World Atlas

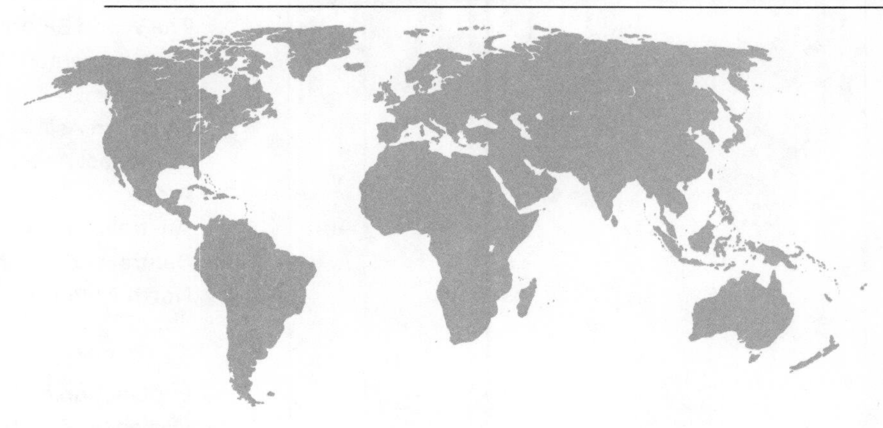

Rand McNally & Company
Chicago · New York · San Francisco

Contents

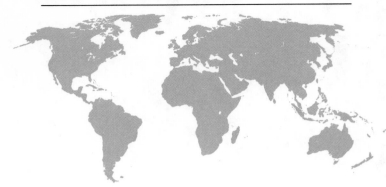

World Wildlife 4A-37A

The Living Earth 4A-5A
The World Before Man 6A-7A
Zoogeography: The Realms of Nature 8A-9A
Europe 10A-13A
Northern Asia 14A-17A
Southeast Asia 18A-21A
Africa 22A-25A
Australia and New Zealand 26A-29A
Central and South America 30A-33A
North America 34A-37A

Map Legend 38A

Explanation of the Map Symbols 38A
Explanation of the Index Reference System 38A

The Political World in Maps 1-89

The World 1-2
Polar Map of the World 1
The World 2

Europe 3-14
Europe 3
British Isles 4
France and the Low Countries 5
Germany, Austria and Switzerland 6
Poland and Czechoslovakia 7
Spain and Portugal 8
Italy 9
Yugoslavia, Hungary, Romania and Bulgaria 10
Norway, Sweden and Finland 11
Western Soviet Union 12
Soviet Union 13
Eastern Mediterranean 14

Asia 15-20
Israel and Arabia 15
Eurasia 16
China, Mongolia, Korea, Japan and Taiwan 17
Japan and Korea 18
Indonesia and the Philippines 19
India, Pakistan, Bangladesh, Burma and Sri Lanka 20

Africa 21-24
Africa 21
Northwestern Africa 22
Northeastern Africa 23
Central and Southern Africa 24

Australia and New Zealand 25-26
Australia 25
Southeastern Australia and New Zealand 26

Library of Congress Catalog Card Number: 73-2278
Printed in the United States of America.

Political Maps Continued

South America — 27-32

South America — 27
Central and Southern Argentina and Chile — 28
Bolivia, Paraguay, Northern Argentina and Chile — 29
Uruguay and Southern Brazil — 30
Peru and Ecuador — 31
Colombia and Venezuela — 32

North America — 33-89

North America — 33
Mexico — 34
West Indies — 35
Canada — 36
  British Columbia — 37
  Alberta — 38
  Saskatchewan — 39
  Manitoba — 40
  Ontario — 41
  Quebec — 42
  Maritime Provinces — 43
  Newfoundland — 44

United States — 45
  Alabama — 46
  Alaska — 47
  Arizona — 48
  Arkansas — 49
  California — 50
  Colorado — 51
  Connecticut — 52
  Delaware — 53
  Florida — 54
  Georgia — 55
  Hawaii — 56
  Idaho — 57
  Illinois — 58
  Indiana — 59
  Iowa — 60
  Kansas — 61
  Kentucky — 62
  Louisiana — 63
  Maine — 64
  Maryland — 53
  Massachusetts — 65
  Michigan — 66
  Minnesota — 67
  Mississippi — 68
  Missouri — 69
  Montana — 70
  Nebraska — 71
  Nevada — 72
  New Hampshire — 73
  New Jersey — 74
  New Mexico — 48
  New York — 75
  North Carolina — 76
  North Dakota — 77
  Ohio — 78
  Oklahoma — 79
  Oregon — 80
  Pennsylvania — 81
  Rhode Island — 52
  South Carolina — 82
  South Dakota — 77
  Tennessee — 83
  Texas — 84
  Utah — 72
  Vermont — 73
  Virginia — 85
  Washington — 86
  West Virginia — 87
  Wisconsin — 88
  Wyoming — 89

World Information — 90-99

World Political Information Table — 90-94
World Facts and Comparisons — 95-99
Movements, Measurements, Inhabitants, Surface and Extremes of Temperature and Rainfall of the Earth — 95
The Continents — 95
Approximate Population of the World, 1650-1978 — 95
Largest Countries of the World in Population — 95
Largest Countries of the World in Area — 95
Principal Mountains of the World — 95
Great Oceans and Seas of the World — 97
Principal Lakes of the World — 97
Principal Rivers of the World — 97
Principal Islands of the World — 97
Largest Metropolitan Areas of the World, 1978 — 98
Principal World Cities and Populations — 99

United States Information — 100-102

Geographical Facts About the United States — 100
Historical Facts About the United States — 100
State Areas and Populations — 100
U.S. State General Information Table — 101
U.S. Population by State or Colony — 102

Index — 103-201

Glossary of Foreign Geographical Terms — 103-104
List of Abbreviations — 105
Explanation of the Map Index — 106

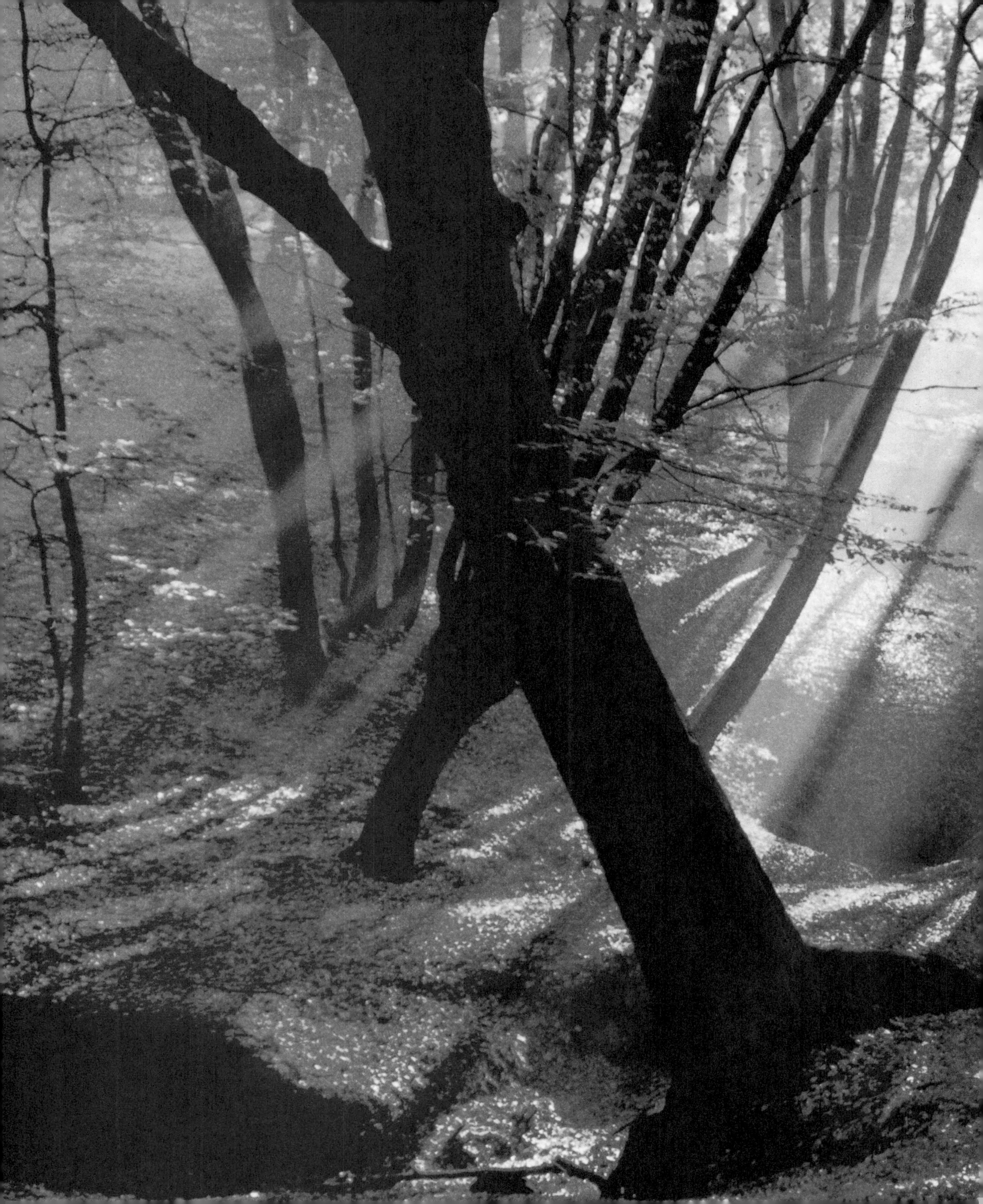

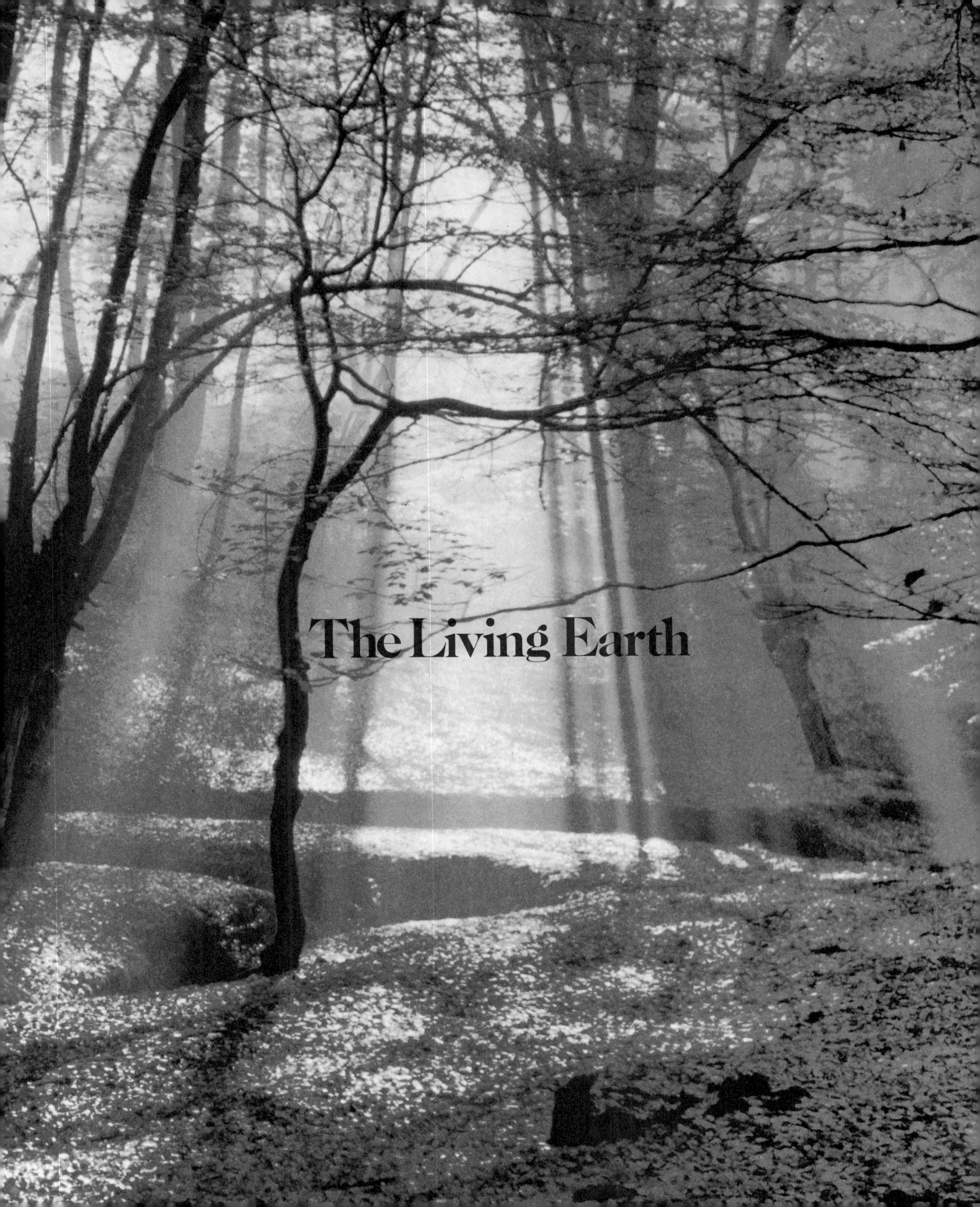

The Living Earth

The World Before Man

To our stolid medieval forefathers the earth was a pattern of unchanging continents and oceans, its wildlife unaltered since the fifth day of Creation. Modern man has discovered that, like his own restless nature, the face of the earth is shifting and changing, and animals and plants have evolved and indeed are still evolving at rates measurable in his own lifetime.

The earth consolidated over four and a half thousand million years ago, and the vapors surrounding it cooled and condensed. Some of the oldest rocks – nearly four thousand million years old by radio-isotope dating – were deposited as sediments, showing that water was present in quantity, and cycles of weathering and erosion were already carving the rocks of the primordial land. The oceans deepened and acquired an increasing concentration of soluble materials from earth and atmosphere. Gradually there developed the rich broth of inorganic molecules in which life was spawned. The first traces of life – humped or branching masses of chalk or silica, believed to have been formed by primitive plants – occur in Precambrian rocks two to three thousand million years old in Canada and the northern United States. The earliest traces of animals are much younger, dating from early Cambrian rocks of Australia approximately 600 million years old.

Five hundred million years ago, at the end of the Cambrian period, the oceans teemed with a variety of simple floating plants, which supported a mixed fauna of primitive sponges, worms, shelled brachiopods and mollusks, trilobites and crustaceans, and echinoderms related to sea urchins and starfish. As yet there were no vertebrates, though pre-chordate ancestors may already have been recognizable among the larvae of invertebrates in the plankton of the ocean surface. Almost certainly there were present the elements of ecological organization which are linked in every modern ecosystem.

The first traces of land animals and land plants appear in Silurian rocks some 400 million years old. Unshaded by vegetation and wide open to the elements, the Silurian landscape cannot have seemed hospitable to its first hesitant colonizers. But the 50 million years of the Devonian period saw the invasion, evolution and spread of plant life.

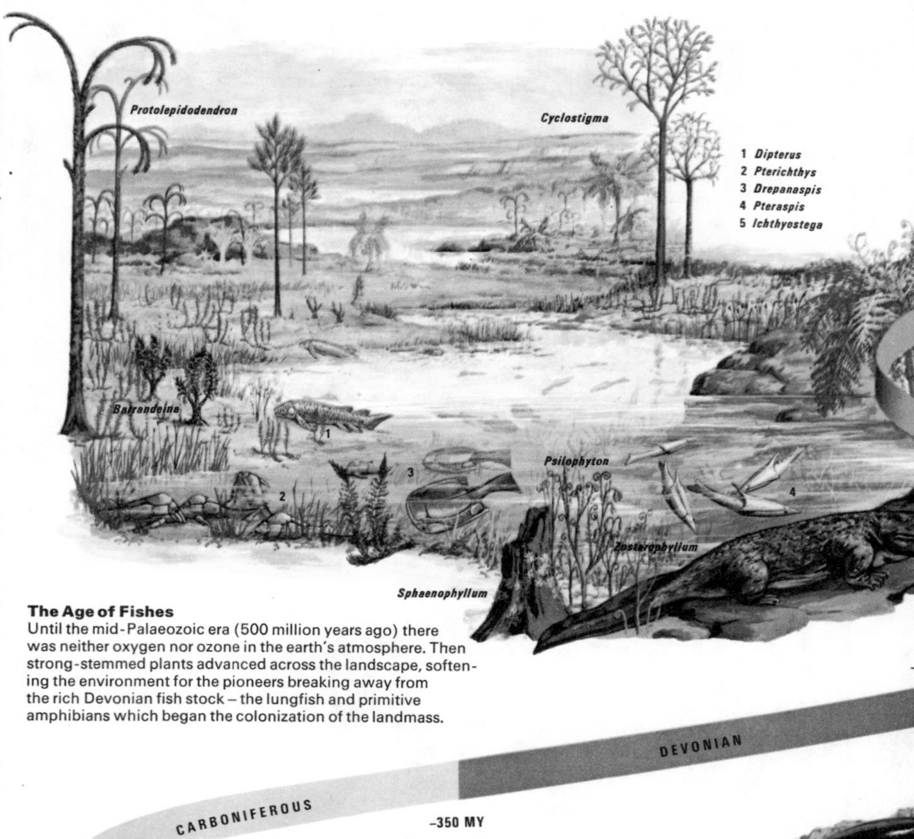

1 Dipterus
2 Pterichthys
3 Drepanaspis
4 Pteraspis
5 Ichthyostega

The Age of Fishes

Until the mid-Palaeozoic era (500 million years ago) there was neither oxygen nor ozone in the earth's atmosphere. Then strong-stemmed plants advanced across the landscape, softening the environment for the pioneers breaking away from the rich Devonian fish stock – the lungfish and primitive amphibians which began the colonization of the landmass.

DEVONIAN

CARBONIFEROUS   −350 MY

−270 MY

PERMIAN   −225 MY

The mammals take over

Forty to 50 million years ago flowering plants had overtaken all other forms of vegetation to clothe the land surface of the earth. The reptiles were no longer dominant; the world was now ruled by mammals, warm-blooded offshoots of reptilian stock. Most modern animals have clearly recognizable Oligocene ancestors.

TRIASSIC   −180 MY

JURASSIC

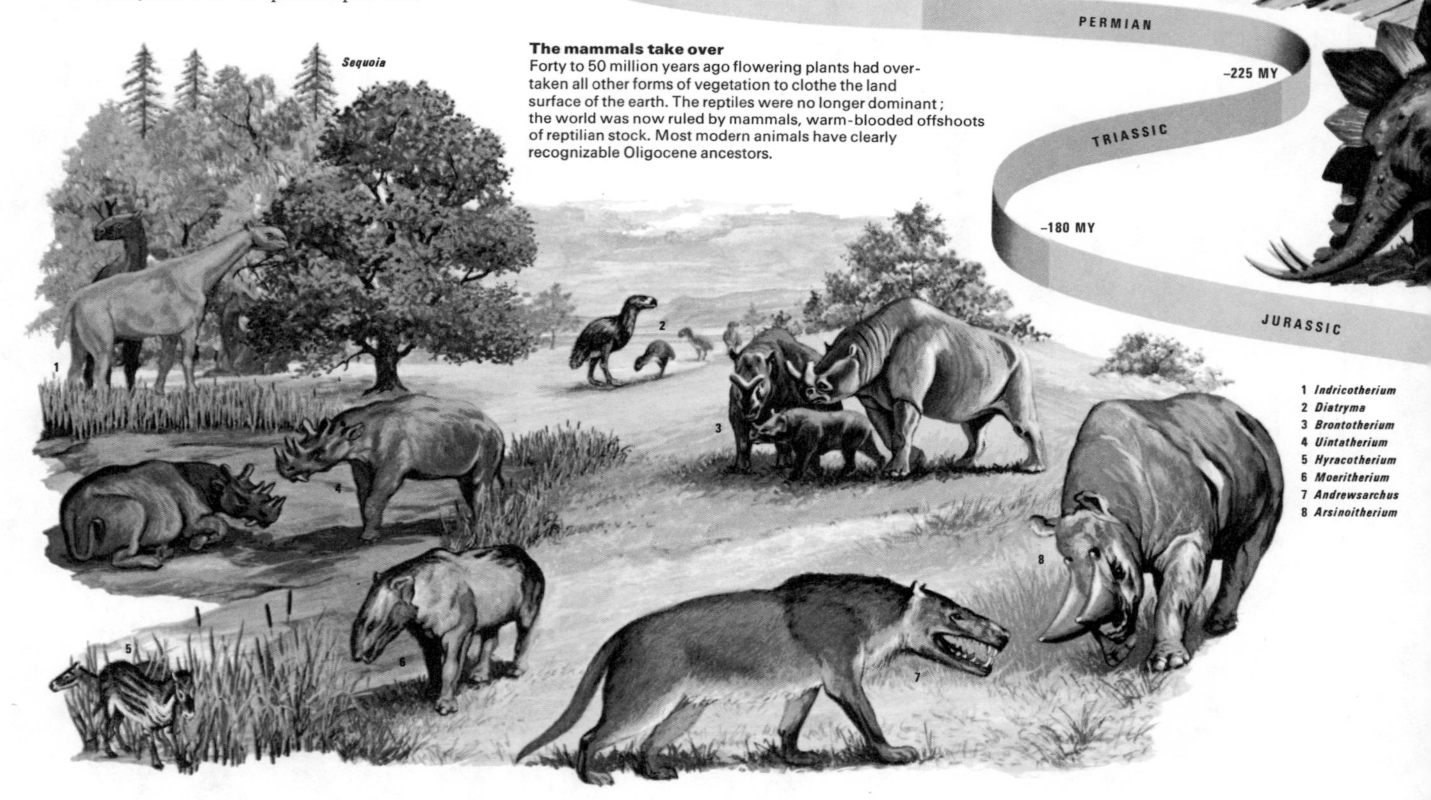

1 Indricotherium
2 Diatryma
3 Brontotherium
4 Uintatherium
5 Hyracotherium
6 Moeritherium
7 Andrewsarchus
8 Arsinoitherium

Ribbon of life *below*

Over the past 600 million years the planet earth has been populated by a remarkable and ever-changing succession of life forms. The major divisions of this span of time, the geological periods, are shown to scale in the diagram, amplified by reconstructions of three of the most significant Ages of evolution.

−600 MY

CAMBRIAN

1 *Pterodactylus*
2 *Rhamphorhynchus*
3 *Diplodocus*
4 *Plesiosaurus*
5 *Peloneustes*
6 *Archaeopteryx*
7 *Antrodemus*
8 *Oligokyphus*
9 *Stegosaurus*

ORDOVICIAN

−440 MY

SILURIAN

Williamsonia

Conifer

Cycads

−135 MY

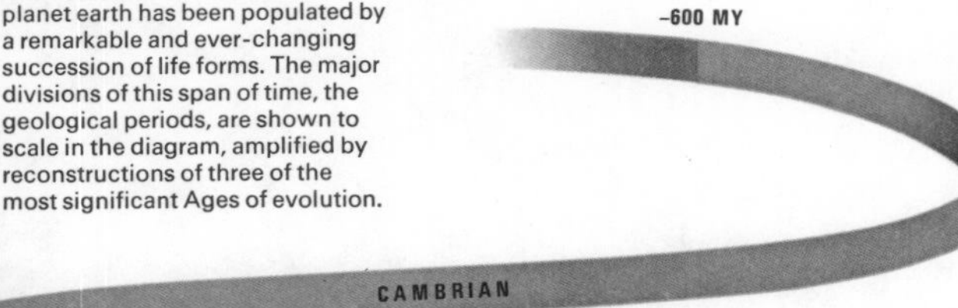

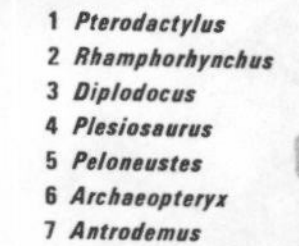

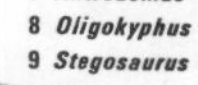

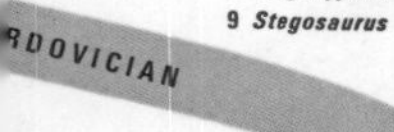

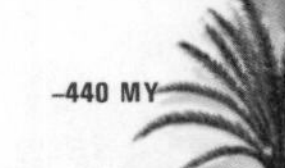

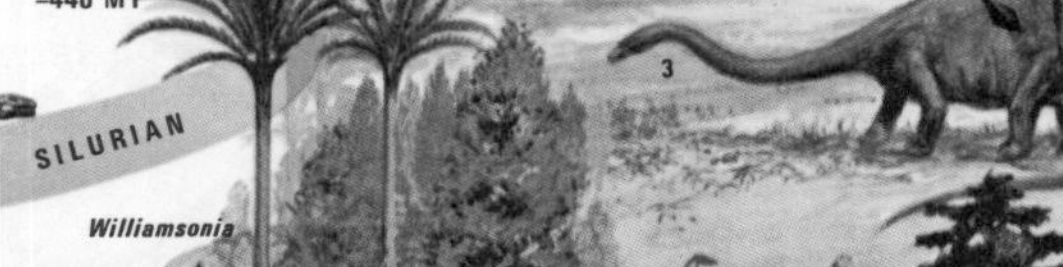

The Age of Reptiles

Throughout the Jurassic (180–135 million years ago) the land was clothed in oxygen-rich vegetation harboring many small terrestrial life forms, notably insects and other small invertebrates. Reptiles, amongst them the 10-ton *Stegosaurus*, were the rulers – dominating all other life forms. Flying reptiles, the pterosaurs, heralded the advent of birds.

CRETACEOUS

Miocene : Rockies, Alps and Himalayas uplifted, temperate and polar regions cooled and grasslands steadily replaced forests. Grazing mammals spread across the plains.

Pleistocene : permanent ice shield developed in northern latitudes of America and Eurasia, and spread to plains a million years ago, advancing and retreating four times.

−70 MY   −60 MY   −40 MY   −25 MY   −12 MY   −3 MY

PALAE OCENE	EOCENE	OLIGOCENE	MIOCENE	PLIOCENE	PLEIST OCENE

Pliocene : world continued to cool, tropical plants and animals retreated to lower latitudes. Camels, horses, antelopes, mastodons lived on northern plains of America and Asia.

Recent : with final retreat of ice sheets just over ten thousand years ago, man evolved from hunter-gatherer to settler-farmer, building his homes in the fertile regions.

The record of the rocks *below*

Beyond six hundred million years ago, traces of life are scarce but the record of rock succession tells of huge supercontinents shifting over the earth, mountain ranges created and destroyed, oceans opened and engulfed.

Life on land — 440 my
Beginnings of fossil record — 600 my
Origins of earth — 4600 my
Oldest dated rocks — 3900 my
Appalachians formed
Rockies formed
PALAEOZOIC ERA
Alps formed
MESOZOIC ERA
CENOZOIC ERA
Urals formed
Himalayas formed
Caledonian mountains formed
First living cells — 3200 my

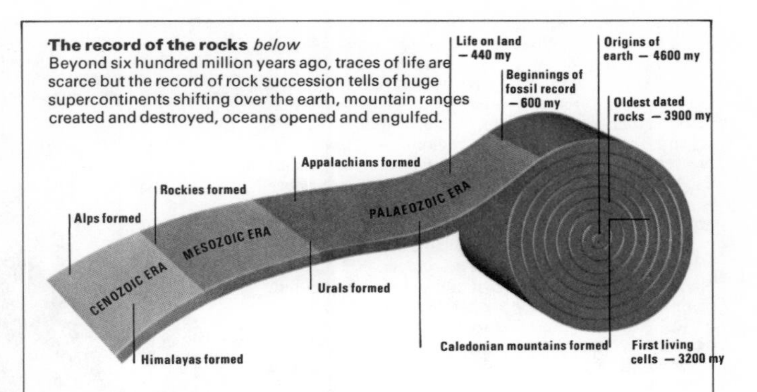

The shifting continents

a Trenches
b Mid-ocean ridges
c Transverse faults
Direction of drift

LAURASIA
TETHYS SEA
GONDWANALAND

Once there was one 'supercontinent' — Pangaea. Outlines of present continents are due to a network of fractures that developed in Pangaea over 200 million years ago.

Pangaea began to split into two major blocks 180 million years ago ; the southern block subdivided later into Austral, Afro-American and Indian fragments.

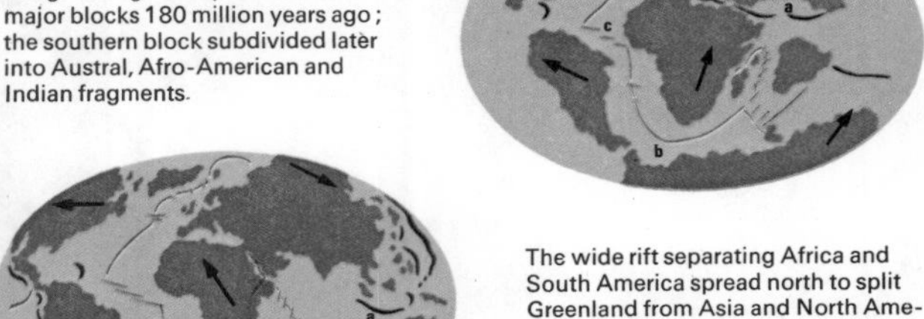

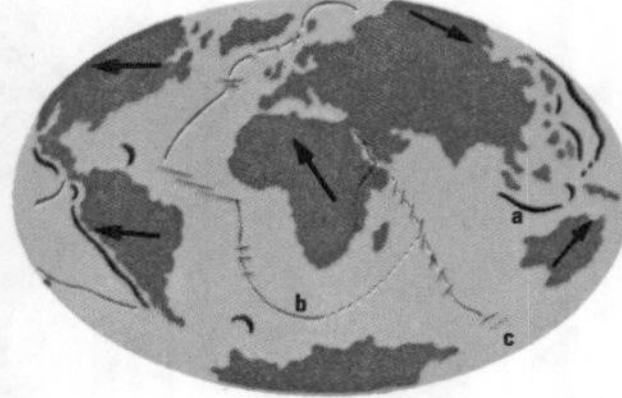

The wide rift separating Africa and South America spread north to split Greenland from Asia and North America 65 million years ago. Australia and Antarctica were still united.

Era	Period	Began my ago	Length my	Development of life
CENOZOIC	Quaternary	3	3	The Pleistocene and recent periods. Widespread dominance of mammals. Evolution of the hominid line leading to *Homo erectus* about 500,000 years ago.
CENOZOIC	Tertiary	70	67	Palaeocene to Pliocene. Ancestral horses, pigs, cattle and primates appear at the dawn of the Age of Mammals. Flowering plants reach full development.
MESOZOIC	Cretaceous	135	65	Great dinosaurs, ammonites and primitive fish extinct during the late Cretaceous. Flowering plants develop. Mammals and primitive birds more numerous.
MESOZOIC	Jurassic	180	45	The Age of Reptiles : many and varied reptile forms dominant in a forest-swamp-plain environment. First winged reptiles and primitive birds evolve.
MESOZOIC	Triassic	225	45	Worldwide desert conditions with seasonal rainfall creating deltas and salt lakes. First primitive mammals. Period of great diversity of reptile groups.
PALAEOZOIC	Permian	270	45	Climax of Carboniferous mountain building period. Rich marine and freshwater life. Modern insects (bugs, beetles) appear. Rise of the reptiles.
PALAEOZOIC	Carboniferous	350	80	Lycopods and tree ferns dominant on land. First appearance of gymnosperms. Winged insects evolve along with spiders and land scorpions. First reptiles appears.
PALAEOZOIC	Devonian	400	50	Remarkable evolution of fishes invading freshwater environments and giving rise to the first airbreathing amphibians. Insects numerous on land.
PALAEOZOIC	Silurian	440	40	Seaweeds abundant in shallow seas giving rise to the first land plants. Freshwater and estuarine deposits hold fossils of jawed fish and sea-scorpions.
PALAEOZOIC	Ordovician	500	60	Mild climate over much of the earth. Corals, sponges, cephalopods and trilobites abundant in reduced oceans. First fish-like vertebrates appear in North America.
PALAEOZOIC	Cambrian	600	100	First appearance of abundant fossil remains. Trilobites, echinoderms, graptolites and foraminifera common in shallow seas covering much of earth's surface.
PALAEOZOIC	Pre-Cambrian	4600	4000	Evidence of primitive invertebrates – bacteria, sponges and worms. Earliest traces of life are algae and bacteria dated at over 3000 million years old.

Zoogeography: The Realms of Nature

The distinguished early Victorian ornithologist P. L. Sclater first divided the world into six faunal regions, each with its own characteristic assembly of birds. Alfred Wallace, a widely-traveled naturalist (and co-discoverer of natural selection), found that many other animals fitted readily into Sclater's scheme. The six original regions – Palaearctic, Nearctic, Neotropical, Ethiopian, Oriental (or Indian) and Australian – are still valid today, but one more is sometimes added to them – the Antarctic continent, unknown in Sclater's time.

Many animal groups seem to have originated in the warm central landmass of Arctogea (Palearctic, Nearctic, Ethiopian and Oriental regions), spreading from there toward the peripheral regions of southern Africa, Australia and the Americas. This is especially true of the mammals, which appear to have spread outward in waves, each wave representing a new evolutionary development, and to some extent over-taking and replacing the next. The marsupials, an early pattern of mammals which produce their young only a few days after conception and rear them – firmly attached to a teat – in a pouch on the body wall, spread across the world between 60 and 80 million years ago. Fossil remains are found in Europe, and marsupials are still plentiful in Australia and South America. Later came a second wave of more advanced mammals – the placentals, which keep their young longer inside the mother's body and feed the developing embryo through a placenta attached to the wall of the uterus. Placentals, marginally more successful, replaced marsupials wherever the two competed.

Continental movement during the early Tertiary isolated Australia and South America from Arctogea, and in these two outposts marsupials continued to flourish and diversify. Later South America was invaded by placental mammals from North America, but Australia remained almost entirely free of placentals until the arrival of man.

The Nearctic or 'New North' Realm

This realm includes North America down to the high-lands of Mexico ; many of its mammals (including deer and sheep) entered across the Bering land bridge. Others, (among them horses and camels) went the other way.

The Palaearctic or 'Old North' Realm

The Palaearctic is a vast realm extending from Britain to Japan, and from Spitzbergen to Saudi Arabia and Africa north of the Sahara. Many of its animals spread to peripheral Ethiopian, Oriental and Nearctic realms.

The Neotropical or 'New Tropical' Realm

Linked with the Nearctic by the isthmus of Central America the Neotropical reaches down to Cape Horn. Its fauna includes marsupials, sloths, armadillos and forest monkeys with prehensile tails.

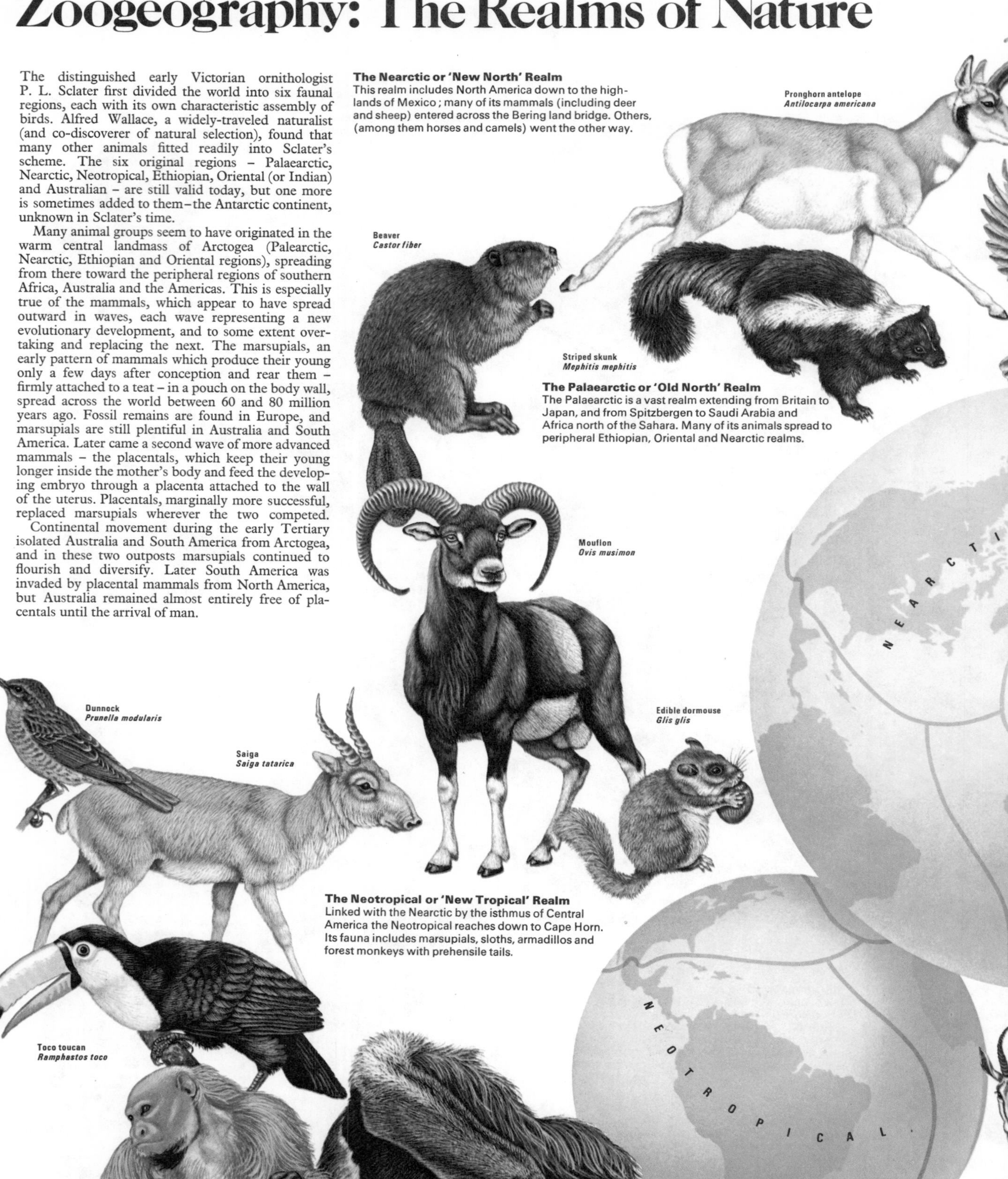

Pronghorn antelope
Antilocarpa americana

Beaver
Castor fiber

Striped skunk
Mephitis mephitis

Mouflon
Ovis musimon

Edible dormouse
Glis glis

Dunnock
Prunella modularis

Saiga
Saiga tatarica

Toco toucan
Ramphastos toco

Bald uakari
Cacajo calvus

Giant anteater
Myrmecophaga tridactyla

Springbuck
Antidorcas marsupialis

NEARCTIC

NEOTROPICAL

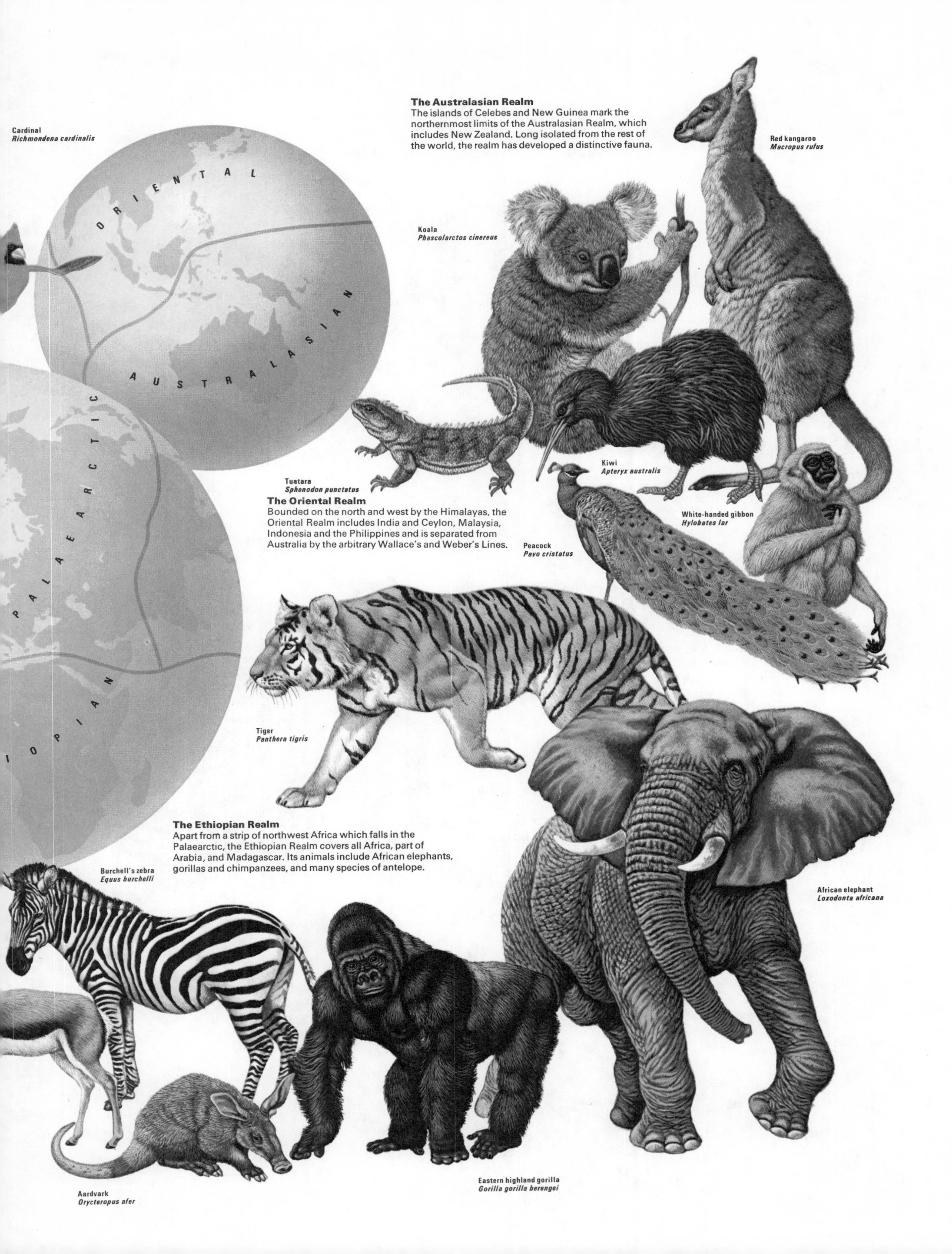

Cardinal
Richmondena cardinalis

The Australasian Realm
The islands of Celebes and New Guinea mark the northernmost limits of the Australasian Realm, which includes New Zealand. Long isolated from the rest of the world, the realm has developed a distinctive fauna.

Red kangaroo
Macropus rufus

Koala
Phascolarctos cinereus

Tuatara
Sphenodon punctatus

The Oriental Realm
Bounded on the north and west by the Himalayas, the Oriental Realm includes India and Ceylon, Malaysia, Indonesia and the Philippines and is separated from Australia by the arbitrary Wallace's and Weber's Lines.

Kiwi
Apteryx australis

Peacock
Pavo cristatus

White-handed gibbon
Hylobates lar

Tiger
Panthera tigris

The Ethiopian Realm
Apart from a strip of northwest Africa which falls in the Palaearctic, the Ethiopian Realm covers all Africa, part of Arabia, and Madagascar. Its animals include African elephants, gorillas and chimpanzees, and many species of antelope.

African elephant
Loxodonta africana

Burchell's zebra
Equus burchelli

Aardvark
Orycteropus afer

Eastern highland gorilla
Gorilla gorilla berengei

Europe

THE PALAEARCTIC REALM 1.

The smallest of the continents with the exception of Australia, Europe is a series of peninsulas within peninsulas, and islands, giving it a coastline longer, in proportion to its size, than any other continent. It is only marginally larger than Canada, and the only continent (apart from Antarctica) that has no tropical lands. Its vegetational and climatic regions form slender bands ranging from the sub-tropical Mediterranean in the south through the broadleaf and coniferous belts to the Arctic tundra. It is faunally impoverished when compared with the other great continents, a fact partly due to the successful occupation of man and to a climatic history in which it has been largely covered by an ice sheet at least four times during the past million years. During the interglacial periods plants and animals moved in, only to be driven back with the advance of yet another ice sheet. Prehistoric man shared the land with many animals that have now vanished from Europe and may have hunted some to extinction, but the real diminution of wildlife has followed intensive agriculture and forest clearance. Yet there remains a fascinating flora and fauna on a smaller, less dramatic scale than that found in other continents, but which is none the less rewarding to the observer. The arrival and departure of migrant birds hint at other climes, and the ability of many small life forms to survive warily in competition with man is demonstrated even in those areas where intensive agriculture, and even industrialization, is found.

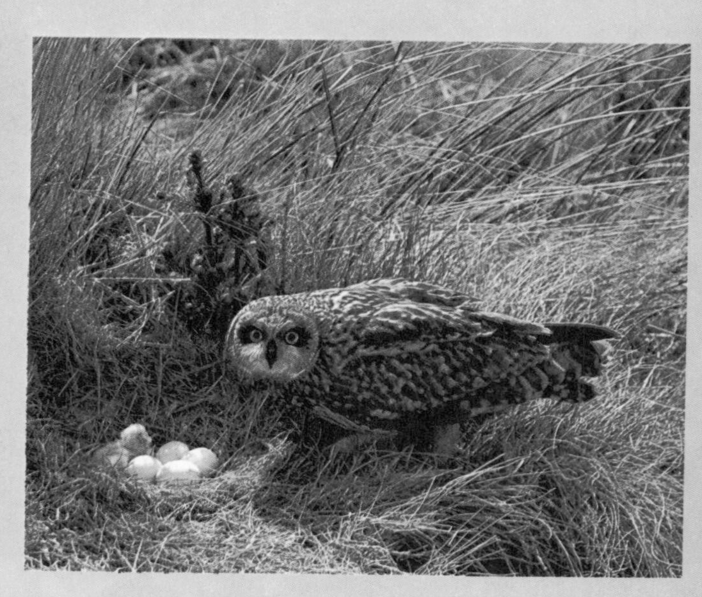

Short-eared owl nesting in heathland, Northern Europe

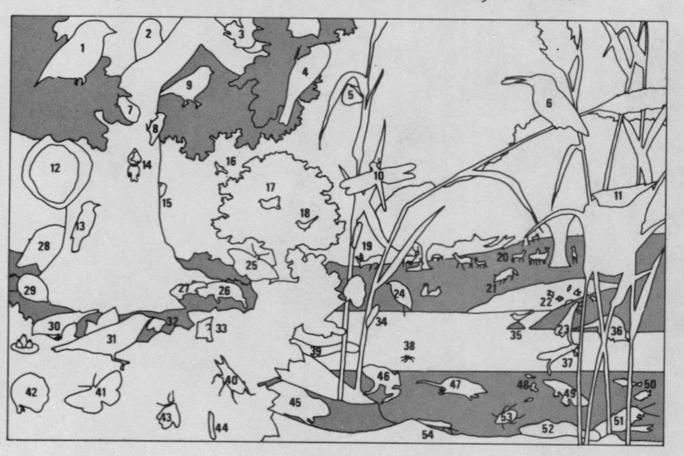

Key to panorama

1 Pied flycatcher	19 Fallow deer	37 Damsel fly
2 Tawny owl	20 Roe deer	38 Pond skater
3 Red squirrel	21 Fox	39 Grass snake
4 Great tit	22 Sand martin	40 Stag beetle
5 Marsh fritillary	23 Bank vole	41 White admiral
6 Kingfisher	24 Grey heron	42 Wood mouse
7 Oak eggar	25 Wood fritillary	43 Red admiral
8 Lesser spotted woodpecker	26 Rabbit	44 Large white caterpillar
9 Jay	27 Weasel	45 Water vole
10 Dragonfly	28 Badger	46 Common frog
11 Reed Warbler	29 Hedgehog	47 Water shrew
12 Tree wasp nest	30 Blackcap	48 Water boatman
13 Green woodpecker	31 Wood warbler	49 Smooth newt
14 Long-eared bat	32 Wood white	50 Stickleback
15 Treecreeper	33 Dormouse	51 Crayfish
16 Sparrowhawk	34 Dragonfly pupa	52 Bullhead
17 Woodpigeon	35 Pied wagtail	53 Water beetle
18 Magpie	36 Otter	54 Dragonfly larva

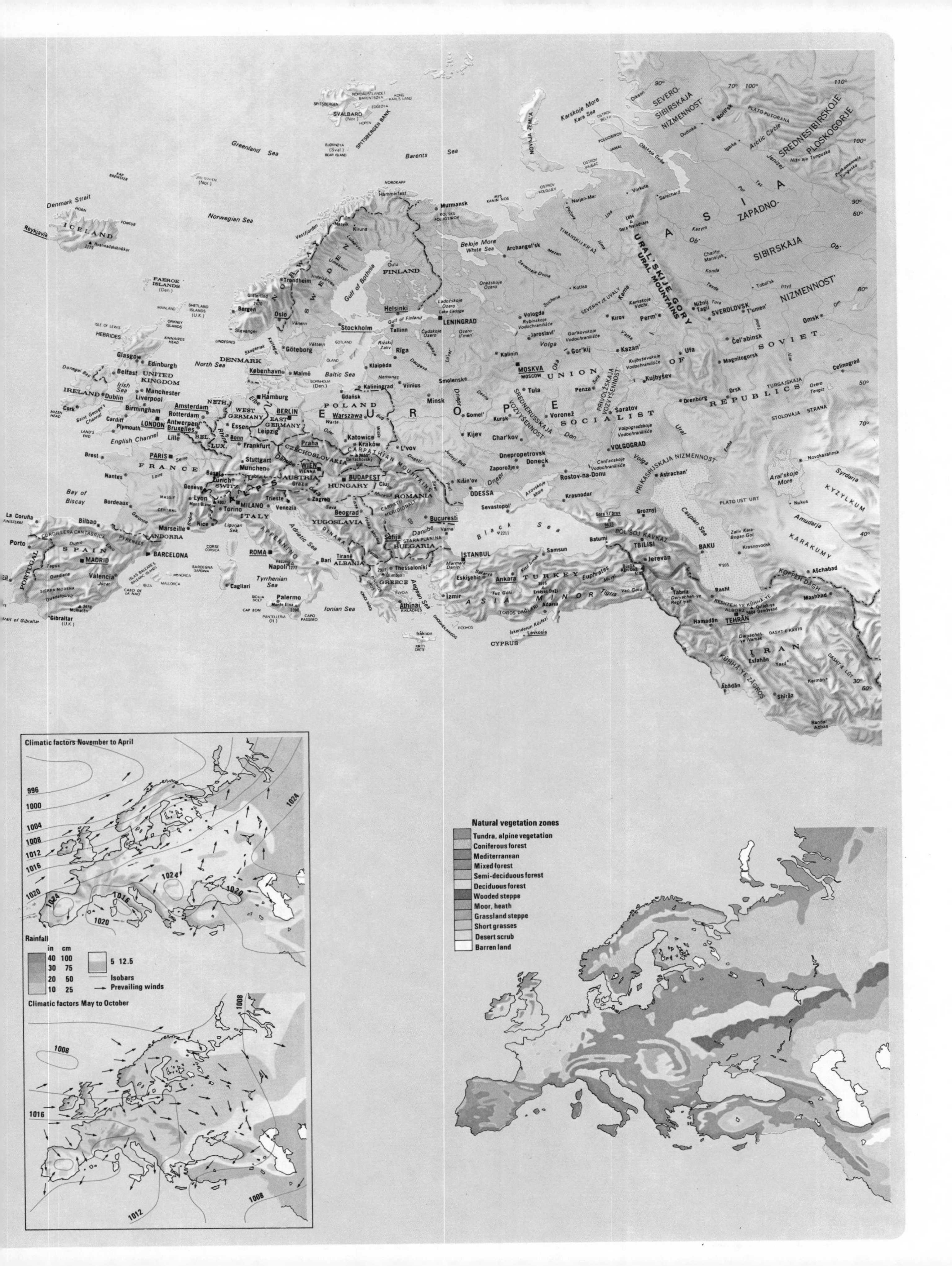

Climatic factors November to April

996
1000
1004
1008
1012
1016
1020
1024

Rainfall

in	cm
40	100
30	75
20	50
10	25

5 12.5

Isobars
Prevailing winds

Climatic factors May to October

Natural vegetation zones

Tundra, alpine vegetation
Coniferous forest
Mediterranean
Mixed forest
Semi-deciduous forest
Deciduous forest
Wooded steppe
Moor, heath
Grassland steppe
Short grasses
Desert scrub
Barren land

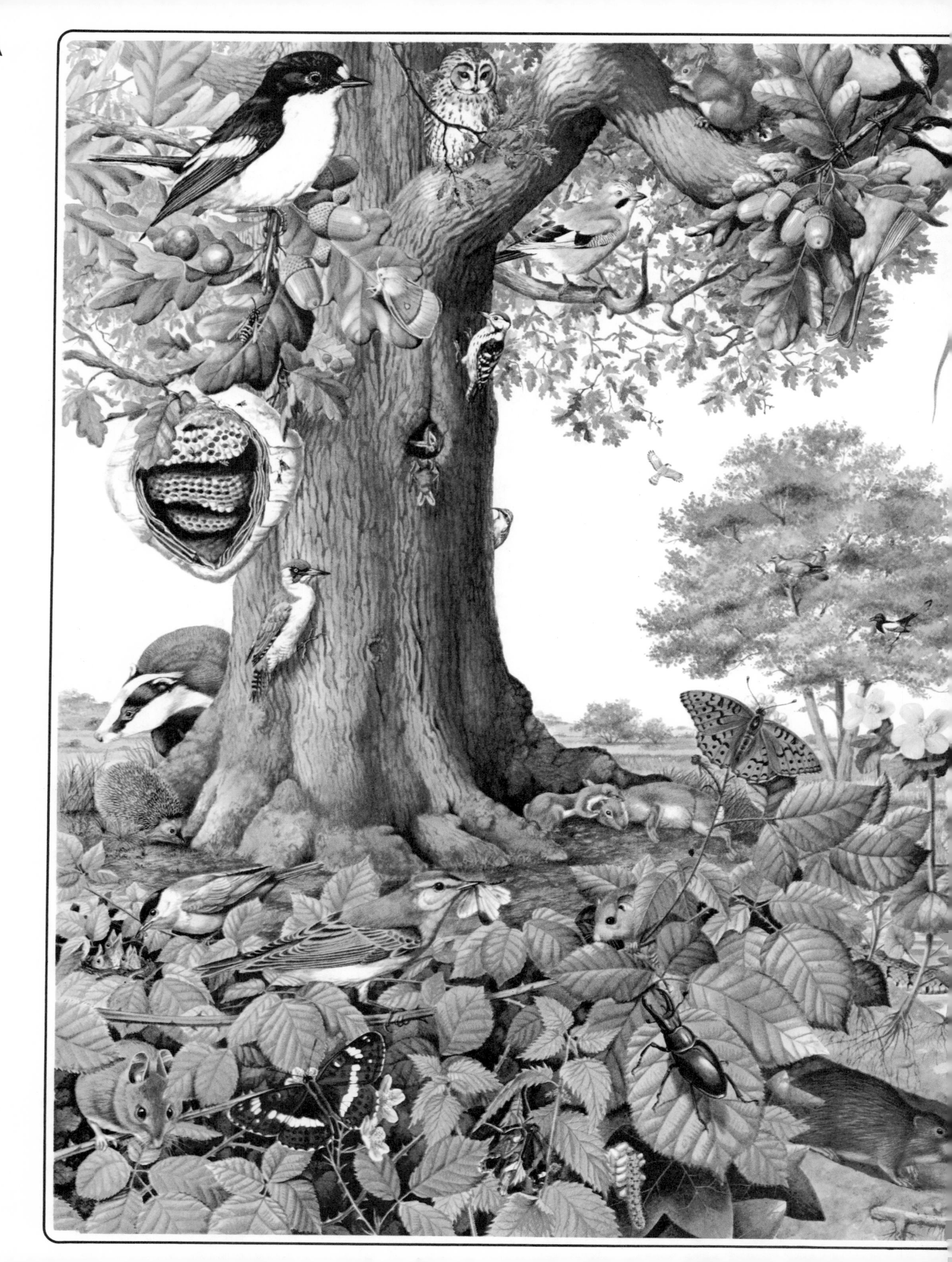

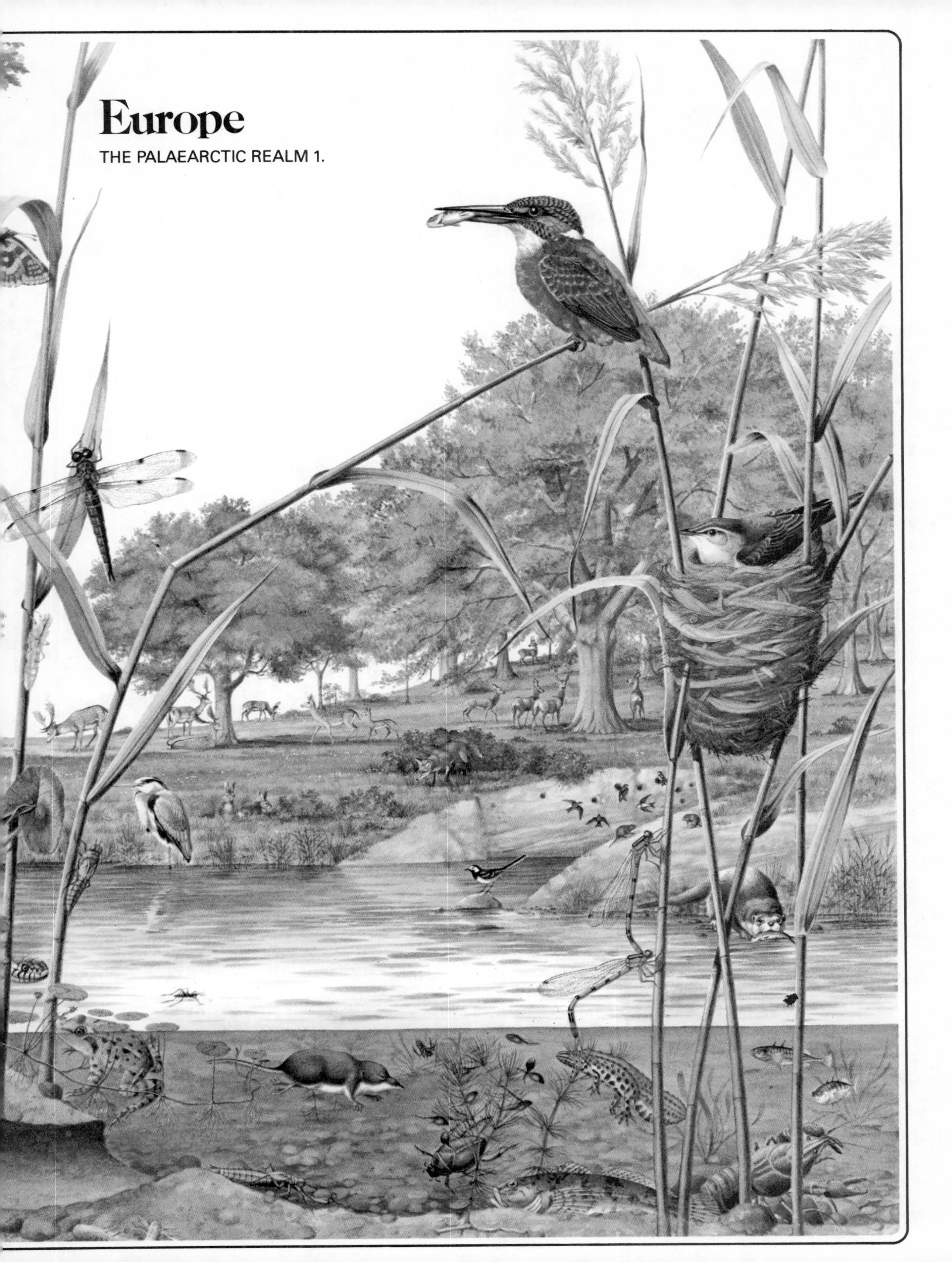

Europe

THE PALAEARCTIC REALM 1.

Northern Asia

THE PALAEARCTIC REALM 2.

Continent is barely adequate a term to describe Asia, the world's largest landmass. Europe, little more than a seafrayed appendage to it, is also a continent. Asia reaches out almost to touch the Americas; Africa, across the man-made ditch of the Suez Canal; and Australia, through the chain of islands of Indonesia. The following pages describe the northern and central regions of the continent – the great, horizontal bands of taiga, steppe and desert bounded to the north by the Arctic tundra and to the south by the soaring mountains of the Karakoram, Pamir and Himalaya. The seemingly endless expanses of conifer in the taiga form the greatest forest in the world, linking the Atlantic (through Scandinavia) with the northern margins of the Pacific. The deserts reach from China to join the Sahara with little interruption and the fertile steppes unroll across the Russian river basins into eastern Europe. The breathtaking scale of everything in Asia is exemplified by the great natural barrier of mountains to the south where any one of a hundred peaks is higher than any mountain in any other part of the world. Each of these unique regions is occupied by life forms peculiar to itself, albeit in diminishing traces like Przewalski's horse, the last of its species in the wild, or the Siberian and Caspian tigers, still holding on to life in a habitat from which their genus first emerged. Conservation authorities have had some notable success in saving indigenous herbivores such as the saiga antelope and the wild ass.

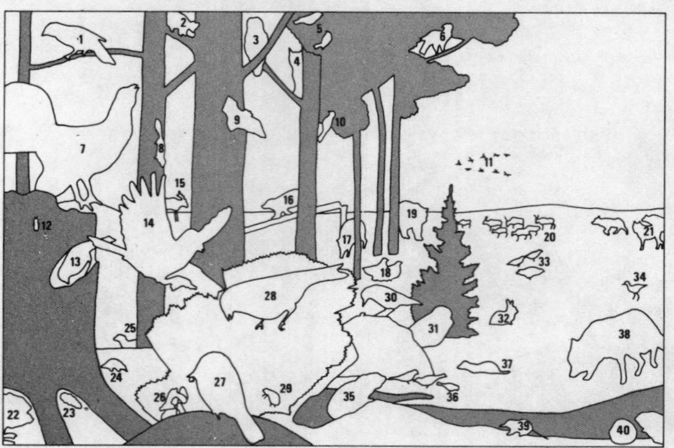

Pine trees damaged by moose, Siberia, U.S.S.R.

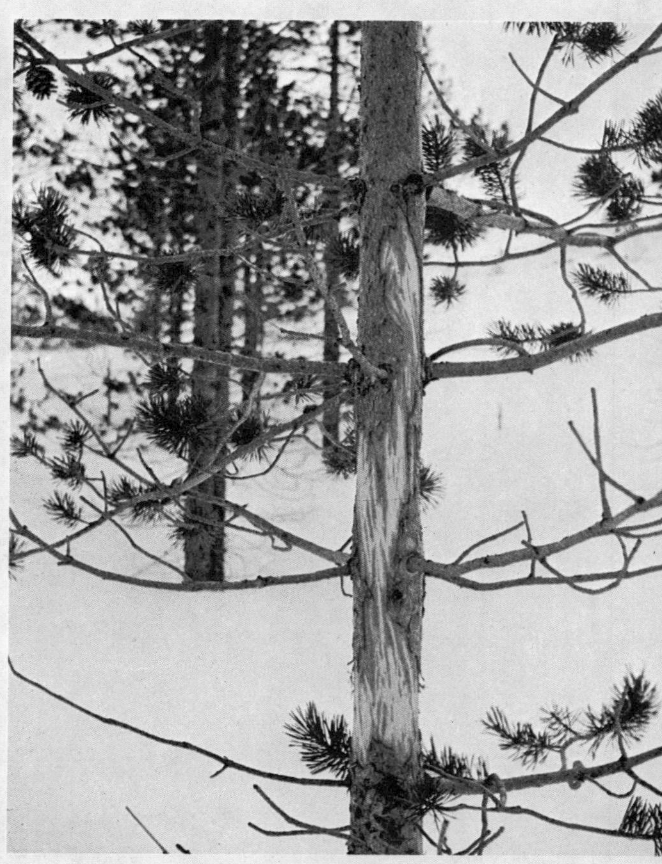

Key to panorama

1 Siberian jay	11 Common cranes	21 Wolves	31 Snowy owl
2 Pine marten	12 Wood-boring beetle	22 Eurasian ground squirrel	32 Blue hare
3 Great grey owl	13 Willow tit	23 Pupa of longhorn beetle	33 Ravens
4 Lynx	14 Siberian rubythroat	24 Pygmy shrew	34 Greenshank
5 Pine grosbeaks	15 Elk	25 Siberian weasel	35 Pika
6 Goshawk	16 Wolverine	26 Ichneumon wasp	36 Bramblings
7 Capercaille	17 Boar	27 Siberian tit	37 Stoat
8 Eurasian flying squirrel	18 Willow grouse	28 Crossbill	38 Arctic fox
9 Northern bat	19 Brown bear	29 Pine weevil	39 Masked shrew
10 Black woodpecker	20 Reindeer	30 Nutcracker	40 Root voles

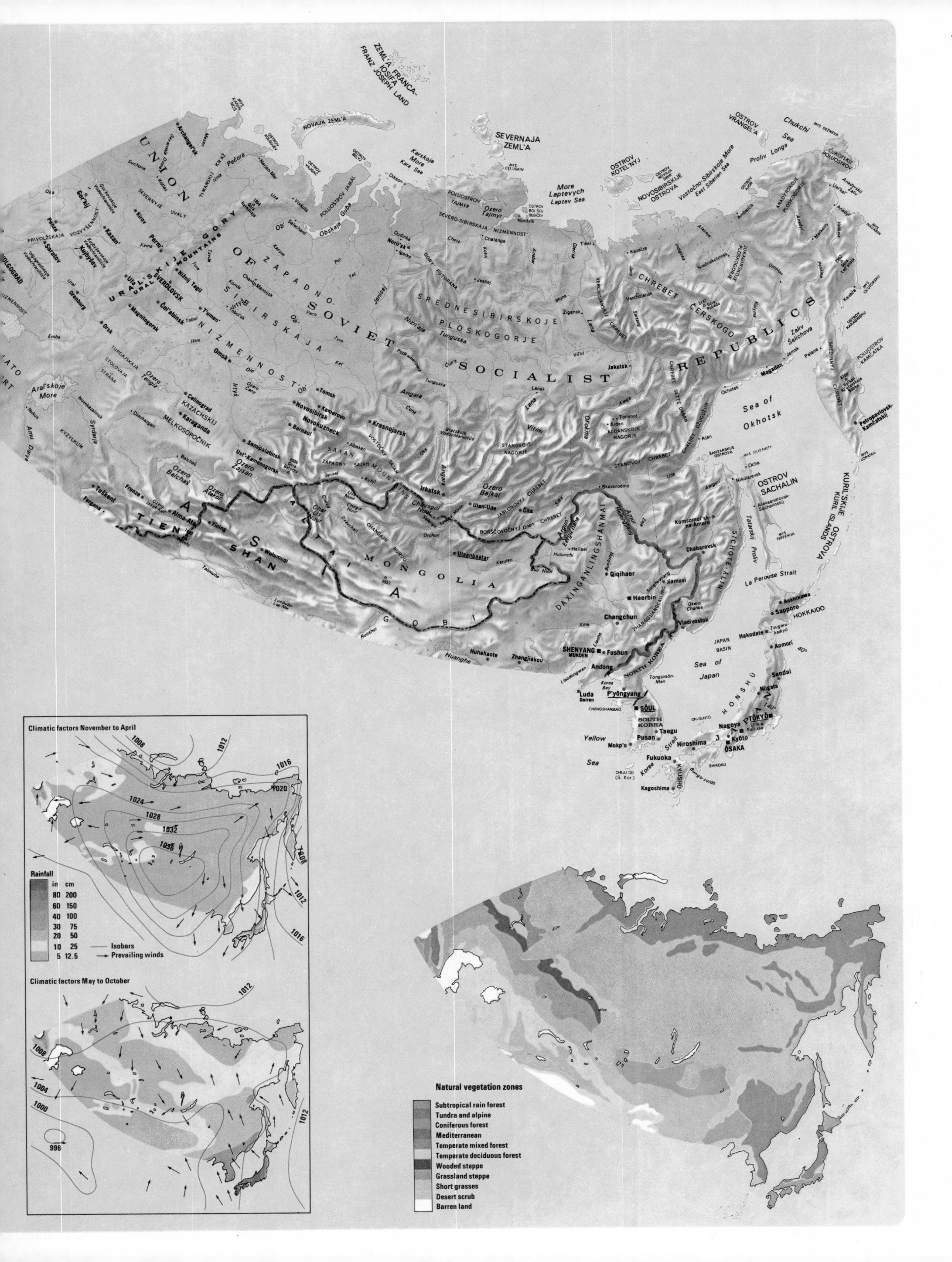

Climatic factors November to April

1008
1012
1016
1020
1024
1028
1032
1036

Rainfall

in	cm
80	200
60	150
40	100
30	75
20	50
10	25
5	12.5

—— Isobars
→ Prevailing winds

Climatic factors May to October

1012
1008
1004
1000
996
1012

Natural vegetation zones

Subtropical rain forest
Tundra and alpine
Coniferous forest
Mediterranean
Temperate mixed forest
Temperate deciduous forest
Wooded steppe
Grassland steppe
Short grasses
Desert scrub
Barren land

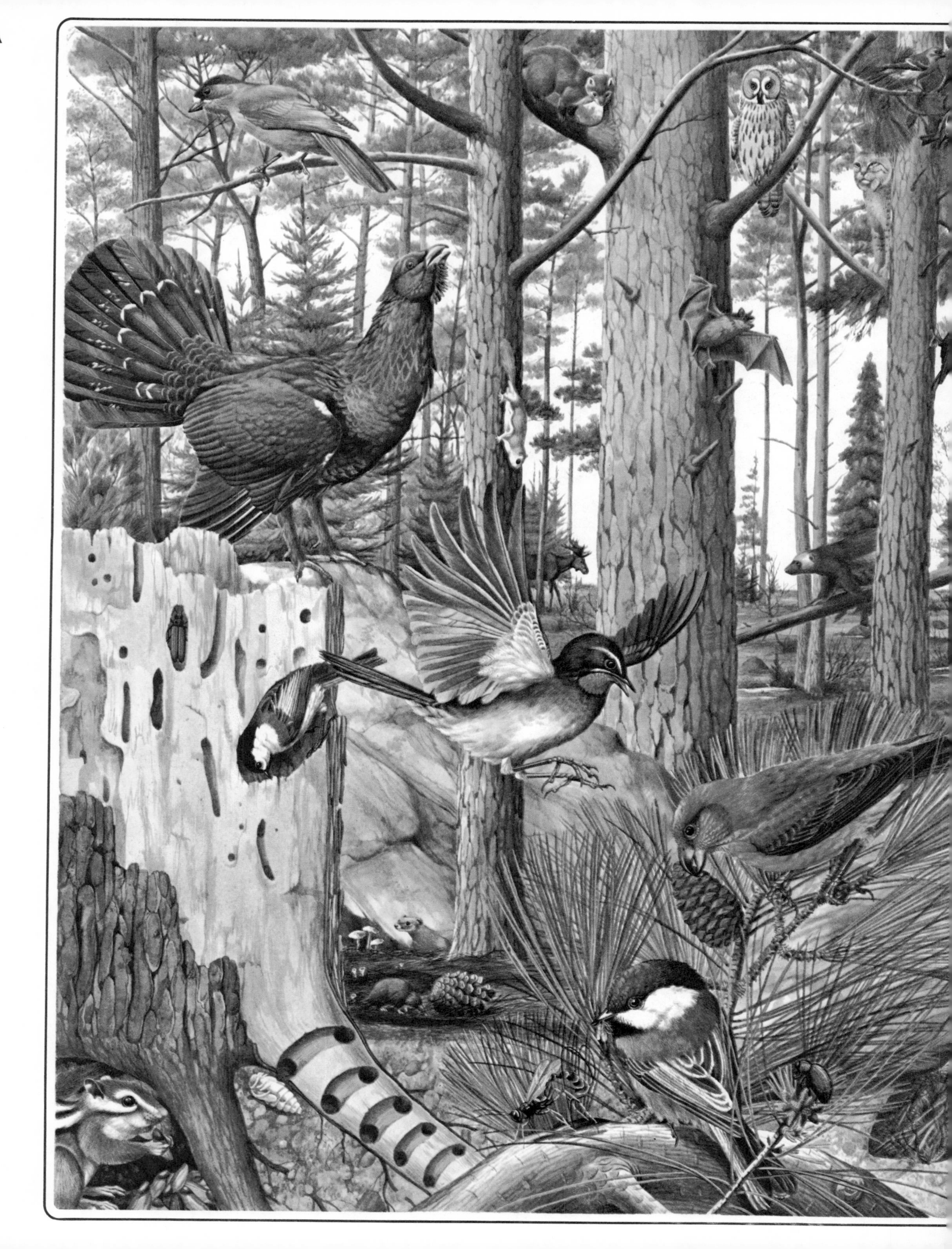

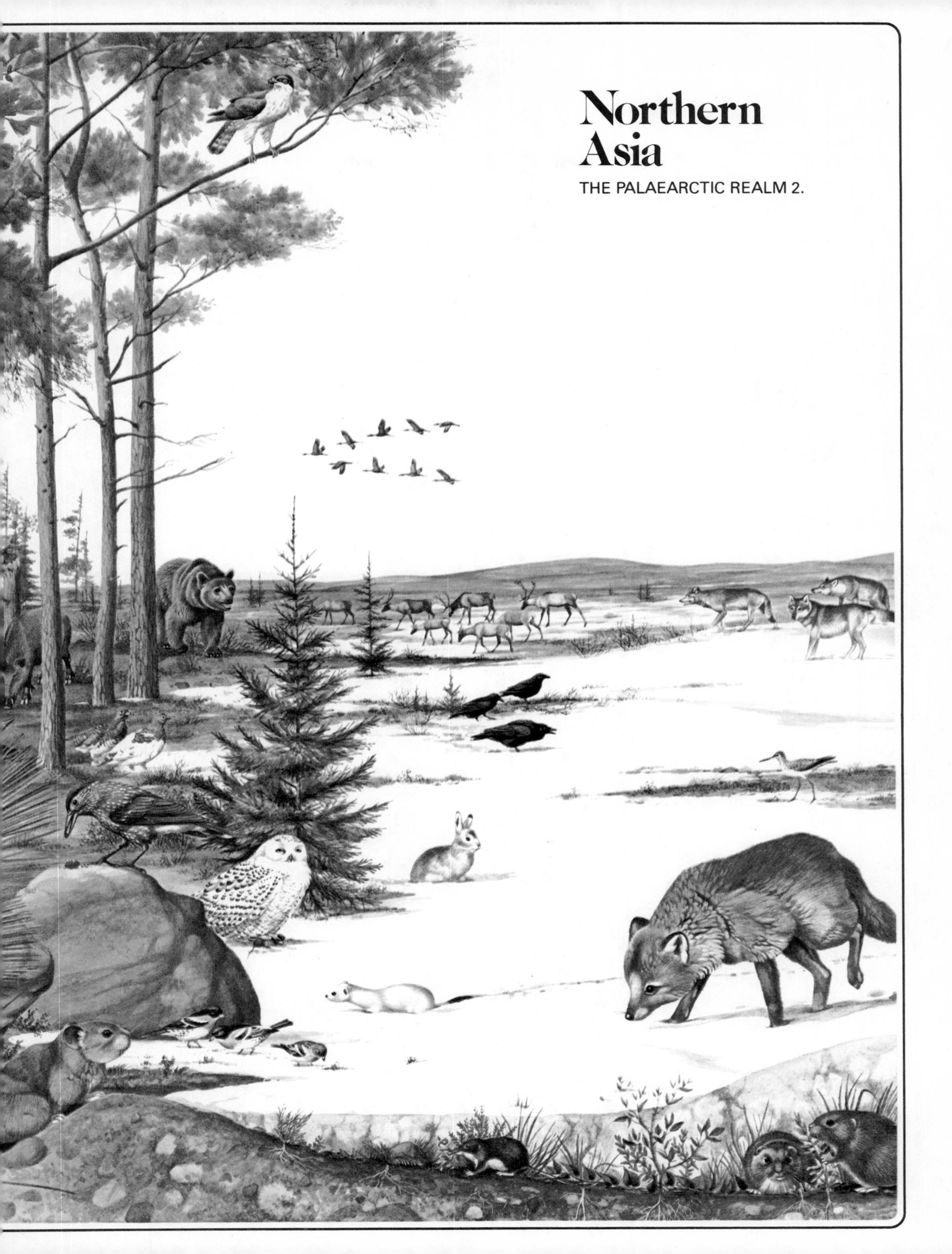

Northern
Asia
THE PALAEARCTIC REALM 2.

Southeast Asia

THE ORIENTAL REALM

The Himalayas, a young giant among mountain ranges, is a natural divide separating northern and central Asia from another, completely different world – the warm, moist south and southeast, a series of ocean-washed peninsulas dominated by a monsoon climate caused by regions of low pressure over Asia drawing in rain-laden winds from the Indian Ocean. The extreme southeast of the continent forming the islands east to Borneo and Java is the least stable region, a volcanic, fragmented tapestry of islands on a shallow shelf of submerged land. Rich in reminders of the spread and extinction – or threatened extinction – of species, the islands remain among the most rewarding, and intriguing, for naturalists as well as being among the most scenically beautiful. The wildlife of India, geologically a newcomer to the old Asian landmass, provides many illustrations of animal invasion when new, amiable habitats present themselves. And lost in the secret fastness of Szechwan, where the Himalayas tumble away into China, there is a faunal crossroads between north and south and a home for some of the rarest of the world's animals, including the giant panda and the gaudier forms of pheasant. The forests of southeast Asia are the home of one of man's closest relatives, the orangutan, the odd proboscis monkey and other primates whose survival depends on their ability to adjust to man and his ways. Races and species of two of the world's great beasts, the tiger and rhinoceros, cling to diminished habitats dotted across the region.

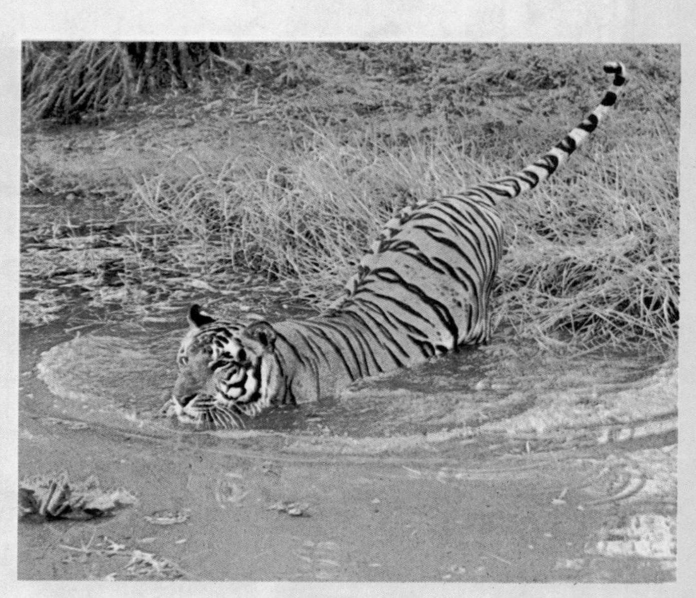

Mature tiger bathing, Sundarbans, West Bengal

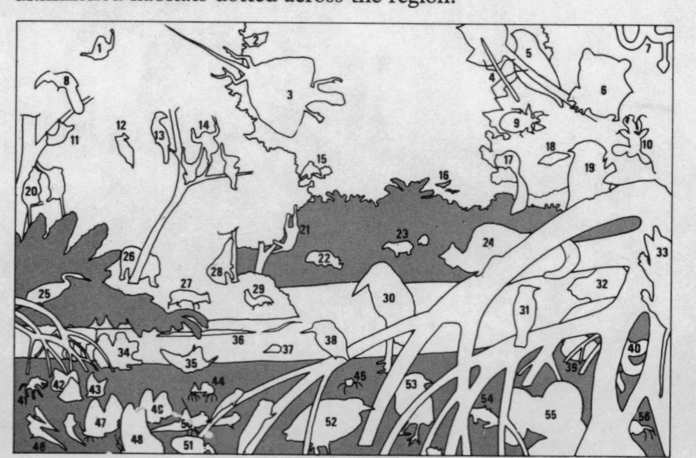

Key to panorama

1 Siamang	20 Silver langurs	39 Binturong
2 Malayan colugo	21 Orang-utan	40 Mangrove snake
3 Flying lizard	22 Sumatran rhinoceros	41 Soldier crabs
4 Stick insect	23 Malayan tapir	42 Yellow appias
5 Lesser-green broadbill	24 Banded linsang	43 Prothaeid butterfly
6 Horsfield's tarsier	25 Indian darter	44 Fiddler crabs
7 Green pit viper	26 Sumatran tiger	45 Soldier crab
8 Wreathed hornbill	27 Indian muntjac	46 Mudskipper
9 Leaf insect	28 Sun bear	47 Sword-tailed swallowtail
10 Orchid mantis	29 Jungle fowl	48 Swallowtail
11 Malayan colugo	30 Lesser adjutant stork	49 Atrophaneuran butterfly
12 Flying fox	31 Black-naped blue monarch	50 Mudskippers
13 Great hornbill	32 Fishing cat	51 Male fiddler crab
14 Lar gibbons	33 Malayan moon rat	52 White-breasted water hen
15 Brahminy kite	34 Crab-eating macaques	53 Blue-winged pitta
16 Flying foxes	35 Graphium butterfly	54 Female fiddler crab
17 Prevost's squirrel	36 Salt water crocodile	55 Reticulated python
18 Common tree shrew	37 Malayan small-clawed otter	56 Soldier crab
19 Yellow-crowned bulbul	38 Indian three-toed kingfisher	

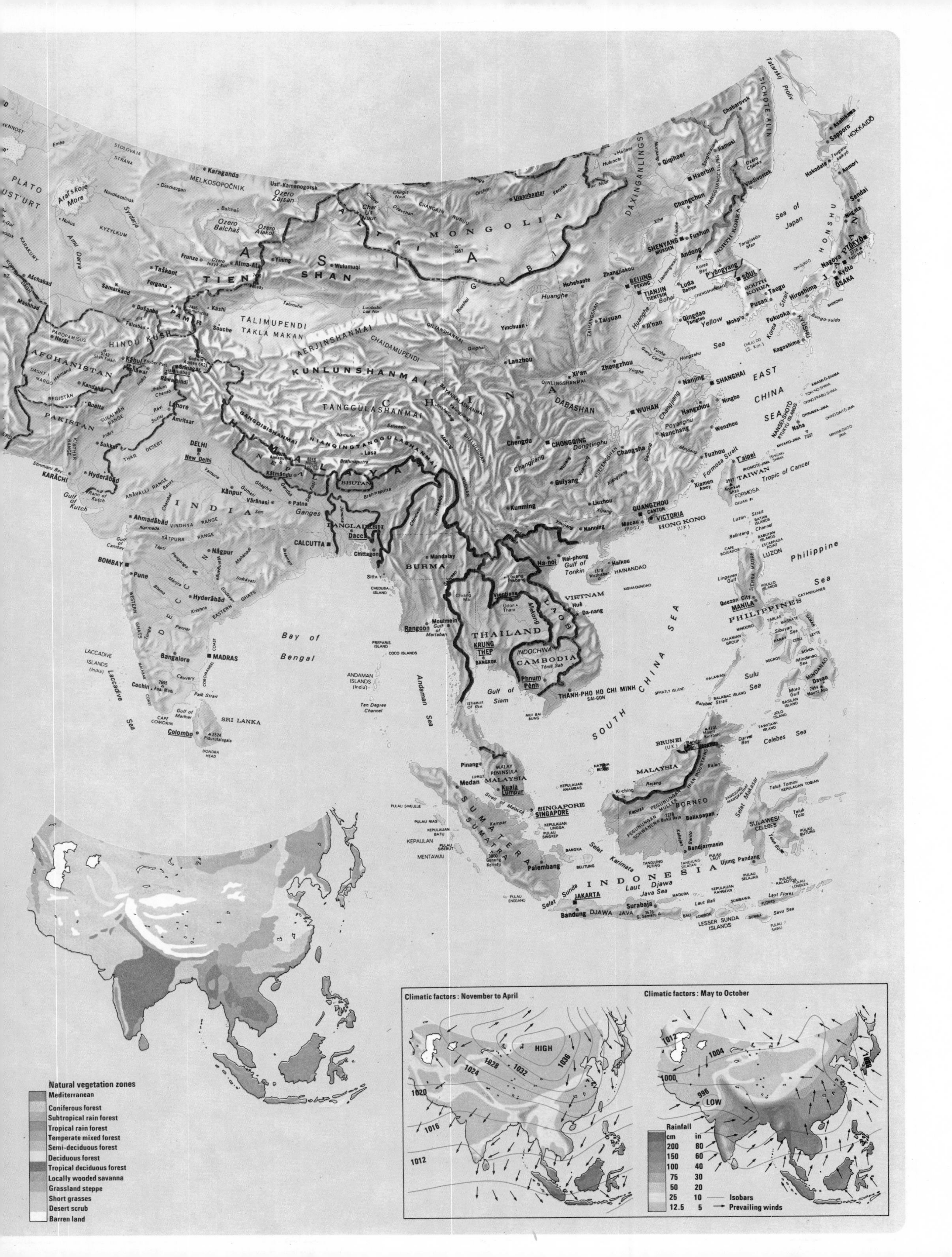

A S I A
MONGOLIA
CHINA
INDIA
PAKISTAN
AFGHANISTAN
BHUTAN
BANGLADESH
BURMA
THAILAND
LAOS
VIETNAM
CAMBODIA
MALAYSIA
BRUNEI
INDONESIA
PHILIPPINES
NORTH KOREA
SOUTH KOREA
TAIWAN
SRI LANKA
TIEN SHAN
HINDU KUSH
PAMIR
HIMALAYA
TALIMUPENDI
TAKLA MAKAN
KUNLUNSHANMAI
TANGGULASHANMAI
GOBI
DAXINGANLINGSHANMAI
SICHOTE-ALIN
HONSHU
HOKKAIDO
KYUSHU
Sea of Japan
Yellow Sea
EAST CHINA SEA
SOUTH CHINA SEA
Philippine Sea
Sulu Sea
Celebes Sea
Java Sea
Bay of Bengal
Andaman Sea
Laccadive Sea
Gulf of Siam
Gulf of Tonkin
Tropic of Cancer
Aral'skoje More
Ozero Balchaš
Ulaanbaatar
BEIJING
TIANJIN
SHANGHAI
WUHAN
CHONGQING
GUANGZHOU
VICTORIA
HONG KONG
T'aipei
SOUL
P'yŏngyang
TŌKYŌ
ŌSAKA
DELHI
New Delhi
BOMBAY
CALCUTTA
MADRAS
KARACHI
Dacca
Rangoon
KRUNG THEP
Ha-noi
Phnum Pénh
THANH-PHO HO CHI MINH
MANILA
SINGAPORE
Kuala Lumpur
JAKARTA
BORNEO
SUMATERA
SULAWESI CELEBES
DECCAN
Colombo
Kābul
Lhasa
Kātmāndu
Natural vegetation zones
Mediterranean
Coniferous forest
Subtropical rain forest
Tropical rain forest
Temperate mixed forest
Semi-deciduous forest
Deciduous forest
Tropical deciduous forest
Locally wooded savanna
Grassland steppe
Short grasses
Desert scrub
Barren land
Climatic factors : November to April
HIGH
1036
1032
1028
1024
1020
1016
1012
Climatic factors : May to October
1012
1004
1000
996
LOW
Rainfall
cm
in
200
80
150
60
100
40
75
30
50
20
25
10
12.5
5
Isobars
Prevailing winds

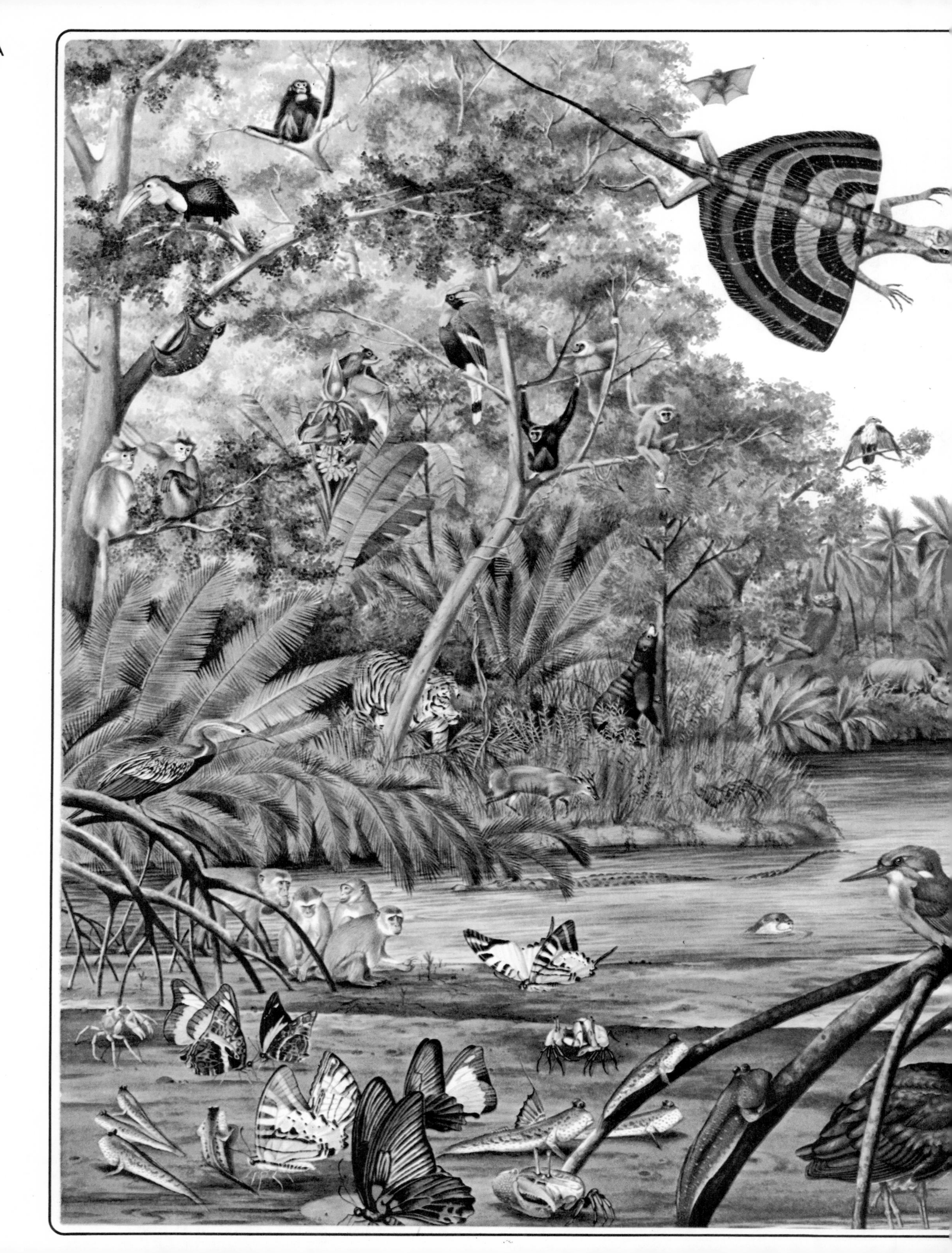

Southeast Asia

THE ORIENTAL REALM

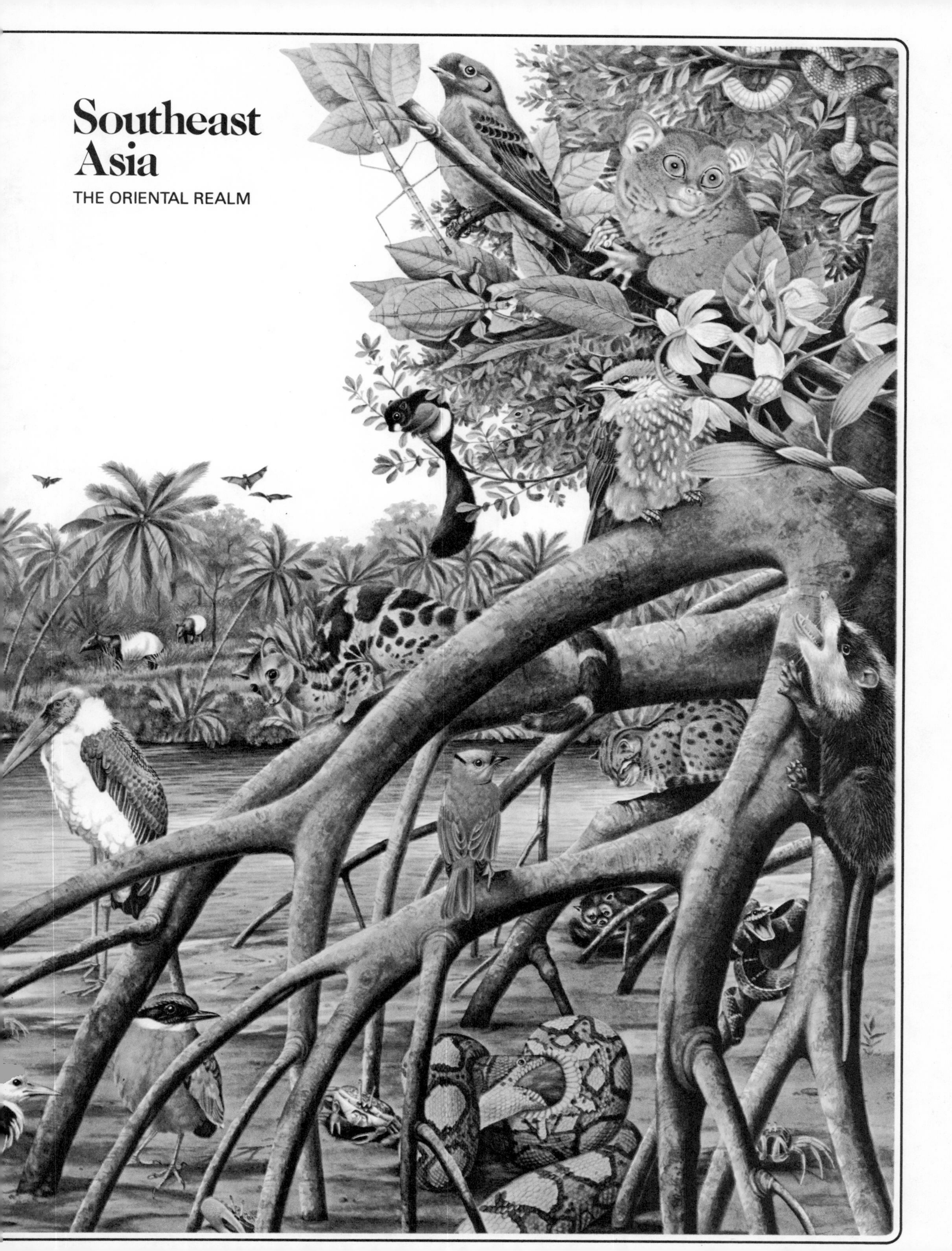

Africa

THE ETHIOPIAN REALM

The richest of all continents in the exuberance and variety of its wildlife, Africa forms an entire zoogeographical realm, the Ethiopian, excluding a narrow coastal strip to the northwest which falls in the Palaearctic. The dominant vegetational cover of the continent's heartland is the tropical rain forest, a green world of even temperature and humidity stretching from the Gulf of Guinea in the west to the highlands and Great Rift Valley (a huge fracture in the surface of the earth) in East Africa. Evidence suggests that this great forest was once even greater before it was supplanted, to its north and south, by grassy savanna – the plains and open skies which provide the backdrop for the world's great herds, the stalking cats which prey upon them, and the ravenous dogs and vultures performing their unpleasant but biologically necessary scavenging tasks. The savanna is the tourists' Africa; to the zoologist, it is one of a series of environments harboring plant and animal communities each uniquely adapted to its niche. The deserts which lie, north and south, beyond the savanna – the Sahara, the Kalahari and the Namib – contain life forms endowed with features which enable them to survive where man cannot. The fauna of African lakes ranges from the threated crocodile basking along the shores to the spectacular flocks of flamingos wading happily in the searingly alkaline waters of the shallow lakes. Alpine highlands, rivers and swamps complete the rich tapestry of the continent where man himself may have originated.

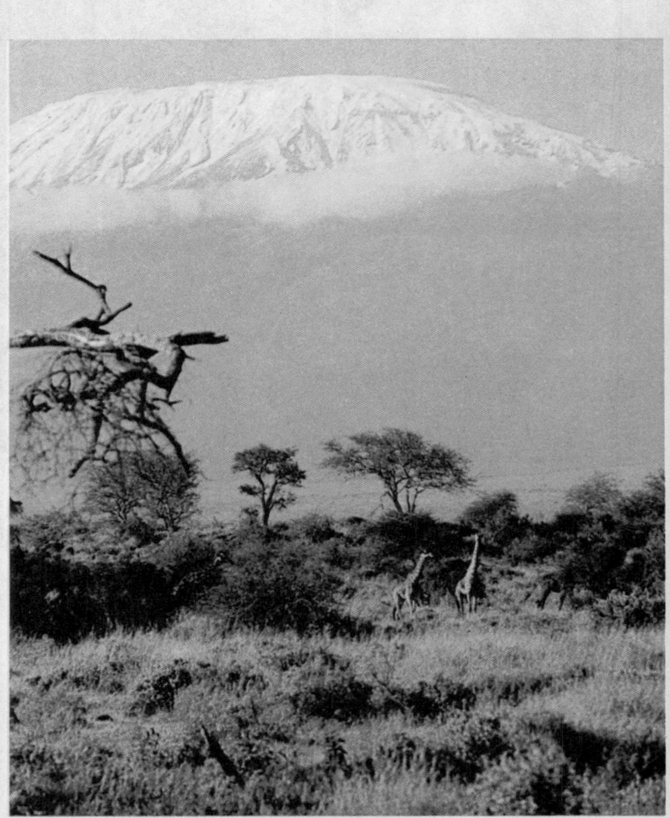

Savanna near Mt. Kilimanjaro, Tanzania, East Africa

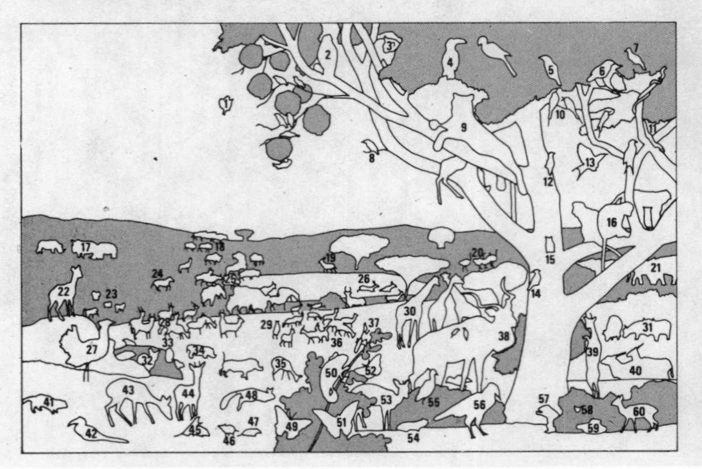

Key to panorama

1 Weaver birds	16 Vervet monkey	31 African buffalo	46 Elephant shrew
2 Auger buzzard	17 White rhinoceros	32 Bat-eared fox	47 Four-striped mouse
3 African wild cat	18 Wildebeest	33 Rock hyrax	48 Spring hare
4 Red-billed hornbill	19 Common waterbuck	34 Warthog	49 Citrus swallowtail
5 Blue glossy starling	20 Ostrich	35 Steinbok	50 Flap-necked chameleon
6 Superb glossy starling	21 Elephant	36 Thomson's gazelle	51 Large-striped swordtail
7 Purple glossy starling	22 Klipspringer	37 Preying mantis	52 Broad-bordered acraea
8 Angola kingfisher	23 Anubis baboon	38 Greater kudu	53 Grimm's duiker
9 Leopard and gazelle	24 Burchell's zebra	39 Gerenuk	54 Dwarf mongoose
10 Carmine bee eater	25 Topi	40 Cape eland	55 Oxpecker
11 Boomslang	26 Red lechwe	41 Zorilla	56 Ground hornbill
12 Nubian woodpecker	27 Kori bustard	42 Yellow-billed hornbill	57 Striped ground squirrel
13 Lilac-breasted roller	28 Kob	43 Oribi	58 Lesser bushbaby
14 Hoopoe	29 Impala	44 Austrida	59 African python
15 Scops owl	30 Kenyan giraffe	45 Two-striped field mouse	60 Kirk's dik-dik

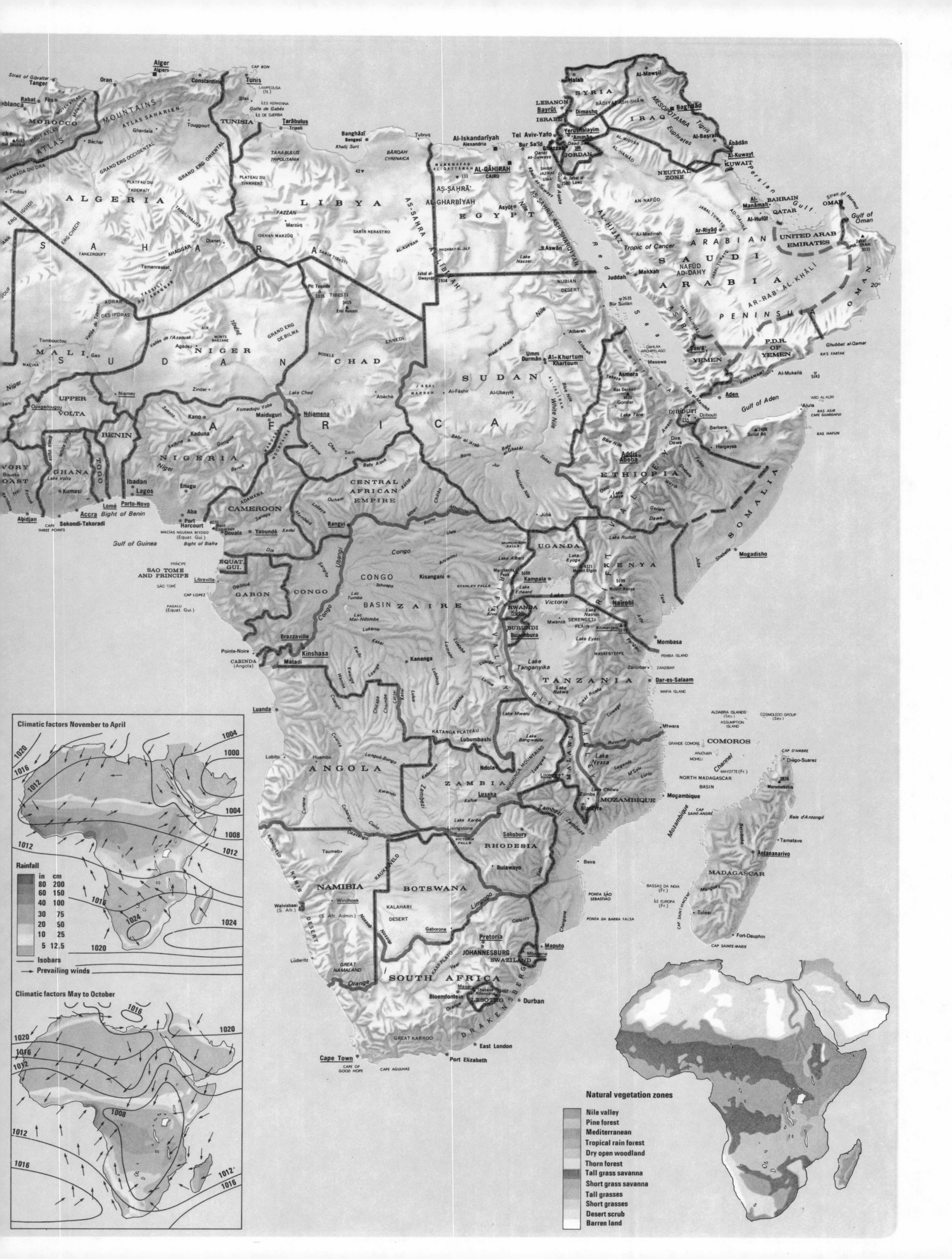

Climatic factors November to April

Rainfall

in	cm
80	200
60	150
40	100
30	75
20	50
10	25
5	12.5

— Isobars
→ Prevailing winds

Climatic factors May to October

Natural vegetation zones

Nile valley
Pine forest
Mediterranean
Tropical rain forest
Dry open woodland
Thorn forest
Tall grass savanna
Short grass savanna
Tall grasses
Short grasses
Desert scrub
Barren land

Africa

THE ETHIOPIAN REALM

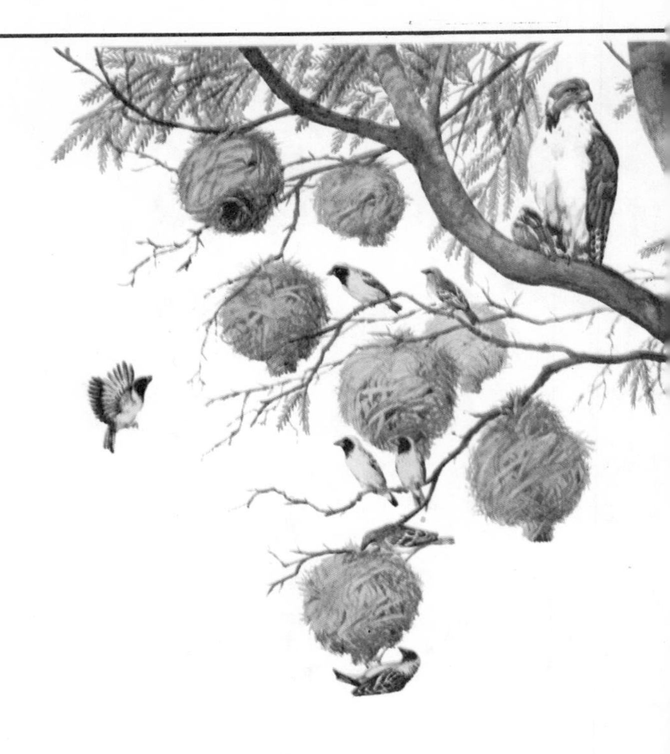

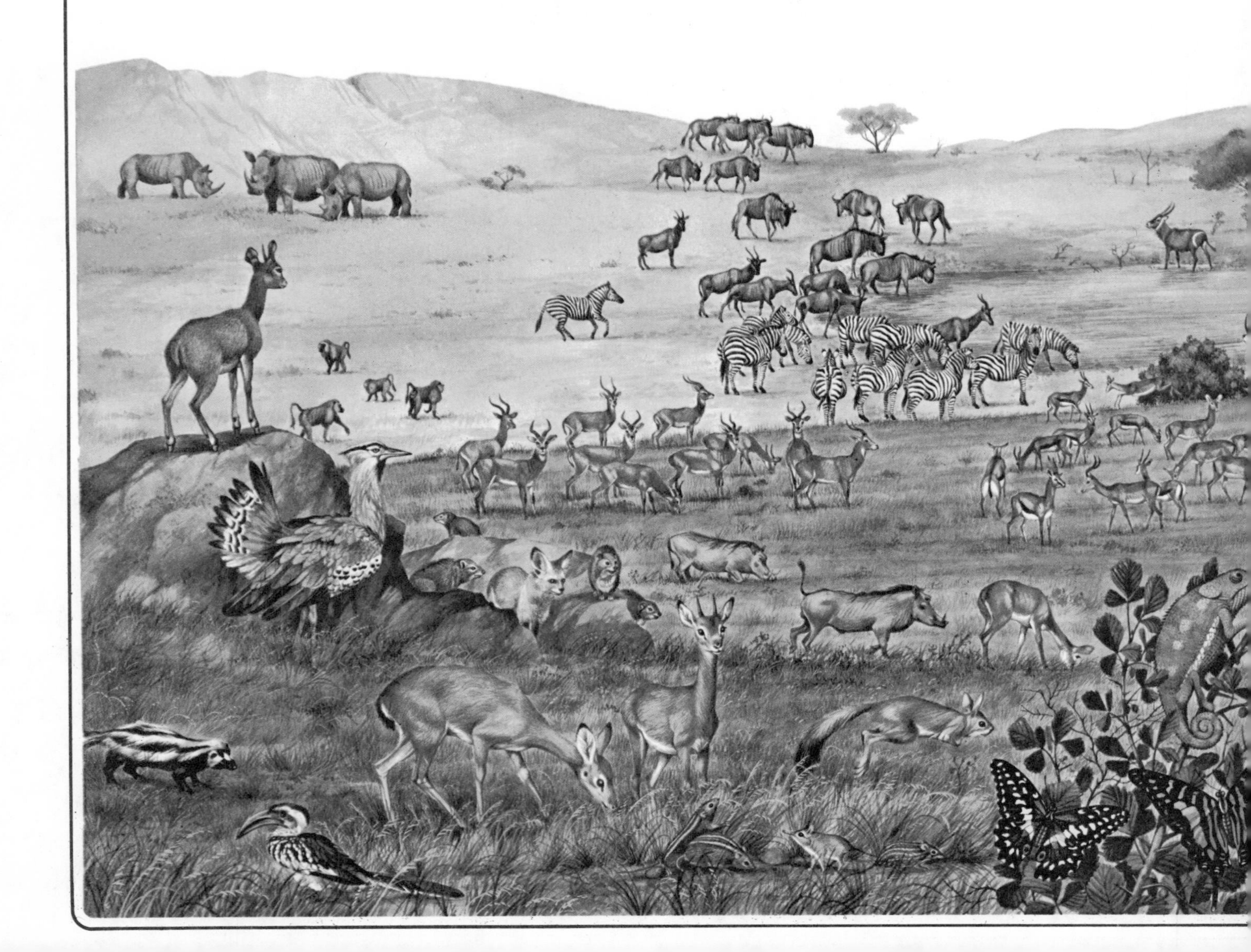

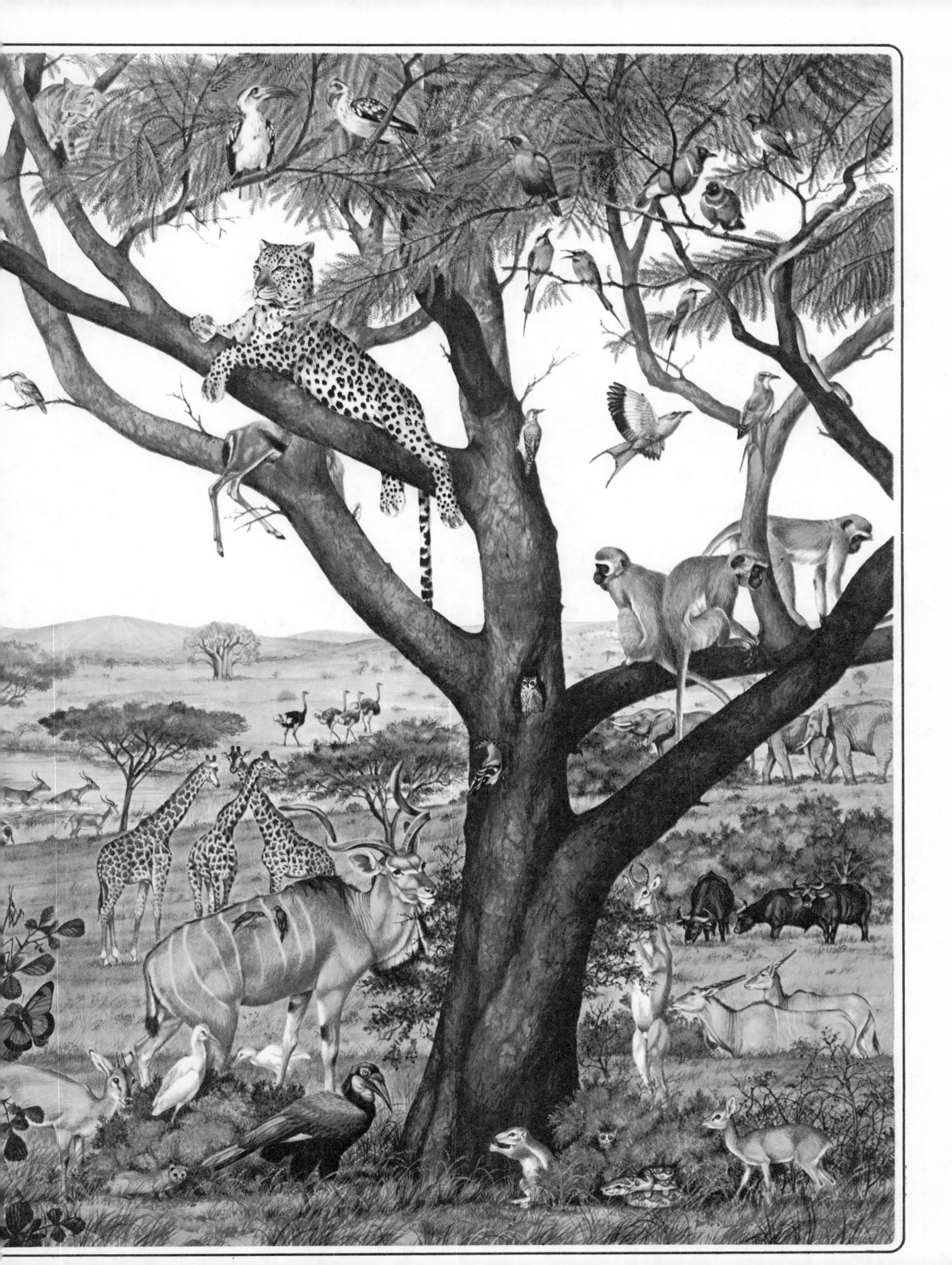

Australia
and
New Zealand

THE AUSTRALASIAN REALM

Isolated, geographically, from the rest of the world for at least 50 million years, Australia is the flattest of continents. Just over half its area is more than 1,000 feet (304 meters) above sea-level and this, mostly, is in an arc of mountains reaching from northern Queensland south to the Bass Strait and beyond into Tasmania. To the west of the mountains is the greater part of the continent and those regions that characterize it best; the deserts of sand, stone and clay. At first forbidding and inhospitable, these deserts are friendless only to modern man for they were the arena where nature best demonstrated the effects of a long, predation-free isolation on life forms which have no counterpart in other continents – except, vestigially, in South America to which it may once have been joined as part of a great, southern continent. These life forms were the marsupials, the 'pouched' animals, which radiated into almost as wide a range of forms and niches as those occupied by their more advanced placental counterparts in the rest of the world; and the even stranger monotremes, a breakaway group tracing its ancestry back to that moment in time when the early reptilians were diverging into primitive mammals. Across 1,000 miles of sea from this ancient landmass, the twin islands of New Zealand were developing another distinct theater of evolution of plants and helpless, peaceful animals – including the reptile relic of a species which vanished elsewhere more than 135 million years ago – unprepared for the invasion of man.

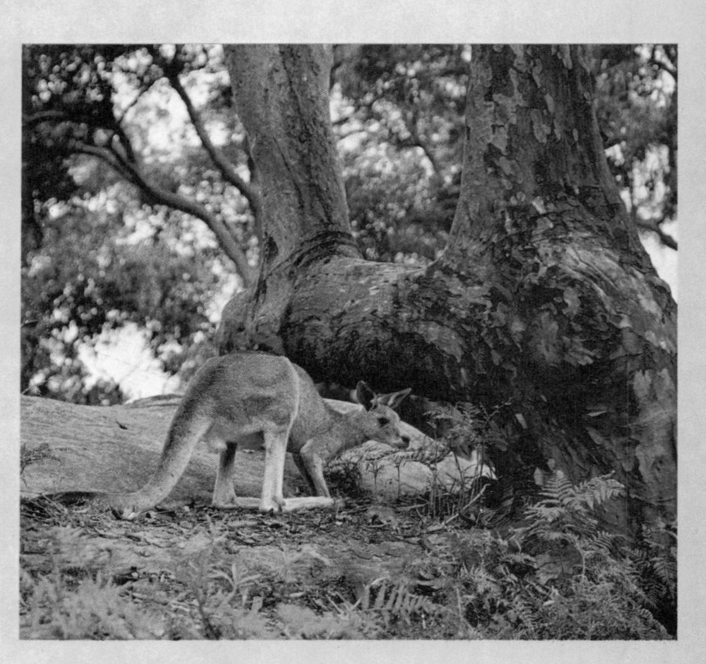

Grey kangaroo in arid scrubland, Eastern Australia

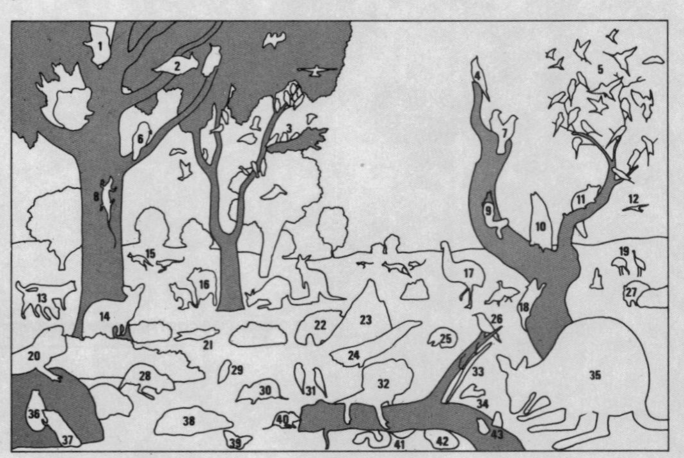

Key to panorama

1 Koala	16 Great grey kangaroo	31 Rainbow lorikeet
2 Sulphur-crested cockatoo	17 Emu	32 Frilled lizard
3 Galah	18 Northern native cat	33 Giant stick insect
4 Cockatiel	19 Brolga crane	34 Little quail
5 Budgerigar	20 Bearded dragon	35 Agile wallaby
6 Kookaburra	21 Red tailed cockatoo	36 Cicada
7 Crimson winged parrots	22 Wedge tailed eagle	37 Marsupial mouse
8 Lace monitor	23 Termite mound	38 Carpet python
9 King brown snake	24 Sand monitor	39 Checkered swallowtail
10 Tawny frogmouth	25 Echidna	40 Jerboa marsupial mouse
11 Sugar glider	26 Rainbow bee eater	41 Death adder
12 Black kite	27 Hairy nosed wombat	42 Holly cross toad
13 Dingo	28 Rufous rat kangaroo	43 Common Australian crow butterfly
14 Wallaroo	29 Turquoise grass parrot	
15 Great red kangaroo	30 Long nosed bandicoot	

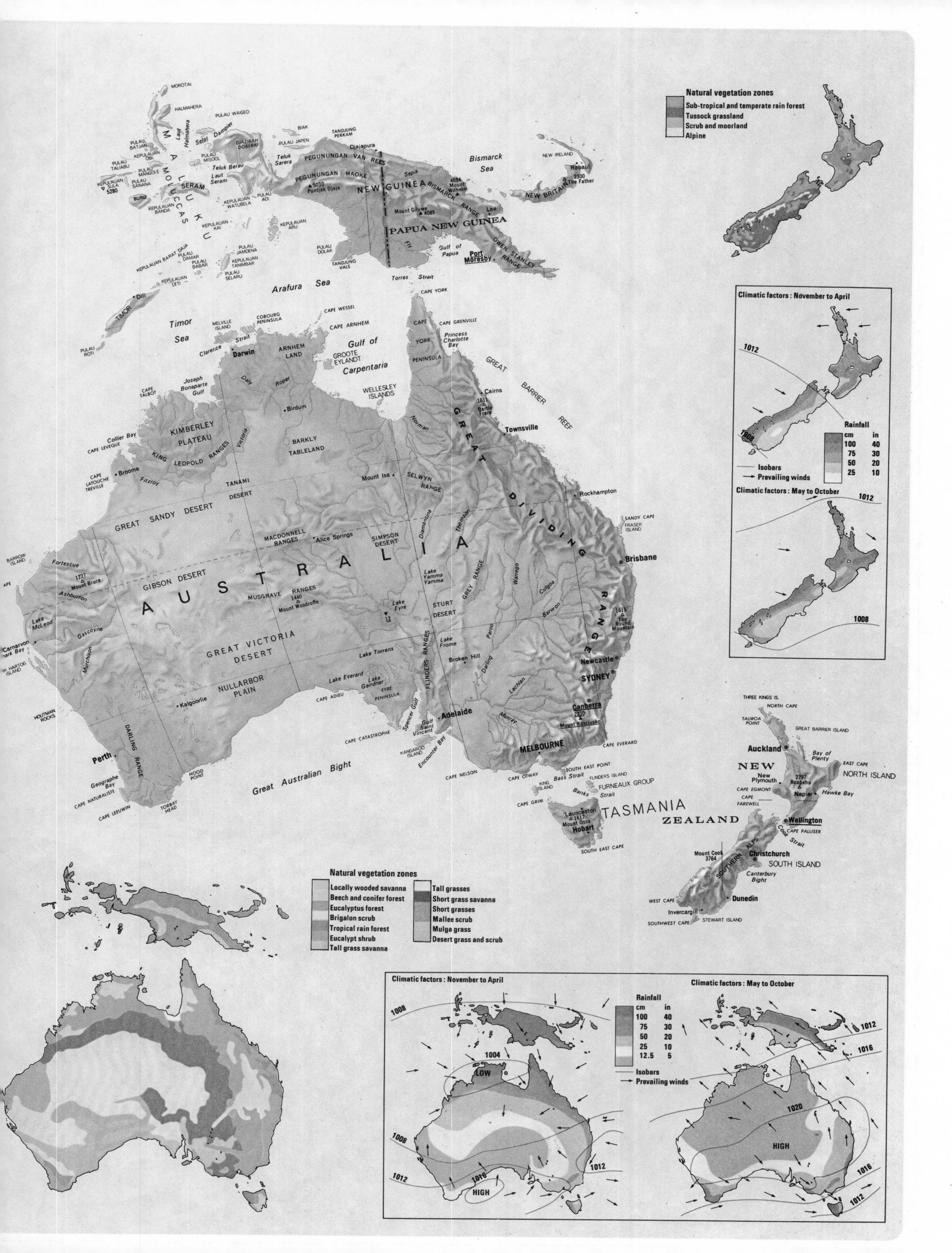

Natural vegetation zones
Sub-tropical and temperate rain forest
Tussock grassland
Scrub and moorland
Alpine
MOROTAI
HALMAHERA
PULAU WAIGEO
MALUKU
MOLUCCAS
SERAM
BURU
Arafura Sea
Timor Sea
TIMOR
Dili
PEGUNUNGAN VAN REES
PEGUNUNGAN MAOKE
NEW GUINEA
PAPUA NEW GUINEA
BISMARCK RANGE
OWEN STANLEY RANGE
Bismarck Sea
NEW BRITAIN
NEW IRELAND
Rabaul
Lae
Port Moresby
Gulf of Papua
Torres Strait
Mount Wilhelm
Mount Giluwe
Puntjak Djaja
Sepik
Fly
CAPE YORK
CAPE YORK PENINSULA
Gulf of Carpentaria
GROOTE EYLANDT
WELLESLEY ISLANDS
MELVILLE ISLAND
COBOURG PENINSULA
CAPE WESSEL
CAPE ARNHEM
ARNHEM LAND
Darwin
Clarence Strait
Joseph Bonaparte Gulf
CAPE TALBOT
KIMBERLEY PLATEAU
KING LEOPOLD RANGES
Collier Bay
CAPE LEVEQUE
Broome
Fitzroy
BARKLY TABLELAND
Birdum
Daly
Roper
Victoria
TANAMI DESERT
GREAT SANDY DESERT
Mount Isa
SELWYN RANGE
GREAT BARRIER REEF
Cairns
Bartle Frere
Townsville
GREAT DIVIDING RANGE
Rockhampton
SANDY CAPE
FRASER ISLAND
Brisbane
MACDONNELL RANGES
Alice Springs
SIMPSON DESERT
AUSTRALIA
GIBSON DESERT
MUSGRAVE RANGES
Mount Woodroffe
Mount Bruce
Fortescue
Ashburton
BARROW ISLAND
Lake McLeod
Gascoyne
Carnarvon
Murchison
Lake Eyre
Lake Yamma Yamma
STURT DESERT
GREY RANGE
Diamantina
Thomson
Warrego
Culgoa
Barwon
Paroo
Darling
Lachlan
Murray
GREAT VICTORIA DESERT
NULLARBOR PLAIN
Kalgoorlie
Lake Torrens
Lake Frome
Lake Everard
Lake Gairdner
EYRE PENINSULA
FLINDERS RANGES
Broken Hill
Newcastle
SYDNEY
Canberra
Mount Kosciusko
Adelaide
Spencer Gulf
Gulf Saint Vincent
KANGAROO ISLAND
Encounter Bay
CAPE ADIEU
CAPE CATASTROPHE
MELBOURNE
CAPE EVERARD
CAPE OTWAY
CAPE NELSON
Bass Strait
KING ISLAND
FLINDERS ISLAND
FURNEAUX GROUP
Banks Strait
CAPE GRIM
TASMANIA
Launceston
Mount Ossa
Hobart
SOUTH EAST CAPE
SOUTH EAST POINT
Perth
DARLING RANGE
Geographe Bay
CAPE NATURALISTE
CAPE LEEUWIN
TORBAY HEAD
HOOD POINT
Great Australian Bight
HOUTMAN ROCKS
THREE KINGS IS.
NORTH CAPE
GREAT BARRIER ISLAND
Auckland
Bay of Plenty
EAST CAPE
NORTH ISLAND
NEW ZEALAND
New Plymouth
CAPE EGMONT
Ruapehu
Napier
Hawke Bay
CAPE FAREWELL
Wellington
CAPE PALLISER
Cook Strait
Mount Cook
SOUTHERN ALPS
Christchurch
SOUTH ISLAND
Canterbury Bight
Dunedin
WEST CAPE
Invercargill
SOUTHWEST CAPE
STEWART ISLAND
Climatic factors : November to April
Rainfall
cm in
100 40
75 30
50 20
25 10
Isobars
Prevailing winds
Climatic factors : May to October
1012
1008
Natural vegetation zones
Locally wooded savanna
Beech and conifer forest
Eucalyptus forest
Brigalon scrub
Tropical rain forest
Eucalypt shrub
Tall grass savanna
Tall grasses
Short grass savanna
Short grasses
Mallee scrub
Mulga grass
Desert grass and scrub
Climatic factors : November to April
Climatic factors : May to October
Rainfall
cm in
100 40
75 30
50 20
25 10
12.5 5
Isobars
Prevailing winds
LOW
HIGH
1004
1008
1012
1016
1020

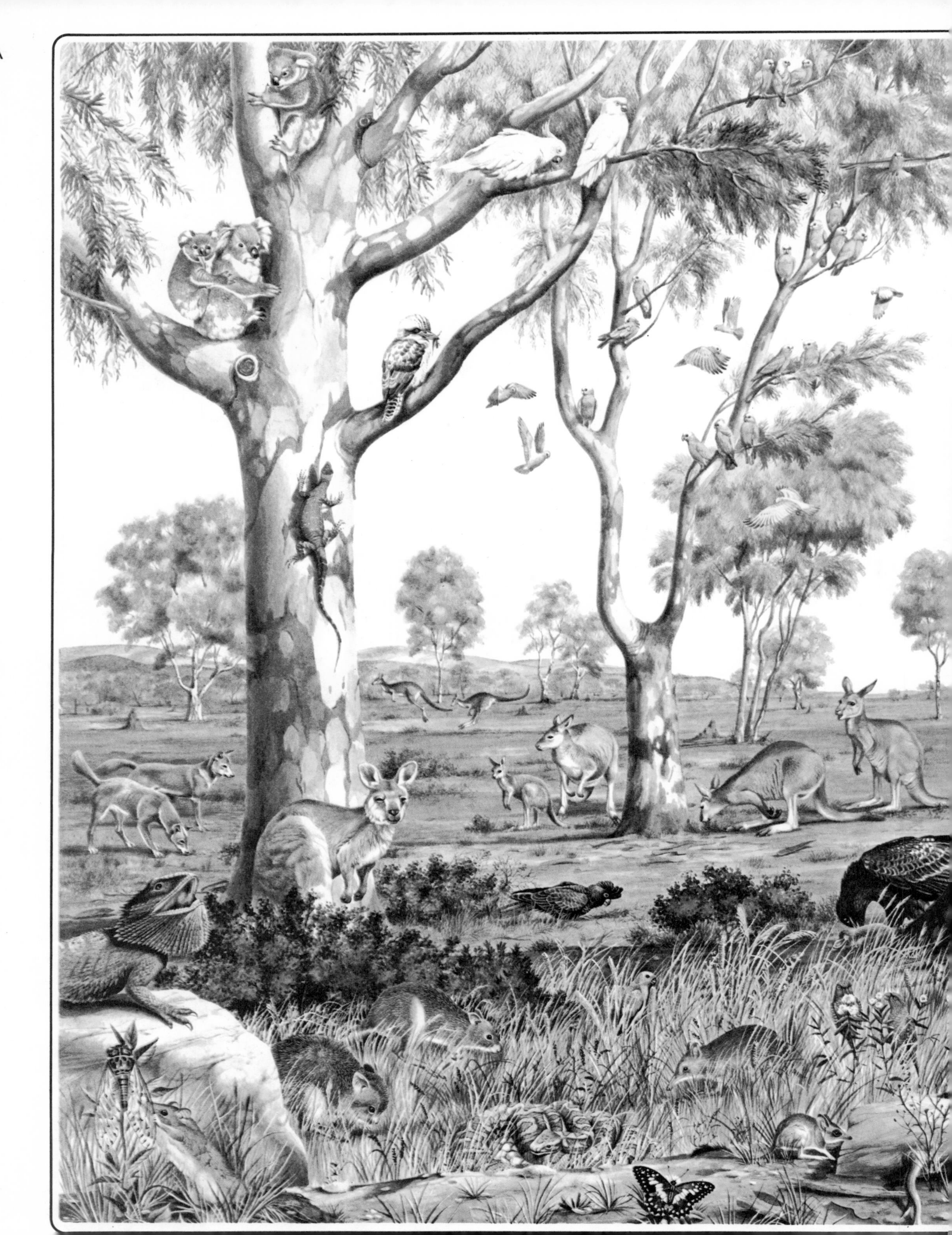

Australia and New Zealand

THE AUSTRALASIAN REALM

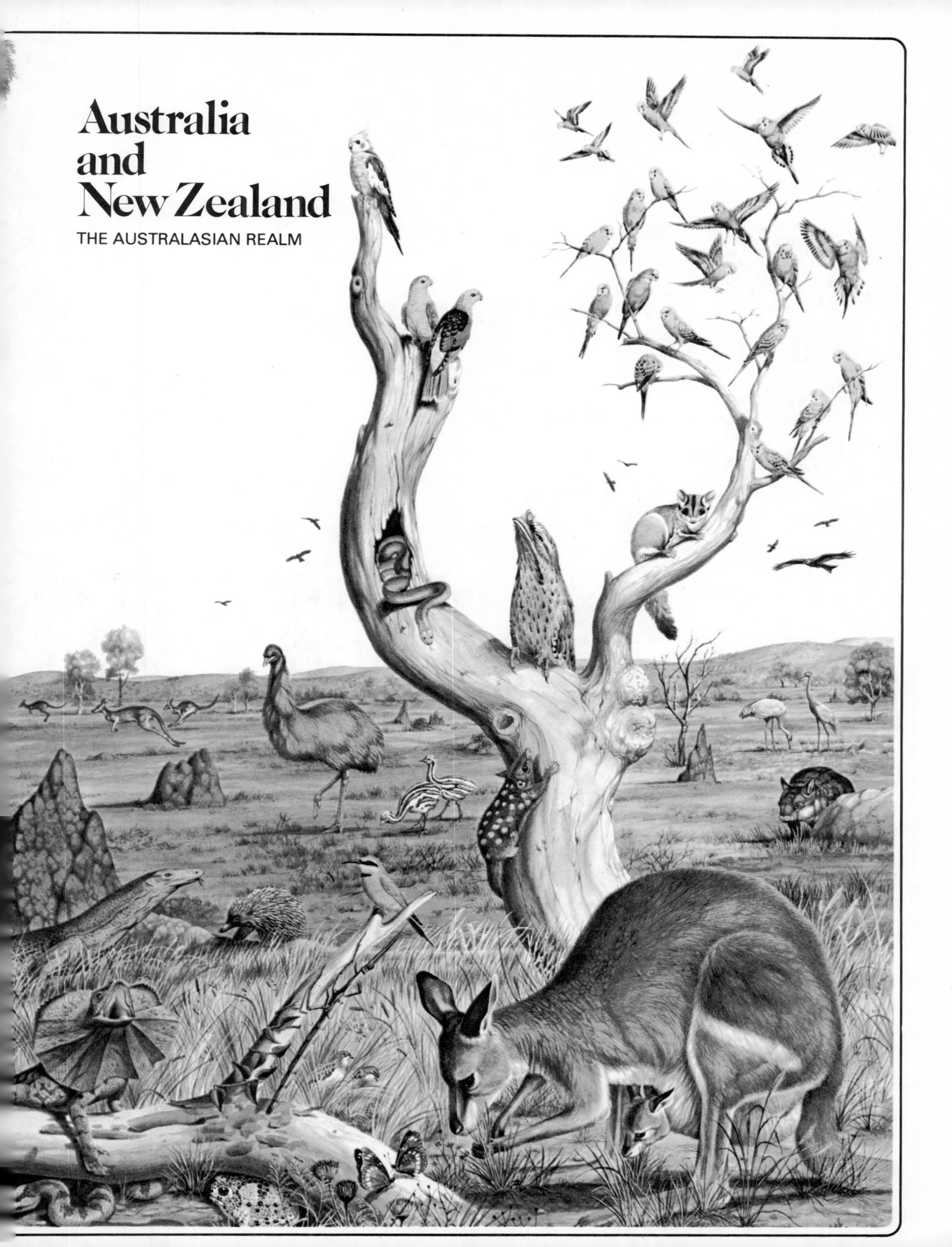

Central and South America

THE NEOTROPICAL REALM

The connexion between South America and the rest of the world has never been more than tenuous and – for much of the history of life on earth – non-existent. It is an isolation that has given to the continent a flora and fauna characteristically its own, but owing some influence to the northern continent and through it, to the great landmass of Eurasia. It is a continent of superlative geography. A mountain spine, the mighty Andes, reaches for thousands of miles from the northern hemisphere almost to touch Antarctica with a rocky finger. It has a river, the Amazon, much greater in almost every sense than any other in the world and a forest of unparalleled size and unbridled luxuriance. Its coastal waters teem with marine life and offshore there are islands, the Galapagos, harboring species which caused traditional theories of evolution to be revised. The great glories are, however, the river and the forest, *Hylea amazonica*, which clothes the basin of the Amazon and its tributaries, 17 of which are more than 1,000 miles (1,600km) long. In this great forest, vegetation and river are largely indivisible. Most life forms must either climb or swim, unless they are birds or fish. The result is a lavish avian fauna and countless, many-hued fish, with a small but exceedingly diverse animal life that will climb, if need be, or take to the water with ease. The highlands of the Andes support a fauna uniquely adapted to its rarified air and deserts as barren as any in the world fringe the Pacific margins.

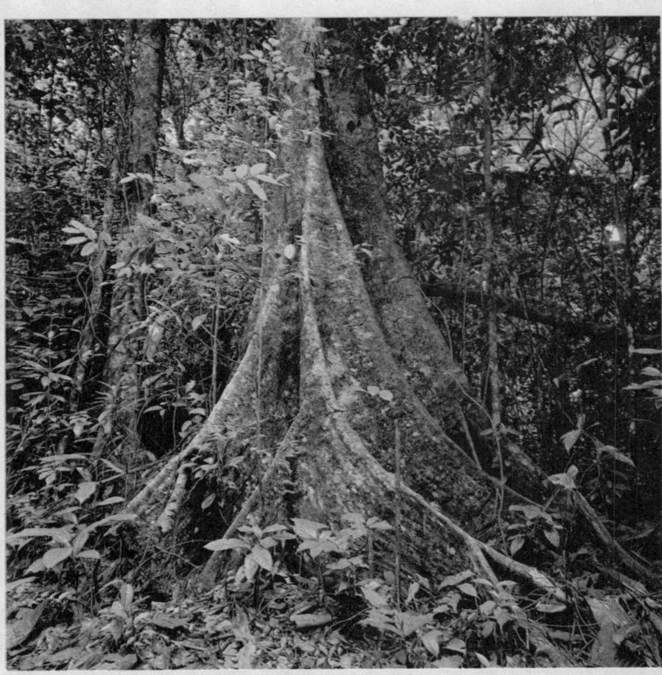

Buttressed roots in mangrove swamp, Amazon basin, South America

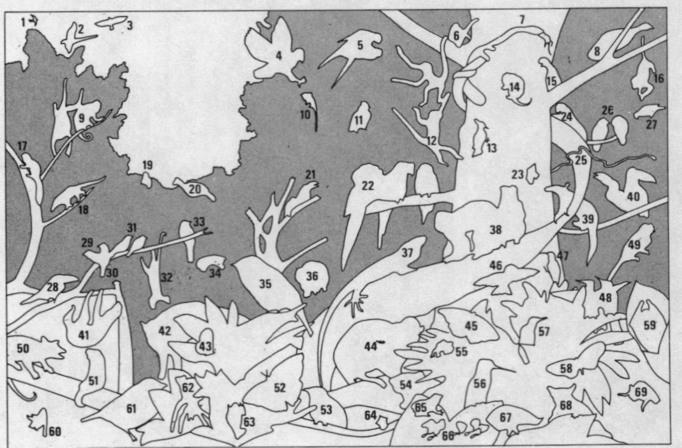

Key to panorama

1 Swifts	24 Tayra	47 Red-billed scythebill
2 Hyacinthine macaw	25 Vine snake	48 Crimson topaz hummingbirds
3 Ornate hawk eagle	26 Yellow-headed Amazon parrot	49 Geoffrey's marmoset
4 Harpy eagle	27 Blue-headed parrot	50 Grey fan-eyed opossum
5 Blue and yellow macaws	28 Lettered aracari	51 Pygmy anteater
6 Geoffrey's spider monkey	29 Paradise tanager	52 Morpho butterfly
7 Boa constrictor	30 Swallow tanager	53 Gould's manakin
8 White crested guan	31 Blue-necked tanager	54 White-eared tufted marmoset
9 Red howler monkey	32 Kinkajou	55 Tree frog
10 Squirrel monkey	33 White-tailed trogan	56 Long-billed star-throat hummingbird
11 Cock of the rock	34 Emerald tree boa	57 Fork-tailed wood nymph
12 Black spider monkey	35 Blue-grey tanager	58 Heliconid butterfly
13 Chestnut woodpecker	36 Cotton-headed tamarins	59 Disk-winged bat
14 Tree porcupine	37 Common iguana	60 Fisherman bats
15 Ornate umbrella bird	38 Black-capped capuchin	61 Beryl-spangled tanager
16 Wooly monkey	39 Tamandua	62 Bird-eating spider
17 Monk saki	40 Sulphur-breasted toucan	63 Tree frog
18 Coatimundi	41 Two-toed sloth	64 Tree hopper
19 Red uakari	42 Margay	65 Tree frog
20 Great razor-billed curassaw	43 Window pane butterfly	66 Parasol ant
21 Toco toucans	44 Squirrel monkey	67 Katydid
22 Scarlet macaws	45 Blue morpho butterfly	68 Mouse opossum
23 False vampire bat	46 Ruby topaz hummingbird	69 Vampire bat

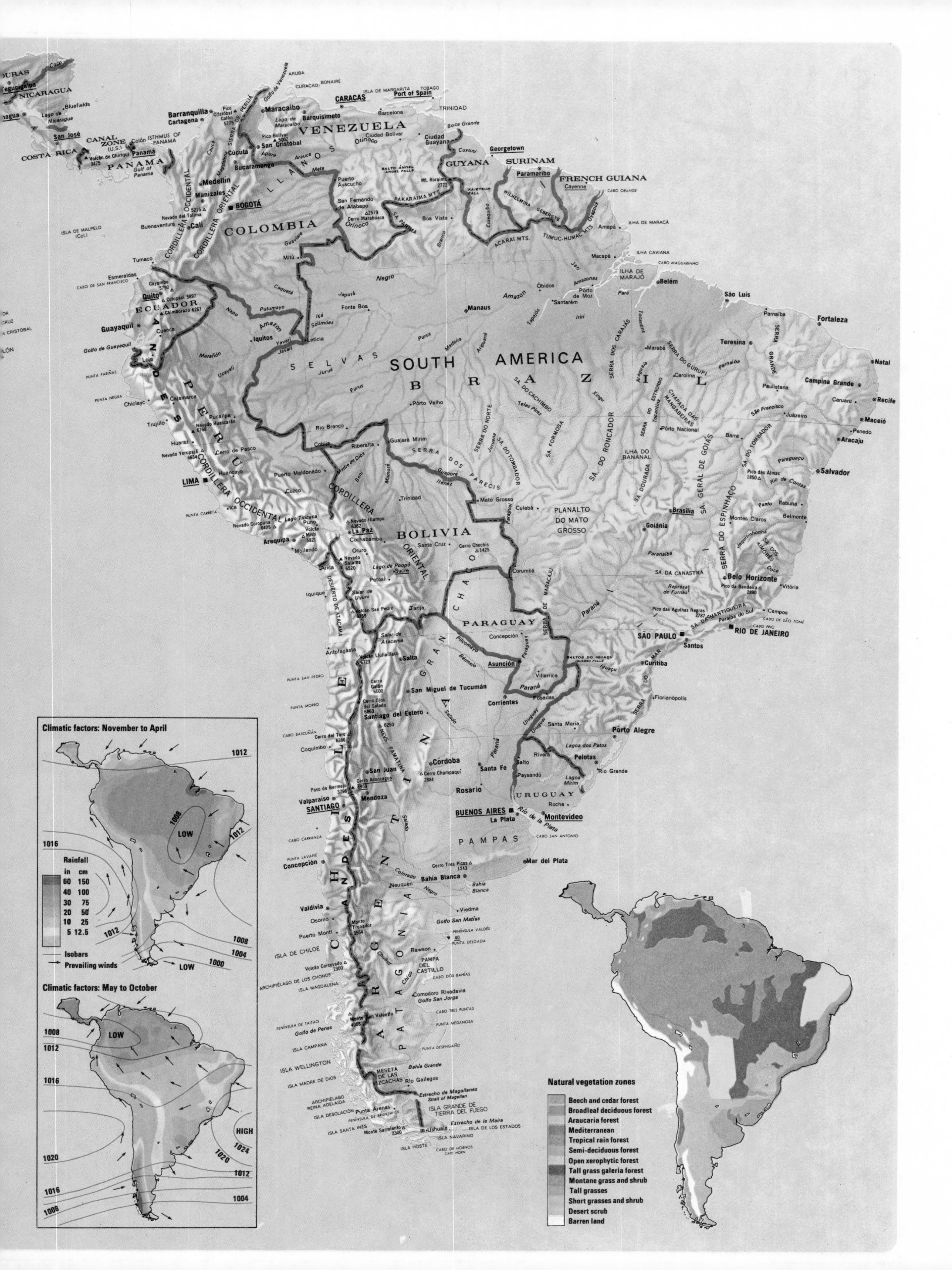
SOUTH AMERICA
BRAZIL
VENEZUELA
COLOMBIA
ECUADOR
PERU
BOLIVIA
PARAGUAY
URUGUAY
ARGENTINA
CHILE
GUYANA
SURINAM
FRENCH GUIANA
NICARAGUA
COSTA RICA
PANAMA
CANAL ZONE (U.S.)
ANDES
SELVAS
LLANOS
GRAN CHACO
PAMPAS
PATAGONIA
PLANALTO DO MATO GROSSO
CARACAS
BOGOTÁ
Quito
LIMA
La Paz
Sucre
Asunción
SANTIAGO
BUENOS AIRES
Montevideo
Georgetown
Paramaribo
Cayenne
Port of Spain
Brasília
SÃO PAULO
RIO DE JANEIRO
Maracaibo
Barranquilla
Cartagena
Medellín
Cali
Guayaquil
Iquitos
Manaus
Belém
São Luís
Fortaleza
Natal
Recife
Maceió
Aracaju
Salvador
Belo Horizonte
Curitiba
Pôrto Alegre
Pelotas
Rio Grande
Córdoba
Rosario
Santa Fe
Mendoza
San Juan
Salta
San Miguel de Tucumán
Corrientes
Mar del Plata
Bahía Blanca
La Plata
Valparaíso
Concepción
Antofagasta
Arica
Arequipa
Cuzco
Puerto Montt
Punta Arenas
Ushuaia
Amazon
Negro
Orinoco
Paraná
Paraguay
Uruguay
Río de la Plata
Lago Titicaca
Lago de Poopó
Salar de Uyuni
DESIERTO DE ATACAMA
Estrecho de Magallanes
ISLA GRANDE DE TIERRA DEL FUEGO
CABO DE HORNOS
Climatic factors: November to April
Climatic factors: May to October
LOW
HIGH
Rainfall
in cm
60 150
40 100
30 75
20 50
10 25
5 12.5
Isobars
Prevailing winds
Natural vegetation zones
Beech and cedar forest
Broadleaf deciduous forest
Araucaria forest
Mediterranean
Tropical rain forest
Semi-deciduous forest
Open xerophytic forest
Tall grass galeria forest
Montane grass and shrub
Tall grasses
Short grasses and shrub
Desert scrub
Barren land

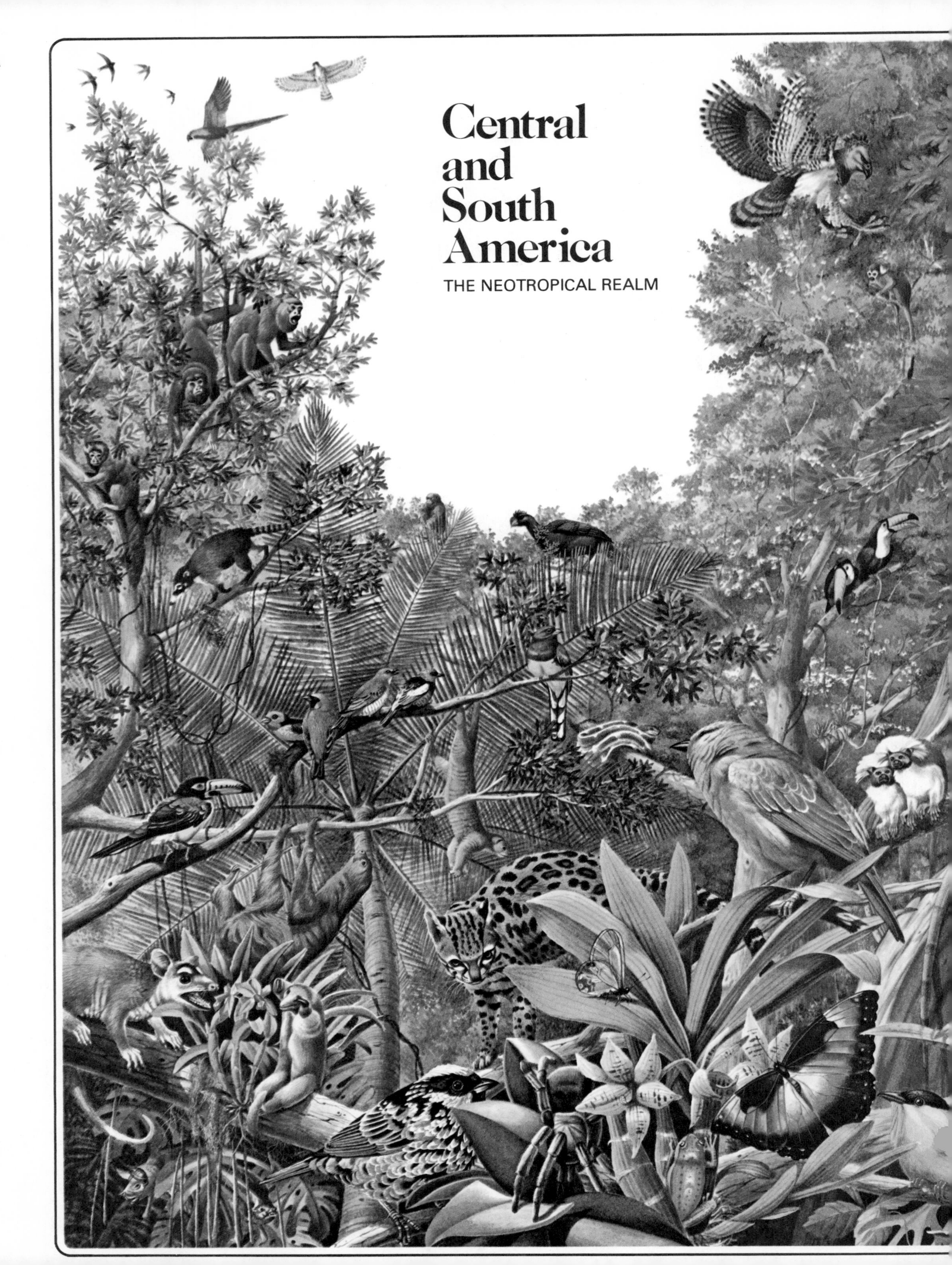

Central and South America

THE NEOTROPICAL REALM

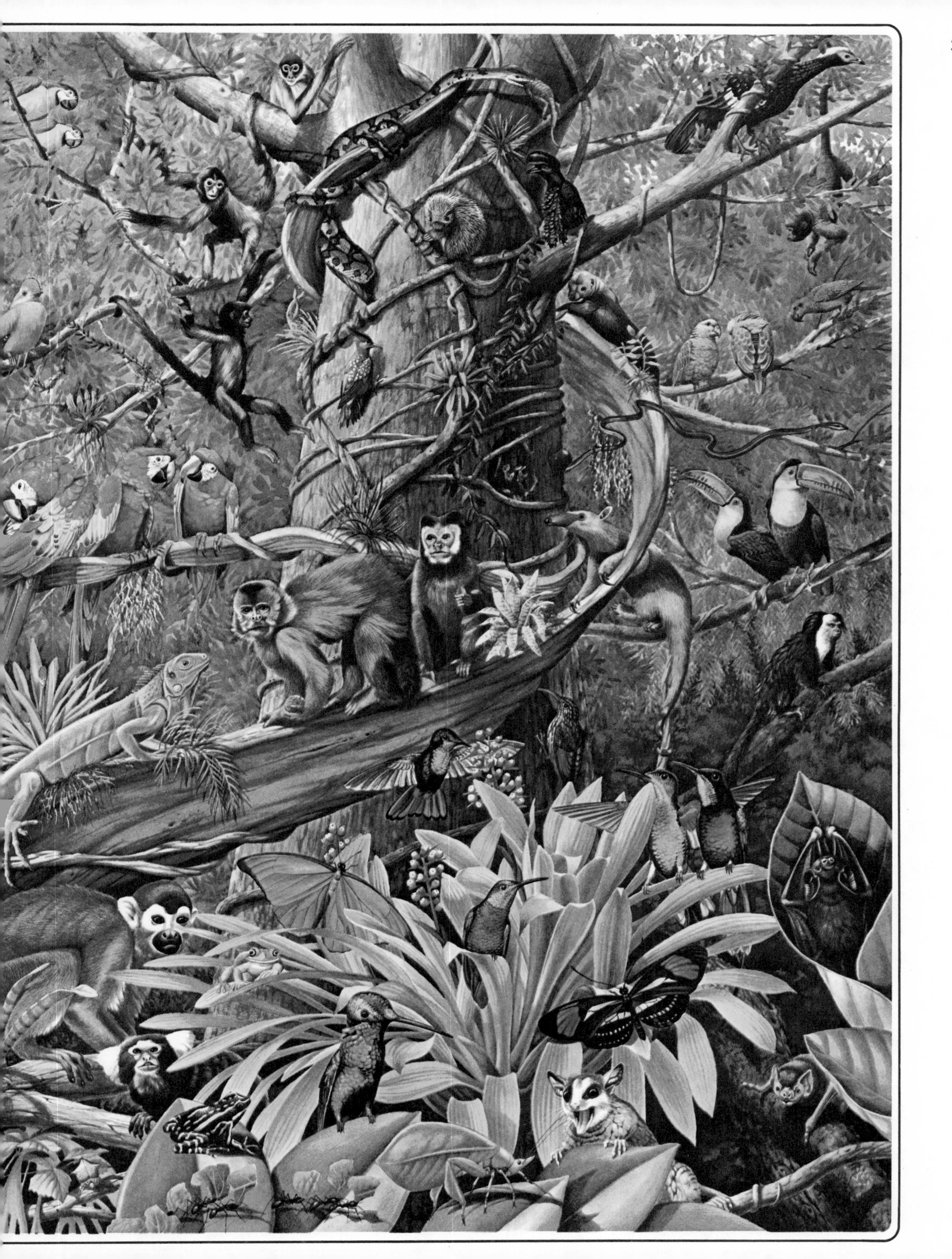

North America

THE NEARCTIC REALM

The first Europeans to colonize the North American continent had little comprehension of the true nature of the land they had settled. The ancient grandeur of its topography and wildlife were perhaps hidden by an immeasurable potential for the creation of a new society, based on an improved image of the one the settlers had left behind. In such an image there was little concern for environment and conservation; these were concepts that had still to come. They arrived too late to save some species that had proliferated in earlier times and are not altogether effective in holding back the demise of others. But the North Americans were the first to introduce the idea of reserves, or national parks, to protect regions of singular value for posterity, and their prophets of conservation are among the most influential. The continent is large enough still to hold surprises for the naturalist fortunate enough to observe them at close hand, from the alpine regions of the Rockies and the misty forests of the Pacific seaboard to the swamplands and bayous of the southeast and Florida, almost touching the Tropic of Cancer. North of the 49th parallel there are still vast expanses where man is still less common than some of the larger animals he hunts and south, across the Rio Grande, the northern areas of the ancient bridge to South America retain much of their age-old faunal flavor. All this is North America, a continent where man has done his worst, and is still doing his best, for the landscape and the animals he shares it with.

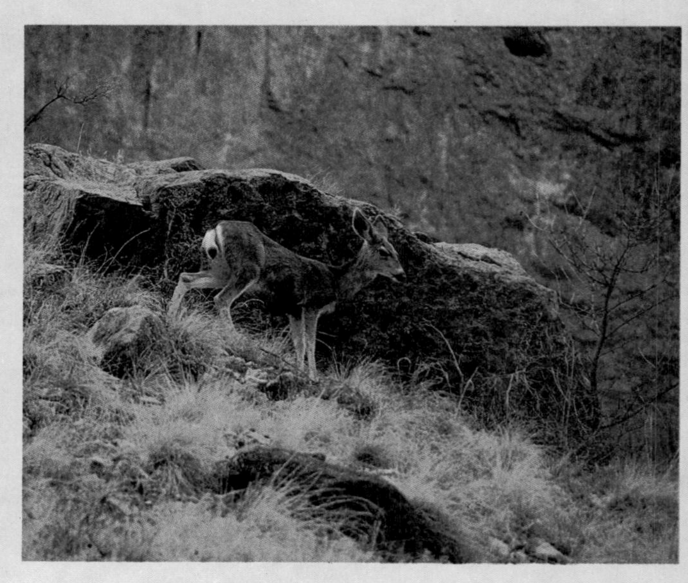

Immature mule deer, Grand Canyon, Arizona U.S.A.

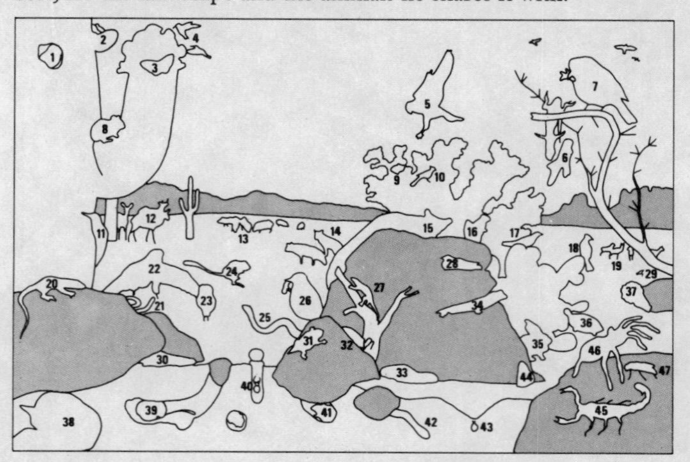

Key to panorama

1 Elf owl	17 Cactus wren	33 Diamond back rattlesnake
2 Black-chinned hummingbird	18 Ashy throated flycatcher	34 Chuckawalla
3 Swallowtail butterfly	19 Pronghorn	35 Jack rabbit
4 Rufous throated hummingbird	20 Collared lizard	36 Desert tortoise
5 Sparrow hawk	21 King snake	37 Skunk
6 Grasshopper	22 Prairie falcon	38 Kit fox
7 Northern shrike	23 Burrowing owl	39 Kangaroo rat
8 Pack rat	24 Kangaroo rat	40 Trapdoor spider
9 White footed mouse	25 Sidewinder	41 Pocket mouse
10 Pyrrhuloxia	26 Road runner	42 Bull snake
11 Gila woodpecker	27 Desert spiny lizard	43 Ant lion
12 Mule deer	28 Poorwill	44 Monarch butterfly
13 Peccaries	29 Bobwhite quail	45 Desert scorpion
14 Coyote	30 Gila monster	46 Tarantula
15 Ringtail	31 Horned lizard	47 Tarantula hawk wasp
16 Chipmunk	32 Grasshopper mouse	

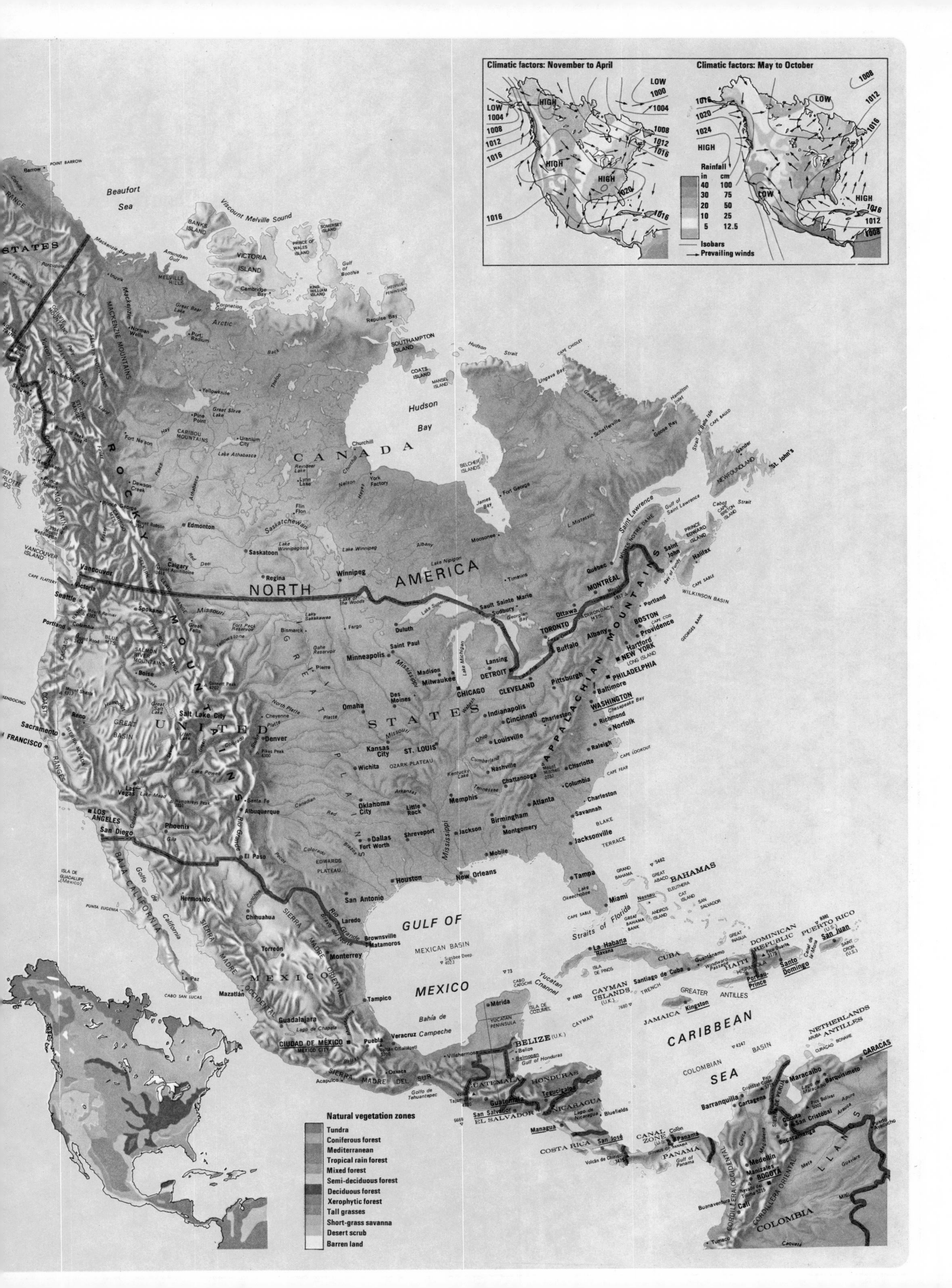

Climatic factors: November to April   Climatic factors: May to October

Rainfall
in   cm
40   100
30   75
20   50
10   25
5   12.5

— Isobars
→ Prevailing winds

Natural vegetation zones

Tundra
Coniferous forest
Mediterranean
Tropical rain forest
Mixed forest
Semi-deciduous forest
Deciduous forest
Xerophytic forest
Tall grasses
Short-grass savanna
Desert scrub
Barren land

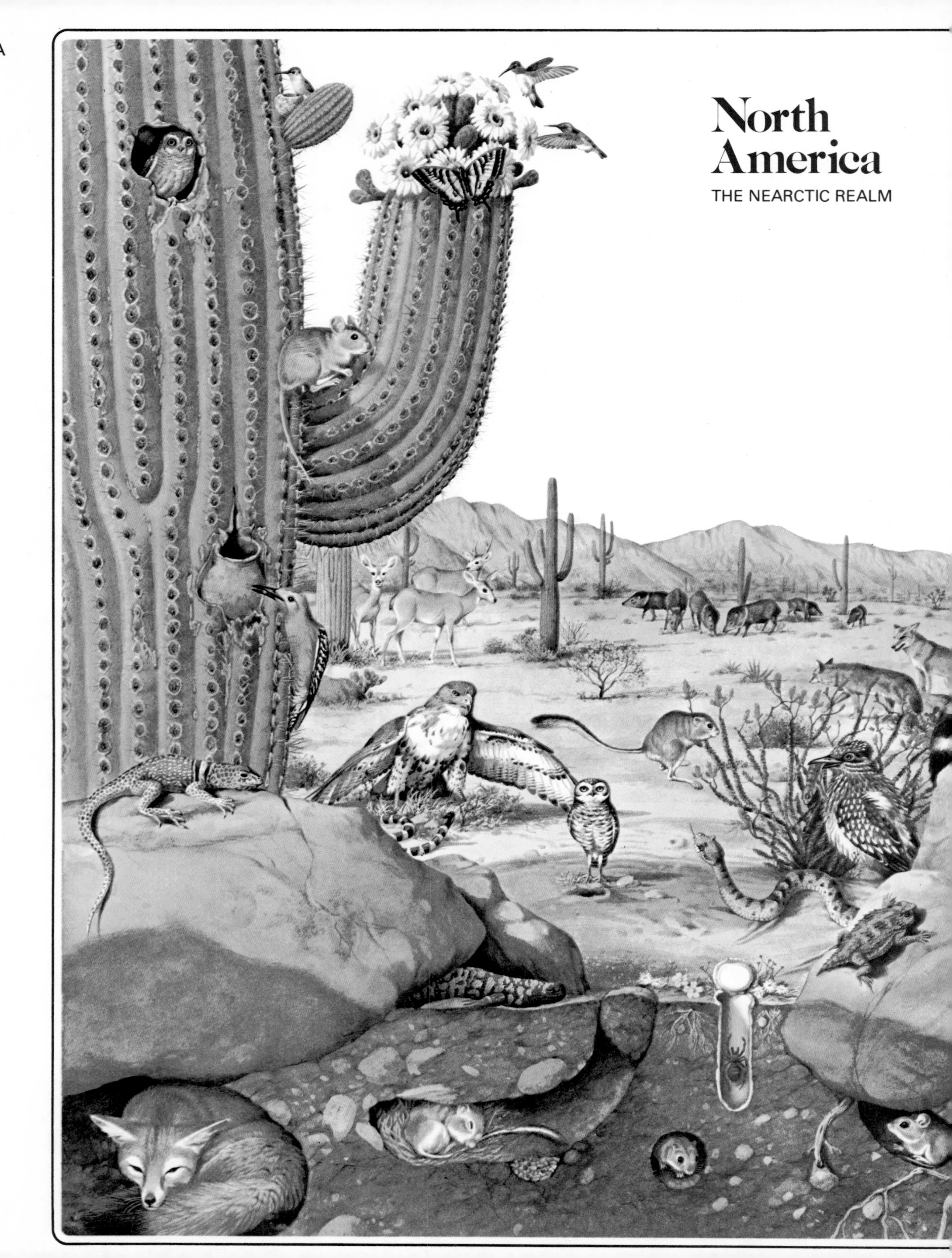

North America
THE NEARCTIC REALM

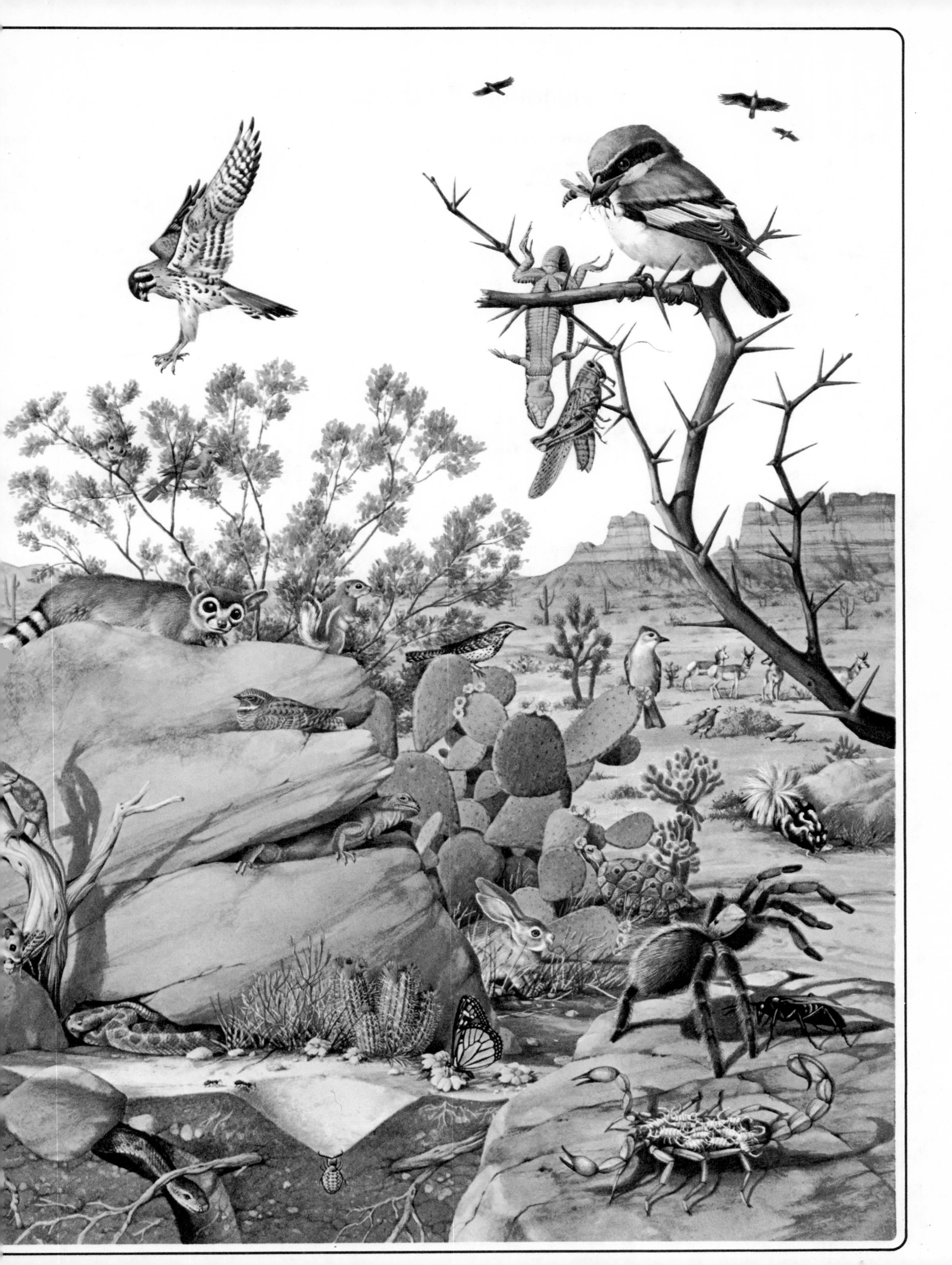

Explanation of Map Symbols

CULTURAL FEATURES

Political Boundaries

International

Secondary (State, province, etc.)

County

Populated Places

Cities, towns, and villages

••••••● Symbol size represents population of the place

Chicago
Gary
Racine
Glenview
Edgewood

Type size represents relative importance of the place

Corporate area of large U.S. and Canadian cities and urban area of other foreign cities

Major Urban Area
Area of continuous commercial, industrial, and residential development in and around a major city

○ Community within a city

⊛ Capital of major political unit

☆ Capital of secondary political unit

◉ Capital of U.S. state or Canadian province

● County Seat

▲ Military Installation

☉ Scientific Station

Miscellaneous

National Park

National Monument

Provincial Park

Indian Reservation

△ Point of Interest

∴ Ruins

■ ♣ Buildings

Race Track

Railroad

Tunnel

Underground or Subway

Dam

Bridge

Dike

LAND FEATURES

Passes =

Point of Elevation above sea level + 8,520 FT.

WATER FEATURES

Coastlines and Shorelines

Indefinite or Unsurveyed Coastlines and Shorelines

Lakes and Reservoirs

Canals

Rivers and Streams

Falls and Rapids

Intermittent or Unsurveyed Rivers and Streams

Directional Flow Arrow

Rocks, Shoals and Reefs

TYPE STYLES USED TO NAME FEATURE

ASIA — Continent

DENMARK CANADA — Country, State, or Province

BÉARN — Region, Province, or Historical Region

CROCKETT — County

PANTELLERIA (ITALY) — Country of which unit is a dependency in parentheses

SRI LANKA (CEYLON) — Former or alternate name

Rome (Roma) — Local or alternate city name

Naval Air Station — Military Installation

MESA VERDE SAN XAVIER — National Park or Monument, Provincial Park, Indian Res.,

UINTA DESERT — Major Terrain Features

MT. MORIAH — Individual Mountain

STROMBOLI NUNIVAK — Island or Coastal Feature

Ocean
Lake
River
Canal — Hydrographic Features

Note: Size of type varies according to importance and available space. Letters for names of major features are spread across the extent of the feature

The Index Reference System

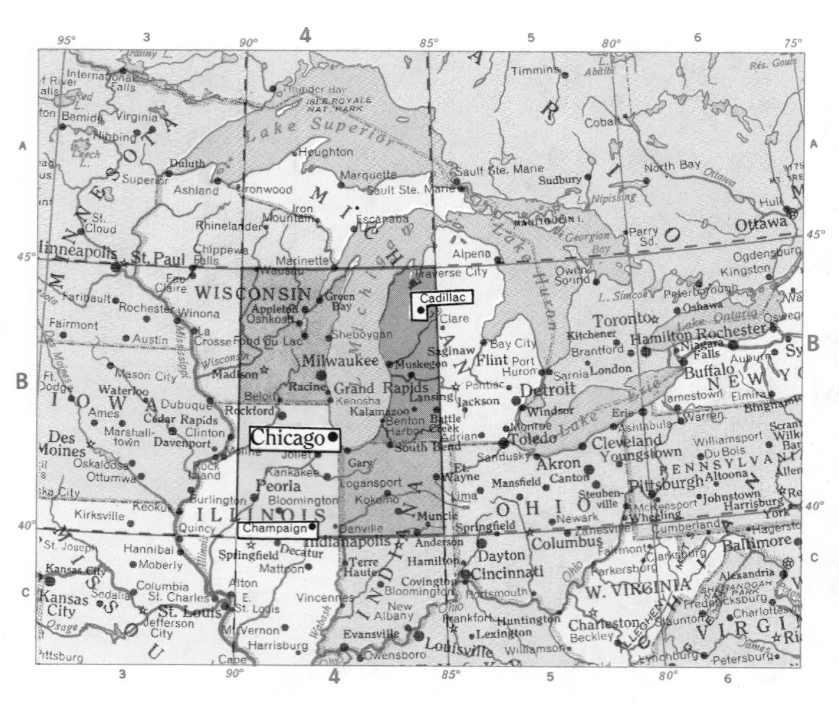

Place	Location	Pop.	Index Key	Page
Cacequi, Braz., 9,976			D2	30
Cacouna, Que., Can., 1,001			B8	42
Caddo, Okla., 886			C5	79
Cadillac, Mich., 9,990			B4	58
Cadiz, Ky., 1,987			D2	62
Cádiz, Sp., 134,342			D2	8
Cadyville, N.Y., 800			f11	75
Chambly, Que., Can., 11,469			D4	42
Chambly, co., Que., Can., 190,946			D4	42
Chambord, Que., Can., 1,106			A5	42
Champaign, Ill., 56,837			B4	58
Champaign, co., Ill., 163,281			C5	58
Champigny-sur-Marne, Fr., 70,419			g11	5
Champion, Ohio, 5,000			A5	78
Champlain, N.Y., 1,426			f11	75
Cheyenne, Wyo., 40,914			E8	89
Chiang Mai, Thai., 83,729			B1	19
Chiapas, state, Mex., 1,381,500			D6	34
Chiari, It., 9,000			B2	9
Chiautla de Tapia, Mex., 5,847			n14	34
Chiba, Jap., 482,133			I10, n19	18
Chiba, pref., Jap., 3,366,624			*I10	18
Chicago, Ill., 3,369,357 (*7,582,700)			B4	58
Chichester, Eng., 20,830			E6	4
Chichibu, Jap., 60,867			m18	18
Chickasaw, co., Iowa, 14,969			A5	60
Chiclana, Sp., 21,524			D2	8
Chiclayo, Peru, 148,932			C2	31

The indexing system used in this atlas is based upon the conventional pattern of parallels and meridians used to indicate latitude and longitude. The index samples beside the map indicate that the cities of *Chicago, Cadillac,* and *Champaign* are all located in *B4.* Each index key letter, *in this case "B,"* is placed between corresponding degree numbers of latitude in the vertical borders of the map. Each index key number, *in this case "4,"* is placed between corresponding degree numbers of longitude in the horizontal borders of the map. Crossing of the parallels above and below the index letter with the meridians on each side of the index number forms a confining "box" in which the given place is certain to be located. It is important to note that location of the place may be anywhere in this confining "box."

Insets on many foreign maps are indexed independently of the main maps by separate index key letters and figures. All places indexed to these insets are identified by the lower case reference letter in the index key. A diamond-shaped symbol in the margin of the map is used to separate the insets from the main map and also to separate key letters and numbers where the spacing of the parallels and meridians is great.

Place-names are indexed to the location of the city symbol. Political divisions and physical features are indexed to the location of their names on the map.

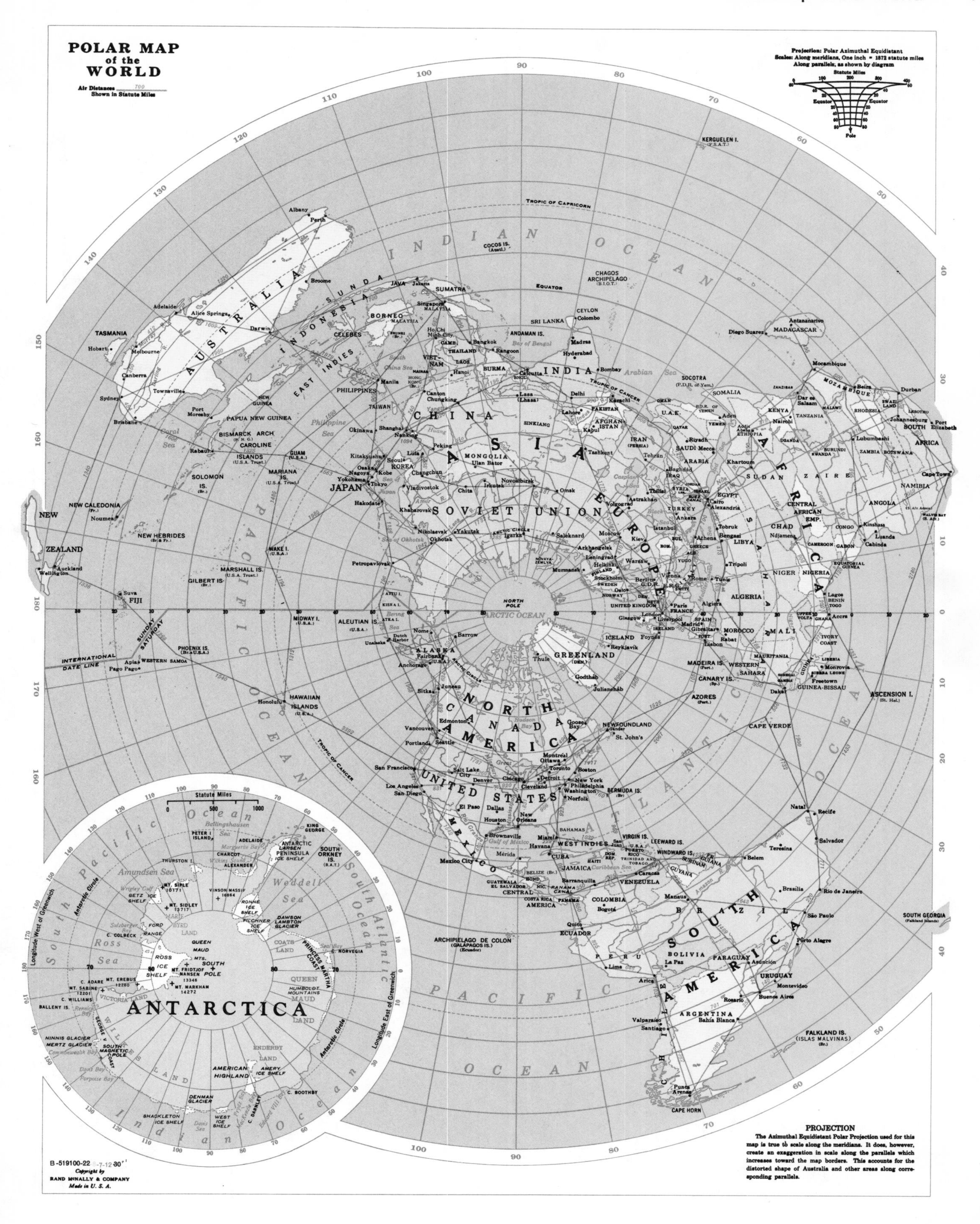

Polar Map of the WORLD

Air Distances ___700___
Shown in Statute Miles

Projection: Polar Azimuthal Equidistant
Scale: Along meridians, One inch = 1872 statute miles
Along parallels, as shown by diagram

PROJECTION
The Azimuthal Equidistant Polar Projection used for this
map is true to scale along the meridians. It does, however,
create an exaggeration in scale along the parallels which
increases toward the map borders. This accounts for the
distorted shape of Australia and other areas along corresponding parallels.

B-519100-22   -7-12-30
Copyright by
RAND MCNALLY & COMPANY
Made in U.S.A.

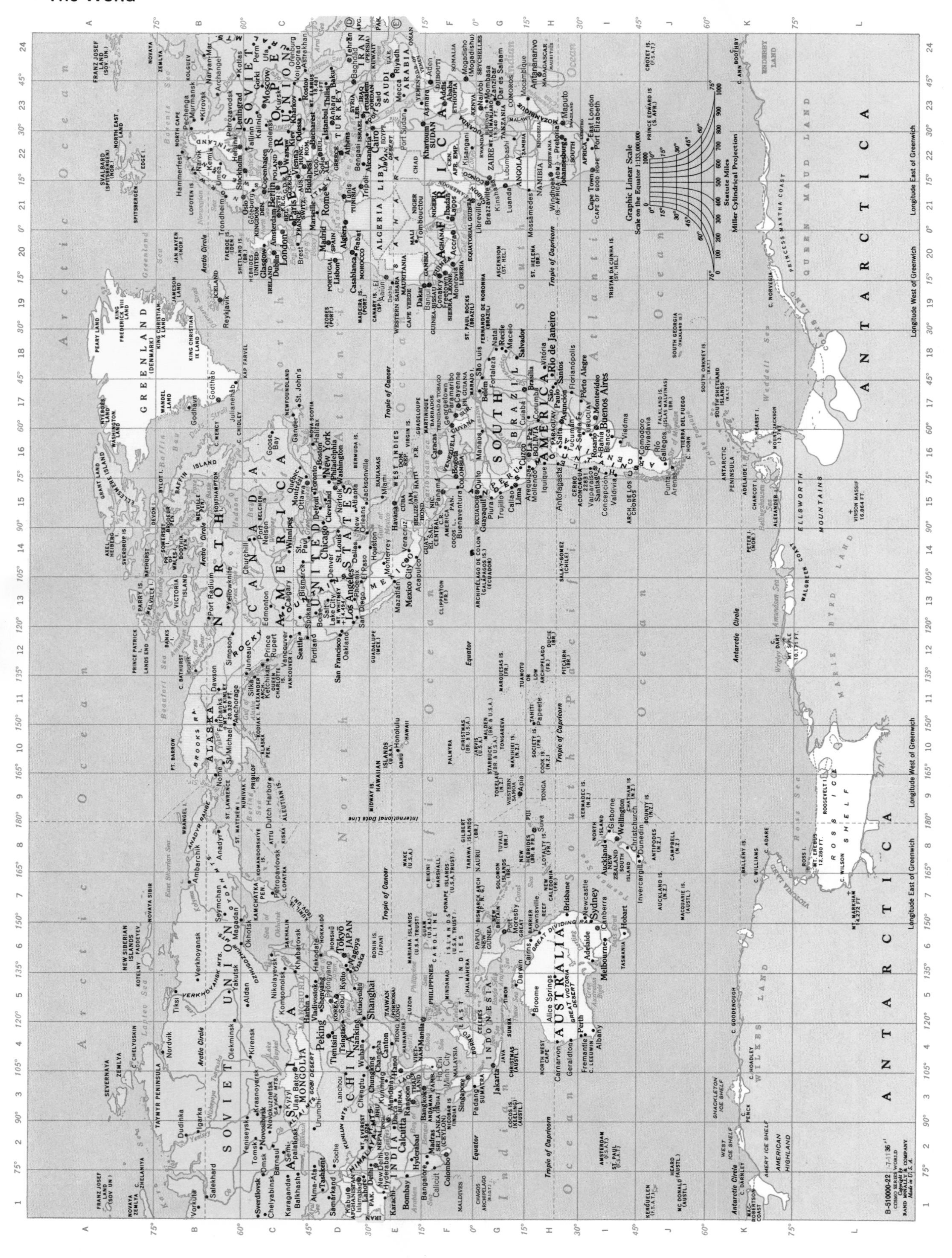
Arctic Ocean
NORTH AMERICA
SOUTH AMERICA
AFRICA
EUROPE
AUSTRALIA
ANTARCTICA
Graphic Linear Scale
Scale on the Equator 1:133,000,000
Statute Miles
Miller Cylindrical Projection
Longitude West of Greenwich
Longitude East of Greenwich
International Date Line
Tropic of Cancer
Equator
Tropic of Capricorn
Arctic Circle
Antarctic Circle

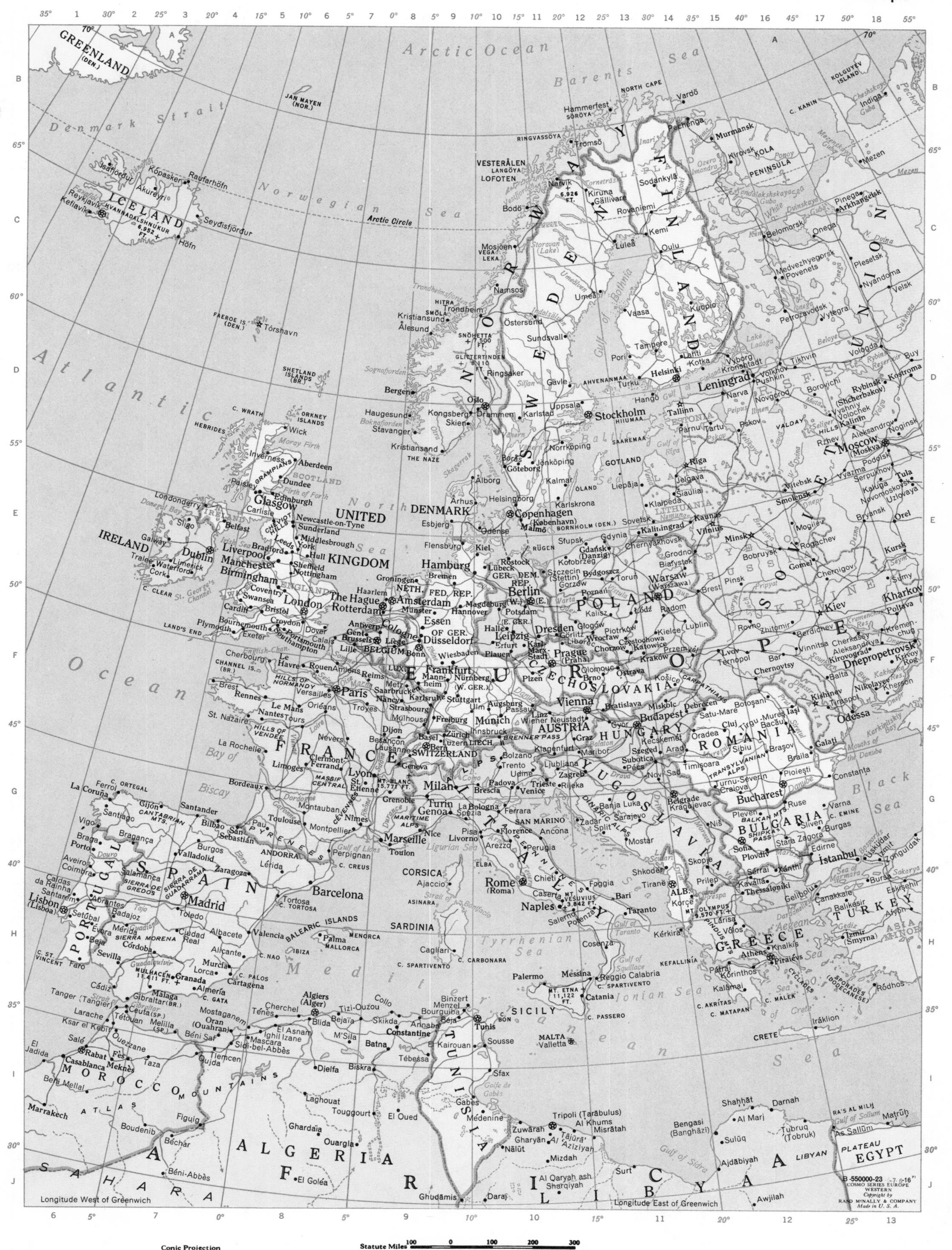

Arctic Ocean

Barents Sea

GREENLAND (DEN.)

Denmark Strait

JAN MAYEN (NOR.)

NORTH CAPE
C. KANIN
KOLGUYEV ISLAND

Norwegian Sea

ICELAND
Reykjavík
Keflavík

Arctic Circle

VESTERÅLEN
LANGØYA
LOFOTEN

Murmansk
KOLA
PENINSULA

FAEROE IS. (DEN.)
Tórshavn

SHETLAND ISLANDS (BR.)

NORWAY
SWEDEN
FINLAND

S.F.S.R.
SOVIET UNION

Atlantic

Leningrad
Moscow
Moskva

DENMARK
Copenhagen
København

IRELAND
Dublin

UNITED KINGDOM
Glasgow
Edinburgh
London

North Sea

Hamburg
Berlin
GER. DEM. REP.
Warsaw
Warszawa
POLAND

NETH.
Amsterdam
Rotterdam
Brussels
BELGIUM
Cologne
Essen
Düsseldorf
Frankfurt
FED. REP. OF GER.

Prague (Praha)
CZECHOSLOVAKIA

Paris
FRANCE

SWITZERLAND
Vienna
AUSTRIA
Budapest
HUNGARY
ROMANIA
Bucharest

Milan
Turin
Genoa
I TALY
Rome (Roma)

YUGOSLAVIA
BULGARIA
Sofia

Ocean

Bay of Biscay

SPAIN
Madrid
Barcelona

PORTUGAL
Lisbon (Lisboa)

CORSICA

SARDINIA

Mediterranean

Naples

SICILY

BALEARIC ISLANDS

GREECE
Athens

TURKEY
ASIA MINOR
Istanbul

Black Sea

Ionian Sea

Tyrrhenian Sea

CRETE

MALTA
Valletta

MOROCCO
Casablanca
Rabat

ALGERIA

TUNISIA
Tunis

ATLAS MOUNTAINS

SAHARA

LIBYA

EGYPT
PLATEAU
LIBYAN

Gulf of Sidra

B-550000-23
COSMO SERIES EUROPE
WESTERN
Copyright by
RAND McNALLY & COMPANY
Made in U.S.A.

Longitude West of Greenwich

Longitude East of Greenwich

Statute Miles
100 0 100 200 300

Kilometers
100 0 100 200 300 400

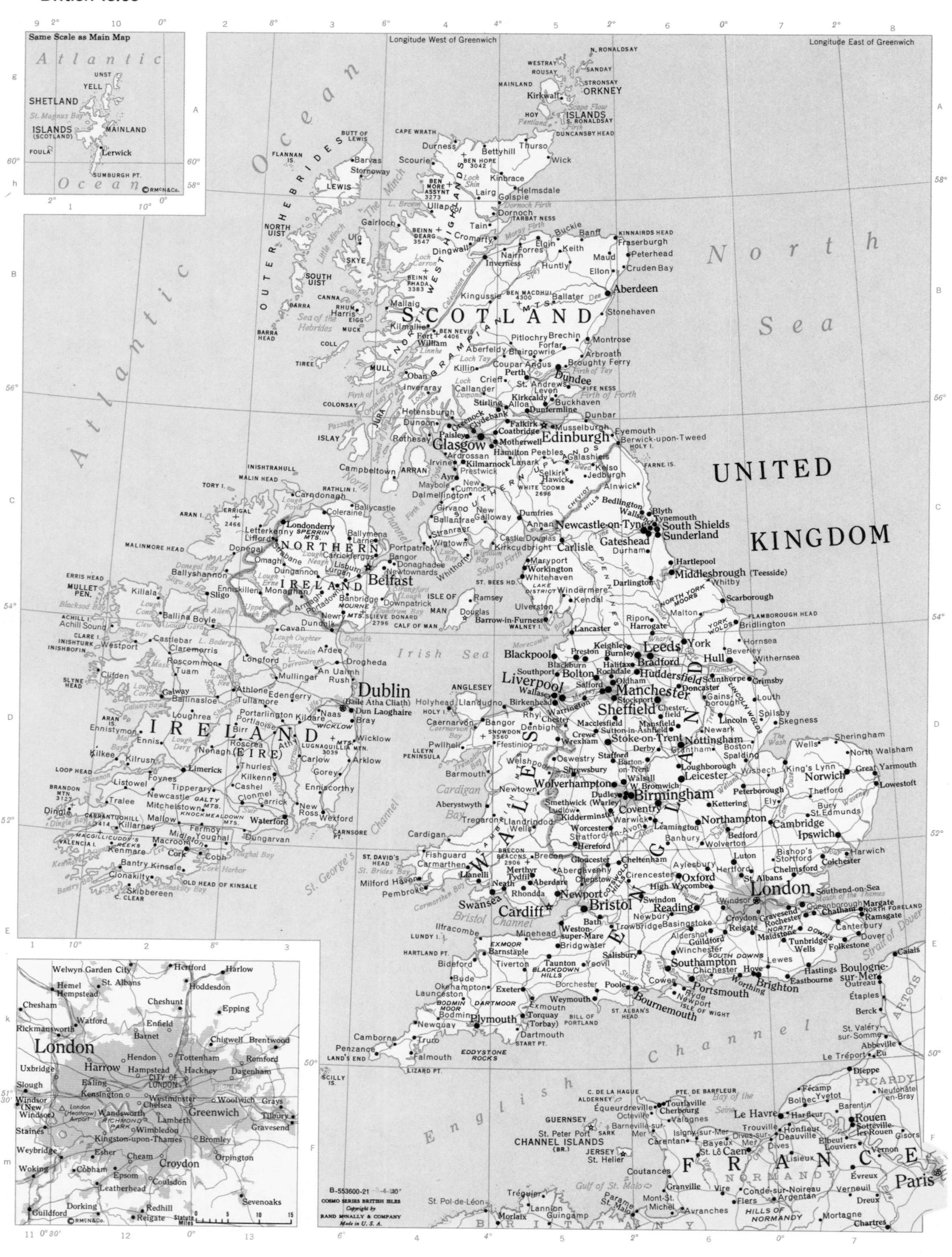

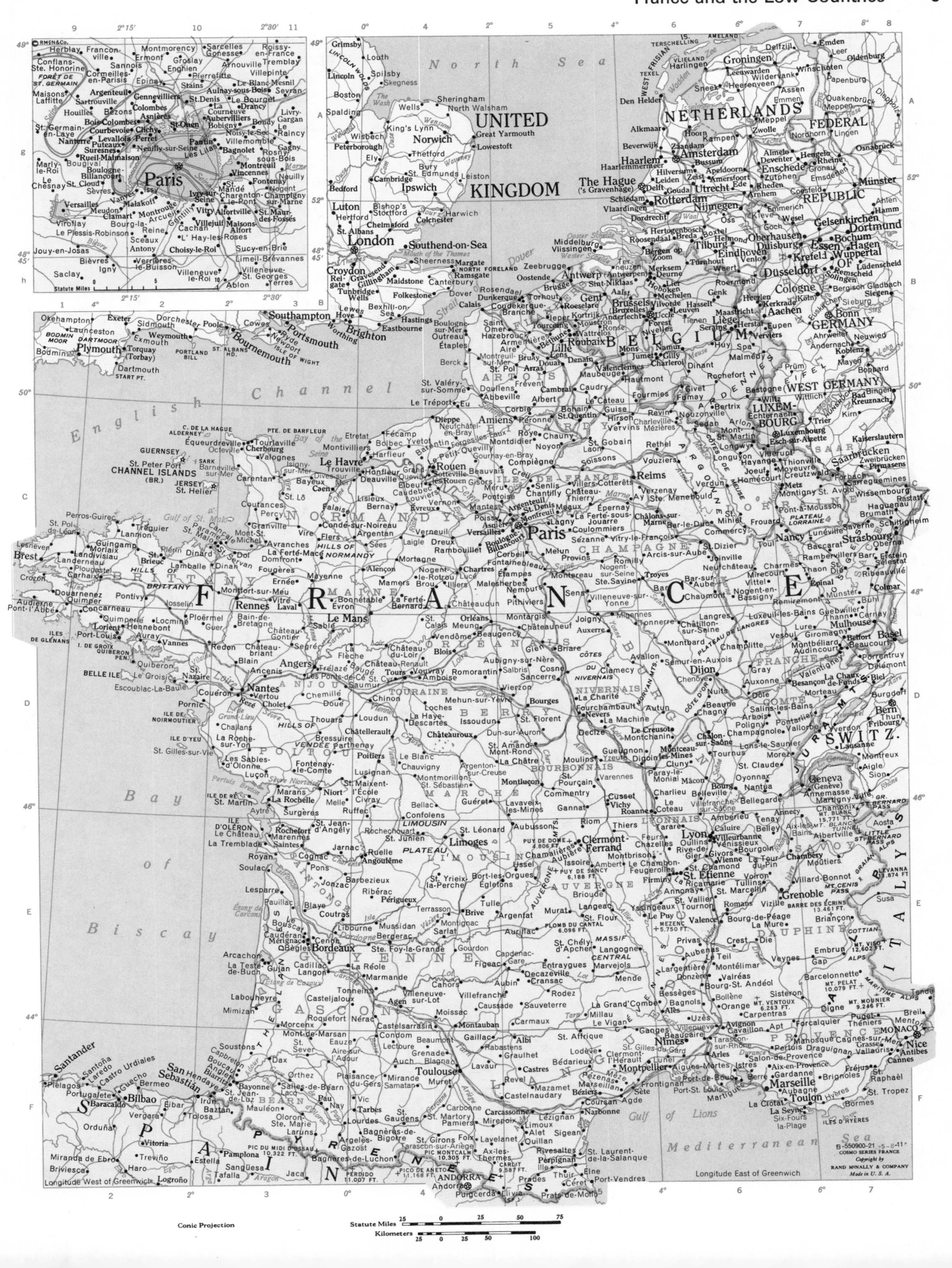

Conic Projection

Statute Miles

Kilometers

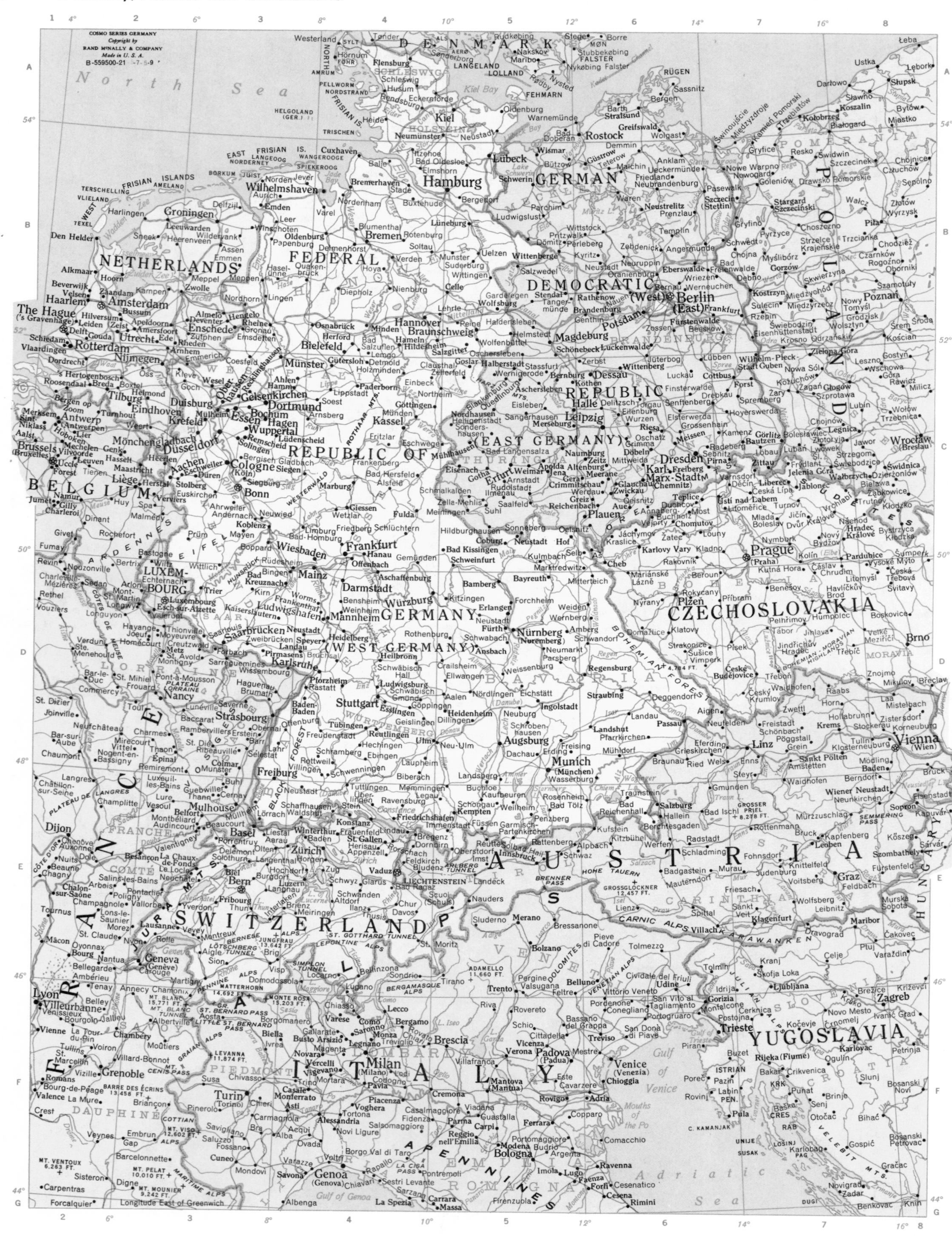
COSMO SERIES GERMANY
Copyright by
RAND McNALLY & COMPANY
Made in U. S. A.
B-559500-21 -7-5-9
North Sea
DENMARK
NETHERLANDS
FEDERAL
REPUBLIC OF
GERMANY
(WEST GERMANY)
GERMAN
DEMOCRATIC
REPUBLIC
(EAST GERMANY)
POLAND
CZECHOSLOVAKIA
BELGIUM
LUXEMBOURG
FRANCE
SWITZERLAND
LIECHTENSTEIN
AUSTRIA
HUNGARY
ITALY
YUGOSLAVIA
Adriatic Sea
Gulf of Venice
Gulf of Genoa
Hamburg
Bremen
Hannover
Berlin (East)
Berlin (West)
Amsterdam
The Hague ('s Gravenhage)
Rotterdam
Brussels (Bruxelles)
Cologne (Köln)
Bonn
Frankfurt
Leipzig
Dresden
Munich (München)
Nürnberg (Nuremberg)
Stuttgart
Prague (Praha)
Vienna (Wien)
Zürich
Bern
Geneva (Genève)
Milan (Milano)
Turin (Torino)
Venice (Venezia)
Genoa (Genova)
Lyon
Longitude East of Greenwich
Statute Miles 25 0 25 50 75
Kilometers 25 0 25 50 100
Conic Projection

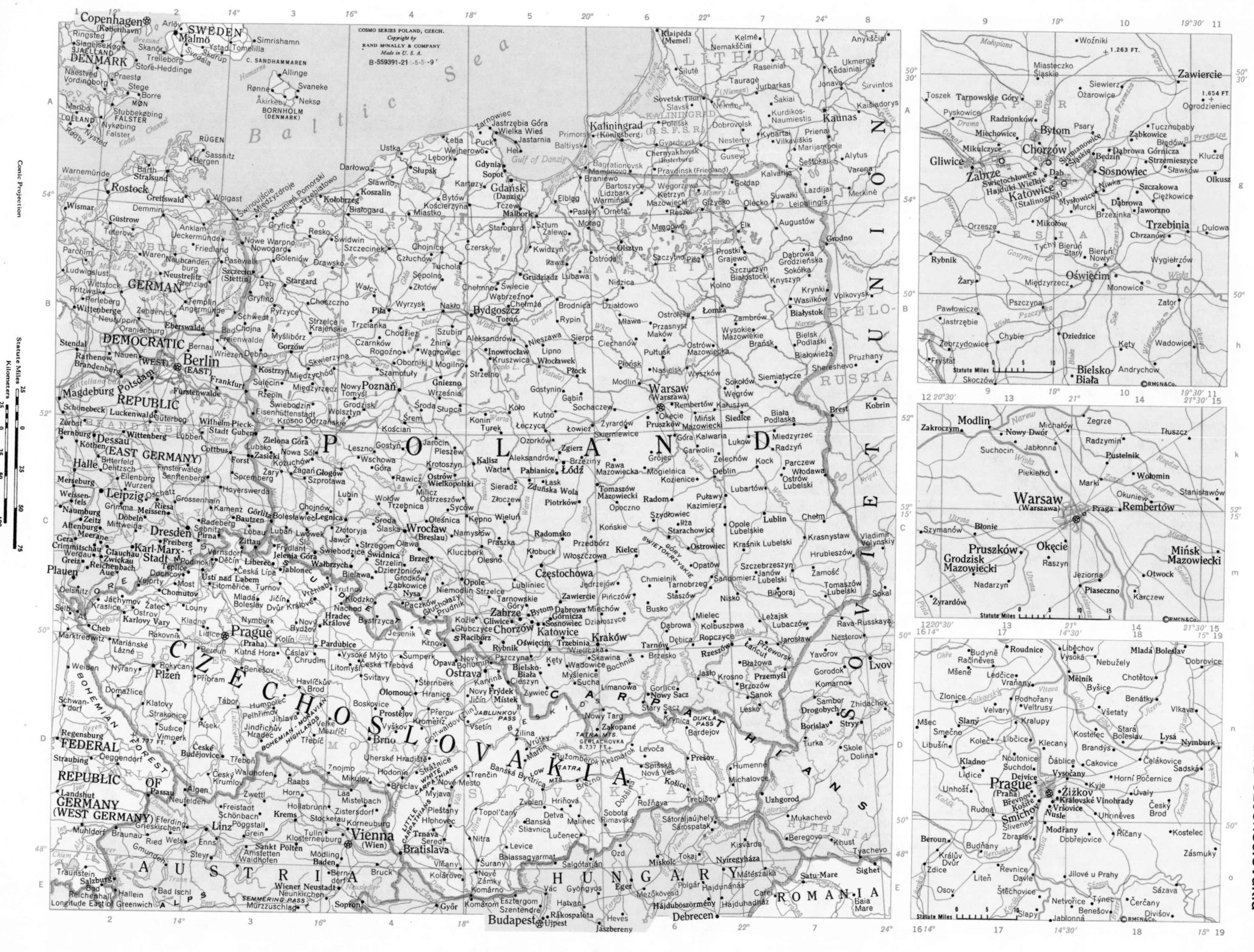

Conic Projection

Statute Miles 25   0   25   50   75

Kilometers 25   0   25   50   100

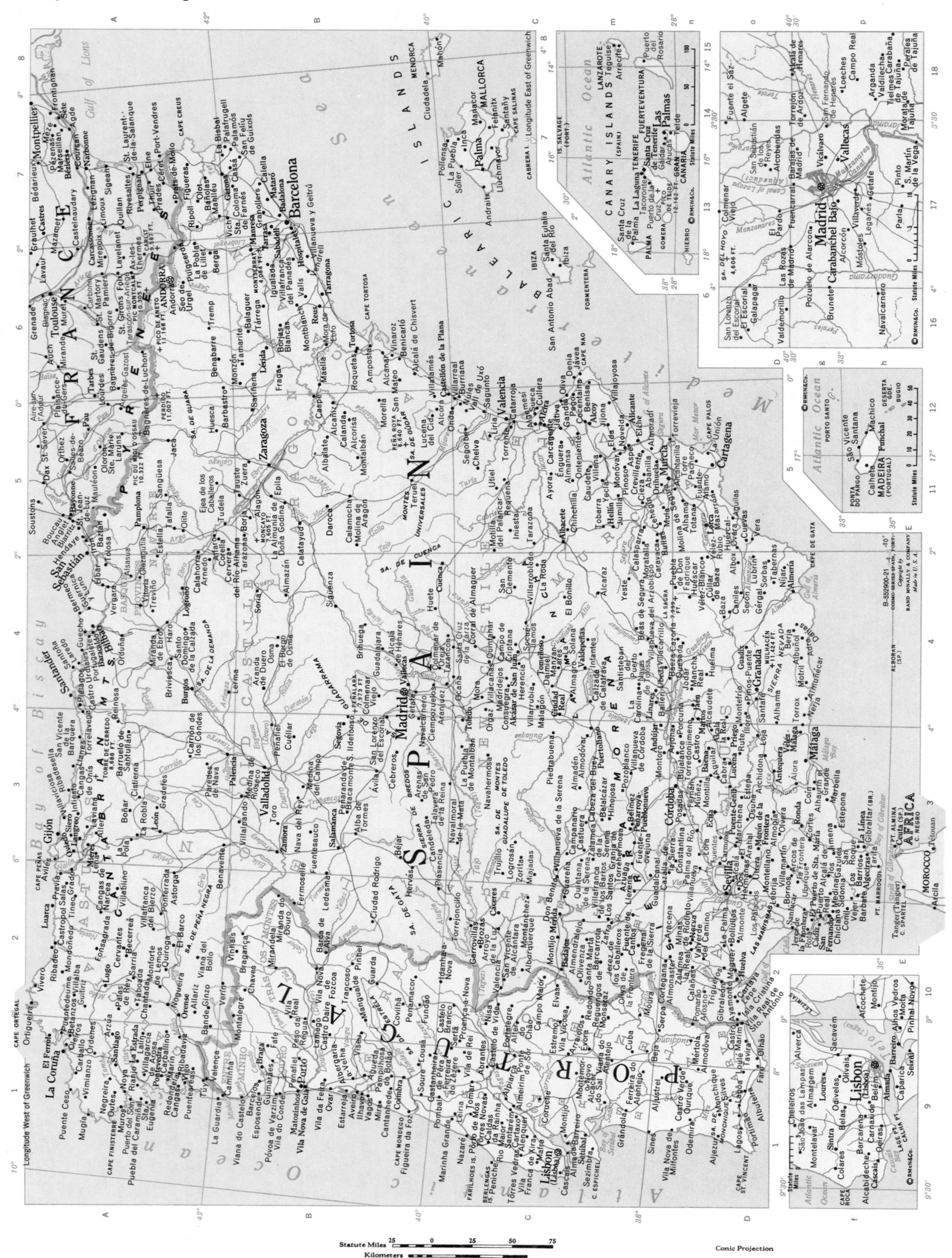

Statute Miles 25   0   25   50   75

Kilometers 25   0   25   50   109

Conic Projection

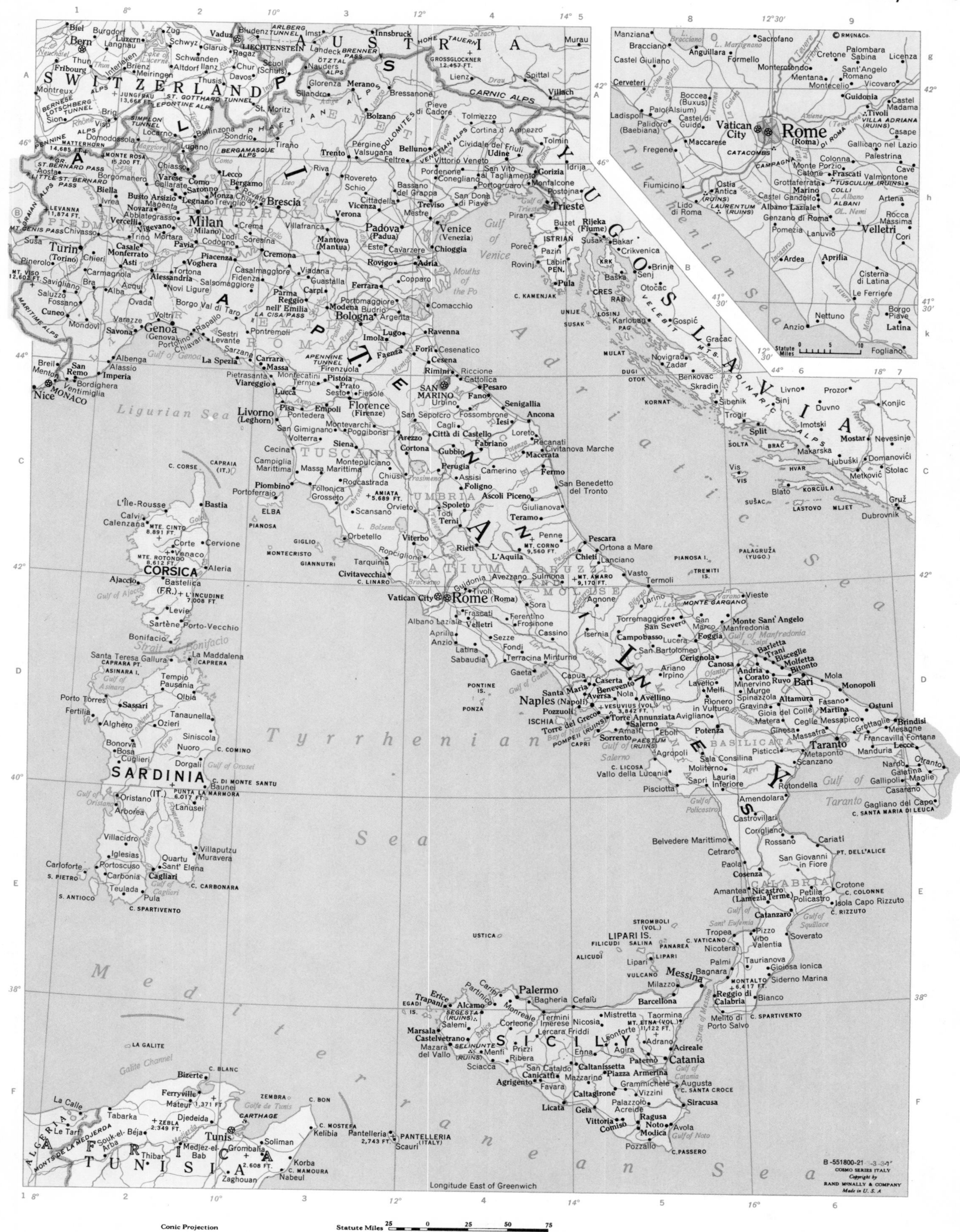
SWITZERLAND
AUSTRIA
LIECHTENSTEIN
YUGOSLAVIA
ITALY
ALPS
APENNINES
Bern
Zurich
Lucerne
Vaduz
Innsbruck
Fribourg
Interlaken
Montreux
JUNGFRAU 13,666 FT.
MATTERHORN 14,685 FT.
MONTE ROSA 15,200 FT.
ST. GOTTHARD TUNNEL
SIMPLON TUNNEL
BRENNER PASS
GROSSGLOCKNER 12,457 FT.
CARNIC ALPS
DOLOMITES
BERGAMASQUE ALPS
LEPONTINE ALPS
MARITIME ALPS
PIEDMONT
LOMBARDY
VENETIA
EMILIA ROMAGNA
TUSCANY
UMBRIA
LATIUM
ABRUZZI AND MOLISE
CAMPANIA
BASILICATA
CALABRIA
APULIA
SICILY
CORSICA (FR.)
SARDINIA (IT.)
SAN MARINO
MONACO
Milan (Milano)
Turin (Torino)
Genoa (Genova)
Venice (Venezia)
Florence (Firenze)
Bologna
Padova (Padua)
Verona
Brescia
Bergamo
Trieste
Trento
Bolzano
Udine
Parma
Modena
Ferrara
Ravenna
Rimini
Pesaro
Ancona
Perugia
Livorno (Leghorn)
Pisa
Lucca
Siena
La Spezia
Savona
Nice
Rome (Roma)
Vatican City
Naples (Napoli)
Salerno
Bari
Brindisi
Taranto
Lecce
Foggia
Pescara
L'Aquila
Potenza
Cosenza
Catanzaro
Reggio di Calabria
Messina
Palermo
Catania
Siracusa
Agrigento
Trapani
Marsala
Cagliari
Sassari
Nuoro
Oristano
Ajaccio
Bastia
Tunis
Bizerte
Ligurian Sea
Tyrrhenian Sea
Adriatic Sea
Mediterranean Sea
Gulf of Venice
Gulf of Genoa
Gulf of Taranto
Strait of Bonifacio
Strait of Messina
LIPARI IS.
ELBA
CAPRI
ISCHIA
PANTELLERIA (ITALY)
MT. ETNA (VOL.) 11,122 FT.
VESUVIUS (VOL.) 3,842 FT.
TUNISIA
ALGERIA
Longitude East of Greenwich
Tiber
Po
Arno
Castel Gandolfo
Frascati
Tivoli
Ostia Antica (RUINS)
Velletri
Latina
Anzio
Nettuno
Fiumicino
Tyrrhenian Sea
Statute Miles 0 5 10
B-551800-21-1-3-3-1
COSMO SERIES ITALY
Copyright by RAND McNALLY & COMPANY
Made in U. S. A.
Conic Projection
Statute Miles 25 0 25 50 75
Kilometers 25 0 25 50 100

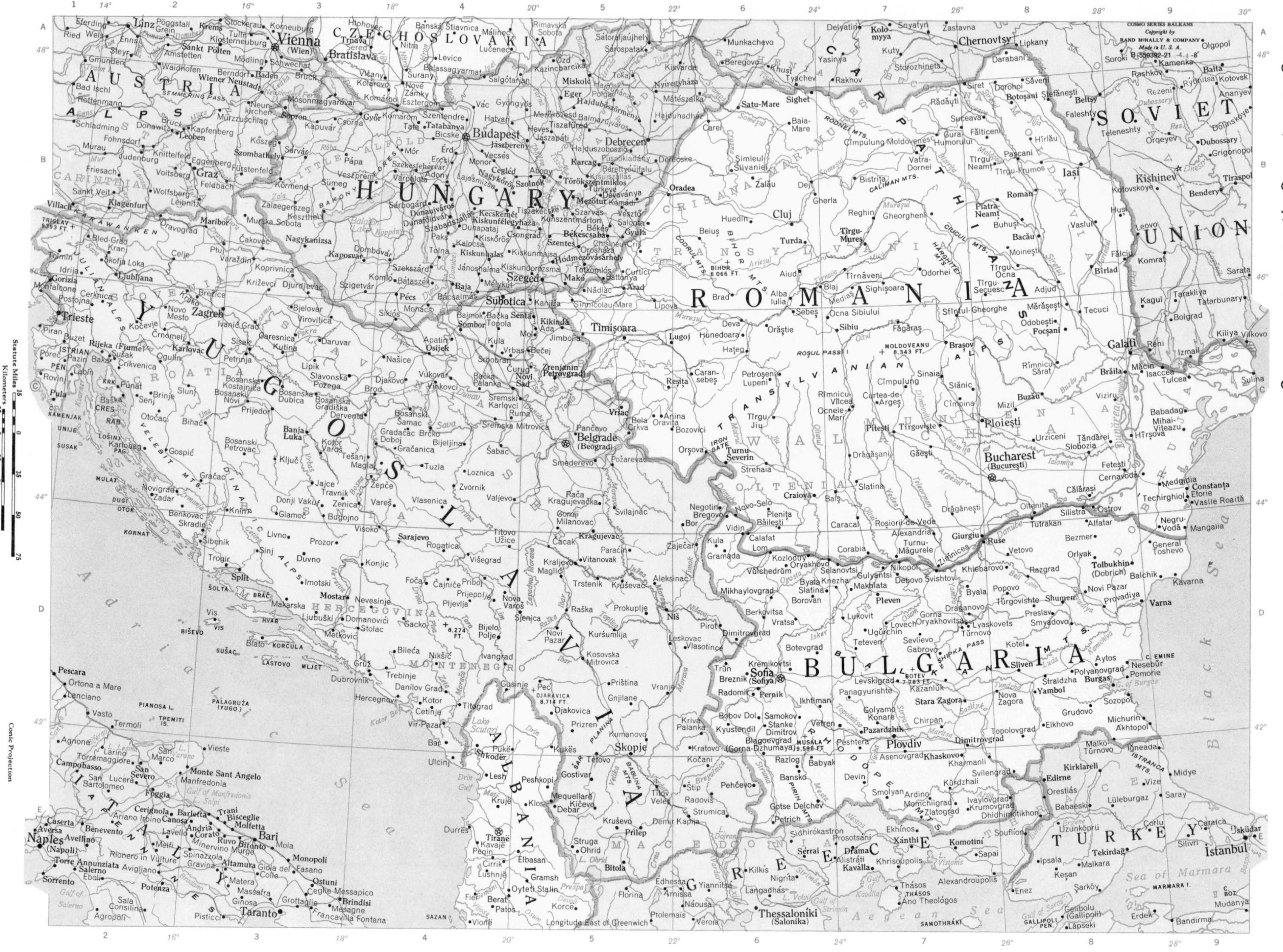
SOVIET UNION
ROMANIA
BULGARIA
YUGOSLAVIA
HUNGARY
CZECHOSLOVAKIA
AUSTRIA
ALBANIA
GREECE
TURKEY
ITALY
Black Sea
Adriatic Sea
Aegean Sea
Sea of Marmara
Bucharest (Bucureşti)
Belgrade (Beograd)
Budapest
Sofia (Sofiya)
Vienna (Wien)
Tiranë
Istanbul
Kishinev
CARPATHIAN MTS.
TRANSYLVANIAN ALPS
DINARIC ALPS
BALKAN MTS.
RHODOPE MTS.
Statute Miles 25 0 25 50 75
Kilometers 25 0 25 50 100
Conic Projection
COSMO SERIES BALKANS
Copyright by RAND McNALLY & COMPANY
Made in U. S. A.

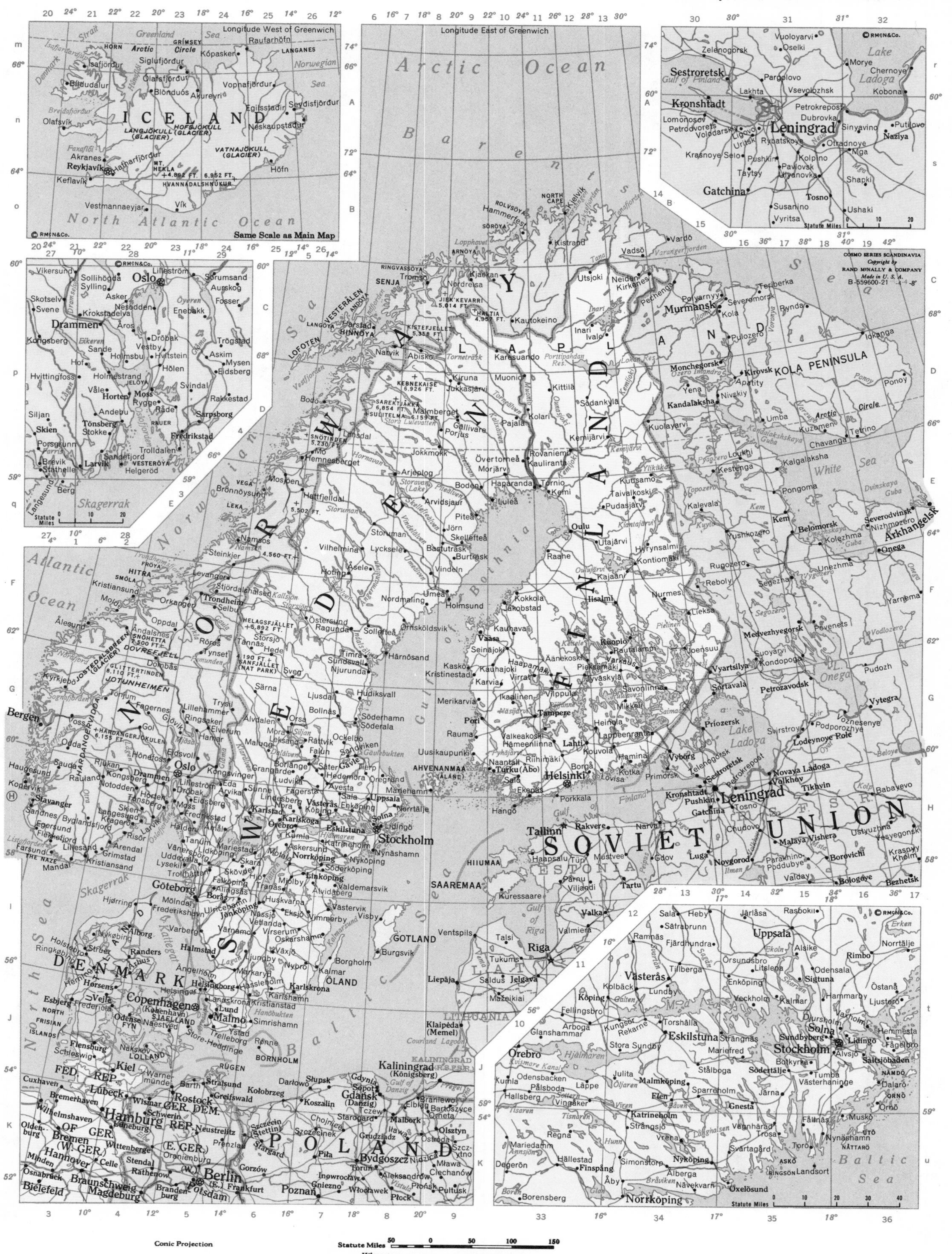

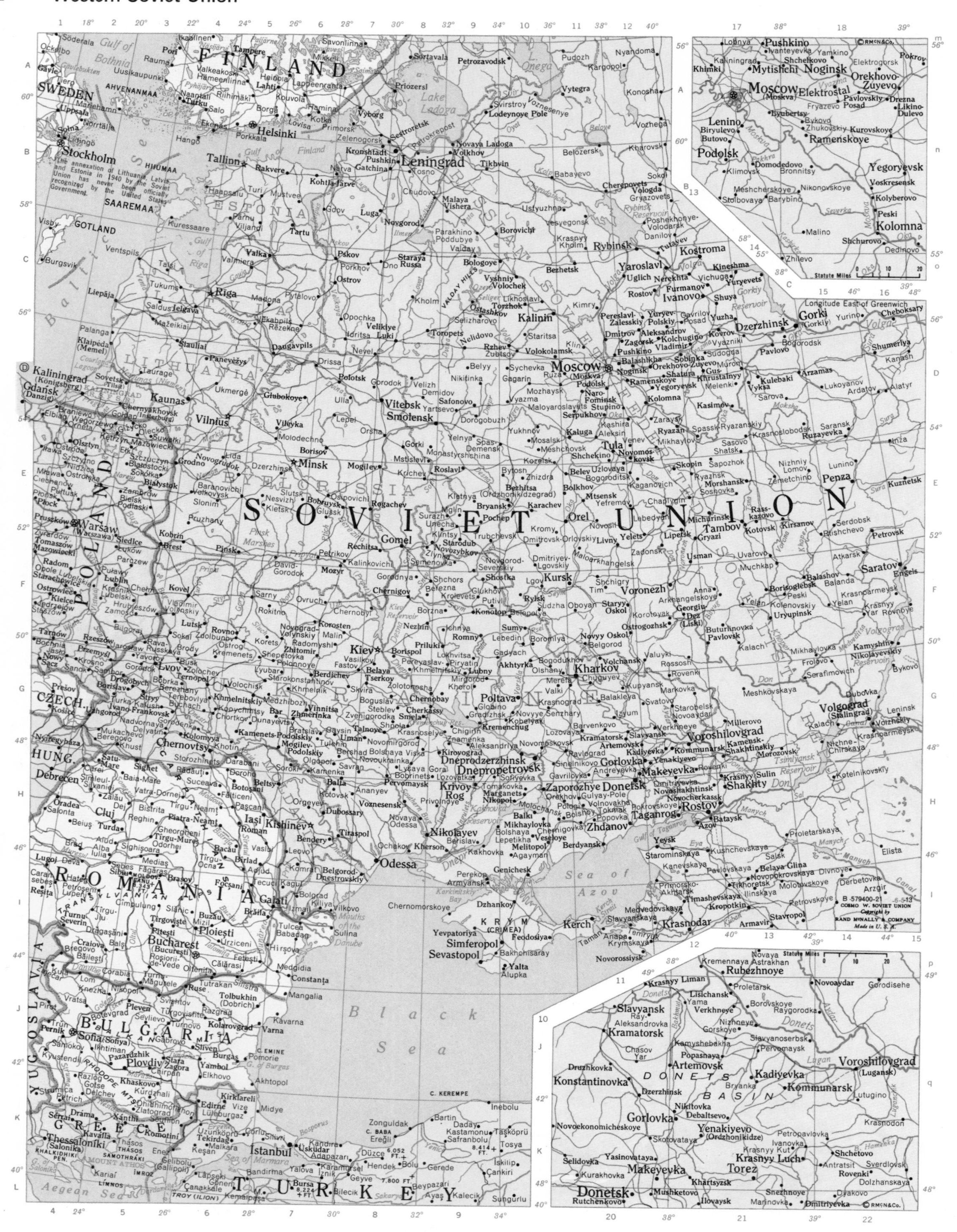

Statute Miles 50 0 50 100 150

Kilometers 50 0 50 100 200

Conic Projection

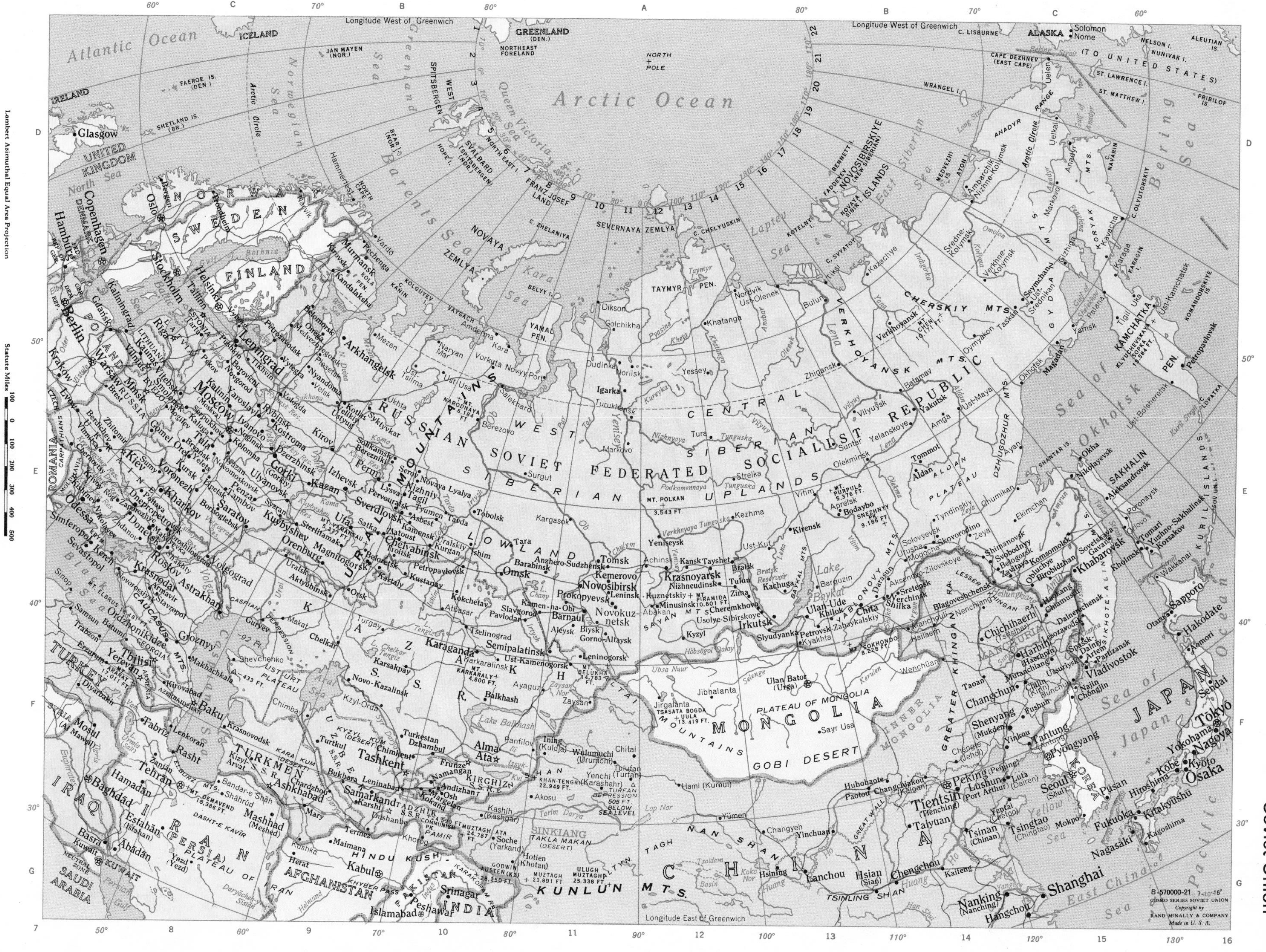

Lambert Azimuthal Equal Area Projection

Statute Miles

Kilometers

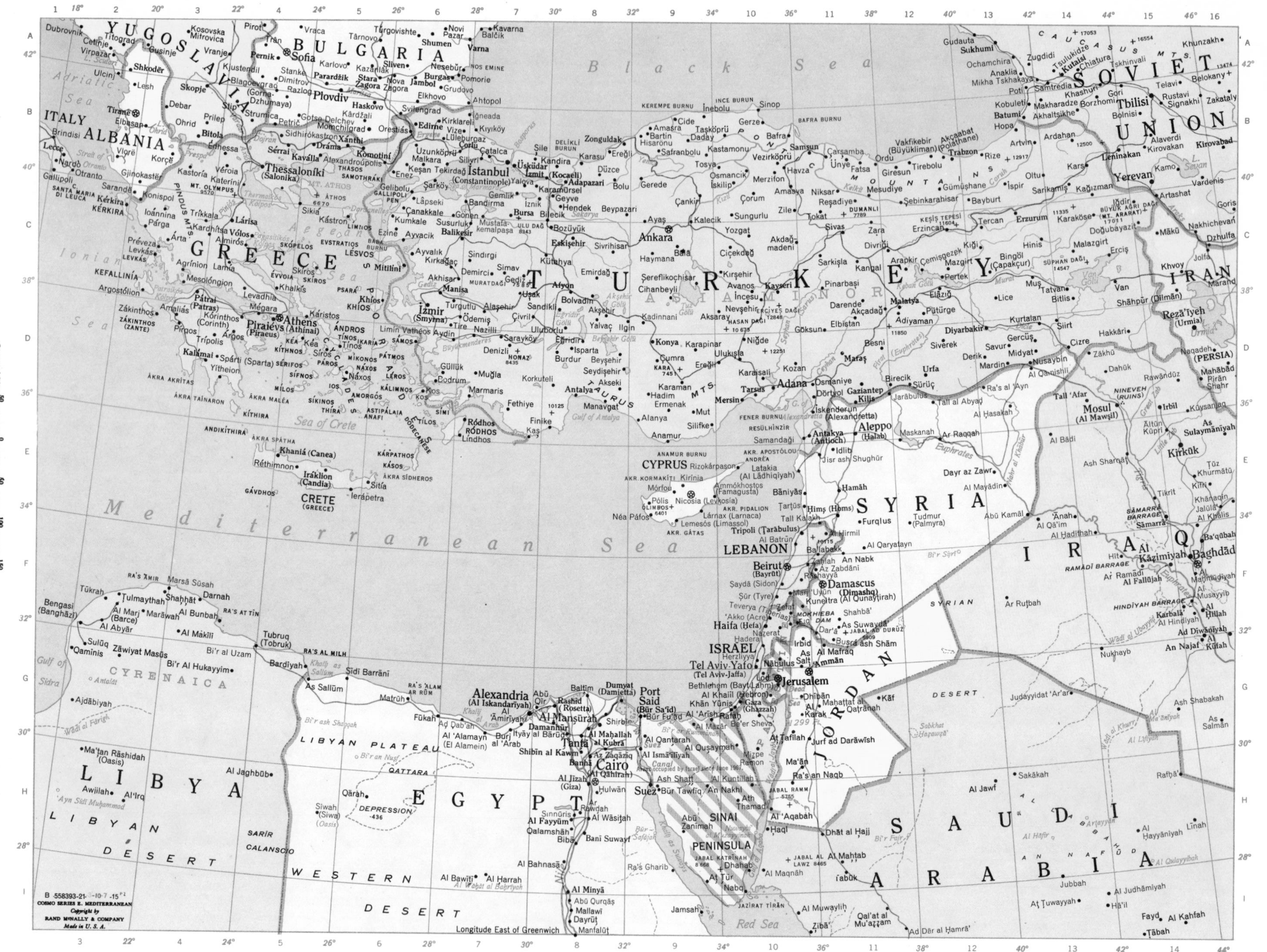
Black Sea
Mediterranean Sea
Ionian Sea
Aegean Sea
Sea of Crete
Red Sea
SOVIET UNION
TURKEY
IRAN
IRAQ
SYRIA
LEBANON
ISRAEL
JORDAN
SAUDI ARABIA
EGYPT
LIBYA
GREECE
BULGARIA
YUGOSLAVIA
ALBANIA
ITALY
CYPRUS
CRETE (GREECE)
SINAI PENINSULA
Ankara
Istanbul (Constantinople)
Athens (Athinai)
Beirut (Bayrūt)
Damascus (Dimashq)
Jerusalem
Amman
Cairo
Alexandria (Al Iskandarīyah)
Baghdād
Aleppo (Halab)
Sofia
Tbilisi
Yerevan
Tiranë
Nicosia (Levkosia)
Port Said (Būr Sa'īd)
Suez
Tel Aviv-Yafo
Bengasi (Banghāzī)
Tubruq (Tobruk)
LIBYAN PLATEAU
QATTARA DEPRESSION
WESTERN DESERT
LIBYAN DESERT
SYRIAN DESERT
CYRENAICA
Longitude East of Greenwich
Statute Miles 50 0 50 100 150
Kilometers 50 0 50 100 200
Lambert Conformal Conic Projection
B 558393-21 -10-7-15 P2
COSMO SERIES E. MEDITERRANEAN
Copyright by RAND McNALLY & COMPANY
Made in U. S. A.

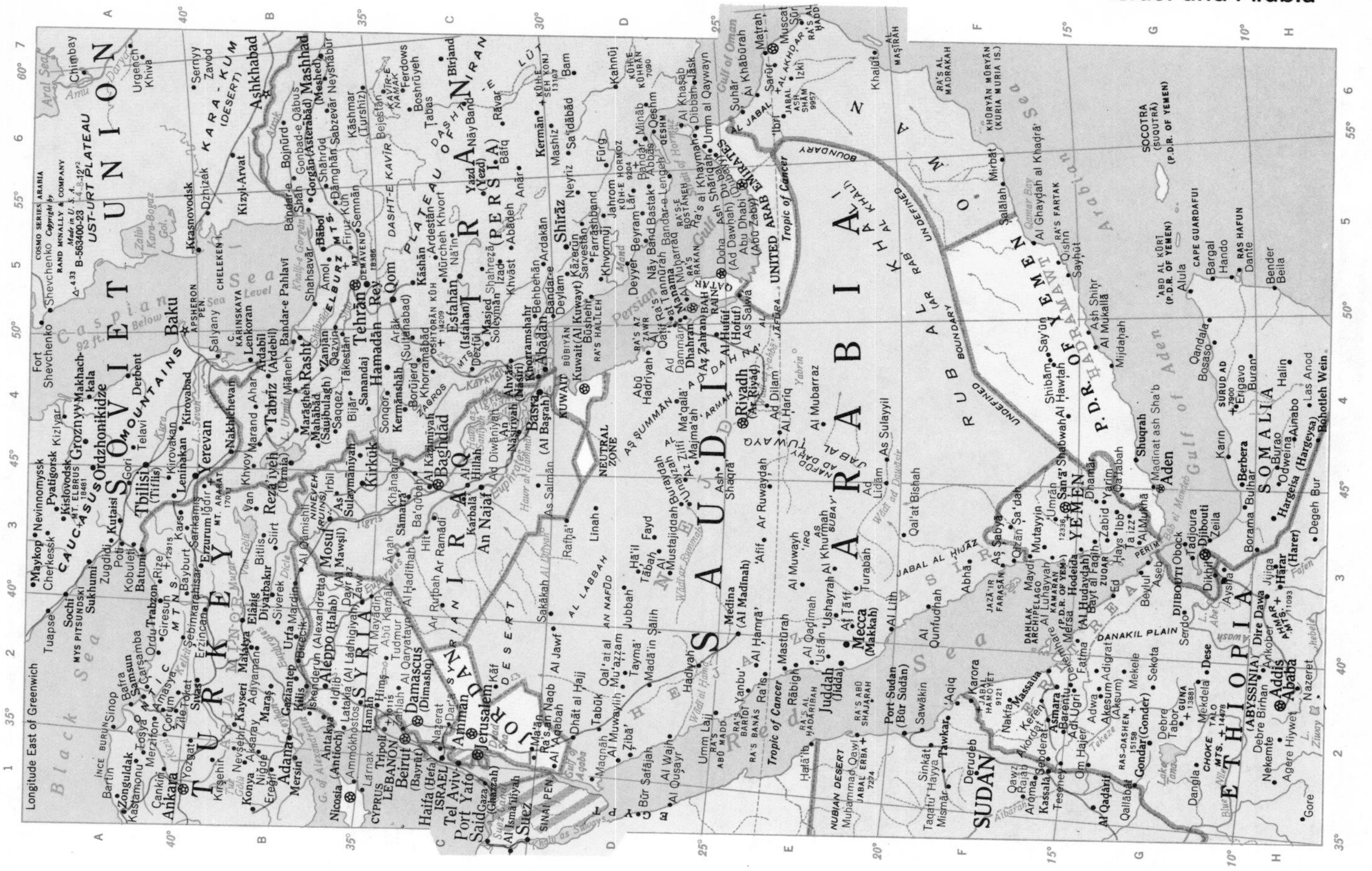

Lambert Conformal Conic Projection

COSMO SERIES ISRAEL.
Copyright by
RAND M^{c}NALLY & COMPANY
B-561800-23 - 3-7.5-12'

Statute Miles

Kilometers

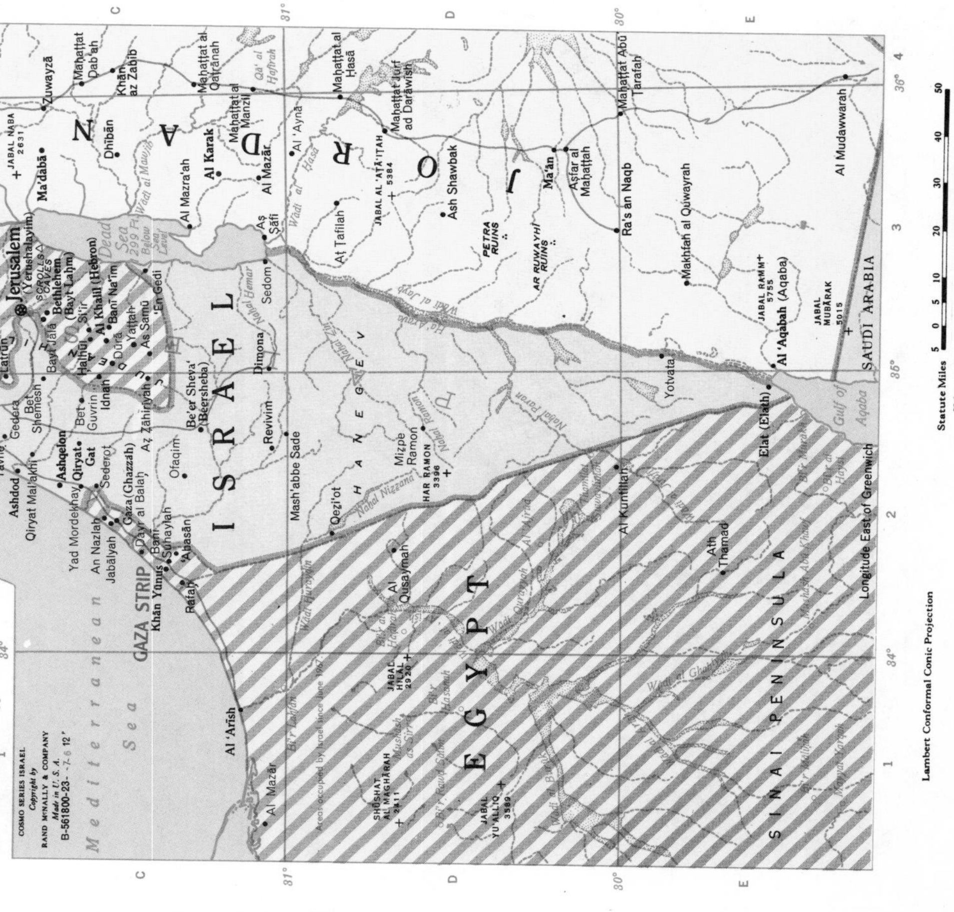

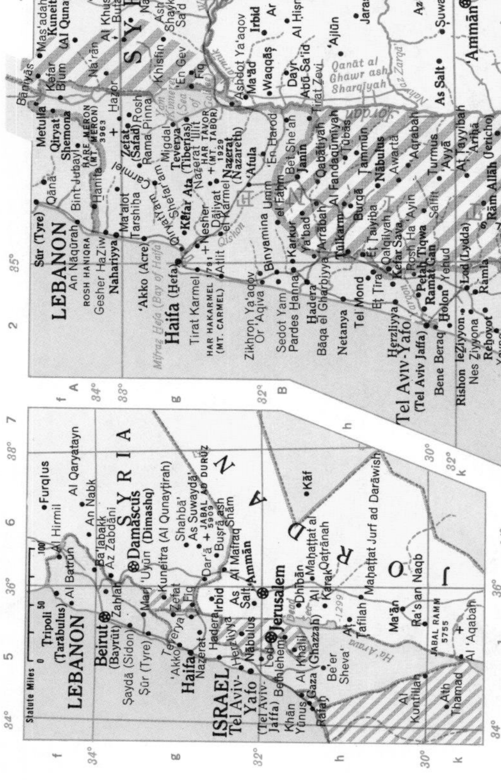

Longitude East of Greenwich

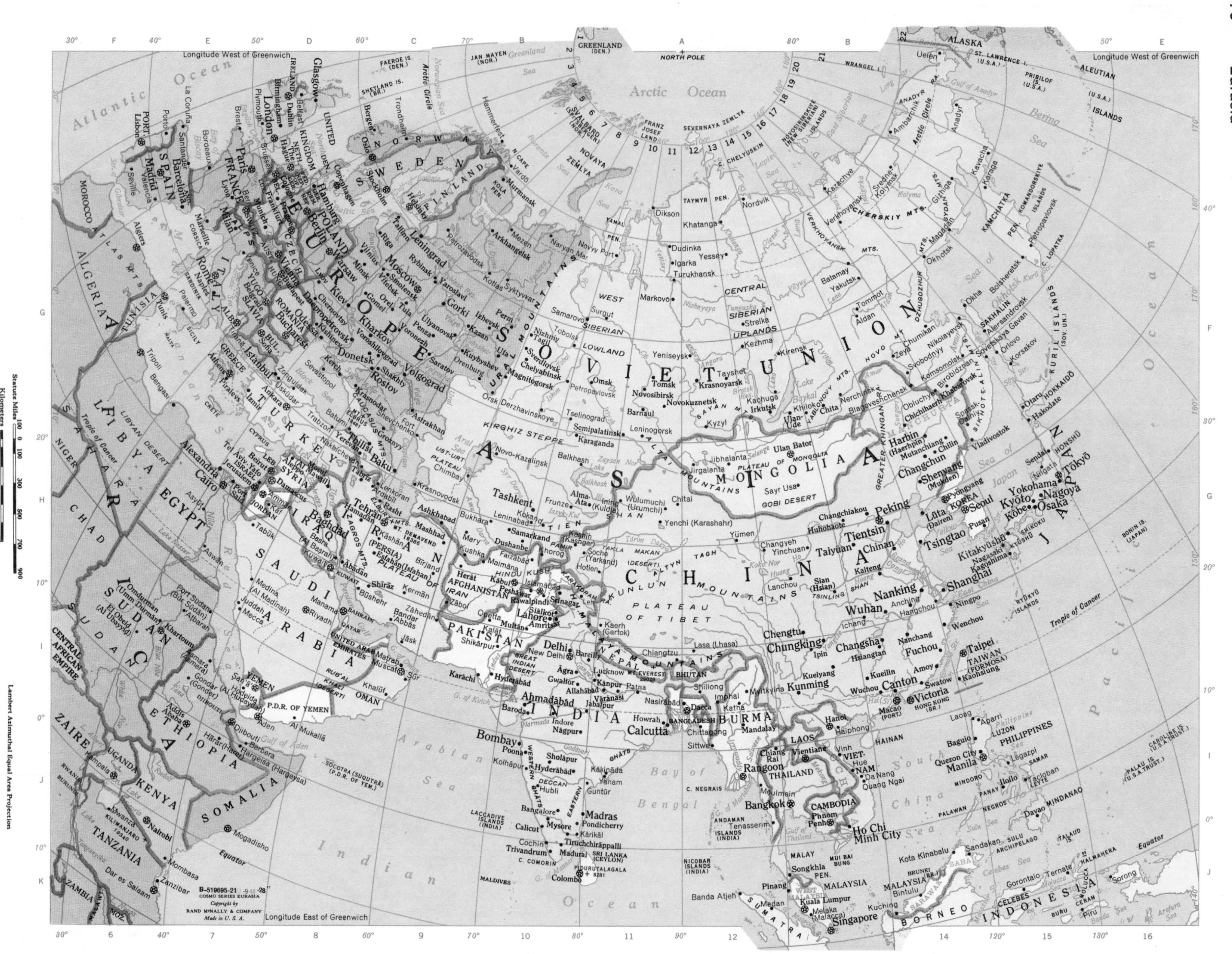

Statute Miles 100 0 100 300 500 700 900

Kilometers 100 0 100 300 700 1100

Lambert Azimuthal Equal Area Projection

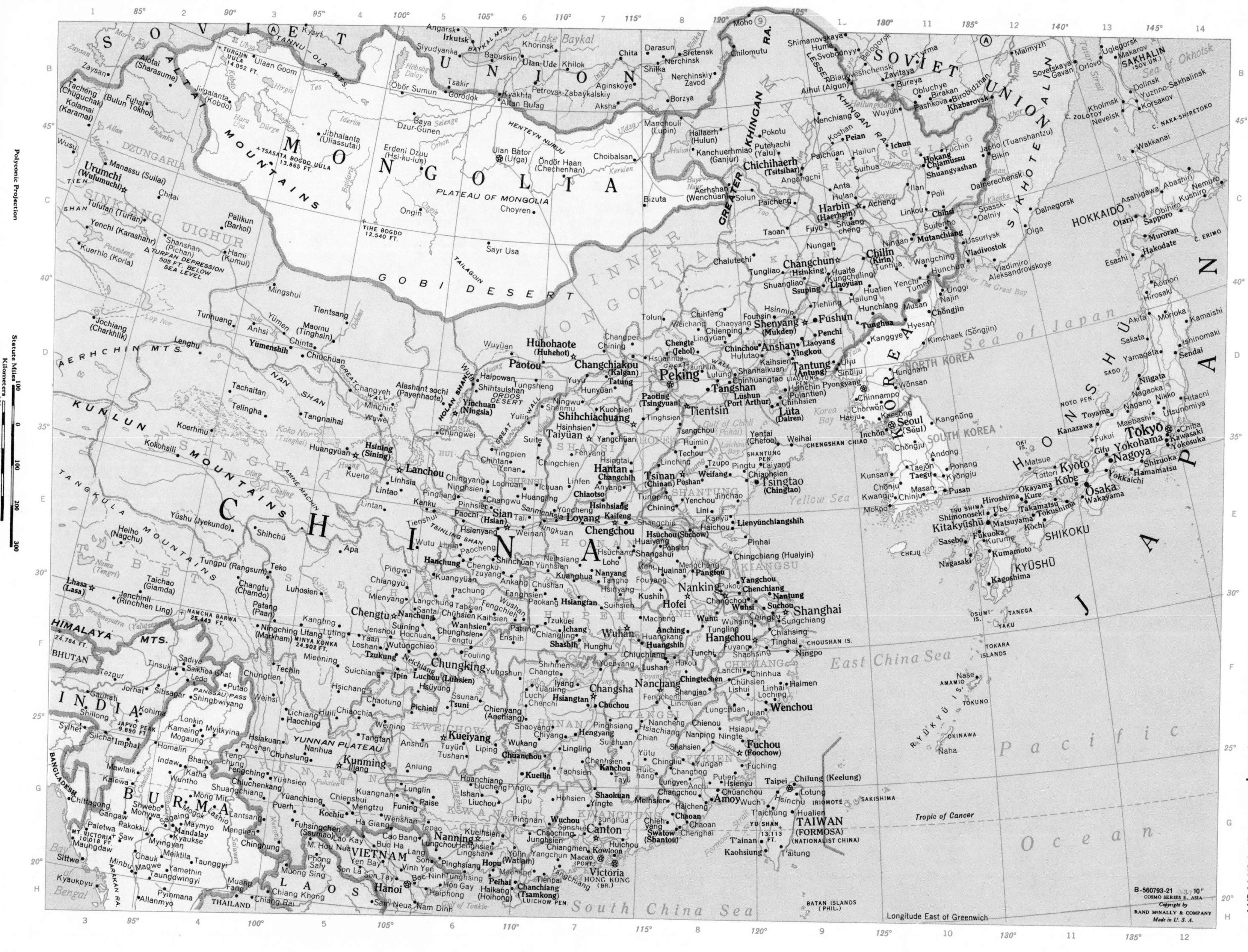

Polyconic Projection

Statute Miles

Kilometers

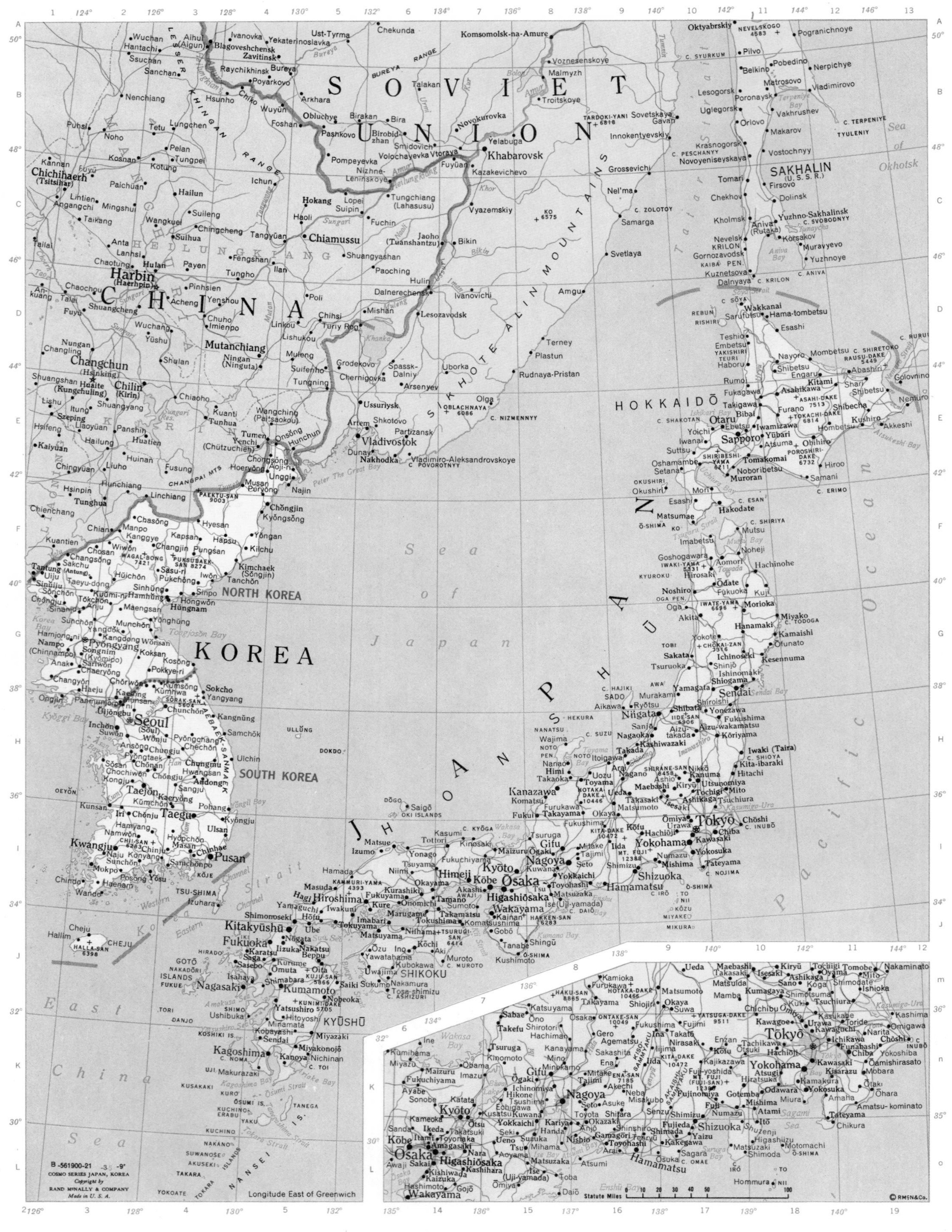

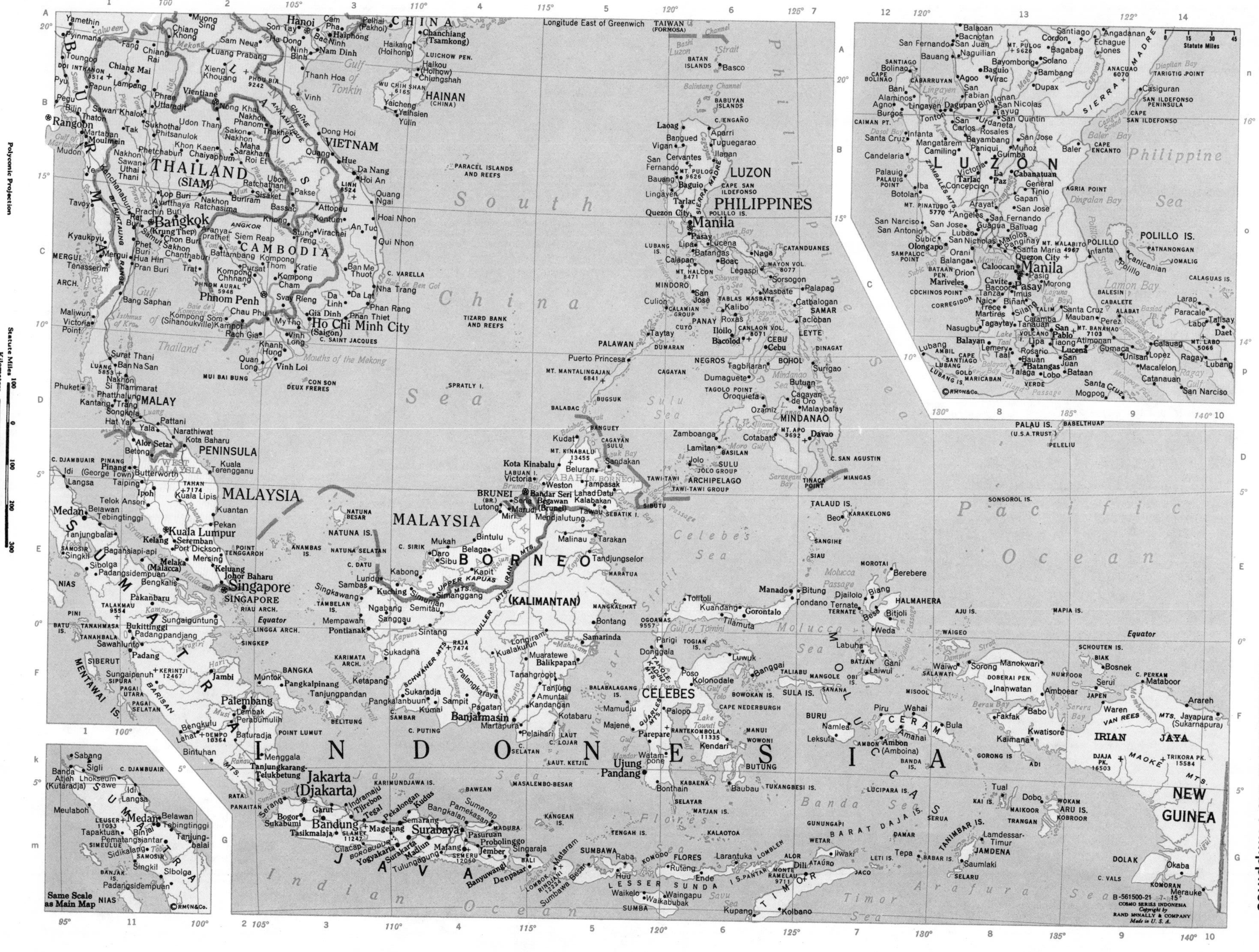

Polyconic Projection

Statute Miles

Kilometers

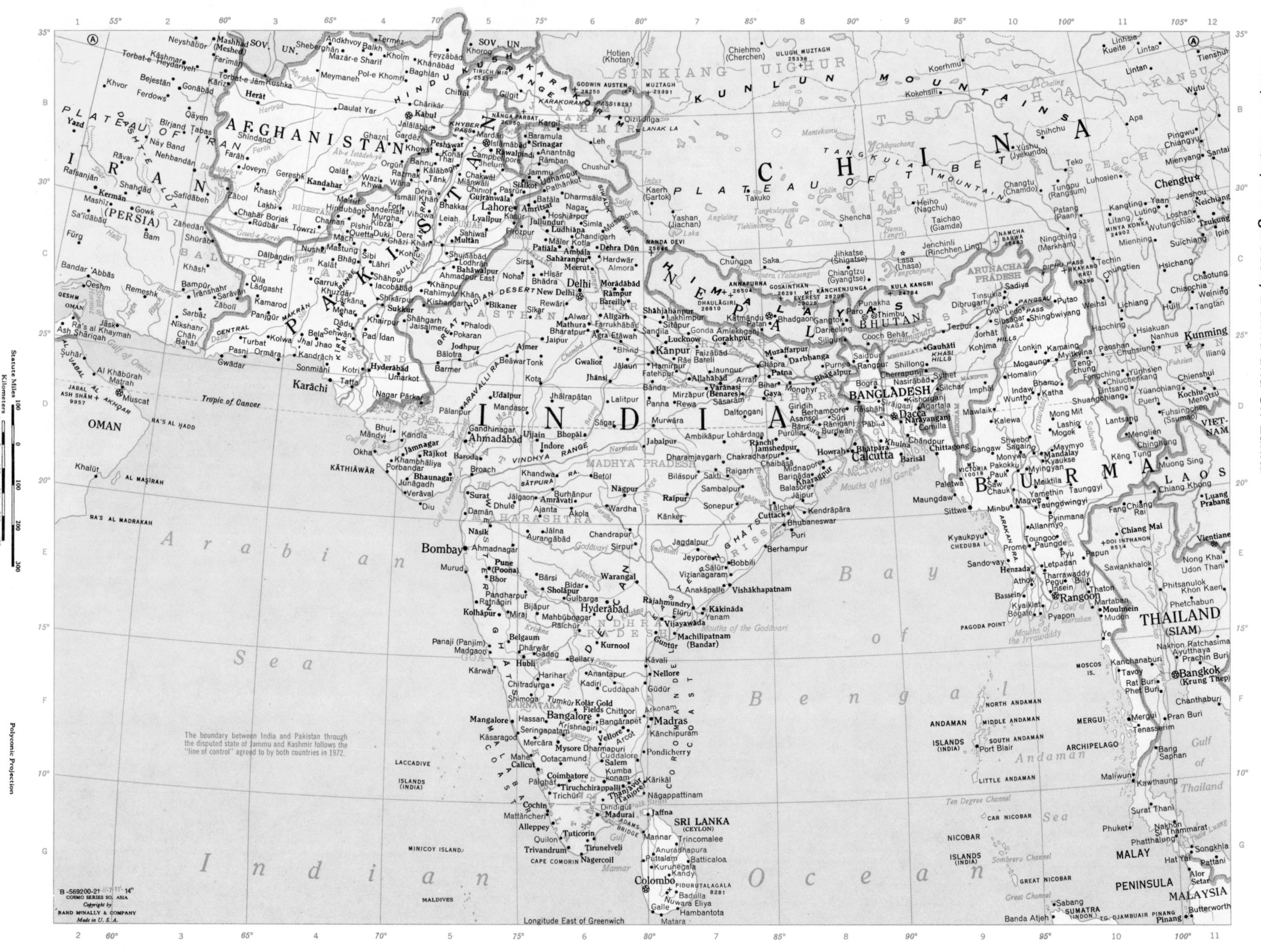

The boundary between India and Pakistan through
the disputed state of Jammu and Kashmir follows the
"line of control agreed to by both countries in 1972.

Statute Miles 100   0   100   200   300
Kilometers 100   0   100   200   300   400

Polyconic Projection

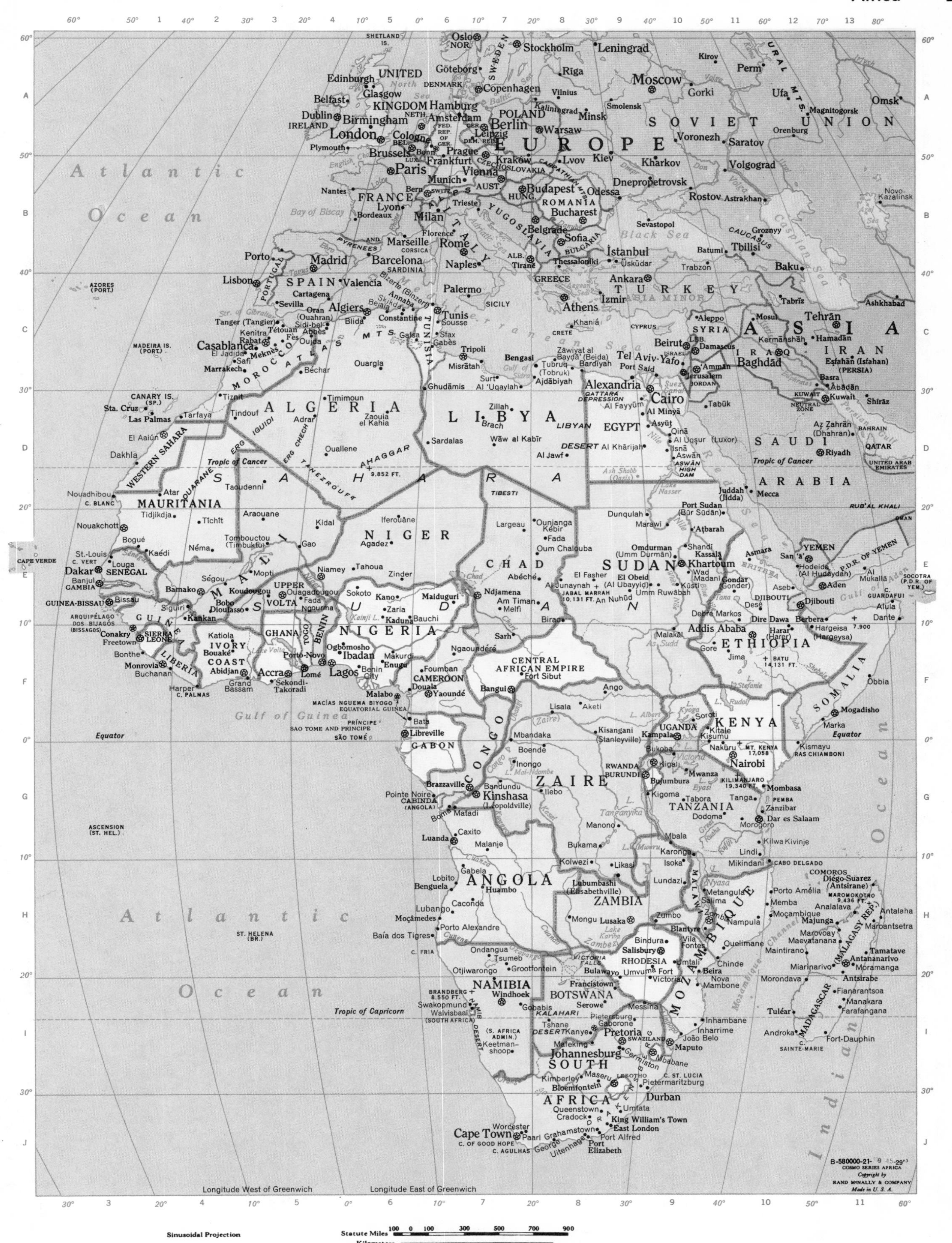

Longitude West of Greenwich   Longitude East of Greenwich

Sinusoidal Projection

Statute Miles

Kilometers

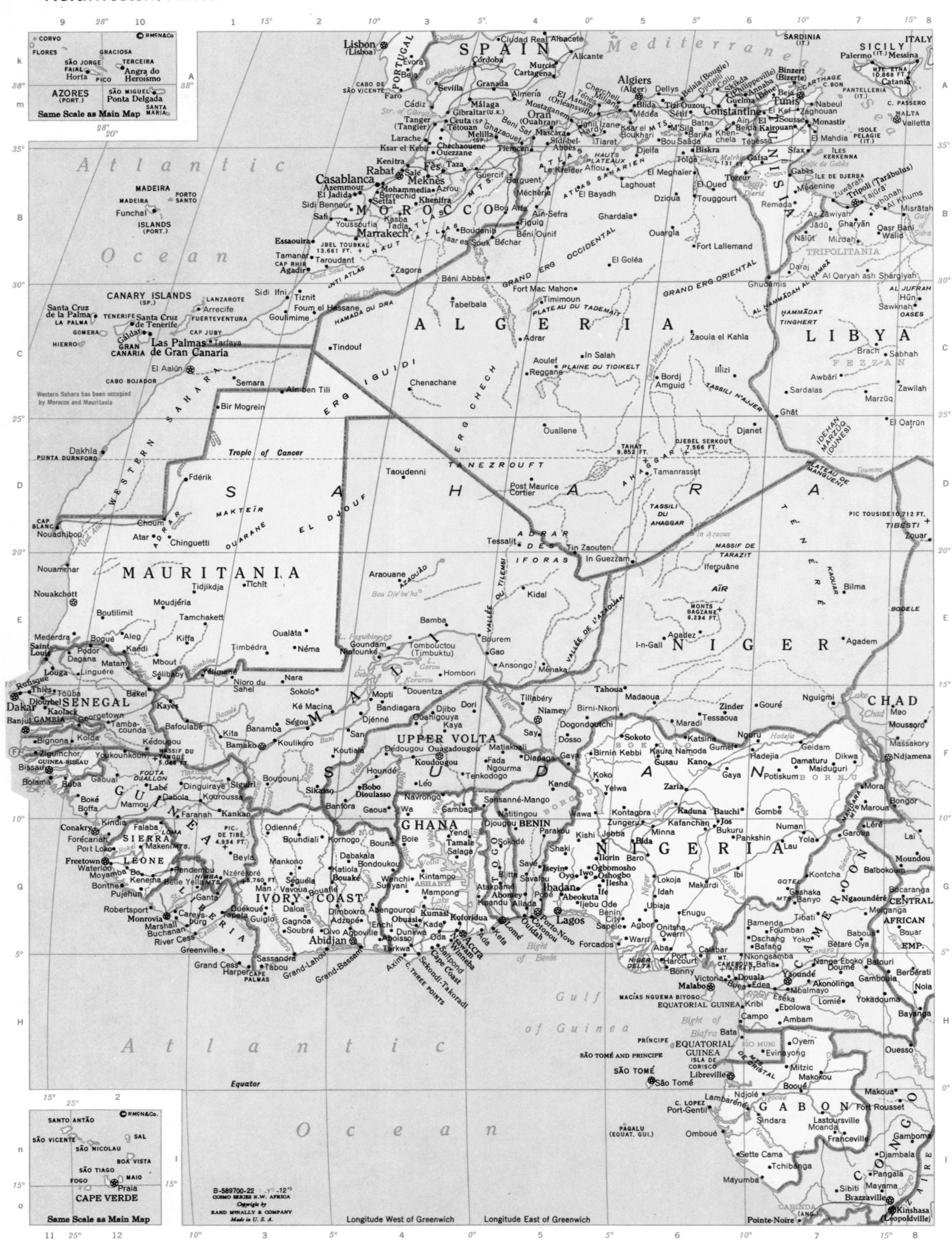

Statute Miles

Kilometers

Sinusoidal Projection

Longitude West of Greenwich   Longitude East of Greenwich

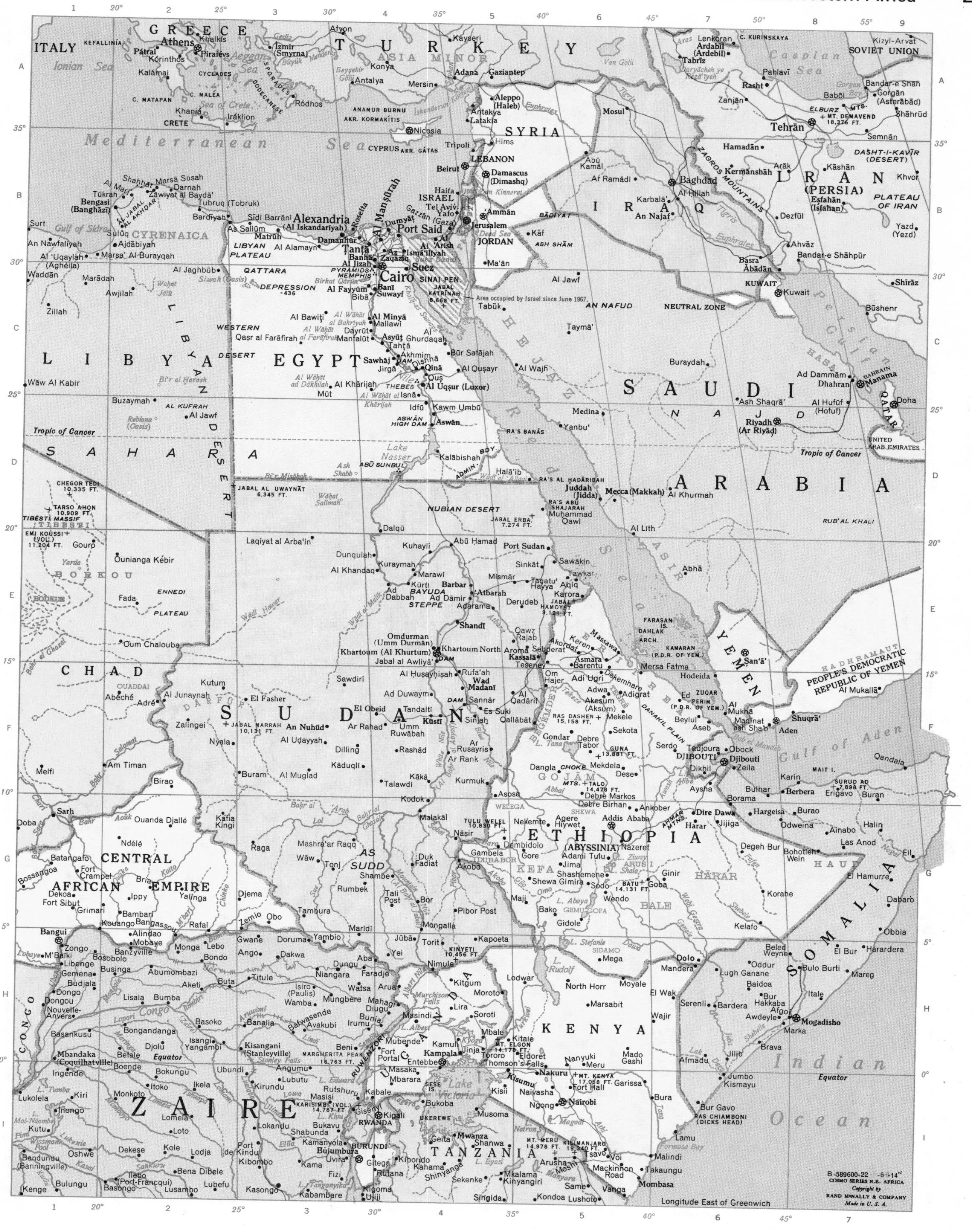

B-589600-22   -6-5-14"
COSMO SERIES N.E. AFRICA
Copyright by
RAND MCNALLY & COMPANY
Made in U.S.A.

Sinusoidal Projection

Statute Miles 100 0 100 200 300
Kilometers 100 0 100 200 300 400

Longitude East of Greenwich

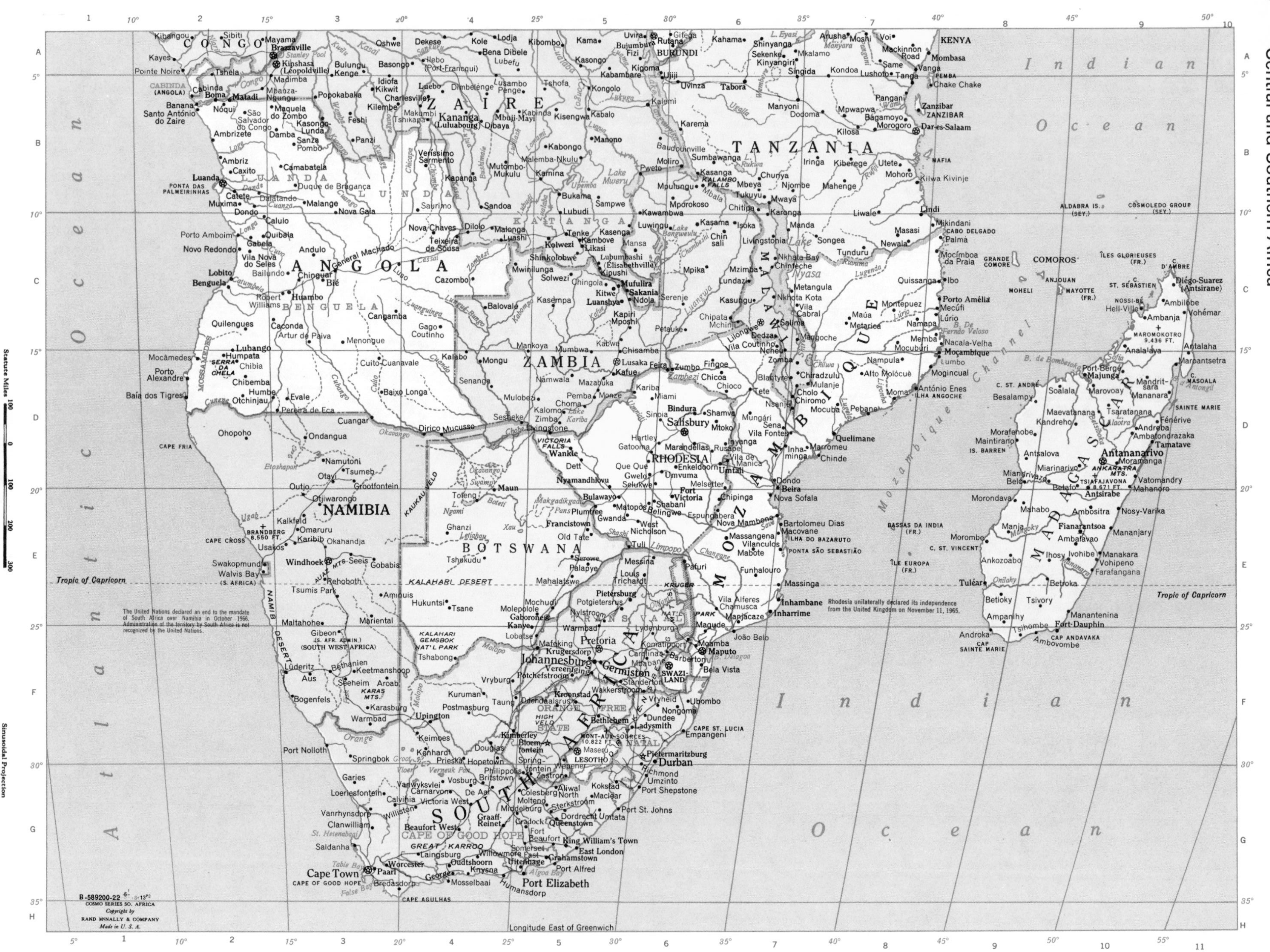

Statute Miles   100   0   100   200   300

Kilometers   100   0   100   200   300   400

Sinusoidal Projection

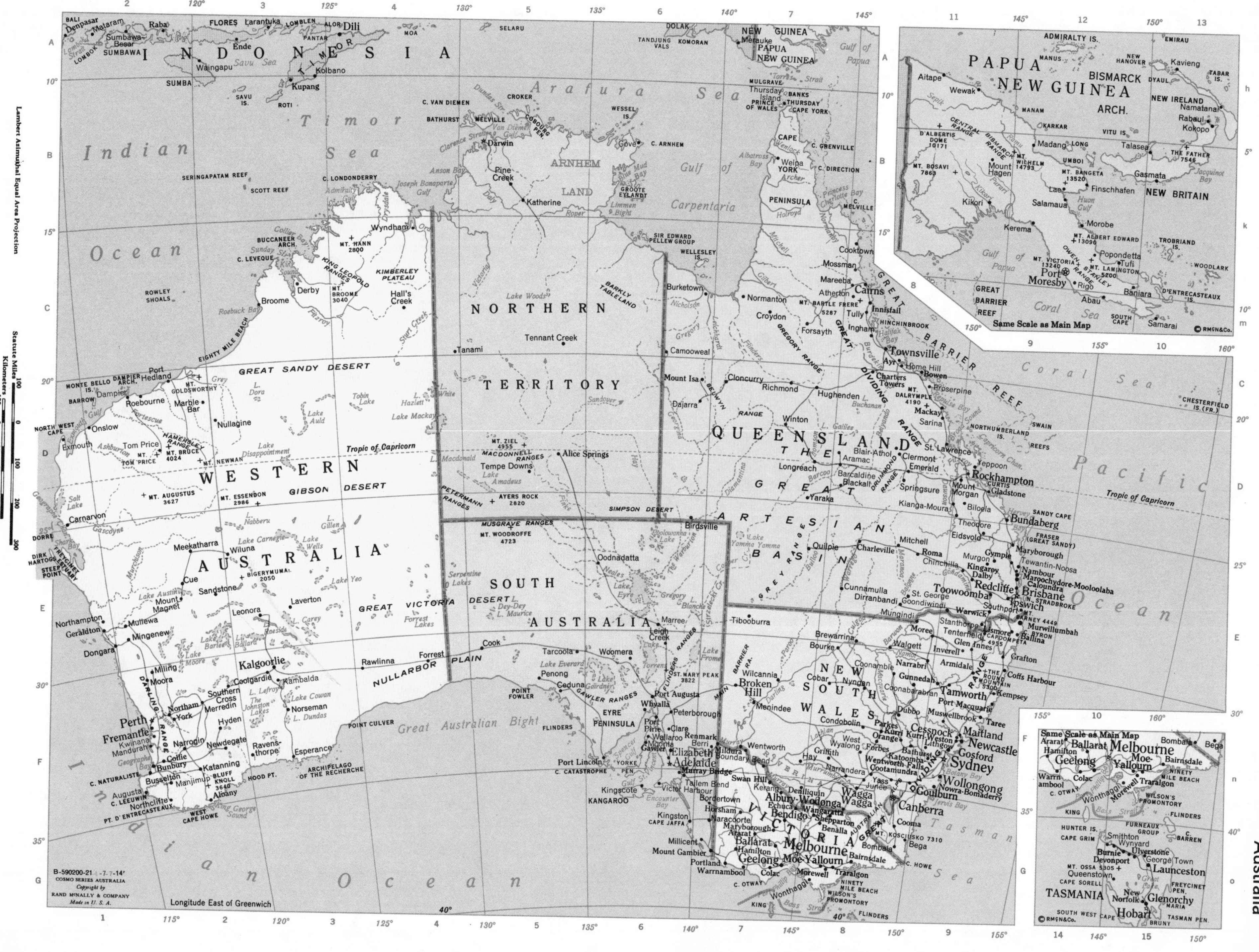

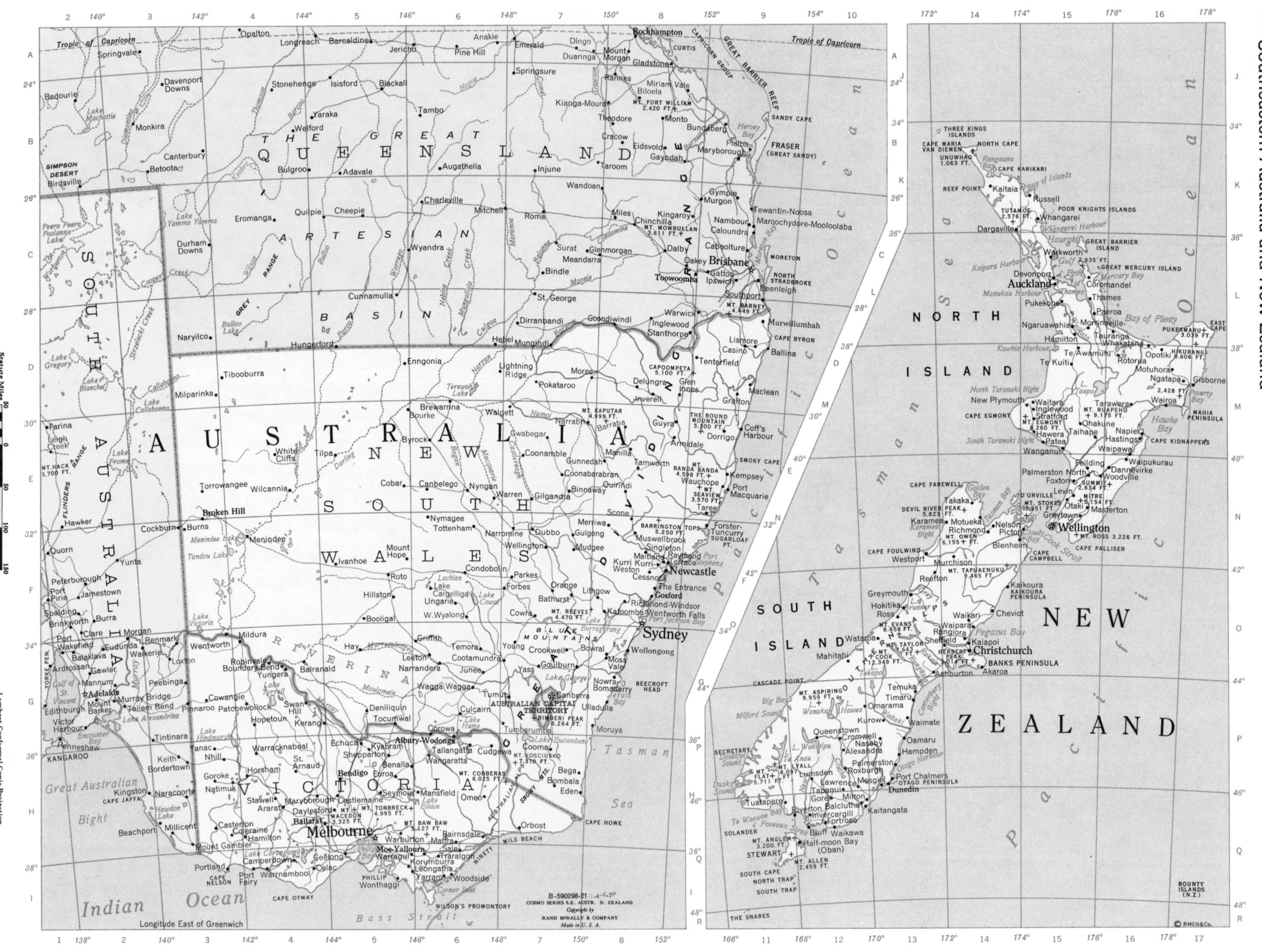

Statute Miles 50 0   50   100   150

Kilometers 50 0 50 100 200

Lambert Conformal Conic Projection

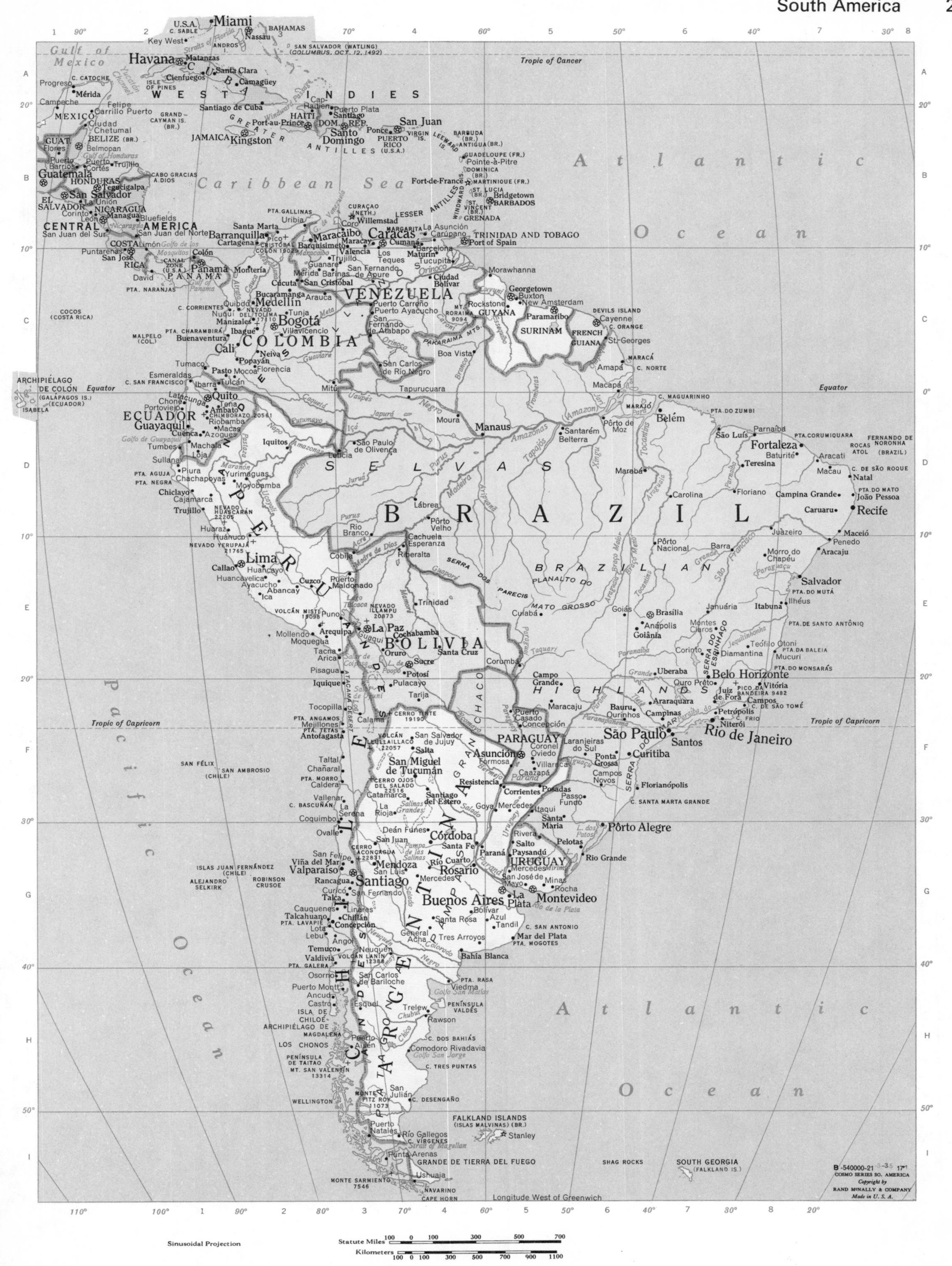

Sinusoidal Projection

Statute Miles
100 0   100   300   500   700

Kilometers
100 0 100   300   500   700   900 1100

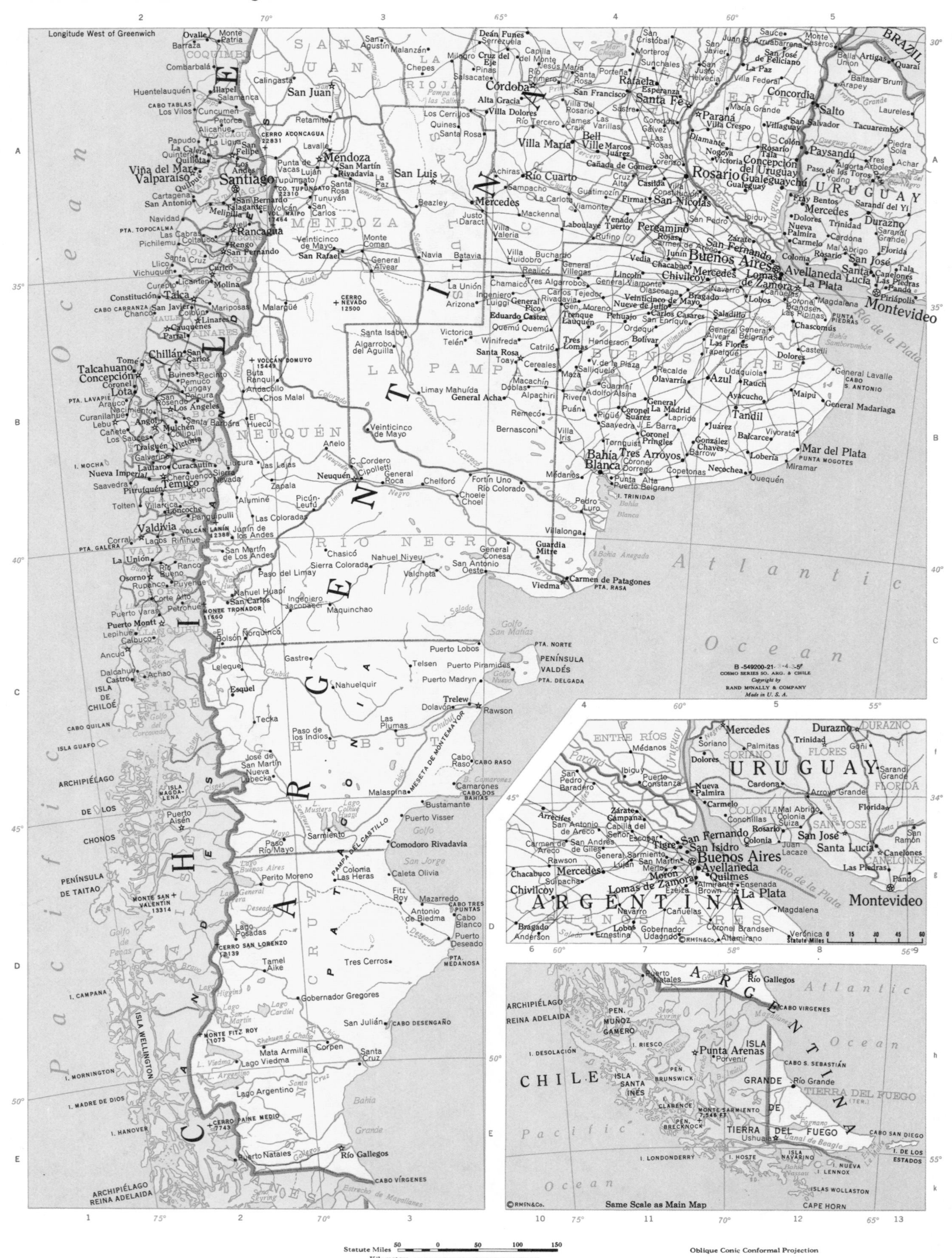

Statute Miles   50   0   50   100   150

Kilometers   50   0   50   100   150   200

Oblique Conic Conformal Projection

Same Scale as Main Map

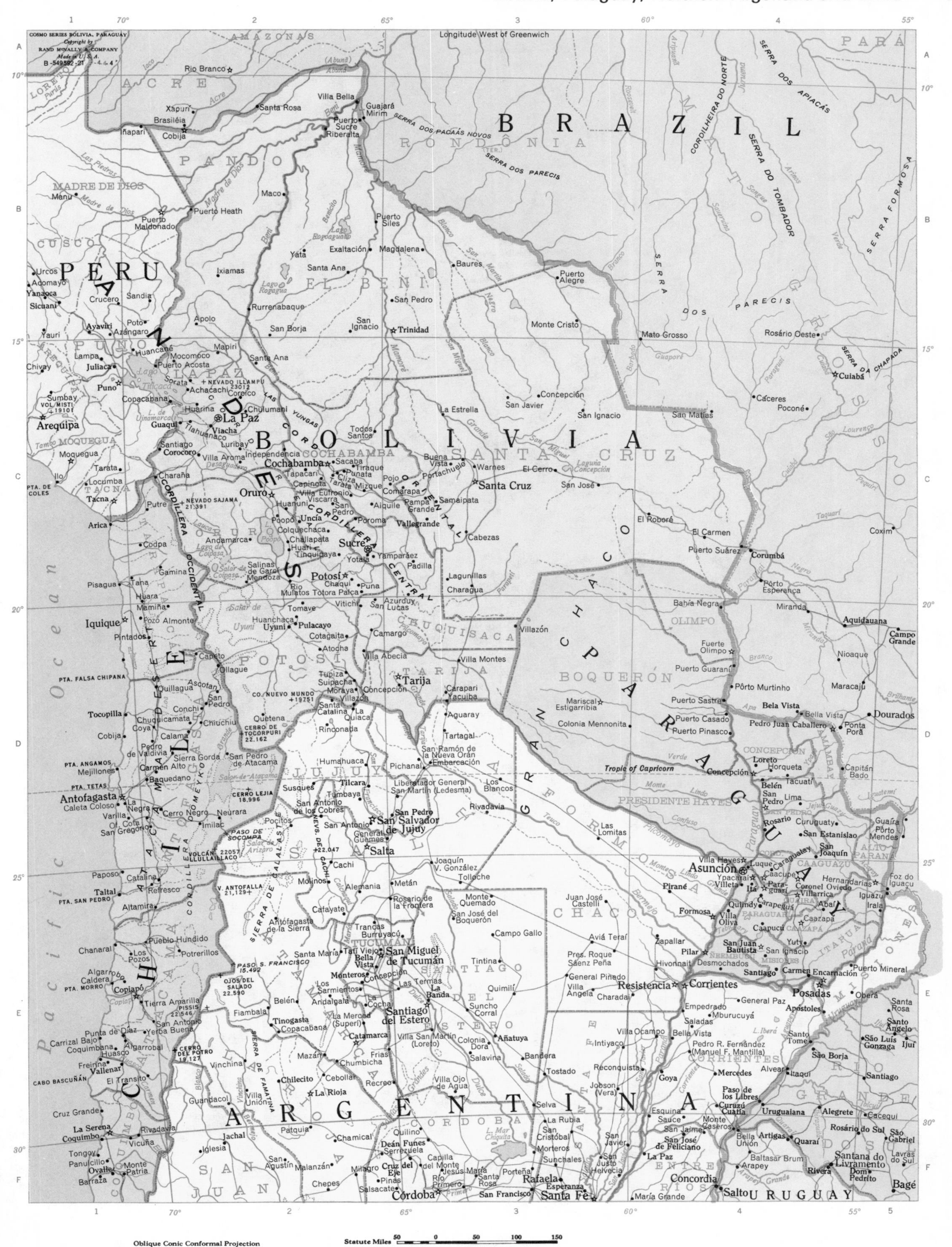

COSMO SERIES BOLIVIA, PARAGUAY
Copyright by
RAND MCNALLY & COMPANY
Made in U.S.A.
B-549592-21

Oblique Conic Conformal Projection

Statute Miles
50   0   50   100   150

Kilometers
50   0   50   100   150   200

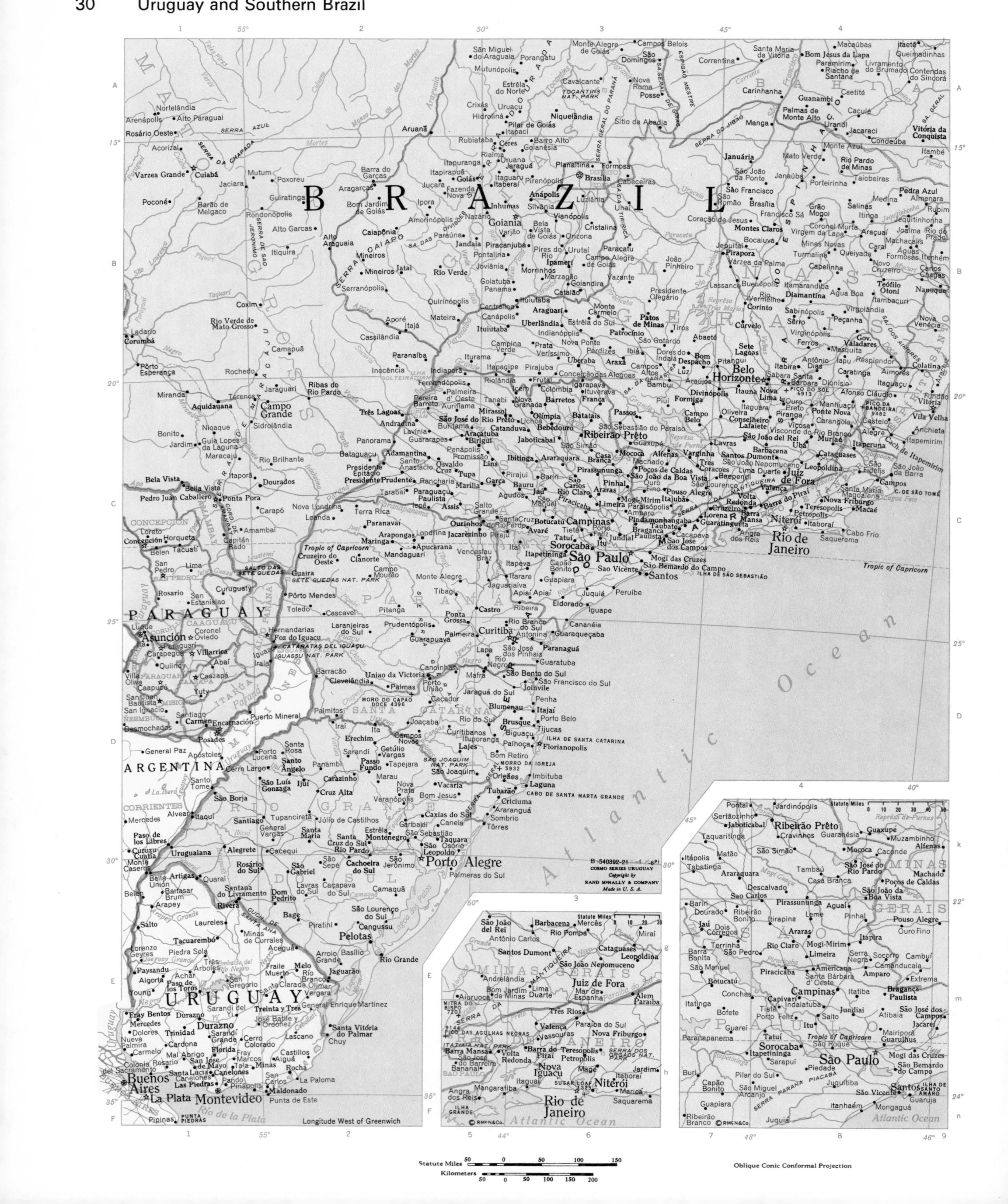
BRAZIL
PARAGUAY
URUGUAY
ARGENTINA
Atlantic Ocean
Tropic of Capricorn
Rio de Janeiro
São Paulo
Belo Horizonte
Pôrto Alegre
Curitiba
Goiânia
Brasília
Campinas
Santos
Niterói
Montevideo
Buenos Aires
La Plata
Asunción
Campo Grande
Florianópolis
Pelotas
Ribeirão Prêto
Juiz de Fora
Uberlândia
Sorocaba
Rio de la Plata
Longitude West of Greenwich
B-540392-21
COSMO SERIES URUGUAY
Copyright by
RAND McNALLY & COMPANY
Made in U. S. A.
Statute Miles
Kilometers
Oblique Conic Conformal Projection

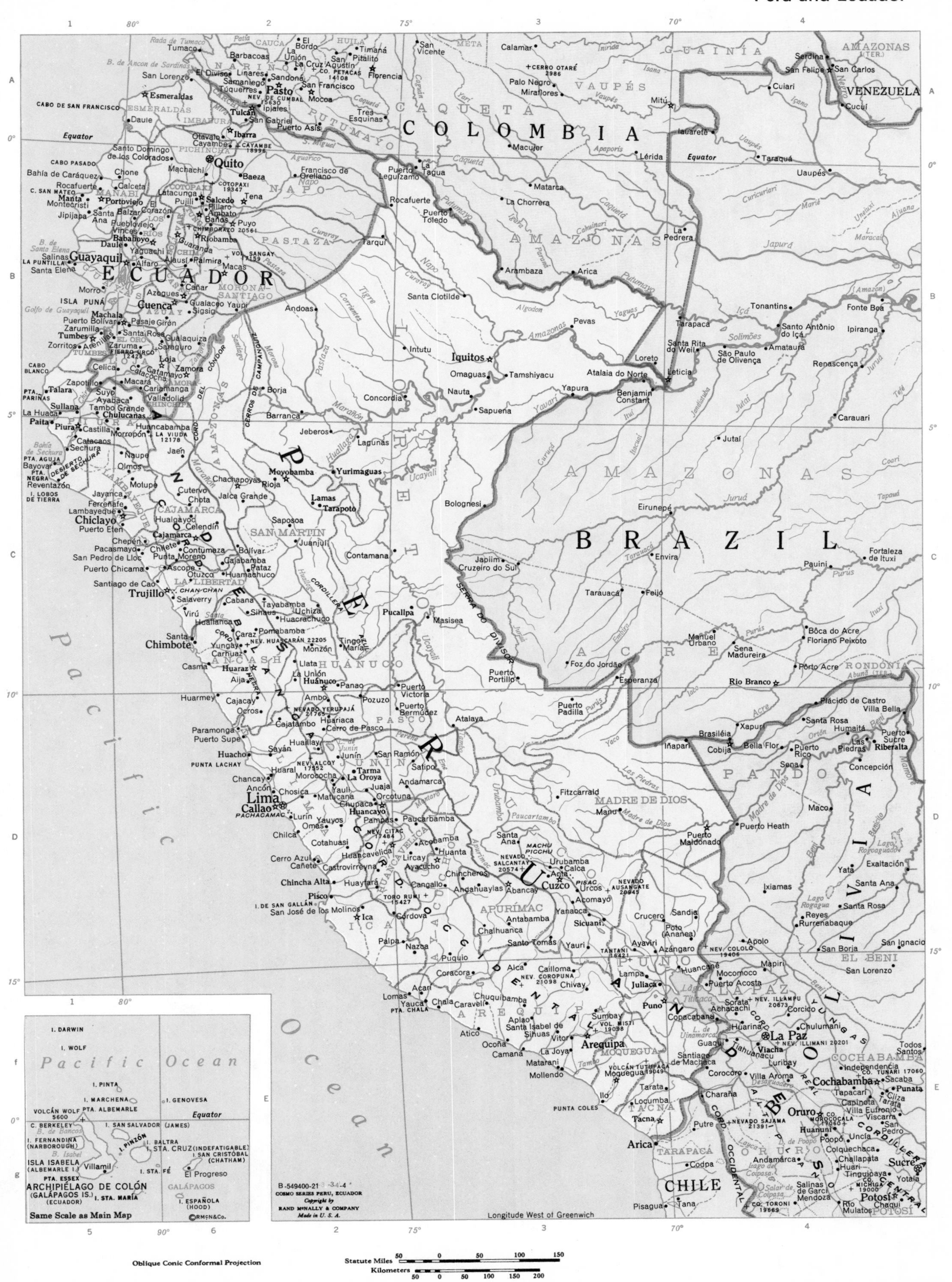

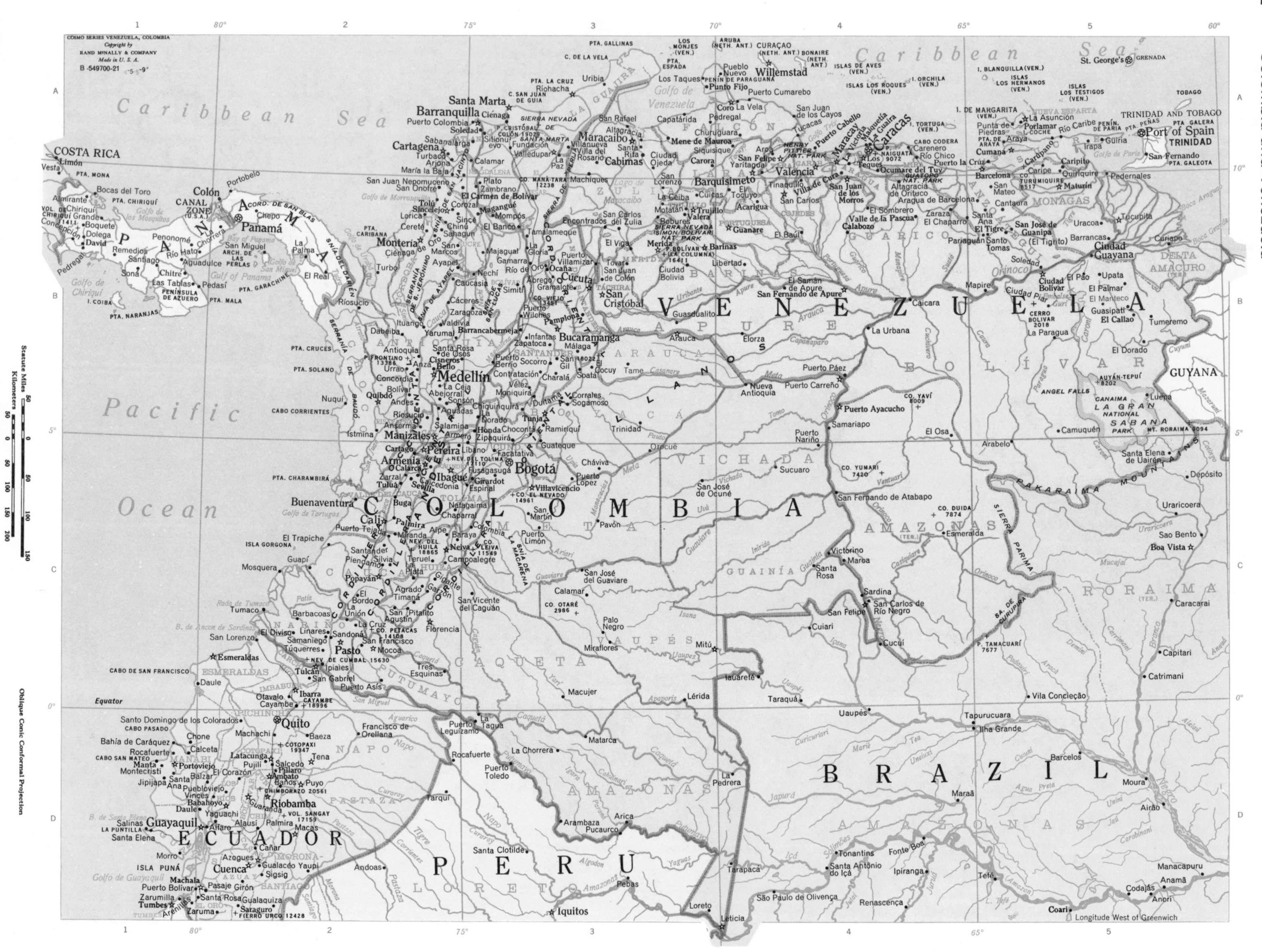
COLOMBIA
VENEZUELA
BRAZIL
PERU
ECUADOR
PANAMA
GUYANA
COSTA RICA
TRINIDAD AND TOBAGO
Caribbean Sea
Pacific Ocean
Bogotá
Caracas
Quito
Panamá
Medellín
Cali
Barranquilla
Cartagena
Maracaibo
Valencia
Barquisimeto
Ciudad Guayana
Port of Spain
Iquitos
Guayaquil
Equator
Longitude West of Greenwich
COSMO SERIES VENEZUELA, COLOMBIA
Copyright by RAND McNALLY & COMPANY
Made in U. S. A.
B-549700-21 -5-5-9-
Statute Miles 50 0 50 100 150
Kilometers 50 0 50 100 150 200
Oblique Conic Conformal Projection

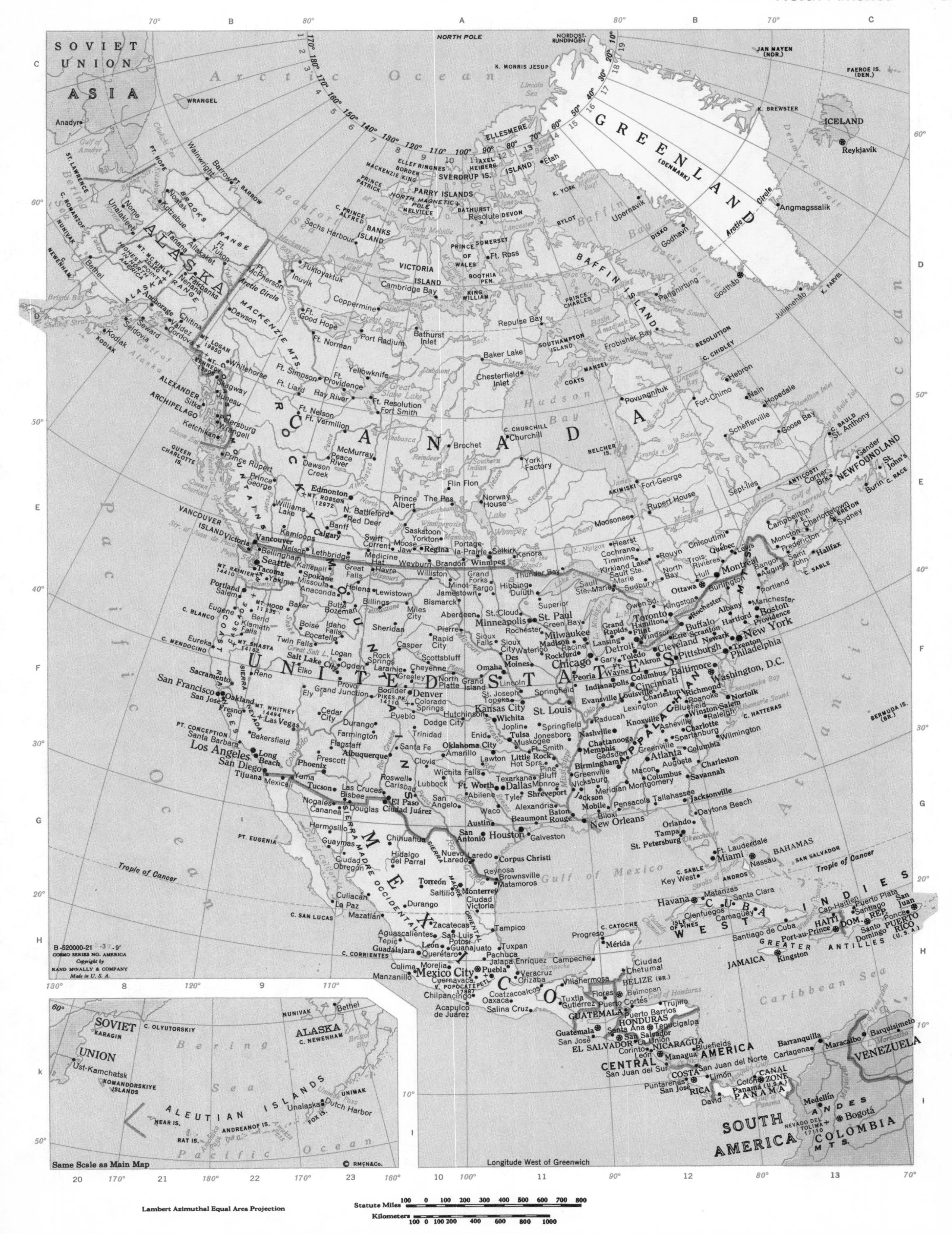

Lambert Azimuthal Equal Area Projection

Statute Miles 100 0 100 200 300 400 500 600 700 800

Kilometers 100 0 100 200 400 600 800 1000

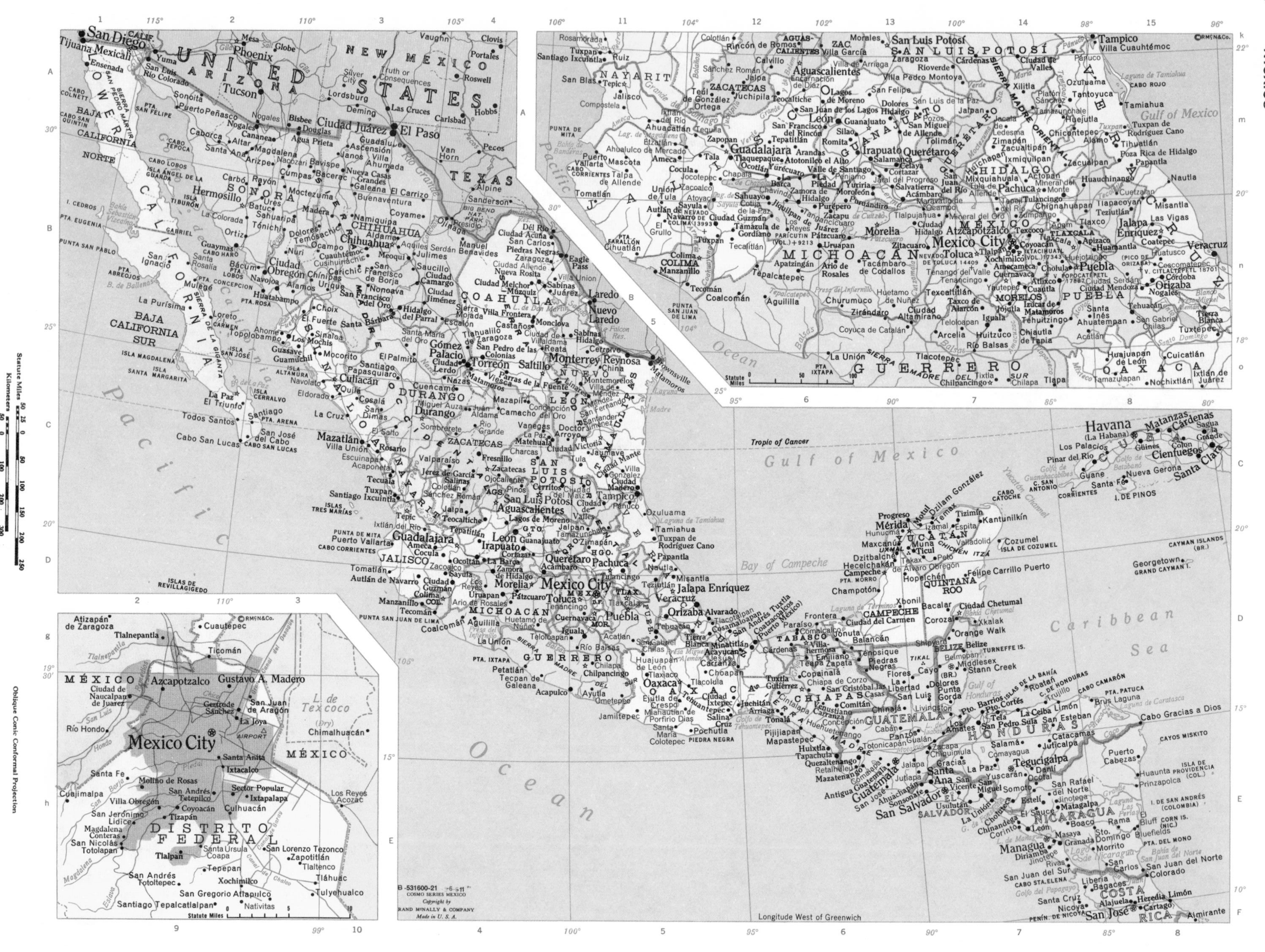

Statute Miles 50 25 0   50   100   150   200   250

Kilometers   50   0   100   200   300

Oblique Conic Conformal Projection

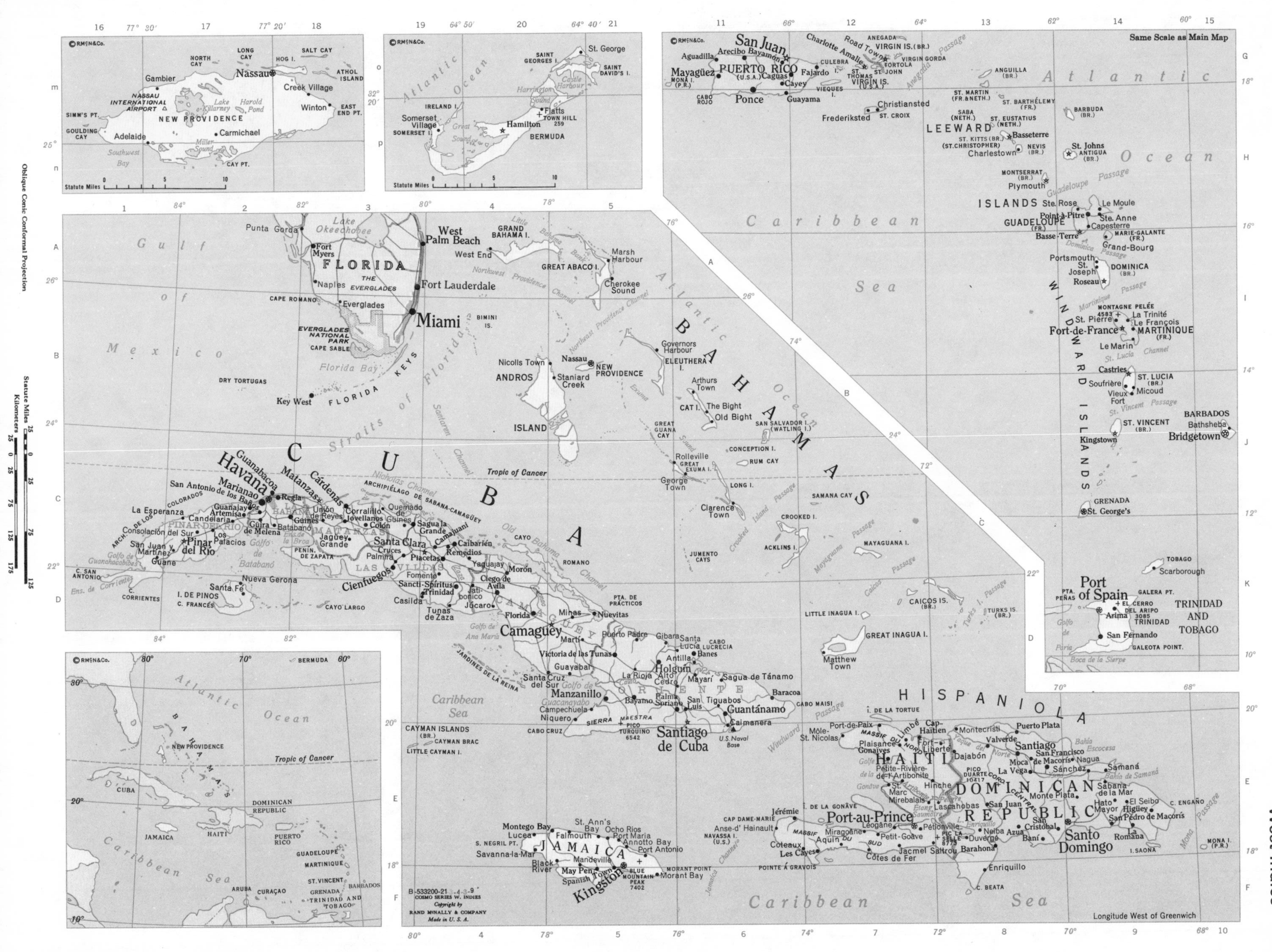

Same Scale as Main Map

Oblique Conic Conformal Projection

Statute Miles 25 0 25 75 125
Kilometers 25 0 25 75 125 175

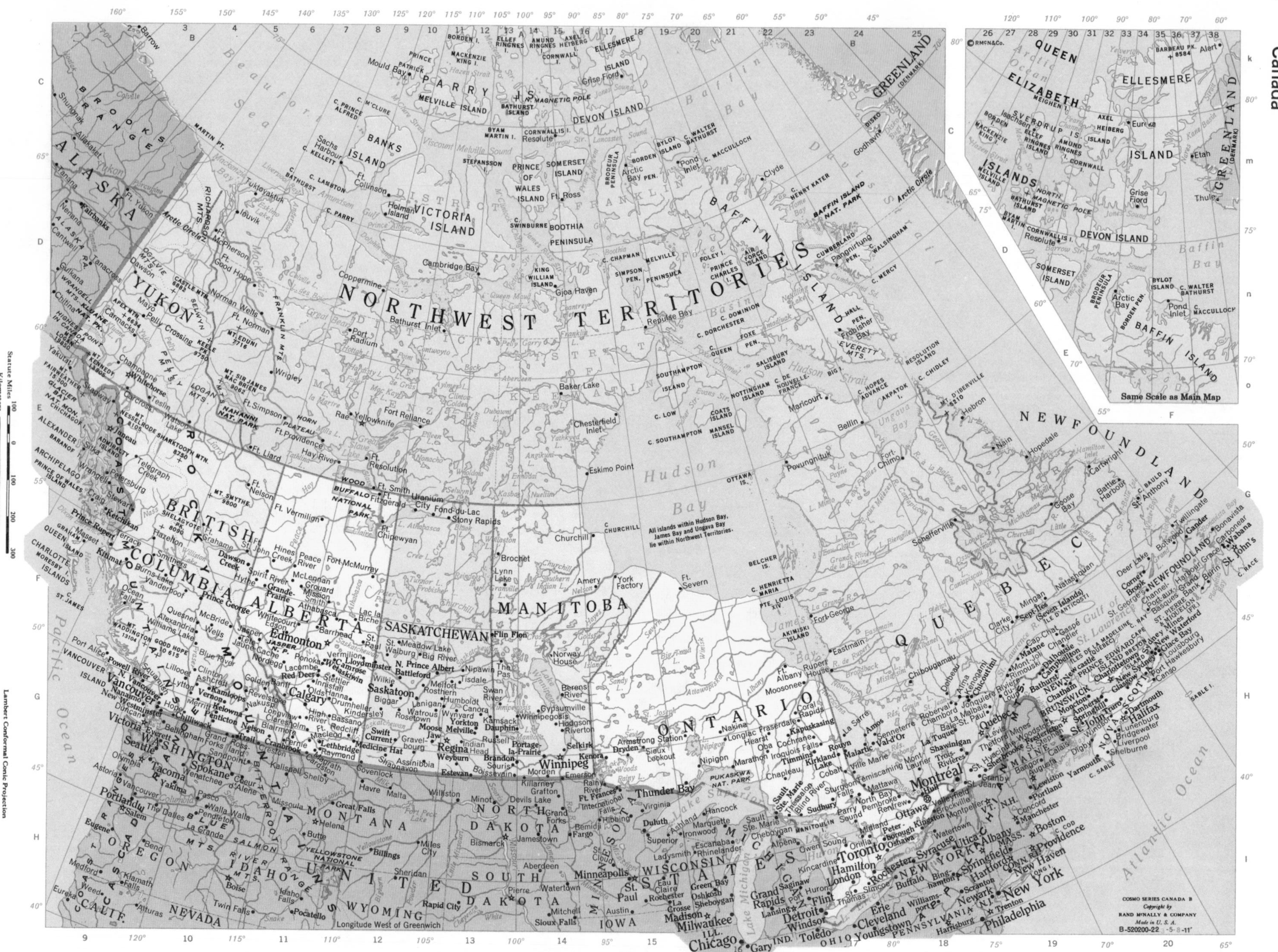

Statute Miles
Kilometers

Lambert Conformal Conic Projection

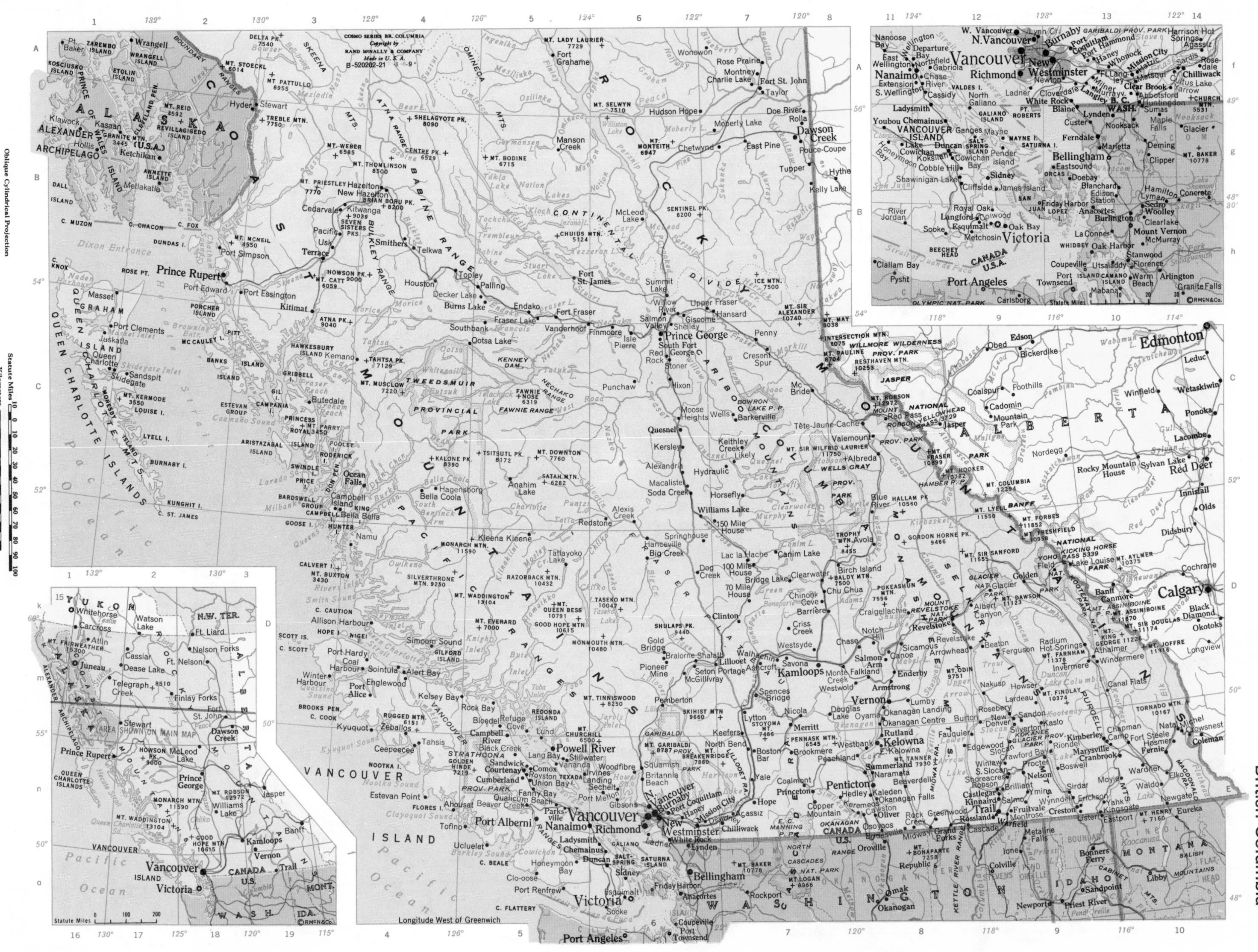

Oblique Cylindrical Projection

Statute Miles
Kilometers

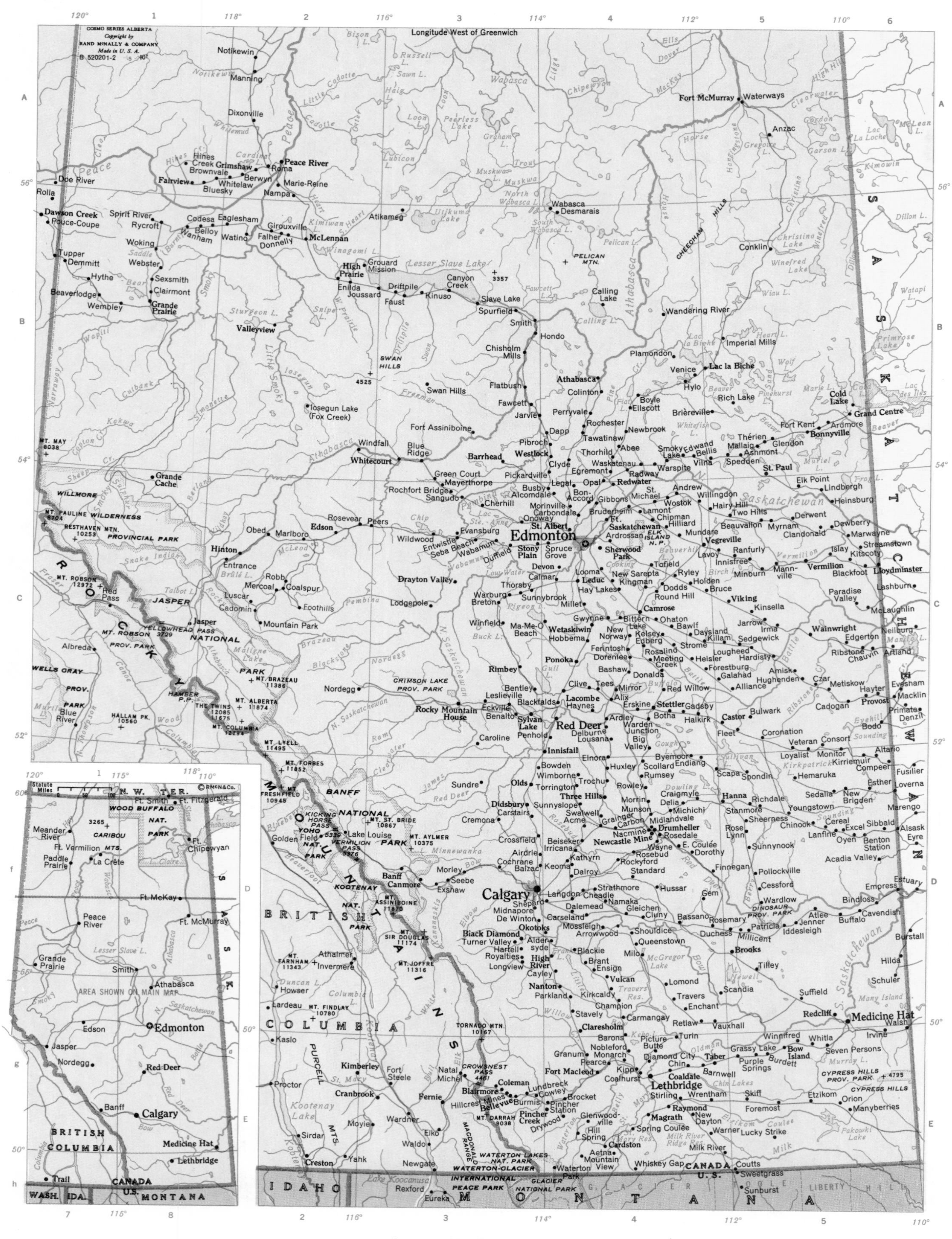

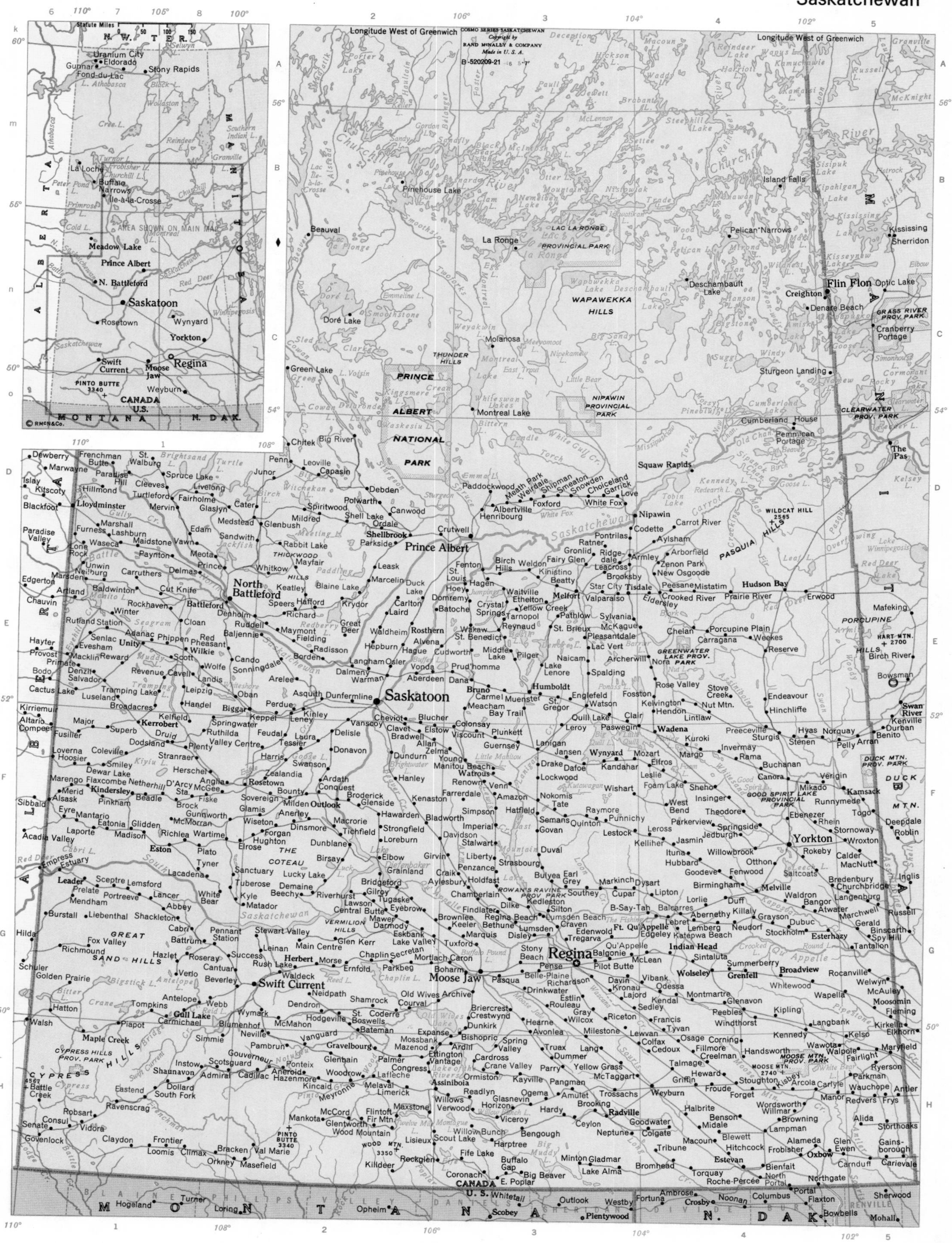

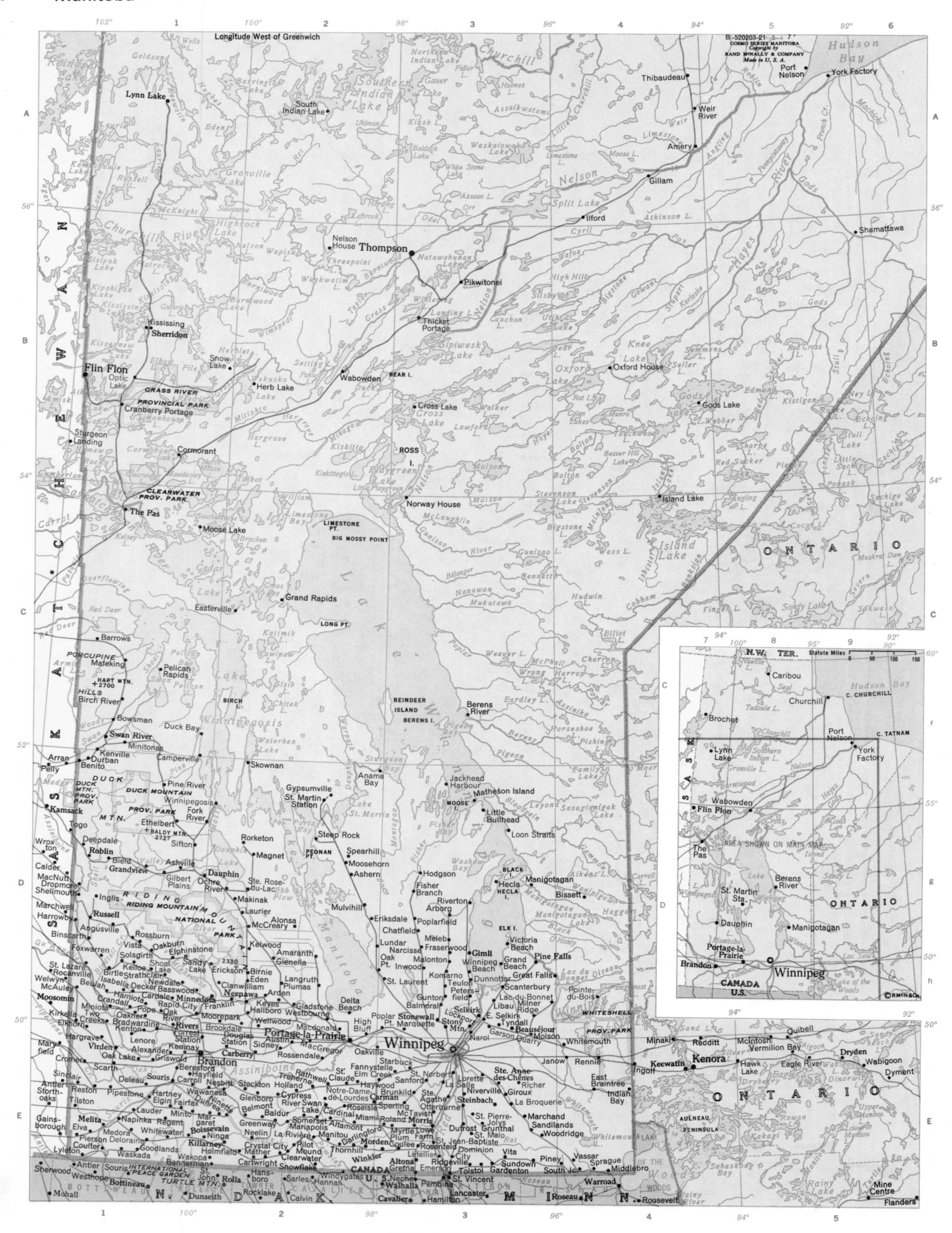

Statute Miles 10 0 10 20 30 40 50 60 70
Kilometers 10 0 10 20 30 40 60 80 100

Oblique Cylindrical Projection

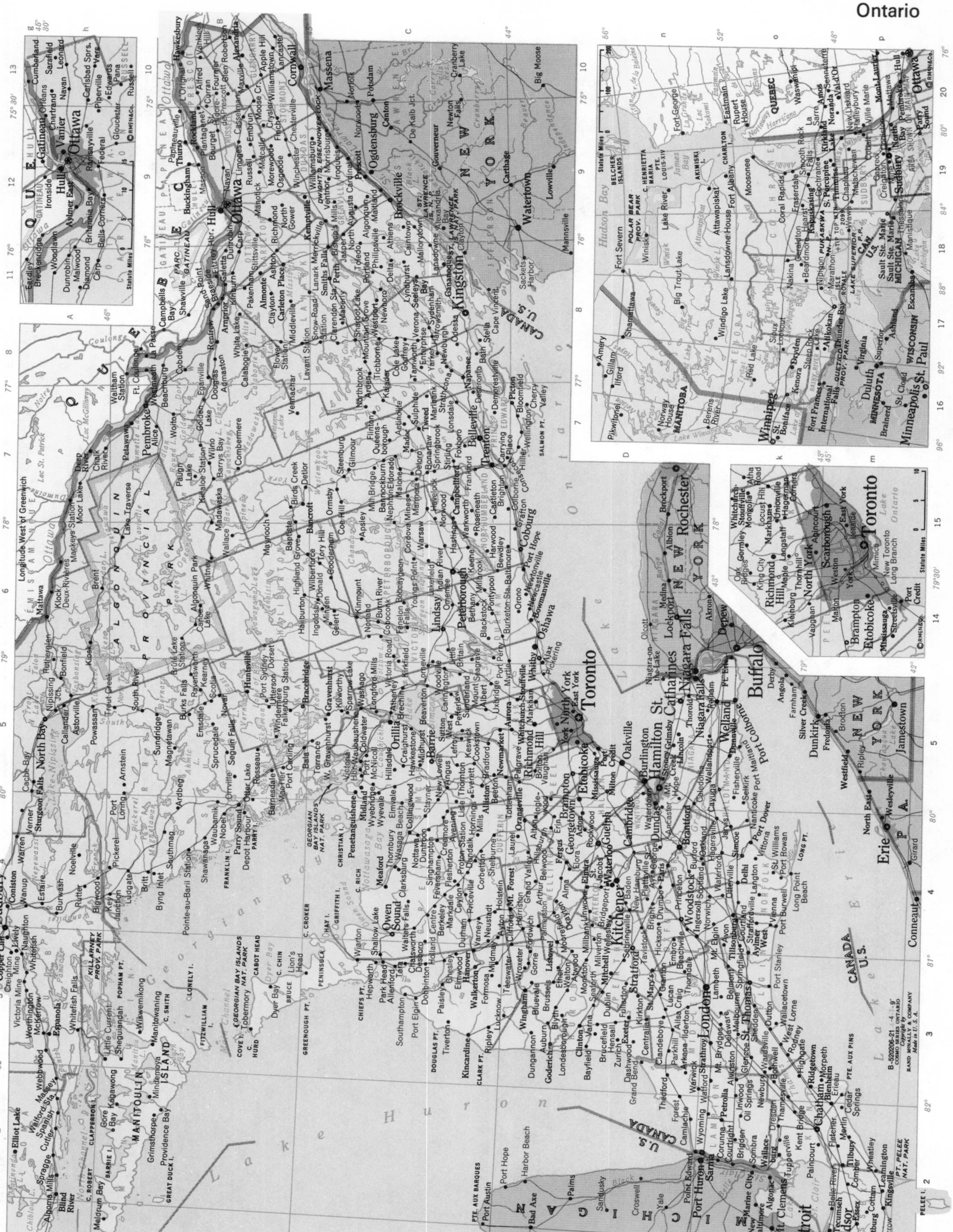

QUEBEC

NEW YORK

ALGONQUIN PROVINCIAL PARK

Lake Ontario

Lake Huron

Lake Erie

Georgian Bay

MANITOULIN ISLAND

CANADA
U.S.

MICHIGAN

PENNA.

Sudbury

North Bay

Ottawa

Hull

Vanier

Toronto

Hamilton

Kingston

Brockville

Cornwall

Detroit

Windsor

Buffalo

Rochester

London

Kitchener

Waterloo

Cambridge

Guelph

Brampton

Mississauga

Oakville

Burlington

St. Catharines

Niagara Falls

Welland

Stratford

Sarnia

Chatham

Owen Sound

Barrie

Orillia

Peterborough

Belleville

Oshawa

Whitby

Pembroke

Massena

Watertown

Ogdensburg

Potsdam

Minneapolis

St. Paul

Duluth

Winnipeg

Sault Ste. Marie

MINNESOTA

WISCONSIN

MANITOBA

Hudson Bay

James Bay

POLAR BEAR PROV. PARK

Oblique Cylindrical Projection

Statute Miles 5 0 5 10 20 30 40 50

Kilometers 5 0 5 15 25 35 45 55 65 75

B-502006-21 -4-'g'
COMO SERIES ONTARIO
RAND McNALLY & COMPANY
Made in U.S.A.

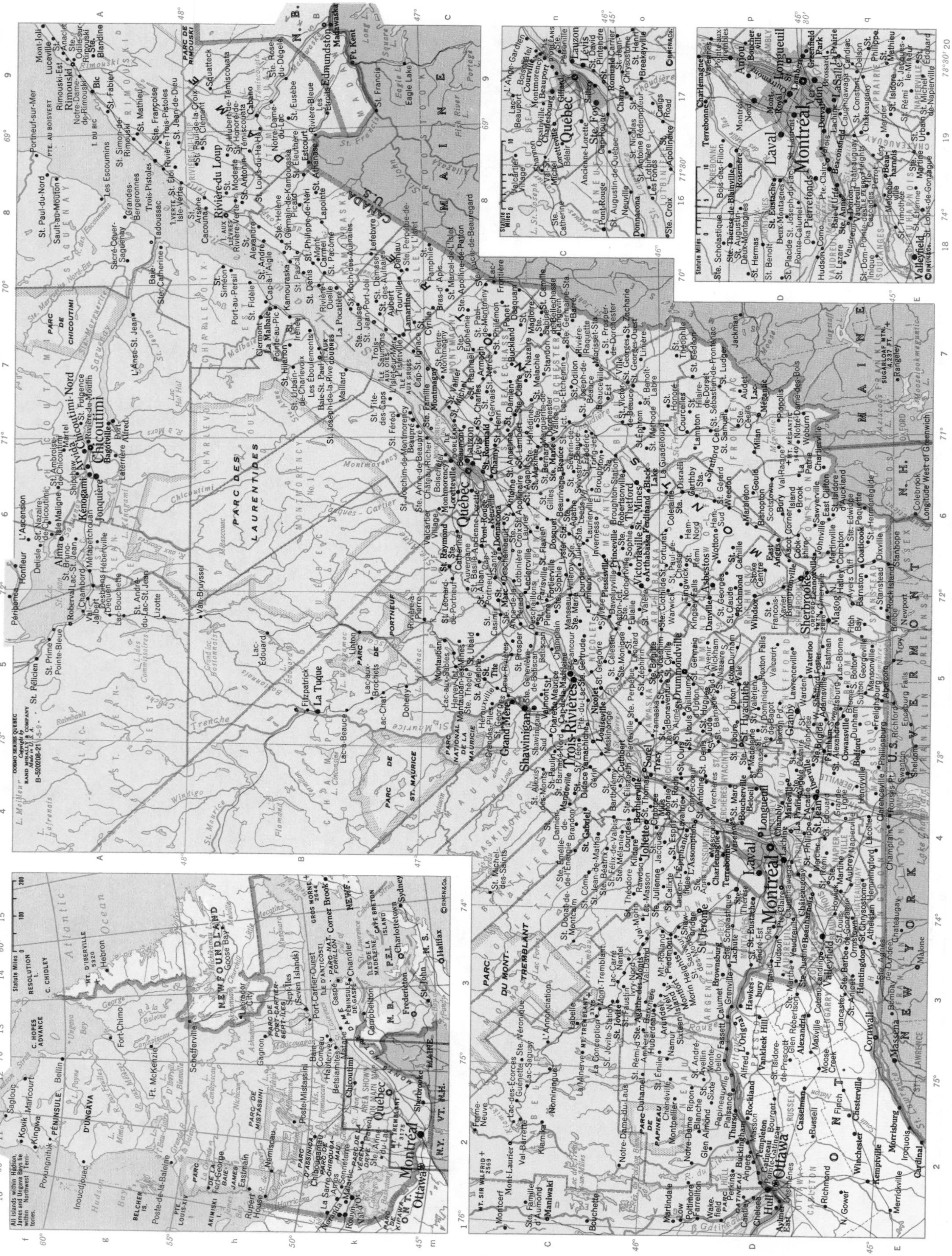

Quebec

Statute Miles 5 0 5 10   20   30   40

Kilometers 5 0 5   15   25   35   45   55

Oblique Cylindrical Projection

COSMO SERIES QUEBEC
Copyright by
RAND MCNALLY & COMPANY
B-50(2026-21) 5-9
Made in U.S.A.

All islands within Hudson,
James and Ungava Bays lie
in Northwest Terri-
tories.

©RMcN&Co.

Longitude West of Greenwich

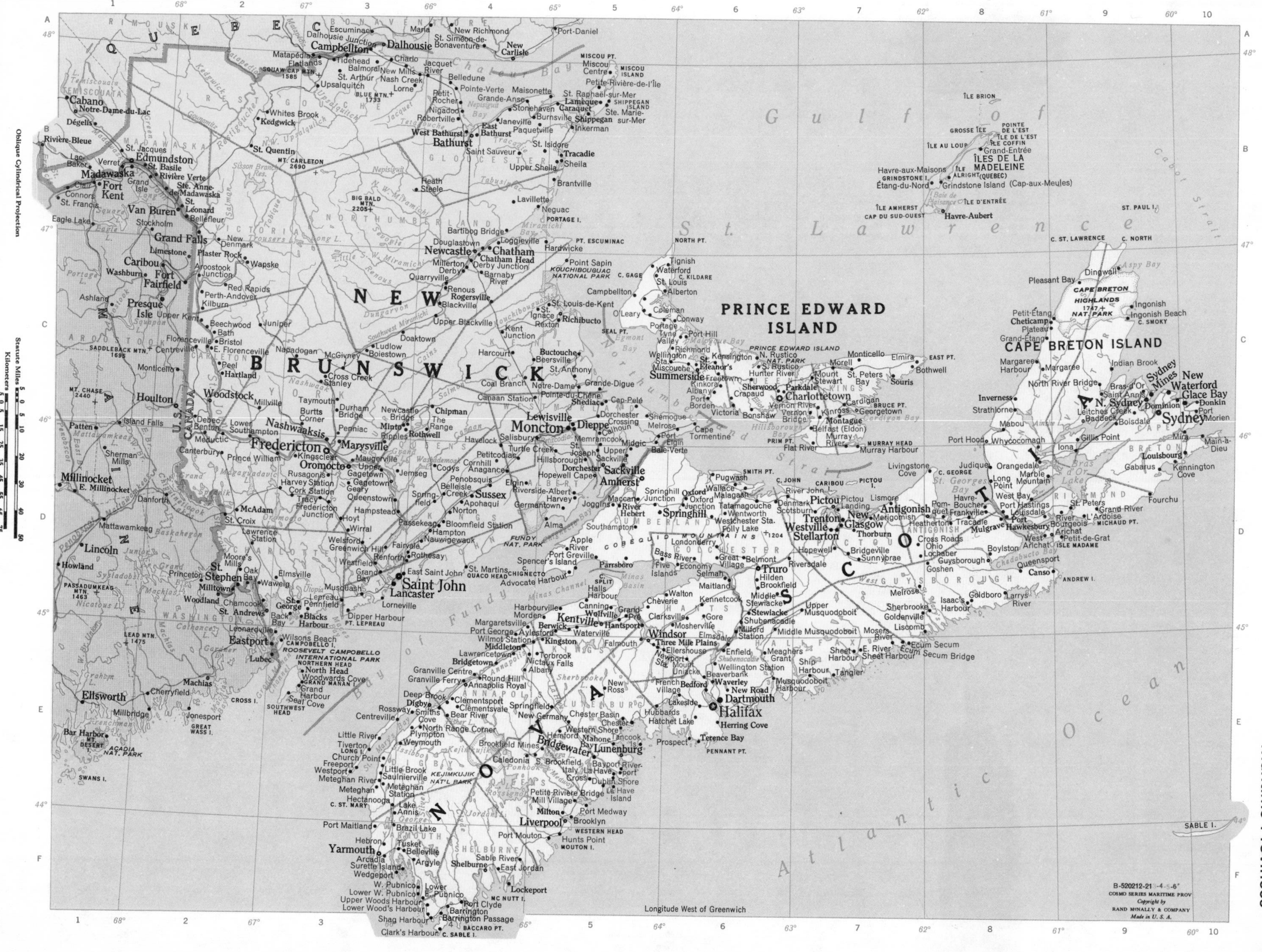

PRINCE EDWARD ISLAND

CAPE BRETON ISLAND

NEW BRUNSWICK

N O V A   S C O T I A

Gulf of St. Lawrence

Atlantic Ocean

B-502012-21-4-5-6"
COSMO SERIES MARITIME PROV.
Copyright by
RAND McNALLY & COMPANY
Made in U.S.A.

Oblique Cylindrical Projection

Statute Miles

Kilometers

Longitude West of Greenwich

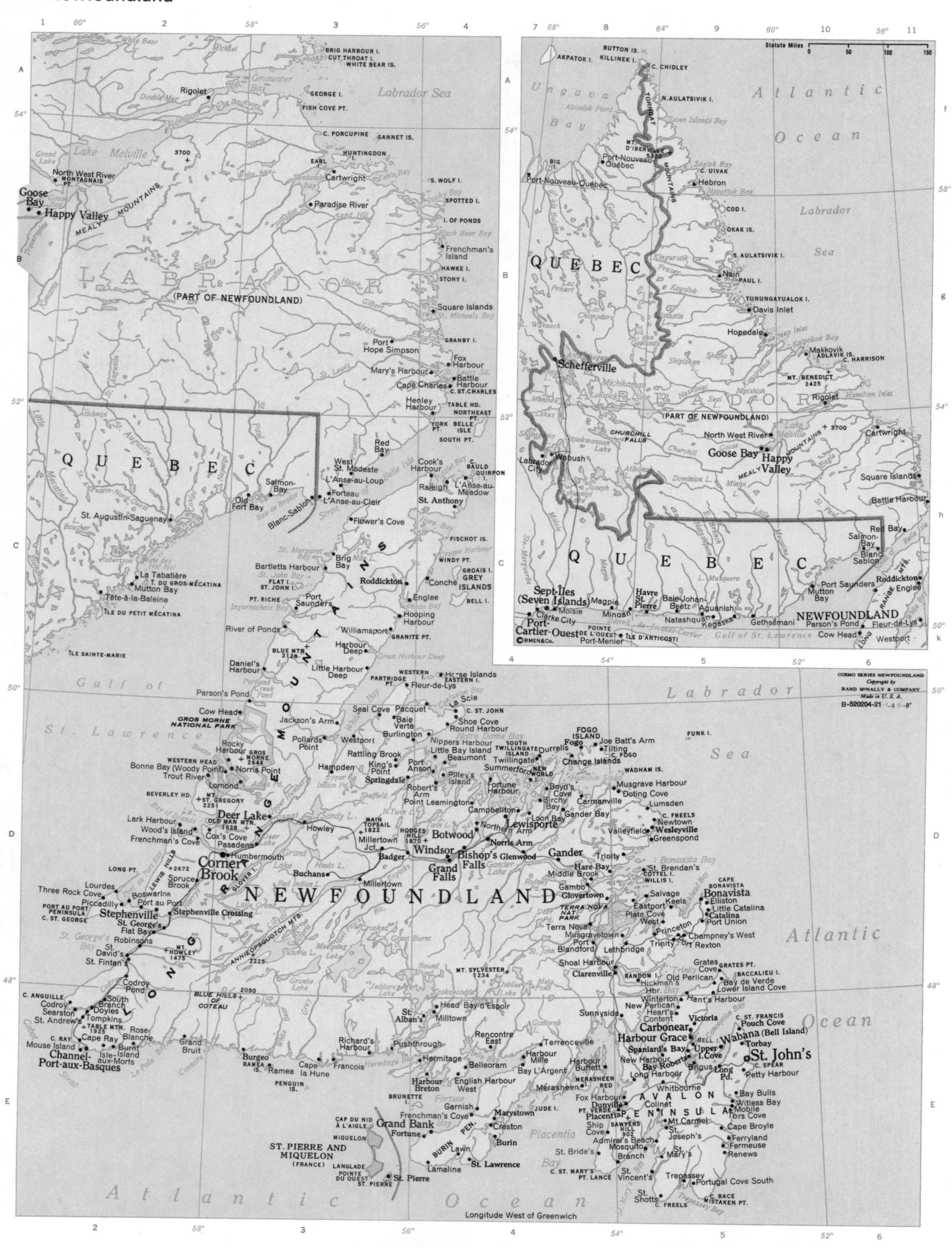
LABRADOR
(PART OF NEWFOUNDLAND)
QUEBEC
NEWFOUNDLAND
Labrador Sea
Gulf of St. Lawrence
Atlantic Ocean
Labrador Sea
AVALON PENINSULA
LONG RANGE MOUNTAINS
MEALY MOUNTAINS
GROS MORNE NATIONAL PARK
TERRA NOVA NAT. PARK
ST. PIERRE AND MIQUELON (FRANCE)
St. John's
Corner Brook
Gander
Grand Falls
Stephenville
Channel-Port-aux-Basques
Goose Bay
Happy Valley
Schefferville
Sept-Îles (Seven Islands)
Longitude West of Greenwich
COSMO SERIES NEWFOUNDLAND
Copyright by RAND McNALLY & COMPANY
Made in U. S. A.
B-520204-21
Statute Miles
Kilometers
Lambert Conformal Conic Projection

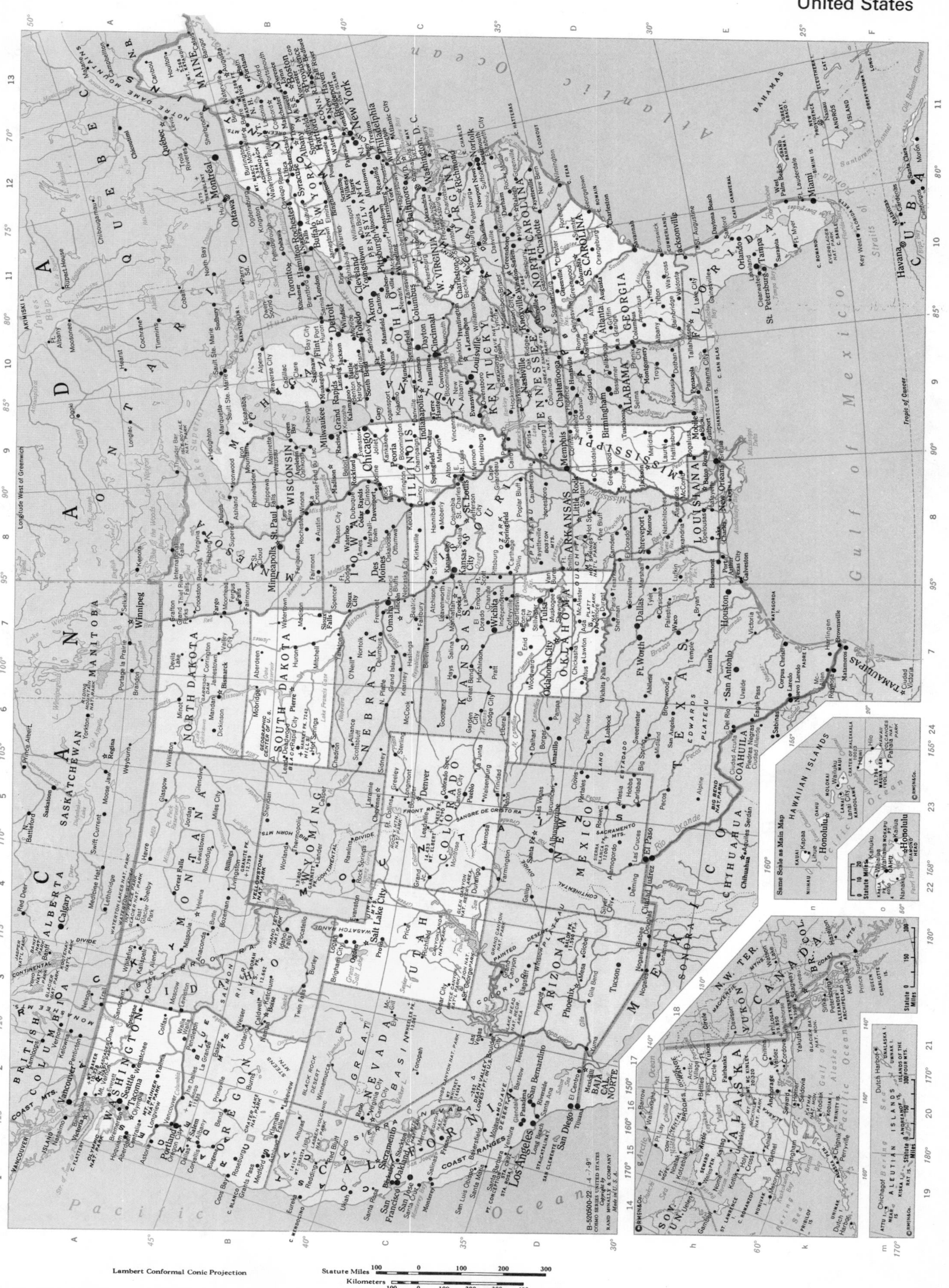

Lambert Conformal Conic Projection

Statute Miles
100   0   100   200   300

Kilometers
100   0   100   200   300   400

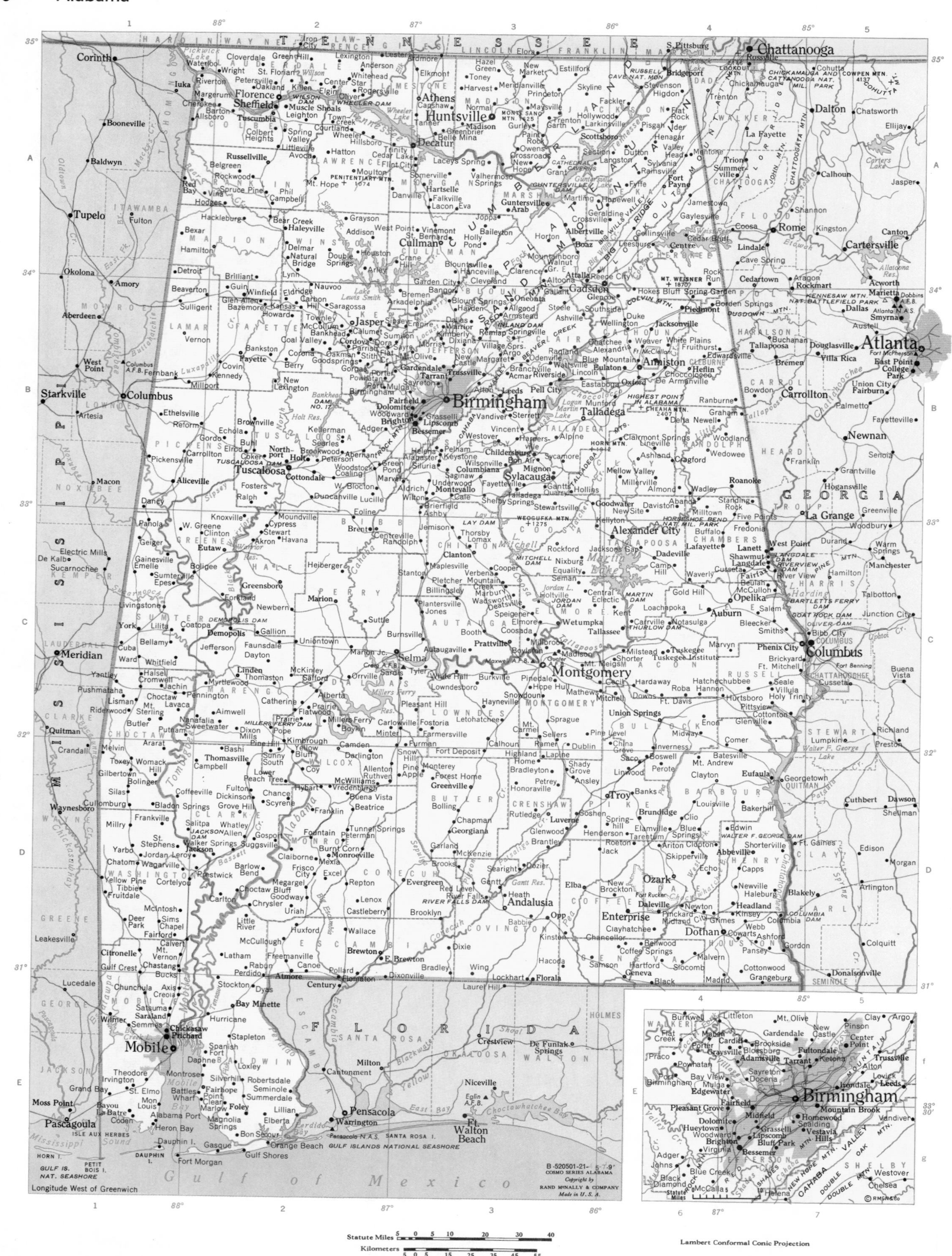

Statute Miles
Kilometers

Longitude West of Greenwich

Lambert Conformal Conic Projection

Polyconic Projection

Statute Miles 50 25 0 50 100 150 200 250
Kilometers 50 0 100 200 300

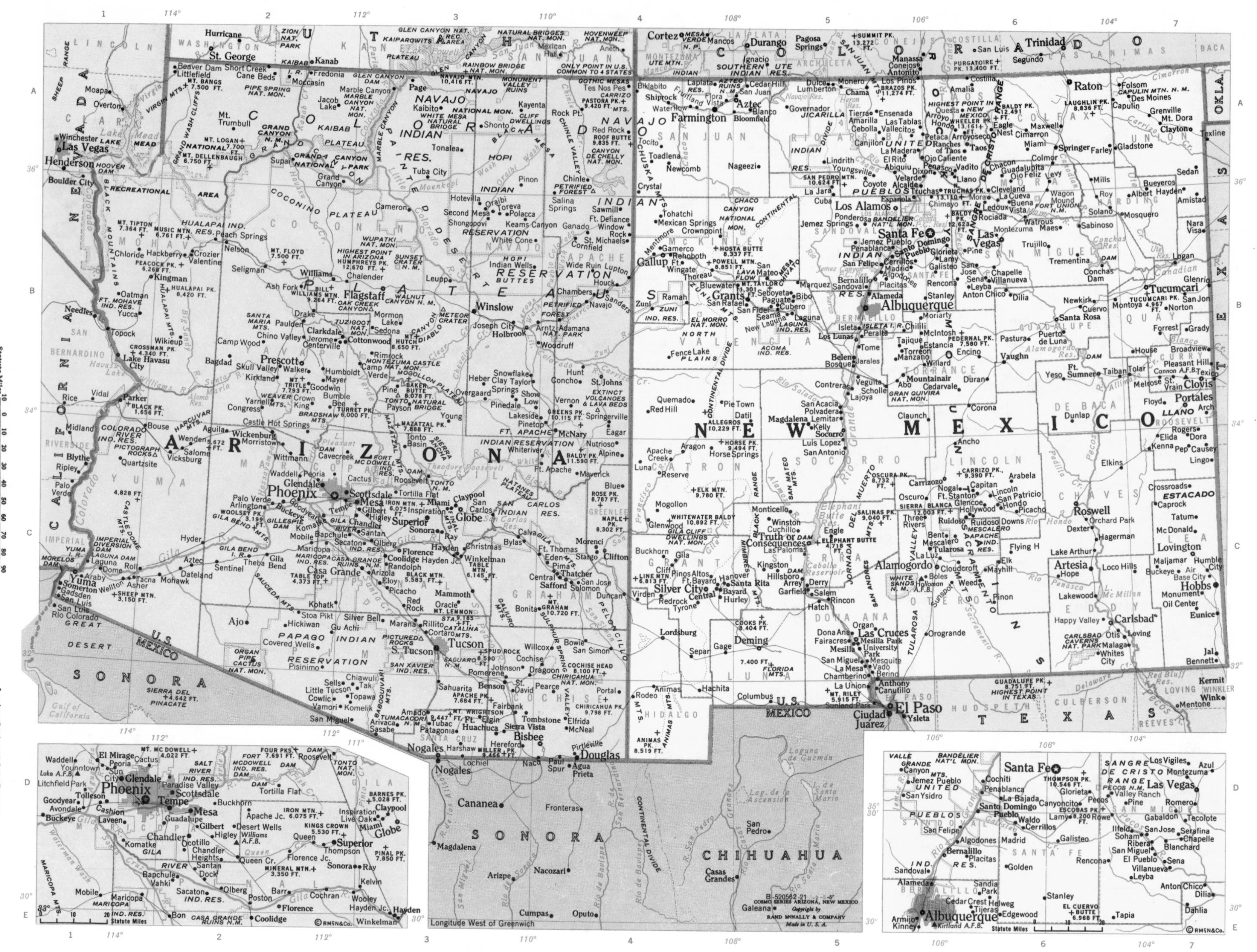

Statute Miles 10 0 10 20 30 40 50 60 70 80 90

Kilometers
10 0 10 20 30 40 60 80 100 120

Lambert Conformal Conic Projection

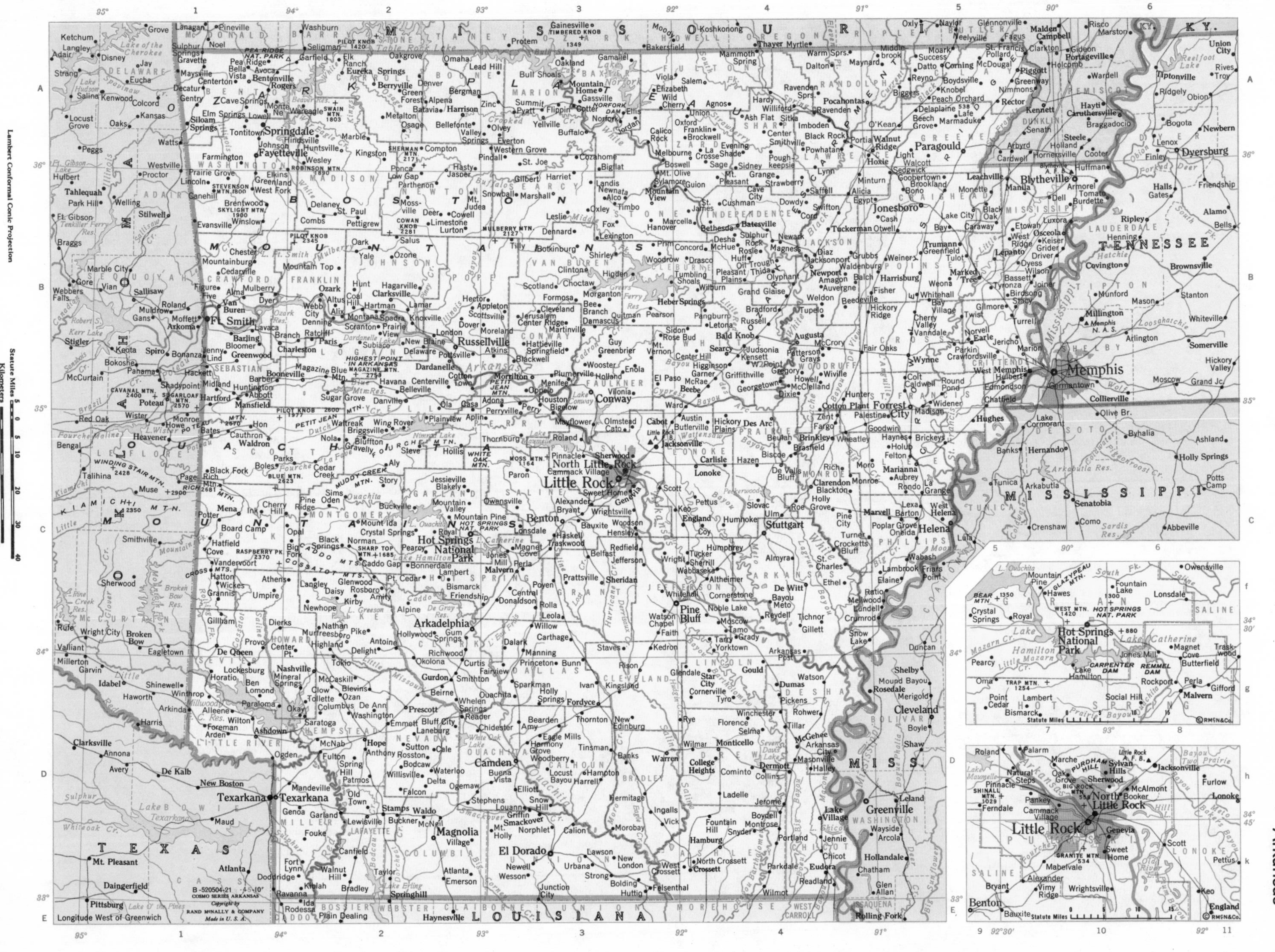

Lambert Conformal Conic Projection

Statute Miles

Kilometers

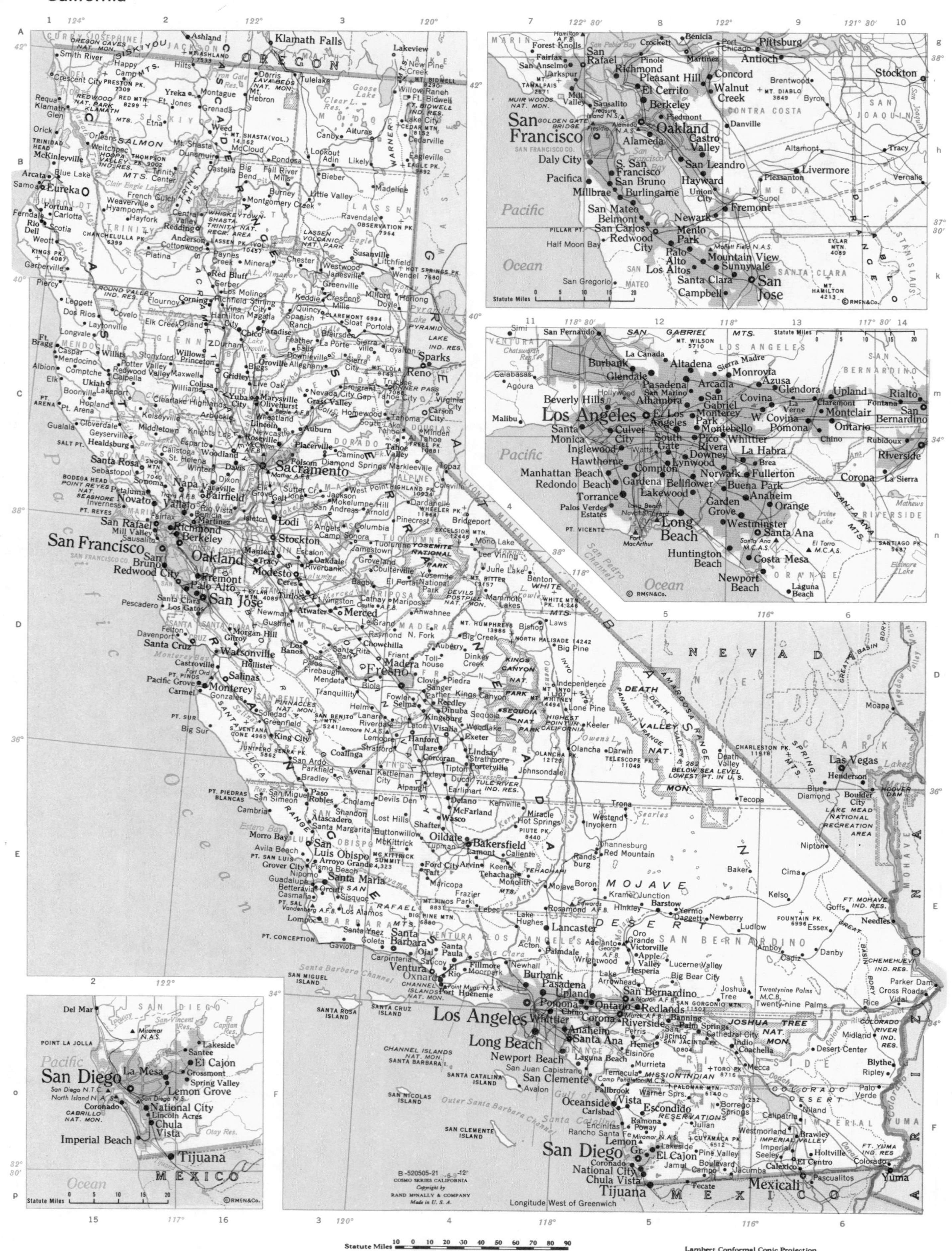

Statute Miles 10 0 10 20 30 40 50 60 70 80 90
Kilometers 10 0 10 20 40 60 80 100 120

Lambert Conformal Conic Projection

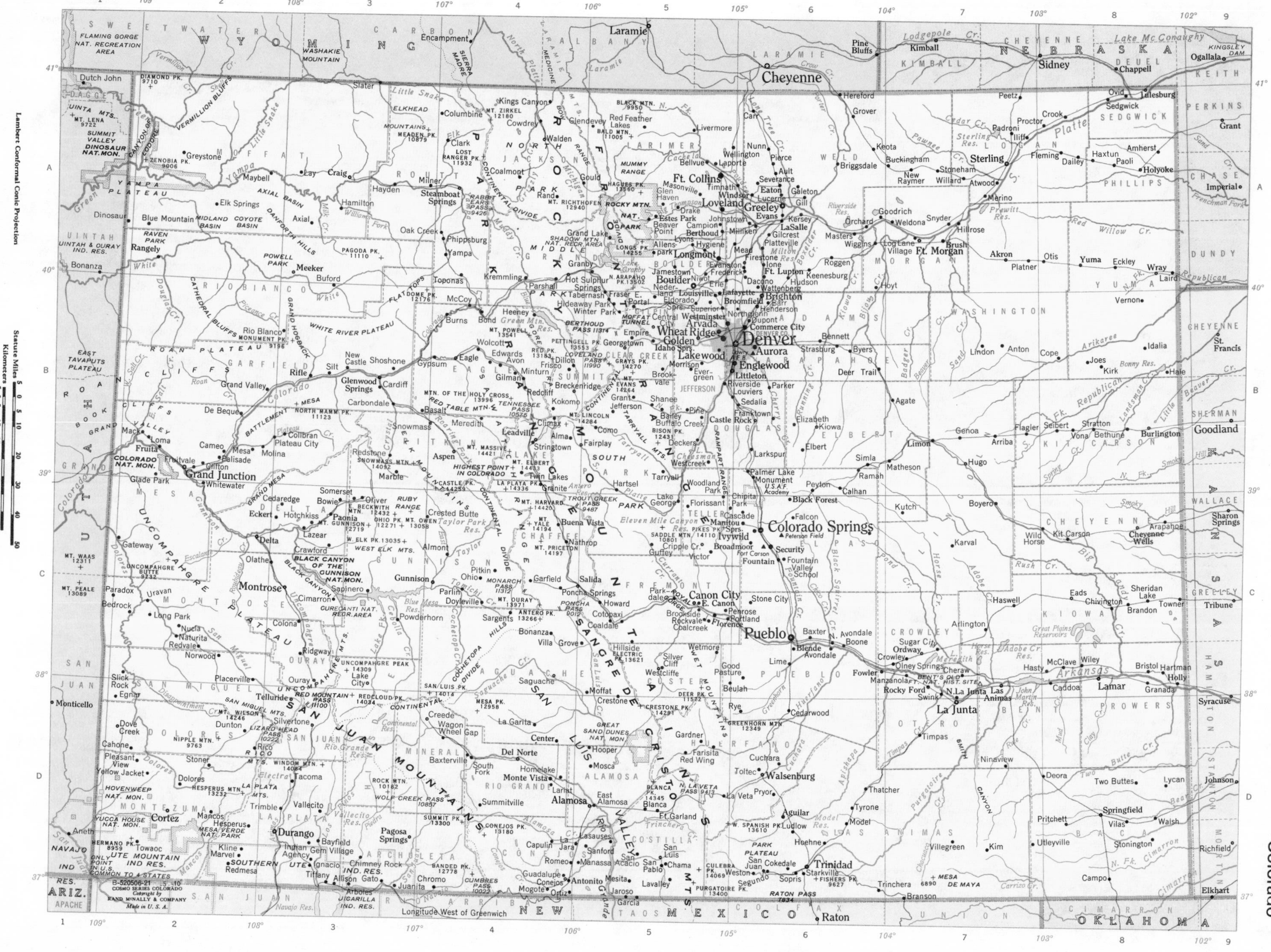

Lambert Conformal Conic Projection

Statute Miles 5 0 5 10   20   30   40   50

Kilometers 5 0 5 15 25 35 45 55 65 75

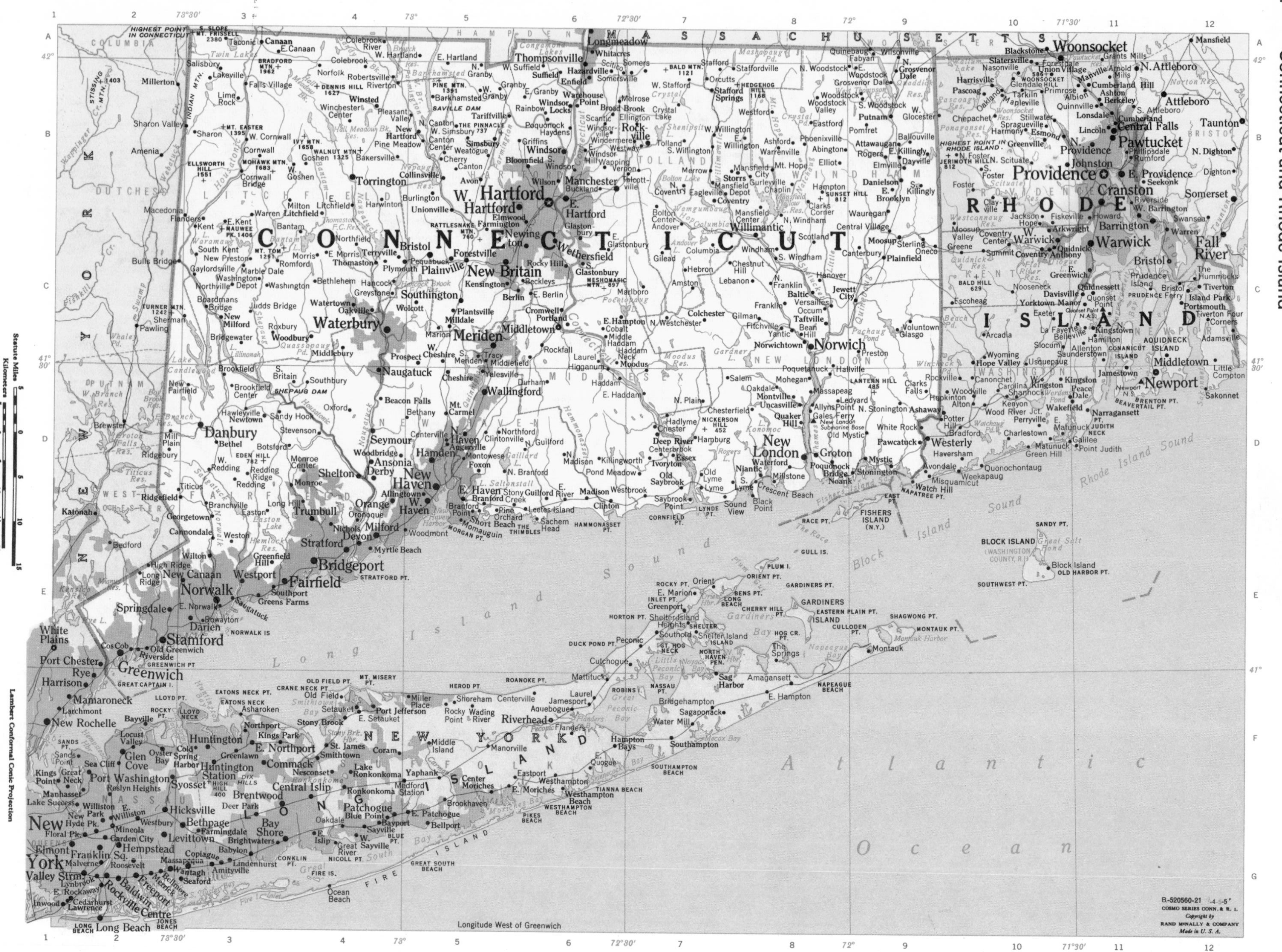

Statute Miles

Kilometers

Lambert Conformal Conic Projection

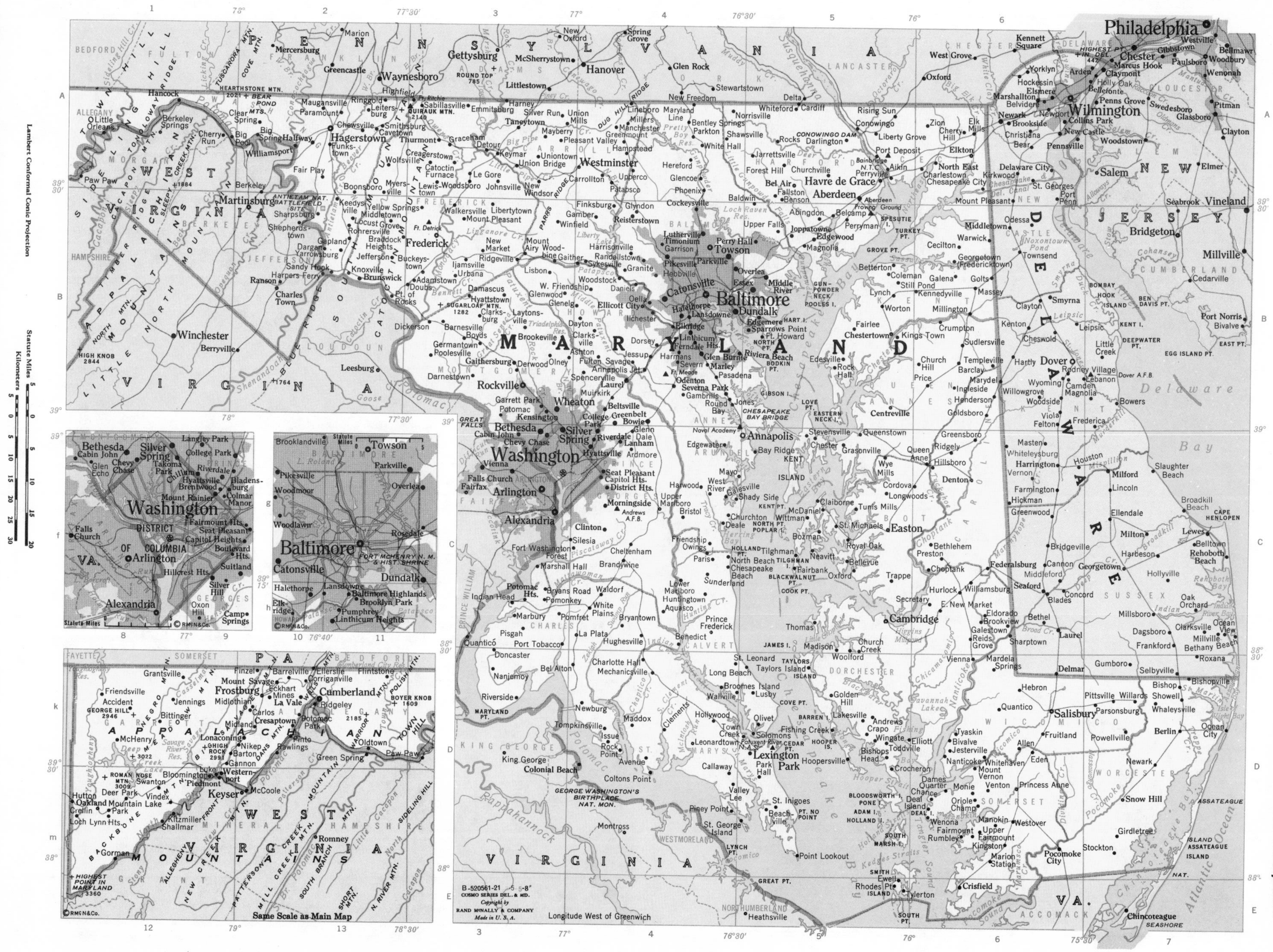

Lambert Conformal Conic Projection

Statute Miles
Kilometers

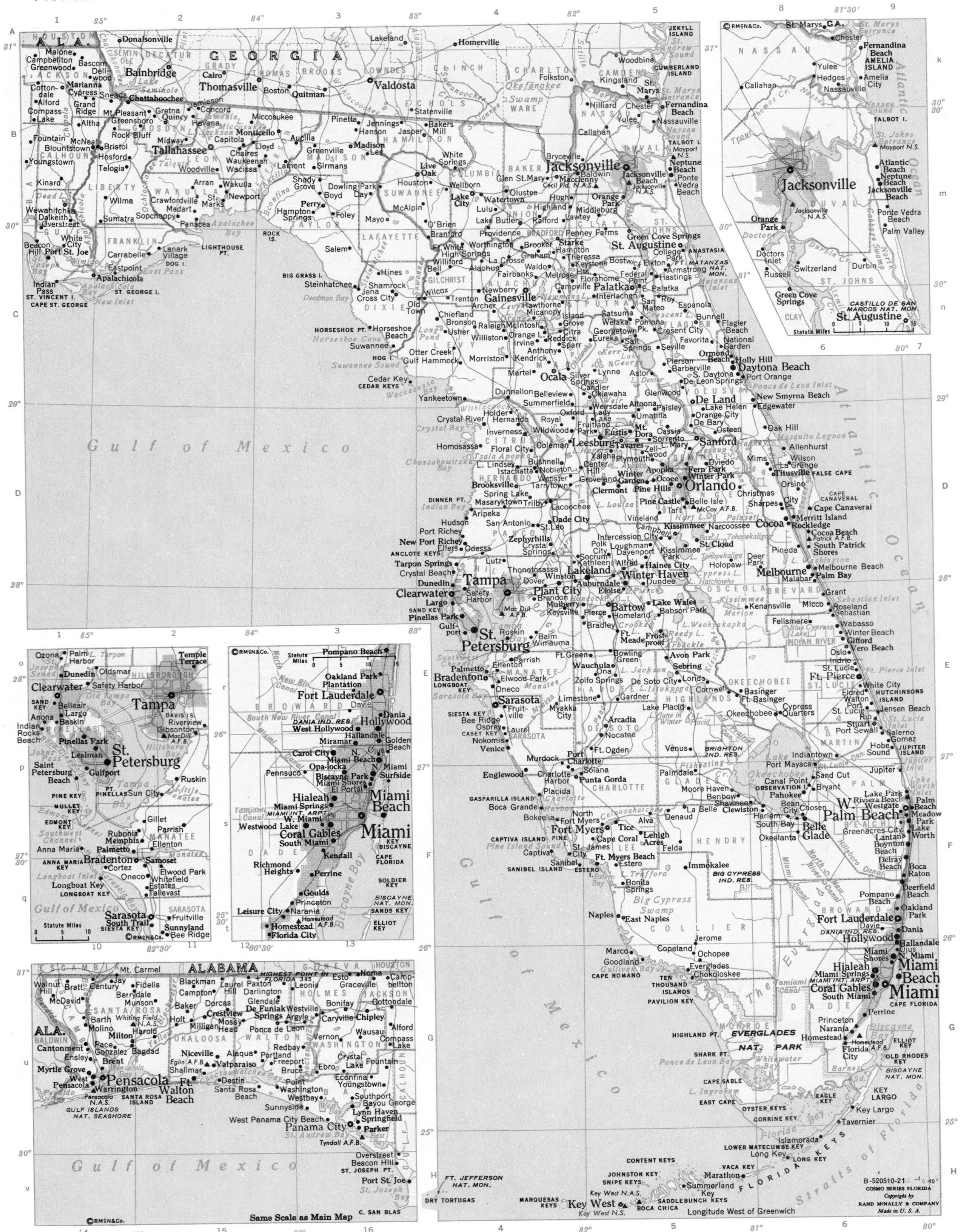
GEORGIA
ALA.
ALABAMA
Gulf of Mexico
Atlantic Ocean
Straits of Florida
Jacksonville
Tallahassee
Pensacola
Gainesville
Ocala
Orlando
Daytona Beach
Tampa
St. Petersburg
Clearwater
Sarasota
Bradenton
Lakeland
Fort Myers
W. Palm Beach
Fort Lauderdale
Hollywood
Miami
Miami Beach
Key West
St. Augustine
Valdosta
Thomasville
Bainbridge
Okefenokee Swamp
Lake Okeechobee
EVERGLADES NAT. PARK
Big Cypress Swamp
FLORIDA KEYS
Same Scale as Main Map
Statute Miles
Kilometers
Lambert Conformal Conic Projection
Longitude West of Greenwich
B-520510-21
COSMO SERIES FLORIDA
Copyright by RAND McNALLY & COMPANY
Made in U. S. A.
©RM&Co.

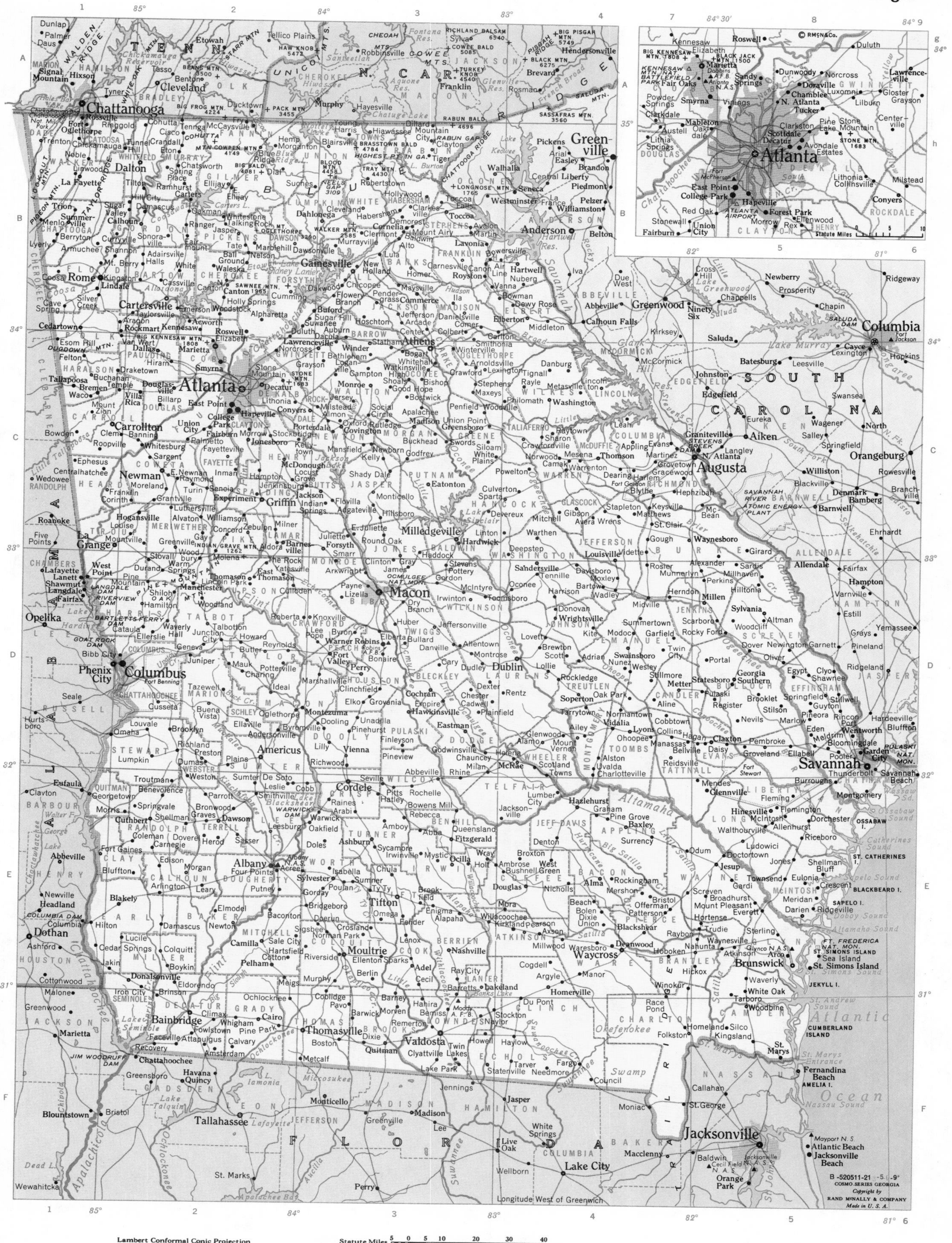

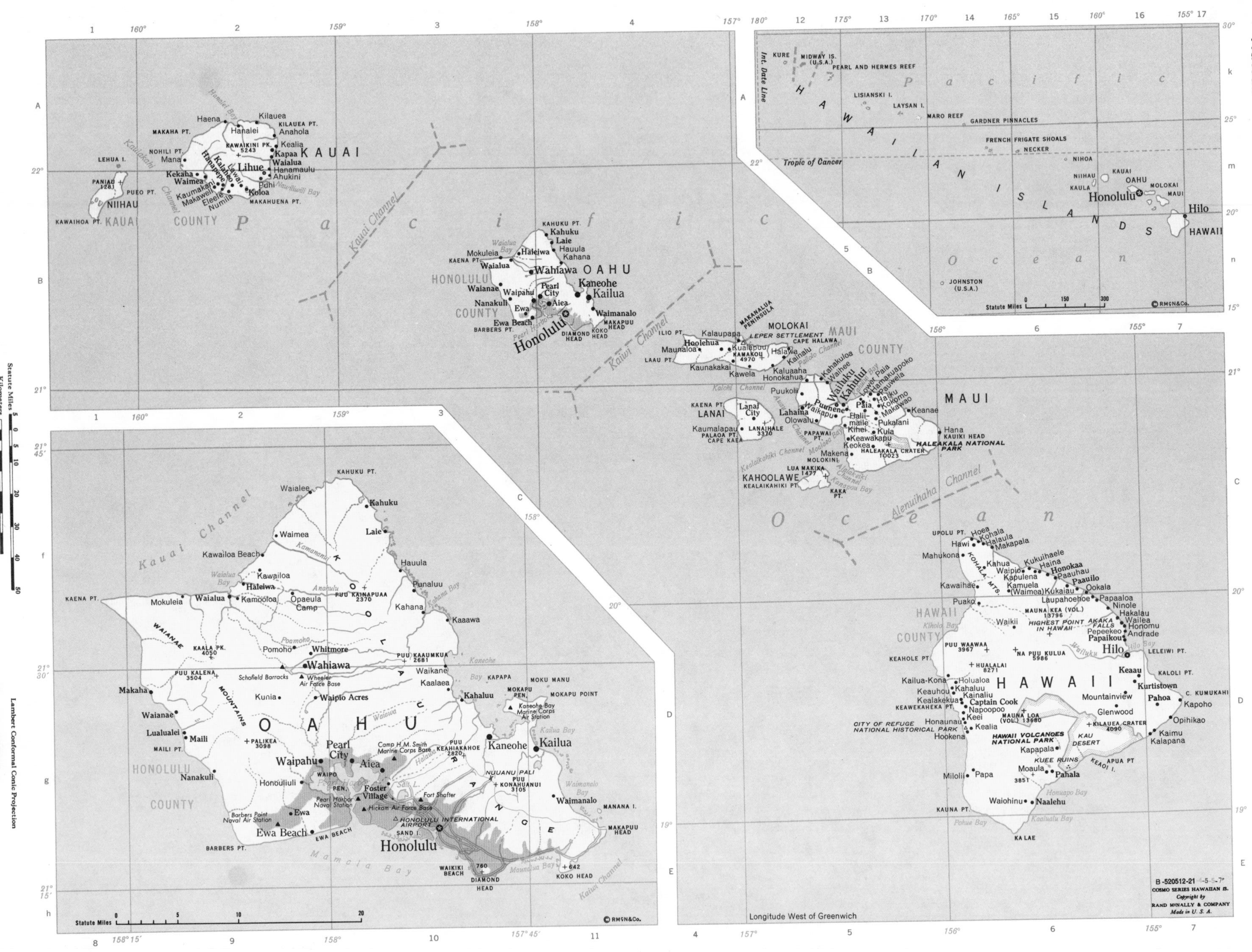
Pacific Ocean
HAWAIIAN ISLANDS
KURE
MIDWAY IS. (U.S.A.)
PEARL AND HERMES REEF
LISIANSKI I.
LAYSAN I.
MARO REEF
GARDNER PINNACLES
FRENCH FRIGATE SHOALS
NECKER
NIHOA
JOHNSTON (U.S.A.)
Tropic of Cancer
Int. Date Line
NIIHAU
KAUAI
OAHU
MOLOKAI
MAUI
HAWAII
LANAI
KAHOOLAWE
Honolulu
Hilo
Kauai Channel
Kaiwi Channel
Kalohi Channel
Alenuihaha Channel
KAUAI COUNTY
HONOLULU COUNTY
MAUI COUNTY
HAWAII COUNTY
Lihue
Kapaa
Waimea
Haleiwa
Wahiawa
Kaneohe
Kailua
Pearl City
Aiea
Waipahu
Ewa Beach
Waimanalo
Kahului
Wailuku
Lahaina
Hana
Lanai City
Kailua-Kona
Captain Cook
Waimea
Honokaa
MAUNA KEA (VOL.) 13796
MAUNA LOA (VOL.) 13680
HALEAKALA NATIONAL PARK
HAWAII VOLCANOES NATIONAL PARK
CITY OF REFUGE NATIONAL HISTORICAL PARK
KOOLAU RANGE
WAIANAE MOUNTAINS
HONOLULU INTERNATIONAL AIRPORT
Hickam Air Force Base
Pearl Harbor Naval Station
Schofield Barracks
WAIKIKI BEACH
DIAMOND HEAD
Mamala Bay
Longitude West of Greenwich
Statute Miles
Kilometers
Lambert Conformal Conic Projection
B-520512-21
COSMO SERIES HAWAIIAN IS.
Copyright by RAND McNALLY & COMPANY
Made in U. S. A.
©RMcN&Co.

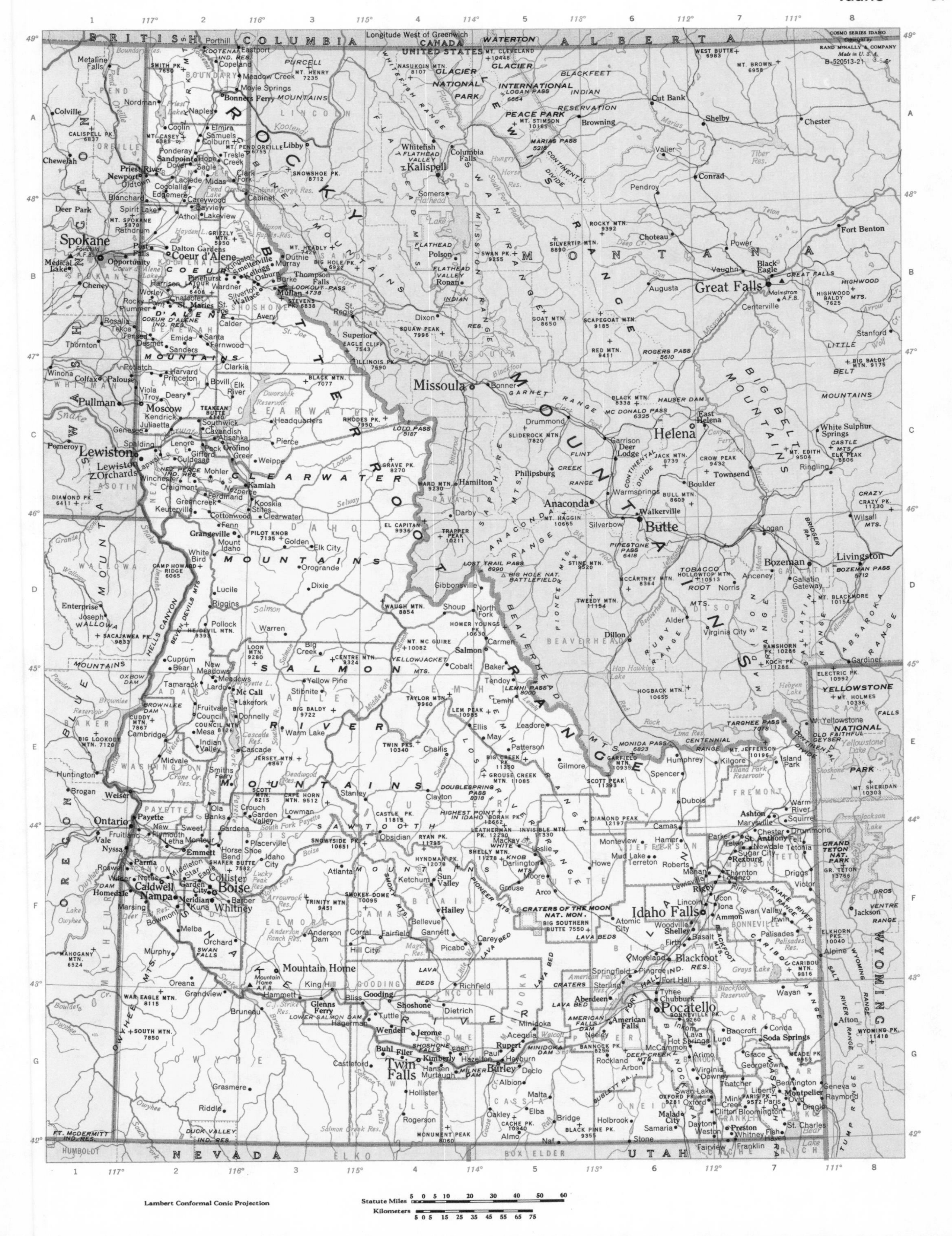
Longitude West of Greenwich
BRITISH COLUMBIA
ALBERTA
CANADA
UNITED STATES
COSMO SERIES IDAHO
Copyright by
RAND McNALLY & COMPANY
Made in U.S.A.
WASHINGTON
OREGON
MONTANA
WYOMING
NEVADA
UTAH
ROCKY MOUNTAINS
BITTERROOT RANGE
CLEARWATER MOUNTAINS
SALMON RIVER MOUNTAINS
BEAVERHEAD MTS.
LEMHI RANGE
LOST RIVER RANGE
SAWTOOTH RANGE
BLUE MOUNTAINS
SEVEN DEVILS MTS.
HELLS CANYON
OWYHEE MTS.
SNAKE RIVER
CRATERS OF THE MOON NAT. MON.
GLACIER NATIONAL PARK
YELLOWSTONE NATIONAL PARK
GRAND TETON NAT. PARK
FORT HALL IND. RES.
COEUR D'ALENE IND. RES.
NEZ PERCE IND. RES.
DUCK VALLEY IND. RES.
BORAH PK. 12662
HIGHEST POINT IN IDAHO
Spokane
Coeur d'Alene
Lewiston
Moscow
Grangeville
McCall
Payette
Ontario
Weiser
Emmett
Caldwell
Nampa
Boise
Mountain Home
Twin Falls
Burley
Pocatello
Idaho Falls
Blackfoot
Rexburg
St. Anthony
Salmon
Challis
Hailey
Sun Valley
Ketchum
Arco
Montpelier
Preston
Malad City
Soda Springs
Missoula
Helena
Butte
Anaconda
Great Falls
Bozeman
Livingston
Kalispell
Sandpoint
Bonners Ferry
Kellogg
Wallace
Orofino
Kamiah
Dillon
Hamilton
Jackson
Lambert Conformal Conic Projection
Statute Miles
0 5 10 20 30 40 50 60
Kilometers
5 0 5 15 25 35 45 55 65 75

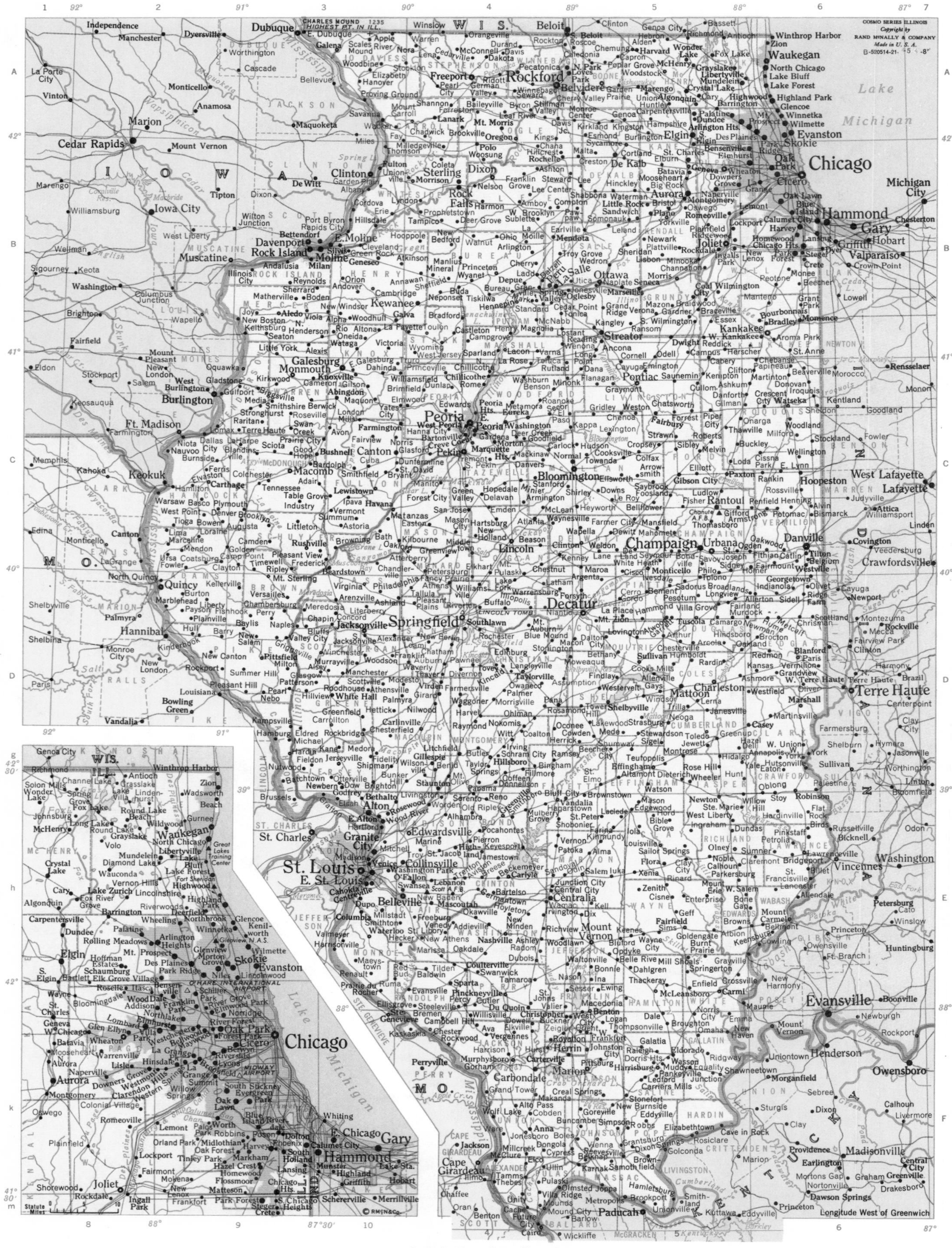

Statute Miles

Kilometers

Lambert Conformal Conic Projection

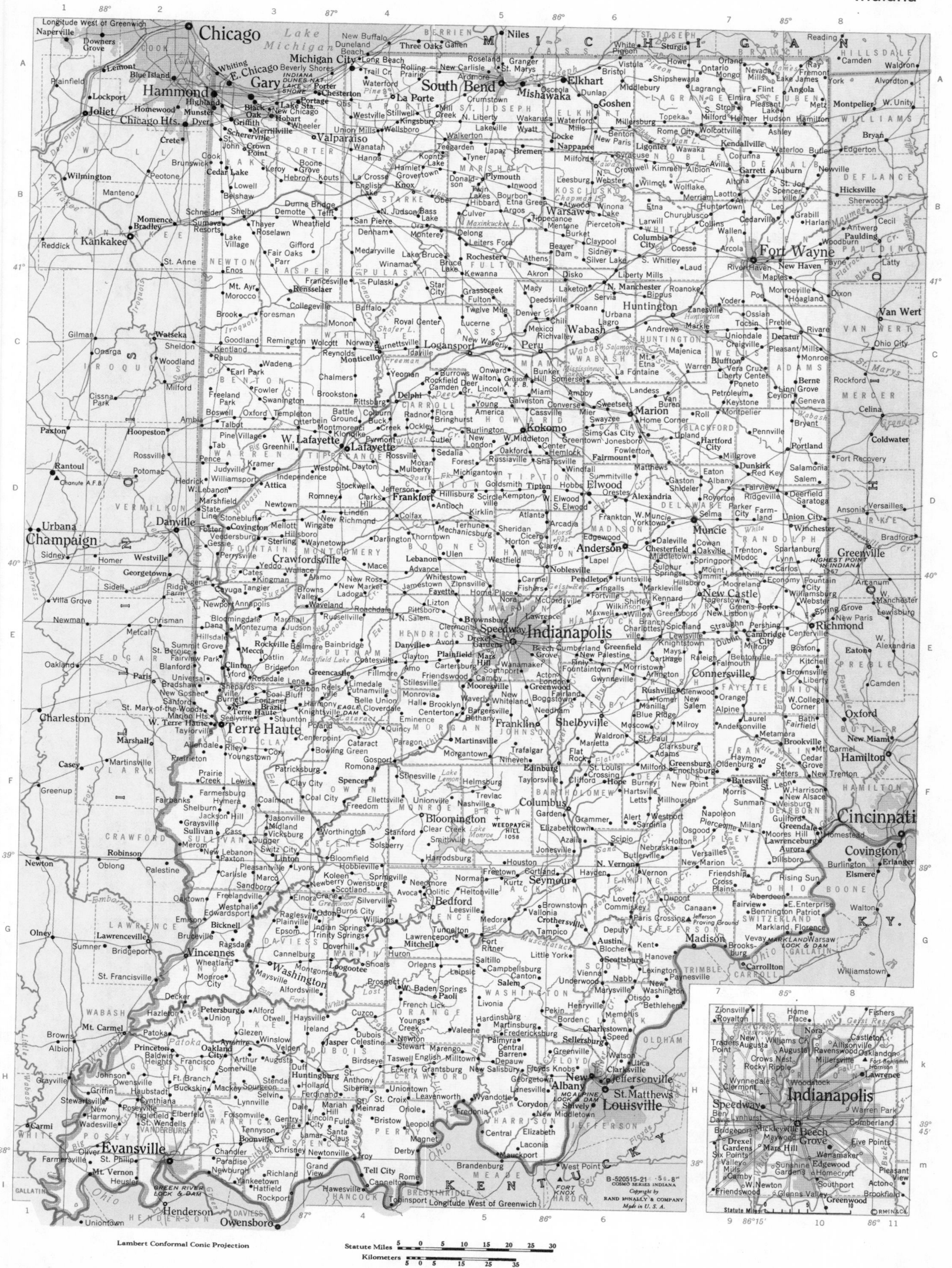

Lambert Conformal Conic Projection

Statute Miles
Kilometers

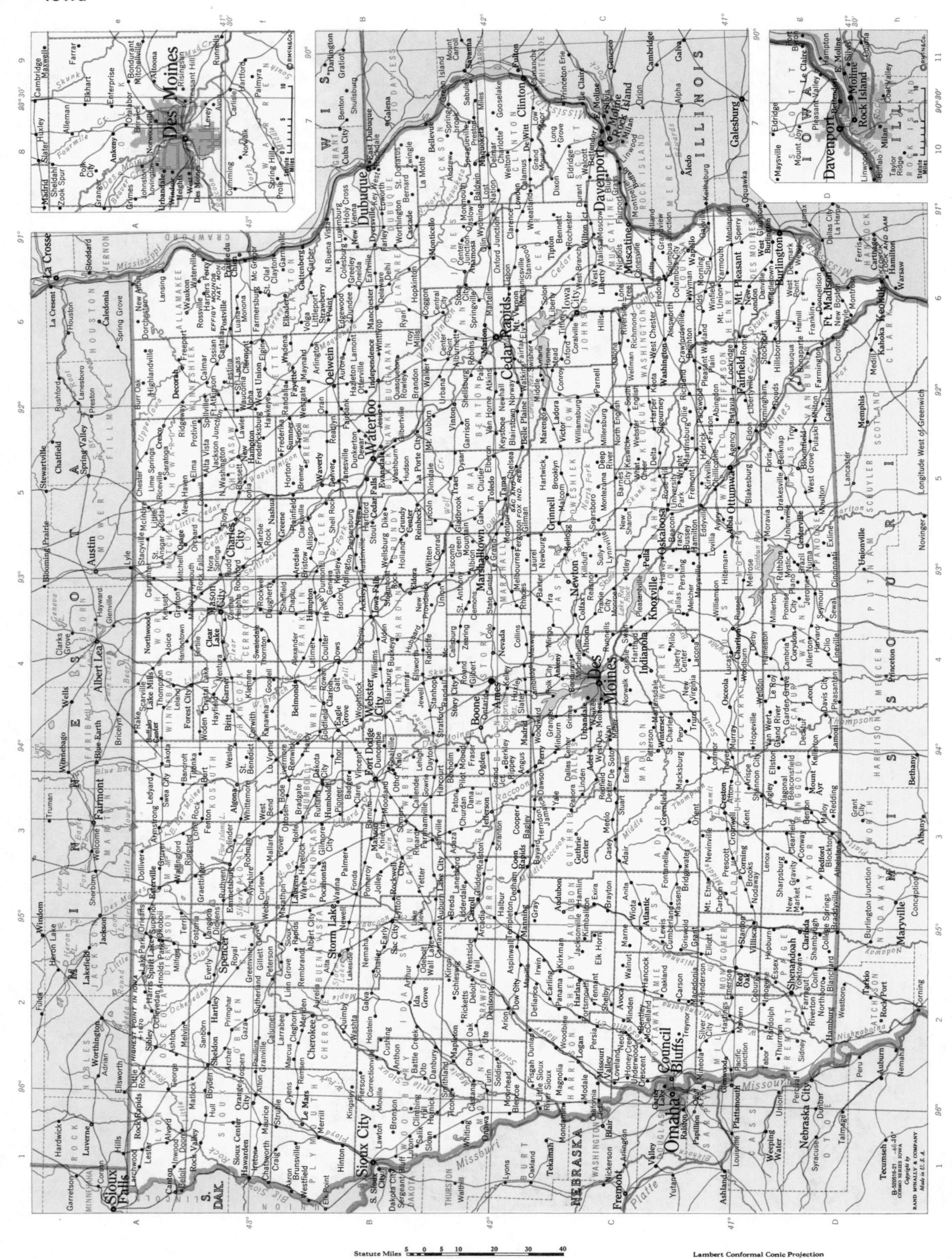

Statute Miles

Kilometers

Lambert Conformal Conic Projection

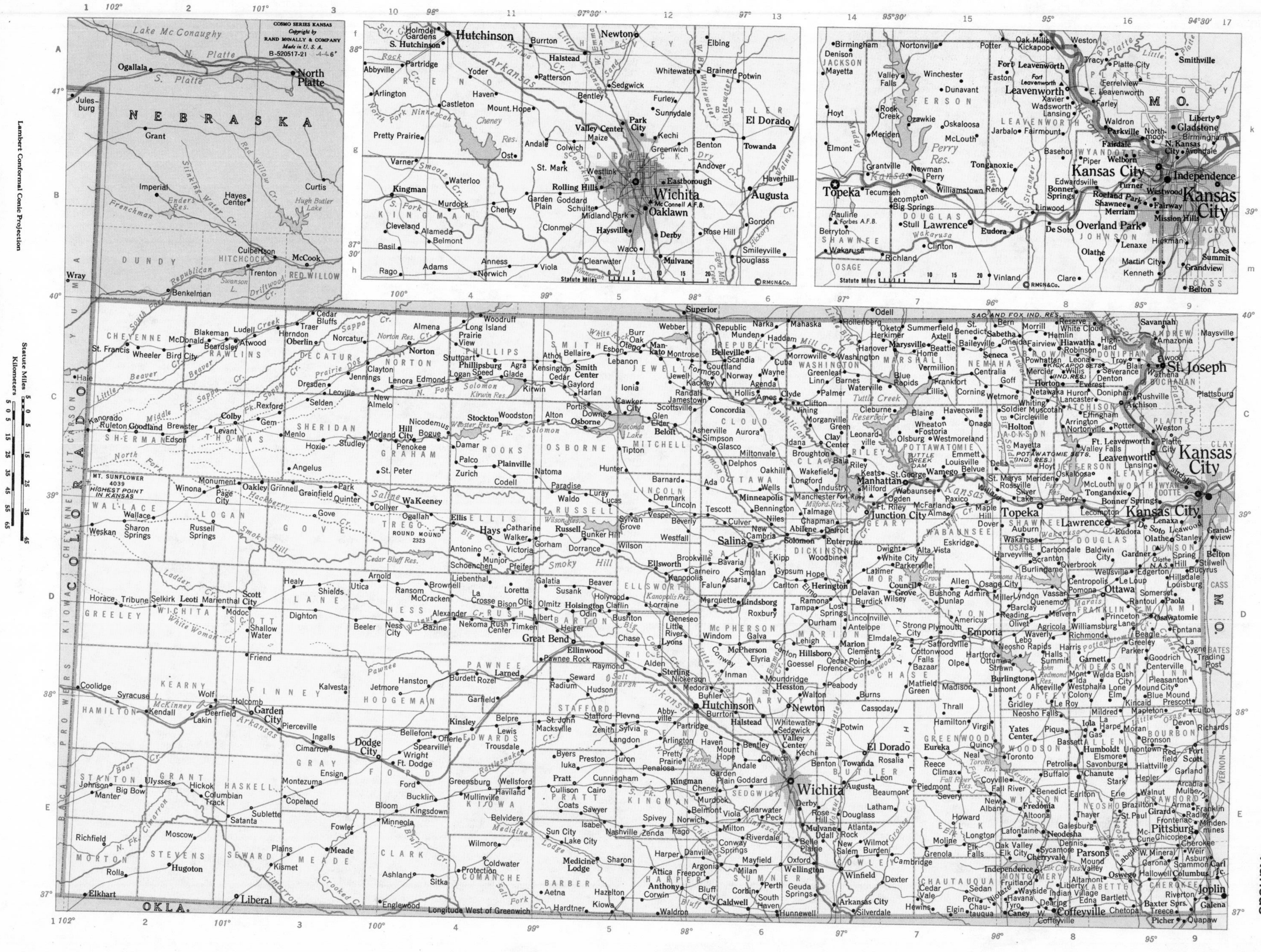

Lambert Conformal Conic Projection

Statute Miles 5 0 5 15 25 35 45
Kilometers 5 0 5 15 25 35 45 55 65

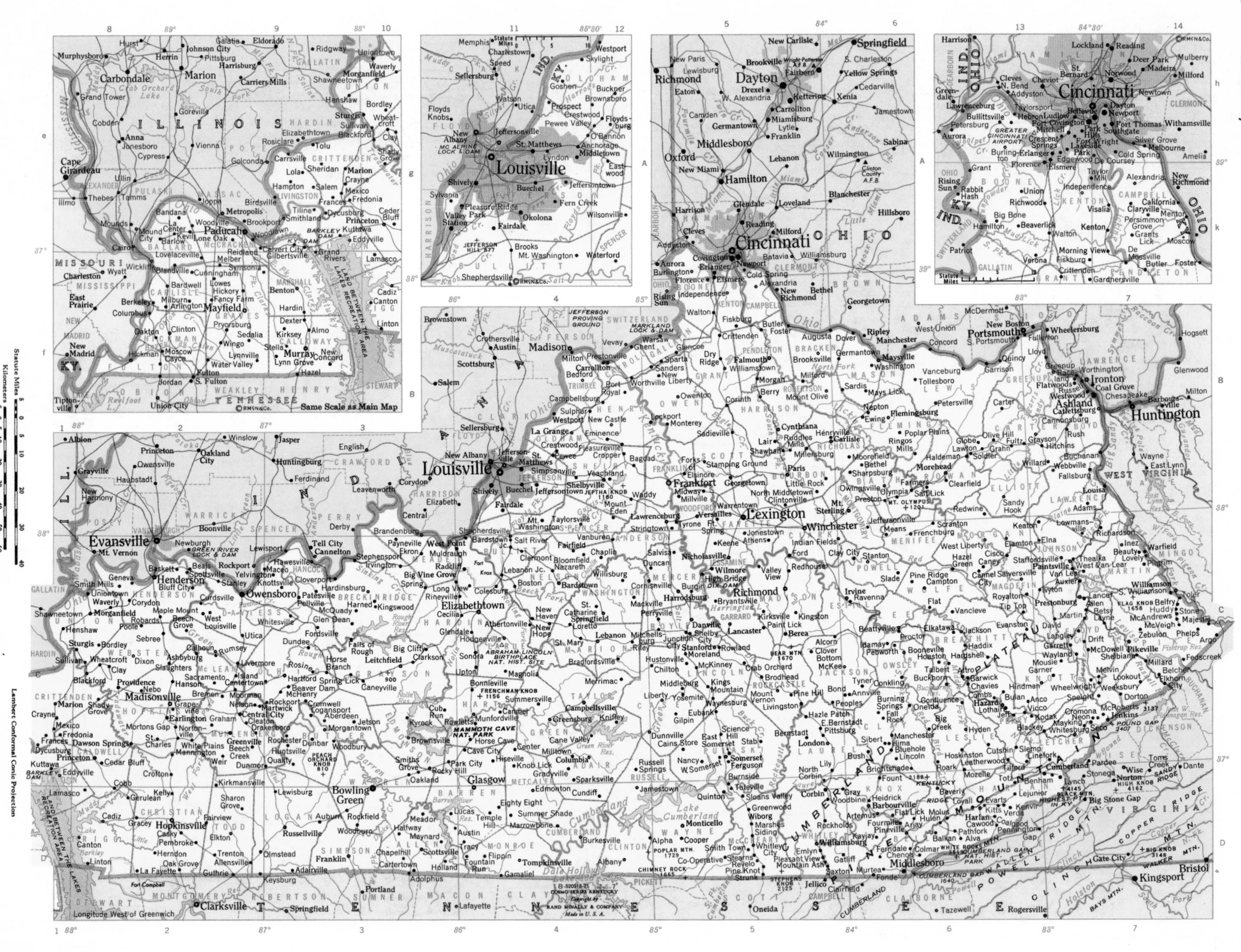

Statute Miles 5 0 5 10 20 30 40
Kilometers 5 0 5 10 20 30 40 50 60

Lambert Conformal Conic Projection

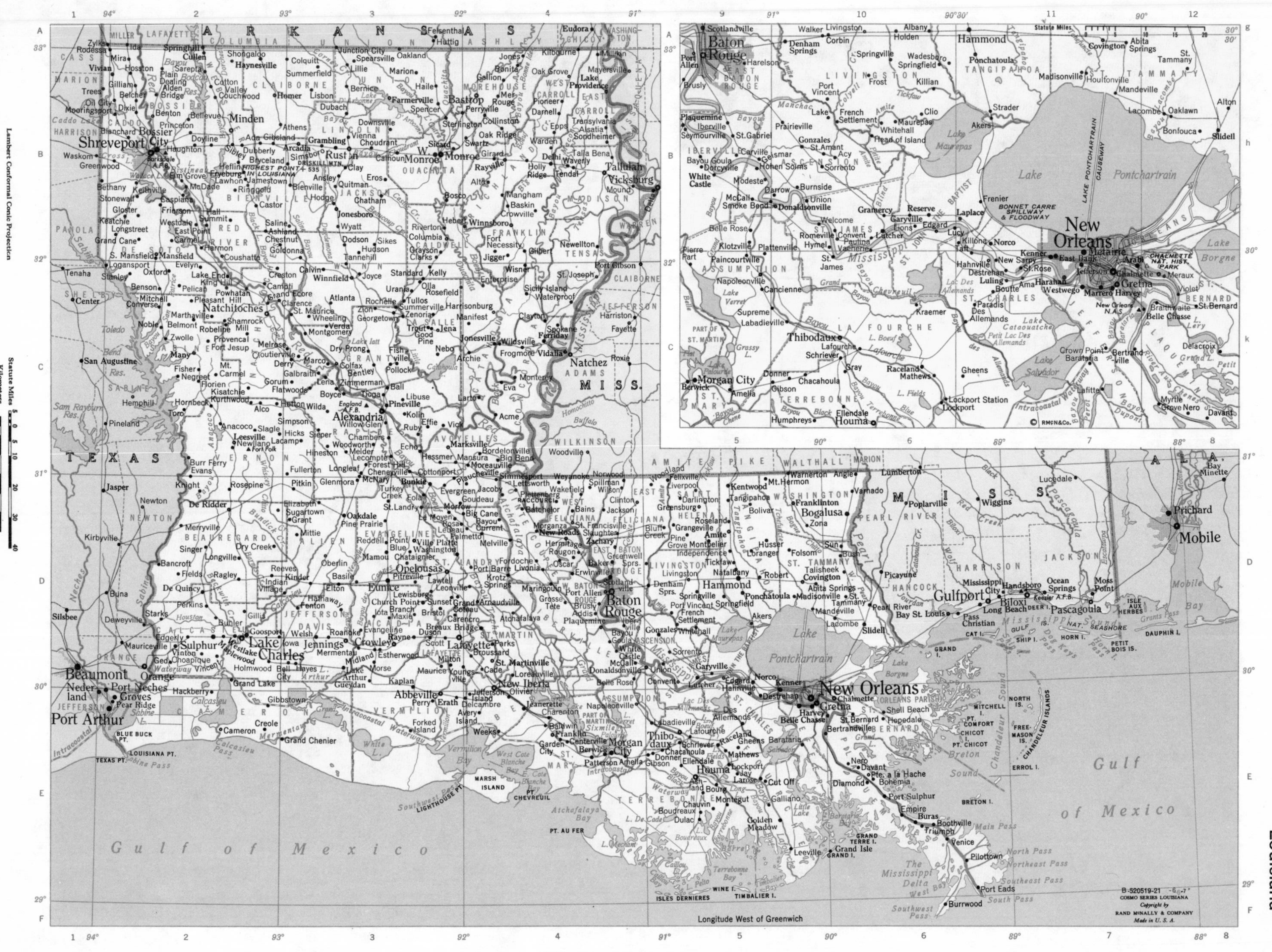

Lambert Conformal Conic Projection

Statute Miles 5 0 5 10   20   30   40
Kilometers 5 0 5 15 25 35 45 55

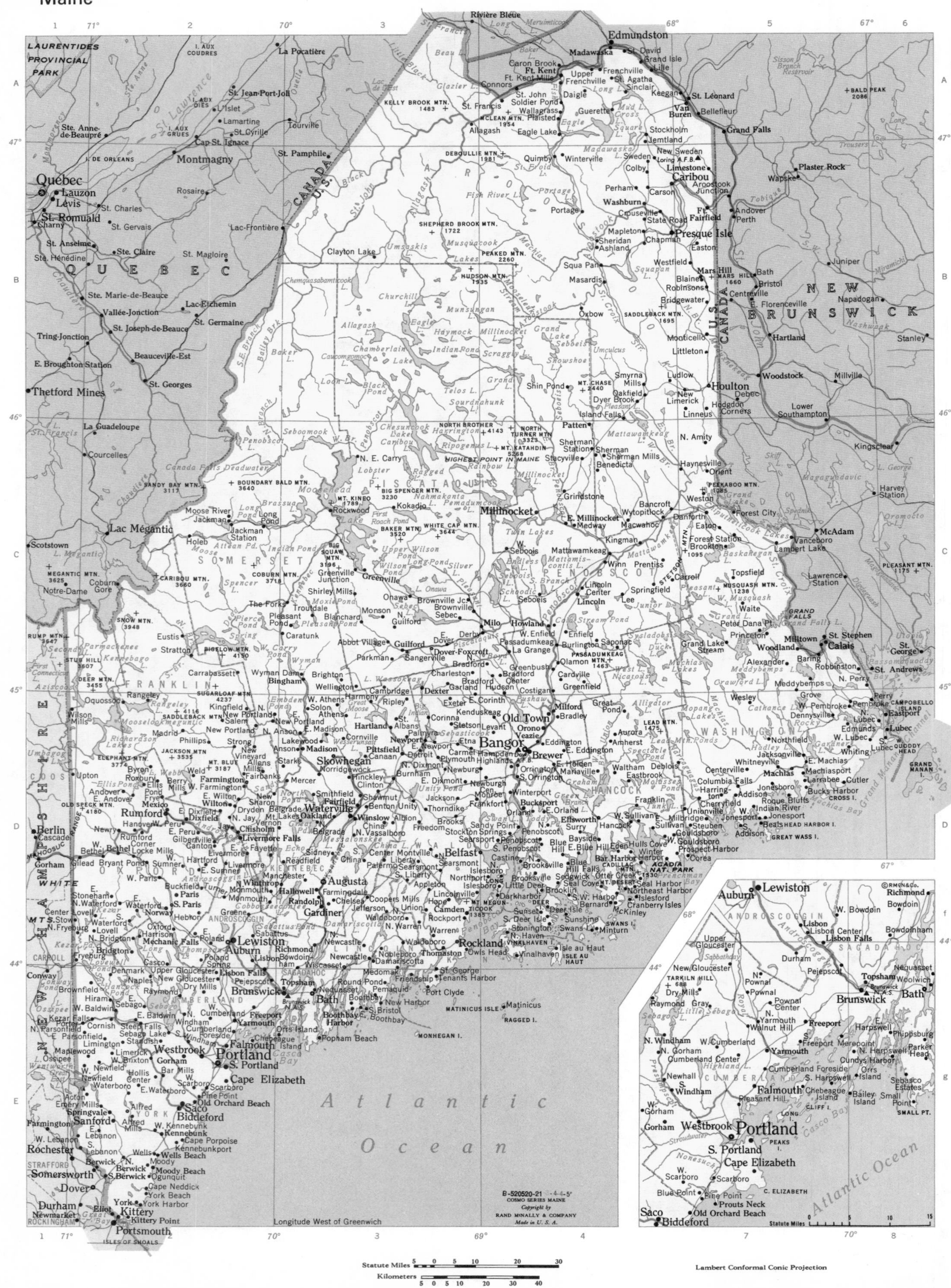
QUEBEC
NEW BRUNSWICK
LAURENTIDES PROVINCIAL PARK
CANADA
U. S.
PISCATAQUIS
SOMERSET
FRANKLIN
PENOBSCOT
WASHINGTON
HANCOCK
OXFORD
KENNEBEC
ANDROSCOGGIN
YORK
CUMBERLAND
SAGADAHOC
LINCOLN
WALDO
KNOX
AROOSTOOK
NEW HAMPSHIRE
WHITE MTS.
Atlantic Ocean
Québec
Lauzon
Levis
Montmagny
Edmundston
Madawaska
Ft. Kent
Caribou
Presque Isle
Houlton
Millinocket
Bangor
Brewer
Old Town
Orono
Augusta
Waterville
Skowhegan
Lewiston
Auburn
Brunswick
Bath
Portland
S. Portland
Cape Elizabeth
Westbrook
Saco
Biddeford
Sanford
Kittery
Portsmouth
Dover
Rochester
Somersworth
Rockland
Belfast
Ellsworth
Bar Harbor
Calais
St. Stephen
Eastport
Lubec
Machias
Rumford
Berlin
Lac Mégantic
Thetford Mines
Woodstock
Grand Falls
Plaster Rock
HIGHEST POINT IN MAINE
MT. KATAHDIN 5268
ACADIA NAT. PARK
Longitude West of Greenwich
B-520520-21
COMO SERIES MAINE
Copyright by RAND McNALLY & COMPANY
Made in U. S. A.
Statute Miles 5 0 5 10 20 30
Kilometers 5 0 5 10 20 30 40
Statute Miles 0 5 10 15
Lambert Conformal Conic Projection

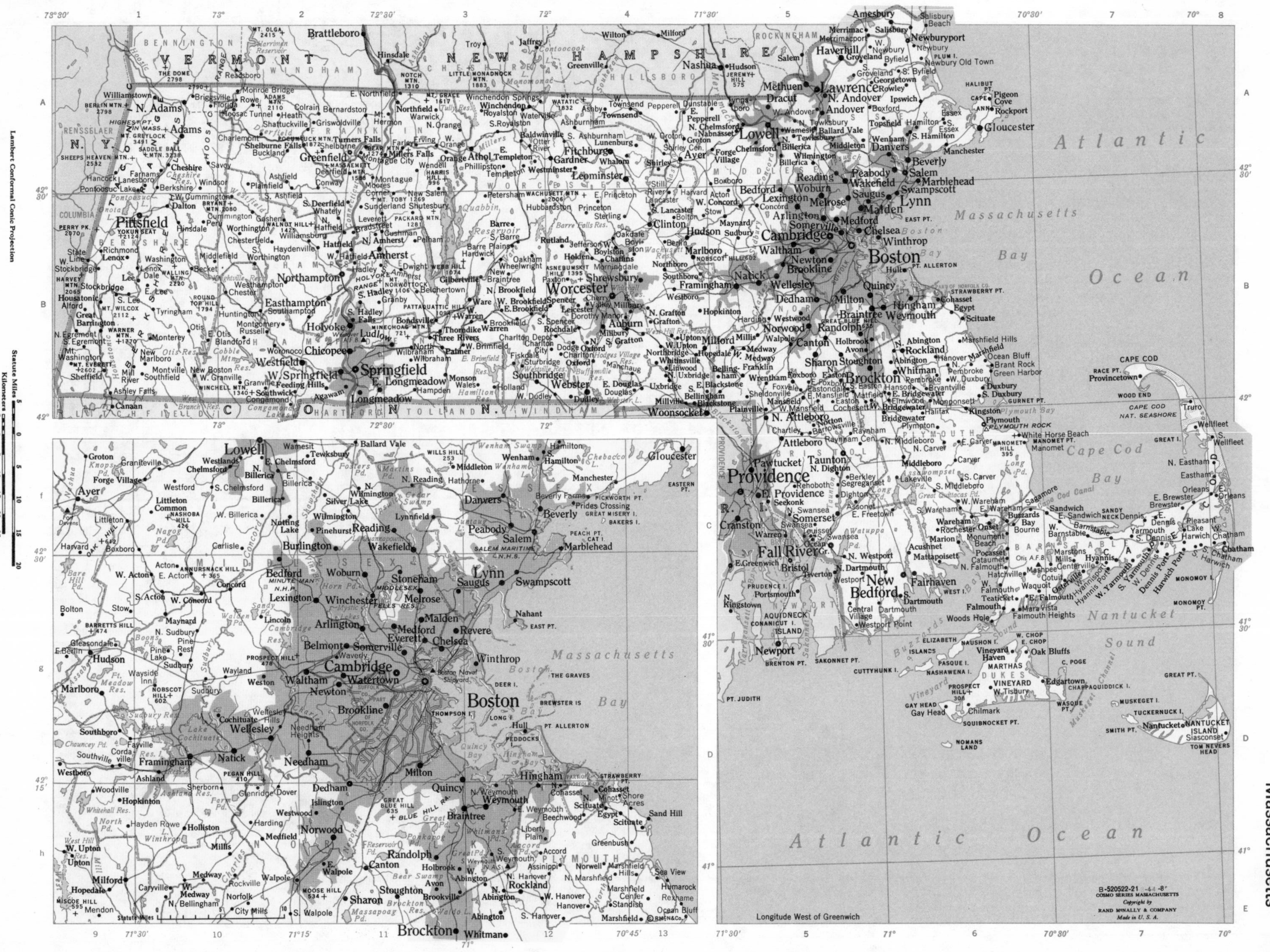

Lambert Conformal Conic Projection

Statute Miles

Kilometers

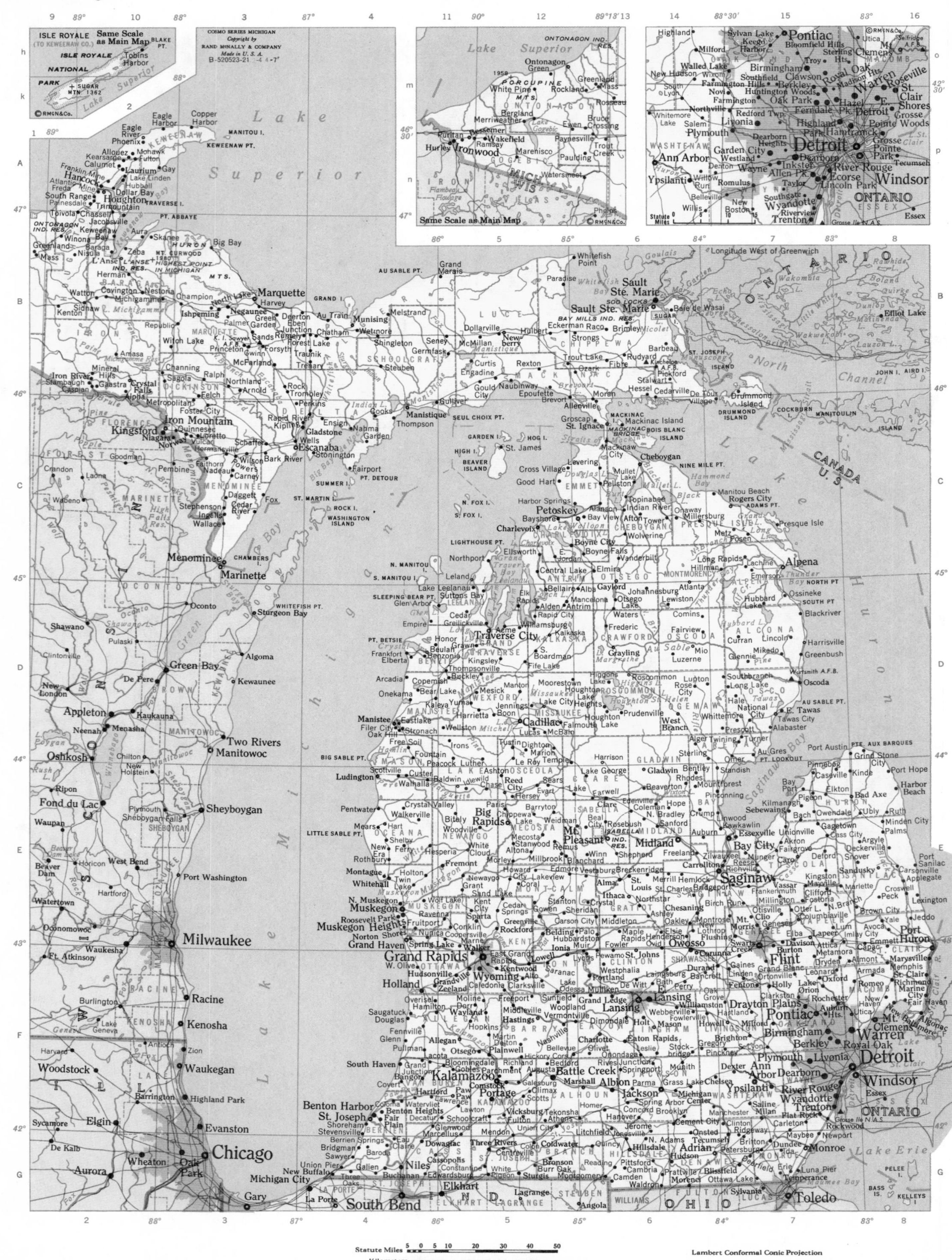

ISLE ROYALE (TO KEWEENAW CO.)
Same Scale as Main Map
ISLE ROYALE NATIONAL PARK
SUGAR MTN. 1362
COSMO SERIES MICHIGAN
Copyright by RAND McNALLY & COMPANY
Made in U. S. A.
Lake Superior
Ironwood
Same Scale as Main Map
Pontiac
Detroit
Windsor
ONTARIO
Ann Arbor
Ypsilanti
Warren
Livonia
Dearborn
Trenton
Wyandotte
Lake Superior
Marquette
Houghton
Hancock
Escanaba
Iron Mountain
Kingsford
Menominee
Marinette
Manistique
Sault Ste. Marie
St. Ignace
Cheboygan
Petoskey
Charlevoix
Alpena
Traverse City
Cadillac
Manistee
Ludington
Muskegon
Grand Rapids
Holland
Kalamazoo
Battle Creek
Jackson
Lansing
Flint
Saginaw
Bay City
Midland
Mt. Pleasant
Big Rapids
Port Huron
Benton Harbor
St. Joseph
Niles
South Bend
Toledo
Monroe
Adrian
Chicago
Milwaukee
Green Bay
Appleton
Oshkosh
Sheboygan
Manitowoc
Two Rivers
Racine
Kenosha
Waukegan
Gary
Lake Michigan
Lake Huron
Saginaw Bay
Lake Erie
North Channel
ONTARIO
CANADA
U.S.
OHIO
Statute Miles 5 0 5 10 20 30 40 50
Kilometers 5 0 5 15 25 35 45 55 65 75
Lambert Conformal Conic Projection

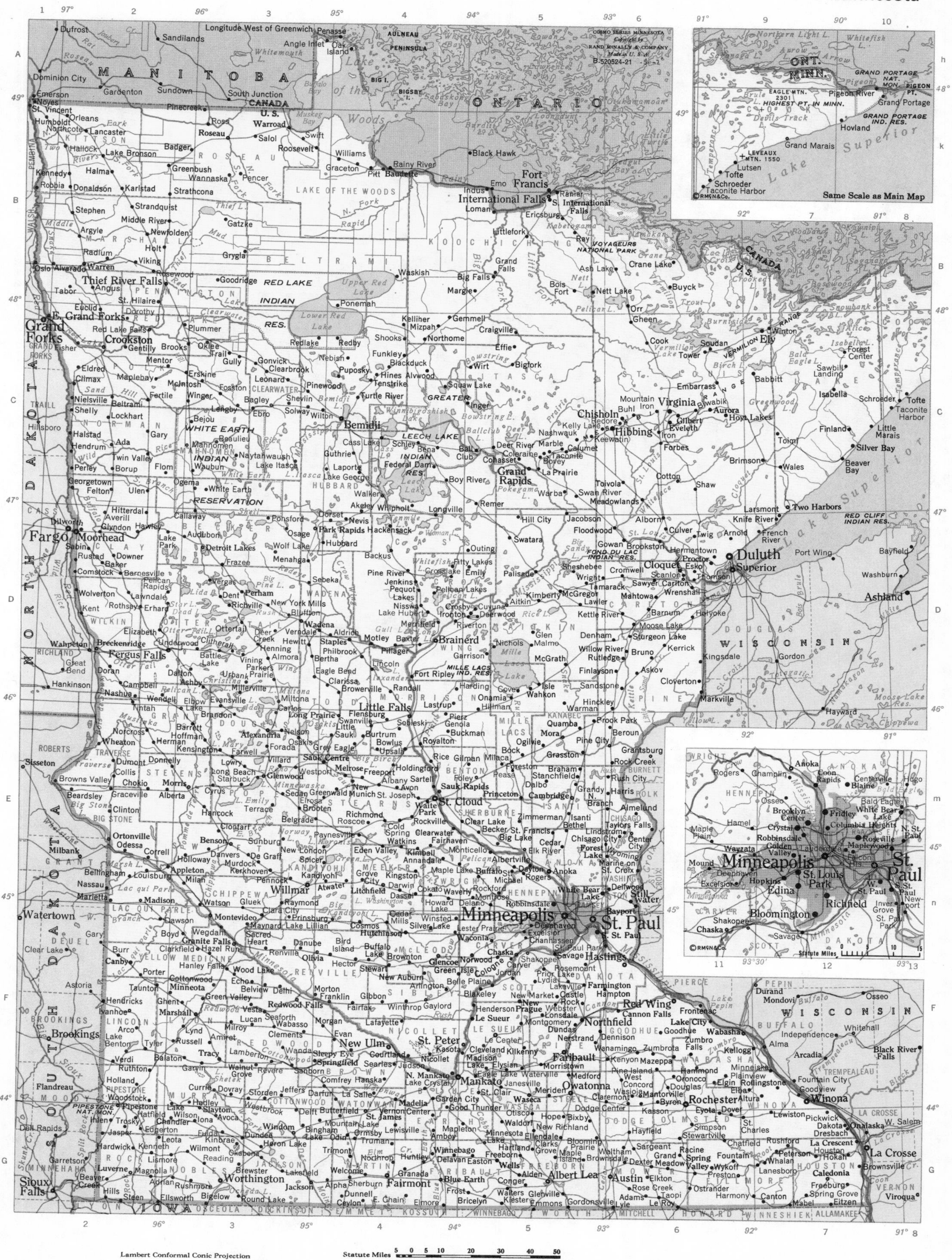

Lambert Conformal Conic Projection

Statute Miles
5 0 5 10 20 30 40 50

Kilometers
5 0 5 15 25 35 45 55 65

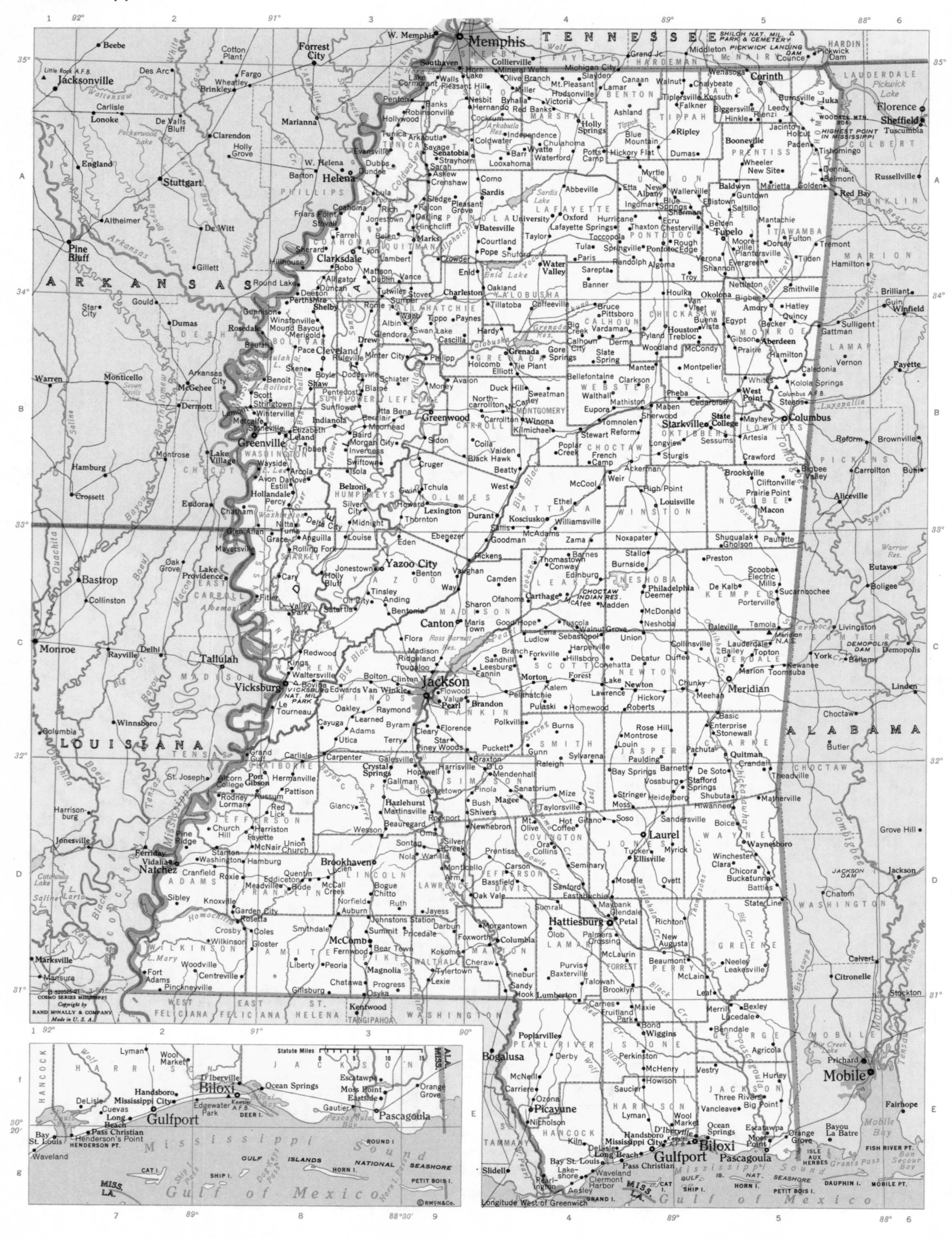

Statute Miles 5 0 5 10   20   30   40
Kilometers
Lambert Conformal Conic Projection

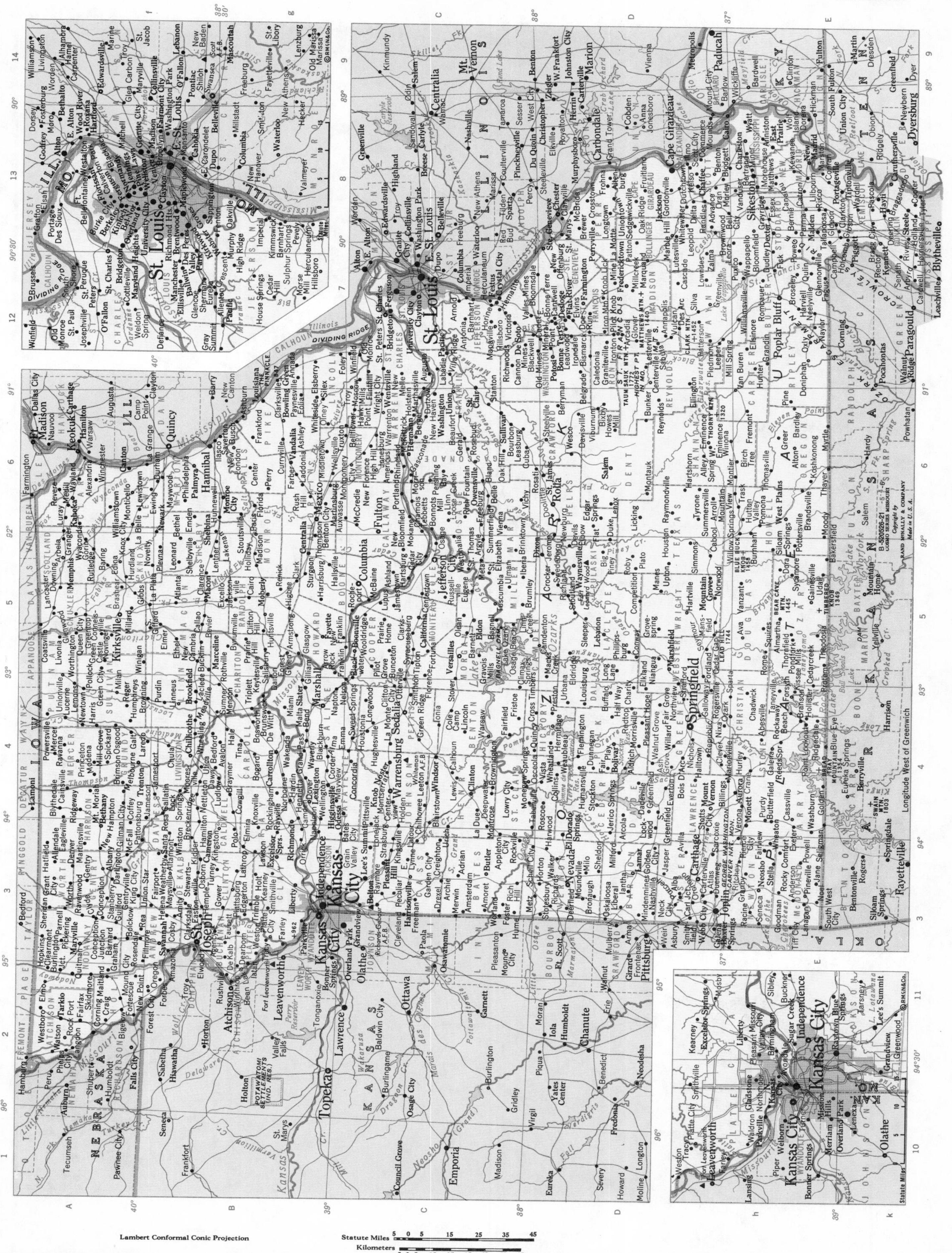

Statute Miles

Kilometers

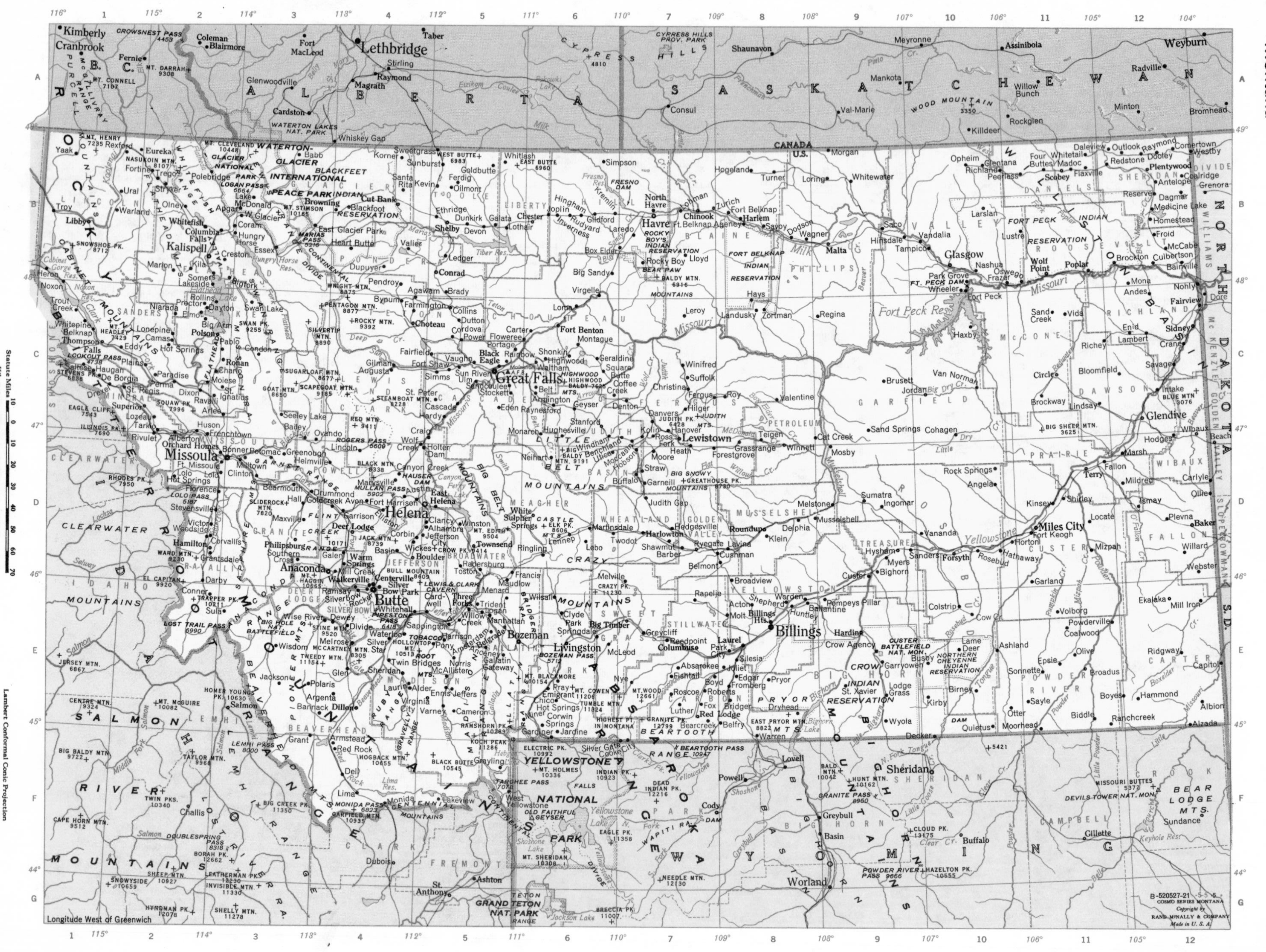

Statute Miles 10 0 10 20 30 40 50 60 70

Kilometers 10 0 10 30 50 70 90

Lambert Conformal Conic Projection

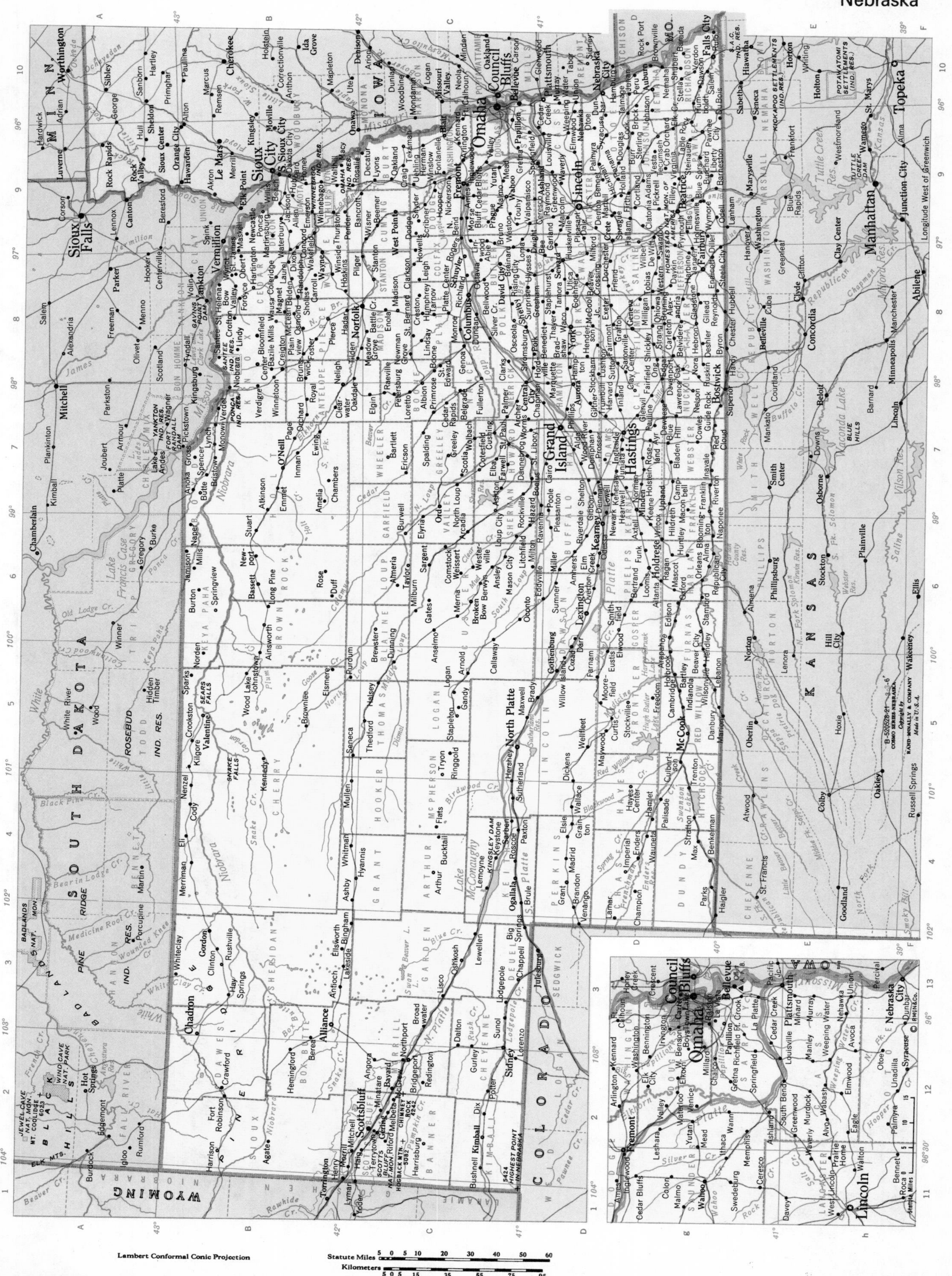

Lambert Conformal Conic Projection

Statute Miles 5 0 5 10 20 30 40 50 60

Kilometers 5 0 5 15 35 55 75 95

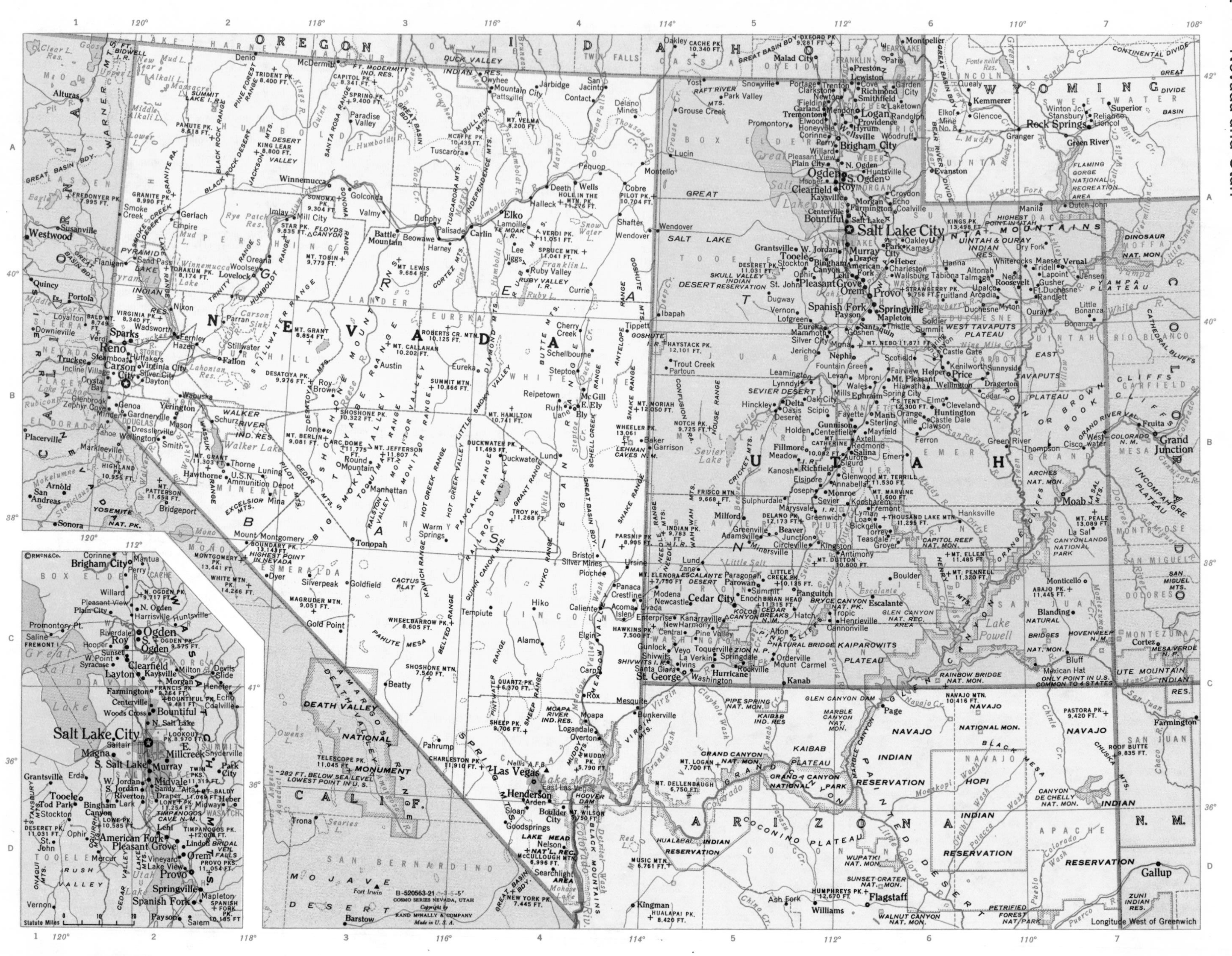

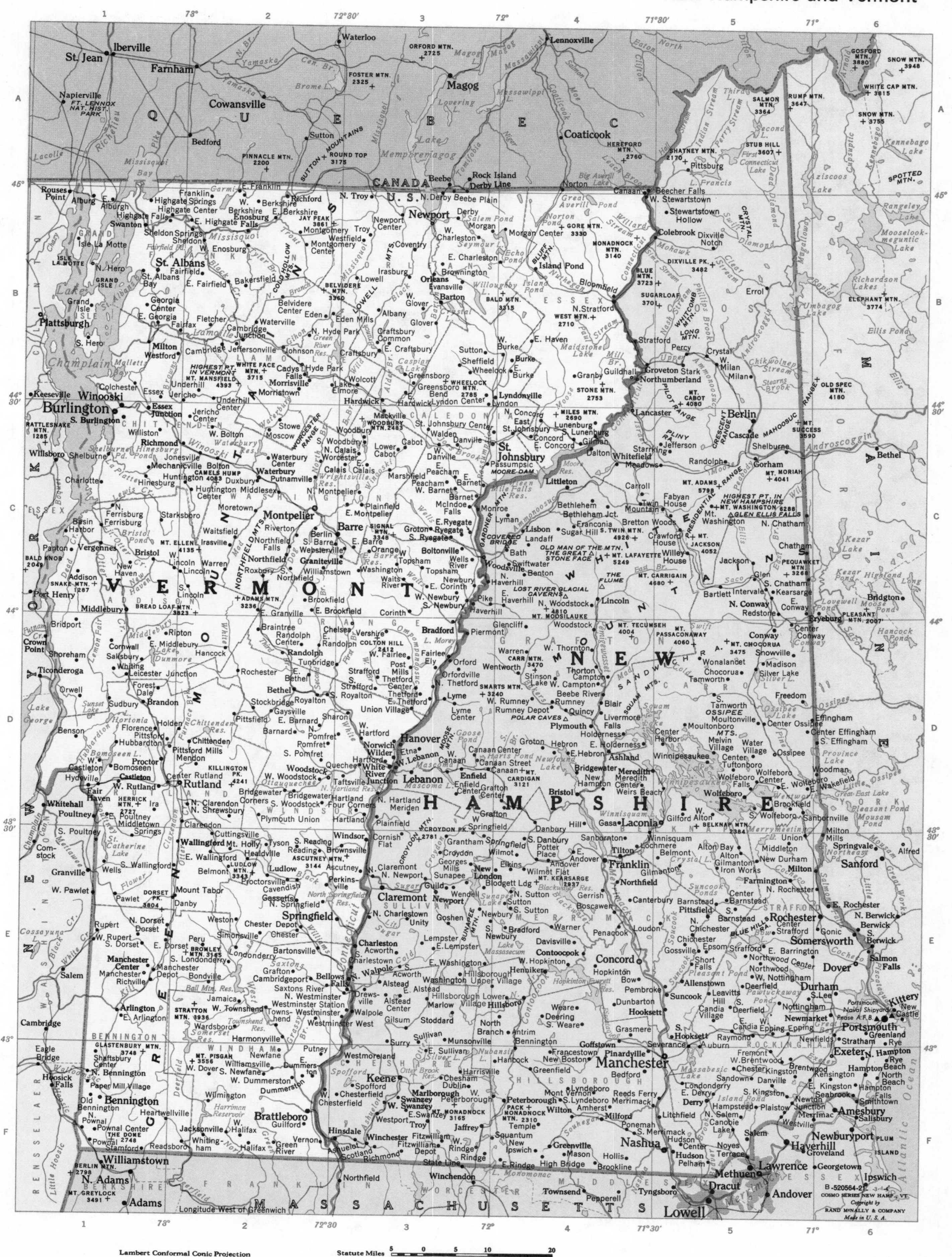

Lambert Conformal Conic Projection

Statute Miles
5   0   5   10   20

Kilometers
5 0 5 10 15 20 25

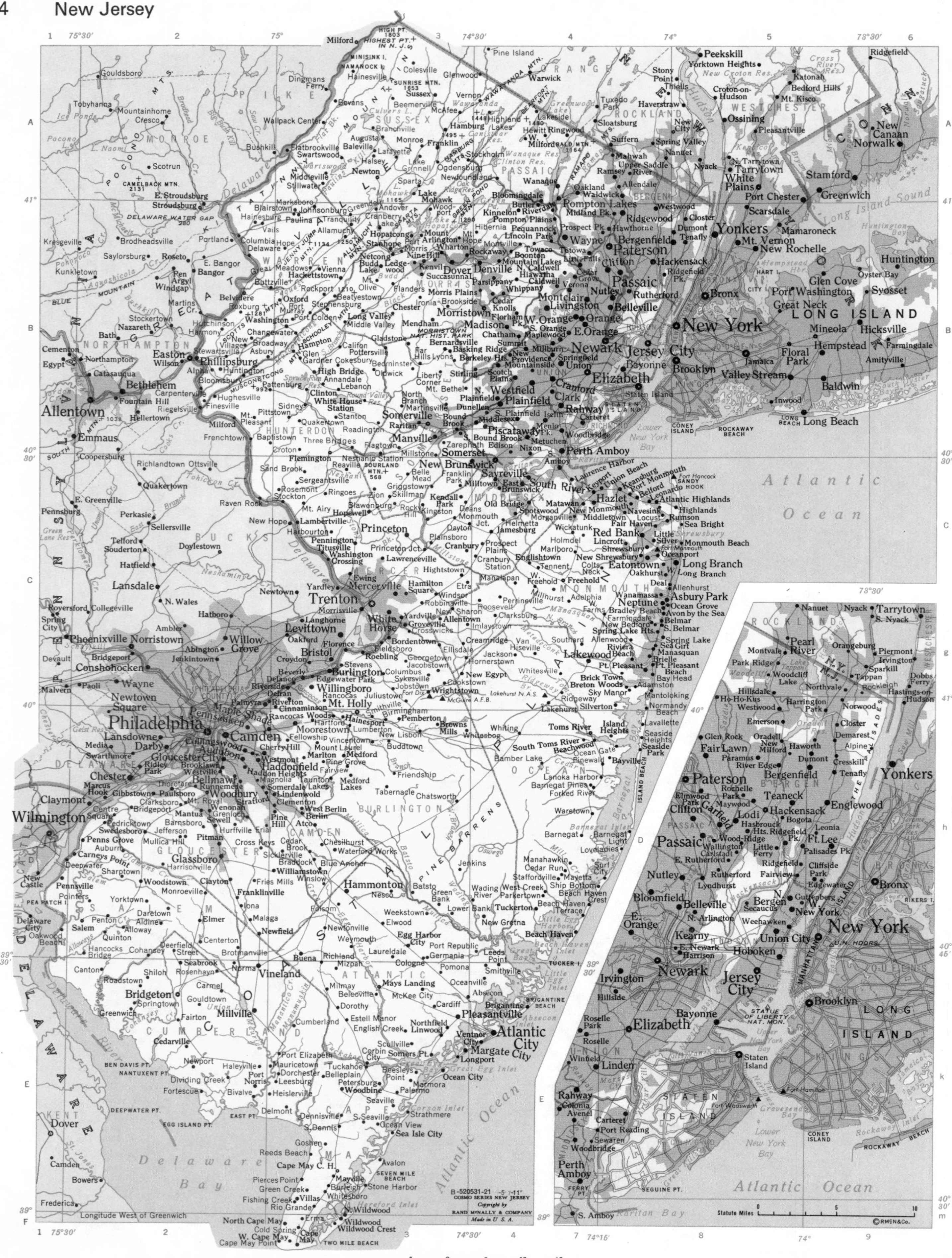
Atlantic Ocean
Delaware Bay
LONG ISLAND
New York
Newark
Jersey City
Elizabeth
Paterson
Passaic
Trenton
Camden
Philadelphia
Atlantic City
Allentown
Wilmington
Yonkers
Bronx
Brooklyn
Staten Island
Princeton
New Brunswick
Perth Amboy
Vineland
Bridgeton
Millville
Hammonton
Toms River
Lakewood
Asbury Park
Long Branch
Red Bank
Morristown
Dover
Phillipsburg
Bethlehem
Easton
Flemington
Somerville
Plainfield
Westfield
Rahway
Bayonne
Hoboken
Hackensack
Englewood
Teaneck
Clifton
Montclair
Bloomfield
Nutley
Kearny
Irvington
Linden
Union City
Burlington
Willingboro
Mt. Holly
Bristol
Levittown
Norristown
Chester
Glassboro
Woodbury
Salem
Pleasantville
Ocean City
Cape May
Wildwood
Dover
Statute Miles
Kilometers
Longitude West of Greenwich
Lambert Conformal Conic Projection
B-520531-21 -5-11'
COSMO SERIES NEW JERSEY
Copyright by
RAND McNALLY & COMPANY
Made in U. S. A.
©RM&Co.

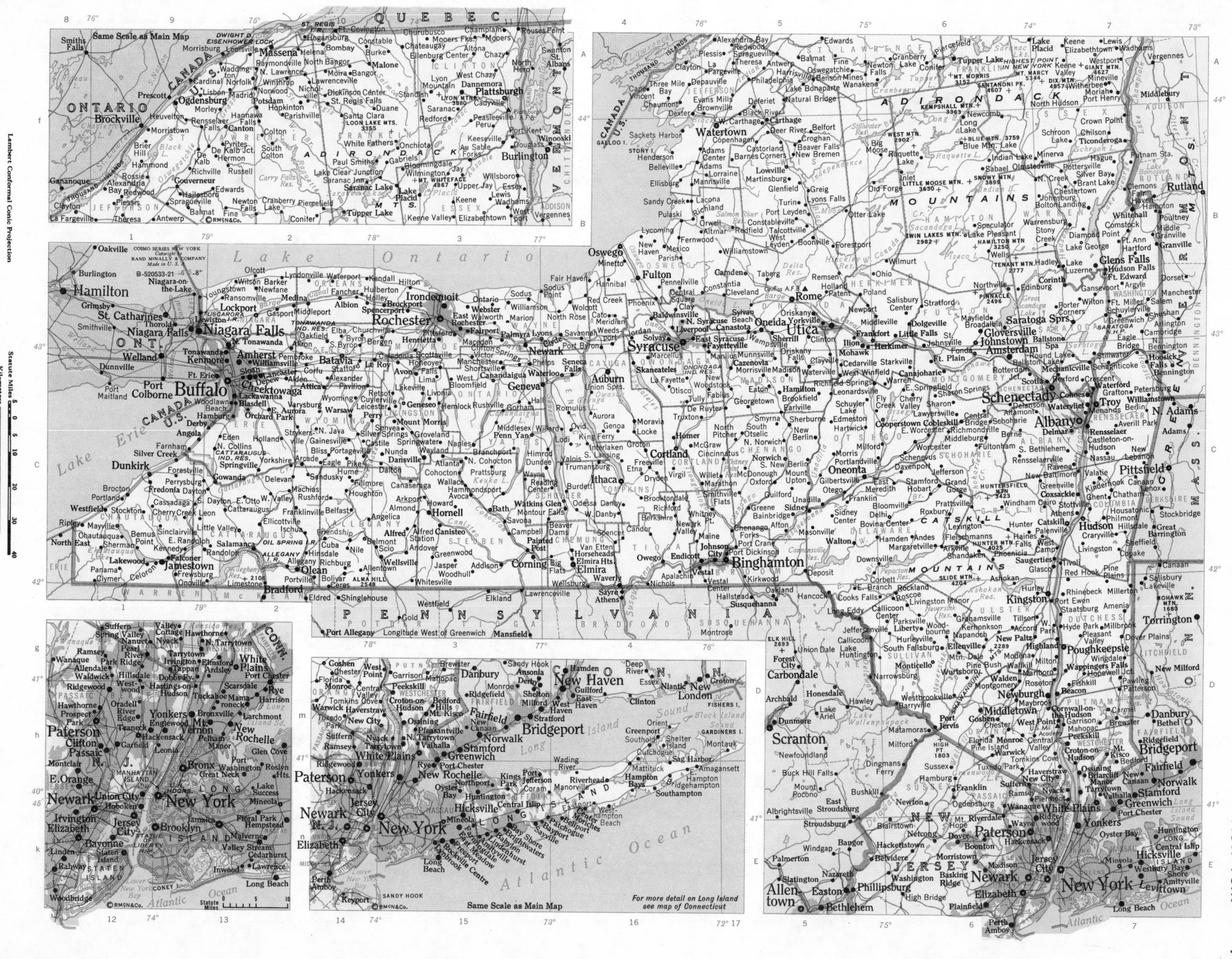

Lambert Conformal Conic Projection

Statute Miles 5 0 5 10 20 30 40

Kilometers 5 0 5 10 15 20 25 30 35 40 45 50 55

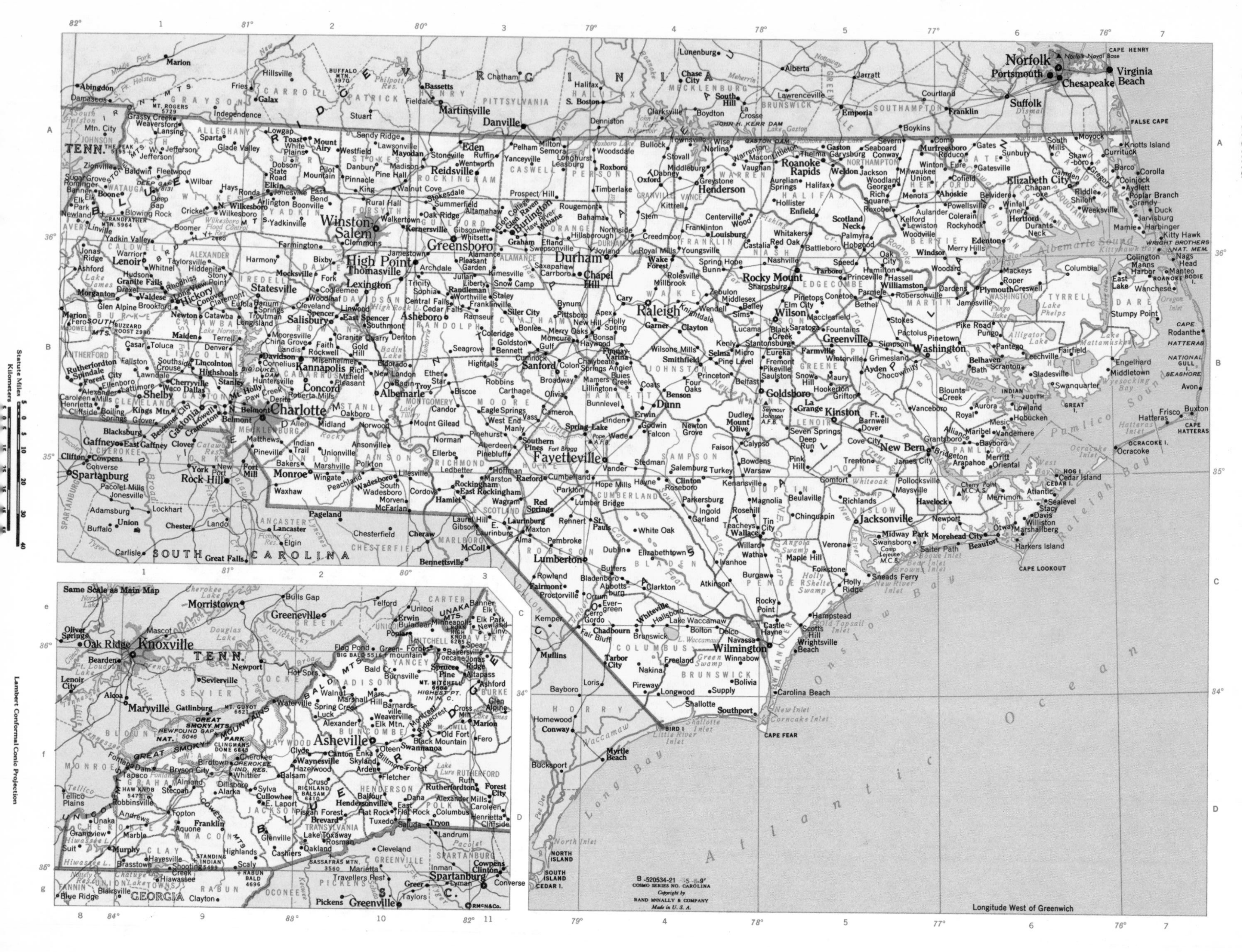
VIRGINIA
Norfolk
Portsmouth
Chesapeake
Virginia Beach
Suffolk
Elizabeth City
Raleigh
Durham
Chapel Hill
Greensboro
Winston-Salem
High Point
Charlotte
Fayetteville
Wilmington
Jacksonville
New Bern
Greenville
Rocky Mount
Goldsboro
Danville
SOUTH CAROLINA
Atlantic Ocean
CAPE HENRY
CAPE HATTERAS
CAPE LOOKOUT
CAPE FEAR
Same Scale as Main Map
Knoxville
Asheville
TENN.
GEORGIA
B-520534-21
COSMO SERIES NO. CAROLINA
Copyright by
RAND McNALLY & COMPANY
Made in U. S. A.
Longitude West of Greenwich
Statute Miles
Kilometers
Lambert Conformal Conic Projection

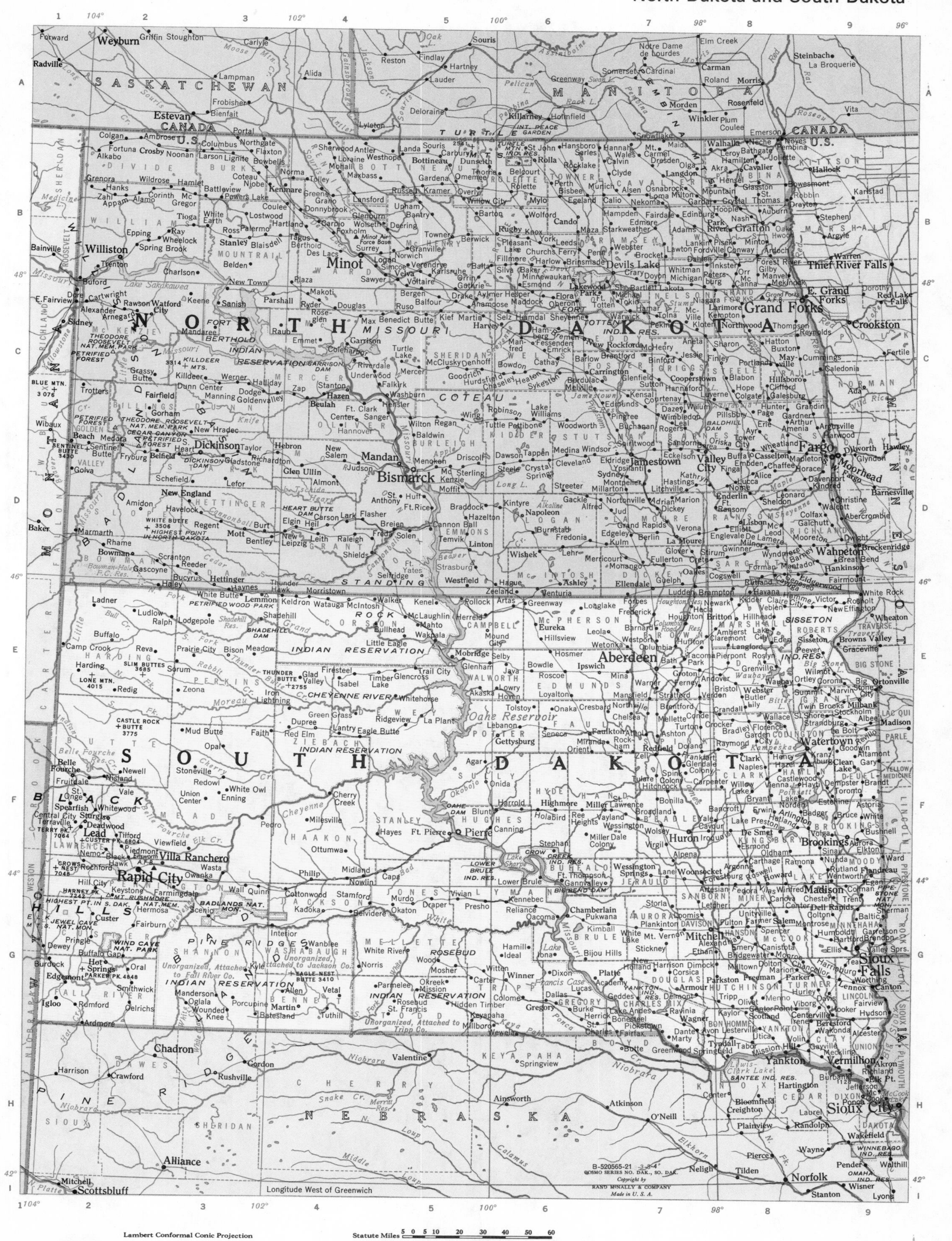
SASKATCHEWAN
MANITOBA
CANADA
U.S.
NORTH DAKOTA
SOUTH DAKOTA
NEBRASKA
MONTANA
WYOMING
MINNESOTA
IOWA
Bismarck
Minot
Grand Forks
Fargo
Mandan
Jamestown
Devils Lake
Williston
Dickinson
Valley City
Wahpeton
Aberdeen
Pierre
Rapid City
Sioux Falls
Watertown
Huron
Mitchell
Brookings
Yankton
Vermillion
Sioux City
Lead
Spearfish
Villa Ranchero
Chadron
Alliance
Scottsbluff
Norfolk
O'Neill
Valentine
Moorhead
Thief River Falls
Crookston
Weyburn
Estevan
Lake Sakakawea
Oahe Reservoir
Lake Francis Case
STANDING ROCK INDIAN RESERVATION
CHEYENNE RIVER INDIAN RESERVATION
PINE RIDGE INDIAN RESERVATION
ROSEBUD INDIAN RESERVATION
FORT BERTHOLD INDIAN RESERVATION
BLACK HILLS
BADLANDS NAT. MON.
TURTLE MTS.
INT. PEACE GARDEN
HIGHEST POINT IN NORTH DAKOTA
WHITE BUTTE 3506
HARNEY PK. 7242
HIGHEST PT. IN S. DAK.
Longitude West of Greenwich
B-520565-21
COSMO SERIES NO. DAK., SO. DAK.
Copyright by
RAND McNALLY & COMPANY
Made in U. S. A.
Lambert Conformal Conic Projection
Statute Miles 5 0 5 10 20 30 40 50 60
Kilometers 5 0 5 15 25 35 45 55 65 75

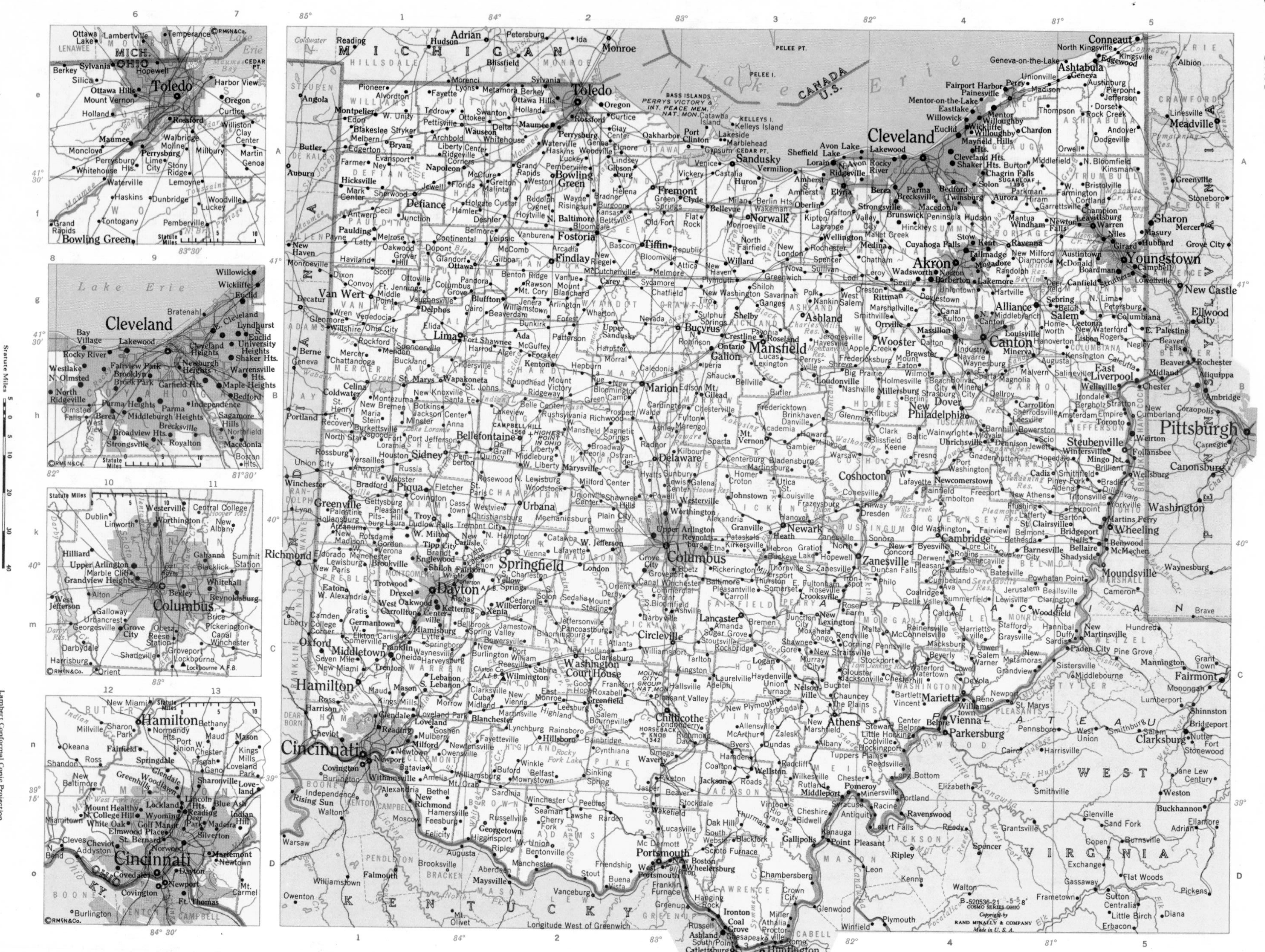

Statute Miles

Kilometers

Lambert Conformal Conic Projection

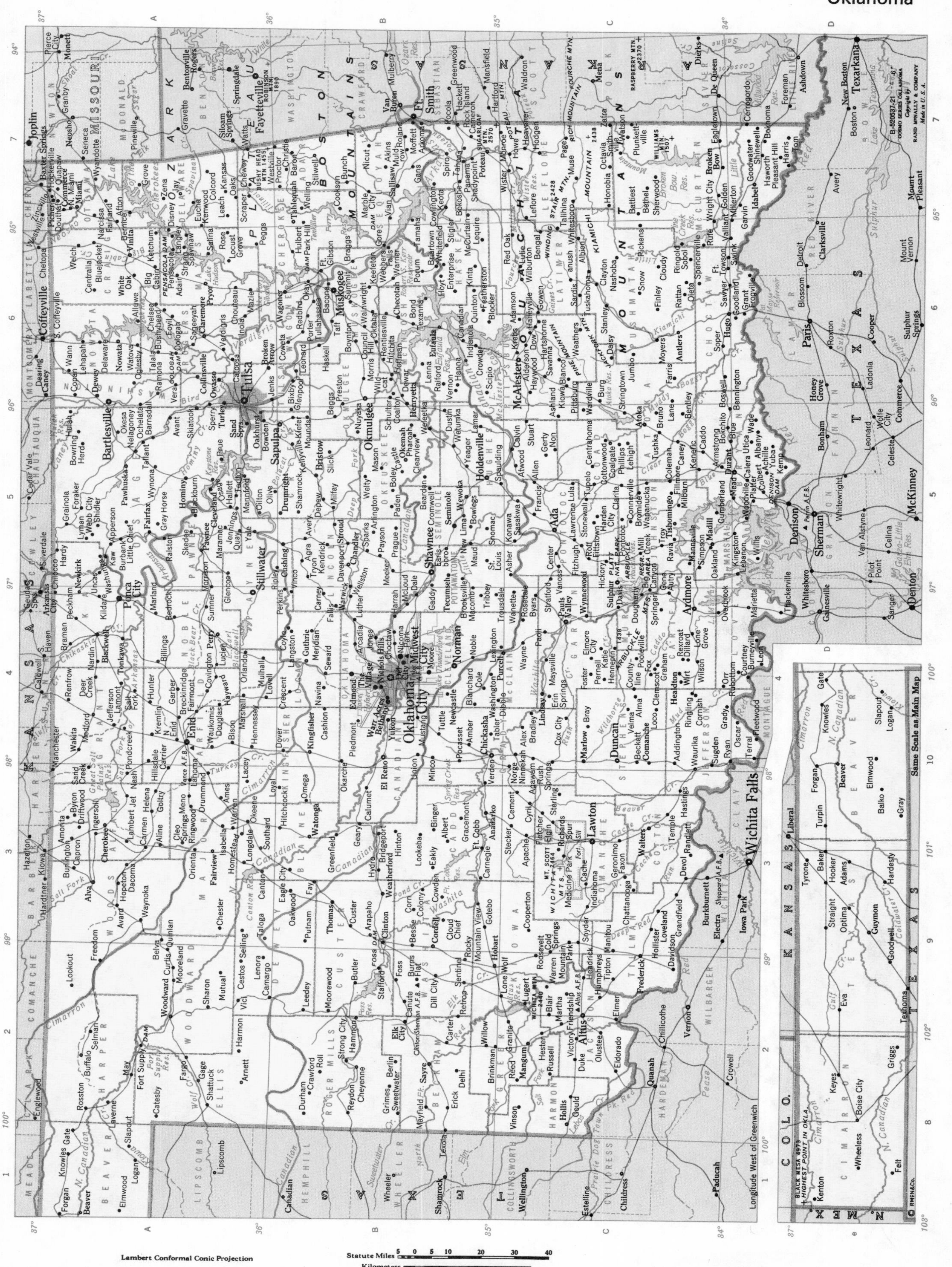

Statute Miles 5 0 5 10 20 30 40
Kilometers 5 0 5 15 25 35 45 55

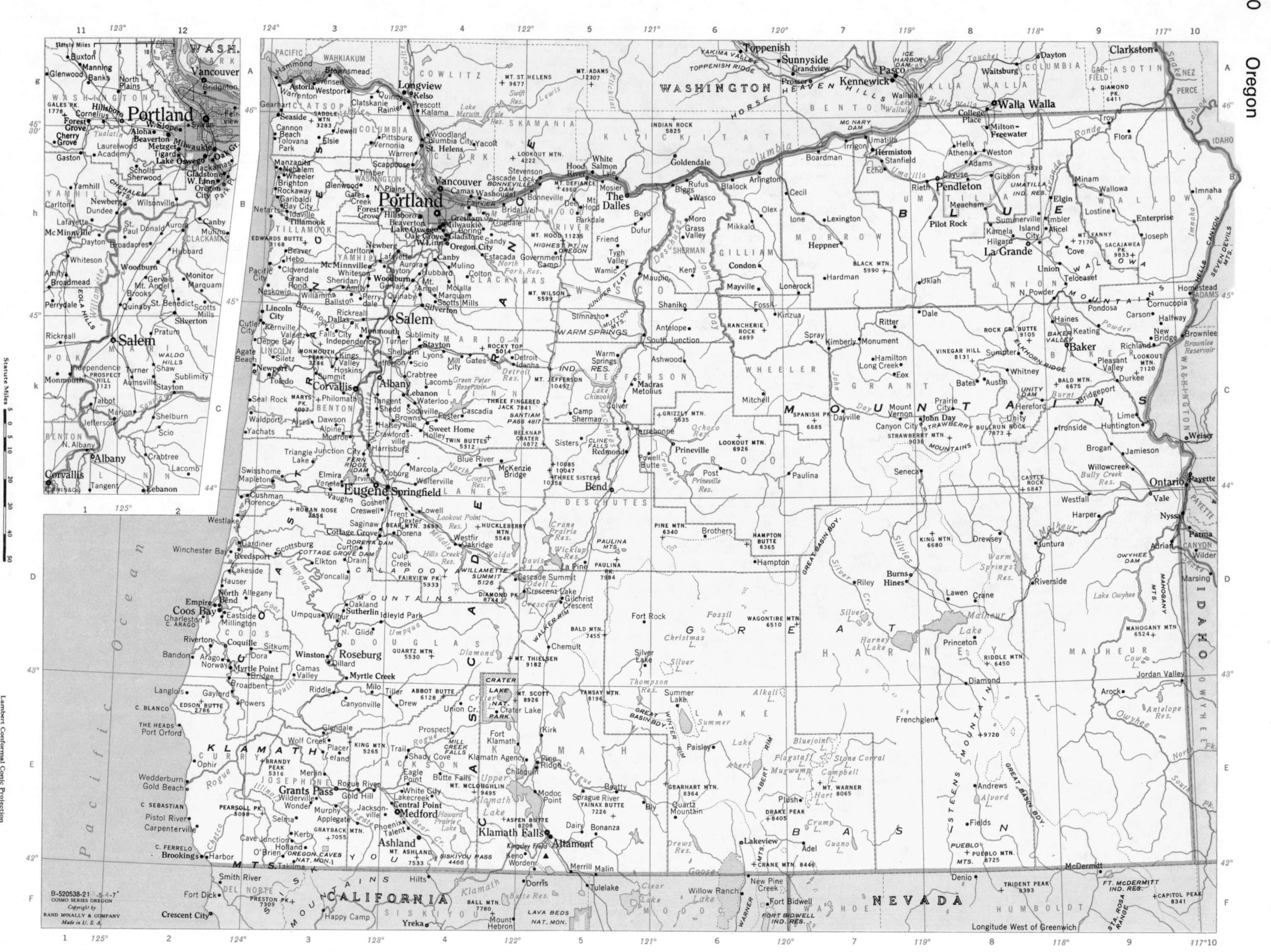

Statute Miles 5 0 5 10 20 30 40 50
Kilometers 5 0 5 15 25 35 45 55 65 75

Lambert Conformal Conic Projection

B-520538-21 -5-7'
COSMO SERIES OREGON
Copyright by
RAND McNALLY & COMPANY
Made in U.S.A.

Lambert Conformal Conic Projection

Statute Miles
5 0 5 10 20 30

Kilometers
5 0 5 15 25 35 45

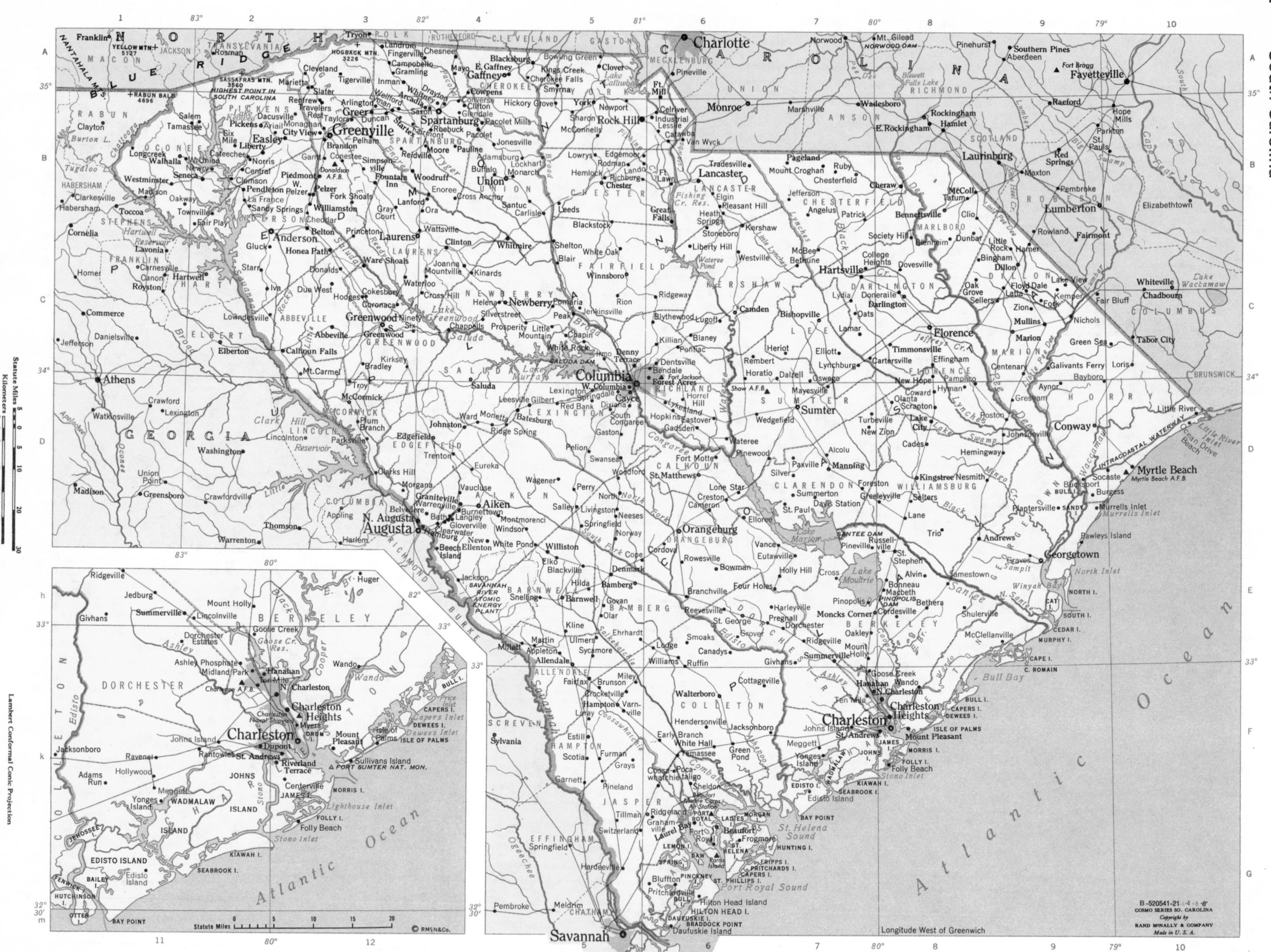
NORTH CAROLINA
GEORGIA
Atlantic Ocean
Charlotte
Columbia
Charleston
Savannah
Greenville
Spartanburg
Florence
Sumter
Myrtle Beach
Georgetown
Conway
Rock Hill
Anderson
Orangeburg
Aiken
Augusta
N. Augusta
Athens
Fayetteville
Lumberton
Laurinburg
Monroe
Greenwood
Newberry
Camden
Lancaster
Union
Gaffney
Laurens
Hartsville
Darlington
Dillon
Marion
Walterboro
Beaufort
Manning
Barnwell
Allendale
Edgefield
Abbeville
Seneca
Easley
Chester
Winnsboro
Saluda
Bamberg
Denmark
Summerville
Moncks Corner
Mount Pleasant
Charleston Heights
Hilton Head Island
Longitude West of Greenwich
B-520541-21
COSMO SERIES SO. CAROLINA
Copyright by RAND McNALLY & COMPANY
Made in U. S. A.
Statute Miles
Kilometers
Lambert Conformal Conic Projection

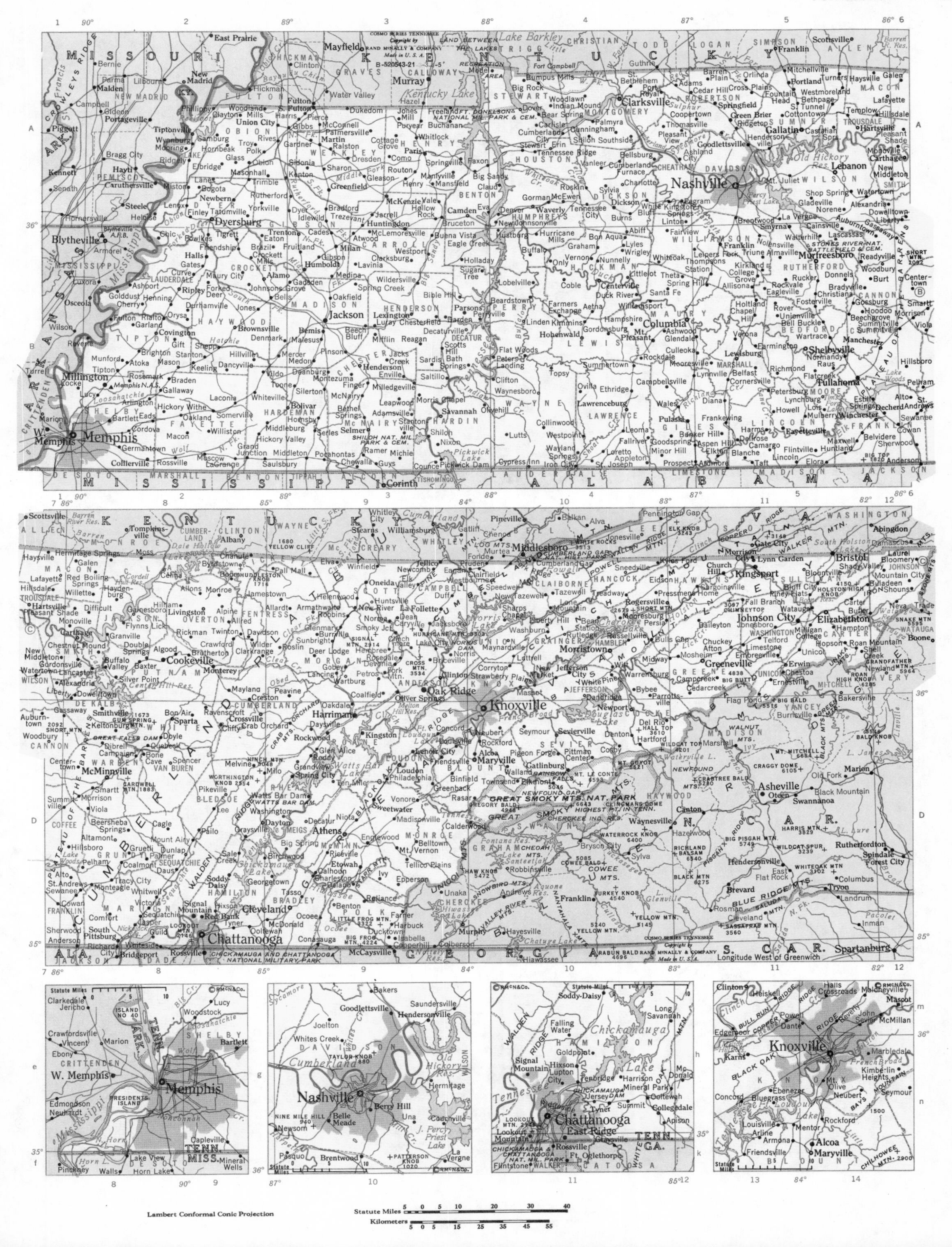

MISSOURI
KENTUCKY
ARKANSAS
MISSISSIPPI
ALABAMA
GEORGIA
S. CAR.
VIRGINIA
Nashville
Memphis
Knoxville
Chattanooga
Jackson
Clarksville
Murfreesboro
Columbia
Oak Ridge
Johnson City
Kingsport
Bristol
Asheville
Cookeville
Dyersburg
Cleveland
Great Smoky Mts. Nat. Park
Kentucky Lake
Lake Barkley
Lambert Conformal Conic Projection
Statute Miles
Kilometers
Longitude West of Greenwich
COSMO SERIES TENNESSEE
Copyright by RAND McNALLY & COMPANY
Made in U. S. A.

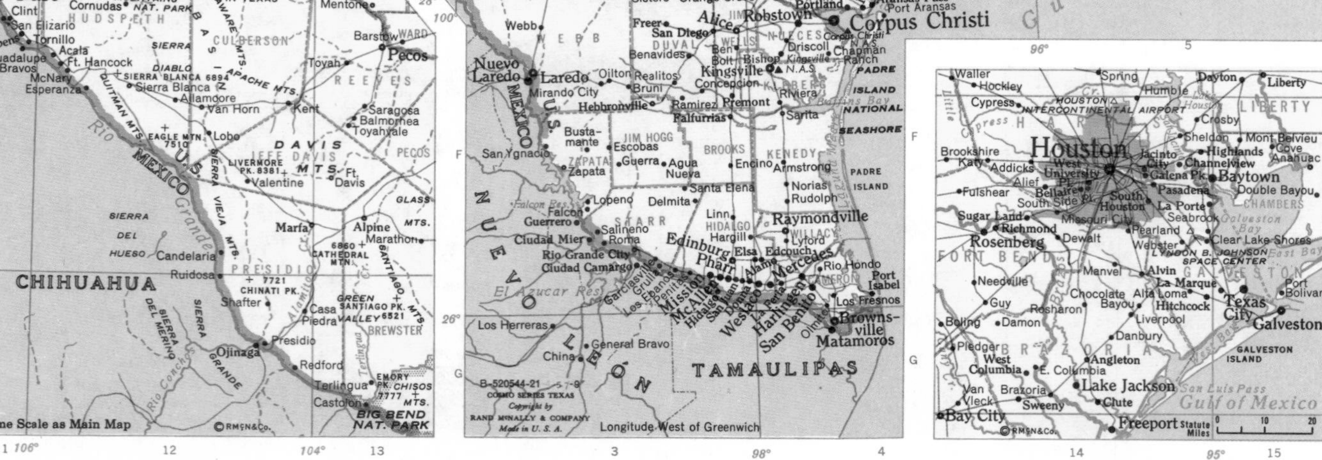
Same Scale as Main Map
Longitude West of Greenwich
TAMAULIPAS
NUEVO LEÓN
CHIHUAHUA
COAHUILA
Gulf of Mexico
Statute Miles 10 0 10 20 30 40 50 60 70 80 90 100
Kilometers 10 0 10 20 40 60 80 100 120 140
Lambert Conformal Conic Projection

Washington

Statute Miles

Kilometers

Lambert Conformal Conic Projection

B-320548-21

Copyright by RAND M?NALLY & COMPANY
Made in U.S.A.

(Full-page reference map of Washington State with numerous city, town, mountain, river, and county labels including Spokane, Seattle, Tacoma, Olympia, Yakima, Walla Walla, Bellingham, Everett, Wenatchee, Ellensburg, Bremerton, Port Angeles, Aberdeen, Vancouver, Longview, Kennewick, Pasco, Richland, Moses Lake, Ephrata, Colville, Newport, Pullman, Clarkston, Coeur d'Alene, Moscow, Lewiston, and others. Bordering labels: BRITISH COLUMBIA, CANADA U.S., IDAHO, OREGON, Pacific Ocean, VANCOUVER ISLAND, Victoria. Physical features include OLYMPIC MOUNTAINS, CASCADE RANGE, MT. RAINIER, Columbia River, Mt. St. Helens, SELKIRK MOUNTAINS, etc. Inset maps show Spokane and Seattle–Tacoma areas.)

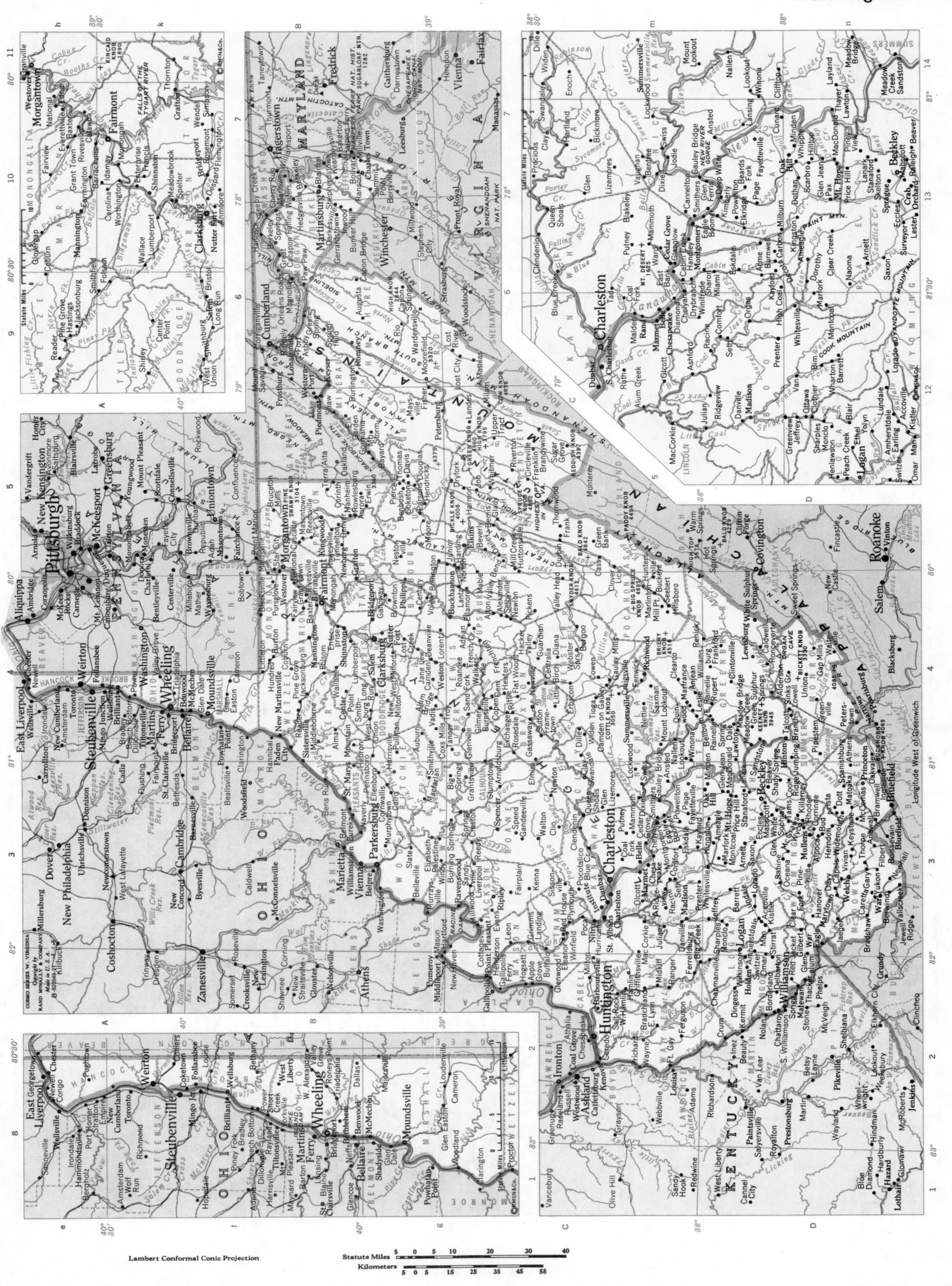

Lambert Conformal Conic Projection

Statute Miles 5 0 5 10 20 30 40
Kilometers 5 0 5 15 25 35 45 55

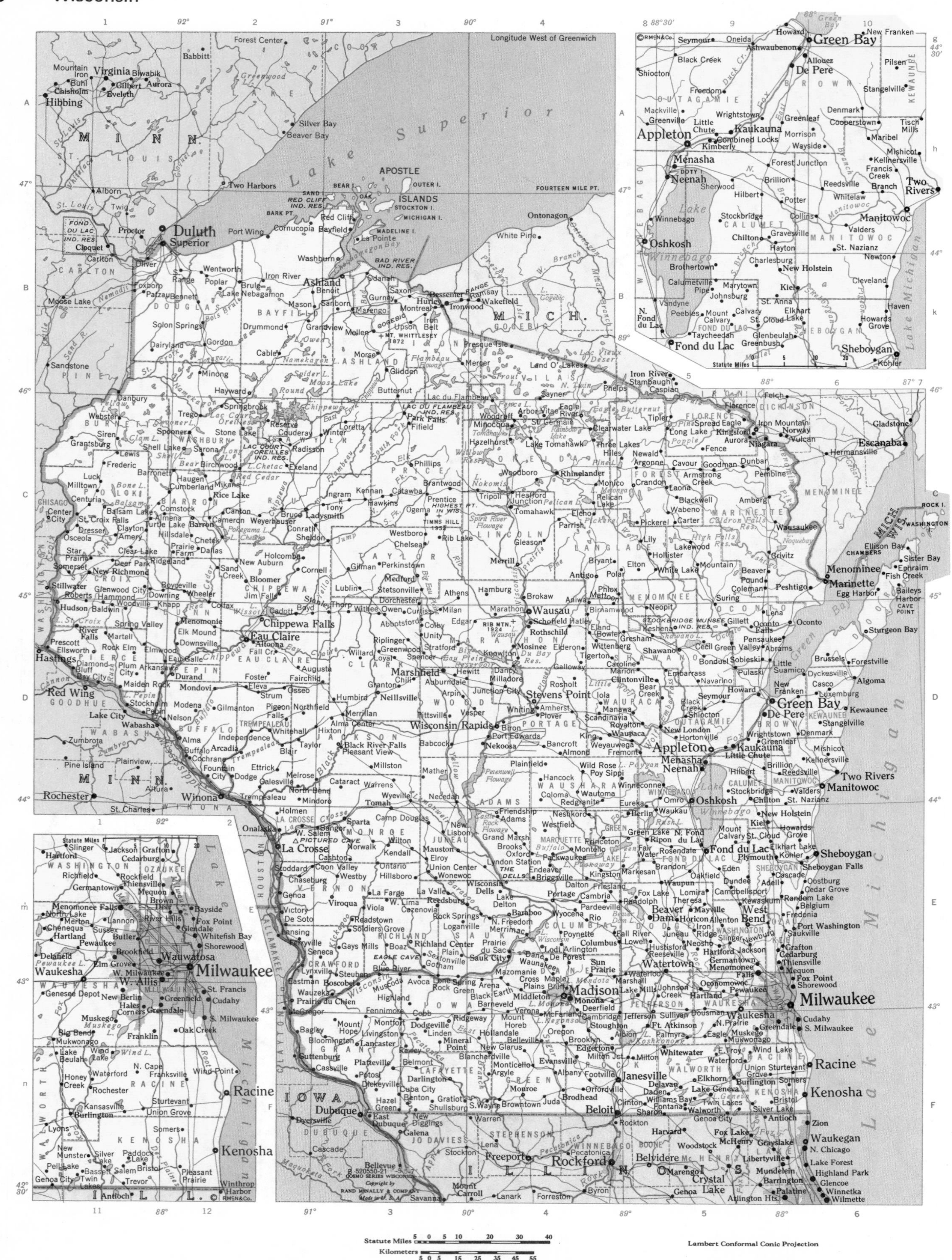

Statute Miles   5 0 5   10   20   30   40
Kilometers   5 0 5   15   25   35   45   55

Lambert Conformal Conic Projection

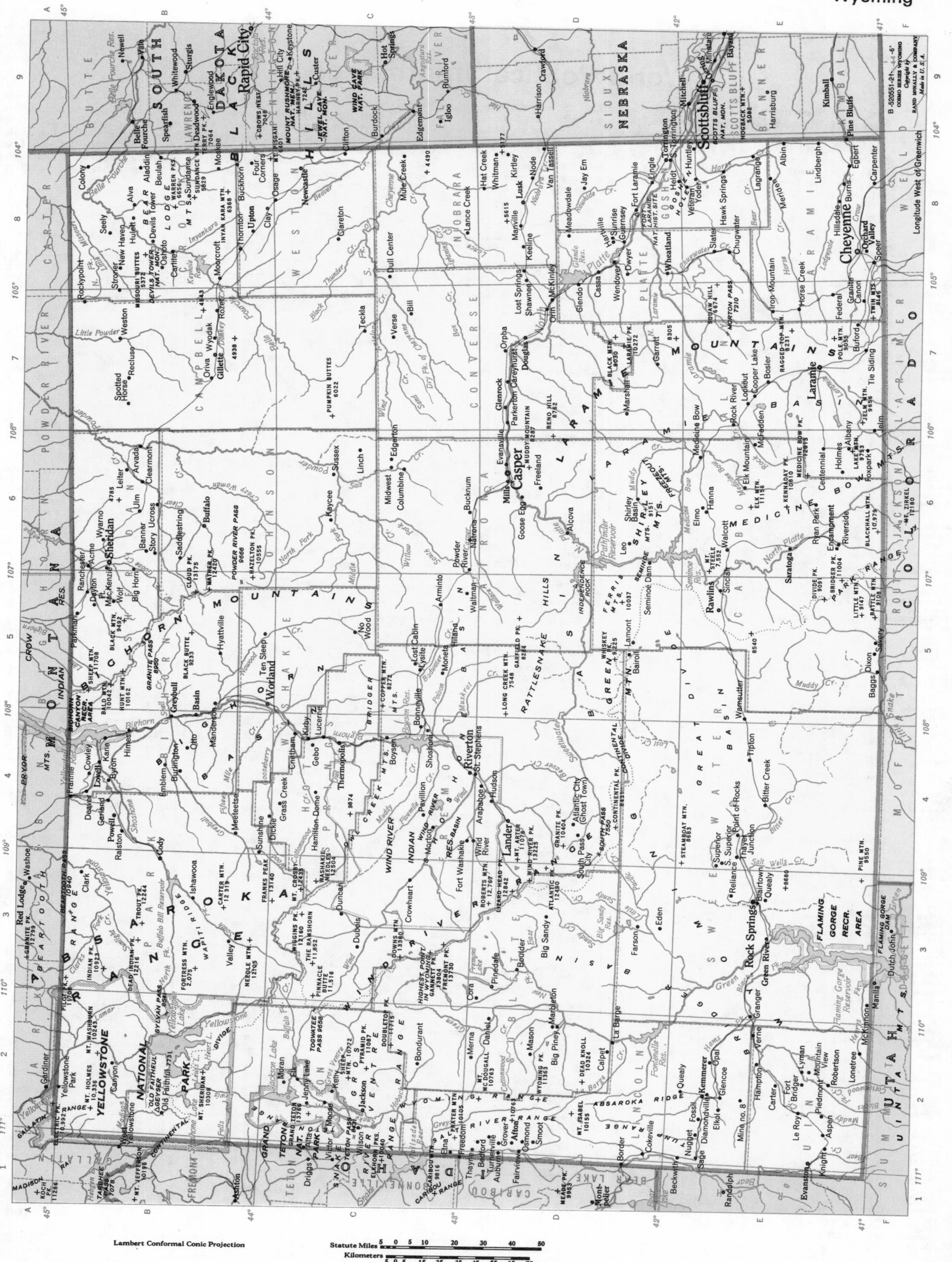

Statute Miles
5 0 5 10   20   30   40   50

Kilometers
5 0 5 15 25 35 45 55 65 75

World Political Information Table

This table lists all countries and dependencies in the world, U.S. States, Canadian provinces, and other important regions and political subdivisions. Besides specifying the form of government for all political areas, the table classifies them into six groups according to their political status. Units labeled **A** are independent sovereign nations. (Several of these are designated as members of the British Commonwealth of Nations.) Units labeled **B** are independent as regards internal affairs, but for purposes of foreign affairs they are under the protection of another country. Areas under military government are also labeled **B**. Units labeled **C** are colonies, overseas territories, dependencies, etc., of other countries. Together the **A**, **B**, and **C** areas comprise practically the entire inhabited area of the world. The areas labeled **D** are physically separate units, such as groups of islands, which are *not* separate countries, but form part of a nation or dependency. Units labeled **E** are States, provinces, Soviet Republics, or similar major administrative subdivisions of important countries. Units in the table with no letter designation are regions or other areas that do not constitute separate political units by themselves.

Region or Political Division	Area in sq. miles	Estimated Population 1/1/1978	Pop. per sq. mi.	Form of Government and Ruling Power	Capital; Largest City (unless same)	Predominant Languages
Aden, see Yemen, P.D.R. of.....						
Afars & Issas, see Djibouti....						
Afghanistan†	250,000	20,565,000	82	Republic...A	Kabul	Pushtu (Afghan), Persian
Africa	11,685,000	429,400,000	37		....; Cairo	
Alabama	51,609	3,725,000	72	State (U.S.)...E	Montgomery; Birmingham	
Alaska	586,412	408,000	0.7	State U.S.)...E	Juneau; Anchorage	English, Indian, Eskimo
Albania†	11,100	2,655,000	239	People's Republic...A	Tiranë	Albanian
Alberta	255,285	1,889,000	7.4	Province (Canada)...E	Edmonton	English
Algeria†	919,595	18,073,000	20	Republic...A	Algiers (Alger)	Arabic, French, Berber
American Samoa	76	33,000	434	Unincorporated Territory (U.S.)...C	Pago Pago	Polynesian, English
Andaman & Nicobar Is.	3,202	132,000	41	Territory (India)...D	Port Blair	Andaman, Nicobar Malay
Andorra	175	28,000	160	Principality...A	Andorra	Catalan
Angola†	481,353	7,214,000	15	Republic...A	Luanda	Bantu languages, Portuguese
Anguilla	35	6,000	171	Colony (U.K.)...C	The Valley	English
Antarctica	5,100,000					
Antigua (incl. Barbuda)	171	75,000	439	Associated State (U.K.)...B	St. Johns	English
Arabian Peninsula	1,145,636	19,682,000	17		....; Riyadh	Arabic
Argentina†	1,072,162	26,075,000	24	Federal Republic...A	Buenos Aires	Spanish
Arizona	113,909	2,360,000	21	State (U.S.)...E	Phoenix	
Arkansas	53,104	2,144,000	40	State (U.S.)...E	Little Rock	
Armenia (S.S.R.)	11,500	2,887,000	251	Soviet Socialist Republic (Sov. Un.)...E	Yerevan	Armenian, Russian
Aruba	69	62,000	899	Division of Netherlands Antilles (Neth.)...D	Oranjestad	Dutch, Spanish, English, Papiamento
Ascension I.	34	2,000	59	Dependency of St. Helena (U.K.)...D	Georgetown	English
Asia	17,085,000	2,432,000,000	142		....; Tōkyō	
Australia†	2,967,909	13,858,000	4.7	Monarchy (Federal) (Br. Commonwealth of Nations)...A	Canberra; Sydney	English
Australian Capital Territory	939	202,000	215	Federal Territory (Australia)...E	Canberra	English
Austria†	32,374	7,500,000	232	Federal Republic...A	Vienna (Wien)	German
Azerbaidzhan (S.S.R.)	33,450	5,801,000	173	Soviet Socialist Republic (Sov. Un.)...E	Baku	Turkic languages, Russian, Armenian
Azores Is.	905	298,000	329	Part of Portugal (3 Districts)...D	....; Ponta Delgada	Portuguese
Baden-Württemberg	13,803	9,088,000	658	State (Federal Republic of Germany)...E	Stuttgart	German
Bahamas†	5,380	222,000	41	Self-Governing Member (Br. Comm. of Nations)...A	Nassau	English
Bahrain†	231	268,000	1,160	Sheikdom...A	Manama	Arabic
Balearic Is.	1,936	577,000	298	Part of Spain (Baleares Province)...D	Palma de Mallorca	Catalan, Spanish
Baltic Republics	67,150	7,439,000	111	Soviet Union	....; Riga	Lithuanian, Latvian, Estonian, Russian
Bangladesh†	55,126	84,605,000	1,535	Republic (Br. Comm. of Nations)...A	Dacca	Bengali, English
Barbados†	166	250,000	1,506	Self-Governing Member (Br. Comm. of Nations)...A	Bridgetown	English
Basutoland, see Lesotho.....						
Bavaria (Bayern)	27,239	10,687,000	392	State (Federal Republic of Germany)...E	Munich (München)	German
Bechuanaland, see Botswana.....						
Belgium†	11,781	10,005,000	849	Monarchy...A	Brussels (Bruxelles)	Dutch, French
Belize (British Honduras)	8,867	150,000	17	Colony (U.K.)...C	Belmopan; Belize	English, Spanish, Indian languages
Benelux	28,549	24,315,000	852		Brussels (Bruxelles)	Dutch, French, Luxembourgeois
Benin†	43,484	3,405,000	78	Republic...A	Porto Novo; Cotonou	Native languages, French
Berlin, West	185	1,991,000	10,762	State (Federal Republic of Germany)...E	Berlin (West)	German
Bermuda	21	59,000	2,810	Colony (U.K.)...C	Hamilton	English
Bhutan†	18,200	1,245,000	68	Monarchy (Indian protection)...B	Thimbu and Paro	Tibetan dialects
Bismarck Archipelago	18,965	454,000	24	Part of Papua New Guinea...D	....; Rabaul	Malay-Polynesian and Papuan languages, English
Bolivia†	424,164	4,887,000	12	Republic...A	Sucre and La Paz; La Paz	Spanish, Quechua, Aymará, Guaraní
Borneo, Indonesian (Kalimantan)	208,286	5,969,000	29	Part of Indonesia (4 Provinces)...D	....; Bandjarmasin	Bahasa Indonesia (Indonesian)
Botswana (Bechuanaland)†	231,805	718,000	3.1	Republic (Br. Commonwealth of Nations)...A	Gaborone; Serowe	Bechuana, other Bantu languages, English
Brazil†	3,286,487	113,815,000	35	Federal Republic...A	Brasília; São Paulo	Portuguese
Bremen	156	714,000	4,577	State (Federal Republic of Germany)...E	Bremen	German
British Antarctic Territory (excl. Antarctic mainland)	2,040	Winter pop. 75		Colony (U.K.)...C	Stanley, Falkland Islands	
British Columbia	366,255	2,534,000	6.9	Province (Canada)...E	Victoria; Vancouver	English
British Commonwealth of Nations	10,676,384	999,352,000	94		London	
British Guiana, see Guyana.....						
British Indian Ocean Territory	18			Colony (U.K.)...C	Victoria, Seychelles	Creole, English, French
Brunei	2,226	190,000	85	Sultanate (U.K. protection)...A	Bandar Seri Begawan (Brunei)	Malay-Polynesian languages, English
Bulgaria†	42,823	8,820,000	206	People's Republic...A	Sofia (Sofiya)	Bulgarian
Burma†	261,790	31,815,000	122	Federal Republic...A	Rangoon	Burmese, English
Burundi (Urundi)†	10,747	4,003,000	372	Republic...A	Bujumbura	Bantu and Hamitic languages, French
Byelorussia (Belorussia) (S.S.R.)†	80,150	9,520,000	119	Soviet Socialist Republic (Sov. Un.)...E	Minsk	Byelorussian, Polish, Russian
California	158,693	22,018,000	139	State (U.S.)...E	Sacramento; Los Angeles	
Cambodia†	69,898	8,712,000	125	Republic...A	Phnom Penh	Cambodian (Khmer), French
Cameroon†	183,569	6,725,000	37	Federal Republic...A	Yaoundé; Douala	Native languages, French
Canada†	3,851,809	23,625,000	6.1	Monarchy (Federal) (Br. Commonwealth of Nations)...A	Ottawa; Montréal	English, French
Canal Zone	558	40,000	72	Under U.S. Jurisdiction...C	Balboa Heights; Balboa	Spanish, English
Canary Is.	2,808	1,271,000	453	Part of Spain (2 Provinces)...D	....; Las Palmas	Spanish
Canton & Enderbury	27			U.K.-U.S. Administration...A	Canton Island	Malay-Polynesian languages, English
Cape Verde†	1,557	314,000	202	Republic...A	Praia; Mindelo	Portuguese
Caroline Is.	463	85,000	184	Part of U.S. Pacific Is. Trust Ter. (4 Districts)...D		Malay-Polynesian languages, English
Cayman Is.	100	12,000	120	Colony (U.K.)...C	Georgetown	English
Celebes (Sulawesi)	72,987	9,891,000	136	Part of Indonesia (2 Provinces)...D	....; Makasar	Bahasa Indonesia (Indonesian), Malay-Polynesian languages
Central African Empire†	240,535	1,923,000	7.9	Empire...A	Bangui	Bantu languages, French
Central America	202,063	20,172,000	100		....; Guatemala	Spanish, Indian languages
Central Asia, Soviet	493,950	23,929,000	48	Soviet Union	....; Tashkent	Uzbek, Russian, Kirghiz, Turkoman, Tadzhik
Ceylon, see Sri Lanka.....						
Chad†	495,800	4,255,000	8.6	Republic...A	Ndjamena (Fort Lamy)	Hamitic languages, Arabic, French
Channel Is. (Guernsey, Jersey, etc.)	75	129,000	1,720		....; St. Helier	English, French
Chile†	292,258	10,740,000	37	Republic...A	Santiago	Spanish
China (excl. Taiwan)†	3,691,500	855,546,000	232	People's Republic...A	Peking (Peiching); Shanghai	Chinese, Mongolian, Turkic, Tungus
China (Nationalist)†, see Taiwan.....						

† Member of the United Nations (1978).

Region or Political Division	Area in sq. miles	Estimated Population 1/1/1978	Pop. per sq. mi.	Form of Government and Ruling Power	Capital; Largest City (unless same)	Predominant Languages
Christmas I. (Indian Ocean)	52	3,600	69	External Territory (Australia)....C		Chinese, Malay, English
Cocos (Keeling) Is.	5	700	140	External Territory (Australia)....C		Malay, English
Colombia†	439,737	25,460,000	58	Republic....A	Bogotá	Spanish
Colorado	104,247	2,644,000	25	State (U.S.)....E	Denver	
Commonwealth of Nations, see Br. Commonwealth of Nations	......	......	......			
Comoros†	694	314,000	452	Republic....A	Moroni	Malagasy, French
Congo (Rep. of Congo; Capital Brazzaville)†	132,000	1,455,000	11	Republic....A	Brazzaville	Bantu languages, French
Congo, The, see Zaire						
Connecticut	5,009	3,143,000	627	State (U.S.)....E	Hartford	
Cook Is.	93	18,000	194	Self-Governing Territory, (New Zealand)....C	Avarua	Malay-Polynesian languages
Corsica	3,352	292,000	87	Part of France (Corse Department)....D	Ajaccio; Bastia	French, Italian
Costa Rica†	19,650	2,079,000	106	Republic....A	San José	Spanish
Cuba†	44,218	9,678,000	219	Republic....A	Havana (La Habana)	Spanish
Curaçao	173	157,000	908	Division of Netherlands Antilles (Neth.)....D	Willemstad	Dutch, Spanish, English, Papiamento
Cyprus †	3,572	645,000	181	Republic (Br. Commonwealth of Nations)....A	Nicosia	Greek, Turkish, English
Czechoslovakia†	49,373	15,095,000	306	People's Republic....A	Prague (Praha)	Czech, Slovak
Dahomey, see Benin						
Delaware	2,057	588,000	286	State (U.S.)....E	Dover; Wilmington	
Denmark†	16,629	5,090,000	306	Monarchy....A	Copenhagen (København)	Danish
Denmark and Possessions	857,169	5,180,000	6.0		Copenhagen (København)	Danish, Faeroese, Greenlandic
District of Columbia	67	689,000	10,284	District (U.S.)....E	Washington	
Djibouti†	8,900	152,000	17	Republic....A	Djibouti	Somali, French
Dominica	290	77,000	266	Associated State (U.K.)....B	Roseau	English, French
Dominican Republic†	18,816	5,041,000	268	Republic....A	Santo Domingo	Spanish
Ecuador†	109,483	8,180,000	75	Republic....A	Quito; Guayaquil	Spanish, Quechua
Egypt (United Arab Republic)†‡	‡‡386,900	39,320,000	102	Republic....A	Cairo (Al Qāhirah)	Arabic
Ellice Is., see Tuvalu						
El Salvador†	8,260	4,290,000	519	Republic....A	San Salvador	Spanish
England (excl. Monmouthshire)	50,332	46,386,000	922	United Kingdom....A	; London	English
England & Wales	58,348	49,151,000	842	Administrative division of United Kingdom....E	London	English, Welsh
Equatorial Guinea†	10,830	325,000	30	Republic....A	Malabo	Bantu languages, Spanish
Estonia (S.S.R.)	17,400	1,456,000	84	Soviet Socialist Republic (Sov. Un.)....E	Tallinn	Estonian, Russian
Ethiopia†	471,778	29,775,000	63	Provisional Military Government....A	Addis Ababa	Amharic and other Semitic languages, English, various Hamitic languages
Eurasia	20,910,000	3,086,000,000	148		; Tōkyō	
Europe	3,825,000	654,000,000	171		; London	
Faeroe Is.	540	40,000	74	Self-Governing Territory (Denmark)....B	Tórshavn	Danish, Faeroese
Falkland Is. (excl. Deps)	4,618	1,900	0.41	Colony (U.K.)....C	Stanley	English
Fernando Poo, see Macías Nguema Biyogo						
Fiji†	7,055	595,000	84	Monarchy (Federal) (Br. Comm. of Nations)....A	Suva	Malaya-Polynesian languages, English, Hindi
Finland†	130,129	4,770,000	37	Republic....A	Helsinki	Finnish, Swedish
Florida	58,560	8,652,000	148	State (U.S.)....A	Tallahassee; Jacksonville	
France†	210,039	53,208,000	253	Republic....A	Paris	French
France and Possessions	238,881	54,986,000	230		Paris	
Franklin	549,253	7,000	0.01	District of Northwest Territories, Canada....E	; Cambridge Bay	English, Eskimo, Indian
French Guiana	35,100	66,000	1.9	Overseas Department (France)....C	Cayenne	French
French Polynesia	1,550	138,000	89	Overseas Territory (France)....C	Papeete	Malay-Polynesian languages, French
French Somaliland, see Djibouti						
French Southern & Antarctic Ter. (excl. Adélie Coast)	2,918	200	0.07	Overseas Territory (France)....C		French
French West Indies	1,112	749,000	674		; Fort-de-France	French
Gabon†	103,347	537,000	5.2	Republic....A	Libreville	Bantu languages, French
Galápagos Is. (Colón, Archipélago de)	3,075	5,100	1.7	Province (Ecuador)....D	Puerto Baquerizo	Spanish
Gambia†	4,361	559,000	128	Republic (Br. Comm. of Nations)....A	Banjul (Bathurst)	Mandingo, Fula, English
Georgia (S.S.R.)	26,900	5,046,000	188	Soviet Socialist Republic (Sov. Un.)....E	Tbilisi	Georgic, Armenian, Russian
Georgia (Entire)	58,876	5,032,000	85	State (U.S.)....E	Atlanta	
Germany (Entire)	137,727	77,765,000	565		; Berlin	German
German Democratic Republic (East Germany)†	41,768	16,695,000	400	People's Republic....A	Berlin (East)	German
Germany, Federal Republic of (West Germany)†	95,959	61,070,000	636	Federal Republic....A	Bonn; Berlin (West)	German
Ghana†	92,100	10,905,000	118	Republic (Br. Commonwealth of Nations)....A	Accra	Twi, Fanti, Ewe-Fon, English
Gibraltar	2	30,000	15,000	Colony (U.K.)....C	Gibraltar	Spanish, English
Gilbert Is.	331	58,000	175	Colony (U.K.)....C	Bairiki	Malay-Polynesian languages, English
Great Britain & Northern Ireland, see United Kingdom	......	......	......			
Greece†	50,944	9,340,000	183	Republic....A	Athens (Athínai)	Greek
Greenland	840,000	50,000	0.06	Overseas Territory (Denmark)....C	Godthåb	Greenlandic, Danish, Eskimo
Grenada†	133	114,000	857	Self-Governing Member (Br. Comm. of Nations)....A	St. George's	English
Guadeloupe (incl. Dependencies)	687	371,000	540	Overseas Department (France)....C	Basse-Terre; Pointe-à-Pitre	French
Guam	212	96,000	453	Unincorporated Territory (U.S.)....C	Agana	English, Chamorro
Guatemala†	42,042	6,525,000	155	Republic....A	Guatemala	Spanish, Indian languages
Guernsey (incl. Dependencies)	30	54,000	1,800	Bailiwick (U.K.)....C	St. Peter Port	English, French
Guinea†	94,926	4,695,000	49	Republic....A	Conakry	Native languages, French
Guinea-Bissau†	13,948	539,000	39	Republic....A	Bissau	Native languages, Portuguese
Guyana†	83,000	781,000	9.4	Republic (Br. Comm. of Nations)....A	Georgetown	English
Haiti†	10,714	4,800,000	448	Republic....A	Port-au-Prince	Creole, French
Hamburg	288	1,710,000	5,938	State (Federal Republic of Germany)....E	Hamburg	German
Hawaii	6,450	914,000	142	State (U.S.)....E	Honolulu	English, Japanese, Hawaiian
Hesse (Hessen)	8,150	5,496,000	674	State (Federal Republic of Germany)....E	Wiesbaden; Frankfurt am Main	German
Hispaniola	29,530	9,841,000	333		; Santo Domingo	French, Spanish
Holland, see Netherlands						
Honduras†	43,277	2,946,000	68	Republic....A	Tegucigalpa	Spanish
Hong Kong	399	4,445,000	11,140	Colony (U.K.)....C	Victoria	Chinese, English
Hungary†	35,920	10,690,000	298	People's Republic....A	Budapest	Hungarian
Iceland†	39,800	225,000	5.7	Republic....A	Reykjavík	Icelandic
Idaho	83,557	855,000	10	State (U.S.)....E	Boise (Boise City)	
Illinois	56,400	11,277,000	200	State (U.S.)....E	Springfield; Chicago	
India (incl. part of Kashmir)†	1,229,210	627,990,000	511	Republic (Br. Commonwealth of Nations)....A	New Delhi; Calcutta	Hindi and other Indo-Aryan languages, Dravidian languages, English
Indiana	36,291	5,306,000	146	State (U.S.)....E	Indianapolis	
Indonesia (incl. West Irian)†	741,034	138,180,000	186	Republic....A	Djakarta	Bahasa Indonesia (Indonesian), Chinese, English
Iowa	56,290	2,881,000	51	State (U.S.)....A	Des Moines	
Iran (Persia)†	636,300	34,160,000	54	Monarchy....A	Tehrān	Persian, Turkish dialects, Kurdish
Iraq†	167,925	12,069,000	72	Republic....A	Baghdād	Arabic, Kurdish
Ireland†	27,137	3,210,000	118	Republic....A	Dublin	English, Irish
Isle of Man	227	64,000	282	Possession (U.K.)....C	Douglas	English
Israel†	‡‡8,019	3,610,000△	450	Republic....A	Jerusalem; Tel Aviv-Yafo	Hebrew, Arabic
Italy†	116,313	56,710,000	488	Republic....A	Rome (Roma); Milan (Milano)	Italian

† *Member of the United Nations (1978).*
‡‡ *Areas for Egypt, Israel, Jordan and Syria do not reflect de facto changes which took place during 1967.*
△ *Population excludes 1,100,000 people in territories administered by Israel.*

92 **World Political Information Table** *Continued*

Region or Political Division	Area in sq. miles	Estimated Population 1/1/1978	Pop. per sq. mi.	Form of Government and Ruling Power	Capital; Largest City (unless same)	Predominant Languages
Ivory Coast†	124,504	7,095,000	57	Republic...A	Abidjan	French, native languages
Jamaica†	4,232	2,080,000	491	Self-Governing Member (Br. Comm. of Nations)...A	Kingston	English
Japan†	143,706	114,650,000	798	Monarchy...A	Tōkyō	Japanese
Java (Djawa) (incl. Madura)	51,040	88,184,000	1,728	Part of Indonesia (5 Provinces)...D	........; Djakarta	Bahasa Indonesia (Indonesian), Chinese, Engli
Jersey	45	75,000	1,667	Bailiwick (U.K.)...C	St. Helier	English, French
Jordan†	‡‡37,738	2,900,000	77	Monarchy...A	'Ammān	Arabic
Kansas	82,264	2,337,000	28	State (U.S.)...E	Topeka; Wichita	
Kashmir, Jammu &	86,024	5,275,000	61	In dispute (India & Pakistan)	Srinagar	Kashmiri, Punjabi
Kazakh S.S.R.	1,048,300	14,592,000	14	Soviet Socialist Republic (Sov. Un.)...E	Alma-Ata	Turkic languages, Russian
Keewatin	228,160	4,000	0.02	District of Northwest Territories, Canada...E	........; Baker Lake	English, Eskimo, Indian
Kentucky	40,395	3,482,000	86	State (U.S.)...E	Frankfort; Louisville	
Kenya†	224,960	14,545,000	65	Republic (Br. Comm. of Nations)...A	Nairobi	Swahili and other Bantu languages, English
Kerguelen	2,700	90	0.03	Part of French Southern & Antarctic Ter. (Fr.)...D		French
Kirghiz S.S.R.	76,650	3,433,000	45	Soviet Socialist Republic (Sov. Un.)...E	Frunze	Turkic languages, Persian, Russian
Korea (Entire)	85,049‡	53,590,000	630		........; Seoul (Sŏul)	Korean
Korea, North	46,540	16,855,000	362	People's Republic...A	Pyongyang	Korean
Korea, South	38,022	36,735,000	966	Republic...A	Seoul (Sŏul)	Korean
Kuwait†	6,200	1,091,000	176	Sheikdom...A	Kuwait (Al Kuwayt)	Arabic
Labrador	112,826	34,000	0.3	Part of Newfoundland Province, Canada...D	........; Labrador City	English, Eskimo
Laos†	91,400	3,485,000	38	Monarchy...A	Vientiane	Lao, French
Latin America	7,925,708	339,947,000	43		........; São Paulo	
Latvia (S.S.R.)	24,600	2,601,000	106	Soviet Socialist Republic (Sov. Un.)...E	Riga	Latvian, Russian
Lebanon†	3,950	3,096,000	784	Republic...A	Beirut (Bayrūt)	Arabic, French, English
Lesotho (Basutoland)†	11,720	1,622,000	138	Monarchy (Br. Comm. of Nations)...A	Maseru	Kaffir, other Bantu languages, English
Liberia†	43,000	1,810,000	42	Republic...A	Monrovia	Native languages, English
Libya†	679,362	2,678,000	3.9	Republic...A	Tripoli	Arabic
Liechtenstein	62	25,000	403	Principality...A	Vaduz	German
Lithuania (S.S.R.)	25,150	3,381,000	134	Soviet Socialist Republic (Sov. Un.)...E	Vilnius	Lithuanian, Polish, Russian
Louisiana	48,523	3,906,000	80	State (U.S.)...E	Baton Rouge; New Orleans	
Lower Saxony (Niedersachsen)	18,299	7,157,000	391	State (Federal Republic of Germany)...E	Hannover (Hanover)	German
Luxembourg†	998	365,000	366	Grand Duchy...A	Luxembourg	Luxembourgeois, French
Macao	6	284,000	47,333	Overseas Province (Portugal)...C	Macao	Chinese, Portuguese
Macías Nguema Biyogo (Fernando Poo)	785	82,000	104	Part of Equatorial Guinea...D	Malabo (Santa Isabel)	Bantu Languages, Spanish
Mackenzie	527,490	33,000	0.06	District of Northwest Territories, Canada...E	........; Yellowknife	English, Eskimo, Indian
Madagascar (Malagasy Republic)†	226,658	8,399,000	37	Republic...A	Antananarivo	French Malagasy
Madeira Is.	308	271,000	880	Part of Portugal (Funchal District)...D	Funchal	Portuguese
Maine	33,215	1,087,000	33	State (U.S.)...E	Augusta; Portland	
Malawi (Nyasaland)†	45,747	5,385,000	118	Republic (Br. Comm. of Nations)...A	Lilongwe; Blantyre	Bantu languages, English
Malaya	50,700	10,805,000	213	Part of Malaysia	Kuala Lumpur	Malay, Chinese, English
Malaysia†	128,430	12,845,000	100	Self-Governing Member (Br. Comm. of Nations)...A	Kuala Lumpur	Malay, Chinese, English
Maldives†	115	141,000	1,226	Republic...A	Male	Arabic, English
Mali†	478,655	6,050,000	13	Republic...A	Bamako	Native languages, French, Arabic
Malta†	122	275,000	2,254	Republic (Br. Comm. of Nations)...A	Valletta	English, Maltese
Manitoba	251,000	1,050,000	4.2	Province (Canada)...E	Winnipeg	English
Mariana Is. (excl. Guam)	184	16,000	87	District of U.S. Pacific Is. Trust Ter...D	Saipan	Malay-Polynesian languages, English
Maritime Provinces (excl. Newfoundland)	51,963	1,668,000	32	Canada	........; Halifax	English
Marshall Is.	70	28,000	400	District of U.S. Pacific Is. Trust Ter...D	Majuro	Malay-Polynesian languages, English
Martinique	425	378,000	889	Overseas Department (France)...C	Fort-de-France	French
Maryland	10,577	4,190,000	396	State (U.S.)...E	Annapolis; Baltimore	
Massachusetts	8,257	5,833,000	706	State (U.S.)...E	Boston	
Mauritania†	397,950	1,484,000	3.7	Republic...A	Nouakchott	Arabic, French
Mauritius (incl. Dependencies)†	789	901,000	1,142	Self-Governing Member (Br. Comm. of Nations)...A	Port Louis	Indo-Aryan languages, French, Creole, English
Mayotte	144	43,000	299	Overseas Territory (France)...C	Dzaoudzi	Malagasy, French
Mexico†	761,604	65,555,000	86	Federal Republic...A	Mexico City	Spanish
Michigan	58,216	9,122,000	157	State (U.S.)...E	Lansing; Detroit	
Middle America	1,055,708	113,947,000	108		........; Mexico City	
Midway Is.	2	2,000	1,000	Possession (U.S.)...C		English
Minnesota	84,068	4,027,000	48	State (U.S.)...E	St. Paul; Minneapolis	
Mississippi	47,716	2,379,000	50	State (U.S.)...E	Jackson	
Missouri	69,686	4,801,000	69	State (U.S.)...E	Jefferson City; St. Louis	
Moldavia (S.S.R.)	13,000	3,902,000	300	Soviet Socialist Republic (Sov. Un.)...E	Kishinëv	Moldavian, Russian, Ukrainian
Monaco	0.6	26,000	43,333	Principality...A	Monaco	French, Italian
Mongolia†	604,200	1,552,000	2.6	People's Republic...A	Ulan Bator	Mongolian
Montana	147,138	764,000	5.2	State (U.S.)...E	Helena; Billings	
Montserrat	39	13,700	351	Colony (U.K.)...C	Plymouth	English
Morocco†	172,415	18,575,000	108	Monarchy...A	Rabat; Casablanca	Arabic, Berber, French
Mozambique†	303,771	9,745,000	32	Republic...A	Maputo	Bantu Languages, Portuguese
Namibia (excl. Walvis Bay)	317,827	910,000	2.9	Mandate (South Africa)**...C	Windhoek	Bantu languages, Afrikaans, English, German
Nauru	8	7,300	913	Republic (Br. Comm. of Nations)...A		Malay-Polynesian languages, Chinese, English
Nebraska	77,227	1,565,000	20	State (U.S.)...E	Lincoln; Omaha	
Nepal†	54,362	13,280,000	244	Monarchy...A	Kātmāndu	Nepali, Tibeto-Burman languages, English
Netherlands†	15,770	13,945,000	884	Monarchy...A	Amsterdam and The Hague ('s Gravenhage); Amsterdam	Dutch
Netherlands and Possessions	16,141	14,187,000	879		Amsterdam and The Hague; Amsterdam	
Netherlands Antilles	371	242,000	652	Self-Governing Territory (Netherlands)...C	Willemstad	Dutch, Spanish, English, Papiamento
Netherlands Guiana, see Surinam						
Nevada	110,540	637,000	5.8	State (U.S.)...E	Carson City; Las Vegas	
New Brunswick	28,354	696,000	25	Province (Canada)...E	Fredericton; Saint John	English, French
New Caledonia (incl. Deps.)	7,358	141,000	19	Overseas Territory (France)...C	Nouméa	Malay-Polynesian languages, French
New England	66,608	12,306,000	185	United States	........; Boston	English
Newfoundland	156,185	573,000	3.7	Province (Canada)...E	St. John's	English
Newfoundland (excl. Labrador)	43,359	539,000	12		........; St. John's	English
New Hampshire	9,304	838,000	90	State (U.S.)...E	Concord; Manchester	
New Hebrides	5,700	100,000	18	Condominium (France-U.K.)...C	Vila	Malay-Polynesian languages, French, English
New Jersey	7,836	7,359,000	939	State (U.S.)...E	Trenton; Newark	
New Mexico	121,666	1,202,000	9.9	State (U.S.)...E	Santa Fe; Albuquerque	English, Spanish
New South Wales	309,433	4,886,000	16	State (Australia)...E	Sydney	English
New York	49,576	18,102,000	365	State (U.S.)...E	Albany; New York	
New Zealand†	103,736	3,245,000	31	Monarchy (Br. Commonwealth of Nations)...A	Wellington; Auckland	English
Nicaragua†	50,200	2,347,000	47	Republic...A	Managua	Spanish
Niedersachsen, see Lower Saxony						
Niger†	489,200	4,925,000	10	Republic...A	Niamey	Hausa, Arabic, French

† Member of the United Nations (1978). *‡ Includes 487 sq. miles of demilitarized zone, not included in North or South Korea figures.*
‡‡ Areas for Egypt, Israel, Jordan, and Syria do not reflect de facto changes which took place during 1967.

Region or Political Division	Area in sq. miles	Estimated Population 1/1/1978	Pop. per sq. mi.	Form of Government and Ruling Power	Capital; Largest City (unless same)	Predominant Languages
Nigeria†	356,669	66,190,000	186	Republic (Br. Commonwealth of Nations)............A	Lagos	Hausa, Ibo, Yoruba, English
Niue	100	3,000	30	Island Territory (New Zealand)....................C	Alofi	Malay-Polynesian languages, English
Norfolk Island	14	2,000	143	External Territory (Australia)...................C	Kingston	English
North America	9,420,000	355,200,000	38		.........; New York	
North Borneo, see Sabah	....	....	......			
North Carolina	52,586	5,539,000	105	State (U.S.)......................................E	Raleigh; Charlotte	
North Dakota	70,665	651,000	9.2	State (U.S.)......................................E	Bismarck; Fargo	
Northern Ireland	5,452	1,537,000	282	Administrative division of United Kingdom........E	Belfast	English
Northern Rhodesia, see Zambia						
Northern Territory	520,280	100,000	0.2	Territory (Australia)............................E	Darwin	English, Aboriginal languages
North Polar Regions						
North Rhine-Westphalia (Nordrhein-Westfalen)	13,144	16,977,000	1,292	State (Federal Republic of Germany)..............E	Düsseldorf; Cologne	German
Northwest Territories	1,304,903	44,000	0.03	Territory (Canada)...............................E	Yellowknife	English, Eskimo, Indian
Norway†	125,050	4,060,000	32	Monarchy...A	Oslo	Norwegian (Riksmål and Landsmål)
Nova Scotia	21,425	851,000	40	Province (Canada)................................E	Halifax	English
Nyasaland, see Malawi						
Oceania (incl. Australia)	3,295,000	21,900,000	6.6		.........; Sydney	
Ohio	41,222	10,669,000	259	State (U.S.)......................................E	Columbus; Cleveland	
Oklahoma	69,919	2,823,000	40	State (U.S.)......................................E	Oklahoma City	
Oman†	82,030	824,000	10	Sultanate..A	Muscat; Maṭraḥ	Arabic
Ontario	412,582	8,492,000	21	Province (Canada)................................E	Toronto	English
Oregon	96,981	2,373,000	24	State (U.S.)......................................E	Salem; Portland	
Orkney Is.	376	18,000	48	Part of Scotland, U.K. (Orkney County)...........D	Kirkwall	English
Pacific Islands Trust Territory	717	129,000	180	Trust Territory (U.S.)...........................C	Saipan	Malay-Polynesian languages, English
Pakistan (incl. part of Kashmir)†	345,753	77,040,000	223	Federal Republic.................................A	Islamabad; Karachi	Urdu, English
Pakistan, East, see Bangladesh						
Panama†	29,209	1,795,000	61	Republic...A	Panamá	Spanish
Papua New Guinea†	178,260	2,950,000	17	Republic...A	Port Moresby	Papuan and Negrito languages, English
Paraguay†	157,048	2,839,000	18	Republic...A	Asunción	Spanish, Guaraní
Pennsylvania	45,333	11,897,000	262	State (U.S.)......................................E	Harrisburg; Philadelphia	
Persia, see Iran						
Peru†	496,224	16,795,000	34	Republic...A	Lima	Spanish, Quechua
Philippines†	115,831	44,505,000	384	Republic...A	Manila	Tagalog and other Malay-Polynesian languages, English
Pitcairn (excl. Dependencies)	2	70	35	Colony (U.K.)....................................C	Adamstown	English
Poland†	120,725	34,865,000	289	People's Republic................................A	Warsaw (Warszawa)	Polish
Portugal†	35,553	9,660,000	272	Republic...A	Lisbon (Lisboa)	Portuguese
Portugal and Possessions	35,559	9,944,000	280		Lisbon (Lisboa)	
Portuguese Guinea, see Guinea-Bissau	....	....	......			
Prairie Provinces	757,985	3,886,000	5.1	Canada	.........; Winnipeg	English
Prince Edward Island	2,184	121,000	55	Province (Canada)................................E	Charlottetown	English
Puerto Rico	3,435	3,345,000	974	Commonwealth (U.S.)..............................C	San Juan	Spanish, English
Qatar†	8,500	100,000	12	Sheikdom...A	Doha	Arabic
Quebec	594,860	6,406,000	11	Province (Canada)................................E	Québec; Montréal	French, English
Queensland	667,000	2,084,000	3.1	State (Australia)................................E	Brisbane	English
Reunion	969	525,000	542	Overseas Department (France).....................C	St. Denis	French
Rhineland-Palatinate (Rhineland-Pfalz)	7,657	3,628,000	474	State (Federal Republic of Germany)..............E	Mainz; Ludwigshafen am Rhein	German
Rhode Island	1,214	922,000	759	State (U.S.)......................................E	Providence	
Rhodesia	150,804	6,860,000	45	Self-Governing Colony (U.K.)*....................B	Salisbury	Bantu languages, English
Rio Muni, see Equatorial Guinea	....	....	......			
Rodrigues	42	27,000	643	Dependency of Mauritius (U.K.)...................D	Port Mathurin	English, French
Romania†	91,699	21,760,000	237	People's Republic................................A	Bucharest (Bucureşti)	Romanian, Hungarian
Russian Soviet Federated Socialist Republic	6,592,850	137,053,000	21	Soviet Federated Socialist Republic (Sov. Un.)...E	Moscow (Moskva)	Russian, Finno-Ugric languages, various Turkic, Iranian, and Mongol languages
Russian S.F.S.R. in Europe	1,527,350	100,559,000	66	Soviet Union	.........; Moscow	Russian, Finno-Ugric languages
Rwanda†	10,169	4,421,000	435	Republic...A	Kigali	Bantu and Hamitic languages, French
Saar (Saarland)	992	1,081,000	1,090	State (Federal Republic of Germany)..............E	Saarbrücken	German
Sabah (North Borneo)	29,388	849,000	29	Administrative division of Malaysia..............E	Kota Kinabalu; Sandakan	Malay, Chinese, English
St. Helena (incl. Dependencies)	162	8,000	49	Colony (U.K.)....................................C	Jamestown	English
St. Kitts-Nevis	103	48,000	466	Associated State (U.K.)..........................B	Basseterre	English
St. Lucia	238	117,000	492	Associated State (U.K.)..........................B	Castries	English
St. Pierre & Miquelon	93	6,200	67	Overseas Territory (France)......................C	St. Pierre	French
St. Vincent	150	117,000	780	Associated State (U.K.)..........................B	Kingstown	English
Samoa (Entire)	1,173	203,000	173		.........; Apia	Malay-Polynesian languages, English
San Marino	24	21,000	875	Republic...A	San Marino	Italian
Sao Tome & Principe†	372	83,000	223	Republic...A	São Tomé	Bantu languages, Portuguese
Sarawak	48,342	1,191,000	25	Administrative division of Malaysia..............E	Kuching	Malay; Chinese, English
Sardinia	9,301	1,571,000	169	Part of Italy (3 Provinces)......................D	.........; Cagliari	Italian
Saskatchewan	251,700	947,000	3.8	Province (Canada)................................E	Regina	English
Saudi Arabia†	830,000	9,645,000	12	Monarchy...A	Riyadh	Arabic
Scandinavia (incl. Finland and Iceland)	509,899	22,450,000	44		.........; Copenhagen (København)	Swedish, Danish, Norwegian, Finnish, Icelandic
Schleswig-Holstein	6,046	2,541,000	420	State (Federal Republic of Germany)..............E	Kiel	German
Scotland	30,414	5,202,000	171	Administrative division of United Kingdom........E	Edinburgh; Glasgow	English, Gaelic
Senegal†	75,955	5,295,000	70	Republic...A	Dakar	Wolof, Poular French
Seychelles†	156	61,000	391	Republic...A	Victoria	French, Creole, English
Shetland Is.	550	19,000	35	Part of Scotland, U.K. (Zetland County)..........D	Lerwick	English
Siam, see Thailand						
Sicily	9,926	4,917,000	495	Part of Italy (Sicilia Autonomous Region)........D	Palermo	Italian
Sierra Leone†	27,699	3,252,000	117	Republic (Br. Commonwealth of Nations)...........A	Freetown	Temne, Mende, English
Singapore†	224	2,320,000	10,357	Republic (Br. Comm. of Nations)..................A	Singapore	Chinese, Malay, English
Solomon Is.	11,500	215,000	19	Protectorate (U.K.)..............................C	Honiara	Malay-Polynesian languages, English
Somalia†	246,201	3,391,000	14	Republic...A	Mogadiscio	Somali
South Africa (incl. Walvis Bay)†	471,879	27,061,000	57	Federal Republic.................................A	Pretoria and Cape Town; Johannesburg	English, Afrikaans, Bantu languages

† *Member of the United Nations (1978).* * *Rhodesia unilaterally declared its independence from the United Kingdom on November 11, 1965.*

Region or Political Division	Area in sq. miles	Estimated Population 1/1/1978	Pop. per sq. mi.	Form of Government and Ruling Power	Capital; Largest City (unless same)	Predominant Languages
South America	6,870,000	226,000,000	33		........; Sao Paulo	
South Australia	380,070	1,273,000	3.3	State (Australia) ....E	Adelaide	English
South Carolina	31,055	2,901,000	93	State (U.S.) ....E	Columbia	
South Dakota	77,047	688,000	8.9	State (U.S.) ....E	Pierre; Sioux Falls	
Southern Rhodesia, see Rhodesia	....	....	......			
South Georgia	1,450	20	0.01	Dependency of Falkland Is. (U.K.) ....D	Grytviken	English, Norwegian
South Polar Regions						
South West Africa, see Namibia						
Soviet Union (Union of Soviet Socialist Republics)†	8,600,350	260,110,000	30	Federal Soviet Republic ....A	Moscow (Moskva)	Russian and other Slavic languages, various Finno-Ugric, Turkic, and Mongol languages, Caucasian languages, Persian
Soviet Union in Europe	1,920,750	171,360,000	89	Soviet Union	........; Moscow (Moskva)	Russian and other Slavic languages, various Finno-Ugric and Caucasian languages
Spain†	194,885	36,530,000	187	Monarchy ....A	Madrid	Spanish, Catalan, Galician, Basque
Spain and Possessions	194,897	36,646,000	188		Madrid	
Spanish Possessions in North Africa	12	116,000	9,667	Five Possessions (no central government) (Spain) C	........; Melilla	Spanish, Arabic, Berber
Spanish Sahara, see Western Sahara	....	....	......			
Spitsbergen, see Svalbard	....	....	......			
Sri Lanka (Ceylon)†	25,332	14,085,000	556	Republic (Br. Comm. of Nations) ....A	Colombo	Sinhalese, Tamil, English
Sudan†	967,500	16,726,000	17	Republic ....A	Khartoum	Arabic, native languages, English
Sumatra (Sumatera)	182,860	24,112,000	132	Part of Indonesia (6 Provinces) ....D	........; Medan	Bahasa Indonesia, English, Chinese
Surinam (Neth. Guiana)†	63,037	454,000	7.2	Republic ....A	Paramaribo	Dutch, Indo-Aryan languages
Svalbard (Spitsbergen)	24,102	Winter pop. 3,000		Dependency (Norway) C	Longyearbyen	Norwegian, Russian
Swaziland†	6,705	515,000	77	Monarchy (Br. Comm. of Nations) ....A	Mbabane	Swazi and other Bantu languages, English
Sweden†	173,649	8,265,000	48	Monarchy ....A	Stockholm	Swedish
Switzerland	15,941	6,270,000	393	Federal Republic ....A	Bern (Berne); Zürich	German, French, Italian
Syria†	71,498	7,968,000	111	Republic ....A	Damascus (Dimashq)	Arabic
Tadzhik S.S.R.	‡‡55,250	3,538,000	64	Soviet Socialist Republic (Sov. Un.) ....E	Dushanbe	Tadzhik, Turkic languages, Russian
Taiwan (Formosa) (Nationalist China)	13,885	16,770,000	1,208	Republic ....A	T'aipei	Chinese
Tanganyika, see Tanzania	....	....	......			
Tanzania (Tanganyika & Zanzibar)†	364,900	16,154,000	44	Republic (Br. Comm. of Nations) ....A	Dar es Salaam	Swahili and other Bantu languages, English, Arabic
Tasmania	26,383	412,000	16	State (Australia) ....E	Hobart	English
Tennessee	42,244	4,276,000	101	State (U.S.) ....E	Nashville; Memphis	
Texas	267,339	12,835,000	48	State (U.S.) ....E	Austin; Houston	
Thailand (Siam)†	198,500	44,600,000	225	Monarchy ....A	Bangkok (Krung Thep)	Thai, Chinese
Tibet	471,700	1,710,000	3.6	Autonomous Region (China) ....E	Lasa (Lhasa)	Tibetan
Togo†	21,600	2,366,000	110	Republic ....A	Lomé	Native languages, French
Tokelau (Union) Is.	4	1,600	400	Island Territory (New Zealand) C	........; Fakaofo	Malay-Polynesian languages, English
Tonga	270	92,000	341	Monarchy (Br. Comm. of Nations) ....A	Nukualofa	Malay-Polynesian languages, English
Transcaucasia	71,850	13,733,000	191	Soviet Union	........; Tbilisi	
Trinidad & Tobago†	1,980	1,118,000	565	Self-Governing Member (Br. Comm. of Nations) ......A	Port-of-Spain	English, Spanish
Tristan da Cunha	40	300	7.5	Dependency of St. Helena (U.K.) ....D	Edinburgh	English
Trucial States, see United Arab Emirates	....	....	......			
Tunisia†	63,379	5,875,000	93	Republic ....A	Tunis	Arabic, French
Turkey†	301,382	41,605,000	138	Republic ....A	Ankara; İstanbul	Turkish
Turkey in Europe	9,121	3,591,000	394	Turkey	........; İstanbul	Turkish
Turkmen S.S.R.	188,450	2,627,000	14	Soviet Socialist Republic (Sov. Un.) ....E	Ashkhabad	Turkic languages, Russian
Turks & Caicos Is.	166	5,000	30	Colony (U.K.) C	Grand Turk	English
Tuvalu (Ellice Is.)	9.5	7,000	737	Colony (U.K.) C	Funafuti	Malay-Polynesian languages, English
Uganda†	91,076	12,521,000	137	Republic (Br. Comm. of Nations) ....A	Kampala	Bantu languages, English
Ukraine (S.S.R.)†	233,100	49,941,000	214	Soviet Socialist Republic (Sov. Un.) ....E	Kiev	Ukrainian, Russian
Union of Soviet Socialist Republics, see Soviet Union	....	....	......			
United Arab Emirates†	32,300	239,000	7.4	Self-Governing Union ....A	Abū Zaby	Arabic
United Arab Republic, see Egypt	....	....	......			
United Kingdom of Great Britain & Northern Ireland†	94,214	55,890,000	593	Monarchy (Br. Commonwealth of Nations) ....A	London	English, Welsh, Gaelic
United Kingdom & Possessions	282,477	68,688,000	243		London	
United States†	*3,675,545	217,513,000	59	Federal Republic ....A	Washington; New York	English
United States and Possessions	3,680,713	221,262,000	60		Washington; New York	English, Spanish
Upper Volta†	105,800	6,376,000	60	Republic ....A	Ouagadougou	Voltaic and Mande languages, French
Uruguay†	68,536	2,826,000	41	Republic ....A	Montevideo	Spanish
Utah	84,916	1,264,000	15	State (U.S.) ....E	Salt Lake City	
Uzbek S.S.R.	173,600	14,332,000	83	Soviet Socialist Republic (Sov. Un.) ....E	Tashkent	Turkic languages, Sart, Russian
Vatican City (Holy See)	0.2	1,000	5,000	Ecclesiastical State ....A	Vatican City	Italian, Latin
Venezuela†	352,144	13,047,000	37	Federal Republic ....A	Caracas	Spanish
Vermont	9,609	483,000	50	State (U.S.) ....E	Montpelier; Burlington	
Victoria	87,884	3,730,000	42	State (Australia) ....E	Melbourne	English
Vietnam†	128,402	48,475,000	378	People's Republic ....A	Hanoi; Ho Chi Minh City (Saigon)	Vietnamese
Virginia	40,817	5,114,000	125	State (U.S.) ....E	Richmond; Norfolk	
Virgin Is., British	59	10,000	169	Colony (U.K.) C	Road Town	English
Virgin Is. of the U.S.	133	102,000	767	Unincorporated Territory (U.S.) C	Charlotte Amalie	English
Wake I.	3	1,000	333	Possession (U.S.) C		English
Wales (incl. Monmouthshire)	8,016	2,765,000	345	United Kingdom	Cardiff	English, Welsh
Wallis & Futuna	98	9,500	97	Overseas Territory (France) C	Mata-Utu	Malay-Polynesian languages, French
Washington	68,192	3,697,000	54	State (U.S.) ....E	Olympia; Seattle	
Western Australia	975,920	1,171,000	1.2	State (Australia) ....E	Perth	English
Western Sahara	102,700	139,000	1.4	Administered by Morocco and Mauritania C	El Aaiún	Arabic
Western Samoa†	1,097	170,000	155	Constitutional Monarchy (Br. Comm. of Nations) ......A	Apia	Malay-Polynesian languages, English
West Indies	92,041	28,220,000	307		........; Havana	
West Virginia	24,181	1,846,000	76	State (U.S.) ....E	Charleston; Huntington	
White Russia, see Byelorussia	....	....	......			
Wisconsin	56,154	4,617,000	82	State (U.S.) ....E	Madison; Milwaukee	
World	57,280,000	4,119,000,000	72		........; Tōkyō	
Wyoming	97,914	407,000	4.2	State (U.S.) ....E	Cheyenne	
Yemen†	75,300	5,690,000	76	Republic ....A	San'a'	Arabic
Yemen, People's Democratic Republic of,†	111,075	1,825,000	16	People's Republic ....A	Aden	Arabic; English
Yugoslavia†	98,766	21,875,000	221	Socialist Federal Republic ....A	Belgrade (Beograd)	Serbo-Croatian, Slovenian, Macedonian
Yukon	207,076	22,000	0.11	Territory (Canada) ....E	Whitehorse	English, Eskimo, Indian
Zaire (Congo The)†	905,567	26,705,000	29	Republic ....A	Kinshasa	Bantu languages, French
Zambia (Northern Rhodesia)†	290,586	5,406,000	19	Republic (Br. Comm. of Nations) ....A	Lusaka	Bantu languages, English
Zanzibar	950	413,000	435	Part of Tanzania ....D	........; Zanzibar	Arabic, English

† *Member of the United Nations (1978).* * *Total area of the United States includes 3,536,855 square miles of land, 78,268 square miles of inland water; and 60,422 square miles of Great Lakes area, not included any State.*

‡ *For 1970 census populations of the United States and each State, see table of Geographical Facts about the United States.*

‡‡ *Areas for Egypt, Israel, Jordan and Syria do not reflect de facto changes which took place during 1967.*

World Facts and Comparisons

MOVEMENTS OF THE EARTH

The earth makes one complete revolution around the sun every 365 days, 5 hours, 48 minutes, and 46 seconds.

The earth makes one complete rotation on its axis in 23 hours and 56 minutes.

The earth revolves in its orbit around the sun at a speed of 66,700 miles per hour.

The earth rotates on its axis at an equatorial speed of more than 1,000 miles per hour.

MEASUREMENTS OF THE EARTH

Estimated age of the earth, at least 3 billion years.
Equatorial diameter of the earth, 7,926.68 miles.
Polar diameter of the earth, 7,899.99 miles.
Mean diameter of the earth, 7,918.78 miles.
Equatorial circumference of the earth, 24,902.45 miles.
Polar circumference of the earth, 24,818.60 miles.
Difference between equatorial and polar circumference of the earth, 83.85 miles.

Weight of the earth, 6,600,000,000,000,000,000,000 tons, or 6,600 billion billion tons.

Total area of the earth, 196,940,400 square miles.

Total land area of the earth (including inland water and Antarctica), 57,280,000 square miles.

THE EARTH'S INHABITANTS

Total population of the earth is estimated to be 4,119,000,000 (January 1, 1978).

Estimated population density of the earth, 72 per square mile.

THE EARTH'S SURFACE

Highest point on the earth's surface, Mount Everest, China (Tibet)–Nepal, 29,028 feet.

Lowest point on the earth's land surface, shores of the Dead Sea, Israel-Jordan, 1,299 feet below sea level.

Greatest ocean depth, the Marianas Trench, south of Guam, Pacific Ocean, 36,198 feet.

EXTREMES OF TEMPERATURE AND RAINFALL OF THE EARTH

Highest temperature ever recorded, 136.4°F. at Al 'Azīzīyah, Libya, Africa, on September 13, 1922.

Lowest temperature ever recorded, −126.9°F. at Vostok, Antarctica, on August 24, 1960.

Highest mean annual temperature, 88°F. at Lugh Ferrandi, Somalia.

Lowest mean annual temperature, −67°F. at Vostok, Antarctica.

At Cilaos, Réunion Island, in the Indian Ocean, 74 inches of rainfall was reported in a 24-hour period, March 15-16, 1952. This is believed to be the world's record for a 24-hour rainfall.

An authenticated rainfall of 366 inches in 1 month—July, 1861—was reported at Cherrapunji, India. More than 131 inches fell in a period of 7 consecutive days in June, 1931. Average annual rainfall at Cherrapunji is 450 inches.

The Continents

CONTINENT	Area (sq. mi.)	Population Estimated Jan. 1, 1978	Population per sq. mi.	Mean Elevation (feet)	Highest Elevation (Feet)	Lowest Elevation (Feet)	Highest Recorded Temperature	Lowest Recorded Temperature
North America	9,420,000	355,200,000	38	2,000	Mt. McKinley, United States (Alaska), 20,320	Death Valley, California, 282 below sea level	Death Valley, California, 134°F.	Snag, Yukon, Canada, −81°F.
South America	6,870,000	226,000,000	33	1,800	Mt. Aconcagua, Argentina, 22,831	Salinas Chicas, Argentina, 138 below sea level	Rivadavia, Argentina, 120°F.	Sarmiento, Argentina, −27.4°F.
Europe	3,825,000	654,000,000	171	980	Mt. Elbrus, Soviet Union, 18,481	Caspian Sea, Soviet Union—Iran, 92 below sea level	Sevilla (Seville), Spain, 122°F.	Ust-Shchugor, Soviet Union, −67°F.
Asia	17,085,000	2,432,000,000	142	3,000	Mt. Everest, China (Tibet)-Nepal, 29,028	Dead Sea, Israel-Jordan, 1,299 below sea level	Tirat Zvi, Israel, 129.2°F.	Oymyakon, Soviet Union, −89.9°F.
Africa	11,685,000	429,400,000	37	1,900	Mt. Kilimanjaro, Tanzania, 19,340	Lac Assal, Afars and Issas, 509 below sea level	Al 'Azīzīyah, Libya, 136.4°F.	Ifrane, Morocco, −11.2°F.
Oceania, incl. Australia	3,295,000	21,900,000	7	.....	Mt. Wilhelm, Papua New Guinea, 14,793	Lake Eyre, South Australia, 52 below sea level	Cloncurry, Queensland, Australia, 127.5°F.	Charlotte Pass, New South Wales, Australia, −8°F.
Australia	2,967,909	13,858,000	5	1,000	Mt. Kosciusko, New South Wales, 7,310	Lake Eyre, South Australia, 52 below sea level	Cloncurry, Queensland, 127.5°F.	Charlotte Pass, New South Wales, −8°F.
Antarctica	5,100,000	Uninhabited	...	6,000	Vinson Massif, 16,864	Unknown	Esperanza (Antarctic Peninsula), 58.3°F.	Vostok, −126.9°F.
World	57,280,000	4,119,000,000	72	.....	Mt. Everest, China (Tibet)-Nepal, 29,028	Dead Sea, Israel-Jordan, 1,299 below sea level	Al 'Azīzīyah, Libya, 136.4°F.	Vostok, −126.9°F.

Approximate Population of the World 1650-1978 *

AREA	1650	1750	1800	1850	1900	1914	1920	1939	1950	1978
North America	*5,000,000*	*5,000,000*	*13,000,000*	*39,000,000*	106,000,000	141,000,000	147,000,000	186,000,000	219,000,000	355,200,000
South America	*8,000,000*	*7,000,000*	*12,000,000*	*20,000,000*	38,000,000	55,000,000	90,000,000	90,000,000	111,000,000	226,000,000
Europe	*100,000,000*	*140,000,000*	*190,000,000*	*265,000,000*	400,000,000	470,000,000	453,000,000	526,000,000	530,000,000	654,000,000
Asia	*335,000,000*	*476,000,000*	*593,000,000*	*754,000,000*	932,000,000	1,006,000,000	1,000,000,000	1,247,000,000	1,418,000,000	2,432,000,000
Africa	*100,000,000*	*95,000,000*	*90,000,000*	*95,000,000*	118,000,000	130,000,000	140,000,000	170,000,000	199,000,000	429,400,000
Oceania, incl. Australia	} *2,000,000*	*2,000,000*	*2,000,000*	*2,000,000*	{ 6,000,000	8,000,000	9,000,000	11,000,000	13,000,000	21,900,000
Australia					4,000,000	5,000,000	6,000,000	7,000,000	8,000,000	13,858,000
World	*550,000,000*	*725,000,000*	*900,000,000*	*1,175,000,000*	1,600,000,000	1,810,000,000	1,810,000,000	2,230,000,000	2,490,000,000	4,119,000,000

* Figures prior to 1978 are rounded to the nearest million. Figures in italics represent very rough estimates.

Largest Countries of the World in Population

	Population 1/1/1978
1 China (excl. Taiwan)	855,546,000
2 India (incl. part of Kashmir)	627,990,000
3 Soviet Union	260,110,000
4 United States	217,513,000
5 Indonesia	138,180,000
6 Japan	114,650,000
7 Brazil	113,815,000
8 Bangladesh	84,605,000
9 Pakistan (incl. part of Kashmir)	77,040,000

	Population 1/1/1978
10 Nigeria	66,190,000
11 Mexico	65,555,000
12 Germany, Federal Republic of (incl. West Berlin)	61,070,000
13 Italy	56,710,000
14 United Kingdom (Great Britain)	55,890,000
15 France	53,208,000
16 Vietnam	48,475,000

	Population 1/1/1978
17 Thailand	44,600,000
18 Philippines	44,505,000
19 Turkey	41,605,000
20 Egypt (United Arab Republic)	39,320,000
21 Korea, South	36,735,000
22 Spain	36,530,000
23 Poland	34,865,000
24 Iran	34,160,000
25 Burma	31,815,000

Largest Countries of the World in Area

	Area (sq. mi.)
1 Soviet Union	8,600,350
2 Canada	3,851,809
3 China (excl. Taiwan)	3,691,500
4 United States	3,675,545
5 Brazil	3,286,487
6 Australia	2,967,909
7 India (incl. part of Kashmir)	1,229,210
8 Argentina	1,072,162

	Area (sq. mi.)
9 Sudan	967,500
10 Algeria	919,595
11 Zaire (The Congo)	905,567
12 Greenland (Den.)	840,000
13 Saudi Arabia	830,000
14 Mexico	761,604
15 Indonesia	741,034
16 Libya	679,362
17 Iran	636,300

	Area (sq. mi.)
18 Mongolia	604,200
19 Peru	496,224
20 Chad	495,800
21 Niger	489,200
22 Angola	481,353
23 Mali	478,655
24 South Africa (incl. Walvis Bay)	471,879
25 Ethiopia	471,778

Principal Mountains of the World

North America

Height (Feet)

McKinley, △Alaska (△United States;
  △North America)............20,320
Logan, △Canada (△St. Elias Mts.)..........19,850
Citlaltépetl (Orizaba), △Mexico..........18,701
St. Elias, Alaska–Canada..........18,008
Popocatépetl, Mexico..........17,887
Foraker, Alaska..........17,400
Ixtacihuatl, Mexico..........17,343
Lucania, Yukon, Canada..........17,147
Whitney, △California..........14,494
Elbert, △Colorado (△Rocky Mts.)..........14,443
Massive, Colorado..........14,421
Harvard, Colorado..........14,420
Rainier, △Washington (△Cascade Range)..........14,410
Williamson, California..........14,375
Blanca Pk., Colorado
  (△Sangre de Cristo Range)..........14,345
Uncompahgre Pk., Colorado
  (△San Juan Mts.)..........14,309
Grays Pk., Colorado (△Front Range)..........14,270
Evans, Colorado..........14,264
Longs Pk., Colorado..........14,255
Wrangell, Alaska..........14,163
Shasta, California..........14,162
Pikes Peak, Colorado..........14,110
Colima, Nevado de, Mexico..........13,993
Tajumulco, △Guatemala (△Central America)..........13,846
Gannett Pk., △Wyoming..........13,804
Mauna Kea, △Hawaii (△Hawaii I.)..........13,796
Grand Teton, Wyoming..........13,766
Mauna Loa, Hawaii..........13,680
Kings Pk., △Utah..........13,528
Cloud Pk., Wyoming (△Big Horn Mts.)..........13,175
Wheeler Pk., △New Mexico..........13,161
Boundary Pk., △Nevada..........13,143
Gunnbjörn, △Greenland..........13,120
Waddington, Canada (△Coast Mts.)..........13,104
Robson, Canada (△Canadian Rockies)..........12,972
Granite Pk., △Montana..........12,799
Borah Pk., △Idaho..........12,662
Humphreys Pk., △Arizona..........12,633
Chirripó Grande, △Costa Rica..........12,533
Adams, Washington..........12,307
San Gorgonio, California..........11,502
Chiriquí, △Panama..........11,411
Hood, △Oregon..........11,235
Lassen Pk., California..........10,457
Duarte, Pico, △Dominican Rep. (△West Indies)..........10,417
Haleakala, Hawaii (△Maui)..........10,023
Parícutin, Mexico..........9,213
La Selle, Pic, △Haiti..........8,773
Guadalupe Pk., △Texas..........8,751
Olympus, Washington (△Olympic Mts.)..........7,965
Monte Cristo, △El Salvador–Guatemala–
  Honduras..........7,936
Blue Mountain Pk., △Jamaica..........7,402
Harney Pk., △South Dakota (△Black Hills)..........7,242
Mitchell, △North Carolina (△Appalachian Mts.)..6,684
Clingmans Dome, North Carolina–
  △Tennessee (△Great Smoky Mts.)..........6,643
Turquino, Pico, △Cuba..........6,542
Washington, △New Hampshire (△White Mts.)..........6,288
Rogers, △Virginia..........5,729
Marcy, △New York (△Adirondack Mts.)..........5,344
Katahdin, △Maine..........5,268
Kawaikini, Hawaii (△Kauai)..........5,243
Spruce Knob, △West Virginia..........4,862
Pelée, △Martinique..........4,583
Mansfield, △Vermont (△Green Mts.)..........4,393
Punta, Cerro de, △Puerto Rico..........4,389
Black Mtn., △Kentucky..........4,145
Kaala Pk., Hawaii (△Oahu)..........4,050

South America

Aconcagua, △Argentina (△Andes Mts.;
  △South America)..........22,831
Ojos del Salado, Argentina–△Chile..........22,516
Tupungato, Argentina–Chile..........22,310
Pissis, Argentina..........22,241
Mercedario, Argentina..........22,211
Huascarán, △Peru..........22,205
Llullaillaco, Argentina–Chile..........22,057
Yerupaja, Peru..........21,765
Incahuasi, Argentina–Chile..........21,719
Sajama, Nevado, △Bolivia..........21,391
Illimani, Bolivia..........21,201
Chimborazo, △Ecuador..........20,561
Cotopaxi, Ecuador..........19,347
Misti, Peru..........19,098
Cristóbal Colón, △Colombia..........19,029

Huila, Colombia (△Cordillera Central)..........18,865
Bolívar (La Columna), △Venezuela..........16,411
Fitz Roy, Argentina..........11,073
Neblina, Pico da, △Brazil..........9,888

Europe

Height (Feet)

Elbrus, Soviet Union (△Caucasus Mts.;
  △Europe)..........18,481
Dykh-Tau, Soviet Union..........17,070
Shkhara, Soviet Union..........16,594
Kazbek, Soviet Union..........16,512
Blanc, Mont, △France–△Italy (△Alps)..........15,771
Rosa, Monte (Dufourspitze) △Switzerland..........15,200
Weisshorn, Switzerland..........14,803
Matterhorn, Italy–Switzerland..........14,685
Finsteraarhorn, Switzerland..........14,026
Jungfrau, Switzerland..........13,668
Grossglockner, △Austria..........12,457
Teide, Pico de, △Spain (△Canary Is.)..........12,162
Mulhacén, △Spain (continental)..........11,424
Aneto, Pico de, Spain (△Pyrenees)..........11,168
Etna, Italy (△Sicily)..........11,122
Perdido (Perdu), Spain..........11,007
Clapier, France–Italy (△Maritime Alps)..........9,993
Zugspitze, Austria–△Germany, Fed. Rep. of..........9,721
Coma Pedrosa, Andorra..........9,665
Musala, △Bulgaria..........9,592
Corno, Italy (△Apennines)..........9,560
Olympus, △Greece..........9,550
Triglav, △Yugoslavia..........9,393
Korab, △Albania–Yugoslavia..........9,068
Ginto, France (△Corsica)..........8,891
Gerlachovka, △Czechoslovakia
  (△Carpathian Mts.)..........8,737
Moldoveanu, △Romania..........8,343
Rysy, Czechoslovakia–△Poland..........8,199
Glittertinden, △Norway (△Scandinavia)..........8,110
Parnassós, Greece..........8,061
Idhi (Ida), Greece (△Crete)..........8,058
Pico, △Portugal (△Azores Is.)..........7,713
Hvannadalshnúkur, △Iceland..........6,952
Kebnekaise, △Sweden..........6,926
Estrela, △Portugal (continental)..........6,539
Narodnaya, Soviet Union (△Ural Mts.)..........6,184
Marmora, Punta la, Italy (△Sardinia)..........6,017
Hekla, Iceland..........4,747
Nevis, Ben, △United Kingdom (△Scotland)..........4,406
Haltia, Finland–Norway..........4,357
Vesuvius, Italy..........3,842
Snowdon, △Wales..........3,560
Carrantuohill, △Ireland..........3,414
Kékes, △Hungary..........3,330
Scafell Pikes, △England..........3,210

Asia

Everest, △China (△Tibet)–△Nepal (△Himalaya
  Mts.; △Asia; △World)..........29,028
Godwin Austen (K²), China–△Pakistan
  (△Kashmir) (△Karakoram Range)..........28,250
Kanchenjunga, Nepal–△India..........28,208
Makalu, China (Tibet)–Nepal..........27,824
Dhaulagiri, Nepal..........26,810
Nanga Parbat, Pakistan (Kashmir)..........26,650
Annapurna, Nepal..........26,504
Gasherbrum, Pakistan (Kashmir)..........26,470
Gosainthan, China (Tibet)..........26,291
Nanda Devi, India..........25,645
Rakaposhi, Pakistan (Kashmir)..........25,550
Kamet, India..........25,447
Namcha Barwa, China (Tibet)..........25,443
Gurla Mandhata, China (Tibet)..........25,354
Ulugh Muztagh, China (△Kunlun Mts.)..........25,338
Tirich Mir, Pakistan (△Hindu Kush)..........25,230
Minya Konka, China..........24,902
Muztagh Ata, China..........24,787
Kula Kangri, △Bhutan..........24,784
Communism Pk., △Soviet Union
  (△Pamir-Alay Mts.)..........24,590
Pobeda Pk., China–Soviet Union (△Tien Shan)..24,406
Lenin Pk., Soviet Union..........23,406
Api, Nepal..........23,399
Khan-Tengri, Soviet Union..........22,949
Kailas, China (Tibet)..........22,031
Hkakabo Razi, △Burma–China..........19,296
Demavend, △Iran..........18,386
Ararat, △Turkey..........17,011
Djaja Pk., △Indonesia (△New Guinea)..........16,503
Klyuchevskaja Sopka, Soviet Union
  (△Kamchatka)..........15,584
Trikora Pk., Indonesia..........15,584

Belukha, Soviet Union..........14,783
Tabun Bogdo (Khuitun), China–△Mongolia–
  Soviet Union (△Altai Mts.)..........14,291
Turgun Uula, Mongolia..........14,052
Kinabalu, △Malaysia (△Borneo)..........13,455
Hsinkao, △Taiwan (Formosa)..........13,113
Erciyeş, Turkey..........12,848
Kerintji, Indonesia (△Sumatra)..........12,467
Fuji, △Japan (△Honshu)..........12,388
Hadūr Shu'ayb, △Yemen
  (△Arabian Peninsula)..........12,336
Rindjani, Indonesia (△Lombok)..........12,224
Semeru, Indonesia (△Java)..........12,060
Munku-Sardyk, Mongolia–Soviet Union
  (△Sayan Mts.)..........11,453
Rantekombola, Indonesia (△Celebes)..........11,335
Sa'uda, Qurnet es, △Lebanon..........10,131
Shām, Jabal ash, △Oman..........9,957
Apo, △Philippines (△Mindanao)..........9,692
Pulog, Philippines (△Luzon)..........9,626
Bia, Phou, △Laos..........9,242
Hermon, Lebanon–△Syria..........9,232
Paektu-san, China–△Korea..........9,003
Anai Mudi, △India (peninsular)..........8,841
Inthanon, Doi, △Thailand..........8,514
Pidurutalagala, △Sri Lanka..........8,281
Mayon, Philippines (Luzon)..........8,077
Asahi, Japan (△Hokkaido)..........7,513
Tahan, Gunong, Malaysia (△Malaya)..........7,174
Olimbos, △Cyprus..........6,401
Kuju-San, Japan (△Kyushu)..........5,866
Meron, △Israel..........3,963
Carmel, Israel..........1,791

Africa

Height (Feet)

Kilimanjaro (Kibo), △Tanzania
  (△Africa)..........19,340
Kenya, △Kenya..........17,058
Margherita Pk., △Zaire–△Uganda..........16,763
Ras Dashen, △Ethiopia..........15,158
Meru, Tanzania..........14,978
Elgon, Kenya–Uganda..........14,178
Toubkal, Jebel, △Morocco (△Atlas Mts.)..........13,665
Cameroun, △Cameroon..........13,353
Thabana Ntlenyana, △Lesotho..........11,425
Koussi, Emi, △Chad (△Tibesti Mts.)..........11,204
Injasuti, △South Africa..........11,182
Neiges, Piton des, △Reunion..........10,069
Santa Isabel, △Equatorial Guinea
  (△Macías Nguema Biyogo)..........9,868
Tahat, △Algeria (△Ahaggar Mts.)..........9,852
Maromokotro, △Madagascar..........9,436
Pico, △Cape Verde..........9,281
Katrīnah, Jabal, △Egypt..........8,668
São Tomé, Pico de, △Sao Tome..........6,640

Oceania

Wilhelm, △Papua New Guinea..........15,400
Giluwe, Papua New Guinea..........14,330
Bangeta, Papua New Guinea..........13,473
Victoria, Papua New Guinea
  (△Owen Stanley Range)..........13,363
Cook, △New Zealand (△South Island)..........12,349
Ruapehu, New Zealand (△North Island)..........9,175
Balbi, △Solomon Is. (△Bougainville)..........9,000
Egmont, New Zealand..........8,260
Sinewit, Papua New Guinea
  (△Bismarck Archipelago)..........8,000
Orohena, △Fr. Polynesia (△Tahiti)..........7,352
Kosciusko, △Australia (△New South Wales)..........7,314
Silisili, Mauga, △Western Samoa..........6,095
Panié, △New Caledonia..........5,341
Ossa, Australia (△Tasmania)..........5,305
Bartle Frere, Australia (△Queensland)..........5,287
Humboldt, New Caledonia..........5,282
Woodroffe, Australia (△South Australia)..........4,970
Tomaniivi (Victoria), △Fiji (△Viti Levu)..........4,341
Bruce, Australia (△Western Australia)..........4,024

Antarctica

Vinson Massif (△Antarctica)..........16,864
Kirkpatrick..........14,856
Markham..........14,272
Jackson..........13,747
Sidley..........13,717
Wade..........13,396

△*Highest mountain in state, country, range, or region named.*

Great Oceans and Seas of the World

OCEANS AND SEAS	Area (sq. mi.)	Average Depth (feet)	Greatest Depth (feet)	OCEANS AND SEAS	Area (sq. mi.)	Average Depth (feet)	Greatest Depth (feet)	OCEANS AND SEAS	Area (sq. mi.)	Average Depth (feet)	Greatest Depth (feet)
Pacific Ocean	63,855,000	14,050	36,201	Bering Sea	876,000	4,710	16,800	Hudson Bay	476,000	402	850
Atlantic Ocean	31,744,000	12,690	27,651	Caribbean Sea	750,000	7,310	24,580	Japan, Sea of	389,000	4,490	12,280
Indian Ocean	28,371,000	13,000	24,442	Gulf of Mexico	596,000	4,960	14,360	North Sea	222,000	310	2,170
Arctic Ocean	5,427,000	5,010	17,880	Okhotsk, Sea of	590,000	2,760	11,400	Black Sea	178,000	3,610	7,360
Mediterranean Sea	967,000	4,780	16,420	East China Sea	482,000	620	9,840	Red Sea	169,000	1,610	7,370
South China Sea	895,000	5,420	18,090	Yellow Sea	480,000	150	300	Baltic Sea	163,000	180	1,440

Principal Lakes of the World

LAKES	Area (sq. mi.)	LAKES	Area (sq. mi.)	LAKES	Area (sq. mi.)
Caspian, Soviet Union–Iran (salt)	152,084	Ontario, United States–Canada	7,540	Torrens, Australia (salt)	△2,200
Superior, United States–Canada	31,820	Ladoga, Soviet Union	7,092	Albert, Uganda–Zaire	2,162
Victoria, Kenya–Uganda–Tanzania	26,828	Balkhash, Soviet Union	6,678	Vänern, Sweden	2,156
Aral, Soviet Union (salt)	26,518	Chad, Chad–Nigeria–Cameroon	△6,300	Winnipegosis, Canada	2,103
Huron, United States–Canada	23,010	Onega, Soviet Union	3,821	Bangweulu, Zambia	△1,900
Michigan, United States	22,400	Eyre, Australia (salt)	△3,700	Nipigon, Canada	1,870
Great Bear, Canada	12,275	Titicaca, Peru–Bolivia	3,500	Manitoba, Canada	1,817
Baykal, Soviet Union	12,159	Athabasca, Canada	3,120	Great Salt, United States (salt)	1,700
Great Slave, Canada	10,980	Nicaragua, Nicaragua	2,972	Koko Nor (Ching Hai), China	1,650
Tanganyika, Zaire–Tanzania–Burundi–Zambia	10,965	Rudolf, Kenya–Ethiopia (salt)	2,473	Dubawnt, Canada	1,600
Nyasa, Malawi–Tanzania–Mozambique	10,900	Reindeer, Canada	2,467	Gairdner, Australia (salt)	△1,500
Erie, United States–Canada	9,940	Issyk-Kul, Soviet Union	2,393	Lake of the Woods, United States–Canada	1,485
Winnipeg, Canada	9,465	Urmia, Iran (salt)	△2,229	Van, Turkey (salt)	1,470

△ Due to seasonal fluctuations in water level, areas of these lakes vary considerably.

Principal Rivers of the World

River	Length (miles)	River	Length (miles)	River	Length (miles)
Nile, Africa	4,132	Amu Darya, Asia	1,628	Si, Asia	930
Amazon (Amazonas), South America	3,900	Kolyma, Asia	1,615	Oka, Europe	920
Mississippi–Missouri–Red Rock, North America	3,860	Murray, Australia	1,600	Canadian, North America	906
Ob-Irtysh, Asia	3,461	Ganges, Asia	1,550	Dnestr, Europe	876
Yangtze (Chang), Asia	3,430	Pilcomayo, South America	1,550	Brazos, North America	870
Huang Ho (Yellow), Asia	2,903	Angara, Asia	1,549	Salado, South America	870
Congo, Africa	2,900	Ural, Asia	1,522	Fraser, North America	850
Amur, Asia	2,802	Vilyuy, Asia	1,513	Parnaíba, South America	850
Irtysh, Asia	2,747	Arkansas, North America	1,450	Colorado, North America (Texas)	840
Lena, Asia	2,653	Colorado, North America (U.S.–Mexico)	1,450	Rhine, Europe	820
Mackenzie, North America	2,635	Irrawaddy, Asia	1,425	Narbada, Asia	800
Mekong, Asia	2,600	Dnepr, Europe	1,420	Athabasca, North America	765
Niger, Africa	2,590	Aldan, Asia	1,392	Donets, Europe	735
Yenisey, Asia	2,566	Negro, South America	1,305	Pecos, North America	735
Missouri, North America	2,466	Paraguay, South America	1,290	Green, North America	730
Paraná, South America	2,450	Kama, Europe	1,261	Elbe, Europe	720
Mississippi, North America	2,348	Juruá, South America	1,250	James, North America	710
Plata-Paraguay, South America	2,300	Xingú, South America	1,230	Ottawa, North America	696
Volga, Europe	2,293	Don, Europe	1,224	White, North America	690
Madeira, South America	2,060	Ucayali, South America	1,220	Cumberland, North America	687
Indus, Asia	1,980	Columbia, North America	1,214	Gambia, Africa	680
Purús, South America	1,900	Saskatchewan, North America	1,205	Yellowstone, North America	671
St. Lawrence, North America	1,900	Peace, North America	1,195	Tennessee, North America	652
Rio Grande, North America	1,885	Orange, Africa	1,155	Gila, North America	630
Brahmaputra (Yalutsangpu), Asia	1,800	Tigris, Asia	1,150	Vistula (Wisla), Europe	630
Orinoco, South America	1,800	Sungari, Asia	1,140	Loire, Europe	625
São Francisco, South America	1,800	Pechora, Europe	1,118	Tagus (Tajo) (Tejo), Europe	625
Yukon, North America	1,800	Tobol, Asia	1,093	North Platte, North America	618
Danube, Europe	1,770	Snake, North America	1,038	Albany, North America	610
Darling, Australia	1,750	Uruguay, South America	1,025	Tisza (Tisa), Europe	607
Salween, Asia	1,730	Red, North America	1,018	Back, North America	605
Euphrates (Firat), Asia	1,675	Churchill, North America	1,000	Ouachita, North America	605
Syr Darya, Asia	1,653	Marañón, South America	1,000	Cimarron, North America	600
Zambezi, Africa	1,650	Ohio, North America	981	Sava, Europe	585
Tocantins, South America	1,640	Magdalena, South America	950	Nemunas (Niemen), Europe	582
Araguaia, South America	1,630	Roosevelt (River of Doubt), South America	950	Branco, South America	580
		Godavari, Asia	930	Oder, Europe	565

Principal Islands of the World

Island	Area (sq. mi.)	Island	Area (sq. mi.)	Island	Area (sq. mi.)
Greenland, Arctic Region	840,000	Hispaniola, West Indies	29,530	Ceram, Indonesia	6,046
New Guinea, Oceania	316,856	Sakhalin, Soviet Union	29,344	New Caledonia, Oceania	5,671
Borneo, Indonesia	286,967	Tasmania, Australia	26,383	Flores, Indonesia	5,513
Madagascar, Indian Ocean	227,800	Ceylon, Indian Ocean	25,332	Samar, Philippines	5,124
Baffin, Canadian Arctic	183,810	Banks, Canadian Arctic	23,230	Negros, Philippines	4,903
Sumatra, Indonesia	182,860	Devon, Canadian Arctic	20,861	Palawan, Philippines	4,500
Honshū, Japan	88,930	Tierra del Fuego, Argentina-Chile	18,600	Panay, Philippines	4,448
Great Britain, North Atlantic Ocean	88,756	Kyūshū, Japan	16,215	Jamaica, West Indies	4,232
Ellesmere, Canadian Arctic	82,119	Melville, Canadian Arctic	16,141	Hawaii, West Indies	4,030
Victoria, Canadian Arctic	81,930	Southampton, Hudson Bay, Canada	15,700	Cape Breton, Canada	3,970
Celebes, Indonesia	72,986	West Spitsbergen, Arctic Region	15,260	Bougainville, Oceania	3,880
South Island, New Zealand	58,093	New Britain, Oceania	14,592	Mindoro, Philippines	3,794
Java, Indonesia	50,745	Formosa, China Sea	13,885	Cyprus, Mediterranean Sea	3,572
North Island, New Zealand	44,281	Hainan, South China Sea	13,127	Kodiak, Gulf of Alaska	3,569
Cuba, West Indies	44,218	Timor, Timor Sea	13,094	Puerto Rico, West Indies	3,435
Newfoundland, North Atlantic Ocean	43,359	Prince of Wales, Canadian Arctic	12,830	Corsica, Mediterranean Sea	3,352
Luzon, Philippines	40,814	Vancouver, Canada	12,408	Crete, Mediterranean Sea	3,217
Iceland, North Atlantic Ocean	39,800	Sicily, Mediterranean Sea	9,926	New Ireland, Oceania	3,205
Mindanao, Philippines	36,906	Somerset, Canadian Arctic	9,370	Leyte, Philippines	3,090
Ireland, North Atlantic Ocean	32,596	Sardinia, Mediterranean Sea	9,301	Wrangel, Soviet Arctic	2,819
Novaya Zemlya, Soviet Arctic	31,390	Shikoku, Japan	7,245	Guadalcanal, Oceania	2,500
Hokkaidō, Japan	29,950	North East Land, Svalbard Group	6,350	Long Island, United States	1,620

Largest Metropolitan Areas of the World, 1978

This table lists the major metropolitan areas of the world according to their estimated population on January 1, 1978. For convenience in reference, the areas are grouped by major region, and the number of areas in each region and size group is given.

There are 25 areas with more than 5,000,000 population each; these are listed in rank order of estimated population, with the world rank given in parentheses following the name. For example, New York's 1978 rank is second. Below the 5,000,000 level, the metropolitan areas are listed alphabetically within region, not in order of size.

For ease of comparison, each metropolitan area has been defined by Rand McNally & Company according to consistent rules. A metropolitan area includes a central city, neighboring communities linked to it by continuous built-up areas, and more distant communities if the bulk of their population is supported by commuters to the central city. Some metropolitan areas have more than one central city, for example Tōkyō–Yokohama or San Francisco–Oakland–San Jose.

POPULATION CLASSIFICATION	UNITED STATES and CANADA	LATIN AMERICA	EUROPE (excl. U.S.S.R.)	U.S.S.R.	ASIA	AFRICA–OCEANIA
Over 15,000,000 (3)	New York, U.S. (2)				Tōkyō–Yokohama, Jap. (1) Ōsaka–Kōbe–Kyōto, Jap. (3)	
10,000,000–15,000,000 (5)		Mexico City, Mex. (4) São Paulo, Braz. (7)	London, Eng. (5)	Moscow (6)	Calcutta, India (8)	
5,000,000–10,000,000 (17)	Los Angeles, U.S. (12) Chicago, U.S. (17) Philadelphia, U.S. (22)	Buenos Aires, Arg. (9) Rio de Janeiro, Braz. (13)	Paris, Fr. (11) Essen–Dortmund–Duisburg (The Ruhr), Ger., Fed. Rep. of (23)	Leningrad (24)	Seoul, Kor. (10) Bombay, India (15) Shanghai, China (16) Jakarta, Indon. (18) Manila, Phil. (19) Delhi, India (20) Peking, China (21) Tehrān, Iran (25)	Cairo, Eg. (14)
3,000,000–5,000,000 (27)	Boston, U.S. Detroit, U.S.–Windsor, Can. San Francisco–Oakland–San Jose, U.S. Washington, U.S.	Bogotá, Col. Caracas, Ven. Lima, Peru Santiago, Chile	Athens, Greece Barcelona, Sp. Berlin, Ger. İstanbul, Tur. Madrid, Sp. Milan, It. Rome, It.		Baghdād, Iraq Bangkok, Thai. Chungking, China Karāchi, Pak. Madras, India Mukden, China Nagoya, Jap. Taipei, Taiwan Tientsin, China Victoria, Hong Kong Wuhan, China	Sydney, Austl.
2,000,000–3,000,000 (45)	Cleveland, U.S. Dallas–Fort Worth, U.S. Houston, U.S. Miami–Fort Lauderdale, U.S. Montréal, Can. Pittsburgh, U.S. St. Louis, U.S. San Diego, U.S.–Tijuana, Mex. Toronto, Can.	Belo Horizonte, Braz. Guadalajara, Mex. Havana, Cuba Recife, Braz.	Birmingham, Eng. Brussels, Bel. Bucharest, Rom. Budapest, Hung. Hamburg, Ger., Fed. Rep. of Katowice–Bytom–Gliwice, Pol. Lisbon, Port. Manchester, Eng. Naples, It. Warsaw, Pol.	Donetsk–Makeyevka Kiev	Ahmādābād, India Bangalore, India Canton, China Dacca, Bngl. Harbin, China Ho Chi Minh City (Saigon), Viet. Hyderābād, India Lahore, Pak. Pusan, Korea Rangoon, Bur. Sian, China Singapore, Singapore Surabaya, Indon.	Alexandria, Eg. Algiers, Alg. Casablanca, Mor. Johannesburg, S. Afr. Kinshasa, Zaire Lagos, Nig. Melbourne, Austl.
1,500,000–2,000,000 (32)	Atlanta, U.S. Baltimore, U.S. Buffalo, U.S. Minneapolis–St. Paul, U.S. Seattle–Tacoma, U.S.	Medellín, Col. Monterrey, Mex. Pôrto Alegre, Braz. San Juan, P.R.	Amsterdam, Neth. Cologne, Ger., Fed. Rep. of Copenhagen, Den. Frankfurt am Main, Ger., Fed. Rep. of Glasgow, Scot. Leeds–Bradford, Eng. Liverpool, Eng. Munich, Ger., Fed. Rep. of Stuttgart, Ger., Fed. Rep. of Turin, It. Vienna, Aus.	Baku Gorki Kharkov Tashkent	Ankara, Tur. Chengtu, China Colombo, Sri Lanka Fukuoka, Jap. Kanpur, India Kitakyūshū–Shimonoseki, Jap. Nanking, China Taiyuan, China	
1,000,000–1,500,000 (81)	Cincinnati, U.S. Denver, U.S. El Paso, U.S.–Ciudad Juárez, Mex. Hartford, U.S. Indianapolis, U.S. Kansas City, U.S. Milwaukee, U.S. New Orleans, U.S. Phoenix, U.S. Portland, U.S. Vancouver, Can.	Cali, Col. Córdoba, Arg. Fortaleza, Braz. Guatemala, Guat. Guayaquil, Ec. Montevideo, Ur. Rosario, Arg. Salvador, Braz.	Antwerp, Bel. Belgrade, Yugo. Düsseldorf, Ger., Fed. Rep. of Hannover, Ger., Fed. Rep. of Lille, Fr. Łódź, Pol. Lyon, Fr. Mannheim, Ger., Fed. Rep. of Marseille, Fr. Newcastle–Sunderland, Eng. Nürnberg, Ger., Fed. Rep. of Porto, Port. Prague, Czech. Rotterdam, Neth. Sofia, Bul. Stockholm, Swe. Valencia, Sp.	Chelyabinsk Dnepropetrovsk Kazan Kuybyshev Minsk Novosibirsk Odessa Omsk Perm Rostov-na-Donu Saratov Sverdlovsk Tbilisi Volgograd Yerevan	Anshan, China Bandung, Indon. Beirut, Leb. Chengchou, China Chittagong, Bngl. Dairen, China Damascus, Syria Fushun, China Hanoi, Viet. Hiroshima–Kure, Jap. Hsinking, China İzmir, Tur. Kaohsiung, Taiwan Kunming, China Lanchou, China Lucknow, India Nāgpur, India Pune, India Pyŏngyang, Kor. Sapporo, Jap. Shihchiachuang, China Taegu, Kor. Tel Aviv–Yafo, Isr. Tsinan, China Tsingtao, China	Addis Ababa, Eth. Brisbane, Austl. Cape Town, S. Afr. Durban, S. Afr. Tunis, Tun.
Total by Region (210)	33	24	48	23	68	14

Principal World Cities and Populations

The populations for all United States cities are estimates for January 1, 1978. For other cities, the populations are recent census figures or official estimates. Metropolitan populations are given for as many cities as possible, and identified by a star symbol (★). Some metropolitan areas, such as Minneapolis-St. Paul, include more than one large city. In such cases, the entry for the first named city carries the entire metropolitan population, and other cities in the metropolitan area carry a reference to the first-named city with a star symbol.

Aachen, Ger., Fed. Rep. of (★540,000)....242,416
Abidjan, Ivory Coast....510,000
Accra, Ghana (★738,498)....633,880
Addis Ababa, Ethiopia....1,161,300
Adelaide, Australia (★900,379)....13,773
Aden, Yemen, People's Democratic Republic of....264,300
Agra, India (★634,622)....591,917
Ahmadabad, India (★1,960,000)....1,585,544
Akron, Ohio (★614,000)....242,600
Albany, New York (★736,400)....106,600
Aleppo (Halab), Syria....639,428
Alexandria (Al Iskandarīyah), Egypt (★2,425,000)....2,161,916
Algiers (Alger), Algeria (★1,800,000)....1,503,720
Allahabad, India (★513,036)....490,622
Alma-Ata, Soviet Union (★905,000)....871,000
'Ammān, Jordan....520,720
Amritsar, India (★458,029)....407,628
Amsterdam, Netherlands (★1,760,000)....740,650
Ankara (Angora), Turkey (★1,750,000)....1,698,542
Anshan, China....1,050,000
Antananarivo, Madagascar....366,530
Antwerp (Antwerpen), Belgium (★1,065,000)....206,786
Asunción, Paraguay (★540,000)....392,753
Athens (Athínai), Greece (★2,540,241)....867,023
Atlanta, Georgia (★1,760,000)....406,000
Auckland, New Zealand (★765,000)....150,708

Baghdād, Iraq (★2,183,800)....1,300,000
Baku, Soviet Union (★1,625,000)....963,000
Baltimore, Maryland (★1,895,000)....814,000
Bamako, Mali....237,000
Bandung, Indonesia (★1,250,000)....1,201,730
Bangalore, India (★1,750,000)....1,540,741
Bangkok (Krung Thep), Thailand (★3,375,000)....3,133,834
Bangui, Central African Empire....187,000
Barcelona, Spain (★3,455,000)....1,816,623
Barranquilla, Colombia (★730,000)....661,920
Basel (Bâle), Switzerland (★555,000)....188,800
Beirut (Bayrūt), Lebanon (★1,010,000)....474,870
Belém (Pará), Brazil (★660,000)....565,097
Belfast, Northern Ireland (★710,000)....363,000
Belgrade (Beograd), Yugoslavia (★1,150,000)....770,140
Belo Horizonte, Brazil (★1,945,000)....1,557,464
Bengasi (Banghāzī), Libya....170,000
Berlin, East, Ger. Dem. Rep. (★Berlin)....1,094,147
Berlin, West, Ger., Fed. Rep. of (★3,850,000)....2,023,987
Bern (Berne), Switzerland (★283,500)....146,800
Bilbao, Spain (★910,000)....431,347
Birmingham, Alabama (★695,000)....267,500
Birmingham, England (★2,680,000)....1,058,800
Bogotá, Colombia (★2,925,000)....2,855,065
Bologna, Italy (★560,000)....485,643
Bombay, India (★6,750,000)....5,970,575
Bonn, Ger., Fed. Rep. of (★535,000)....283,891
Bordeaux, France (★612,456)....223,131
Boston, Massachusetts (★3,825,000)....624,000
Brasília, Brazil (★750,000)....350,000
Brazzaville, Congo....175,000
Bremen, Ger., Fed. Rep. of (★805,000)....579,430
Brighton, England (★425,000)....156,500
Brisbane, Australia (★957,710)....725,000
Bristol, England (★640,000)....416,300
Brussels (Bruxelles), Belgium (★2,040,000)....152,850
Bucharest (Bucureşti), Romania (★2,000,000)....1,807,044
Budapest, Hungary (★2,535,000)....2,083,000
Buenos Aires, Argentina (★8,625,000)....2,972,453
Buffalo, New York (★1,532,000)....387,000
Bujumbura, Burundi....78,810

Cairo (Al Qāhirah), Egypt (★8,000,133)....5,084,463
Calcutta, India (★9,100,000)....3,148,746
Cali, Colombia....923,446
Canberra, Australia (★215,414)....193,000
Canton (Kuangchou), China....2,250,000
Cape Town (Kaapstad), South Africa (★1,125,000)....697,514
Caracas, Venezuela (★2,475,000)....1,658,500
Cardiff, Wales (★625,000)....281,500
Casablanca, Morocco (★1,575,000)....1,506,373
Changchiakou (Kalgan), China....350,000
Changchun (Hsinking), China....1,200,000
Changsha, China....750,000
Chelyabinsk, Soviet Union (★1,195,000)....1,007,000
Chengchou, China....900,000
Chengtu, China....1,450,000
Chicago, Illinois (★7,635,000)....2,980,000
Chichihaerh (Tsitsibar), China....825,000
Chilin (Kirin), China....583,000
Chittagong, Bangladesh (★1,050,000)....416,733
Chungking (Chungching), China....2,600,000
Cincinnati, Ohio (★1,425,000)....390,000
Cleveland, Ohio (★2,255,000)....595,000
Cologne (Köln), Ger., Fed. Rep. of (★1,700,000)....1,022,075
Colombo, Sri Lanka (★1,475,000)....618,000
Columbus, Ohio (★922,000)....527,000
Conakry, Guinea....197,267
Copenhagen (København), Denmark (★1,505,000)....545,350
Córdoba, Argentina (★825,000)....798,663
Coventry, England (★650,000)....336,800

Dacca, Bangladesh (★2,400,000)....1,310,976
Dakar, Senegal (★735,000)....667,000
Dallas, Texas (★2,495,000)....800,000
Damascus (Dimashq), Syria (★1,100,000)....836,668
Dar es Salaam, Tanzania....343,900
Dayton, Ohio (★905,000)....187,400
Delhi, India (★4,500,000)....3,706,558
Denver, Colorado (★1,305,000)....473,900
Detroit, Michigan (★4,410,000)....1,245,000
Dnepropetrovsk, Soviet Union (★1,410,000)....995,000
Donetsk (Stalino), Soviet Union (★2,025,000)....984,000
Dortmund, Ger., Fed. Rep. of (★Essen)....636,954
Dresden, Ger. Dem. Rep. (★640,000)....507,692
Dublin (Baile Átha Cliath), Ireland (★835,000)....567,866
Durban, South Africa (★1,040,000)....736,852
Düsseldorf, Ger., Fed. Rep. of (★1,150,000)....675,437

Edinburg, Scotland (★650,000)....467,097
Edmonton, Canada (★554,228)....461,361
El Paso, Texas (★1,020,000)....402,000
Essen, Ger., Fed. Rep. of (★5,350,000)....684,147

Florence (Firenze), Italy (★660,000)....464,792
Fortaleza, Brazil (★1,175,000)....1,109,837
Fort Worth Texas (★Dallas)....340,000
Frankfurt [am Main], Ger., Fed. Rep. of (★1,825,000)....652,037
Freetown, Sierra Leone (★335,000)....274,000
Fuchou (Foochow), China....700,000
Fukuoka, Japan (★1,445,000)....1,021,623
Fushun, China....1,350,000

Gdańsk (Danzig), Poland (★775,000)....421,000
Genève (Geneva), Switzerland (★400,000)....152,600
Genoa (Genova), Italy (★870,000)....800,532
Gent (Ghent), Belgium (★335,000)....248,671
Georgetown, Guyana (★164,039)....63,184
Glasgow, Scotland (★1,890,000)....856,012
Gorki (Gorkiy), Soviet Union (★1,835,000)....1,319,000
Göteborg, Sweden (★665,000)....444,651
Guadalajara, Mexico (★1,900,000)....1,478,400
Guatemala, Guatemala (★945,000)....717,322
Guayaquil, Ecuador....814,064

Halle [an der Saale], Ger. Dem. Rep. (★475,000)....241,425
Hamburg, Ger., Fed. Rep. of (★2,250,000)....1,733,802
Hamilton, Canada (★529,371)....312,003
Hangchou, China....875,000
Hannover (Hanover), Ger., Fed. Rep. of (★980,000)....562,951
Hanoi, Vietnam (★643,576)....414,620
Harbin (Haerhpin), China....2,100,000
Hartford, Connecticut (★1,071,000)....130,100
Havana (La Habana), Cuba (★1,800,000)....1,755,400
Helsinki, Finland (★863,000)....502,961
Hiroshima, Japan (★1,425,000)....863,273
Ho Chi Minh City (Saigon), Vietnam (★2,750,000)....1,804,900
Honolulu, Hawaii (★728,000)....328,000
Houston, Texas (★2,345,000)....1,460,000
Howrah, India (★Calcutta)....737,877
Hsüchou (Süchow), China....825,000
Hyderabad, India (★2,000,000)....1,607,396
Hyderabad, Pakistan (★660,000)....600,000

Ibadan, Nigeria....758,000
Inchŏn, Korea (South)....799,982
Indianapolis, Indiana (★1,078,000)....711,000
Irkutsk, Soviet Union....532,000
İstanbul, Turkey (★3,675,000)....2,534,839
Ivanovo, Soviet Union....458,000
İzmir (Smyrna), Turkey (★945,000)....636,078

Jabalpur (Jubbulpore), India (★534,845)....426,224
Jacksonville, Florida (★619,000)....547,000
Jaipur, India....615,258
Jakarta (Djakarta), Indonesia (★4,650,000)....4,576,009
Jamshedpur, India (★456,146)....341,576
Jerusalem, Israel (★375,000)....355,500
Johannesburg, South Africa (★2,550,000)....654,232
Juddah, Saudi Arabia....561,104

Kabul, Afghanistan (★498,800)....318,094
Kampala, Uganda....330,700
Kanpur, India (★1,320,000)....1,154,388
Kansas City, Missouri (★1,235,000)....454,000
Karachi, Pakistan (★3,498,634)....2,850,000
Karaganda, Soviet Union....576,000
Karl-Marx-Stadt (Chemnitz), Ger. Dem. Rep. (★460,000)....303,811
Katmandu, Nepal (★215,000)....150,402
Katowice, Poland (★2,450,000)....343,700
Kaunas, Soviet Union....352,000
Kawasaki, Japan (★Tōkyō)....1,025,455
Kazan, Soviet Union (★1,015,000)....970,000
Khabarovsk, Soviet Union....524,000
Kharkov, Soviet Union (★1,680,000)....1,405,000
Khartoum, Sudan (★790,000)....333,921
Kiev (Kiyev), Soviet Union (★2,290,000)....2,079,000
Kigali, Rwanda....59,100
Kingston, Jamaica....603,717
Kinshasa, Zaire....2,008,000
Kitakyūshū, Japan (★1,510,000)....1,063,990
Kōbe, Japan (★Ōsaka)....1,363,992
Kowloon, Hong Kong (★Victoria)....715,440
Kraków (Cracow), Poland....684,600
Krasnoyarsk, Soviet Union....769,000
Krivoy Rog, Soviet Union....641,000
Kuala Lumpur, Malaysia (★750,000)....451,728
Kueiyang, China....530,000
Kunming, China....1,100,000
Kuwait, Kuwait (★780,000)....78,116
Kuybyshev, Soviet Union (★1,420,000)....1,204,000
Kyōto, Japan (★Ōsaka)....1,461,567

Lagos, Nigeria (★1,250,000)....901,000
Lahore, Pakistan (★2,200,000)....2,050,000
Lanchou, China....875,000
La Paz Bolivia....654,713
La Plata, Argentina (★510,000)....408,300
Leeds, England (★1,555,000)....744,500
Le Havre, France (★264,422)....217,881
Leicester, England (★495,000)....289,400
Leipzig, Ger. Dem. Rep. (★725,000)....570,972
Leningrad, Soviet Union (★5,150,000)....3,961,000
Libreville, Gabon....73,000
Liège, Belgium (★545,000)....221,404
Lille, France (★1,015,000)....172,280
Lima, Peru (★3,350,000)....340,339
Lisbon (Lisboa), Portugal (★1,950,000)....829,900
Liverpool, England (★1,575,000)....539,700
Łodź, Poland (★980,000)....798,300
Lomé, Togo....144,300
London, England (★11,175,000)....7,028,200
Los Angeles, California (★9,200,000)....2,765,000
Louisville, Kentucky (★867,000)....319,800
Loyang, China....500,000
Luanda, Angola....475,328
Lubumbashi, Zaire....404,000
Lucknow, India (★840,000)....749,239
Lusaka, Zambia....483,000
Lüta (Dairen), China (★1,200,000)....1,150,000
Luxembourg, Luxembourg (★104,000)....78,300
Lvov, Soviet Union....642,000
Lyon (Lyons), France (★1,170,660)....456,716

Macao, Macao (★248,636)....241,413
Madras, India (★3,200,000)....2,469,449
Madrid, Spain (★3,860,000)....3,274,043
Madurai, India (★725,000)....549,114
Magdeburg, Ger. Dem. Rep. (★390,000)....276,089
Managua, Nicaragua....375,278
Manchester, England (★2,835,000)....490,000
Manila, Philippines (★5,375,000)....1,438,300
Mannheim, Ger., Fed. Rep. of (★1,390,000)....320,508
Maputo (Lourenço Marques), Mozambique....341,922
Maracaibo, Venezuela....651,574
Marseille (Marseilles), France (★1,070,912)....908,600
Mecca (Makkah), Saudi Arabia....366,801
Medan, Indonesia....635,562
Medellín, Colombia (★1,500,000)....1,100,082
Melbourne, Australia (★2,603,578)....65,065
Memphis, Tennessee (★825,000)....655,000
Mexico City, Mexico (★11,250,000)....8,299,200
Miami, Florida (★2,420,000)....348,000
Middlesbrough (Teesside), England (★580,000)....153,900
Milan (Milano), Italy (★3,780,000)....1,705,086
Milwaukee, Wisconsin (★1,382,000)....641,000
Minneapolis, Minnesota (★1,950,000)....359,000
Minsk, Soviet Union (★1,250,000)....1,215,000
Mogadisho, Somalia....230,000
Monrovia, Liberia....100,000
Monterrey, Mexico (★1,550,000)....1,006,200
Montevideo, Uruguay (★1,350,000)....1,229,748
Montréal, Canada (★2,802,485)....1,080,546
Moscow (Moskva), Soviet Union (★10,925,000)....7,644,000
Munich (München), Ger., Fed. Rep. of (★1,850,000)....1,323,434

Nagasaki, Japan....449,371
Nagoya, Japan (★3,565,000)....2,080,050
Nagpur, India (★950,000)....866,076
Nairobi, Kenya....630,000
Nanchang, China....520,000
Nanking (Nanching), China....1,750,000
Naples (Napoli), Italy (★2,030,000)....1,223,927
Nashville, Tennessee (★560,000)....459,000
Ndjamena (Fort Lamy), Chad....179,000
Newark, New Jersey (★New York)....324,000
Newcastle-on-Tyne, England (★1,325,000)....295,800
New Delhi, India (★Delhi)....301,801
New Orleans, Louisiana (★1,125,000)....560,000
New York, New York (★17,040,000)....7,420,000
Niamey, Niger....130,300
Nice, France (★437,566)....344,481
Norfolk, Virginia (★764,000)....266,400
Nottingham, England (★655,000)....280,300
Novokuznetsk, Soviet Union....537,000
Novosibirsk, Soviet Union (★1,435,000)....1,304,000
Nürnberg (Nuremberg), Ger., Fed. Rep. of (★1,035,000)....509,813

Oakland, California (★San Francisco)....326,000
Odessa, Soviet Union (★1,100,000)....1,039,000
Oklahoma City, Oklahoma (★691,000)....371,000
Omaha, Nebraska (★576,000)....382,900
Omsk, Soviet Union....1,026,000
Oran (Ouahran), Algeria....485,139
Ōsaka, Japan (★14,800,000)....2,750,418
Oslo, Norway (★725,000)....461,881
Ostrava, Czechoslovakia (★710,000)....300,945
Ottawa, Canada (★693,288)....304,462
Ouagadougou, Upper Volta....172,661

Palembang, Indonesia....582,961
Palermo, Italy....673,163
Panamá, Panama (★500,000)....371,070
Paris, France (★9,150,000)....2,299,830
Patna, India (★625,000)....473,001
Peking (Peiping), China (7,570,000▲)....★4,800,000
Perm, Soviet Union (★1,045,000)....972,000
Perth, Australia (★805,489)....87,576
Philadelphia, Pennsylvania (★5,320,000)....1,805,000
Phnom Penh, Cambodia....393,995
Phoenix, Arizona (★1,270,000)....669,000
Pinang (George Town), Malaysia (★450,000)....270,019
Pittsburgh, Pennsylvania (★2,190,000)....430,000
Port-au-Prince, Haiti (★493,932)....458,675
Portland, Oregon (★1,109,000)....348,000
Porto (Oporto), Portugal (★1,150,000)....335,700
Pôrto Alegre, Brazil (★1,760,000)....1,043,964
Port of Spain, Trinidad & Tobago (★350,000)....60,450
Porto Novo, Benin....104,000
Port Said (Būr Sa'īd), Egypt....262,620
Portsmouth, England (★500,000)....198,500
Poznań, Poland (★585,000)....516,000
Prague (Praha), Czechoslovakia (★1,250,000)....1,169,567
Pretoria, South Africa (★575,000)....545,450
Providence, Rhode Island (★871,000)....158,600
Pune (Poona), India (★1,175,000)....856,105
Pusan, Korea (South)....2,454,051
Pyŏngyang, Korea (North)....840,000

Québec, Canada (★542,158)....177,082
Quezon City, Philippines (★Manila)....994,700
Quito, Ecuador....597,133

Rabat, Morocco (★540,000)....367,620
Rangoon, Burma....2,055,365
Rawalpindi, Pakistan (★725,000)....375,000
Recife (Pernambuco), Brazil (★2,100,000)....1,249,821
Reykjavik, Iceland (★117,761)....84,493
Richmond, Virginia (★540,000)....222,600
Riga, Soviet Union (★895,000)....816,000
Rio de Janeiro, Brazil (★8,235,000)....4,857,716
Riyadh (Ar Riyāḍ), Saudi Arabia....666,840
Rochester, New York (★808,500)....285,100
Rome (Roma), Italy (★3,150,000)....2,883,996
Rosario, Argentina (★875,000)....750,455
Rostov-na-Donu, Soviet Union (★1,065,000)....921,000
Rotterdam, Netherlands (★1,090,000)....600,978

Sacramento, California (★783,000)....261,500
St. Louis, Missouri (★2,250,000)....495,000
St. Paul, Minnesota (★Minneapolis)....271,000
St. Petersburg, Florida (★649,000)....238,200
Salisbury, Rhodesia (★569,000)....107,600
Salt Lake City, Utah (★594,500)....164,500
Salvador, Brazil (★1,270,000)....1,237,373
Şan'ā', Yemen....135,000
San Antonio, Texas (★960,000)....804,000
San Bernardino, California (★665,000)....104,400
San Diego, California (★2,100,000)....820,000
San Francisco, California (★4,500,000)....658,000
San Jose, California (★San Francisco)....590,100
San José, Costa Rica (★493,300)....228,300
San Juan, Puerto Rico (★1,185,000)....452,749
San Salvador, El Salvador (★655,000)....366,000
Santiago, Chile (★2,925,000)....517,473
Santo Domingo, Dominican Republic....673,470
Santos, Brazil (★610,000)....341,317
São Paulo, Brazil (★9,900,000)....7,198,608
Sapporo, Japan (★1,315,000)....1,276,547
Saratov, Soviet Union (★1,075,000)....856,000
Seattle, Washington (★1,855,000)....481,000
Sendai, Japan (★815,000)....615,473
Seoul, Korea (South) (★8,625,000)....6,889,470
Sevilla (Seville), Spain (★680,000)....589,721
Shanghai, China (10,820,000▲)....★7,900,000
Sheffield, England (★725,000)....558,000
Shenyang (Mukden), China....3,000,000
Shihchiachuang, China....750,000
Shizuoka, Japan (★730,000)....450,322
Sian (Hsian), China....1,750,000
Singapore, Singapore (★2,225,000)....2,074,507
Sofia (Sofiya), Bulgaria (★1,060,000)....937,100
Southampton, England (★400,000)....213,700
Springfield, Massachusetts (★504,000)....188,000
Srinagar, India (★415,271)....403,413
Stockholm, Sweden (★1,357,558)....665,202
Stoke-on-Trent, England (★445,000)....256,200
Strasbourg, France (★390,000)....253,384
Stuttgart, Ger., Fed. Rep. of (★1,875,000)....613,263
Suchou (Soochow), China....725,000
Sucre, Bolivia....63,259
Surabaya, Indonesia (★1,650,000)....1,556,255
Sverdlovsk, Soviet Union (★1,400,000)....1,187,000
Sydney, Australia (★3,021,299)....52,152
Syracuse, New York (★559,000)....177,000
Szczecin (Stettin), Poland....369,700

Taegu, Korea (South)....1,311,078
Taipei, Taiwan (★3,175,000)....2,043,300
Taiyüan (Yangkü), China....1,350,000
Tallinn, Soviet Union....415,000
Tampa, Florida (★541,000)....278,000
Tanger (Tangier), Morocco....187,894
Tangshan, China....900,000
Tashkent, Soviet Union (★1,880,000)....1,689,000
Tbilisi, Soviet Union (★1,205,000)....1,042,000
Tegucigalpa, Honduras....273,894
Tehrān, Iran (★4,350,000)....3,774,000
Tel Aviv-Yafo, Israel (★1,260,000)....353,800
The Hague ('s Gravenhage), Netherlands (★800,000)....471,137
Thessaloníki (Salonika), Greece (★557,360)....345,799
Tientsin (Tienching), China (4,280,000▲)....★3,800,000
Tiranë, Albania....174,800
Tōkyō, Japan (★24,700,000)....8,590,142
Toledo, Ohio (★573,000)....366,000
Toronto, Canada (★2,803,101)....633,318
Toulouse, France (★509,939)....373,796
Tripoli (Tarābulus), Libya....264,000
Tsinan (Chinan), China....1,100,000
Tsingtao (Chingtao), China....1,350,000
Tula, Soviet Union (★605,000)....510,000
Tunis, Tunisia (★950,000)....550,404
Turin (Torino), Italy (★1,675,000)....1,190,621

Ufa, Soviet Union....942,000
Ulan Bator, Mongolia....267,400
Utrecht, Netherlands (★465,000)....245,269

Valencia, Spain (★1,040,000)....707,915
Valletta, Malta (★202,000)....15,200
Valparaíso, Chile (★530,000)....250,358
Vancouver, Canada (★1,166,348)....410,188
Varanasi (Benares), India (★606,271)....583,856
Venice (Venezia), Italy (★445,000)....362,494
Victoria, Hong Kong (★3,575,000)....521,612
Vienna (Wien), Austria (★1,940,000)....1,614,841
Vientiane, Laos....174,229
Vladivostok, Soviet Union....536,000
Volgograd (Stalingrad), Soviet Union (★1,205,000)....931,000
Voronezh, Soviet Union....779,000

Warsaw (Warszawa), Poland (★1,950,000)....1,436,100
Washington, D.C. (★3,200,000)....689,000
Wellington, New Zealand (★349,628)....139,566
Wiesbaden, Ger., Fed. Rep. of (★750,000)....252,017
Winnipeg, Canada (★578,217)....560,874
Wrocław (Breslau), Poland....575,900
Wuhan, China....2,900,000
Wuhsi (Wusih), China....650,000
Wuppertal, Ger., Fed. Rep. of (★920,000)....412,403

Yaoundé, Cameroon....165,800
Yaroslavl, Soviet Union....584,000
Yerevan, Soviet Union (★1,065,000)....956,000
Yokohama, Japan (★Tōkyō)....2,658,545
Youngstown, Ohio (★496,000)....118,600

Zagreb, Yugoslavia....566,084
Zaporozhye, Soviet Union....772,000
Zürich, Switzerland (★775,000)....383,000

★ *Population of metropolitan area, including suburbs. See headnote.*
▲ *Population of entire municipality or district, including rural area. Starred population in these entries refers to urban portion of municipality only.*

Geographical Facts about the United States

ELEVATION

The highest elevation in the United States is Mount McKinley, Alaska, 20,320 feet.

The lowest elevation in the United States is in Death Valley, California, 282 feet below sea level.

The average elevation of the United States is 2,500 feet.

EXTREMITIES

Direction	Location	Latitude	Longitude
North	Point Barrow, Alaska	71°23′N.	156°29′W.
South	South Cape, Hawaii	18°56′N.	155°41′W.
East	West Quoddy Head, Maine	44°49′N.	66°57′W.
West	Cape Wrangell, Alaska	52°55′N.	172°27′E.

The two places in the United States separated by the greatest distance are Kure Island, Hawaii, and Mangrove Point, Florida. These points are 5,848 miles apart.

LENGTH OF BOUNDARIES

The total length of the Canadian boundary of the United States is 5,525 miles.

The total length of the Mexican boundary of the United States is 1,933 miles.

The total length of the Atlantic coastline of the United States is 2,069 miles.

The total length of the Pacific and Arctic coastline of the United States is 8,683 miles.

The total length of the Gulf of Mexico coastline of the United States is 1,631 miles.

The total length of all coastlines and land boundaries of the United States is 19,841 miles.

The total length of the tidal shoreline and land boundaries of the United States is 96,091 miles.

GEOGRAPHIC CENTERS

The geographic center of the United States (including Alaska and Hawaii) is in Butte County, South Dakota at 44°58′N., 103°46′W.

The geographic center of North America is in North Dakota, a few miles west of Devils Lake, at 48°10′N., 100°10′W.

EXTREMES OF TEMPERATURE

The highest temperature ever recorded in the United States was 134°F., at Greenland Ranch, Death Valley, California, on July 10, 1913.

The lowest temperature ever recorded in the United States w —76°F., at Tanana, Alaska, in January, 1886.

PRECIPITATION

The average annual precipitation for the United States approximately 29 inches.

Hawaii is the wettest state, with an average annual rainfall 82.48 inches. Nevada, with an average annual rainfall 8.81 inches, is the driest state.

The greatest local average annual rainfall in the United Sta is at Mt. Waialeale, Kauai, Hawaii, 460 inches.

Greatest 24-hour rainfall in the United States, 23.22 inches New Smyrna, Florida, October 10–11, 1924.

Extreme minimum rainfall records in the United States inclu a total fall of only 3.93 inches at Bagdad, California, for period of 5 years, 1909–13, and an annual average of 1. inches at Death Valley, California.

Heavy snowfall records include 76 inches at Silver Lak Colorado, in 1 day; 42 inches at Angola, New York, in days; 87 inches at Giant Forest, California, in 3 days; a 108 inches at Tahoe, California, in 4 days.

Greatest seasonal snowfall, 1,000.3 inches, more than 83 feet, Paradise Ranger Station, Washington, during the winter 1955–56.

Historical Facts about the United States

TERRITORIAL ACQUISITIONS

Accession	Date	Area (sq. mi.)	Cost in Dollars
Original territory of the Thirteen States	1790	888,685	....
Purchase of Louisiana Territory, from France	1803	827,192	$11,250,000.00
By treaty with Spain: Florida	1819	58,560	$ 5,000,000.00
Other areas	1819	13,443	
Annexation of Texas	1845	390,144	....
Oregon Territory, by treaty with Great Britain	1846	285,580	....
Mexican Cession	1848	529,017	$15,000,000.00
Gadsden Purchase, from Mexico	1853	29,640	$10,000,000.00
Purchase of Alaska, from Russia	1867	586,412	7,200,000.00
Annexation of Hawaiian Islands	1898	6,450	....
Puerto Rico, by treaty with Spain	1899	3,435	....
Guam, by treaty with Spain	1899	212	....
American Samoa, by treaty with Great Britain and Germany	1900	76	....
Panama Canal Zone, by treaty with Panama	1904	553	*$10,000,000.00
Virgin Islands, by purchase from Denmark	1917	133	$25,000,000.00
Total		3,619,532	$83,450,000.00

Note: The Philippines, ceded by Spain in 1898 for $20,000,000.00, were a territorial possession of the United States from 1898 to 1946. On July 4, 1946 they became the independent republic of the Philippines.

* $25,000,000.00 was also paid to the republic of Colombia, out of whose territory the republic of Panama was created. In addition, an annual payment of $1,930,000 is made to the republic of Panama.

WESTWARD MOVEMENT OF CENTER OF POPULATION

Year	U.S. Population Total at Census	Approximate Location
1790	3,929,214	23 miles east of Baltimore, Md.
1800	5,308,483	18 miles west of Baltimore, Md.
1810	7,239,881	40 miles northwest of Washington, D.C.
1820	9,638,453	16 miles east of Moorefield, W. Va.
1830	12,866,020	19 miles southwest of Moorefield, W. Va.
1840	17,069,453	16 miles south of Clarksburg, W. Va.
1850	23,191,876	23 miles southeast of Parkersburg, W. Va.
1860	31,443,321	20 miles southeast of Chillicothe, Ohio
1870	39,818,449	48 miles northeast of Cincinnati, Ohio
1880	50,155,783	8 miles southwest of Cincinnati, Ohio
1890	62,947,714	20 miles east of Columbus, Ind.
1900	75,994,575	6 miles southeast of Columbus, Ind.
1910	91,972,266	Bloomington, Ind.
1920	105,710,620	8 miles southeast of Spencer, Ind.
1930	122,775,046	3 miles northeast of Linton, Ind.
1940	131,669,275	2 miles southeast of Carlisle, Ind.
1950	150,697,361	8 miles northwest of Olney, Ill.
1960	179,323,175	6 miles northwest of Centralia, Ill.
1970	204,816,296	5 miles southeast of Mascoutah, Ill.

State Areas and Populations

STATE	Land Area (square miles)	Water Area (square miles)	Total Area (square miles)	Rank in Area	Apportionment Population in 1970‡	Resident Population in 1970	Population Per Square Mile in 1970	Population in 1960	Population in 1950	Rank in Population in 1970	Rank in Population in 1960	Rank in Population in 1950
Alabama	50,851	758	51,609	29	3,475,885	3,444,165	67	3,266,740	3,061,743	21	19	17
Alaska	566,432	19,980	586,412	1	304,067	302,173	0.5	226,167	128,643	50	50	50
Arizona	113,563	346	113,909	6	1,787,620	1,772,482	16	1,302,161	749,587	33	35	37
Arkansas	52,175	929	53,104	27	1,942,303	1,923,295	36	1,786,272	1,909,511	32	31	30
California	156,537	2,156	158,693	3	20,098,863	19,953,134	126	15,717,204	10,586,223	1	2	2
Colorado	103,794	453	104,247	8	2,226,771	2,207,259	21	1,753,947	1,325,089	30	33	34
Connecticut	4,870	139	5,009	48	3,050,693	3,032,217	605	2,535,234	2,007,280	24	25	28
Delaware	1,982	75	2,057	49	551,928	548,104	266	446,292	318,085	46	46	47
District of Columbia†	61	6	67	..	762,971‡	756,510	11,291	763,956	802,178	..	..	..
Florida	54,136	4,424	58,560	22	6,855,702	6,789,443	116	4,951,560	2,771,305	9	10	20
Georgia	58,197	679	58,876	21	4,627,306	4,589,575	78	3,943,116	3,444,578	15	16	13
Hawaii	6,425	25	6,450	47	784,901	769,913	119	632,772	499,794	40	43	45
Idaho	82,677	880	83,557	13	719,921	713,008	8.5	667,191	588,637	42	42	43
Illinois	55,875	525	56,400	24	11,184,320	11,113,976	197	10,081,158	8,712,176	5	4	4
Indiana	36,189	102	36,291	38	5,228,156	5,193,669	143	4,662,498	3,934,224	11	11	12
Iowa	56,043	247	56,290	25	2,846,920	2,825,041	50	2,757,537	2,621,073	25	24	22
Kansas	82,056	208	82,264	14	2,265,846	2,249,071	27	2,178,611	1,905,299	28	28	31
Kentucky	39,851	544	40,395	37	3,246,481	3,219,311	80	3,038,156	2,944,806	23	22	19
Louisiana	45,131	3,392	48,523	31	3,672,008	3,643,180	75	3,257,022	2,683,516	20	20	21
Maine	30,933	2,282	33,215	39	1,006,320	993,663	30	969,265	913,774	38	36	35
Maryland	9,891	686	10,577	42	3,953,698	3,922,399	371	3,100,689	2,343,001	18	21	23
Massachusetts	7,833	424	8,257	45	5,726,676	5,689,170	689	5,148,578	4,690,514	10	9	9
Michigan	56,817	1,399	58,216	23	8,937,196	8,875,083	152	7,823,194	6,371,766	7	7	7
Minnesota	79,289	4,779	84,068	12	3,833,173	3,805,069	45	3,413,864	2,982,483	19	18	18
Mississippi	47,358	358	47,716	32	2,233,848	2,216,912	46	2,178,141	2,178,914	29	29	26
Missouri	69,046	640	69,686	19	4,718,034	4,677,399	67	4,319,813	3,954,653	13	13	11
Montana	145,603	1,535	147,138	4	701,573	694,409	4.7	674,767	591,024	43	41	42
Nebraska	76,522	705	77,227	15	1,496,820	1,483,791	19	1,411,330	1,325,510	35	34	33
Nevada	109,889	651	110,540	7	492,396	488,738	4.4	285,278	160,083	47	49	49
New Hampshire	9,033	271	9,304	44	746,284	737,681	79	606,921	533,242	41	45	44
New Jersey	7,532	304	7,836	46	7,208,035	7,168,164	915	6,066,782	4,835,329	8	8	8
New Mexico	121,445	221	121,666	5	1,026,664	1,016,000	8.4	951,023	681,187	37	37	39
New York	47,869	1,707	49,576	30	18,338,055	18,241,266	368	16,782,304	14,830,192	2	1	1
North Carolina	48,880	3,706	52,586	28	5,125,230	5,082,059	97	4,556,155	4,061,929	12	12	10
North Dakota	69,280	1,385	70,665	17	624,181	617,761	8.7	632,446	619,636	45	44	41
Ohio	41,018	204	41,222	35	10,730,200	10,652,017	258	9,706,397	7,946,627	6	5	5
Oklahoma	68,983	936	69,919	18	2,585,486	2,559,253	37	2,328,284	2,233,351	27	27	25
Oregon	96,209	772	96,981	10	2,110,810	2,091,385	22	1,768,687	1,521,341	31	32	32
Pennsylvania	45,025	308	45,333	33	11,884,314	11,793,909	260	11,319,366	10,498,012	3	3	3
Rhode Island	1,049	165	1,214	50	957,798	949,723	782	859,488	791,896	39	39	36
South Carolina	30,280	775	31,055	40	2,617,320	2,590,516	83	2,382,594	2,117,027	26	26	27
South Dakota	75,956	1,091	77,047	16	673,247	666,257	8.6	680,514	652,740	44	40	40
Tennessee	41,367	878	42,244	34	3,961,060	3,924,164	93	3,567,089	3,291,718	17	17	16
Texas	262,970	4,369	267,339	2	11,298,787	11,196,730	42	9,579,677	7,711,194	4	6	6
Utah	82,381	2,535	84,916	11	1,067,810	1,059,273	12	890,627	688,862	36	38	38
Vermont	9,274	335	9,609	43	448,327	444,732	46	389,881	377,747	48	47	46
Virginia	39,841	976	40,817	36	4,690,742	4,648,494	114	3,966,949	3,318,680	14	14	15
Washington	66,683	1,529	68,192	20	3,443,487	3,409,169	50	2,853,214	2,378,963	22	23	24
West Virginia	24,084	97	24,181	41	1,763,331	1,744,237	72	1,860,421	2,005,552	34	30	29
Wisconsin	54,466	1,688	56,154	26	4,447,013	4,417,933	79	3,951,777	3,434,575	16	15	14
Wyoming	97,281	633	97,914	9	335,719	332,416	3.4	330,066	290,529	49	48	48
United States	3,540,911	74,212	3,675,545*	..	204,816,296‡	203,235,298	55	179,323,175	151,325,798	..	..	..

† District. * Includes the United States parts of the Great Lakes (60,422 square miles). These are not included in state figures.

‡ The apportionment population represents the resident population plus members of the armed forces overseas and other U. S. citizens who were abroad at the time of the census. A total U. S. apportionmen population of 204,053,325 was used to compute the 1971 Congressional apportionment among the 50 States. This total excludes the District of Columbia, ignored in Congressional apportionment.

U.S. State General Information

STATE	CAPITAL	LARGEST CITY	Date of Entry	Rank of Entry	Greatest N-S Measurement (miles)	Greatest E-W Measurement (miles)	HIGHEST POINT Location	Altitude (feet)	STATE FLOWER	STATE BIRD	STATE NICKNAME
Alabama	Montgomery	Birmingham	Dec. 14, 1819	22	330	200	Cheaha Mountain	2,407	Camellia	Yellowhammer	Yellowhammer
Alaska	Juneau	Anchorage	Jan. 3, 1959	49	1,332	2,250	Mt. McKinley	20,320	Forget-me-not	Willow Ptarmigan	Last Frontier
Arizona	Phoenix	Phoenix	Feb. 14, 1912	48	390	335	Humphreys Peak	12,633	Saguaro Cactus	Cactus Wren	Grand Canyon
Arkansas	Little Rock	Little Rock	June 15, 1836	25	240	275	Magazine Mtn.	2,753	Apple Blossom	Mockingbird	Land of Opportunity
California	Sacramento	Los Angeles	Sept. 9, 1850	31	800	375	Mt. Whitney	14,494	Golden Poppy	California Valley Quail	Golden
Colorado	Denver	Denver	Aug. 1, 1876	38	270	380	Mt. Elbert	14,433	Rocky Mountain Columbine	Lark Bunting	Centennial
Connecticut*	Hartford	Hartford	Jan. 9, 1788	5	75	90	S. slope of Mt. Frissell	2,380	Mountain Laurel	American Robin	Constitution
Delaware*	Dover	Wilmington	Dec. 7, 1787	1	95	35	Ebright Road, New Castle Co.	442	Peach Blossom	Blue Hen Chicken	First
District of Columbia†	Washington	Washington	March 3, 1791	..	15	15	Tenleytown	410	American Beauty Rose	Wood Thrush	
Florida	Tallahassee	Jacksonville	March 3, 1845	27	460	400	N. boundary, Walton Co.	345	Orange Blossom	Mockingbird	Sunshine
Georgia*	Atlanta	Atlanta	Jan. 2, 1788	4	315	250	Brasstown Bald (mtn.)	4,784	Cherokee Rose	Brown Thrasher	Peach State
Hawaii	Honolulu	Honolulu	Aug. 21, 1959	50	...	1,600	Mauna Kea	13,796	Red Hibiscus	Nene (Hawaiian Goose)	The Aloha
Idaho	Boise	Boise	July 3, 1890	43	480	305	Borah Peak	12,662	Syringa	Mountain Bluebird	Gem
Illinois	Springfield	Chicago	Dec. 3, 1818	21	380	205	Charles Mound	1,235	Native Violet	Cardinal	Prairie
Indiana	Indianapolis	Indianapolis	Dec. 11, 1816	19	265	160	Near Spartanburg	1,257	Peony	Cardinal	Hoosier
Iowa	Des Moines	Des Moines	Dec. 28, 1846	29	205	310	N. W. corner Osceola Co.	1,670	Wild Rose	Eastern Goldfinch	Hawkeye
Kansas	Topeka	Wichita	Jan. 29, 1861	34	205	410	Mt. Sunflower	4,039	Sunflower	Western Meadowlark	Sunflower
Kentucky	Frankfort	Louisville	June 1, 1792	15	175	350	Black Mountain	4,145	Goldenrod	Kentucky Cardinal	Bluegrass
Louisiana	Baton Rouge	New Orleans	April 30, 1812	18	275	300	Driskill Mountain	535	Magnolia	Eastern Brown Pelican**	Pelican
Maine	Augusta	Portland	March 15, 1820	23	310	210	Mt. Katahdin	5,268	White Pine Cone and Tassel	Chickadee	Pine Tree
Maryland*	Annapolis	Baltimore	April 28, 1788	7	120	200	Backbone Mountain	3,360	Black-eyed Susan	Baltimore Oriole	Free
Massachusetts*	Boston	Boston	Feb. 6, 1788	6	110	190	Mt. Greylock	3,491	Mayflower	Chickadee	Bay
Michigan	Lansing	Detroit	Jan. 26, 1837	26	400	310	Mt. Curwood	1,980	Apple Blossom	Robin	Wolverine
Minnesota	St. Paul	Minneapolis	May 11, 1858	32	400	350	Eagle Mtn.	2,301	Showy Lady's-slipper	Loon	Gopher
Mississippi	Jackson	Jackson	Dec. 10, 1817	20	340	180	Woodall Mountain	806	Magnolia	Mockingbird	Magnolia
Missouri	Jefferson City	St. Louis	Aug. 10, 1821	24	280	300	Taum Sauk Mountain	1,772	Hawthorne	Bluebird	Show Me
Montana	Helena	Billings	Nov. 8, 1889	41	315	570	Granite Peak	12,799	Bitterroot	Western Meadowlark	Treasure
Nebraska	Lincoln	Omaha	March 1, 1867	37	210	415	S.W. corner Kimball Co.	5,426	Goldenrod	Western Meadowlark	Cornhusker
Nevada	Carson City	Las Vegas	Oct. 31, 1864	36	485	315	Boundary Peak	13,143	Sagebrush	Mountain Bluebird**	Battle Born
New Hampshire*	Concord	Manchester	June 21, 1788	9	185	90	Mt. Washington	6,288	Purple Lilac	Purple Finch	Granite
New Jersey*	Trenton	Newark	Dec. 18, 1787	3	166	70	High Point	1,803	Purple Violet	Eastern Goldfinch	Garden
New Mexico	Santa Fe	Albuquerque	Jan. 6, 1912	47	390	350	Wheeler Peak	13,161	Yucca	Road Runner	Land of Enchantment
New York*	Albany	New York	July 26, 1788	11	310	330	Mt. Marcy	5,344	Rose	Bluebird**	Empire
North Carolina*	Raleigh	Charlotte	Nov. 21, 1789	12	200	520	Mt. Mitchell	6,684	Dogwood	Cardinal	Tar Heel
North Dakota	Bismarck	Fargo	Nov. 2, 1889	39	210	360	White Butte	3,506	Wild Prairie Rose	Western Meadowlark	Flickertail
Ohio	Columbus	Cleveland	March 1, 1803	17	230	205	Campbell Hill	1,550	Scarlet Carnation	Cardinal	Buckeye
Oklahoma	Oklahoma City	Oklahoma City	Nov. 16, 1907	46	210	460	Black Mesa	4,973	Mistletoe	Scissor-tailed Flycatcher	Sooner
Oregon	Salem	Portland	Feb. 14, 1859	33	290	375	Mt. Hood	11,235	Oregon Grape	Western Meadowlark	Beaver
Pennsylvania*	Harrisburg	Philadelphia	Dec. 12, 1787	2	180	310	Mt. Davis	3,213	Mountain Laurel	Ruffed Grouse	Keystone
Rhode Island*	Providence	Providence	May 29, 1790	13	50	35	Jerimoth Hill	812	Violet	Rhode Island Red	Little Rhody
South Carolina*	Columbia	Columbia	May 23, 1788	8	215	285	Sassafras Mountain	3,560	Carolina Jessamine	Carolina Wren	Palmetto
South Dakota	Pierre	Sioux Falls	Nov. 2, 1889	40	240	360	Harney Peak	7,242	Pasque	Ringnecked Pheasant	Coyote
Tennessee	Nashville	Memphis	June 1, 1796	16	120	430	Clingmans Dome	6,643	Iris	Mockingbird	Volunteer
Texas	Austin	Houston	Dec. 29, 1845	28	710	760	Guadalupe Peak	8,751	Bluebonnet	Mockingbird	Lone Star
Utah	Salt Lake City	Salt Lake City	Jan. 4, 1896	45	345	275	Kings Peak	13,528	Sego Lily	Seagull	Beehive
Vermont*	Montpelier	Burlington	March 4, 1791	14	155	90	Mt. Mansfield	4,393	Red Clover	Hermit Thrush	Green Mountain
Virginia*	Richmond	Norfolk	June 25, 1788	10	205	425	Mt. Rogers	5,729	American Dogwood	Cardinal	Old Dominion
Washington	Olympia	Seattle	Nov. 11, 1889	42	230	340	Mt. Rainier	14,410	Rhododendron	Willow Goldfinch	Evergreen
West Virginia*	Charleston	Huntington	June 20, 1863	35	200	225	Spruce Knob	4,862	Rhododendron	Cardinal	Mountain
Wisconsin	Madison	Milwaukee	May 29, 1848	30	300	290	Timms Hill	1,952	Violet	Robin	Badger
Wyoming	Cheyenne	Cheyenne	July 10, 1890	44	275	365	Gannett Peak	13,804	Indian Paint Brush	Meadowlark	Equality
United States	Washington, D.C.	New York	..	..	..	..	Mt. McKinley, Alaska	20,320	...	Bald Eagle	

*One of the Thirteen Original States. **Unofficial. †District.

U.S. Population by State or Colony 1650-1970

STATES	1650	1700	1750	1770	1790	1800	1820	1840	1860	1880	1900	1920	1930	1940	1950	1960	1970
Alabama							127,901	590,756	964,201	1,262,505	1,828,697	2,348,174	2,646,248	2,832,961	3,061,743	3,266,740	3,444,165
Alaska										33,426	63,592	55,036	59,278	72,524	128,643	226,167	302,173
Arizona										40,440	122,931	334,162	435,573	499,261	749,587	1,302,161	1,772,482
Arkansas							14,273	97,574	435,450	802,525	1,311,564	1,752,204	1,854,482	1,949,387	1,909,511	1,786,272	1,923,295
California									379,994	864,694	1,485,053	3,426,861	5,677,251	6,907,387	10,586,223	15,717,204	19,953,134
Colorado									34,277	194,327	539,700	939,629	1,035,791	1,123,296	1,325,089	1,753,947	2,207,259
Connecticut	4,139	25,970	111,280	183,881	237,946	251,002	275,248	309,978	460,147	622,700	908,420	1,380,631	1,606,903	1,709,242	2,007,280	2,535,234	3,032,217
Delaware	185	2,470	28,704	35,496	59,096	64,273	72,749	78,085	112,216	146,608	184,735	223,003	238,380	266,505	318,085	446,292	548,104
District of Columbia						8,144	23,336	33,745	75,080	177,624	278,718	437,571	486,869	663,091	802,178	763,956	756,510
Florida								54,477	140,424	269,493	528,542	968,470	1,468,211	1,897,414	2,771,305	4,951,560	6,789,443
Georgia			5,200	23,375	82,548	162,686	340,989	691,392	1,057,286	1,542,180	2,216,331	2,895,832	2,908,506	3,123,723	3,444,578	3,943,116	4,589,575
Hawaii											154,001	255,881	368,300	422,770	499,794	632,772	769,913
Idaho										32,610	161,772	431,866	445,032	524,873	588,637	667,191	713,008
Illinois							55,211	476,183	1,711,951	3,077,871	4,821,550	6,485,280	7,630,654	7,897,241	8,712,176	10,081,158	11,113,976
Indiana						5,641	147,178	685,866	1,350,428	1,978,301	2,516,462	2,930,390	3,238,503	3,427,796	3,934,224	4,662,498	5,193,669
Iowa								43,112	674,913	1,624,615	2,231,853	2,404,021	2,470,939	2,538,268	2,621,073	2,757,537	2,825,041
Kansas									107,206	996,096	1,470,495	1,769,257	1,880,999	1,801,028	1,905,299	2,178,611	2,249,071
Kentucky				15,700	73,677	220,955	564,317	779,828	1,155,684	1,648,690	2,147,174	2,416,630	2,614,589	2,845,627	2,944,806	3,038,156	3,219,311
Louisiana							153,407	352,411	708,002	939,946	1,381,625	1,798,509	2,101,593	2,363,880	2,683,516	3,257,022	3,643,180
Maine[4]				31,257	96,540	151,719	298,335	501,793	628,279	648,936	694,466	768,014	797,423	847,226	913,774	969,265	993,663
Maryland	4,504	29,604	141,073	202,599	319,728	341,548	407,350	470,019	687,049	934,943	1,188,044	1,449,661	1,631,526	1,821,244	2,343,001	3,100,689	3,922,399
Massachusetts[4]	16,603	55,941	188,000	235,308	378,787	422,845	523,287	737,699	1,231,066	1,783,085	2,805,346	3,852,356	4,249,614	4,316,721	4,690,514	5,148,578	5,689,170
Michigan							8,896	212,267	749,113	1,636,937	2,420,982	3,668,412	4,842,325	5,256,106	6,371,766	7,823,194	8,875,083
Minnesota									172,023	780,773	1,751,394	2,387,125	2,563,953	2,792,300	2,982,483	3,413,864	3,805,069
Mississippi						8,850	75,448	375,651	791,305	1,131,597	1,551,270	1,790,618	2,009,821	2,183,796	2,178,914	2,178,141	2,216,912
Missouri							66,586	383,702	1,182,012	2,168,380	3,106,665	3,404,055	3,629,367	3,784,664	3,954,653	4,319,813	4,677,399
Montana										39,159	243,329	548,889	537,606	559,456	591,024	674,767	694,409
Nebraska									28,841	452,402	1,066,300	1,296,372	1,377,963	1,315,834	1,325,510	1,411,330	1,483,791
Nevada									6,857	62,266	42,335	77,407	91,058	110,247	160,083	285,278	488,738
New Hampshire	1,305	4,958	27,505	62,396	141,885	183,858	244,161	284,574	326,073	346,991	411,588	443,083	465,293	491,524	533,242	606,921	737,681
New Jersey		14,010	71,393	117,431	184,139	211,149	277,575	373,306	672,035	1,131,116	1,883,669	3,155,900	4,041,334	4,160,165	4,835,329	6,066,782	7,168,164
New Mexico									93,516	119,565	195,310	360,350	423,317	531,818	681,187	951,023	1,016,000
New York	4,116	19,107	76,696	162,920	340,120	589,051	1,372,812	2,428,921	3,880,735	5,082,871	7,268,894	10,385,227	12,588,066	13,479,142	14,830,192	16,782,304	18,241,266
North Carolina		10,720	72,984	197,200	393,751	478,103	638,829	753,419	992,622	1,399,750	1,893,810	2,559,123	3,170,276	3,571,623	4,061,929	4,556,155	5,082,059
North Dakota[3]										36,909	319,146	646,872	680,845	641,935	619,636	632,446	617,761
Ohio						45,365	581,434	1,519,467	2,339,511	3,198,062	4,157,545	5,759,394	6,646,697	6,907,612	7,946,627	9,706,397	10,652,017
Oklahoma[5]											790,391	2,028,283	2,396,040	2,336,434	2,233,351	2,328,284	2,559,253
Oregon									52,465	174,768	413,536	783,389	953,786	1,089,684	1,521,341	1,768,687	2,091,385
Pennsylvania		17,950	119,666	240,057	434,373	602,365	1,049,458	1,724,033	2,906,215	4,282,891	6,302,115	8,720,017	9,631,350	9,900,180	10,498,012	11,319,366	11,793,909
Rhode Island	785	5,894	33,226	58,196	68,825	69,122	83,059	108,830	174,620	276,531	428,556	604,397	687,497	713,346	791,896	859,488	949,723
South Carolina		5,704	64,000	124,244	249,073	345,591	502,741	594,398	703,708	995,577	1,340,316	1,683,724	1,738,765	1,899,804	2,117,027	2,382,594	2,590,516
South Dakota[3]									4,837	98,268	401,570	636,547	692,849	642,961	652,740	680,514	666,257
Tennessee				1,000	35,691	105,602	422,823	829,210	1,109,801	1,542,359	2,020,616	2,337,885	2,616,556	2,915,841	3,291,718	3,567,089	3,924,164
Texas									604,215	1,591,749	3,048,710	4,663,228	5,824,715	6,414,824	7,711,194	9,579,677	11,196,730
Utah									40,273	143,963	276,749	449,396	507,847	550,310	688,862	890,627	1,059,273
Vermont				10,000	85,425	154,465	235,981	291,948	315,098	332,286	343,641	352,428	359,611	359,231	377,747	389,881	444,732
Virginia[6]	18,731	58,560	231,033	447,016	691,737	807,557	938,261	1,025,227	1,219,630	1,512,565	1,854,184	2,309,187	2,421,851	2,677,773	3,318,680	3,966,949	4,648,494
Washington									11,594	75,116	518,103	1,356,621	1,563,396	1,736,191	2,378,963	2,853,214	3,409,169
West Virginia[6]					55,873	78,592	136,808	224,537	376,688	618,457	958,800	1,463,701	1,729,205	1,901,974	2,005,552	1,860,421	1,744,237
Wisconsin								30,945	775,881	1,315,497	2,069,042	2,632,067	2,939,006	3,137,587	3,434,575	3,951,777	4,417,933
Wyoming										20,789	92,531	194,402	225,565	250,742	290,529	330,066	332,416
Total[1]	50,368	250,888	1,170,760	2,148,076	3,929,214	5,308,483	9,638,453	17,069,453[2]	31,443,321	50,189,209	76,212,168	106,021,537	123,202,624	132,164,569	151,325,798	179,323,175	203,235,298

[1] All figures prior to 1890 exclude uncivilized Indians. Figures for 1650 through 1770 include only the British colonies that later became the United States. No areas are included prior to their annexation to the United States. However, many of the figures refer to territories prior to their admission as States. U.S. total includes Alaska from 1880 through 1970 and Hawaii from 1900 through 1970.

[2] U.S. total for 1840 includes 6,100 persons on public ships in service of the United States, not credited to any State.

[3] South Dakota figure for 1860 represents entire Dakota Territory. North and South Dakota figures for 1880 are for the parts of Dakota Territory which later constituted the respective States.

[4] Maine figures for 1770 through 1800 are for that area of Massachusetts which became the State of Maine in 1820. Massachusetts figures exclude Maine from 1770 through 1800, but include it from 1650 through 1750. Massachusetts figure for 1650 also includes population of Plymouth (1,566), a separate colony until 1691.

[5] Oklahoma figure for 1900 includes population of Indian Territory (392,060).

[6] West Virginia figures for 1790 through 1860 are for that area of Virginia which became West Virginia in 1863. These figures are excluded from the figures for Virginia from 1790 through 1860.

Glossary of Foreign Geographical Terms

rab.....Arabic | Kor.....Korean
antu.....Bantu | Lao.....Laotian
ur.....Burmese | Lapp.....Lappish
amb.....Cambodian | Mal.....Malayan
lt.....Celtic | Mong.....Mongolian
hn.....Chinese | Nor.....Norwegian
ech.....Czech | Per.....Persian
an.....Danish | Pol.....Polish
u.....Dutch | Port.....Portuguese
.....Finnish | Rom.....Romanian
.....French | Rus.....Russian
.....German | Siam.....Siamese
rc.....Greek | So. Slav.....Southern Slavonic
.....Hungarian | Sp.....Spanish
.....Icelandic | Swe.....Swedish
dia.....India | Tib.....Tibetan
dian.....American Indian | Tur.....Turkic
.....Italian | Viet.....Vietnamese
ap.....Japanese

A

Dan., Nor. ...river
, Du. ...at, on
d, India, Per ...dwelling, town
, abou, Arab ...father
n, Nor ...spit
elf, Swe ...river
, Ger ...mountain
, Ger ...old
a, -o, It., Port., Sp ...high
piano, It ...plateau
, älven, Swe ...river
arillo, Sp ...yellow
quipélago, Port ...archipelago
oyo, Sp ...brook, dry bed of stream
Dan,. Nor., Swe ...hill, ridge
stral, Sp ...southern

B

ai, Du ...bay
, Arab ...gate, strait
ch, Arab ...brook, stream
ke, Swe ...hill
d, Ger ...bath
hía, Port., Sp ...bay, gulf
hr, Arab ...bay, river
ia, It ...bay, gulf
ie, Fr ...bay, gulf
io, Sp ...low, lower
kke, Dan., Nor ...hill
lkan, Tur ...mountain range
n, Lao, Mal ...village
n, Siam ...house
na, Jap ...cape
ndar ...harbor
dar, Mal ...river
tang, Mal ...river
yy, belaya, Rus ...white
n, Celt ...mountain, summit
nder, bandar, Arab., India ...market town, port
ni, bani, Arab ...sons of, tribe of
rg, Du., Ger., Nor., Swe ...mountain, hill
bi'r, Arab ...well
kat, Arab ...pool, well
li, -a, -o, So. Slav ...white
bjaerg, Dan., Nor ...mountain
anc, Fr ...white
anco, Sp ...white
au, Ger ...blue
eu, Fr ...blue
dden, Ger ...ground
gaz, bogazi, Tur ...strait
is, Fr ...forest, wood
loto, Rus ...marsh
lshoy, bolshoye, Rus ...great
real, Sp ...northern
rg, Dan., Nor., Swe ...castle
rgo, It ...town
sch, Du ...forest, wood
ouche, Fr ...river mouth
urg, Fr ...town, borough
o, Dan., Nor., Swe ...bridge
rücke, brücken, Ger ...bridge, bridges
un, Fr ...brown
cht, Ger ...bay, bight
gt, Dan., Nor ...bay, gulf
kt, bukten, Swe ...bay, gulf
lak, Tur ...spring
r, Arab ...port
rg, Du., Ger ...castle, town
ri, Siam ...city

burun, burnu, Tur ...cape
büyük, Tur ...great
by, Dan., Nor., Swe ...town, village

C

cabeza, Sp ...summit
cabo, Port., Sp ...cape
cairn, carn, Celt ...rocky headland
campo, It., Port., Sp ...field
campos, Port. (Brazil) ...plains
cañon, Sp ...canyon
cap, Fr ...cape
capo, It ...cape
casa, It., Port., Sp ...house
castello, It., Port ...castle, fort
castillo, Sp ...castle, fort
catingas, Port. (Brazil) ...open brushlands
cayo, Sp ...rock, shoal, islet
central, Fr ...middle
cerro, Sp ...hill
chai, ciai, Tur ...river
champ, Fr ...field
chapada, Port. (Brazil) ...hills, ridge
chateau, Fr ...castle
cherniy, chernyaya, Rus ...black
chin, Chn ...market town
chott, shat, Arab ...salt river or lake
chou, Chn ...island
cidade, Port ...city
città, It ...town, city
ciudad, Sp ...town, city
col, Fr ...pass
colina, Sp ...hill
colorado, Sp ...red
cordillera, Sp ...mountain chain
costa, It., Port., Sp ...coast
côte, côtes, Fr ...coast, hills, peak, ridge
crkva, So. Slav ...church
crni, So. Slav ...black
cuchilla, Sp ...mountain range
cumbre, Sp ...peak, ridge

D

daal, dal, Du ...valley
dag, Tur ...mountain
daglari, Tur ...mountains, range
dake, take, Jap ...peak, ridge
dal, Dan., Du., Nor., Swe ...valley
dalay, Mong ...lake
dar, Arab ...land, country
darya, daria, Per ...river, sea
dasht, Per ...plain, desert
dawhat, Arab ...bay, inlet
deccan, India ...south
deir, Arab ...convent
denis, -z, Tur ...sea, lake
désert, Fr ...desert
deserto, It ...desert
desierto, Sp ...desert
détroit, Fr ...strait
djebel, jebel, Arab ...mountain
dolok, Mal ...mountain
dorf, Ger ...village
dorp, Du ...village
drift, Du., Ger ...current
duinen, Du ...dunes
dun, Celt ...fortified hill
dyk, Du ...dam, dyke
dzong, Tib ...fort, administrative capital

E

eau, Fr ...water
ecuador, Sp ...equator
eiland, Du ...island
elf, älf, Swe ...river
elv, Dan., Nor ...river
erg, Arab ...dune, region of dunes
eski, Tur ...old
est, Fr ...east
estado, Sp ...state
este, It., Port., Sp ...east
estrecho, Sp ...strait
étang, Fr ...pond, lake
état, Fr ...state
étroit, Fr ...narrow

F

feld, Ger ...field, plain
fels, Ger ...rock
festung, Ger ...fort
firth, Scotch ...estuary
fiume, It ...river
fjäll, fjället, Swe ...mountain
fjärd, Swe ...bay, inlet
fjeld, Nor ...mountain, hill
fjell, Nor ...mountain
fjord, fjorden, Dan., Nor ...fiord, inlet
fjördhur, Ice ...fiord, inlet
fleuve, Fr ...river
flod, Dan., Swe ...river
flói, Ice ...bay
fluss, Ger ...river
foce, It ...river mouth
fontein, Du ...a spring
fors, Swe ...waterfall, torrent
forst, Ger ...forest
fos, Dan., Nor ...waterfall
fuente, Sp ...spring, fountain
fuerte, Sp ...fort
furt, Ger ...ford

G

gamla, Swe ...old
gamle, Dan., Nor ...old
gat, Dan., Nor ...passage, channel
gavan', Rus ...harbor
gebel, Arab ...mountain
gebergte, Du ...mountain range
gebiet, Ger ...district, territory
gebirge, Ger ...range, mountains
ghat, India ...mountain pass, river passage
gobi, Mong ...desert
göl, gölu, Tur ...lake
golf, Du., Ger ...gulf, bay
golfe, Fr ...gulf, bay
golfo, It., Port., Sp ...gulf, bay
gong, India ...village
gora, Pol., Rus., So. Slav ...mountain
gornji, -a, -o, So. Slav ...upper
gorny, Pol ...upper
gorod, grad, Rus., So. Slav ...town
grand, grande, Fr ...large, great
grande, It., Port., Sp ...large, great
grod, gorod, Pol., Rus ...town
grön, Dan ...green
groot, Du ...great
gross, Ger ...great
guba, Rus ...bay, gulf
gunto, Jap ...archipelago

H

haf, Swe ...sea
hafen, Ger ...port, harbor
haff, Ger ...gulf, inland sea
hai, Chn ...sea, lake
hamn, Swe ...harbor
hamun, Per ...swampy lake, plain
haus, hausen, Ger ...house, houses
haut, Fr ...high, summit, upper
havet, Nor ...bay
havn, Dan., Nor ...harbor, port
havre, Fr ...harbor, port
hawr, Arab ...lake, marsh
haz, -a, Hung ...house, dwelling of
heim, Ger ...hamlet
hem, Swe ...hamlet
higashi, Jap ...east
hinterland, Ger ...back country
hissar, hisar, Tur ...castle, fort
ho, Chn ...river
hoch, Ger ...high
hoek, Du ...cape
hof, Ger ...court, farm house
höfn, Ice ...harbor
hoku, Jap ...north
holm, Dan., Nor., Swe ...island
hora, Czech ...mountain
horn, Ger ...peak
hoved, Dan., Nor ...cape, headland
hsien, Chn ...district, district capital
hügel, Ger ...hill

huk, Dan., Nor., Swe ...point
hus, Dan., Nor., Swe ...house
hwang, Chn ...yellow

I

ile, Fr ...island
ilha, Port ...island
indre, Dan., Nor ...inner
indsö, Dan., Nor ...lake
inférieur, Fr ...lower
insel, Ger ...island
insjö, Swe ...lake
irmak, Tur ...river
isla, Sp ...island
isola, It ...island
istmo, It., Sp ...isthmus

J

jabal, Arab ...mountain, plateau, ridge
järvi, Fin ...lake
jebel, djebel, Arab ...mountain
jima, shima, Jap ...island
jökel, jökelen, Nor ...glacier
joki, Fin ...river
jökull, Ice ...ice-covered mountain
juzna, So. Slav ...south, southern

K

kaap, Du ...cape
kafr, kefr, Arab ...village
kaikyo, Jap ...strait
kaise, Lapp ...mountain
kala, kalat, Arab., Per ...castle, fortress, village
kale, Tur ...castle, fort
kamen', Rus ...rock
kang, Chn ...village
kap, Nor ...cape
kapp, Nor ...cape
kara, Tur ...black
kaupunki, Fin ...town, city
kavir, Per ...salt desert
kebir, Arab ...great
kefr, kafr, Arab ...village
ken, Jap ...prefecture
kend, kand, Per ...village
khalij, Arab ...bay, gulf
khrebet, Rus ...mountain range
ki, Jap ...tree, forest
kil, cill, Celt ...church, cell
kirche, Ger ...church
kirchen, Ger ...parish
kio, kyo, Jap ...town, capital
kis, Hung ...little, small
klein, Du., Ger ...small
köbstad, Dan ...city
köl, Mong., Tur ...lake, marsh
kompong, Camb ...village
kong, Chn ...river
kopf, Ger ...head, summit, peak
köping, Swe ...market, borough
kraal, Du ...native village
krasniy, krasnaya, Rus ...beautiful, fair, red
kuala, Mal ...junction, river mouth
kuchuk, Tur ...small
kuh, koh, Per ...mountain
kul, Mong., Tur ...lake
kum, qum, Tur ...desert
kuppe, Ger ...summit
küste, Ger ...coast
kyzyl, kizil, Tur ...red

L

laag, Du ...low
lac, Fr ...lake
lago, It., Sp ...lake
lâgoa, Port ...lagoon
laguna, It., Port., Sp ...lagoon, lake
lahti, Fin ...bay, gulf
län, Swe ...county
landsby, Dan., Nor ...village
lao, Viet ...island
lilla, Swe ...small

Glossary of Foreign Geographical Terms *Continued*

lille, *Dan., Nor.*......small
liman, *Tur.*......bay, port
ling, *Chn.*......mountain, range
llanos, *Sp.*......prairies, plains
loch, *Celt.*......lake, bay (Scotland)
lough, *Celt.*......lake, bay (Ireland)

M

maha, *India*......great
malyy, malaya, *Rus.*......small
mar, *Port., Sp.*......sea
mare, *It., Rom.*......sea
mare, *Rom.*......great
mark, *Ger.*......boundary, limit
massif, *Fr.*......mountain range
mato, *Port.*......jungle, copse
medio, *Sp.*......middle
meer, *Du., Ger.*......lake, sea
mer, *Fr.*......sea
mesa, *Sp.*......flat-topped mountain
meseta, *Sp.*......hill
midden, *Du.*......middle
mina, *Port., Sp.*......mine
mittel, *Ger.*......middle
mont, *Fr.*......mount, mountain
montagna, *It.*......mountain
montagne, *Fr.*......mountain
montaña, *Sp.*......mountain
monte, *It., Port., Sp.*......mount, mountain
more, *Rus., So. Slav.*......sea
morro, *Port., Sp.*......hill
moyen, *Fr.*......middle
mühle, *Ger.*......mill
mund, munde, *Ger.*......river mouth
mündung, *Ger.*......river mouth
muong, *Lao.*......town, village
mura, *Jap.*......village
muz, *Tur.*......ice
mys, *Rus.*......cape, point

N

nada, *Jap.*......sea
nadi, *India*......river, creek
naes, näs, *Dan., Nor., Swe.*......cape
nagar, nagon, *India*......town, city
nagy, *Hung.*......large, great
naka, *Jap.*......middle
neder, *Du.*......low
nedre, *Nor.*......lower
negro, *It., Port., Sp.*......black
nejd, *Arab*......highland
neu, *Ger.*......new
nevado, *Sp.*......mountain
nez, *Fr.*......point, cape
nieder, *Ger.*......low, lower
nieuw, *Du.*......new
nizhne, nizhniy, nizhnyaya, *Rus.*......lower
noir, *Fr.*......black
nong, *Siam*......marsh, pond, lake
noord, *Du.*......north
nor, *Tib.*......lake
nord, *Dan., Fr., Ger., It., Nor.*......north
norr, norra, *Swe.*......north
norte, *Port., Sp.*......north
nos, *Rus.*......cape
nouvelle, *Fr.*......new
novi, -a, -o, *So. Slav.*......new
novo, *Port.*......new
novy, -e, -a, *Czech.*......new
novyy, novyye, novaya, novo, *Rus.*......new
nowa, nowy, *Pol.*......new
nuevo, *Sp.*......new
nuovo, *It.*......new
nuur, *Mong.*......lake
ny, *Dan., Swe.*......new
nyasa, *Bantu*......lake

O

o, *Jap.*......great, large
ö, *Dan., Nor., Swe.*......island
ober, *Ger.*......upper
occidental, *Sp.*......western

odde, *Dan., Nor.*......point, cape
oedjoeng, *Mal.*......cape
oeste, *Port., Sp.*......west
ojo, *Sp.*......spring
oost, *Du.*......east
op, *Du.*......on
oriental, *Sp.*......eastern
oro, *Sp.*......gold
óros, *Grc.*......mountain
ost, *Ger., Swe.*......east
öst, öster, östre, *Dan., Nor., Swe.*......east, eastern
ostrog, *Rus.*......fort
ostrov, *Rus.*......island
ouadi, *Arab*......intermittent stream
ouest, *Fr.*......west
öy, *Nor.*......island
ozero, *Rus.*......lake

P

paa, *Fin.*......mountain
padang, *Mal.*......plain, field
pampas, *Sp. (Argentina)*......grassy plains
para, *Indian (Brazil)*......river
pas, *Fr.*......channel, strait, pass
paso, *Sp.*......mountain pass
passo, *It., Port.*......mountain pass
patam, *India*......city, town
pequeño, *Sp.*......small
peresheyek, *Rus.*......isthmus
pertuis, *Fr.*......strait
peski, *Rus.*......desert, sands
petit, petite, *Fr.*......small, little
pic, *Fr.*......mountain peak
piccolo, *It.*......small
pico, *Port., Sp.*......mountain peak
piedra, *Sp.*......stone, rock
pik, *Rus.*......peak
planalto, *Port.*......plateau
plata, *Sp.*......silver
plato, *Rus.*......plateau
playa, *Sp.*......shore, beach
po, *Chn.*......lake
pointe, *Fr.*......point
polder, *Du., Ger.*......reclaimed marsh
polje, *So. Slav.*......field
poluostrov, *Rus.*......peninsula
pont, *Fr.*......bridge
ponta, *Port.*......point, headland
ponte, *It., Port.*......bridge
pore, pur, *India*......city, town
porto, *It.*......port, harbor
pôrto, *Port.*......port, harbor
prado, *Sp.*......field, meadow
presqu'ile, *Fr.*......peninsula
proliv, *Rus.*......strait
pu, *Chn.*......commercial village
pueblo, *Sp.*......town, village
puerto, *Sp.*......port, harbor
pulau, *Mal.*......island
punkt, *Ger.*......point
punt, *Du.*......point
punta, *It., Sp.*......point
pur, pura, *India*......city, town
puy, *Fr.*......peak

R

rann, *India*......wasteland
ra's, *Arab*......cape, summit
reg, *Arab*......coarse gravel desert
reka, *Rus., So. Slav.*......river
represa, *Port.*......reservoir
retto, *Jap.*......archipelago
ria, *Sp.*......river mouth
ribeira, -ão, *Port.*......stream, river
rio, *It., Port.*......river
río, *Sp.*......river
rivière, *Fr.*......river
roca, *Sp.*......rock
rochedos, *Port. (Brazil)*......rocks in water
rouge, *Fr.*......red
rud, *Per.*......river

S

saari, *Fin.*......island
sable, *Fr.*......sand
sahra, *Arab*......desert
sal, *Sp.*......salt
samar, *Mong.*......path, route
san, *Chn., Jap., Kor.*......mountain, hill
san, santa, santo, *It., Port., Sp.*......saint
são, *Port.*......saint
sat, satu, *Rom.*......village
schloss, *Ger.*......castle, fort
sebkha, *Arab*......salt marsh
see, *Ger.*......lake, sea
sehir, shehr, *Tur.*......town
selat, *Mal.*......channel, strait
selatan, *Mal.*......south, southern
selvas, *Port. (Brazil)*......tropical rain forests
seno, *Sp.*......bay
serra, *It., Port.*......pass, mountain ridge
serranía, *Sp.*......mountain ridge
seto, *Jap.*......strait, channel
severnaya, *Rus.*......north
shahr, shehr, *Per.*......town
sha'ib, *Arab*......depression, intermittent stream
shan, *Chn.*......range, mountain, hill
shatt, chott, *Arab*......salt river or lake
shima, sima, *Jap.*......island
shimo, *Jap.*......lower
shiu, *Chn., Jap.*......province
shoto, *Jap.*......archipelago
si, *Chn.*......west, western
sierra, *Sp.*......mountain range
sint, *Du.*......saint
sjö, *Nor., Swe.*......lake, sea
sö, *Dan., Nor.*......lake, sea
söder, *Swe.*......south
soengai, sungei, *Mal.*......river
sopka, *Rus.*......extinct volcano
source, *Fr.*......spring
spitze, *Ger.*......summit, point
sredniy, sredne, srednyaya, *Rus.*......middle
staat, *Ger.*......state
stad, *Dan., Du., Nor., Swe.*......city, town
stadt, *Ger.*......city, town
stari, -a, -o, *So. Slav.*......old
stary, *Czech., Pol.*......old
staryy, staraya, *Rus.*......old
stato, *It.*......state
sten, *Dan., Nor., Swe.*......stone
step, *Rus.*......treeless plain, steppe
stor, *Dan., Nor., Swe.*......great, large
straat, *Du.*......strait
strand, *Dan., Du., Ger., Nor., Swe*......shore, beach
stretto, *It.*......strait
strom, *Ger.*......stream
ström, *Dan., Nor., Swe.*......river
stroom, *Du.*......stream, river
su, suyu, *Tur.*......water, river
sud, *Fr., Sp.*......south
süd, *Ger.*......south
sul, *Port.*......south, southern
sund, *Dan., Nor., Swe.*......sound
supérieure, *Fr.*......upper
sur, *Fr.*......on
sur, *Sp.*......south
syd, *Dan., Nor., Swe.*......south

T

tafelland, *Du., Ger.*......plateau, tableland
tagh, *Mong., Tur.*......mountain
tai, *Jap.*......large, great
taiga, *Rus.*......northern coniferous forest
take, dake, *Jap.*......peak, ridge
tandjung, tanjong, *Mal.*......cape
tao, -u, *Chn.*......island
targ, targu, *Rom.*......market, town
tash, *Per., Tur.*......rock, stone
tau, *Tur.*......mountain range
tell, tel, *Arab*......hill
terra, *It.*......land
terre, *Fr.*......earth, land

thal, *Ger.*......val
tierra, *Sp.*......earth, la
torp, *Swe.*......village, cott
torre, *It., Port., Sp.*......tow
tsi, *Chn.*......village, boro
tsu, *Jap.*......
tundra, *Rus.*......marshy arctic pla
tung, *Chn.*......east, east
turn, turnu, *Rom.*......tow
tuz, *Tur.*......

U

udd, udde, *Swe.*......ca
ufer, *Ger.*......beach, shore, river ba
uj, *Hung.*......
ulan, *Mong.*......
umi, *Jap.*......sea, g
unter, *Ger.*......lo
ura, *Jap.*......bay, shore, cr
ust, *Rus.*......river mo
uula, *Mong.*......mountain, ra
utara, *Mal.*......north, north

V

vall, *Swe.*......
valle, *Port., Sp.*......val
vallée, *Fr.*......val
valli, *It.*......lake, lago
var, *Hung.*......fort
varos, *Hung., So. Slav.*......to
varre, *Lapp.*......mount
vecchio, *It.*......
veld, *Du.*......open plain, fi
velho, *Port.*......
velikiy, *Rus., So. Slav.*......gr
verde, *It., Port., Sp.*......gre
verkhniy, verkhnyaya, *Rus.*......upper, hig
vert, *Fr.*......gre
ves, *Czech.*......villa
vest, *Dan., Nor., Swe.*......w
viejo, *Sp.*......
vieux, *Fr.*......
vik, viken, *Swe.*......
villa, *Port., Sp.*......small to
villar, *Sp.*......village, ham
ville, *Fr.*......town, c
vinh, *Viet.*......b
vishni, visni, *Rus.*......hi
vostok, *Rus.*......e
volcán, *Sp.*......volca

W

wadi, wādī, wad, *Arab*......intermittent strea
wald, *Ger.*......forest, woodla
wan, *Chn., Jap.*......bay, g
weiler, *Ger.*......hamlet, villa
weiss, *Ger.*......wh
westersch, *Du.*......weste
wiek, *Du.*......b
wüste, *Ger.*......dese

Y

yama, *Jap.*......mounta
yang, *Chn.*......chann
yeni, *Tur.*......n
yokara, *Tur.*......upp
yoma, *Bur.*......mountain ran
yug, *Rus.*......sou
yuzhno, *Rus.*......south, southe

Z

zaki, saki, *Jap.*......ca
zaliv, *Rus.*......bay, gu
zapad, zapadnyy, *Rus.*......we
zapadni, -a, -o, *So. Slav.*......west, weste
zee, *Du.*......s
zemlya, *Rus.*......lan
zuid, *Du.*......sou

Abbreviations

admin . . . . administered
Afg . . . . Afghanistan
Afr . . . . Africa
Ala . . . . Alabama
Alb . . . . Albania
Alg . . . . Algeria
Alsk . . . . Alaska
Alta . . . . Alberta
Am . . . . American
Am. Sam . . . . American Samoa
And . . . . Andorra
Ang . . . . Angola
Ant . . . . Antarctica
Arc . . . . Arctic
arch . . . . archipelago
Arg . . . . Argentina
Ariz . . . . Arizona
Ark . . . . Arkansas
Atl. O . . . . Atlantic Ocean
Aus . . . . Austria
Austl . . . . Australia, Australian
auton . . . . autonomous
Az. Is . . . . Azores Islands
Ba . . . . Bahamas
Barb . . . . Barbados
B. C . . . . British Columbia
Bel . . . . Belgium, Belgian
Bhu . . . . Bhutan
Bis. Arch . . . . Bismarck Archipelago
Bngl . . . . Bangladesh
Bol . . . . Bolivia
Bots . . . . Botswana
Br . . . . British
Braz . . . . Brazil
Bru . . . . Brunei
Bul . . . . Bulgaria
Bur . . . . Burma
Calif . . . . California
Cam . . . . Cameroon
Camb . . . . Cambodia
Can . . . . Canada
Can. Is . . . . Canary Islands
Cen. Afr. Emp . . . . Central African Empire
Cen. Am . . . . Central America
co . . . . county
Col . . . . Colombia
Colo . . . . Colorado
Con . . . . Congo
Conn . . . . Connecticut
cont . . . . continent
C. R . . . . Costa Rica
C. V . . . . Cape Verde
Cyp . . . . Cyprus
C.Z . . . . Canal Zone
Czech . . . . Czechoslovakia
D.C . . . . District of Columbia
Del . . . . Delaware
Den . . . . Denmark
dep . . . . dependency, dependencies
dept . . . . department
dist . . . . district
div . . . . division
Dji . . . . Djibouti
Dom. Rep . . . . Dominican Republic
Ec . . . . Ecuador
Eg . . . . Egypt
Eng . . . . England
Equat. Gui . . . . Equatorial Guinea
Eth . . . . Ethiopia
Eur . . . . Europe
Falk. Is . . . . Falkland Islands
Fed . . . . Federation
Fin . . . . Finland
Fla . . . . Florida
Fr . . . . France, French
Fr. Gu . . . . French Guiana
Ga . . . . Georgia
Gam . . . . Gambia
Ger., Fed. Rep. of . . . . Federal Republic
of Germany
Ger. Dem. Rep . . . . German Democratic
Republic
Gib . . . . Gibraltar

Grc . . . . Greece
Grnld . . . . Greenland
Guad . . . . Guadeloupe
Guat . . . . Guatemala
Guy . . . . Guyana
Hai . . . . Haiti
Haw . . . . Hawaii
Hond . . . . Honduras
Hung . . . . Hungary
I . . . . Island
I.C . . . . Ivory Coast
Ice . . . . Iceland
Ill . . . . Illinois
incl . . . . includes, including
Ind . . . . Indiana
Indian res . . . . Indian reservation
Indon . . . . Indonesia
I. of Man . . . . Isle of Man
Ire . . . . Ireland
is . . . . islands
isl . . . . island
Isr . . . . Israel
It . . . . Italy
Jam . . . . Jamaica
Jap . . . . Japan
Kans . . . . Kansas
Ken . . . . Kenya
Kor . . . . Korea
Kuw . . . . Kuwait
Ky . . . . Kentucky
La . . . . Louisiana
Leb . . . . Lebanon
Le. Is . . . . Leeward Islands
Leso . . . . Lesotho
Lib . . . . Liberia
Liech . . . . Liechtenstein
Lux . . . . Luxembourg
Mad . . . . Madagascar
Mad. Is . . . . Madeira Islands
Mala . . . . Malaysia
Man . . . . Manitoba
Mart . . . . Martinique
Mass . . . . Massachusetts
Maur . . . . Mauritania
Md . . . . Maryland
Medit . . . . Mediterranean
Mex . . . . Mexico
Mich . . . . Michigan
Minn . . . . Minnesota
Miss . . . . Mississippi
Mo . . . . Missouri
Mong . . . . Mongolia
Mont . . . . Montana
Mor . . . . Morocco
Moz . . . . Mozambique
mtn . . . . mount, mountain
mts . . . . mountains
mun . . . . municipality
N.A . . . . North America
nat. mon . . . . national monument
nat. park . . . . national park
N.B . . . . New Brunswick
N.C . . . . North Carolina
N. Cal . . . . New Caledonia
N. Dak . . . . North Dakota
Nebr . . . . Nebraska
Nep . . . . Nepal
Neth . . . . Netherlands
Nev . . . . Nevada
Newf . . . . Newfoundland
New Hebr . . . . New Hebrides
N.H . . . . New Hampshire
Nic . . . . Nicaragua
Nig . . . . Nigeria
N. Ire . . . . Northern Ireland
N.J . . . . New Jersey
N. Mex . . . . New Mexico
Nor . . . . Norway, Norwegian
N.S . . . . Nova Scotia
N.W. Ter . . . . Northwest Territories
N.Y . . . . New York
N.Z . . . . New Zealand
occ . . . . occupied area
Okla . . . . Oklahoma

Om . . . . Oman
Ont . . . . Ontario
Oreg . . . . Oregon
Pa . . . . Pennsylvania
Pac. O . . . . Pacific Ocean
Pak . . . . Pakistan
Pan . . . . Panama
Pap. N. Gui . . . . Papua New Guinea
Par . . . . Paraguay
par . . . . parish
P.D.R. of Yem . . . . Yemen, People's
Democratic Republic of
P.E.I . . . . Prince Edward Island
pen . . . . peninsula
Phil . . . . Philippines
Pol . . . . Poland
pol. dist . . . . political district
pop . . . . population
Port . . . . Portugal, Portuguese
poss . . . . possession
P.R . . . . Puerto Rico
pref . . . . prefecture
prot . . . . protectorate
prov . . . . province, provincial
pt . . . . point
Que . . . . Quebec
reg . . . . region
rep . . . . republic
res . . . . reservation, reservoir
Rh . . . . Rhodesia
R.I . . . . Rhode Island
riv . . . . river
Rom . . . . Romania
S. A . . . . South America
S. Afr . . . . South Africa
Sal . . . . El Salvador
Sask . . . . Saskatchewan
Sau. Ar . . . . Saudi Arabia
S.C . . . . South Carolina
Scot . . . . Scotland
S. Dak . . . . South Dakota
Sen . . . . Senegal
S.L . . . . Sierra Leone
Sol. Is . . . . Solomon Islands
Som . . . . Somalia
Sov. Un . . . . Soviet Union
Sp . . . . Spain, Spanish
St., Ste . . . . Saint, Sainte
Sud . . . . Sudan
Sur . . . . Surinam
Swaz . . . . Swaziland
Swe . . . . Sweden
Switz . . . . Switzerland
Syr . . . . Syria
Tan . . . . Tanzania
Tenn . . . . Tennessee
ter . . . . territories, territory
Tex . . . . Texas
Thai . . . . Thailand
Trin . . . . Trinidad & Tobago
trust . . . . trusteeship
Tun . . . . Tunisia
Tur . . . . Turkey
U.A.E . . . . United Arab Emirates
Ug . . . . Uganda
U.K . . . . United Kingdom
Ur . . . . Uruguay
U.S . . . . United States
Va . . . . Virginia
Ven . . . . Venezuela
Viet . . . . Vietnam
Vir. Is . . . . Virgin Islands
vol . . . . volcano
Vt . . . . Vermont
Wash . . . . Washington
W.I . . . . West Indies
Win. Is . . . . Windward Islands
Wis . . . . Wisconsin
W. Sah . . . . Western Sahara
W. Sam . . . . Western Samoa
W. Va . . . . West Virginia
Wyo . . . . Wyoming
Yugo . . . . Yugoslavia

Explanation of the Map Index

This universal index includes in a single alphabetical list all important names that appear on the reference maps. Each place name is followed by its location; the population figure, when available; the map index key; and the page number of the map.

State locations are given for all places in the United States. Province and country locations are given for all places in Canada. All other place name entries show only country locations.

United States populations, including counties, metropolitan areas, and incorporated cities are final 1970 census figures. Populations for the States, foreign countries, dependencies and other major regions and political divisions are estimates for January 1, 1974. Populations for individual foreign cities and minor political divisions are from the latest available official census figures and estimates. A triangle symbol (▲) denotes a population figure for an *entire* township, district, or other minor civil division. For some larger cities a second population figure is given accompanied by a star (*). The second figure indicates the population of the city's entire metropolitan area including suburbs, as: Chicago, 3,369,357 (*7,582,700).

The index reference key, always a letter and figure combination, and the map page number are the last items in each entry. Because some places are shown on both a main map and an inset map, more than one index key may be given for a single map page number. Reference also may be made to more than a single map. In each case, however, the index key *letter and figure* precede

the map page number to which reference is made. A lower case key letter indicates reference to an inset map which has been keyed separately.

All major and minor political divisions are followed by both a descriptive term (co., dist., region, prov., dept., state, etc.), indicating political status, and by the country in which they are located. U. S. counties are listed with state locations; all others are given with county references.

The more important physical names that are shown on the maps are listed in the index. Each entry is followed by a descriptive term (bay, hill, range, riv., mtn., isl., etc.), to indicate its nature.

Country locations are given for each name, except for features entirely within States of the United States or provinces of Canada, in which case these divisions are also given.

Some names are included in the index that were omitted from the maps because of scale size or lack of space. These entries are identified by an asterisk (*) and reference is given to the approximate location on the map.

A long name may appear on the map in a shortened form, with the full name given in the index. The part of the name not on the map then appears in brackets, thus: St. Gabriel [-de-Brandon].

The system of alphabetizing used in the index is standard. When more than one name with the same spelling is shown, place names are listed *first* and political divisions *second*.

Index

A

Aachen, Ger., Fed. Rep. of, 239,619 (*475,000)......C3 6
Aalen, Ger., Fed. Rep. of, 50,572..............D5 6
Aalst, Bel., 46,518.......B6 5
Äänekoski, Fin., 7,200...F11 11
Aarau, Switz., 16,500. (*51,800).............E4 6
Aargau, canton, Switz., 427,000.............*E3 6
Aba, Nig., 131,003........G6 22
Ābādān, Iran, 272,962.....B7 23
Abaetetuba, Braz., 19,197.............*D6 27
Abakan, Sov. Un., 90,000.............D12 13
Abancay, Peru, 12,172....D3 31
Abashiri, Jap., 35,000 (43,904 ▲)...........D12 18
Abbeville, Ala., 2,996.....D4 46
Abbeville, Fr., 23,999.....B4 5
Abbeville, La., 10,996.....E3 63
Abbeville, S.C. 5,515......C3 82
Abbeville, co., S.C., 21,112...............C2 82
Abbiategrasso, It., 25,900..C2 82
Abbotsford, B.C., Can., 888................f13 37
Abbotsford, Wis., 1,375...D3 88
Åbenrå, co., Den., 49,769.............*J3 11
Abeokuta, Nig., 187,292...G5 22
Aberdare, Wales, 37,780...E5 4
Aberdeen, Idaho, 1,542....G6 57
Aberdeen, Md., 12,375.....A5 53
Aberdeen, Miss., 6,507....B5 68
Aberdeen, N.C., 1,592.....B3 76
Aberdeen, Scot., 181,785 (*210,000)..........B5 4
Aberdeen, S. Dak., 26,476............E7 77
Aberdeen, Wash., 18,489...C2 86
Aberdeen, co., Scot., 320,523............*B5 4
Abergavenny, Wales, 9,290..............E5 4
Abernathy, Tex., 2,625....C2 84
Aberystwyth, Wales, 12,150.............D4 4
Abidjan, I.C., 285,000....G4 22
Abilene, Kans., 6,661.....D6 61
Abilene, Tex., 89,653 (*92,100)............C3 84
Abingdon, Ill., 3,936......C3 58
Abingdon, Va., 4,376.....f10 85
Abington, Mass., 4,700...........B6, h12 65
Abington, Pa., 7,900.....o21 81
Abitibi, co., Que., Can., 114,725............*h12 42
Åbo, see Turku, Fin.
Abomey, Benin, 18,900....G5 22

Abony, Hung., 12,633.....B5 10
Abra, prov., Phil., 115,193..........*B6 19
Abruzzi, reg., It., 1,205,200..........C4 9
Abruzzi e Molise, pol. dist., It., 1,564,318.........C4 9
Absecon, N.J., 6,094......E3 74
Abū Dhabi (Abū Zaby), U.A.E., 22,000......E5 15
Abū Kamāl, Syr., 8,266..E13 14
Aby, Swe., 2,795.........u34 11
Acadia, par., La., 52,109..D3 63
Acámbaro, Mex., 32,257.........C4, m13 34
Acaponeta, Mex., 11,844..C4 34
Acapulco [de Juárez], Mex., 174,378.........D5 34
Acarigua, Ven., 57,470....B4 32
Acatlán [de Osorio], Mex., 7,624............D5, m14 34
Acayucan, Mex., 21,173...D6 34
Accomack, co., Va., 29,004..............C7 85
Accoville, W. Va., 500................D3, n12 87
Accra, Ghana, 615,800....G4 22
Achinsk, Sov. Un., 97,000.............D12 13
Acireale, It., 29,100 (47,600 ▲)..........F5 9
Ackerman, Miss., 1,502....B4 68
Ackley, Iowa, 1,794.......B4 60
Acmetonia, Pa., 1,200....*E1 81
Aconcagua, prov., Chile, 159,800..........A2 28
Aconcagua, peak, Arg....A3 28
Acqui, It., 12,200.........B2 9
Acre, state, Braz., 216,200..C3 31
Acre, riv., Braz..........D4 31
Acton, Ont., Can., 5,031..D4 41
Acton Vale, Que., Can., 4,564............D5 42
Açu, Braz., 13,268.......*D7 27
Acushnet, Mass., 7,767...C6 65
Acworth, Ga., 3,929......B2 55
Ada, Minn., 2,076........C2 67
Ada, Ohio, 5,309.........B2 78
Ada, Okla., 14,859.......C5 79
Ada, Yugo., 12,282.......C5 10
Ada, co., Idaho, 112,230..F2 57
Adair, co., Iowa, 9,487...C3 60
Adair, co., Ky., 13,037...C4 62
Adair, co., Mo., 22,472...A5 69
Adair, co., Okla., 15,141..B7 79
Adairsville, Ga., 1,676....B2 55
Adam, mtn., Wash........C4 86
Adamantina, Braz., 18,164............C2 30
Adams, Mass., 11,772....A1 65
Adams, Minn., 771.......G6 67
Adams, N.Y., 1,951......B4 75

Adams, Wis., 1,440.......E4 88
Adams, co., Colo., 185,789............B6 51
Adams, co., Idaho, 2,877..E2 57
Adams, co., Ill., 70,861...D2 58
Adams, co., Ind., 26,871..C8 59
Adams, co., Iowa, 6,322...C3 60
Adams, co., Miss., 37,293..D2 68
Adams, co., Nebr., 30,553..D7 71
Adams, co., N. Dak., 3,832..............D3 77
Adams, co., Ohio, 18,957..D2 78
Adams, co., Pa., 56,937...G7 81
Adams, co., Wash., 12,014..B7 86
Adams, co., Wis., 9,234...D4 88
Adams, mtn., Mass.......A2 65
Adams, mtn., Wash.......C4 86
Adams Center, N.Y., 800..B5 75
Adamston, N.J., 1,300....C4 74
Adamstown, Pa., 1,202...F9 81
Adamsville, Ala., 2,412....f7 46
Adamsville, Tenn., 1,344..B3 83
Adana, Tur., 347,454....D10 14
Adapazari, Tur., 101,283..B8 14
Ad Dāmir, Sud., 7,700....E4 23
Addis Ababa, Eth., 912,090............G5 23
Addison, Ill., 24,482......k9 58
Addison, co., Vt., 24,266..C1 73
Ad Dīwānīyah, Iraq, 60,553............C3 15
Ad Duwaym, Sud., 12,319..F4 23
Addyston, Ohio, 1,336...o12 78
Adel, Ga., 4,972.........C3 55
Adel, Iowa, 2,419........C3 60
Adelaide, Austl., 16,331 (*842,611)..........F6 25
Adelphi, Md., 12,000....*C4 53
Aden, P.D.R. of Yem., 150,000 (*225,000)...G4 15
Adena, Ohio, 1,134......B5 78
Adigrat, Eth., 9,071.....F5 23
Adirondack, mts., N.Y..........A6, f10 75
Adi Ugri, Eth., 11,920....F5 23
Adiyaman, Tur., 31,263..C12 14
Adjuntas, P.R., 5,319 (18,691 ▲).........*G11 35
Admiralty, is., Pap. N. Gui..........h12 25
Ado-Ekiti, Nig., 157,519..*E6 22
Adrano, It., 32,500.......F5 9
Adria, It., 15,700 (22,700 ▲)..........B4 9
Adrian, Mich., 20,382....G6 66
Adrian, Minn., 1,350.....G3 67
Adrian, Mo., 1,259.......C3 69
Adrianople, see Edirne, Tur.
Adwā, Eth., 17,670......F5 23
Afars & Issas, see Djibouti, country, Afr.
Affton, Mo., 24,898......C7 69

Afghanistan, country, Asia, 18,475,000......B4 20
Africa, cont., 383,200,000.... 21
Afton, Iowa, 823........C3 60
Afton, N.Y., 1,064.......C5 75
Afton, Okla., 1,022......A7 79
Afton, Wyo., 1,290......D2 89
'Afula, Isr., 17,400......B3 15
Afyon, Tur., 53,497......C8 14
Agadez, Niger, 4,700.....E6 22
Agadir, Mor., 61,192.....B3 22
Agana, Guam, 2,400 (*25,000)...........*F6 2
Agartala, India, 59,625...D9 20
Agate Beach, Oreg., 700...C2 80
Agawam, Mass., 10,000...B2 65
Agboville, I.C., 13,000...G4 22
Agde, Fr., 7,696.........F5 5
Agematsu, Jap..........n16 18
Agen, Fr., 34,949........E4 5
Agira, It., 14,079........F5 9
Agnone, It., 9,888........D5 9
Agra, India, 591,917 (*634,622)..........C6 20
Agrícola Oriental, Mex., 124,900...........*D5 34
Agrigento, It., 45,500 (51,700 ▲).........F4 9
Agrínion, Grc., 30,973 (*41,794)..........C3 14
Aguada, P.R., 3,759....*G11 35
Aguadas, Col., 10,822....B2 32
Aguadilla, P.R., 21,031 (51,355 ▲).........G11 35
Aguascalientes, Mex., 181,277.........C4, m12 34
Aguascalientes, state, Mex., 273,300....C4, k12 34
Aguilar, Colo., 699......D6 51
Aguijita, Mex., 5,463...*B4 34
Agusan prov., Phil., 271,010...........*D7 19
Ahlen, Ger., Fed. Rep. of, 50,852.............C3 6
Ahmadabad, India, 1,585,544 (*1,950,000)..D5 20
Ahmadnagar, India, 118,236 (*148,405).....E5 20
Ahmadpur East, Pak., 34,423............C5 20
Ahoskie, N.C., 5,105.....A6 76
Ahrweiler, Ger., Fed. Rep. of, 23,619....C3 6
Ahuachapan, Sal., 17,242............E7 34
Ahualulco de Mercado, Mex., 9,321........m12 34
Ahvāz, Iran, 206,375....B7 23
Ahvenanmaa (Åland), prov., Fin., 21,500....G8 11
Aibonito, P.R., 7,582 (20,044 ▲).........*G11 35

Aichi, pref., Jap., 5,386,163 . . . . . *I8 18
Aiea, Haw., 12,560 . . . B4, g10 56
Aihui (Aigun), China, 25,000 . . . . . A10 17
Aikawa, Jap G9 18
Aiken, S.C., 13,436 . . . . . D4 82
Aiken, co., S.C.,91,023 . . . D4 82
Aiken West, S.C., 2,689 . . . *D4 82
Aimorés, Braz., 12,641 . . . . B4 30
Ain, dept., Fr., 339,262 . . . *D6 5
Aïn-Sefra, Alg., 8,369 . . . . . B4 22
Ainsworth, Nebr., 2,073 . . . B6 71
Aire-sur-la-Lys, Fr., 5,528 . . . . . B5 5
Aisén, prov., Chile, 50,100 . . . . . D2 28
Aitkin, Minn., 1,553 . . . . . D5 67
Aitkin, co., Minn., 11,403 . . . . . D5 67
Aitolía kai Akarnania, prov., Grc., 228,719 . . . *C3 14
Aitolikón, Grc., 4,832 . . . . C3 24
Aiud, Rom., 11,886 . . . . . B6 10
Aix-[en-Provence], Fr., 89,566 . . . . . F6 5
Aix-la-Chapelle, see Aachen, Ger., Fed. Rep. of
Aix-les-Bains, Fr.,20,627 . . . E6 5
Aiyina, Grc., 5,704 . . . . . D4 14
Aiyion, Grc., 18,829 (*23,756) C4 14
Aizu-wakamatsu, Jap., 104,065 . . . . . H9 18
Ajaccio, Fr., 40,834 . . . . . D2 9
Ajax, Ont., Can., 12,515 . . D6 41
Ajmer, India, 262,851 . . . . C5 20
Ajo, Ariz., 5,881 . . . . . C2 48
Akashi, Jap., 206,525 . . . . . I7 18
Akcaabat, Tur., 9,500 . . . B12 14
Akershus, co., Nor., 300,800 . . . . . *H4 11
Aketi, Zaire, 12,100 . . . . . H2 23
Akhaïa (Achaea), prov., Grc., 238,594 . . . . . *C3 14
Akharnaí, Grc., 24,621 . . . g11 14
Akhisar, Tur., 48,796 . . . . . C6 14
Akhtyrka, Sov. Un., 41,000 . . . . . F10 12
Aki, Jap., 13,800 (24,498 ▲) . J6 18
Akita, Jap., 235,873 . . . . . G10 18
Akita, pref., Jap., 1,241,376 . . . . . *G1 18
Akkeshi, Jap., 5,476 . . . . . E12 18
'Akko (Acre), Isr., 34,400 . . . . . B3, g5 15
Akola, India, 168,438 . . . . D6 20
Akron, Colo., 1,775 . . . . . A7 51
Akron, Ind., 1,019 . . . . . B5 59
Akron, Iowa, 1,324 . . . . . B1 60
Akron, N.Y., 2,863 . . . . . B2 75
Akron, Ohio, 275,425 (*635,300) A4 78
Akron, Pa., 3,149 . . . . . F9 81
Aksaray, Tur., 30,138 . . . . C10 14
Akşehir, Tur., 32,591 . . . . . C8 14
Aksenovo-Zilovskove, Sov. Un., 10,000 . . . . . D14 13
Aktyubinsk, Sov. Un., 150,000 . . . . . D8 13
Akureyri, Ice., 10,500 . . . . n23 11
Alabama, state, U.S., 3,523,000 46
Alabaster, Ala., 2,642 . . . . . B3 46
Alachua, Fla., 2,252 . . . . . C4 54
Alachua, co., Fla., 104,764 . . . . . C4 54
Alagoa Grande, Braz., 12,741 . . . . . *D7 27
Alagôas, state, Braz., 1,606,174 . . . . . *D7 27
Alagoinhas, Braz., 53,891 . . . . . *E7 27
Alajuela, C.R., 27,300 . . . . E8 34
Al 'Alamayn (El Alamein), Eg., 970 . . . . . G7 14
Alamance, co., N.C., 96,362 . . . . . B3 76
Alameda, Calif., 70,968 . . . . h8 50
Alameda, N. Mex., 4,000 . . . . . B5, D5 48
Alameda, co., Calif., 1,073,184 . . . . . D3 50
Alamo, Calif., 4,560 . . . . . *D3 50
Alamo, Tenn., 2,499 . . . . . B2 83
Alamo, Tex., 4,291 . . . . . F3 84
Alamogordo, N. Mex., 23,035 . . . . . C6 48
Alamo Heights, Tex., 6,933 . . . . . E3, k7 84
Alamosa, Colo., 6,985 . . . . D5 51
Alamosa, co., Colo., 11,422 . . . . . D5 51
Alanya, Tur., 15,011 . . . . . D9 14
Alaşehir, Tur., 20,300 . . . . C7 14
Alaska, State, U.S., 337,000 47
Alassio, It., 8,544 . . . . . C2 9
Alatyr, Sov. Un., 43,000 . . . . . D16 12
Alava, prov., Sp., 187,300 . . . . . *A4 8
Alba, It., 20,800 (26,500 ▲) B2 9
Albacete, Sp., 79,000 (93,062 ▲) C5 8
Alba Iulia, Rom., 22,200 . . B6 10
Albania, country, Eur., 2,380,000 . . . . . B2 14
Albano Laziale, It., 19,300 (24,400 ▲) . . . D4, h9 9
Albany, Ga., 72,623 (*87,600) E2 55
Albany, Ind., 2,293 . . . . . D7 59
Albany, Ky., 1,891 . . . . . D4 62
Albany, Minn., 1,599 . . . . . E4 67
Albany, Mo., 1,804 . . . . . A3 69
Albany, N.Y., 115,781 (*726,900) C7 75
Albany, Oreg., 18,181 . . . . . C3, k11 80
Albany, Tex., 1,978 . . . . . C3 84
Albany, Wis., 875 . . . . . F4 88
Albany, co., N.Y., 286,742 . . . . . C6 75
Albany, co., Wyo., 26,431 . . E6 89
Albany, riv., Ont o18 41
Al Batrūn, Leb., 2,500 . . . . f5 15
Albay, prov., Phil., 514,980 . . . . . *C6 19
Albemarle, N.C., 11,126 . . . B2 76
Albemarle, co., Va., 37,780 . . . . . C4 85
Albenga, It., 8,700 . . . . . B2 9
Albert, Fr., 10,960 . . . . . B5 5
Albert, co., N.B., Can., 12,485 . . . . . D5 43
Albert, lake, Ug., Zaire . . . H4 23
Alberta, prov., Can., 1,700,000 38
Alberta, mtn., Alta., Can C2 38
Albert Edward, mtn., Pap. N. Gui k12 25
Albert Lea, Minn., 19,418 . . . . . G5 67
Albertson, N.Y., 11,420 . . . . . *G2 52
Albertville, Ala., 9,963 . . . . A3 46
Albertville, Fr., 12,159 . . . . . E7 5
Albi, Fr., 42,930 . . . . . F5 5
Albia, Iowa 4,151 . . . . . C5 60
Albion, Ill., 1,791 . . . . . E5 58
Albion, Ind., 1,498 . . . . . B7 59
Albion, Mich., 12,112 . . . . . F6 66
Albion, Nebr., 2,074 . . . . . C7 71
Albion, N.Y., 5,122 . . . . . B2 75
Albion, R.I., 700 . . . . . B11 52
Ålborg, Den., 83,900 (*123,500) I3 11
Albuñol, Sp., 7,989 . . . . . D4 8
Albuquerque, N. Mex., 243,751 (*327,700) B5, D5 48
Alburquerque, Sp., 9,756 . . C2 8
Alburtis, Pa., 1,142 . . . . . F10 81
Albury-Wodonga, Austl., 37,916 . . . . . G8 25
Alcalá [de Guadaira], Sp., 27,378 (31,004 ▲) D3 8
Alcalá de Henares, Sp., 57,354 . . . . . B4, p18 8
Alcalá de los Gazules, Sp., 9,693 . . . . . D3 8
Alcamo, It., 42,800 . . . . . F4 9
Alcanar, Sp., 6,944 . . . . . B6 8
Alcañiz, Sp., 10,035 . . . . . B5 8
Alcaraz, Sp., 5,864 . . . . . C4 8
Alcaudete, Sp., 18,442 . . . . D3 8
Alcázar de San Juan, Sp., 24,963 . . . . . C4 8
Alcazarquivir, see Ksar el Kebir, Mor.
Alcira, Sp., 26,669 . . . . . C5 8
Alco, La., 15 . . . . . C2 63
Alcoa, Tenn., 7,739 . . . . . D10, n14 83
Alcona, co., Mich., 7,113 . . D7 66
Alcorn, co., Miss., 27,179 . . A5 68
Alcoy, Sp., 61,061 . . . . . C5 8
Alcoy, Nevado, mtn., Peru D2 31
Aldan, Pa., 5,001 . . . . . *G11 81
Aldan, Sov. Un., 18,000 . . . . . D15 13
Aldan, riv., Sov. Un C16 13
Alden, Iowa, 876 . . . . . B4 60
Alden, N.Y., 2,651 . . . . . C2 75
Alden, Pa., 800 . . . . . D9 81
Aldershot, Eng., 33,900 (*210,000) E6 4
Alderson, W. Va., 1,278 . . . D4 87
Alderwood Manor, Wash., 3,800 . . . . . B3 86
Aledo, Ill., 3,325 . . . . . B3 58
Alegre, Braz., 8,312 . . . . . C4 30
Alegrete, Braz., 45,522 . . . . D1 30
Aleksandriya, Sov. Un., 69,000 . . . . . G9 12
Aleksandrov, Sov. Un., 50,000 . . . . . C12 12
Aleksandrovsk [-Sakhalinskiy], Sov. Un., 20,000 . . . . . D17 13
Aleksandrów, Pol., 8,489 . . . B5 7
Aleksinac, Yugo., 12,022 . . . D5 10
Alençon, Fr., 31,656 . . . . . C4 5
Aleppo (Ḥalab), Syr., 639,361 . . . . . D11 14
Alert Bay, B.C., Can., 825 . . . . . D4 37
Alès, Fr., 42,818 . . . . . E6 5
Alessandria, It., 86,900 . . . . B2 9
Alesund, Nor., 39,000 . . . . . F2 11
Alexander, co., Ill.,12,015 . . F4 58
Alexander, co., N.C., 19,466 . . . . . B1 76
Alexander City, Ala., 12,358 . . . . . C4 46
Alexander Mills, N.C., 988 . . . . . B1, f11 76
Alexandria, Ont., Can., 3,240 . . . . . B10 41
Alexandria (Al Iskandarīyah), Eg., 1,875,000 (*2,075,000) . G7 14
Alexandria, Ind., 5,600 . . . D6 59
Alexandria, Ky., 3,844 . . . . . B5, k14 62
Alexandria, La., 41,557 (*93,500) C3 63
Alexandria, Minn., 6,973 . . E3 67
Alexandria, Rom., 19,294 . . D7 10
Alexandria (Independent City), Va., 110,927 . . . . . B5, g12 85
Alexandria Bay, N.Y., 1,440 . . . . . A5, f9 75
Alexandria Southwest, La., 2,782 . . . . . *C3 63
Alexandroúpolis, Grc., 22,995 . . . . . B5 14
Alexis, Ill., 946 . . . . . B3 58
Aleysk, Sov. Un., 32,000 . . . . . D11 13
Alfalfa, co., Okla., 7,224 . . . A3 79
Al Fallūjah, Iraq, 38,072 . . F14 14
Alfaro, Sp., 8,570 . . . . . A5 8
Al Fayyūm Eg., 133,616 . . . . . H8 14
Alfenas, Braz., 20,806 . . C3, k9 30
Alfortville, Fr., 35,023 . . . . g10 5
Alfred, Ont., Can., 1,230 . . . . . B10 41
Alfred, N.Y., 3,804 . . . . . C3 75
Algarve, prov., Port., 328,231 . . . . . D1 8
Algarve, reg., Port., 315,400 . . . . . *D2 8
Algeciras, Sp., 79,997 . . . D3 8
Algemesí, Sp., 19,057 . . . . . C5 8
Alger, Ohio, 1,071 . . . . . B2 78
Alger, co., Mich., 8,568 . . . . B4 66
Algeria, country, Afr., 16,000,000 . . . . . C3 22
Alghero, It., 25,600 . . . . . D2 9
Al Ghurdaqah, Eg., 2,082 . . . . . C4 23
Algiers (Alger), Alg., 1,000,000 (*1,175,000) . . A5 22
Algoma, dist., Ont., Can . . . A2 41
Algoma, Wis., 4,023 . . . . . D6 88
Algona, Iowa, 6,032 . . . . . A3 60
Algona, Wash., 1,276 . . B3, f11 86
Algonac, Mich., 3,684 . . . . . F8 66
Algonquin, Ill., 3,515 . . A5, h8 58
Al Ḥadīthah, Iraq, 6,870 . . E14 14
Alhama, Sp., 9,849 . . . . . D5 8
Alhambra, Calif., 62,125 . . . . . m12 50
Alhaurín el Grande, Sp., 11,525 . . . . . D3 8
Al Ḥillah, Iraq, 84,717 . . . F15 14
Al Hufūf (Hofuf), Sau. Ar., 85,000 . . . . . D4 15
Al Ḥuṣayḥiṣah, Sud., 6,600 . F4 23
Alicante, Sp., 181,550 . . . . . C5 8
Alice, Tex., 20,121 . . . . . F3 84
Alice Southwest, Tex., 1,908 . . . . . *F3 84
Aliceville, Kans., 65 . . . . . D8 61
Alīgarh, India, 252,314 . . . . C6 20
Alingsås, Swe., 20,217 . . . . . I5 11
Aliquippa, Pa., 22,277 . . . . . E1, h13 81
Al Iskandarīyah, see Alexandria, Eg.
Al Ismā 'īlīyah, Eg., 144,163 . . . . . G9 14
Alistráti, Grc., 2,702 . . . . . B4 14
Aliwal North, S. Afr., 10,762 . . . . . G5 24
Al Jawf (Jauf), Sau. Ar., 20,000 . . . . . D2 15
Al Jīzah (Giza), Eg., 329,810 . . . . . H8 14
Al Junaynah, Sud., 11,817 . . F2 23
Aljustrel, Port., 5,844 . . . . . D1 8
Al Karak, Jordan, 7,422 . . . . . C3, h5 15
Al Kāẓimīyah, Iraq, 99,086 . . . . . F14 14
Al Khābūrah, Om D2 20
Al Khalil (Hebron), Jordan, 38,348 . . . . . C3, h5 15
Al Khārijah, Eg., 15,719 . . C4 23
Alkmaar, Neth., 60,375 (*94,000) A6 5
Al Kūfah, Iraq, 30,862 . . . F15 14
Al Lādhiqīyah, see Latakia, Syr.
Allahābād, India (*513,036) C7 20
Allamakee, co., Iowa, 14,968 . . . . . A6 60
Allanmyo, Bur., 15,580 . . . E10 20
Allariz, Sp., 9,403 . . . . . A2 8
Allaykha, Sov. Un., 800 . . B17 13
Allegan, Mich., 4,516 . . . . . F5 66
Allegan, co., Mich., 66,575 . . . . . F4 66
Allegany, N.Y., 2,050 . . . . . C2 75
Allegany, co., Md., 84,044 . . . . . A1 53
Allegany, co., N.Y., 46,458 . . . . . C2 75
Allegany, co., N.C., 8,134 . . A1 76
Allegheny, co., Pa., 1,605,133 . . . . . E1 81
Allegany, co., Va., 12,461 . . C3 85
Allegheny, mts., U.S C10 45
Allegheny, riv., Pa E2 81
Allen, Okla., 974 . . . . . C5 79
Allen, co., Ind., 280,454 . . . B7 59
Allen, co., Kans., 15,043 . . . E8 61
Allen, co., Ky., 12,598 . . . . . D3 62
Allen, co., Ohio, 111,144 . . B1 78
Allen, par., La., 20,794 . . . . D3 63
Allendale, N.J., 6,240 . . . . . A4 74
Allendale, S.C., 3,620 . . . . . E5 82
Allendale, co., S.C., 9,692 . . . . . F5 82
Allen Park, Mich., 40,747 . . . . . p15 66
Allenport, Pa., 762 . . . . . F1 81
Allenstein, see Olsztyn, Pol.
Allentown, N.J., 1,603 . . . . . C3 74
Allentown, Pa., 109,871 (*502,000) E11 81
Alleppey, India, 160,166 . . . G6 20
Aller (Cabañaquinta), Sp., 828 . . . . . A3 8
Alliance, Nebr., 6,862 . . . . . B3 71
Alliance, Ohio, 26,547 . . . . B4 78
Allier, dept., Fr., 386,533 D5 5
Allinge, Den., 2,114 . . . . . A3 7
Allison, Iowa, 1,071 . . . . . B5 60
Allison, Pa., 1,040 . . . . . G2 81
Allison Park, Pa., 5,600 . . . h14 81
Alliston, Ont., Can., 3,176 . . . . . C5 41
Al Līth, Sau. Ar., 10,000 . . D6 23
Alloa, Scot., 14,110 . . . . . B5 4
Allouez, Wis., 13,753 . . . . . h9 88
Al Luhayyah, Yemen, 5,000 . . . . . F3 15
Alma, Ark., 1,613 . . . . . B1 49
Alma, Ga., 3,756 . . . . . E4 55
Alma, Kans., 905 . . . . . C7 61
Alma, Mich., 9,611 . . . . . E6 66
Alma, Nebr., 1,299 . . . . . D6 71
Alma, Wis., 956 . . . . . D2 88
Alma-Ata, Sov. Un., 753,000 . . . . . E10 13
Almada, Port., 11,995 . . . . . f9 8
Almadén, Sp., 13,443 . . . . . C3 8
Al Madīnah, see Medina, Sau. Ar.
Almagro, Sp., 9,681 . . . . . C4 8
Al Maḥallah al Kubrā, Eg., 225,323 . . . . . G8 14
Almansa, Sp., 15,391 . . . . . C5 8
Al Manṣūrah, Eg., 191,459 . . . . . G8 14
Al Marj, Libya, 10,600 . . . . B2 23
Al Mawṣil, see Mosul, Iraq
Almeirim, Port., 7,104 . . . . . C1 8
Almelo, Neth., 59,821 . . . . . A7 5
Almendralejo, Sp., 21,884 . . . . . C2 8
Almería Sp., 114,298 . . . . . D4 8
Al Minyā, Eg., 112,580 . . . C4 23
Almiros, Grc., 5,680 . . . . . C4 14
Almodóvar, Sp., 14,633 . . . . C3 8
Almogía, Sp., 8,341 . . . . . D3 8
Almon, Ga., 350 . . . . . C3 55
Almonesson, N.J., 2,000 . . . D2 74
Almont, Mich., 1,634 . . . . . F7 66

Almonte, Ont., Can., 3,696..........B8 41
Almora, Minn., 100......*D3 67
Almoradí, Sp., 3,998......C5 8
Al Mukallā, P.D.R. of Yem., 25,000..........G4 15
Al Mukhā, Yemen, 5,000..G3 15
Almuñécar, Sp., 6,235.....D4 8
Alnwick, Eng., 7,220......C6 4
Aloha, Oreg., 5,000......h12 80
Alora, Sp., 5,960.........D3 8
Alor Setar, Mala., 66,260..D2 19
Alorton (Fireworks), Ill., 3,573..........*E3 58
Alosno, Sp., 5,814........D2 8
Alotai (Sharasume), China, 25,000..........B2 17
Alpaugh, Calif., 800.......E4 50
Alpena, Mich., 13,805.....C7 66
Alpena, co., Mich., 30,708..C7 66
Alpes-Maritimes, dept., Fr., 722,070..........*F7 5
Alpha, N.J., 8,829.......B2 74
Alpharetta, Ga., 2,455.....B2 55
Alpiarça, Port., 6,680.....C1 8
Alpine, Calif., 1,570.....*F5 50
Alpine, N.J., 1,344........h9 74
Alpine, Tex., 5,971.......o13 84
Alpine, co., Calif., 484.....C4 50
Alpoca, W. Va., 250.......D3 87
Al Qadarif, Sud., 17,537...F5 23
Al Qāhirah, see Cairo, Eg.
Al Qanṭarah, Eg., 2,000...G9 14
Al Qaṭīf, Sau. Ar., 30,000..D4 15
Al Qunayṭirah, see Kuneitra, Syr.
Alsfeld, Ger., Fed. Rep. of 10,300..........C4 6
Alsip, Ill., 11,141.........B6 58
Alta, Iowa, 1,717.........B2 6
Altadena, Calif., 41,700..m12 50
Alta Gracia, Arg., 11,628..A4 28
Alta Loma, Tex., 1,536...r14 84
Altamont, Ill., 1,929......D5 58
Altamont, N.Y., 1,561.....C6 75
Altamont, Oreg., 15,746...E5 80
Altamonte Springs, Fla., 4,391..........*D5 54
Altamura, It., 46,000......D6 9
Altavista, Va., 2,708......C3 85
Altdorf, Switz., 8,647......E4 6
Altenburg, Mo., 277.......D8 69
Altheimer, Ark., 1,037.....C4 49
Alto, Tex., 1,045.........D5 84
Alto Alentejo, prov., Port., 400,374.........*C2 8
Alton, Ill., 39,700.........E3 58
Alton, Iowa, 1,018........B1 60
Altona, Man., Can., 2,122.E3 40
Altoona, Ala., 781.........A3 46
Altoona, Iowa, 2,883.......C4 6
Altoona, Pa., 63,115 (*102,800)..........F5 81
Altoona, Wis., 2,842......D2 88
Alto Paraná, dept., Par., 24,067..........D4 29
Alturas, Calif., 2,799......B3 50
Altus, Okla., 23,302.......C2 79
Alula, Som., 1,300.......F8 23
Al Uqṣur (Luxor), Eg., 77,578..........C4 23
Alva, Ky., 100...........D6 62
Alva, Okla., 7,440........A3 79
Alvarado, Tex., 2,129..C4, n9 84
Alvin, Tex., 10,671....E5, r14 84
Älvsborg, co., Swe., 395,200..........*H5 11
Alwar, India, 100,378.....C6 20
Alx, mtn., Wash..........C4 86
Alytus, Sov. Un., 27,900...A8 7
Amador, co., Calif., 11,821..........C3 50
Amagansett, N.Y., 1,500..n16 75
Amagasaki, Jap., 553,696..o14 18
Amål, Swe., 10,617.......H5 11
Amalias, Grc., 14,177.....D3 14
Amambay, dept., Par., 34,505..........D4 29
Amantea, It., 5,822.......E6 9
Amapá, Braz., 1,923......C5 27
Amarillo, Tex., 127,010 (*132,200)..........B2 84
Amaroúsion, Grc., 27,122.g11 14
Amasya (Amasia), Tur., 36,646..........B10 14
Amazonas, comisaría, Col., 14,900..........D3 32
Amazonas, dept., Peru, 129,003..........B2 31
Amazonas, state, Braz., 960,934..........C3 31
Amazonas, (Amazon), riv., Braz., Peru..........D5 27
Amazon, see Amazonas, riv., Braz., Peru
Ambāla, India, 83,633 (*186,126)..........B6 20
Ambarchik, Sov. Un., 800.C19 13
Ambato, Ec., 67,100.......B2 31
Amberg, Ger., Fed. Rep. of 48,104..........D5 6
Ambérieu [-en-Bugey], Fr., 7,748..........E6 5
Amberley, Ohio, 4,761...*C1 78
Ambikāpur, India, 23,087..D7 20
Ambler, Pa., 7,800...F11, o21 81
Amboise, Fr., 8,625.......D4 5
Ambon (Amboina), Indon., 79,636..........F7 19
Amboy, Ill., 2,184........B4 58
Ambridge, Pa., 11,324..........E1, h13 81
Ambridge Heights, Pa., 5,022..........*E1 81
Amderma, Sov. Un., 10,000..........C9 13
Ameca, Mex., 21,018..........C4, m11 34
Amecameca [de Juárez], Mex., 16,276..........n14 34
Amelia, La., 2,292.....E4, k9 63
Amelia, Ohio, 820........C1 78
Amelia, co., Va., 7,592....C4 85
Amelia Court House, Va., 600..........C5 85
Amenia, N. Dak., 80......D8 77
Amenia, N.Y., 1,157......D7 75
American Falls, Idaho, 2,769..........G6 57
American Fork, Utah, 7,713..........A6, D2 72
American Samoa, U.S. dep., Oceania, 30,000..*G9 2
Americus, Ga., 16,091.....D2 55
Amersfoort, Neth., 79,876 (*118,000)..........A6 5
Amery, Wis., 2,126.......C1 88
Ames, Iowa, 39,505 (*51,000)..........B4 60
Amesbury, Mass., 11,388...A6 65
Amfissa, Grc., 6,605......C4 14
Amga, Sov. Un., 800.....C16 13
Amherst, N.S., Can., 9,966..........D5 43
Amherst, Mass., 17,926....B2 65
Amherst (Eggertsville), N.Y., 54,700..........*C2 75
Amherst, Ohio, 9,902......A3 78
Amherst, Tex., 825........B1 84
Amherst, Va., 1,108.......C3 85
Amherst, co., Va., 26,072..C3 85
Amherstburg, Ont., Can., 5,169..........E1 41
Amherstdale, W. Va., 850..........D3, n12 87
Amiens, Fr., 117,888 (*138,000)..........C5 5
Amite, La., 3,593.........D5 63
Amite, co., Miss., 13,763...D3 68
Amityville, N.Y., 9,794..........E7, n15 75
'Ammān, Jordan., 330,200..........C3, h5 15
Ammon, Idaho, 2,545.....F7 57
Amory, Miss., 7,236.......B5 68
Amos, Que., Can., 6,984..o20 41
Amoy (Hsiamen), China, 308,000..........G8 17
Amparo, Braz., 19,349..........C3, m8 30
Amqui, Que., Can., 3,797..........*k13 42
Amrāvati, India, 193,800 (*221,277)..........D6 20
Amritsar, India, 407,628 (*458,029)..........B5 20
Amsterdam, Neth., 791,769 (*1,800,000)....A6 5
Amsterdam, N.Y., 25,524..C6 75
Amsterdam, Ohio, 882.....B5 78
Amstetten, Aus., 13,334....D7 6
Amu Darya, riv., Sov. Un..F9 13
Amur, riv., China, Sov. Un.......E16 13
'Ānah, Iraq, 6,884........C3 15
Anaconda, Mont., 9,771...D4 70
Anacortes, Wash., 7,701...A3 86
Anadarko, Okla., 6,682....B3 79
Anadyr, Sov. Un., 5,000..C20 13
Anaheim, Calif., 166,408..........F5, n13 50
Anahuac, Tex., 1,881..E5, r15 84
Anakāpalle, India, 57,273..E7 20
Analalava, Mad., 1,900....C9 24
Anamosa, Iowa, 4,389.....B6 60
Anandale, La., 1,779......*C3 63
Anantapur, India, 80,069..F6 20
Anantnāg, India, 27,643...B6 20
Ananyev, Sov. Un., 5,000. H7 12
Anápolis, Braz., 89,405....B3 30
Añatuya, Arg., 11,753.....E3 29
Anawalt, W. Va., 801.....D3 87
Ancash, dept., Peru, 605,548..........C2 31
Anchorage, Alsk., 48,081 (*123,800)........C10, g17 47
Anchorage, Ky., 1,477....g11 62
Anchor Bay Gardens, Mich., 1,000..........*F8 66
Ancienne Lorette, Que., Can., 8,304........C6, n17 42
Ancon, C.Z., 1,151.........B2 32
Ancona, It., 108,300......C4 9
Andalusia, Ala., 10,098....D3 46
Andalusia, reg., Sp., 6,168,000..........D3 8
Andaman and Nicobar Islands, ter., India, 115,133..........F9, G9 20
Anderlecht, Bel., 103,712...B6 5
Andernach, Ger., Fed. Rep. of, 27,229....C3 6
Anderson, Calif., 5,492....B2 50
Anderson, Ind., 70,787 (*142,000)..........D6 59
Anderson, Mo., 1,065......E3 69
Anderson, S.C., 27,556 (*57,600)..........B2 82
Anderson, co., Kans., 8,501..........D8 61
Anderson, co., Ky., 9,358..C4 62
Anderson, co., S.C., 105,474..........B2 82
Anderson, co,. Tenn., 60,300..........C9 83
Anderson, co., Tex., 27,789..........D5 84
Anderson, mtn., Wash.....B2 86
Andes, Col., 11,135.......B2 32
Andhra Pradesh, state, India, 43,502,708.......E6 20
Andizhan, Sov. Un., 188,000..........E10 13
Andkhui, Afg., 18,438.....A4 20
Andong, Kor., 64,000 (76,434 ▲)..........H4 18
Andorra, And., 600.......A6 8
Andorra, country, Eur., 23,000..........A6 8
Andover, Mass., 12,000 (23,695 ▲)..........A5 65
Andover, N.B., Can., 848..C2 43
Andover, N.Y., 1,214......C3 75
Andover, Ohio, 1,179.....A5 78
Andraitx, Sp., 5,077.......C7 8
Andrew, co., Mo., 11,913..B3 69
Andrew Jackson, mtn., Ant..........K16 2
Andrews, Ind., 1,207......C6 59
Andrews, N.C., 1,384......f9 76
Andrews, S.C., 2,879......E8 82
Andrews, Tex., 8,625......C1 84
Andrews, co., Tex., 10,372..........C1 84
Andreyevka, Sov. Un., 10,000..........G11 12
Andria, It., 76,500........D6 9
Androscoggin, co., Maine, 91,279..........D2 64
Andros, isl., Ba..........B4 35
Andrychów, Pol., 13,800..h10 7
Andújar, Sp., 23,897 (32,185 ▲)..........C3 8
Aneto, mtn., Sp..........A6 8
Angara, riv., Sov. Un....D13 13
Angarsk, Sov. Un., 203,000..........*D13 13
Ängelholm, Swe., 14,160...I5 11
Angelica, N.Y., 948.......C2 75
Angelina, co., Tex., 49,349..........D5 84
Angels Camp, Calif., 1,710..........C3 50
Angermunde, Ger. Dem. Rep., 11,700..........B7 6
Angers, Fr., 128,533 (*165,000)..........D3 5
Angier, N.C., 1,431.......B4 76
Anglesey, is., Wales.......D4 4
Anglet, Fr., 21,190........F3 5
Angleton, Tex., 9,770.E5, r14 84
Ango, Zaire............H3 23
Angol, Chile, 18,637.......B2 28
Angola, Ind., 5,117.......A8 59
Angola, N.Y., 2,676.......C1 75
Angola, country, Afr., 5,945,000..........C3 24
Angoulême, Fr., 47,822 (*92,000)..........E4 5
Angra do Heroismo, Port., 10,296..........k10 22
Angra dos Reis, Braz., 16,513..........C4, h5 30
Angus, co., Scot., 280,130.*B5 4
Angwin, Calif., 2,690.....*C2 50
Anhwei, prov., China, 33,560,000..........E8 17
Anina, Rom., 11,837.......C5 10
Anita, Iowa, 1,101........C3 60
Anita, Pa., 600..........D4 81
Aniva (Rutaka), Sov. Un., 10,000..........C11 18
Anjo, Jap., 94,307........o16 18
Anjou, Que., Can., 33,886..........p19 42
Anjou, former prov. Fr....D3 5
Anju, Kor., 21,861........G2 18
Ankang, China,..........E6 17
Ankara, Tur., 1,236,152 (*1,270,000)..........C9 14
Ankeny, Iowa, 9,151...C4, e8 60
Anklam, Ger. Dem. Rep. 19,400..........B6 6
Ankuang, China, 5,000....D1 18
Annaba (Bône), Alg., 168,790..........A6 22
An Najaf, Iraq, 128,096...C3 15
Annalee Heights, Va., 2,000..........*B5 85
Annam, reg., Viet., 8,000,000..........*B3 19
Annandale, Minn., 1,234...E4 67
Annandale, Va., 32,000...g12 85
Annapolis, Md., 30,095....C5 53
Annapolis Royal, N.S., Can., 800..........E4 43
Annapurna 1, peak, Nep...C7 20
Ann Arbor, Mich., 99,797..........F7, p14 66
An Nasiriya, Iraq, 60,405..C4 15
Anne Arundel, co., Md., 298,042..........B4 53
Annecy, Fr., 54,484 (*82,000)..........E7 5
Annemasse, Fr., 17,166....D7 5
Anniston, Ala., 31,533 (*94,900)..........B4 46
Annonay, Fr., 20,757......E6 5
An Nuhūd, Sud., 16,499...F3 23
Annville, Pa., 4,704.......F8 81
Anoka, Minn., 13,298..........E5, m12 67
Anoka, co., Minn., 154,556.E5 67
Ansbach, Ger., Fed. Rep. of, 40,309..........D5 6
Anserma, Col., 14,129.....B2 32
Anshan, China, 1,050,000..C9 17
Anson, Maine, 870 (2,168 ▲)..........D3 64
Anson, Tex., 2,615........C3 84
Anson, co., N.C., 23,488...B2 76
Ansong, Kor., 17,400 (25,788 ▲)..........H3 18
Ansonia, Conn., 21,160....D4 52
Ansonia, Ohio, 1,044......B1 78
Ansted, W. Va., 1,511..........C3, m13 87
Anta, China, 5,000........C2 18
Anta, Peru, 1,542.........D3 31
Antakya (Antioch), Tur., 66,520..........D11 14
Antalaha, Mad., 12,100..........C10 24
Antalya (Adalia), Tur., 95,616..........D8 14
Antananarive Mad., 332,900..........D9 24
Antarctic, pen., Ant......K16 2
Antelope, co., Nebr., 9,047..........B7 71
Antequera, Sp., 28,400 (42,327 ▲)..........D3 8
Anthon, Iowa, 711........B2 60
Anthony, Kans., 2,653.....E5 61
Anthony, N. Mex., 1,728..D5 48
Anthony, R. I., 5,000.....C10 52
Antibes, Fr., 47,547.......F7 5
Antigo, Wis., 9,005........C4 88
Antigonish, N.S., Can., 5,489..........D8 43
Antigonish, co., N.S., Can., 14,890..........D8 43
Antigua, Br. dep., N.A., 74,000..........H14 35
Antigua Guatemala, Guat., 17,692..........E6 34
Antilla, Cuba, 8,000 (10,000 ▲)..........D6 35
Antioch, Calif., 28,060 (*72,500)..........h9 50
Antioch, Ill., 3,189....A5, h8 58
Antioquia, Col., 3,998.....B2 32
Antioquia, dept., Col., 2,828,000..........B2 32
Antique, prov., Phil., 238,405..........*C6 19
Antlers, Okla., 2,685......C6 79
Antofagasta, Chile, 132,500..........D1 29
Antofagasta, prov., Chile, 250,665..........D1 29
Anton, Tex., 1,034........C1 84
Antonina, Braz., 10,737...D3 30
António Enes, Moz., 11,628..........D7 24
Antonito, Colo., 1,113.....D5 51
Antony, Fr., 56,638.......g10 5
Antratsit, Sov. Un., 55,000..........g22 12
Antrim, co., Mich., 12,612..........C5 66

Antrim, co., N. Ire., 352,549......*C3 4
Antsirabe, Mad., 12,900...D9 24
Antwerp, N.Y., 872....A5, f9 75
Antwerp, Ohio, 1,735.....A1 78
Antwerp (Antwerpen), Bel., 222,775 (*1,055,000)....B6 5
Antwerpen, prov., Bel., 1,523,300......*B6 5
Anuradhapura, Sri Lanka, 34,836......G7 20
Anvers, see Antwerp, Bel.
Anyang, China, 124,900...D7 17
Anzhero-Sudzhensk, Sov. Un., 106,000.....D11 13
Anzio, It., 16,900......D4, k7 9
Anzoátegui, state, Ven., 382,002......B5 32
Aomori, Jap., 240,063....F10 18
Aomori, pref., Jap., 1,427,520......*F10 18
Aosta, It., 35,300......B1 9
Apa, China......B11 20
Apache, Okla., 1,421......C3 79
Apache, co., Ariz., 32,304......B4 48
Apache, mts., Tex......o12 84
Apache Junction, Ariz., 3,000......D2 48
Apalachicola, Fla., 3,102...C2 54
Apalachin, N.Y., 900......C4 75
Apam, Mex., 13,705......n14 34
Aparri, Phil., 14,597......B6 19
Apatin, Yugo., 17,523.....C4 10
Apeldoorn, Neth., 128,610......A6 5
Apex, N.C., 2,234......B4 76
Apia, W. Sam., 25,480....G9 2
Apizaco, Mex., 21,189....n14 34
Aplao, Peru, 840......E3 31
Aplington, Iowa, 936......B5 60
Apo, vol., Phil......D7 19
Apolda, Ger. Dem. Rep., 28,504......C5 6
Apollo, Pa., 2,308......E2 8
Apopka, Fla., 4,045......D5 54
Appalachia, Va., 2,161.....f9 85
Appalachian, mts., U.S...F12 33
Appanoose, co., Iowa, 15,007......D5 60
Appenzell, canton, Switz., 61,900......*B7 6
Apple Orchard, mtn., Va..C3 85
Appleton, Minn., 1,789....E2 67
Appleton, Wis., 56,377 (*152,400)......D5, h9 88
Appleton City, Mo., 1,058......C3 69
Appleyard, Wash., 950....B5 86
Appling, co., Ga., 12,726...E4 55
Appomattox, Va., 1,400...C4 85
Appomattox, co., Va., 9,784......C4 85
Aprelsk, Sov. Un., 800...D14 13
Apt, Fr., 5,521......F6 5
Apulia, reg., It......D6 9
Apure, riv., Ven......B4 32
Apurímac, riv., Peru......D3 31
Aquidauana, Braz., 16,534......C1 30
Arab, Ala., 4,399......A3 46
Arabi, La., 12,500......k11 63
Arabia, see Saudi Arabia, Asia
Aracaju, Braz., 179,512....E7 27
Aracati, Braz., 14,509.....D7 27
Araçatuba, Braz., 85,660...C2 30
Arad, Rom., 126,000 (136,900 ▲)......B5 10
Aragon, Ga., 1,023......B1 55
Aragua, state, Ven., 313,274......A4 32
Araguaia, riv., Braz......D6 27
Araguari, Braz., 48,702...*E5 27
Arai, Jap., 14,863......o16 18
Arāk (Sultanabad), Iran, 71,925......B7 23
Aral, sea, Sov. Un......E8 13
Aranda de Duero, Sp., 13,454......B4 8
Arandas, Mex., 18,934...m12 34
Aranjuez, Sp., 27,251......B4 8
Aranos, S.W. Afr., 1,112...B2 24
Aransas, co., Tex., 8,902...E4 84
Aransas Pass, Tex., 5,813...F4 84
Aranyaprathet, Thai., 11,078......C2 19
Arapahoe, Nebr., 1,147...D6 71
Arapkir, Tur., 7,793......C12 14
Arapohoe, co., Colo., 162,142......B6 51
Araraquara, Braz., 82,607......C3, k7 30
Araras, Braz., 40,945..C3, m8 30
Ararat, Austl., 8,317..G7, n14 25
Ararat, see Büyük Ağrı Dağı, mtn., Tur.
Arauca, Col., 4,280......B3 32
Arauca, intendencia, Col., 28,900......B3 32
Arauco, prov., Chile 105,300......B2 28
Araxá, Braz., 31,498......B3 30
Arboga, Swe., 13,596......t33 11
Arborg, Man., Can., 811..D3 40
Arbor Terrace, Mo., 1,440......*C7 69
Arbroath, Scot., 22,764....B5 4
Arbuckle, Calif., 950......C2 50
Arcachon, Fr., 14,986 (*39,000)......E3 5
Arcade, N.Y., 1,972......C2 75
Arcadia, Calif., 45,138...m12 50
Arcadia, Fla., 5,658......E5 54
Arcadia, Ind., 1,338......D5 59
Arcadia, La., 2,970......B3 63
Arcadia, S.C., 2,000......B3 82
Arcadia, Wis., 2,159......D2 88
Arcanum, Ohio, 1,993.....C1 78
Arcata, Calif., 8,985......B1 50
Archangel, see Arkhangelsk, Sov. Un.
Archbald, Pa., 6,118.....m18 81
Archbold, Ohio, 3,047.....A1 78
Archdale, N.C., 6,103.....B3 76
Archer, co., Tex., 5,759....C3 84
Archer City, Tex., 1,722...C3 84
Archidona, Sp., 7,962.....D3 8
Archuleta, co., Colo., 2,733......D3 51
Arcila, Mor., 10,839......E2 8
Arco, Ga., 5,417......E5 55
Arco, Idaho, 1,244......F5 57
Arcola, Ill., 2,276......D5 58
Arcoverde, Braz., 33,308..*D6 27
Arctic, ocean......A6 2
Arcueil, Fr., 21,877......g10 5
Ardabil (Ardebil), Iran, 83,596......B4 15
Ardatov, Sov. Un., 5,000..D16 12
Ardèche, dept., Fr., 256,927......*E6 5
Arden (Ardentown), Del., 555......A7 53
Arden Hills, Minn., 5,149......*E7 67
Ardennes, dept., Fr., 309,380......*C6 5
Ardmore, Okla., 20,881....C4 79
Ardmore, Pa., 13,600.....g20 81
Ardrossan, Scot., 10,604...C4 4
Ardsley, N.Y., 4,470......g13 75
Arecibo, P.R., 35,484 (73,468 ▲)......g11 35
Areia Branca, Braz., 10,778......*D7 27
Arenac, co., Mich., 11,149......D7 66
Arendal, Nor., 11,300.....H3 11
Arequipa, Peru, 98,605 (*304,653)......E3 31
Arequipa, dept., Peru, 407,163......E3 31
Arezzo, It., 62,100......C3 9
Argenta, Ill., 1,034......D5 58
Argenta, It., 4,600......B3 8
Argentan, Fr., 14,558.....C4 5
Argenteuil, Fr., 90,480......C5, g10 5
Argenteuil, co., Que., Can., 31,200......D3 42
Argentina, country, S.A., 24,450,000......G4 27
Argenton-sur-Creuse, Fr., 6,400......D4 5
Argolis, prov., Grc., 89,044......*D4 14
Argos, Grc., 18,890......D4 14
Argos, Ind., 1,393......B5 59
Argostólion, Grc., 7,060...C3 14
Argyll, co., Scot., 58,088..*B4 4
Århus, Den., 113,100 (*190,000)......I4 11
Århus, co., Den., 239,600..*I4 11
Ariail, S.C., 1,150......B2 82
Ariano Irpino, It., 10,900..D5 9
Arica, Chile, 43,344......C1 29
Ariège, dept., Fr., 138,478......*F4 5
Arīḥā (Jericho), Jordan, 6,829......C3 15
Ario de Rosales, Mex., 8,774......D4, n13 34
Aripo, El Cerro del, mtn., Trin......K14 35
Arizona, state, U.S., 2,064,000...... 48
Arjay, Ky., 650......D6 62
Arjona, Col., 16,510......A2 32
Arjona, Sp., 8,154......D3 8
Arkadelphia, Ark., 9,841...C2 49
Arkadhia (Arcadia), prov., Grc., 112,068......*D4 14
Arkansas, state, U.S., 1,994,000...... 49
Arkansas, co., Ark., 23,347......C4 49
Arkansas, riv., U.S......C8 45
Arkansas City, Ark., 615...D4 49
Arkansas City, Kans., 13,216......E6 61
Arkhangelsk, Sov. Un., 343,000......C7 13
Arkoma, Okla., 2,098......B7 79
Arkonam, India, 43,347....F6 20
Arkport, N.Y., 984......C3 75
Arkwright, R.I., 200.....C10 52
Arkwright, S.C., 1,300....*B4 82
Arles, Fr., 33,576......F6 5
Arlington, Ga., 1,698......E2 55
Arlington, Mass., 53,534......B5, g11 65
Arlington, Minn., 1,823....F4 67
Arlington, N.Y., 11,203...*D7 75
Arlington, Ohio, 1,066.....B2 78
Arlington, S.C., 700......B3 82
Arlington, S. Dak., 954....F8 77
Arlington, Tex., 90,032....n9 84
Arlington, Vt., 800......E1 73
Arlington, Va., 174,284......B5, g12 85
Arlington, Wash., 2,261....A3 86
Arlington, co., Va., 174,284......B5, g12 85
Arlington Heights, Ill., 64,884......A5, a9 58
Arlington Heights, Ohio, 1,476......*C1 78
Arlon, Bel., 13,655......C6 5
Arma, Kans., 1,348......E9 61
Armada, Mich., 1,352......F8 66
Armagh, N. Ire., 12,297...C3 4
Armagh, Que., Can., 914..C7 42
Armagh, co., N. Ire., 133,196......*C3 4
Armavir, Sov. Un., 145,000......I13 12
Armenia, Col., 156,100....C2 32
Armenia (S.S.R.), rep., Sov. Un., 2,645,000.....A4 15
Armentières, Fr., 26,916 (*55,000)......B5 5
Armero, Col., 17,495......C3 32
Armidale, Austl., 18,137...F9 25
Armijo, N. Mex., 9,000....E5 48
Armona, Calif., 1,302....*D4 50
Armonk, N.Y., 5,000.....*D7 75
Armour, S. Dak., 925......G7 77
Armstrong, B.C., Can., 1,648...... D8 37
Armstrong, Iowa, 1,061....A3 60
Armstrong, co., Pa., 75,590......E3 81
Armstrong, co., Tex., 1,895......B2 84
Arnaudville, La., 1,673....D4 63
Arnedo, Sp., 7,958......A4 8
Arnhem, Neth., 129,633 (*276,985)......B6 5
Arnissa, Grc., 1,396......E5 10
Arnold, Mo., 17,381......C7 69
Arnold, Nebr., 752......C5 71
Arnold, Pa., 8,174......h14 81
Arnolds Park, Iowa, 970...A2 60
Arnouville [-les-Gonesse], Fr., 10,227......g10 5
Arnprior, Ont., Can., 6,016 (*10,089)......B8 41
Arnsberg, Ger., Fed. Rep. of, 22,296......C4 6
Arnstadt, Ger. Dem. Rep., 29,503......C5 6
Aroostook, co., Maine, 94,078......B4 64
Arp, Tex., 816......C5 84
Arrah, India, 92,919......C7 20
Ar Ramādī, Iraq, 28,723..F14 14
Ar Raqqah, Syr., 37,186..E12 14
Arras, Fr., 49,144 (*72,000)......B5 5
Arrecife, Sp., 12,886.....m15 8
Arrecifes, Arg., 10,397.....g6 28
Arroyo, P.R., 3,741.....*G11 35
Arroyo Grande, Calif., 7,454......E3 50
Árta, Grc., 19,498......C3 14
Arta, prov., Grc., 78,039..*C3 14
Artem, Sov. Un., 61,000..E16 13
Artemisa, Cuba, 31,200....C2 35
Artemovsk, Sov. Un., 82,000......G12, o21 12
Arter, mtn., Wyo......D4 89
Artesia, Calif., 14,757.....*F4 50
Artesia, N. Mex., 10,315......C6 48
Arthabaska, Que., Can., 4,479......C6 42
Arthabaska, co., Que., Can., 49,567......C5 42
Arthur, Ill., 2,214......D5 58
Arthur, co., Nebr., 606....C4 71
Artigas, Ur., 23,429......E1 30
Artigas, dept., Ur., 52,261......*E1 30
Artois, former prov., Fr....B5 5
Arunachal Pradesh, ter., India, 467,511......C9 20
Arusha, Tan., 10,038......I5 23
Arvada, Colo., 46,814.....B5 51
Arvida, Que., Can., 18,448......A6 42
Arvidsjaur, Swe., 3,541....E8 11
Arvika, Swe., 18,880......H5 11
Arvin, Calif., 5,199......E4 50
Arzamas, Sov. Un., 67,000......D14 12
Arzúa, Sp., 1,368......A1 8
As, Czech., 11,891......C2 7
Asahi-Dake, mtn., Jap....E11 18
Asahikawa, Jap., 288,492......E11 18
Asan, Guam, 543......*F6 2
Asansol, India, 155,968 (*925,000)......D8 20
Asbest, Sov. Un., 76,000...D9 13
Asbestos, Que., Can., 9,749 (*15,674)......D6 42
Asbury Park, N.J., 16,533..C4 74
Ascension, par., La., 37,086......D5 63
Ascension Isl., Br. dep., Atl. O., 1,500......G20 2
Aschaffenburg, Ger., Fed. Rep. of, 55,088 (*125,000)......D4 6
Aschersleben, Ger. Dem. Rep., 37,007......C5 6
Ascoli Piceno, It., 41,600...C4 9
Asenovgrad, Bul., 37,433...E7 10
Ashaway, R.I., 1,559......D9 52
Ashburn, Ga., 4,209......E3 55
Ashburnham, Mass., 1,013 (3,484 ▲)......A4 65
Ashburton, N.Z., 13,500..O13 26
Ashby, Ala., 100......B3 46
Ashcroft, B.C., Can., 1,916......D7 37
Ashdown, Ark., 3,522.....D1 49
Ashe, co., N.C., 19,571....A1 76
Asheboro, N.C., 10,797....B3 76
Asheboro South, N.C., 1,998......*B3 76
Asheboro West, N.C., 1,158......*B3 76
Asherton, Tex., 1,645......E3 84
Asheville, N.C., 57,681 (*126,600)......f10 76
Ashford, Ala., 1,980......D4 46
Ash Grove, Mo., 934......D4 69
Ashikaga, Jap., 156,004......H9, m18 18
Ashio, Jap., 11,202......H9 18
Ashkhabad, Sov. Un., 259,000......F8 13
Ashland, Ala., 1,921......B4 46
Ashland, Ill., 1,128......D3 58
Ashland, Kans., 1,244.....E4 61
Ashland, Ky., 29,245......B7 62
Ashland, Maine, 600 (1,761 ▲)......B4 64
Ashland, Mass., 8,882.....g10 65
Ashland, Nebr., 2,176......C9, g12 71
Ashland, N.H., 1,391......D4 73
Ashland, Ohio, 19,872.....B3 78
Ashland, Oreg., 12,342.....E4 80
Ashland, Pa., 4,737......E9 81
Ashland, Va., 2,934......C5 85
Ashland, Wis., 9,615......B3 88
Ashland, co., Ohio, 43,303......B3 78
Ashland, co., Wis., 16,743......B3 88
Ashland, mtn., Oreg......E4 80
Ashland City, Tenn., 2,027......A4 83
Ashley, N. Dak., 1,236....D6 77
Ashley, Ohio, 1,034......B5 78
Ashley, Pa., 4,095......n17 81
Ashley, co., Ark., 24,976...D4 49
Ashmūn, Eg., 26,100.....*G8 14
Ashqelon, Isr., 43,100.....C2 15
Ash Shāmīyah, Iraq, 13,334......*G15 14
Ash Shaṭṭ, Eg., 2,000.....H9 14
Ash Shiḥr, P.D.R. of Yem..C6 15
Ashtabula, Ohio, 24,313...A5 78
Ashtabula, co., Ohio, 98,237......A5 78
Ashton, Idaho, 1,187......E7 57
Ashton, Ill., 1,112......B4 58
Ashton, R.I., 2,000......B11 52
Ashville, Ala., 986......B3 46
Ashville, Ohio, 1,772......C3 78
Ashwaubenon, Wis., 10,042......g9 88
Asia, cont., 2,273,200,000..F9 16
Asir, reg., Sau. Ar......E6 23

Asmara, Eth., 249,110......E5   23
Asnières [-sur-Seine], Fr.,
  80,113.................g10   5
Asotin, co., Wash., 13,799..C8   86
Aspe, Sp., 10,279........C5   8
Aspen, Colo., 2,437.......B4   51
Aspermont, Tex., 1,198...C2   84
Aspinwall, Pa., 3,541....k14   81
As Salt, Jordan,
  16,176.............B3, g5   15
Assam, state, India,
  14,625,152.............C9   20
Assateague, isl., Va......C7   85
Assen, Neth., 42,410......A7   5
Assens, co., Den., 57,661..*J3   11
Assiniboia, Sask., Can.,
  2,675..................H3   39
Assiniboine, mtn., Alta.,
  Can................D3   38
Assini, I.C., 1,000.......G4   22
Assis, Braz., 45,531......C2   30
Assisi, It., 5,400........C4   9
As Sulaymānīyah, Iraq,
  86,822.................B3   15
Assumption, Ill., 1,487...D4   58
Assumption, par., La.,
  19,654.................E4   63
As Suwaydā, Syr., 29,598..F11 14
Asti, It., 58,400.........B2   9
Aston, Pa., 1,200........*G11 81
Astorga, Sp., 10,101......A2   8
Astoria, Ill., 1,281......C3   58
Astoria, Oreg., 10,244....A3   80
Astrakhan, Sov. Un.,
  410,000................E7   13
Asturias, reg., Sp.,
  1,040,300..............A2   8
Asunción, Par., 392,753
  (*540,000)............E4   29
Aswan, Eg., 127,594......D4   23
Asyut, Eg., 153,956......C4   23
Atacama, prov., Chile
  161,900................E1   29
Atami, Jap., 51,281.....n18   18
Atascadero, Calif., 7,000..E3   50
Atascosa, co., Tex.,
  18,696.................E3   84
'Atbarah, Sud., 48,300....E4   23
Atbasar, Sov. Un.,
  37,000.................D9   13
Atchison, Kans., 12,565...C8   61
Atchison, co., Kans.,
  19,165.................C8   61
Atchison, co., Mo., 9,240..A2   69
Atco, N.J., 2,100........D3   74
Athabasca, Alta., Can.,
  1,765..............B4, g8   38
Athabasca, lake, Alta.,
  Sask., Can...........m6   39
Athabasca, riv., Can....E11   36
Athena, Oreg., 872.......B8   80
Athens, Ala., 14,360.....A3   46
Athens, Ont., Can., 1,071..C9   41
Athens, Ga., 44,342......C3   55
Athens (Athínai), Grc.,
  867,023
  (*2,540,241)..........C4   14
Athens, Ill., 1,158......D4   58
Athens, Mich., 996.......F5   66
Athens, N.Y., 1,718......C7   75
Athens, Ohio, 24,168.....C3   78
Athens, Pa., 4,173.......C9   81
Athens, Tenn., 11,790....D9   83
Athens, Tex., 9,582......C5   84
Athens, W. Va., 967......D3   87
Athens, co., Ohio, 55,747..C3   78
Atherton, Austl., 3,081...C8   25
Atherton, Calif., 8,085...*D2   60
Athis-Mons, Fr., 27,640...h10   5
Athleague, Ire., 132.....D3   4
Athok, Bur., 4,770......E10   20
Athol, Mass., 11,185.....A3   65
Atibaia, Braz, 8,957.....m8   30
Atikokan, Ont., Can.,
  6,007.................E8   41

Atkarsk, Sov. Un.,
  29,000...............F15   12
Atkins, Ark., 2,015......B3   49
Atkinson, Ill., 1,053....B3   58
Atkinson, Nebr., 1,406...B7   71
Atkinson, co., Ga., 5,879..E4   55
Atlanta, Ga., 497,421
  (*1,513,600)......C2, h8   55
Atlanta, Ill., 1,640.....C4   58
Atlanta, Tex., 5,007.....C5   84
Atlantic, Iowa, 7,306....C2   60
Atlantic, N.C., 800......C6   76
Atlantic, co., N.J.,
  175,043...............E3   74
Atlantic, ocean.........D17   2
Atlantic, peak, Wyo.....D3   89
Atlantic Beach, N.Y.,
  1,640................n15   75
Atlantic City, N.J., 47,859
  (*153,300)...........E4   74
Atlantic Highlands, N.J.,
  5,102.................C4   74
Atlántico, dept., Col.,
  833,900...............A2   32
Atlas, Pa., 1,527.......*D8   81
Atlixco, Mex., 41,967...n14   34
Atmore, Ala., 8,293......D2   46
Atna, peak, B.C., Can....C3   37
Atoka, Okla., 3,346......C5   79
Atoka, co., Okla., 10,972..C5   79
Atotonilco el Alto, Mex.,
  16,271...............m12   34
Atrisco, N. Mex., 4,000..*B5   48
Atsugi, Jap., 82,888....n18   18
Aṭ Ṭafīlah, Jordan,
  4,506.............D3, h5   15
Aṭ Ṭā'if, Sau. Ar., 30,000..C3   15
Attala, co., Miss., 19,570..B4   68
Attalla, Ala., 7,510.....A3   46
Aṭ Ṭayyibah, Jordan,
  1,677.................C3   15
Attica, Ind., 4,262......D3   59
Attica, Kans., 639.......E5   61
Attica, N.Y., 2,911......C2   75
Attica, Ohio, 1,005......A3   78
Attika (Attica), prov.,
  Grc., 2,294,140.......*C4   14
Attleboro, Mass., 32,907..C5   65
Atvidaberg, Swe., 8,385..H6   11
Atwater, Calif., 11,955..D3   50
Atwater, Minn., 956......E4   67
Atwood, Ill., 1,264......D5   58
Atwood, Kans., 1,658.....C2   61
Atzcapotzalco
  (Azcapotzalco),
  Mex., 63,857......h9, n14   34
Atzmon, mtn., Isr.......A3   15
Aubagne, Fr., 18,069....F3   5
Aube, dept., Fr., 270,325. *C6   5
Aubervilliers, Fr., 73,695..g10   5
Aubin, Fr., 7,821.......E5   5
Auburn, Ala., 22,767....C4   46
Auburn, Ill., 2,594......D4   58
Auburn, Ind., 7,388......B7   59
Auburn, Kans., 261......D8   61
Auburn, Ky., 1,160......D3   62
Auburn, Maine,
  24,151.............D2, f7   64
Auburn, Mass., 15,347...B4   65
Auburn, Mich., 1,919....E6   66
Auburn, Nebr., 3,650...D10   71
Auburn, N.Y., 34,599....C4   75
Auburn, Pa., 895........E9   81
Auburn, Wash.,
  21,653............B3, f11   86
Auburndale, Fla., 5,386...D5   54
Auburn Heights, Mich.,
  6,000.................F7   66
Aubusson, Fr., 5,934....E5   5
Auch, Fr., 21,462......F4   5
Auckland, N.Z., 151,900
  (*690,000)..........L15   26
Aude, dept., Fr.,
  278,323.............*C6   5
Audincourt, Fr., 13,488...D7   5
Audrain, co., Mo., 25,362..B6   69
Audubon, Iowa, 2,907....C3   60

Audubon, N.J., 10,802....D2   74
Audubon, co., Iowa,
  9,595.................C3   60
Audubon Park, N.J.,
  1,492...............*C3   74
Aue, Ger. Dem. Rep.,
  32,885................C6   6
Auglaize, co., Ohio,
  38,602................B1   78
Augsburg, Ger., Fed. Rep. of,
  257,036 (*375,000)....D5   6
Augusta, Ark., 2,777....B4   49
Augusta, Ga., 59,864
  (*218,800)...........C5   55
Augusta, Ill., 824......C3   58
Augusta, It., 31,600....F6   9
Augusta, Kans.,
  5,977.............E6, g13   61
Augusta, Ky., 1,434.....B5   62
Augusta, Maine, 21,945...D3   64
Augusta, Mich., 1,025...F5   66
Augusta, Wis., 1,242....D2   88
Augusta, co., Va.,
  44,220................B3   85
Augustów, Pol., 19,700...B7   7
Augustus, mtn., Austl...D2   25
Aulander, N.C., 947.....A5   76
Aulnay-sous-Bois, Fr.,
  61,521...............g11   5
Aurangābād, India,
  150,483 (*165,253)....E6   20
Auray, Fr., 8,449.......D2   5
Aurelia, Iowa, 1,065....B2   60
Aurich, Ger., Fed. Rep. of,
  34,045................B3   6
Aurillac, Fr., 28,226...E5   5
Aurora, Ont., Can.,
  13,614................D5   42
Aurora, Colo., 74,974...B6   51
Aurora, Ill., 74,182..B5, k8   58
Aurora, Ind., 4,293.....F8   59
Aurora, Minn., 2,531....C6   67
Aurora, Mo., 5,359......E4   69
Aurora, Nebr., 3,180....D7   71
Aurora, Ohio, 6,549.....A4   78
Aurora, co., S. Dak.,
  4,183.................G7   77
Au Sable Forks, N.Y.,
  2,100................f11   75
Aust-Agder, co., Nor.,
  79,400..............*H3   11
Austell, Ga., 2,632.....h7   55
Austin, Ind., 4,902.....G6   59
Austin, Minn., 26,210...C6   67
Austin, Tex., 251,808
  (*296,600)...........D4   84
Austin, co., Tex., 13,831..E4   84
Austintown, Ohio, 24,000..A5   78
Australia, country,
  Oceania, 13,335,000....   25
Australian Capital
  Territory, Austl.,
  170,000.............*G8   25
Austria, country, Eur.,
  7,550,000.............E6   6
Autauga, co., Ala.,
  24,460................C3   46
Autlán de Navarro,
  Mex., 20,398......D4, n11   34
Autun, Fr., 18,398.....D6   5
Auvergne, former prov., Fr. E5   5
Auxerre, Fr., 35,784....D5   5
Auxier, Ky., 900........C7   62
Ava, Mo., 2,504........E5   69
Avalon, Calif., 1,520...F4   50
Avalon, Pa., 7,010.....h13   81
Avanos, Tur., 6,890....C10   14
Avaré, Braz., 29,878....C3   30
Aveiro, Port., 16,011...B1   8
Avella, Pa., 1,109......F1   81
Avellaneda, Arg.,
  337,538...........A5, g7   28
Avellino, It., 43,700...D5   9
Avenal, Calif., 3,147...E3   50
Avenel, N.J., 13,000....k7   74
Aversa, It., 47,000.....D5   9
Avery, co., N.C., 12,655..e11   76

Avesta, Swe., 21,290......G7   11
Aveyron, dept., Fr.,
  281,568..............*E5   5
Avezzano, It., 25,700....C4   9
Avigliano, It., 4,554....D5   9
Avignon, Fr., 86,096.....F6   5
Ávila, Sp., 30,080......B3   8
Avilés, Sp., 82,433
  (*120,000)...........A3   8
Avilla, Ind., 881.......B7   59
Avis, Pa., 1,749........D7   81
Avoca, Ala., 50.........A2   46
Avoca, Iowa, 1,535......C2   60
Avoca, N.Y., 1,153......C3   75
Avoca, Pa., 3,543......m18   81
Avola, It., 29,100......F5   9
Avon, Conn., 300........B5   52
Avon, Ill., 1,013......C3   58
Avon, Mass., 5,295...B5, a11   65
Avon, N.Y., 3,260......C3   75
Avon, Ohio, 7,214......A3   78
Avon, Pa., 1,271.......*F9   81
Avon by the Sea, N.J.,
  2,163.................C4   74
Avondale, Ariz., 6,626...D1   48
Avondale, Pa., 1,025...G10   81
Avondale Estates, Ga.,
  1,735................h8   55
Avon Lake, Ohio, 12,261..A3   78
Avonmore, Pa., 1,267....E3   81
Avon Park, Fla., 6,712...E5   54
Avoyelles, par., La.,
  37,751................C3   63
Avranches, Fr., 9,775...C3   5
Axim, Ghana, 5,600......H4   22
Axis, Ala., 600.........E1   46
Ay, Fr., 6,806.........C5   5
Ayabe, Jap., 30,000
  (44,983 ▲)...........n14   18
Ayacucho, Arg., 10,004...B5   28
Ayacucho, Peru, 34,593...D3   31
Ayacucho, dept., Peru,
  430,289...............D3   31
Ayaguz, Sov. Un., 36,000.E11 13
Ayamonte, Sp., 8,908....D2   8
Ayan, Sov. Un., 9,300...D16 13
Ayaviri, Peru, 7,500....D3   31
Ayden, N.C., 3,450......B5   76
Aydin, Tur., 50,566.....D6   14
Ayer, Mass., 7,393...A4, f9   65
Ayion Oros (Mount Athos),
  prov., Grc., 1,713...*B5   14
Áyios Dhimítrios, Grc.,
  40,968..............*C4   14
Aylesbury, Eng., 41,100..E6   4
Aylesford, N.S., Can., 964..D5   43
Aylmer East, Que., Can.,
  7,198.................D2   42
Aylmer West, Ont., Can.,
  4,755.................E4   41
Ayora, Sp., 6,067.......C5   8
Ayr, Scot., 48,021
  (*96,000)............C4   4
Ayr, co., Scot., 361,041...*C4   4
Aytos, Bul., 17,766.....D8   10
Ayutthaya, Thai., 37,213..C2   19
Ayvalik, Tur., 17,661...C6   14
Azalea Park, Fla., 7,367..*D5   54
Azemmour, Mor., 17,182...B3   22
Azerbaidzhan (S.S.R.),
  rep., Sov. Un.,
  5,425,000...........*E7   16
Azle, Tex., 4,493......n9   84
Azogues, Ec., 8,075.....B2   31
Azores Islands, reg.,
  Port., 270,000.......C3   21
Azov, Sov. Un., 59,000...H12 12
Azrou, Mor., 20,756.....B3   22
Aztec, N. Mex., 3,354...A5   48
Azua, Dom. Rep., 18,600..E8   35
Azuay, prov., Ec.,
  305,400...............B2   31
Azul, Arg., 37,000......B5   28
Azusa, Calif., 25,217..m13   50
Az Zaqāzīq, Eg., 151,186..B4   23
Az Zarqā', Jor., 200,000..*B4   15

B

Babaeski, Tur., 11,700.....E8   10
Babahoyo, Ec., 20,300.....B2   31
Babayevo, Sov. Un.,
  10,000...............B11   12
Babbitt, Minn., 3,076.....C7   67
Babbitt, Nev., 1,579....*B2   72

Bābol, Iran, 49,973.......A8   23
Babson Park, Fla., 900....E5   54
Babyak, Bul., 6,211......E6   10
Babylon, N.Y., 12,897...n15   75
Baca, co., Colo., 5,674..D8   51
Bacalar, Mex., 2,121....D7   34

Bacău, Rom., 73,500
  (*87,500)............B8   10
Baccarat, Fr., 5,856....C7   5
Back, riv., Can.......C12   36
Bac Kan, Viet.,
  10,000.............*G5   17

Backa Palanka, Yugo.,
  21,109...............C4   10
Backa Topola, Yugo.,
  15,057...............C4   10
Bac Lieu, Viet., 58,920..*D3   19
Bacliff, Tex., 2,000...*E5   84

Bac Ninh, Viet., 25,000....G6 17
Bacolod, Phil., 187,300....C6 19
Bacon, co., Ga., 8,233.....E4 55
Bacsalmas, Hung., 7,344...B4 10
Bács-Kiskun, co., Hung., 572,988..............*B4 10
Badajoz, Sp., 75,000 (100,551 ▲)...........C2 8
Badalona, Sp., 163,374....B7 8
Bad Axe, Mich., 2,999.....E8 66
Baddeck, N.S., Can., 825..C9 43
Bad Doberan, Ger. Dem. Rep., 12,600..........A5 6
Baden, Aus., 22,629.......D8 6
Baden, Ont., Can., 977....D4 41
Baden, Pa., 5,536.........E1 81
Baden, Switz., 13,700 (*66,400)..........E4 6
Baden, reg., Ger., Fed. Rep. of..........D4 6
Baden-Baden, Ger., Fed. Rep. of, 44,904........D4 6
Baden-Württemberg, state, Ger., Fed. Rep. of, 9,195,000.............*D4 6
Bad Freienwalde, Ger. Dem. Rep., 12,200......B7 6
Badger, Newf., Can., 1,036.D3 44
Bad Hersfeld, Ger., Fed. Rep. of, 29,015........C4 6
Badin, N.C., 1,626.........B2 76
Bad Ischl, Aus., 12,735....E6 6
Bad Kissingen, Ger., Fed. Rep. of, 22,016........C5 6
Bad Kreuznach, Ger., Fed. Rep. of, 43,149.........D3 6
Bad Langensalza, Ger. Dem. Rep., 16,934......C5 6
Bad Oldesloe, Ger., Fed. Rep. of, 19,618........B5 6
Bad Reichenhall, Ger., Fed. Rep. of, 13,273........E6 6
Bad Salzuflen, Ger., Fed. Rep. of, 51,109........B4 6
Bad Tölz, Ger., Fed. Rep. of, 12,644..........E5 6
Badulla, Sri Lanka, 34,658.G7 20
Baffin, isl., Can..........B19 36
Bafra, Tur., 28,950.......B10 14
Bagdad, Ariz., 1,800.......B2 48
Bagdad, Fla., 900.........u14 54
Bagé, Braz., 57,036.......E2 30
Baghdād, Iraq, 1,200,000 (*1,900,000)..........C3 15
Bagheria, It., 36,600......E4 9
Baghlan, Afg., 24,410......A4 20
Bagley, Minn., 1,314......C3 67
Bagnara [Calabra], It., 10,000..................F5 9
Bagnères-de-Bigorre, Fr., 8,996..................F4 5
Bagnolet, Fr., 34,038.....g10 5
Bagnols [-sur-Cèze], Fr., 12,905................E6 5
Bagot, co., Que., Can., 22,968................D5 42
Bagotville, Que., Can., 6,041..................A7 42
Bahamas, country, N.A., 205,000.........B11 35
Bahāwalpur, Pak., 134,000.C5 20
Bahia, see Salvador, Braz.
Bahia, state, Braz., 7,583,140..............A4 30
Bahía Blanca, Arg., 155,000................B4 28
Bahia de Caráquez, Ec., 8,845..................B1 31
Bahrain (Bahrein), country, Asia, 235,000..........C8 23
Baia-Mare, Rom., 62,800 (108,700 ▲)...........B6 10
Baie-Comeau, Que., Can., 25,290..................k13 42
Baie-St. Paul, Que., Can., 4,163..................B7 42
Baie Verte, Newf., Can., 2,397..................D3 44
Baile Atha Cliath, see Dublin, Ire.
Bailén, Sp., 11,245........C4 8
Băilesti, Rom., 15,932.....C6 10
Bailey, co., Tex., 8,487....B1 84
Bailundo, 4,897...........C3 24
Bainbridge, Ga., 10,887....F2 55
Bainbridge, N.Y., 1,674....C5 75
Bainbridge, Ohio, 1,057...C2 78
Baird, Tex., 1,538.........C3 84
Baixo Alentejo, prov., Port..................*C2 8
Baja, Hung., 34,360.......B4 10
Baja California, state, Mex., 845,700..........A1 34
Baja California Sur, ter., Mex., 93,300..........C2 34
Baker, La., 8,281........*D4 63
Baker, Mont., 2,584......D12 70
Baker, Oreg., 9,354.......C9 80
Baker, co., Fla., 9,242.....B4 54
Baker, co., Ga., 3,875.....E2 55
Baker, co., Oreg., 14,919..C9 80
Bakersfield, Calif., 69,515 (*187,600)...........E4 50
Bakerton, see Elmora, Pa.
Baku, Sov. Un., 870,000 (*1,435,000)...........E7 13
Baʻlabakk, Leb., 16,000....g6 15
Bala-Cynwyd, Pa., 8,600...............*F11 81
Balaguer, Sp., 8,342.......B6 8
Balakleya, Sov. Un., 5,000................G11 12
Balanda, Sov. Un., 10,000.................F15 12
Balanga, Phil., 1,298.....*C6 19
Balashov, Sov. Un., 83,000................F14 12
Balasore, India, 46,239....D8 20
Balassagyarmat, Hung., 13,745................A4 10
Balboa, C.Z., 2,569......*B2 32
Balcarce, Arg., 21,000.....B5 28
Balch, Ark., 50...........B4 49
Balcones Heights, Tex., 2,504.................*E3 84
Bald Eagle, Minn., 1,700..E7 67
Bald Knob, Ark., 2,094....B4 49
Baldwin, La., 2,117.......E4 63
Baldwin, Mich., 612.......E5 66
Baldwin, N.Y., 34,800.....G2 52
Baldwin, Pa., 26,729.....*k14 81
Baldwin, Wis., 1,399......D1 88
Baldwin, co., Ala., 59,382..E2 46
Baldwin, co., Ga., 34,240..C3 55
Baldwin City, Kans., 2,520.................D8 61
Baldwin Park, Calif., 47,285.................*F4 50
Baldwinsville, N.Y., 6,298..B4 75
Baldwinville, Mass., 1,739..A3 65
Baldwyn, Miss., 2,366.....A5 68
Balearic, is., Sp..........C6 8
Baler, Phil., 3,081........B6 19
Balfour, N.C., 500........f10 76
Balikesir, Tur., 85,004.....C6 14
Balikpapan, Indon., 137,340..................F5 19
Balkh, Afg., 12,466........A4 20
Balkhash, Sov. Un., 76,000................E10 13
Balkhash, lake, Sov. Un...E10 13
Balki, Sov. Un., 25,000...H10 12
Ballarat, Austl., 39,605 (*58,854).........G7, n14 25
Ballard, co., Ky., 8,276....e8 62
Ballard Vale, Mass., 1,500..............A5, f11 65
Ballina, Austl., 6,133......E9 25
Ballina, Ire., 6,063........C2 4
Ballinasloe, Ire., 5,969.....D2 4
Ballinger, Tex., 4,203.....D3 84
Ballston Lake, N.Y., 930...C7 75
Ballston Spa, N.Y., 4,968...B7 75
Ballville, Ohio, 1,652.....*A2 78
Ballwin, Mo., 10,656......g12 69
Bally, Pa., 1,197..........F10 81
Ballymena, N. Ire., 16,487..................C3 4
Balm, Fla., 350...........E4 54
Balmazújváros, Hung., 16,312..................B5 10
Balmville, N.Y., 3,214....*D6 75
Balş, Rom., 6,956.........C7 10
Balta, Sov. Un., 20,000....H7 12
Baltic, Conn., 900........C8 52
Baltic, sea, Eur...........I8 11
Baltimore, Ohio, 2,418....C3 78
Baltimore, co., Md., 620,409..................B4 53
Baltimore (Independent City), Md., 905,787 (*1,892,800)...........B4, g11 53
Baluchistan, reg., Iran, Pak...................C4 20
Bamako, Mali, 182,000....F3 22
Bamberg, Ger., Fed. Rep. of, 76,378 (*108,000)....D5 6
Bamberg, S.C., 3,406......E5 82
Bamberg, co., S.C., 15,950..................E5 82
Banat, reg., Rom., 1,285,300...............C5 10
Banbridge, N. Ire., 6,864...C3 4
Banbury, Eng., 29,320.....D6 4
Bancroft, Ont., Can., 2,276..................B7 41
Bancroft, Iowa, 1,103......A3 6
Bānda, India, 50,575......C7 20
Banda Atjeh (Kutaradja), Indon., 53,668..........k11 19
Bandar ʻAbbās, Iran, 34,627................*D6 15
Bandar-e Pahlavī, Iran, 41,785..................B7 23
Bandar Seri Begawan (Brunei), Bru, 17,410....E4 19
Bande, Sp., 6,275.........A2 8
Bandeira, peak, Braz......C4 30
Bandera, Tex., 891........E3 84
Bandera, co., Tex., 4,747..E3 84
Bandirma, Tur., 39,525....B6 14
Bandon, Oreg., 1,832.....D2 80
Bandung, Indon., 1,201,730..............G3 19
Banes, Cuba, 27,100 (39,300 ▲).............D6 35
Banff, Alta., Can., 3,219..................D3, g7 38
Banff, co., Scot., 43,749...*B5 4
Bangalore, India, 1,540,741 (*1,750,000)...........F6 20
Banggai, Indon...........F6 19
Bangkok (Krung Thep), Thai., 1,867,297 (*3,125,000)...........C2 19
Bangladesh, country, Asia 77,450,000..............D9 20
Bangor, Maine, 33,168 (*78,400)..............D4 64
Bangor, Mich., 2,050......F4 66
Bangor, N. Ire., 35,178....C4 4
Bangor, Pa., 5,425.......E11 81
Bangor, Wales, 15,730.....D4 4
Bangor, Wis., 974.........E3 88
Bangs, Tex., 1,214........D3 84
Bangued, Phil., 10,482.....B6 19
Bangui, Cen. Afr. Emp., 150,000................H1 23
Bangweulu, lake, Zambia..C6 24
Banhā, Eg., 63,849........G8 14
Baní, Dom. Rep., 23,700...E8 35
Banī Suwayf, Eg., 90,425..C4 23
Banja Luka, Yugo., 89,866.C3 10
Banjarmasin, Indon., 281,673..................F4 19
Banjul, Gam., 30,900 (*44,000)..............F1 22
Banks, co., Ga., 6,833.....B3 55
Banks, isl., Can...........B9 36
Bānkura, India, 79,129....D8 20
Banner, co., Nebr., 1,034...C2 71
Bannertown, N.C., 1,138..*A2 76
Bannock, co., Idaho, 52,200..................G6 57
Bannu, Pak., 20,509.......B5 20
Bañolas, Sp., 8,075........A7 8
Banska Bystrica, Czech., 40,082..................D5 7
Banska Stiavnica, Czech., 9,500...................D5 7
Bansko, Bul., 6,161........E6 10
Bantam, Conn., 881........C4 52
Banyuwangi, Indon., 89,303..................G4 19
Baʻqūbah, Iraq, 34,575.....C3 15
Bar, Sov. Un., 22,100.....G6 12
Barabinsk, Sov. Un., 37,000................D10 13
Baraboo, Wis., 7,931......E4 88
Baracaldo, Sp., 109,185....A4 8
Baracoa, Cuba, 20,900 (35,600 ▲).............D6 35
Baradero, Arg., 8,253......F7 28
Baraga, Mich., 1,116......B2 66
Baraga, co., Mich., 7,789.. B2 66
Barahona, Dom. Rep., 37,900..................E8 35
Baramula India, 26,334...B5 20
Baranovichi, Sov. Un., 101,000.................E3 12
Baranya, co., Hung., 279,715................*B4 10
Barataria, La., 900....E5, k11 63
Barbacena, Braz., 57,766............C4, g6 30
Barbados, country, N.A., 250,000...................J15 35
Barbar, Sud., 12,900......E4 23
Barbastro, Sp., 10,227.....A6 8
Barbate, Sp., 10,720.......D3 8
Barber, co., Kans., 7,016...E5 61
Barberton, Ohio, 33,052...A4 78
Barberton, S. Afr., 12,232..F6 24
Barbour, co., Ala., 22,543..D4 46
Barbour, co., W. Va., 14,030..................B4 87
Barboursville, W. Va., 2,279..................C2 87
Barbourville, Ky., 3,549...D6 62
Barbuda, isl., Antigua....H14 35
Barcarrota, Sp., 7,898.....C2 8
Barcellona [Pozzo di Gotto], It., 23,700..............E5 9
Barcelona, Sp., 1,741,979 (*2,800,000)..........B7 8
Barcelona, Ven., 76,410...A5 32
Barcelos, Port., 7,875......B1 8
Bardejov, Czech., 12,254...D6 7
Bardstown, Ky., 5,816.....C4 62
Bardwell, Ky., 1,049.......f8 62
Bareilly, India, 296,248 (*326,106)...........C6 2
Baresville, Pa., 1,700.....*G8 81
Barguzin, Sov. Un., 5,600.D13 13
Bar Harbor, Maine, 2,392 (3,716 ▲)........D4 64
Bari, It., 348,900.........D6 9
Barinas, state, Ven., 139,271..................B3 32
Baripāda, India, 28,725....D8 20
Barirí, Braz., 11,532...C3, m7 30
Barisāl, Bngl., 69,936.....D9 20
Barking, Eng., 72,100......k13 4
Bar-le-Duc, Fr., 19,159....C6 5
Barletta, It., 75,100.......D6 9
Barling, Ark., 1,739.......B1 49
Barmer, India, 38,630.....C5 20
Barnaul, Sov. Un., 439,000 (*495,000)....D11 13
Barnegat, N.J., 554.......D4 74
Barnes, co., N. Dak., 14,669..................C7 77
Barnesboro, Pa., 2,708.....E4 81
Barnesville, Ga., 4,935.....C2 55
Barnesville, Minn., 1,782..D2 67
Barnesville, Ohio, 4,292...C4 78
Barnhill, Ohio, 339........B4 78
Barnsboro, N.J., 500......D2 74
Barnsdall, Okla., 1,579....A5 79
Barnsley, Eng., 74,900 (*199,000)..............*D6 4
Barnstable, Mass., 1,202 (19,842 ▲).............C7 65
Barnstable, co., Mass., 96,656..................C7 65
Barnstaple, Eng., 17,590...E4 4
Barnwell, S.C., 4,439......E5 82
Barnwell, co., S.C., 17,176..................E4 82
Baroda, India, 466,696....D5 20
Barquisimeto, Ven., 334,333..................A4 32
Barra, Braz., 8,774.......*E5 27
Barraba, Austl., 1,469.....E8 26
Barrackville, W. Va., 1,545..............B4, h10 87
Barra do Piraí, Braz., 42,713..............C4, h6 30
Barra Mansa, Braz., 75,006..............C4, h6 30
Barrancabermeja, Col., 68,300..................B3 32
Barranquilla, Col., 590,300 (*640,000)......A3 32
Barre, Mass., 1,098 (3,825 ▲)..............B3 65
Barre, Vt., 10,209.........C3 73
Barreiras, Braz., 9,855....*E5 27
Barreiro, Port., 22,190..C1, f9 8
Barreiros, Braz., 17,347...*D7 27
Barren, co., Ky., 28,677...D4 62
Barretos, Braz., 53,050....C3 30
Barrett, Tex., 2,750......*E5 84
Barrhead, Alta., Can., 2,803..................B3 38
Barrie, Ont., Can., 27,676 (*38,176)..............C5 41
Barrigada, Guam, 1,729...*F6 2
Barrington, Ill., 8,674..A5, h8 58
Barrington, N.J., 8,409...*D2 74
Barrington, R.I., 13,500 (17,554 ▲)......C11 52
Barrington Hills, Ill., 2,712..................*A5 58
Barron, Wis., 2,337........C2 88
Barron, co., Wis., 33,955...C2 88
Barrow, Alsk., 2,104.......A8 47
Barrow, co., Ga., 16,859...B3 55
Barrow-in-Furness, Eng., 63,860..................C5 4
Barruelo de Santullán, Sp., 7,770..................A3 8
Barry, Ill., 1,444.........D2 58
Barry, co., Mich., 38,166...F5 66
Barry, co., Mo., 19,597....E4 69
Barrys Bay, Ont., Can., 1,432..................B7 41
Bārsi, India, 62,374.......E6 20
Barstow, Calif., 17,442.....E5 50
Barth, Fla., 180..........u14 54
Barth, Ger. Dem. Rep., 12,200..................A6 6
Bartholomew, co., Ind., 57,022..................F6 59
Bartin, Tur., 15,926.......B9 14
Bartle Frere, mtn., Austl...C8 25
Bartlesville, Okla., 29,683..A6 79
Bartlett, Ill., 3,501........h8 58
Bartlett, Tex., 1,622.......D4 84
Barton, Ala., 200..........A2 46
Barton, Ohio, 800.........B5 78
Barton, Vt., 1,051.........B3 73
Barton, co., Kans., 30,663..D5 61
Barton, co., Mo., 10,431...D3 69
Bartonville, Ill., 7,221.....C4 58
Bartow, Fla., 12,891.......E5 54
Bartow, co., Ga., 32,663...B2 55
Barvas, Scot..............A3 4
Barvenkovo, Sov. Un., 15,000................G11 12
Basel, Switz., 205,100 (*560,000)............E3 6

Basel-Land, sub canton, Switz., 194,500........*E3 6
Basel-Stadt, sub canton, Switz., 235,000........*E3 6
Basildon, Eng., 122,800...*E7 4
Basile, La., 1,779.........D3 63
Basilicata, pol. dist., It....*D5 9
Basin, Wyo., 1,145........B4 89
Basingstoke, Eng., 53,080..E6 4
Baskin, Fla., 500.........P10 54
Basking Ridge, N.J., 4,800..................B3 74
Basque Provinces, reg., Sp., 1,752,600..........A4 8
Basra, Iraq, 370,900.......B7 23
Bas-Rhin, dept., Fr., 827,367..............*C7 5
Bassac, Laos, 5,000........C3 19
Bassano, Alta., Can., 861..D4 38
Bassano del Grappa, It., 30,000..................B3 9
Bassein, Bur., 77,905......E9 20
Basses-Alpes, dept., Fr., 104,813..............*E7 5
Basses-Pyrénées, dept., Fr., 508,734...............*F3 5
Basse-Terre, Guad., 15,690 (*24,000).......I14 35
Basseterre, St. Kitts-Nevis-Anguilla, 13,055.......H13 35
Bassett, Nebr., 983........B6 71
Bassett, Va., 3,058........D3 85
Bastia, Fr., 49,375........C2 9
Bastogne, Bel., 6,827......B6 5
Bastrop, La., 14,713.......B4 63
Bastrop, co., Tex., 17,297..D4 84
Basutoland, see Lesotho, country, Afr.
Bata, Equat., Gui., 4,000..H6 22
Bataan, prov., Phil., 145,323..............*C6 19
Batāla, India, 58,200......B6 20
Batanes, prov., Phil., 10,309...............*A6 19
Batangas, Phil., 18,174 (108,868 ▲)...........p13 19
Batangas, prov., Phil., 681,414..............*C6 19
Bátaszék, Hung., 6,235....B4 10
Batatais, Braz., 21,061.....C3 30
Batavia, Ill., 8,994.....B5, k8 58
Batavia, N.Y., 17,338.....C2 75
Batavia, Ohio, 1,894......C1 78
Batavia, see Jakarta, Indon.
Bataysk, Sov. Un., 85,000..............H12 12
Bates, co., Mo., 15,468....C3 69
Batesburg, S.C., 4,036.....D4 82
Batesville, Ark., 7,209.....B4 49
Batesville, Ind., 3,799......F7 59
Batesville, Miss., 3,796.....A4 68
Bath, Eng., 85,600.........E5 4
Bath, Maine, 9,679....E3, g8 64
Bath, N.Y., 6,053.........C3 75
Bath, Pa., 1,829.........E11 81
Bath, S.C., 1,576.........D4 82
Bath, co., Ky., 9,235.......B6 62
Bath, co., Va., 5,192......B3 85
Bathurst, Austl., 17,169....F8 25
Bathurst, N.B., Can., 16,674..................B4 43
Bathurst, see Banjul, Gam.
Batna, Alg., 54,924........H6 22
Baton Rouge, La., 165,921 (*336,600).........D4, h9 63
Batouri, Cam............H7 22
Battambang, Camb., 38,800................C2 19
Batticaloa, Sri Lanka, 36,761.................G7 20
Battle Creek, Mich., 38,931 (*110,100)............F5 66
Battleford, Sask., Can., 1,803..................E1 39
Battle Ground, Ind., 818...C4 59
Battle Ground, Wash., 1,438.................D3 86
Battonya, Hung., 9,216....B5 10
Batumi, Sov. Un., 101,000................E7 13
Batu Pahat (Bandar Penggaram), Mala., 53,291...............*E2 19
Baturité, Braz., 8,799......D7 27
Bat Yam, Isr., 99,800.....*B2 15
Bauchi, Nig., 37,778........F6 22
Baudette, Minn., 1,547....B4 67
Bauru, Braz., 120,178.....C3 30
Bautzen, Ger. Dem. Rep., 45,041..................C7 6
Bauxite, Ark., 100.....C3, k9 49
Bavaria, reg., Ger., Fed. Rep. of..........D5 6
Bavispe, Mex., 1,040......A3 34
Bawcomville, La., 1,500..*B3 63
Baxley, Ga., 3,503........E4 55
Baxter, Minn., 1,556......D4 67
Baxter, co., Ark., 15,319...A3 49
Baxter Estates, N.Y., 1,026................*E7 75
Baxter Springs, Kans., 4,489..................E9 61
Bay, co., Fla., 75,283..B1, u16 54
Bay, co., Mich., 117,339...E6 66
Baya Dzur-Gunen, Mong..B5 17
Bayamo, Cuba, 71,700 (92,700 ▲).............D5 35
Bayamón, P.R., 147,552..G11 35
Bayanovka, Sov. Un.......C8 13
Bayard, Nebr., 1,338......C2 71
Bayard, N. Mex., 2,908....C4 48
Baybay, Phil., 10,021.....*C6 19
Bayburt, Tur., 20,145.....B13 14
Bay City, Mich., 49,449 (*175,100).............E7 66
Bay City, Oreg., 898.......B3 80
Bay City, Tex., 13,445.............E5, s14 84
Bay de Verde, Newf., Can., 884..............D5 44
Bayern, state, Ger., Fed. Rep. of, 10,810,000....*D5 6
Bayeux, Fr., 11,451.......C3 5
Bayfield, Wis., 874........B3 88
Bayfield, co., Wis., 11,683.................B2 88
Bay Harbor Island, Fla., 4,619..................*F3 54
Bay Head, N.J., 1,083.....C4 74
Bayindir, Tur., 11,300....*C6 14
Baykal, lake, Sov. Un.....D13 13
Baylor, co., Tex., 5,221.....C3 84
Bay Minette, Ala., 6,727...E2 46
Bayombong, Phil., 11,697.*B6 19
Bayonne, Fr., 42,743 (*110,000).............F3 5
Bayonne, N.J., 72,743..B4, k8 74
Bayou Cane, La., 9,077...*E5 63
Bayou LaBatre, Ala., 2,664..................E1 46
Bay Park, N.Y., 3,000....*E7 75
Bayport, Minn., 2,987...................E6 67
Bayport, N.Y., 8,232......n15 75
Bayreuth, Ger., Fed. Rep. of, 66,800.............D5 6
Bay Roberts, Newf., Can., 3,702..................E5 44
Bay St. Louis, Miss., 6,752..............E4, g7 68
Bay Shore, N.Y., 31,061............E7, n15 75
Bayshore Gardens, Fla., 2,297..................*E4 54
Bayside, Wis., 4,461.......m12 88
Bay Springs, Miss., 1,801..D4 68
Bayt Laḥm, see Bethlehem, Jordan
Baytown, Tex., 43,980.............E5, r15 84
Bay View, Ala., 830.........f7 46
Bayview, Calif., 1,800.....*B1 50
Bayview, Mass., 30.........A6 65
Bay Village, Ohio, 18,163..................h9 78
Bayville, N.Y., 6,147......F2 52
Baztán, Sp., 1,534.........A5 8
Beach, N. Dak., 1,408.....D2 77
Beach City, Ohio, 1,133...B4 78
Beach Haven, N.J., 1,488..D4 74
Beachville, Ont., Can., 849..................D4 41
Beachwood, N.J., 4,390...*D4 74
Beachwood, Ohio, 9,631...A4 78
Beacon, N.Y., 13,255......D7 75
Beacon Falls, Conn., 1,900..................D4 52
Beacon Hill, Wash., 1,263..................*C3 86
Beaconsfield, Que., Can., 19,389..................D8 42
Beadle, co., S. Dak., 20,877..................F7 77
Bearden, Ark., 1,272......D3 49
Beardstown, Ill., 6,222.....C3 58
Bear Lake, co., Idaho, 5,801..................G7 57
Bear River, N.S., Can., 830...................E4 43
Bear Town, Miss., 1,085...D3 68
Beas de Segura, Sp., 9,251..................C4 8
Beatrice, Nebr., 12,389....D9 71
Beattyville, Ky., 923......C6 62
Beaucaire, Fr., 8,243.......F6 5
Beauce, co., Que., Can., 64,275..................C7 42
Beauceville Est, Que., Can., 2,192..................C7 42
Beauceville, Ouest, Que., Can., 2,098.............*C7 42
Beaufort, N.C., 3,368......C6 76
Beaufort, S.C., 9,434......G6 82
Beaufort, co., N.C., 35,980.................B5 76
Beaufort, co., S.C., 51,136.................G6 82
Beaufort West, S. Afr., 17,730..................G4 24
Beauharnois, Que., Can., 8,121.............D4, q19 42
Beauharnois, co., Que., Can., 51,942...........D3 42
Beaumont, Calif., 5,484...*F5 50
Beaumont, Tex., 115,919 (*266,300)............D5 84
Beaumont Place, Tex., 1,600..................*E5 84
Beaune, Fr., 16,874.......D6 5
Beaupré, Que., Can., 2,862..................B7 42
Beauregard, par., La., 22,888..................D2 63
Beaurepaire, Que., Can., 2,400..................D8 42
Beauséjour, Man., Can., 2,236..................D3 40
Beauvais, Fr., 46,777......C5 5
Beaver, Okla., 1,853..A1, e10 79
Beaver, Pa., 6,100.........E1 81
Beaver, Utah, 1,453.......B5 72
Beaver, co., Okla., 6,282...A1 79
Beaver, co., Pa., 208,418...E1 81
Beaver, co., Utah, 3,800....B5 72
Beaver Bank, N.S., Can., 870..................E6 43
Beaver City, Nebr., 802....D6 71
Beaverdale, Pa., 1,579.....F4 81
Beaver Dam, Ky., 2,622...C3 62
Beaver Dam, Wis., 14,265..E5 88
Beaver Falls, Pa., 14,375...E1 81
Beaver (Glen Hedrick), W. Va., 1,500......D3, n13 87
Beaverhead, co., Mont., 8,187..................E3 70
Beaverlodge, Alta., Can., 897...................B1 38
Beaver Meadows, Pa., 1,274..............E10 81
Beaverton, Ont., Can., 1,217..................C5 42
Beaverton, Mich., 954......E6 66
Beaverton, Oreg., 18,577............B4, h12 80
Beāwar, India, 66,114......C5 20
Bebedouro, Braz., 28,824..C3 30
Bečej, Yugo., 26,470......C5 10
Béchar, Alg., 46,505.......B4 22
Bechuanaland, see Botswana, country, Afr.
Becker, co., Minn., 24,372. D3 67
Beckham, co., Okla., 15,754..................B2 79
Beckley, W. Va., 19,884 (*46,000)....D3, n13 87
Bédarieux, Fr., 7,135......F5 5
Bedford, N.S., Can........E6 43
Bedford, Que., Can., 2,786..................D5 42
Bedford, Eng., 72,880.....D6 4
Bedford, Ind., 13,087......G5 59
Bedford, Iowa, 1,733......D3 60
Bedford, Mass., 13,513............B5, g10 65
Bedford, Ohio, 17,552............A4, h9 78
Bedford, Pa., 3,302........F4 81
Bedford, Tex., 10,049.....*C4 84
Bedford, Va., 6,011.......C3 85
Bedford, co., Eng., 465,300..................*D6 4
Bedford, co., Pa., 42,353...G4 81
Bedford, co., Tenn., 25,039..................B5 83
Bedford, co., Va., 26,728..C3 85
Bedford Heights, Ohio, 13,063..................*A4 78
Bedford Hills, N.Y., 3,500..................m15 75
Bedlington, Eng., 28,230...C6 4
Bedminster, N.J., 500......B3 74
Będzin, Pol., 42,700.......g10 7
Bee, co., Tex., 22,737......E4 84
Beebe, Ark., 2,805.........B4 49
Beebe, Que., Can., 1,363...D5 42
Beecher, Ill., 1,770........B6 58
Beech Grove, Ind., 13,559............E5, m10 59
Beenleigh, Austl., 2,451....C9 26
Bee Ridge, Fla., 900..E4, q11 54
Be'er Sheva' (Beersheba), Isr., 84,100..........C2, h5 15
Beeskow, Ger. Dem. Rep., 7,571..................B7 6
Beeton, Ont., Can., 1,061..C5 41
Beeville, Tex., 13,506......E4 84
Bègles, Fr., 27,330.........E3 5
Beida, Libya, 12,800......B2 23
Beira, Moz., 80,000.......D6 24
Beira, reg., Port., 2,097,200..............B2 8
Beira Alta, prov., Port....*B2 8
Beira Baixa, prov., Port...*C2 8
Beira Litoral, prov., Port..*B1 8
Beirut (Bayrūt), Leb., 474,870 (*1,010,000)....g5 15
Beja, Port., 15,702........C2 8
Béja, Tun., 28,145.........A6 22
Bejaïa (Bougie), Alg., 49,930..................A5 22
Bejeda (Ras Dashan), mtn., Eth.....................F5 23
Békés, Hung., 17,661 (21,699 ▲)..............B5 10
Békés, co., Hung., 447,196.*B5 10
Békéscsaba, Hung., 48,261 (55,408 ▲)............B5 10
Bela, India, 27,909........C7 20
Bela Crkva, Yugo., 11,129..C5 10
Bel Air, Md., 6,307........A5 53
Belalcázar, Sp., 8,793......C3 8
Bela Vista, Braz., 10,563...C1 30
Belaya Tserkov, Sov. Un., 109,000................G8 12
Belchertown, Mass., 950 (5,186 ▲)............B3 65
Belding, Mich., 5,121......E5 66
Belém, Braz., 565,097 (*660,000)............D6 27
Belen, N. Mex., 4,823......B5 48
Belén, Par., 6,647.........D4 29
Belev, Sov. Un., 18,000...E11 12
Belfair, Wash., 400.......B3 86
Belfast, Maine, 5,957......D3 64
Belfast, N.Y., 900..........C2 75
Belfast, N.C., 900..........B4 76
Belfast, N. Ire., 360,150 (*720,000)............C4 4
Belfield, N. Dak., 1,130....D3 77
Belford, N.J., 6,000.......C4 74
Belfort, Fr., 53,214 (*72,000)..............D7 5
Belfort, dept., Fr., 109,371..............*D7 5
Belfry, Ky., 900..........C7 62
Belgaum, India, 192,427 (*213,872)..............E5 20
Belgium, country, Eur., 9,760,000................B6 5
Belgorod, Sov. Un., 151,000................F11 12
Belgorod-Dnestrovskiy, Sov. Un., 33,000.......H8 12
Belgrade, Mont., 1,307....E5 70
Belgrade (Beograd), Yugo., 770,140 (*1,150,000)....C5 10
Belhaven, N.C., 2,259.....B6 76
Belington, W. Va., 1,567...B5 87
Belize, Belize, 39,332......D7 34
Belize, Br. dep., N.A., 130,000..................D7 34
Belknap, co., N.H., 32,367.D5 73
Bell, Calif., 21,836.......*F4 50
Bell, co., Ky., 31,087......D6 62
Bell, co., Tex., 124,483....D4 84
Bell Acres, Pa., 1,264.....*E1 81
Bellaire, Ohio, 9,655.......C5 78
Bellaire, Tex., 19,009......r14 84
Bellary, India, 125,183....E6 20
Bella Unión, Ur., 2,519....E1 30
Bella Vista, Arg., 6,816....E2 29
Bella Vista, Arg., 8,334....E4 29
Bella Vista, Par., 5,762....D4 29
Bellbrook, Ohio, 1,268.....C1 78
Belle, Mo., 1,133..........C6 69
Belle, W. Va., 1,786.......C6 87
Belleair, Fla., 2,962.......p10 54
Belle Center, Ohio, 985....B2 78
Bellechasse, co., Que., Can., 24,045..................C7 42
Bellefontaine, Ohio, 11,255..B2 78
Bellefontaine Neighbors, Mo., 14,084...........*C7 69
Bellefonte, Del., 1,442.....A7 53
Bellefonte, Pa., 6,828......E6 81
Belle Fourche, S. Dak., 4,236..................F2 77
Bellegarde [-sur-Valserine], Fr., 9,249................D6 5
Belle Glade, Fla., 11,273...F6 54
Belle Isle, Fla., 2,705......D5 54
Bellemead, Md., 1,000....*C4 53
Belle Plaine, Iowa, 2,810..C5 60
Belle Plaine, Kans., 1,553..E6 61
Belle Plaine, Minn., 2,328..F5 67
Belle River, Ont., Can., 2,877..................*E2 41
Belle Rose, La., 700....D4, h9 63
Bellerose, N.Y., 1,136.....*E7 75
Belleterre, Que., Can., 638..................*o20 41
Belle Vernon, Pa., 1,496...F2 81
Belleview, Fla., 916.......C4 54
Belleville, Ont., Can., 35,128..................C7 41
Belleville, Ill., 41,699......E4 58
Belleville, Kans., 3,063....C6 61
Belleville, Mich., 2,406....p15 66
Belleville, N.J., 37,629..B4, h8 74
Belleville, Pa., 1,817.......E6 81
Belleville, Wis., 1,063......F4 88

Bellevue, Ill., 1,189......*C4 58
Bellevue, Iowa, 2,336......B7 60
Bellevue, Ky., 8,847......h13 62
Bellevue, Mich., 1,297......F5 66
Bellevue, Nebr., 21,953............C10, g3 71
Bellevue, Ohio, 8,604......A3 78
Bellevue, Wash., 61,196...e11 86
Belley, Fr., 4,609..........E6 5
Bellflower, Calif., 51,454..n12 50
Bell Gardens, Calif., 29,308...............*F4 50
Bellingham, Mass., 4,228 (13,967 ▲).........B5, h10 65
Bellingham, Wash., 39,375.A3 86
Bellinzona, Switz., 17,100 (*30,600)..............E4 6
Bellmawr, N.J., 15,618....D2 74
Bellmead, Tex., 7,698....*D4 84
Bellmore, N.Y., 18,431....G2 52
Bello, Col., 118,100.........B2 32
Bellows Falls, Vt., 3,505...E3 73
Bellport, N.Y., 3,046......G5 52
Bells, Tenn., 1,474.........B2 83
Belluno, It., 28,900........A4 9
Bell Ville, Arg., 21,000....A4 28
Bellville, Ohio, 1,685......B3 78
Bellville, Tex., 2,371......E4 84
Bellwood, Ill., 22,096......k9 58
Bellwood, Pa., 2,395.......E5 81
Belmar, N.J., 5,782........C4 74
Bélmez, Sp., 8,068........C3 8
Belmond, Iowa, 2,358......B4 60
Belmont, Calif., 23,538.....h8 50
Belmont, Mass., 28,285....g11 65
Belmont, Miss., 1,237......A5 68
Belmont, N.Y., 1,102.......C2 75
Belmont, N.C., 5,054.......B1 76
Belmont, co., Ohio, 80,917.................C4 78
Belmonte, Braz., 7,072....*E7 27
Belmopan, Belize, 5,000..................D7 34
Bel-Nor, Mo., 2,247.........f13 69
Beloeil, Que., Can., 12,274.D4 42
Belo Horizonte, Braz., 1,235,001 (*1,550,000)...B4 30
Beloit, Kans., 4,121........C5 61
Beloit, Ohio, 921...........B5 78
Beloit, Wis., 35,729 (*57,800)..............F4 88
Beloit West, Wis., 1,903...*F4 88
Belomorsk, Sov. Un., 17,000..................C6 13
Belopolye, Sov. Un., 19,000................F10 12
Beloretsk, Sov. Un., 67,000.................D8 13
Belovo, Sov. Un., 108,000..............*D11 13
Belpre, Ohio, 7,819.........C4 78
Bel-Ridge, Mo., 5,346....*C7 69
Belton, Mo., 12,179........C3 69
Belton, S.C., 5,257.........B3 82
Belton, Tex., 8,696.........D4 84
Beltrami, co., Minn., 26,373..................B3 67
Beltsville, Md., 8,912.......B4 53
Beltsy, Sov. Un., 101,000..H6 12
Belukha, mtn., Sov. Un...E11 13
Belvedere, Calif., 2,599...*C2 50
Belvedere, Va., 1,500.....*B5 85
Belvedere Marittimo, It....E5 9
Belvidere, Del., 1,500......A6 53
Belvidere, Ill., 14,061......A5 58
Belvidere, N.J., 2,722......B2 74
Belzoni, Miss., 3,394.......B3 68
Bement, Ill., 1,638.........D5 58
Bemidji, Minn., 11,490.....C4 67
Bemis, Tenn., 1,883........B3 83
Benalla, Austl., 8,235......G8 25
Benares, see Varānasi, India
Benavente, Sp., 11,080.....A3 8
Ben Avon, Pa., 2,713.....*E1 81
Benbrook, Tex., 8,169....*C4 84
Bend, Oreg., 13,710.........C5 80
Bendale, S.C., 1,500.......C6 82
Bendery, Sov. Un., 72,000.H7 12
Bendigo, Austl., 31,972 (*46,564)..............G7 25
Bene Beraq, Isr., 74,100....B2 15
Benešov, Czech., 10,083 ....D3, o18 7
Benevento, It., 49,400......D5 9
Benewah, Idaho, 6,036.....B2 57
Benewah, co., Idaho, 6,230.B2 57
Bengal, reg., Bngl., India...D8 20
Bengasi (Banghāzī), Libya, 247,400.................B2 23
Bengkulu, Indon., 31,866...F2 19
Benguela, Ang., 23,256.....C2 24
Benguela, dist., Ang........C3 24
Benham, Ky., 1,000.........D7 62
Ben Hill, co., Ga., 13,171..D3 55
Benicarló, Sp., 10,627......B6 8
Benicia, Calif., 7,349...C2, g8 50
Benin, country, Afr., 2,935,000..............G5 22
Benin City, Nig., 100,694..G6 22
Benisa, Sp., 6,036.........C6 8
Benkelman, Nebr., 1,349...D4 71
Benld, Ill., 1,736..........D4 58
Ben Lomond, Calif., 1,814................*D2 50
Bennett, co., S. Dak., 3,088.................G4 77
Bennettsville, S.C., 7,468...B8 82
Bennettsville Southwest, S.C., 1,726................*B8 82
Ben Nevis, mtn., Scot......B4 4
Bennington, Vt., 7,950.....F1 73
Bennington, co., Vt., 29,282.................E1 73
Bensenville, Ill., 12,833.B6, k9 58
Bensheim, Ger., Fed. Rep. of, 33,290.........D4 6
Benson, Ariz., 2,839.......D3 48
Benson, Minn., 3,484......E3 67
Benson, N.C., 2,267.......B4 76
Benson, co., N. Dak., 8,245..................B6 77
Bent, co., Colo., 6,493.....D7 51
Bentleyville, Pa., 2,714.....F1 81
Benton, Ark., 16,499...C3, k9 49
Benton, Ill., 6,833.........E5 58
Benton, Ky., 3,652..........f9 62
Benton, La., 1,493.........B2 63
Benton, Pa., 1,027.........D9 81
Benton, Tenn., 749.........D9 83
Benton, Wis., 873...........F3 88
Benton, co., Ark., 50,476...A1 49
Benton, co., Ind., 11,262...C3 59
Benton, co., Iowa, 22,885..B5 60
Benton, co., Minn., 20,841.E4 67
Benton, co., Miss., 7,505...A4 68
Benton, co., Mo., 9,695....C4 69
Benton, co., Oreg., 53,776..C3 80
Benton, co., Tenn., 12,126..A3 83
Benton, co., Wash., 67,540.C6 86
Benton City, Wash., 1,070..C6 86
Benton Harbor, Mich., 16,481 (*98,200).........F4 66
Benton Heights, Mich., 6,000..................F4 66
Bentonville, Ark., 5,508....A1 49
Benwood, W. Va., 2,737..................A4, f8 87
Benzie, co., Mich., 8,593...D4 66
Beograd, see Belgrade, Yugo.
Beppu, Jap., 123,786.......J5 18
Berat, Alb., 23,900........*B2 14
Berat, pref., Alb., 176,000.*B2 14
Berbera, Som., 14,000......F7 23
Berchtesgaden, Ger., Fed. Rep. of, 4,343..........E6 6
Berck, Fr., 13,690..........B4 5
Berdichev, Sov. Un., 71,000..................G7 12
Berdyansk, Sov. Un., 100,000..............H11 12
Berea, Ky., 6,956...........C5 62
Berea, Ohio, 22,465....A4, h9 78
Beregovo, Sov. Un., 5,000..G4 12
Beresford, S. Dak., 1,655...G9 77
Berettyóujfalu, Hung., 11,377..................B5 10
Berezhany, Sov. Un., 5,000..................G5 12
Berezna, Sov. Un., 10,000..F8 12
Berezniki, Sov. Un., 146,000.................D8 13
Berg, Nor. q27 11
Berga, Sp., 9,822...........A6 8
Bergama, Tur., 27,044....*C6 14
Bergamo, It., 124,600 (*300,000).............B2 9
Bergen, Ger. Dem. Rep., 10,500...................A6 6
Bergen, N.Y., 1,018........B3 75
Bergen, Nor., 116,300 (*227,000)..............G1 11
Bergen, see Mons, Bel.
Bergen, co., N.J., 897,148..A4 74
Bergen, co., Nor., 116,300...............*G1 11
Bergenfield, N.J., 29,000.............B5, h8 74
Bergen op Zoom, Neth., 42,072..................B6 5
Bergerac, Fr., 27,165.......E4 5
Bergholz, Ohio, 914........B5 78
Bergisch Gladbach, Ger., Fed. Rep. of, 51,759....C3 6
Berhampore, India, 72,605 (*78,909)........D8 20
Berhampur, India, 117,662.E7 20
Bering, sea, Alsk., Sov. Un..............D21 16
Berislav, Sov. Un., 10,000..H9 12
Berja, Sp., 6,425...........D4 8
Berkeley, Calif., 116,716...D2 50
Berkeley, Ill., 6,152.......*B6 58
Berkeley, Mo., 19,743.......f13 69
Berkeley, R.I., 2,000 ......B11 52
Berkeley, co., S.C., 56,199..E7 82
Berkeley, co., W. Va., 36,356.................B6 87
Berkeley Heights, N.J., 13,078.................B4 74
Berkeley Springs (Bath), W. Va., 944............B6 87
Berkley, Mich., 21,879............F7, o15 66
Berkovitsa, Bul., 6,870.....D6 10
Berks, co., Pa., 296,382....F9 81
Berkshire, Md., 1,200.....*C4 53
Berkshire, co., Eng., 647,010...............*E6 4
Berksire, co., Mass., 104,200.................B1 65
Berlin, Md., 1,942.........D7 53
Berlin, N.H., 17,821.......C5 73
Berlin, N.J., 4,997.........D3 74
Berlin, N.Y., 800...........C7 75
Berlin, Pa., 1,766..........G4 81
Berlin, Wis., 5,338.........E5 88
Berlin, East, Ger. Dem. Rep., 1,088,828.........B6 6
Berlin, West, Ger., Fed. Rep. of, 2,062,615 (*3,875,000)...........B6 6
Berlin, West, state, Ger., Fed. Rep. of, 2,062,615 . *B6 6
Bermeo, Sp., 13,781........A4 8
Bermuda, Br. dep., N.A., 56,000.................p20 35
Bern, Switz., 156,900 (*282,200)...............p20 35
Bern, canton, Switz., 980,000...............*E3 6
Bernalillo, N. Mex., 2,016...............B5, D6 48
Bernalillo, co., N. Mex., 315,774..................B5 48
Bernardsville, N.J., 6,652...B3 74
Bernau, Ger. Dem. Rep., 13,600..................B6 6
Bernay, Fr., 7,418.........C4 5
Bernburg, Ger. Dem. Rep., 44,871..................C5 6
Berndorf, Aus., 8,191.......E8 6
Berne, Ind., 2,988..........C8 59
Bernice, La., 1,794.........B3 63
Bernie, Mo., 1,641..........E8 69
Bernville, Pa., 848..........F9 81
Beroun, Czech., 17,809 (*24,000)..........D3, o17 7
Berri, Austl., 2,712.........F7 25
Berrien, co., Ga., 11,556....E3 55
Berrien, co., Mich., 163,940..................F4 66
Berrien Springs, Mich., 1,951..................G4 66
Berry, former prov., Fr....D4 5
Berry Hill, Tenn., 1,551 ...g10 83
Berryville, Ark., 2,271......A2 49
Berryville, Va., 1,569......A5 85
Bershad, Sov. Un., 10,000..G7 12
Berthier, co., Que., Can., 27,035.................C3 42
Berthierville, Que., Can., 4,080...................C4 42
Berthoud, Colo., 1,446.....A5 51
Bertie, co., N.C., 20,528...A5 76
Bertram, Tex., 758.........D4 84
Bertrand, Mich., 3,500....*G4 66
Berwick, N.S., Can., 1,412...................D5 43
Berwick, La., 4,168........E4 63
Berwick, Maine, 1,765 (3,136 ▲)...............E2 64
Berwick, Pa., 12,274.......D9 81
Berwick, co., Scot., 20,641...............*C5 4
Berwick-upon-Tweed, Eng., 11,650..................C6 4
Berwind, W. Va., 700.......D3 87
Berwyn, Ill., 52,502.........k9 58
Berwyn, Pa., 9,000.........o20 81
Berwyn Heights, Md., 3,934.................*B4 53
Besa, Indon. E7 19
Besancon, Fr., 113,220....D7 5
Besni, Tur., 12,025........D11 14
Bessèges, Fr., 5,770........E6 5
Bessemer, Ala., 33,663..B3, g7 46
Bessemer, Mich., 2,805....n11 66
Bessemer, Pa., 1,427.......E1 81
Bessemer City, N.C., 4,991...................B1 76
Bethalto, Ill., 7,074.......E3 58
Bethany, Conn., 800.......D5 52
Bethany, Ill., 1,235........D5 58
Bethany, Mo., 2,914........A3 69
Bethany, Okla., 22,694.....B4 79
Bethany, W. Va., 602........f8 87
Bethayres-Huntingdon Valley, Pa., 2,500.....*F11 81
Bethel, Alsk., 2,416........C7 47
Bethel, Conn., 10,945......D3 52
Bethel, Maine, 950 (2,220 ▲)..................D2 64
Bethel, N.C., 1,514.........B6 76
Bethel, Ohio, 2,214........D1 78
Bethel (Bethel Park), Pa., 34,758................k13 81
Bethesda, Md., 75,000..C3, f8 53
Bethesda, Ohio, 1,157......B4 78
Bethlehem (Bayt Laḩm), Jordan, 16,313......C3, h5 15
Bethlehem, Pa., 72,686...E11 81
Bethlehem, S. Afr., 29,460..F5 24
Bethlehem, W. Va., 2,461...f8 87
Bethpage, N.Y., 29,700....G3 52
Béthune, Fr., 27,154 (*56,000)..............B5 5
Bettendorf, Iowa, 22,126............C7, g11 60
Betūl, India, 30,862........D6 20
Beulah, N. Dak., 1,344.....C4 77
Beulaville, N.C., 1,156.....C5 76
Beverley, Eng., 17,130.....D6 4
Beverly, Mass., 38,348..............A6, f12 65
Beverly, N.J., 3,105........C3 74
Beverly, Ohio, 1,396.......C4 78
Beverly Gardens, Ohio, 2,400................*C1 78
Beverly Hills, Calif., 33,416................m12 50
Beverly Hills, Mich., 13,598.................*F7 66
Beverwijk, Neth., 39,517...A6 5
Bexar, co., Tex., 830,460...E3 84
Bexhill-on-Sea, Eng., 33,500..................E7 4
Bexley, Ohio, 14,888......m11 78
Beypazari, Tur., 12,830....B8 14
Bezerros, Braz., 17,919 ...*D7 27
Bezhetsk, Sov. Un., 30,000..................C11 12
Bezhitsa, Sov. Un., 85,000..................E10 12
Béziers, Fr., 80,492.........F5 5
Bezons, Fr., 24,475.........g9 5
Bhadgaon, Nep., 37,100...C8 20
Bhāgalpur, India, 172,202..................C8 20
Bhakkar, Pak., 12,397.....B5 20
Bhamo, Bur., 9,817.......D10 20
Bharatpur, India, 68,036...C6 20
Bhātpāra, India, 204,750..D8 20
Bhaunagar, India, 225,358 .D5 20
Bhind, India, 42,371.......C6 20
Bhopāl, India, 298,022 (*384,859)..............D6 20
Bhor, India, 10,707 ....E5 20
Bhuj, India, 52,177.........D4 20
Bhutan, country, Asia, 990,000..................C9 20
Biała Podlaska, Pol., 26,100..................B7 7
Białogard, Pol., 20,500.....A4 7
Białystok, Pol., 166,600....B7 7
Bianco, It., 5,057..........E6 9
Biarritz, Fr., 26,750.......F3 5
Bibai, Jap., 36,000 (47,369 ▲)............E10 18
Bibb, co., Ala., 13,812 .....C2 46
Bibb, co., Ga., 143,418.....D3 55
Bibb City, Ga., 812........D2 55
Biberach, Ger., Fed. Rep. of, 27,547..........D4 6
Bic, Que., Can., 1,177.....A9 42
Bicknell, Ind., 3,717.......G3 59
Bicske, Hung., 8,148.......B4 10
Bida, Nig., 55,007.........G6 22
Bīdar, India, 50,670........E6 20
Biddeford, Maine, 19,983.............E2, g7 64
Bideford, Eng., 11,850.....E4 4
Biel, Switz., 62,800 (*89,700)..............E3 6
Bielawa, Pol., 30,900......C4 7
Bielefeld, Ger., Fed. Rep. of, 320,997 (*330,000)...B4 6
Biella, It., 53,800..........B2 9
Bielsko-Biala, Pol., 105,600...........D5, h10 7
Bielsk Podlaski, Pol., 14,000..................B7 7
Bienfait, Sask., Can., 842..H4 39
Bienville, par., La., 16,024..................B2 63
Biga, Tur., 10.800........*B7 14
Big Bear City, Calif., 800...E5 50
Big Bear Lake, Calif., 2,800...............*E5 50
Big Beaver, Pa., 2,739.....*E1 81
Big Flats, N.Y., 2,509......C4 75
Biggar, Sask., Can., 2,607..E1 39
Biggs, Calif., 1,115.........C3 50
Big Horn, co., Mont., 10,057..................E9 70
Big Horn, co., Wyo., 10,202..................B4 89
Big Lake, Tex., 2,489.......D2 84
Biglerville, Pa., 977........G7 81
Big Pine, Calif., 950........D4 50
Big Rapids, Mich., 11,995..E5 66

Big River, Sask., Can., 836 . . . D2 39
Big Run, Pa., 826 . . . E4 81
Big Sandy, Mont., 827 . . . B6 70
Big Spring, Tex., 28,735 . . . C2 84
Big Stone, co., Minn., 7,941 . . . E2 67
Big Stone Gap, Va., 4,153 . . . f9 85
Big Timber, Mont., 1,592 . . . E7 70
Big Wells, Tex., 711 . . . E3 84
Bihac, Yugo., 24,026 . . . C2 10
Bihar, India, 100,046 . . . C8 20
Bihar, state, India, 56,353,369 . . . D8 20
Bijāpur, India, 103,931 . . . E6 20
Bijeljina, Yugo., 24,722 . . . C4 10
Bikaner, India, 188,518 . . . C5 20
Bikin, Sov. Un., 10,000 . . . C7 18
Bilāspur, India, 98,410 (*130,740) . . . D7 20
Bilbao, Sp., 405,908 (*810,000) . . . A4 8
Bileca, Yugo., 2,489 . . . D4 10
Bilin, Bur., 5,265 . . . E10 20
Billerica, Mass., 3,000 (17,867 ▲) . . . A5, f10 65
Billings, Mont., 61,581 (*74,800) . . . E8 70
Billings, co., N. Dak., 1,198 . . . C2 77
Billings Heights, Mont., 4,000 . . . E8 70
Biloela, Austl., 4,022 . . . B8 26
Biloxi, Miss., 48,486 . . . E5, f8 68
Bilqās Qism Awwal, Eg., 41,067 . . . *G8 14
Biltmore Forest, N.C., 1,298 . . . f10 76
Binalbagan, Phil., 17,456 . . . *C6 19
Bindura, Rh., 5,530 . . . D6 24
Bingen, Ger., Fed. Rep. of, 25,571 . . . D3 6
Bingham, Maine, 1,180 (1,308 ▲) . . . C3 64
Bingham, co., Idaho, 29,167 . . . F6 57
Bingham Canyon, Utah, 31 . . . A5, D2 72
Binghamton, N.Y., 64,123 (*248,500) . . . C5 75
Binjai, Indon., 59,882 . . . m11 19
Bintulu, Mala., 5,307 . . . E4 19
Binzert (Bizerte), Tun., 51,708 . . . A6 22
Bío-Bío, prov., Chile, 196,000 . . . B2 28
Birakan, Sov. Un., 5,000 . . . B5 18
Bi'r Ar Rummānah, Eg., 1,000 . . . G9 14
Birch Cliff, Ont., Can . . . *D5 41
Birch Run, Mich., 932 . . . E7 66
Bird Island, Minn., 1,309 . . . F4 67
Birdsboro, Pa., 3,196 . . . F10 81
Birecik, Tur., 18,392 . . . D11 14
Bir Hasanah, well, Eg . . . *G8 14
Birkenhead, Eng., 138,090 . D5 4
Birlad, Rom., 41,100 . . . B8 10
Birmingham, Ala., 300,910 (*647,500) . . . B3, f7 46
Birmingham, Eng., 1,013,420 (*2,630,000) . . D6 4
Birmingham, Mich., 26,170 . . . F7, o15 66
Birobidzhan, Sov. Un., 56,000 . . . E16 12
Birtle, Man., Can., 846 . . . D1 40
Bisbee, Ariz., 8,328 . . . D4 48
Biscayne Park, Fla., 2,717 . . s13 54
Bisceglie, It., 44,300 . . . D6 9
Biscoe, N.C., 1,244 . . . B3 76
Bishop, Calif., 3,498 . . . D4 50
Bishop, Tex., 3,466 . . . F4 84
Bishop's Falls, Newf., Can., 4,133 . . . D4 44
Bishop's Stortford, Eng., 21,120 . . . E7 4
Bishopville, S.C., 3,404 . . . C7 82
Biskra, Alg., 59,275 . . . B6 22
Bismarck, Mo., 1,387 . . . D7 69
Bismarck, N. Dak., 34,703 . . D5 77
Bissau, Guinea-Bissau, 18,309 . . . F1 22
Bissett, Man., Can., 857 . . . D4 40
Bistrita, Rom., 20,292 . . . B7 10
Bitlis, Tur., 20,842 . . . C14 14
Bitola, Yugo., 65,851 . . . E5 10
Bitonto, It., 41,700 . . . D6 9
Bitterfeld, Ger. Dem. Rep., 27,705 (*110,000) . . . *C6 6
Biwabik, Minn., 1,483 . . . C6 67
Bixby, Okla., 3,973 . . . B6 79
Biysk, Sov. Un., 186,000 . . D11 12
Bizerte, see Binzert, Tun.
Bizuta, Mong . . . B8 17
Bjelovar, Yugo., 20,971 . . . C3 10
Black, mtn., Ky. . . . D7 62
Black, sea, Eur . . . G14 3
Blackburn, Eng., 101,130 (*230,000) . . . D5 4
Black Diamond, Alta., Can., 1,043 . . . D3 38
Black Diamond, Wash., 1,160 . . . B4, f11 86
Black Eagle, Mont., 2,200 . . C5 70
Blackford, co., Ind., 15,888 . . . D7 59
Black Forest, Colo., 2,700 . . C6 51
Black Hawk, co., Iowa, 132,916 . . . B5 60
Black Lake, Que., Can., 4,123 . . . C6 42
Black Mountain, N.C., 3,204 . . . f10 76
Black Oak, Ind., 16,500 . . . *A3 59
Black Point, Calif., 650 . . . *C2 50
Blackpool, Eng., 149,770 (*275,000) . . . D5 4
Black River, N.Y., 1,307 . . . A5 75
Black River Falls, Wis., 3,273 . . . D3 88
Blacksburg, S.C., 1,977 . . . A4 82
Blacksburg, Va., 9,384 . . . C2 85
Blackshear, Ga., 2,624 . . . E4 55
Blackstone, Mass., 2,500 (5,130 ▲) . . . B4 65
Blackstone, Va., 3,412 . . . C5 85
Blackville, S.C., 2,395 . . . E5 82
Blackwell, Okla., 8,645 . . . A4 79
Blackwood, N.J., 3,500 . . . *D2 74
Bladen, co., N.C., 26,477 . . . C4 76
Bladenboro, N.C., 783 . . . C4 76
Bladensburg, Md., 7,488 . . . f9 53
Blagoevgrad (Gorna-Dzhumaya), Bul., 32,680 . . . D6 10
Blagoveshchensk, Sov. Un., 128,000 . . . D15 13
Blain, Fr., 2,009 . . . D3 5
Blaine, Minn., 20,573 . . . m12 67
Blaine, Wash., 1,955 . . . A3 86
Blaine, co., Idaho, 5,749 . . . F4 57
Blaine, co., Mont., 6,727 . . . B7 70
Blaine, co., Nebr., 847 . . . C5 71
Blaine, Okla., 11,794 . . . B3 79
Blair, Nebr., 6,106 . . . C9 71
Blair, Okla., 1,114 . . . C2 79
Blair, Wis., 1,036 . . . D2 88
Blair, co., Pa., 135,356 . . . E5 81
Blairgowrie [& Rattray], Scot., 5,557 . . . B5 4
Blairmore, Alta., Can., 2,037 (*6,738) . . . E3 38
Blairsville, Pa., 4,411 . . . F3 81
Blaj, Rom., 8,731 . . . B7 10
Blakely, Ga., 5,267 . . . E2 55
Blanc, mtn., Fr . . . E7 5
Blanca, pk., Colo., 212 . . . D5 51
Blanchard, Okla., 1,580 . . . B4 79
Blanchester, Ohio, 3,080 . . . C2 78
Blanco, co., Tex., 3,567 . . . D3 84
Bland, co., Va., 5,423 . . . C1 85
Blanding, Utah, 2,250 . . . C7 72
Blandinsville, Ill., 922 . . . C3 58
Blankenburg, Ger. Dem. Rep., 19,009 . . . C5 6
Blantyre, Malawi, 109,795 . D6 24
Blasdell, N.Y., 3,910 . . . C2 75
Blato, Yugo., 5,140 . . . D3 10
Blauvelt, N.Y., 5,426 . . . *D6 75
Blawnox, Pa., 1,907 . . . k14 81
Bleckley, co., Ga., 10,291 . . D3 55
Bled-Grad, Yugo., 4,156 . . . B2 10
Bledsoe, co., Tenn., 7,643 . . D8 83
Blekinge, co., Swe., 151,000 . . . *I6 11
Blenheim, Ont., Can., 3,490 . . . E2 41
Blenheim, N.Z., 15,250 . . . N14 26
Blida, Alg., 99,238 . . . A5 22
Blind River, Ont., Can., 3,450 . . . A2 41
Blissfield, Mich., 2,753 . . . G7 66
Blitar, Indon., 67,856 . . . *G4 19
Bloemfontein, S. Afr., 148,282 (*180,179) . . . F5 24
Blois, Fr., 42,264 . . . D4 5
Błonie, Pol., 12,400 . . . m13 7
Bloomer, Wis., 3,143 . . . C2 88
Bloomfield, Ont., Can., 803 . . . D7 41
Bloomfield, Conn., 9,000 . . B6 52
Bloomfield, Ind., 2,565 . . . F4 59
Bloomfield, Iowa, 2,718 . . . D5 60
Bloomfield, Ky., 1,072 . . . C4 62
Bloomfield, Mo., 1,584 . . . E8 69
Bloomfield, Nebr., 1,287 . . . B8 71
Bloomfield, N.J., 52,029 . . . h8 74
Bloomfield, N. Mex., 1,574 . A5 48
Bloomfield Hills, Mich., 3,672 . . . o15 66
Bloomfield Village, Mich., 4,000 . . . *F7 66
Bloomingdale, Ga., 900 . . . D5 55
Bloomingdale, Ill., 2,974 . . *B5 58
Bloomingdale, N.J., 7,797 . . A4 74
Blooming Prairie, Minn., 1,804 . . . G5 67
Bloomington, Calif., 11,800 . . . *F5 50
Bloomington, Ill., 39,992 (*72,400) . . . C4 58
Bloomington, Ind., 43,262 (*75,300) . . . F4 59
Bloomington, Minn., 81,970 . . . n12 67
Bloomington, Tex., 1,800 . . E4 84
Bloomsburg, Pa., 11,652 . . . E9 81
Bloomsbury, N.J., 879 . . . B2 74
Bloomville, Ohio, 884 . . . A2 78
Blossburg, Pa., 1,753 . . . C7 81
Blossom Hill, Pa., 1,300 . . . *G9 81
Blount, co., Ala., 26,853 . . . B3 46
Blount, co., Tenn., 63,744 . . . D10 83
Blountstown, Fla., 2,384 . . . B1 54
Bludenz, Aus., 12,262 . . . E4 6
Blue Ash, Ohio, 8,324 . . . o13 78
Blue Bell, Pa., 1,600 . . . *F11 81
Blue Earth, Minn., 3,965 . . G4 67
Blue Earth, co., Minn., 52,322 . . . F4 67
Bluefield, Va., 5,286 . . . e10 85
Bluefield, W. Va., 15,921 . . D3 87
Bluefields, Nic., 14,542 . . . E8 34
Blue Hills, Conn., 3,500 . . . *B6 52
Blue Island, Ill., 22,958 . . . B6, k9 58
Blue Lake, Calif., 1,112 . . . B2 50
Blue Mound, Ill., 1,181 . . . D4 58
Blue Mountain, pk., Jam . . . F5 35
Blue Point, N.Y., 3,100 . . . G4 52
Blue Rapids, Kans., 1,148 . . . C7 61
Blue Ridge, Ga., 1,602 . . . B2 55
Blue Ridge, Va., 925 . . . C3 85
Blue Ridge, mts., U.S . . . C10 45
Blue Springs, Mo., 6,779 . . . h11 69
Bluff City, Tenn., 985 . . . C11 83
Bluff Park, Ala., 12,000 . . . g7 46
Bluffton, Ind., 8,297 . . . C7 59
Bluffton, Ohio, 2,935 . . . B2 78
Blumenau, Braz., 85,942 . . . D3 30
Blyth, Eng., 34,800 . . . C6 4
Blythe, Calif., 7,047 . . . F6 50
Blytheville, Ark., 24,752 . . . B6 49
Boac, Phil., 3,497 . . . C6 19
Boalsburg, Pa., 800 . . . E6 81
Boardman, Ohio, 33,300 . . . A5 78
Boaz, Ala., 5,621 . . . A3 46
Bobbili, India, 30,649 . . . E7 20
Bobcaygeon, Ont., Can., 1,518 . . . C6 41
Bobigny, Fr., 39,453 . . . g10 5
Bobo Dioulasso, Upper Volta, 45,000 . . . F4 22
Bobrinets, Sov. Un., 10,000 . . . G9 12
Bobrka, Sov. Un., 10,000 . . G5 12
Bobruysk, Sov. Un., 138,000 . . . E7 12
Bobtown, Pa., 1,055 . . . G2 81
Bobures, Ven., 2,159 . . . B3 32
Boca Raton, Fla., 28,506 . . . F6 54
Bochnia, Pol., 14,500 . . . D6 7
Bochum, Ger., Fed. Rep. of, 339,167 . . . C3 6
Bodaybo, Sov. Un., 14,700 . . . D14 13
Boden, Swe., 23,543 . . . E9 11
Bodmin, Eng., 9,260 . . . E4 4
Bodö, Nor., 28,100 . . . D6 11
Boerne, Tex., 2,432 . . . E3, h7 84
Bogalusa, La., 18,412 . . . D6 63
Bogata, Tex., 1,287 . . . C5 84
Boger City, N.C., 2,203 . . . B1 76
Bogo, Phil., 6,786 . . . C6 19
Bogodukhov, Sov. Un., 18,000 . . . F10 12
Bogor (Buitenzorg), Indon., 195,882 . . . G3 19
Bogoroditsk, Sov. Un., 32,000 . . . E12 12
Bogorodsk, Sov. Un., 37,000 . . . C14 12
Bogotá, Col., 2,148,400 (*2,250,000) . . . C3 32
Bogota, N.J., 8,960 . . . h8 74
Bogra, Bngl., 25,303 . . . D8 20
Boguslav, Sov. Un., 10,000 . . . G8 12
Bohain [-en-Vermandois], Fr., 7,090 . . . C5 5
Bohemia, N.Y., 8,926 . . . n15 75
Bohemia (Cěchy), reg., Czech., 6,256,800 . . . D3 7
Bohol, prov., Phil., 592,194 . . . D6 19
Boiling Springs, N.C., 2,284 . . . B1 76
Boiling Springs, Pa., 1,521 . . F7 81
Boischâtel, Que., Can., 1,685 . . . C6, n17 42
Bois-Colombes, Fr., 28,934 . . . G10 5
Bois-des-Filion, Que., Can., 4,061 . . . p19 42
Boise, Idaho, 74,990 (*106,100) . . . F2 57
Boise, co., Idaho, 1,763 . . . F3 57
Boise City, Okla., 1,993 . . . e8 79
Boissevain, Man., Can., 1,506 . . . E1 40
Boissevain, Va., 800 . . . e10 85
Bolbec, Fr., 12,716 . . . C4 5
Bolgrad, Sov. Un., 17,000 . . I7 12
Boling, Tex., 950 . . . E5, r14 84
Bolívar, Arg., 16,500 . . . B4 28
Bolivar, Mo., 4,769 . . . D4 69
Bolivar, N.Y., 1,379 . . . C2 75
Bolivar, Ohio, 1,084 . . . B4 78
Bolivar, Tenn., 6,674 . . . B3 83
Bolivar, co., Miss., 49,409 . . B3 68
Bolívar, dept., Col., 791,900 . . . B2 32
Bolívar, prov., Ec., 165,100 . . . B2 31
Bolívar, state, Ven., 213,543 . . . B4 32
Bolivar (La Columna), pk., Ven . . . B3 32
Bolivia, country, S.A., 5,385,000 . . . C2 29
Bolkhov, Sov. Un., 10,000 . . . E11 12
Bollinger, co., Mo., 8,820 . . D7 69
Bollnäs, Swe., 17,339 . . . G7 11
Bollullos, Sp., 10,947 . . . D2 8
Bologna, It., 490,700 (*535,000) . . . B3 9
Bologoye, Sov. Un., 34,000 . . . C10 12
Bolshaya Lepetikha, Sov. Un., 5,000 . . . H9 12
Bolshaya Viska, Sov. Un., 10,000 . . . G8 12
Bolshoy Tokmak, Sov. Un., 10,000 . . . H10 12
Bolton, Ont., Can., 2,984 . . D5 41
Bolton, Eng., 154,360 . . . D5 4
Bolton Landing, N.Y., 900 . . . B7 75
Bolu, Tur., 26,944 . . . B8 14
Bolvadin, Tur., 25,417 . . . C8 14
Bolzano, It., 103,500 . . . A3 9
Boma, Zaire, 31,500 . . . B2 24
Bombay, India, 5,970,575 (*6,750,000) . . . E5 20
Bom Conselho, Braz., 10,973 . . . *D7 27
Bom Despacho, Braz., 18,783 . . . B3 30
Bon Air, Pa., 525 . . . *G11 81
Bon Air, Va., 10,771 . . . m17 85
Bonaventure, Que., Can., 804 . . . *k13 42
Bonaventure, co., Que., Can., 43,624 . . . A3 43
Bonavista, Newf., Can., 4,215 . . . D5 44
Bond, co., Ill., 14,012 . . . E4 58
Bondy, Fr., 51,652 . . . G10 5
Bone, see Annaba, Alg.
Bonham, Tex., 7,698 . . . C4 84
Bon Homme, co., S. Dak., 8,577 . . . G8 77
Bonifay, Fla., 2,068 . . . G3 54
Bonin, is., Jap . . . E6 2
Bonita, Calif., 2,000 . . . *E5 50
Bonita Springs, Fla., 900 . . . F5 54
Bonn, Ger., Fed. Rep. of, 281,089 (*505,000) . . . C3 6
Bonner, co., Idaho, 15,560 . . . A2 57
Bonners Ferry, Idaho, 1,909 . . . A2 57
Bonner Springs, Kans., 3,662 . . . C9, k16 61
Bonne Terre, Mo., 3,622 . . D7 69
Bonneville, co., Idaho, 52,457 . . . F7 57
Bonnyville, Alta., Can., 2,587 . . . B5 38
Bonorva, It., 6,669 . . . D2 9
Bonoua, I.C., 12,844 . . . *E4 22
Bonthain, Indon., 9,974 . . . G5 19
Bontoc, Phil., 3,336 . . . *B6 19
Boomer, W. Va., 1,657 . . . C3, m13 87
Boone, Iowa, 12,468 . . . B4 60
Boone, N.C., 8,754 . . . A1 76
Boone, co., Ark., 19,073 . . . A2 49
Boone, co., Ill., 25,440 . . . A5 58
Boone, co., Ind., 30,870 . . . D4 59
Boone, co., Iowa, 26,470 . . . B4 60
Boone, co., Ky., 32,812 . . . B5 62
Boone, co., Mo., 80,911 . . . B5 69
Boone, co., Nebr., 8,190 . . . C7 71
Boone, co., W. Va., 25,118 . . . C3 87

Booneville, Ark., 3,239....B2 49
Booneville, Miss., 5,895....A5 68
Boonsboro, Md., 1,410....A2 53
Boon Terrace, Pa., 400....*F1 81
Boonton, N.J., 9,261....B4 74
Boonville, Calif., 950....C2 50
Boonville, Ind., 5,736....H3 59
Boonville, Mo., 7,514....C5 69
Boonville, N.Y., 2,488....B5 75
Boothbay Harbor, Maine, 1,800 (2,320 ▲)....E3 64
Boothwyn, Pa., 6,500....*G11 81
Boppard, Ger., Fed. Rep. of, 8,600....C3 6
Boquerón, dept., Par., 40,405....D3 29
Borah, pk., Idaho....E3 57
Borås, Swe., 72,099 (*94,643)....I5 11
Bordeaux, Fr., 266,662 (*560,000)....E3 5
Borden, co., Tex., 888....C2 84
Borden Springs, Ala., 60....B4 46
Bordentown, N.J., 4,490....C3 74
Bordighera, It., 9,700....C1 9
Borgå, Fin., 11,800....G11 11
Borger, Tex., 14,195....B2 84
Borgomanero, It., 7,900....B2 9
Borgo Val di Taro, It., 11,809....B2 9
Borislav, Sov. Un., 34,000....G7 12
Borisoglebsk, Sov. Un., 64,000....F13 12
Borisov, Sov. Un., 84,000....D7 12
Borispol, Sov. Un., 32,000....F8 12
Borja, Sp., 4,381....B5 8
Borkou, reg., Chad....E1 23
Borlänge, Swe., 45,194....G6 11
Borneo (Kalimantan), isl., Asia....E4 19
Bornholm, co., Den., 48,500....*A3 7
Bornos, Sp., 8,697....D3 8
Boromlya, Sov. Un., 10,000....F10 12
Borovan, Bul., 5,905....D6 10
Borovichi, Sov. Un., 55,000....B9 12
Borovskoye, Sov. Un., 5,000....q21 12
Borsod-Abauj-Zemplen, co., Hung., 608,368....*A5 10
Bort-les-Orgues, Fr., 5,115....E5 5
Borūjerd, Iran, 71,486....C4 15
Borzna, Sov. Un., 10,000....F9 12
Bosa, It., 8,169....D2 9
Bosanska Gradiska, Yugo., 6,373....C3 10
Bosanska Kostajnica, Yugo., 2,037....C3 10
Bosanski Novi, Yugo., 7,082....C3 10
Boscobel, Wis., 2,510....E3 88
Boskovice, Czech., 6,396....D4 7
Bosnia, reg., Yugo....C3 10
Bosnia-Hercegovina, rep., Yugo., 3,277,948....*C3 10
Bosque, co., Tex. 10,966....D4 84
Bossier, par. La., 63,703....B2 63
Bossier City, La., 41,595....B2 63
Boston, Eng., 26,030....D6 4
Boston, Ga., 1,443....F3 55
Boston, Mass., 641,071 (*3,762,900)....B5, g11 65
Boston, Pa., 1,200....*E1 81
Boswell, Ind., 998....C3 59
Botetourt, co., Va. 18,193....C3 85
Botevgrad, Bul., 5,925....D6 10
Bothwell, Ont., Can., 819....E3 41
Botkins, Ohio, 1,057....B1 78
Botosani, Rom., 35,200....E8 10
Botswana, country, Afr., 585,000....E4 24
Bottineau, N. Dak., 2,760....A5 77
Bottineau, co., N. Dak., 9,496....B5 77
Botucatu, Braz., 42,252....C3, m7 30
Botwood, Newf., Can., 4,115....D4 44
Bouaké, I.C., 53,000....G3 22
Boucherville, Que., Can., 19,997....D4, p20 42
Bouches-du-Rhône, dept., Fr., 1,470,271....*F6 5
Bougie, see Bejaïa, Alg.
Boulder, Colo., 66,870 (*80,100)....A5 51
Boulder, Mont., 1,342....D4 70
Boulder, co., Colo., 131,889....A5 51
Boulder City, Nev., 5,223....D4 72
Boulder Creek, Calif., 1,306....*D2 50
Boulogne-Billancourt, Fr., 109,008....C5 5
Boulogne-sur-Mer, Fr., 49,276 (*106,000)....B4 5
Boundary, co., Idaho, 5,484....A2 57
Boundary, pk., Nev....C2 72
Bound Brook, N.J., 10,450....B3 74
Bountiful, Utah, 27,751....A6, C2 72
Bourbon, Ind., 1,606....B5 59
Bourbon, co., Kans., 15,215....E9 61
Bourbon, co., Ky., 18,476....B5 62
Bourbonnais, Ill., 5,909....B6 58
Bourbonnais, former prov., Fr....D5 5
Bourg, La., 900....E5 63
Bourg-de-Péage, Fr., 8,597....E6 5
Bourg [-de-Bresse], Fr., 37,887....D6 5
Bourges, Fr., 70,814....D5 5
Bourg-la-Reine, Fr., 18,711....g10 5
Bourgoin [-Jallieu], Fr., 19,941....E6 5
Bournemouth, Eng., 148,990 (*298,000)....E6 4
Bovey, Minn., 858....C5 67
Bovina, Tex., 1,428....B1 84
Bowdon, Ga., 1,753....C1 55
Bowie, Md., 35,028....B4 53
Bowie, Tex., 5,185....C4 84
Bowie, co., Tex., 67,813....C5 84
Bow Island, Alta., Can., 1,122....E5 38
Bowling Green, Fla., 1,357....E5 54
Bowling Green, Ky., 36,705....D3 62
Bowling Green, Mo., 2,936....B6 69
Bowling Green, Ohio, 21,760....A2, f6 78
Bowling Green, S.C., 700....A5 82
Bowman, N. Dak., 1,762....D2 77
Bowman, S.C., 1,095....E6 82
Bowman, co., N. Dak., 3,901....D2 77
Bowmanstown, Pa., 864....E10 81
Bowmanville, Ont., Can., 8,947....D6 41
Bowral, Austl., 5,913....G8 26
Box Butte, co., Nebr., 10,094....B2 71
Box Elder, co., Utah, 28,129....A5 72
Boxtel, Neth., 16,370....B6 5
Boyacá, dept., Col., 1,144,400....B3 32
Boyce, La., 1,240....C3 63
Boyd, co., Ky., 52,376....B7 62
Boyd, co., Nebr., 3,752....B7 71
Boyertown, Pa., 4,428....F10 81
Boyes Hot Springs, Calif., 2,462....*C2 50
Boyle, co., Ky., 21,090....C5 62
Boylston, Ala., 1,500....C3 46
Boyne City, Mich., 2,969....C5 66
Boynton Beach, Fla., 18,115....F6 54
Boys Town, Nebr., 989....g12 71
Bozeman, Mont., 18,670....E5 70
Bozüyük, Tur., 13,307....C8 14
Bra, It., 16,400....B1 9
Brabant, prov., Bel., 2,157,300....*B6 5
Bracciano, It., 6,460....g8 9
Bracebridge, Ont., Can., 6,903....B5 41
Bracken, co., Ky., 7,227....B5 62
Brackenridge, Pa., 4,796....h15 81
Brackettville, Tex., 1,539....E2 84
Brad, Sov. Un., 9,963....B6 10
Bradbury Heights, Md., 1,000....*C3 53
Braddock, Pa., 8,795....k14 81
Braddock Heights, Md., 800....B2 53
Braddock Hills, Pa., 2,459....*E1 81
Bradenton, Fla., 21,040....E4, q10 54
Bradenton Beach, Fla., 1,370....*E4 54
Bradenville, Pa., 1,200....F3 81
Bradford, Ont., Can., 3,401....C5 41
Bradford, Eng., 294,740....D6 4
Bradford, Ill., 885....B4 58
Bradford, Ohio, 2,163....B1 78
Bradford, Pa., 12,672....C4 81
Bradford, R.I., 1,333....D10 52
Bradford, co., Fla., 14,625....C4 54
Bradford, co., Pa., 57,962....C8 81
Bradfordwoods, Pa., 970....h13 81
Bradley, Fla., 1,035....E5 54
Bradley, Ill., 9,881....B6 58
Bradley, co., Ark., 12,778....D3 49
Bradley, co., Tenn., 50,686....D9 83
Bradley Beach, N.J., 4,163....C4 74
Bradley Gardens, N.J., 3,250....*B3 74
Bradner, Ohio, 1,140....A2 78
Bradshaw, W. Va., 1,048....D3 87
Brady, Tex., 5,557....D3 84
Braga, Port., 40,977....B1 8
Bragado, Arg., 22,000....B4, g6 28
Bragança, Braz., 16,642....*D6 27
Bragança, Port., 8,075....B2 8
Bragança Paulista, Braz., 39,573....C3, m8 30
Brahmaputra, riv., Asia....C9 20
Braidwood, Ill., 2,323....B5 58
Brăila, Rom., 138,600 (144,300 ▲)....C8 10
Brainerd, Minn., 11,667....D4 67
Braintree, Mass., 35,050....B5, h11 65
Brampton, Ont., Can., 41,211....D5, m14 41
Bramwell, W. Va., 1,125....D3 87
Branch, co., Mich., 37,906....G5 66
Branchville, N.J., 911....A3 74
Branchville, S.C., 1,011....E6 82
Branco, riv., Braz....C5 32
Brandenburg, Ger. Dem. Rep., 94,240....B6 6
Brandenburg, Ky., 1,637....B3 62
Brandenburg, former state, Ger. Dem. Rep., 2,527,492....B6 6
Brandenburg, reg., Ger. Dem. Rep. B6 6
Brandon, Man., Can., 31,150....E2, h7 40
Brandon, Fla., 3,000....E4 54
Brandon, Miss., 2,685....C4 68
Brandon, S.C., 2,200....B3 82
Brandon, Vt., 1,720....D1 73
Brandys [nad Labem], Czech., 14,596....n18 7
Branford, Conn., 2,080....D5 52
Branson, Mo., 2,175....E4 69
Brant, co., Ont., Can., 90,945....D4 41
Brantford, Ont., Can., 64,421 (*80,284)....D4 41
Brant Lake, N.Y., 800....B7 75
Brantley, Ala., 1,066....D3 46
Brantley, co., Ga., 5,940....E4 55
Bras-d'or, N.S., Can., 947....C9 43
Brasília, Braz., 272,002....B3 30
Brasilia (Federal District), Braz., 546,015....B3 30
Brașov, Rom., 163,300 (263,200 ▲)....C7 10
Bratenahl, Ohio, 1,613....g9 78
Bratislava, Czech., 283,539....D4 7
Bratsk, Sov. Un., 155,000....*D13 13
Bratslav, Sov. Un., 10,000....G7 12
Brattleboro, Vt., 12,239....F2 73
Braunau [am Inn], Aus., 16,414....D6 6
Braunschweig, Ger., Fed. Rep. of, 220,244 (*355,000)....B5 6
Brawley, Calif., 13,746....F6 50
Braxton, co., W. Va., 12,666....C4 87
Bray, Ire., 14,467....D3 4
Braymer, Mo., 919....B4 69
Brazil, Ind., 8,163....E3 59
Brazil, country, S.A., 103,270,000....C3 30
Brazoria, Tex., 1,681....r14 84
Brazoria, co., Tex., 108,312.E5 84
Brazos, co., Tex., 57,978....D4 84
Brazzaville, Con., 175,000....A3 24
Brčko, Yugo., 25,422....C4 10
Brea, Calif., 18,447....n13 50
Breathitt, co., Ky., 14,221....C6 62
Breaux Bridge, La., 4,942....D4 63
Brechin, Scot., 6,702....B5 4
Breckenridge, Mich., 1,257....E6 66
Breckenridge, Minn., 4,200....D2 67
Breckenridge, Tex., 5,944....C3 84
Breckenridge Hills, Mo., 7,011....*C7 69
Breckenridge, co., Ky., 14,789....C3 62
Brecknock, co., Wales, 54,400....*E5 4
Brecksville, Ohio, 9,137....A4, h9 78
Břeclav, Czech., 13,131....D4 7
Brecon, Wales, 6,260....E5 4
Breda, Neth., 121,181....B6 5
Breese, Ill., 2,885....E4 58
Bregenz, Aus., 23,171....E4 6
Bregovo, Bul., 5,271....C6 10
Bremen, Ga., 3,484....C1 55
Bremen, Ger., Fed. Rep. of, 589,825 (*820,000)....B4 6
Bremen, Ind., 3,487....B5 59
Bremen, Ohio, 1,413....C3 78
Bremen, state, Ger., Fed. Rep. of, 745,000....*B4 6
Bremer, co., Iowa, 22,737....B5 60
Bremerhaven, Ger., Fed Rep. of, 144,505 (*198,000)....B4 6
Bremerton, Wash., 35,307 (*87,700)....B3, e10 86
Bremerton East (Enetai), Wash., 2,539....*B3 86
Bremond, Tex., 822....D4 84
Brenham, Tex., 8,922....D4 84
Brent, Ala., 2,093....C2 46
Brent, Fla., 4,100....u14 54
Brenton, W. Va., 500....D3 87
Brentwood, Calif., 2,649....h9 50
Brentwood, Md., 3,426....F9 53
Brentwood, Mo., 11,248....f13 69
Brentwood, N.Y., 54,186....F4 52
Brentwood, Pa., 13,732....k14 81
Brescia, It., 204,400....B3 9
Breslau, see Wroclaw, Pol.
Bressanone, It., 11,300....A3 9
Bressler, Pa., 850....*F8 81
Bressuire, Fr., 6,528....D3 5
Brest, Fr., 154,023....C1 5
Brest, Sov. Un., 122,000....E4 12
Breton Woods, N.J., 1,200....C4 74
Brevard, co., Fla., 230,006.E6 54
Brevard, N.C., 5,243....f10 76
Brewer, Maine, 9,300....D4 64
Brestwer, N.Y., 1,638....D7, m15 75
Brewster, Ohio, 2,020....B4 78
Brewster, Wash., 1,059....A6 86
Brewster, co., Tex., 7,780....p13 84
Brewton, Ala., 6,747....D2 46
Brezno [nad Hronom], Czech., 12,726....D5 7
Briançon, Fr., 8,215....E7 5
Briarcliff, Pa., 9,000....*G11 81
Briarcliff Manor, N.Y., 6,521....D7 75
Briceville, Tenn., 800....C9 83
Bridge City, Tex., 4,677....*D6 84
Bridgehampton, N.Y., 900....n16 75
Bridgeport, Ala., 2,908....A4 46
Bridgeport, Ont., Can., 2,375....*D4 41
Bridgeport, Conn., 156,542 (*457,200)....E4 52
Bridgeport, Ill., 2,262....E6 58
Bridgeport, Mich., 1,900....E7 66
Bridgeport, Nebr., 1,490....C2 71
Bridgeport, Ohio, 3,001....B5 78
Bridgeport, Pa., 5,630....F11, o20 81
Bridgeport, Tex., 3,614....C4 84
Bridgeport, Wash., 952....B6 86
Bridgeport, W. Va., 4,777....B4, k10 87
Bridgeton, Mo., 19,992....C7, f13 69
Bridgeton, N.J., 20,435 (*35,800)....E2 74
Bridgetown, Barb, 8,789 (*115,000)....J15 35
Bridgetown, N.S., Can., 1,043....E4 43
Bridgetown, Ohio, 7,350....*C1 78
Bridgeview, Ill., 12,522....*B6 58
Bridgeville, Del., 1,317....C6 53
Bridgeville, Pa., 6,717....k13 81
Bridgewater, N.S., Can., 5,231....E5 43
Bridgewater, Mass., 4,032 (11,829 ▲)....C6 65
Bridgewater, Va., 2,828....B4 85
Bridgman, Mich., 1,621....G4 66
Bridgton, Maine, 1,779 (2,967 ▲)....D2 64
Bridgwater, Eng., 26,740....E5 4
Bridlington, Eng., 26,770....C6 4
Brielle, N.J., 3,594....C4 74
Brigantine, N.J., 6,741....E4 74
Brigham City, Utah, 14,007....A5, C2 72
Brighton, Ala., 2,277....B3, g7 46
Brighton, Colo., 8,309....B6 51
Brighton, Eng., 163,860 (*430,000)....E6 4
Brighton, Ill., 1,889....D3 58
Brighton, Mich., 2,457....F7 66
Brighton, N.Y., 35,065....*B3 75
Brightwaters, N.Y., 3,808....n15 75
Brignoles, Fr., 5,347....F7 5
Brilliant, Ohio, 2,178....B5 78
Brillion, Wis., 2,588....D5, h9 88
Brindisi, It., 80,400....D6 9
Brinkley, Ark., 5,275....C4 49
Brioude, Fr., 7,195....E5 5

Brisbane, Austl., 699,371 (*866,207)....E9 25
Brisbane, Calif., 3,033....*D2 50
Briscoe, co., Tex., 2,794....B2 84
Bristol, Conn., 55,487....C5 52
Bristol, Eng., 426,170 (*635,000)....E4 4
Bristol, Ind., 1,100....A6 59
Bristol, N.H., 1,080....D4 73
Bristol, Pa., 12,085....F12 81
Bristol, R.I., 17,860....C11 52
Bristol, Tenn., 20,064 (*65,800)....C11 83
Bristol, Vt., 1,737....C1 73
Bristol (Independent City), Va., 14,857....f9 85
Bristol, co., Mass., 444,301....C5 65
Bristol, co., R.I., 45,937..C11 52
Bristow, Okla., 4,653....B5 79
Brittania Beach, B.C., Can., 775....E6 37
British Columbia, prov., Can., 2,330,000.... 37
British Guiana, see Guyana, country, S.A.
British Honduras, see Belize, Br. dep., N.A.
British Indian Ocean Territory, ter., Ind. O., 1,000....*B9 24
British North Borneo, see Sabah, reg., Mala.
Britt, Iowa, 2,069....A4 60
Brittany (Bretagne), former prov., Fr....C2 5
Britton, S. Dak., 1,465....E8 77
Brive [-la-Gaillarde], Fr., 46,561....E4 5
Brno, Czech., 335,918....D4 7
Broach, India, 91,589....D5 20
Broadalbin, N.Y., 1,452....B6 75
Broad Brook, Conn., 1,548..B6 52
Broadmoor, Colo., 1,900...C6 51
Broadview, Sask., Can., 1,008....G4 39
Broadview, Ill., 9,623....*B6 58
Broadview, Ind., .2,362....*F4 59
Broadview Heights, Ohio, 11,463....B2 78
Broadwater, co., Mont., 2,526....D5 70
Brockport, N.Y., 7,878....B3 75
Brockton, Mass., 89,040....B5, h11 65
Brockville, Ont., Can., 19,765....C9 41
Brockway, Pa., 2,529....D4 81
Brocton, Ill., 349....D6 58
Brod, Yugo., 38,762....C4 10
Broderick, Calif., 9,900...*C3 50
Brodhead, Wis., 2,515....F4 88
Brodnica, Pol., 17,300....B5 7
Brody, Sov. Un., 16,000...F5 12
Broken Arrow, Okla., 11,787....A6 79
Broken Bow, Nebr., 3,734..C6 71
Broken Bow, Okla., 2,980..C7 79
Broken Hill, Austl., 29,743....F7 25
Broken Hill, Zambia, 44,600....C5 24
Brome, co., Que., Can., 14,190....D5 42
Bromptonville, Que., Can., 2,771....D6 42
Bronson, Mich., 2,390....G5 66
Bronte, Tex., 925....D2 84
Bronx, borough and co., N.Y., 1,471,701....E7 75
Bronxville, N.Y., 6,674....h13 75
Brook, Ind., 919....C3 59
Brooke, co., W. Va., 29,685....A4 87
Brookfield, Ill., 20,284....k9 58
Brookfield, Mass., 1,197 (2,063 ▲)....B3 65
Brookfield, Mo., 5,491....B4 69
Brookfield, Wis., 31,761..m11 88
Brookhaven, Miss., 10,700....D3 68
Brookhaven, Pa., 7,370..*G11 81
Brookings, Oreg., 2,720....E2 80
Brookings, S. Dak., 13,717.F9 77
Brookings, co., S. Dak., 22,158....F9 77
Brooklands, Man., Can., 4,369....*E3 40
Brooklands, Mich., 2,500..*F7 66
Brooklawn, N.J., 2,870....D2 74
Brookline, Mass., 58,689....B5, g11 65
Brooklyn, Conn., 800....B9 52
Brooklyn, Ind., 911....E5 59
Brooklyn, Iowa, 1,410....C5 60
Brooklyn, Mich., 1,112....F6 66
Brooklyn, Ohio, 13,142....h9 78
Brooklyn (Lovejoy), Ill., 1,702....g13 69
Brooklyn, borough, N.Y., 2,602,012....k13 75
Brooklyn Center, Minn., 35,173....E6 67
Brooklyn Park, Minn., 26,230....*E6 67
Brookneal, Va., 1,037....C4 85
Brook Park, Ohio, 30,774..h9 78
Brookport, Ill., 1,046....F5 58
Brooks, Alta., Can., 3,986..D5 38
Brooks, co., Ga., 13,739....F3 55
Brooks, co., Tex., 8,005....F3 84
Brookshire, Tex., 1,683....E5, r14 84
Brookside, Ala., 990....f7 46
Brookside, Del., 4,000....A6 53
Brookside, N.J., 800....B3 74
Brookston, Ind., 1,232....C4 59
Brooksville, Fla., 4,060....D4 54
Brookville, Ind., 2,864....F7 59
Brookville, Mass., 900....h11 65
Brookville, N.Y., 3,212....*G2 52
Brookville, Ohio, 4,403....C1 78
Brookville, Pa., 4,314....D3 81
Broomall, Pa., 25,040....*G11 81
Broome, co., N.Y., 221,815....C5 75
Broomfield, Colo., 7,261...B5 51
Broughton, Pa., 2,800....*E1 81
Broussard, La., 1,707....D4 63
Broward, co., Fla., 620,100..F6 54
Brown, co., Ill., 5,586....D3 58
Brown, co., Ind., 9,057....F5 59
Brown, co., Kans., 11,685..C8 61
Brown, co., Minn., 28,887..F4 67
Brown, co., Nebr., 4,021...B6 71
Brown, co., Ohio, 26,635..D2 78
Brown, co., S. Dak., 36,920....E7 77
Brown, co., Tex., 25,877...D3 84
Brown, co., Wis., 158,244..D6 88
Brown City, Mich., 1,142..E8 66
Brown Deer, Wis., 12,582....m12 88
Brownfield, Tex., 9,647....C1 84
Browning, Mont., 1,700....B3 70
Brownlee Park, Mich., 2,985....*F5 66
Brownsburg, Que., Can., 3,481....D3 42
Brownsburg, Ind., 5,751...E5 59
Browns Mills, N.J., 7,144..D3 74
Brownstown, Ind., 2,376...G5 59
Brownstown, Pa., 1,035...*E4 81
Browns Valley, Minn., 906.E2 67
Brownsville, La., 3,000....*B3 63
Brownsville, Oreg., 1,034..C4 80
Brownsville, Pa., 4,856....F2 81
Brownsville, Tenn., 7,011..B2 83
Brownsville, Tex., 52,522 (*188,000)....G4 84
Brownville, Ala., 501....B2 46
Brownville, N.Y., 1,187....A5 75
Brownville Junction, Maine, 800....C3 64
Brownwood, Tex., 17,368..D3 84
Broxton, Ga., 957....E4 55
Brozas, Sp., 5,634....C2 8
Bruay [en-Artois], Fr., 28,628 (*115,000)....B5 5
Bruce, mtn., Austl....D2 25
Bruce, Miss., 2,033....B4 68
Bruceton, Tenn., 1,450....A3 83
Bruchsal, Ger., Fed. Rep. of, 37,160....D4 6
Bruck [ander Leitha], Aus., 7,468....D8 6
Bruck [an der Mur], Aus., 16,369 (*50,000)....E7 6
Brugge (Bruges), Bel., 118,023....B5 5
Brule, co., S. Dak., 5,870..G6 77
Brumath, Fr., 6,801....C7 5
Brundidge, Ala., 2,709....D4 46
Brunei, see Bandar Seri Begawan, Bru.
Brunei, Br. dep., Asia, 149,000....E4 19
Brunswick, Ga., 19,585....E5 55
Brunswick, Maine, 12,546 (16,195 ▲)....E3, g8 64
Brunswick, Md., 3,566....B2 53
Brunswick, Mo., 1,370....B4 69
Brunswick, Ohio, 15,852...A4 78
Brunswick, co., N.C., 24,223....C4 76
Brunswick, co., Va., 16,172....D5 85
Brush, Colo., 3,377....A7 51
Brusly, La., 1,282....D4, h9 63
Brusque, Braz., 32,427....D3 30
Brussels (Bruxelles), Bel., 158,188 (*2,010,000)....B6 5
Brussels, Ont., Can., 844...D3 41
Bruxelles, see Brussels, Bel.
Bryan, Ohio, 7,008....A1 78
Bryan, Tex., 33,719 (*53,700)....D4 84
Bryan, co., Ga., 6,539....D5 55
Bryan, co., Okla., 25,552..D5 79
Bryansk, Sov. Un., 318,000....E10 12
Bryant, Fla., 400....F6 54
Bryantville, Mass., 800....B6 65
Bryn Athyn, Pa., 970....o21 81
Bryn Mawr, Pa., 9,500....o20 81
Bryn Mawr, Wash., 2,300..D2 86
Bryson City, N.C., 1,290....f9 76
Bryte, Calif., 2,780....*C3 50
Brzeg, Pol., 30,700....C4 7
Brzeziny, Pol., 7,629....C5 7
Bsa, It., 16,400....B1 9
Bucaramanga, Col., 264,900....B3 32
Buchanan, Mich., 4,645...G4 66
Buchanan, N.Y., 2,110...*D7 75
Buchanan, Va., 1,326....C3 85
Buchanan, co., Iowa, 21,746....B6 60
Buchanan, co., Mo., 86,915....B3 69
Buchanan, co., Va., 32,071..e9 85
Buchans, Newf., Can., 1,907....D3 44
Bucharest (București), Rom., 1,432,000 (*1,590,000)....C8 10
Buchloe, Ger., Fed. Rep. of, 5,700....D5 6
Buckeye, Ariz., 2,599..C2, D1 48
Buckeye Lake, Ohio, 2,961.C3 78
Buckhannon, W. Va., 7,261....C4 87
Buckhaven [& Methil], Scot., 18,302....B5 4
Buckhorn, Ariz., 1,200....D2 48
Buckie, Scot., 8,028....B5 4
Buckingham, Que., Can., 7,304....D2 42
Buckingham, co., Eng., 592,750....*E6 4
Buckingham, co., Va., 10,597....C4 85
Buckley, Wash., 3,446..B3, f11 86
Bucknell Manor, Va., 2,500....*B5 85
Buckner, Mo., 1,695....*B3 69
Bucks, co., Pa., 416,728...F11 81
Bucksport, Maine, 2,456 (3,756 ▲)....D4 64
Bucksport, S.C., 800....D9 82
Bucovina, reg., Rom....B7 10
Bucovina, reg., Sov. Un....B7 10
București, see Bucharest, Rom.
Bucyrus, Ohio, 13,111....B3 78
Budapest, Hung., 1,940,212 (*2,325,000)...B4 10
Budd Lake, N.J., 3,168....B3 74
Bude, Eng., 5,540....E4 4
Bude, Miss., 1,146....D3 68
Budrio, It., 16,364....B3 9
Buechel, Ky., 8,000...B4, g11 62
Buena, N.J., 3,283....D3 74
Buena Park, Calif., 63,646....n13 50
Buenaventura, Col., 78,700 (108,600 ▲)....C2 32
Buena Vista, Colo., 1,962..C4 51
Buena Vista, Ga., 1,486...D2 55
Buena Vista (Independent City), Va., 6,425....C3 85
Buena Vista, co., Iowa, 20,693....B2 60
Buenos Aires, Arg., 2,972,453 (*8,625,000)....A5, g7 28
Buenos Aires, prov., Arg., 6,766,108....B4, g7 28
Buffalo, Iowa, 1,513..C7, h10 60
Buffalo, Minn., 3,275....E5 67
Buffalo, Mo., 1,915....D4 69
Buffalo, N.Y., 462,768 (*1,265,200)....C2 75
Buffalo, Ohio, 700....C4 78
Buffalo, Okla., 1,579....A2 79
Buffalo, S.C., 1,461....B4 82
Buffalo, Tex., 1,242....D4 84
Buffalo, Wyo., 3,394....B6 89
Buffalo, co., Nebr., 31,222....D6 71
Buffalo, co., S. Dak., 1,739....F6 77
Buffalo, co., Wis., 13,743..D2 88
Buffalo Center, Iowa, 1,118....A4 60
Buffalo Grove, Ill., 11,799....*A6 58
Buford, Ga., 4,640....B3 55
Buga, Col., 74,000....C2 32
Bugojno, Yugo., 5,411....C3 10
Buhl, Idaho, 2,975....G4 57
Buhl, Minn., 1,303....C6 67
Buhler, Kans., 1,019....D6 61
Buhuși, Rom., 12,382....B8 10
Bujalance, Sp., 11,475....D3 8
Bujumbura, Burundi, 71,000....I3 23
Bukama, Zaire....B5 24
Bukavu, Zaire, 33,500....I3 23
Bukhara, Sov. Un., 112,000....F9 13
Bukidnon, prov., Phil., 194,368....*D6 19
Bukittinggi, Indon., 63,132.F2 19
Bukoba, Tan., 5,297....I4 23
Bulacan, prov., Phil., 555,819....*C6 19
Bulan, Ky., 500....C6 62
Bulan, Phil., 19,716....*C6 19
Bulawayo, Rh., 225,000 (*270,000)....E5 24
Bulgaria, country, Eur., 8,680,000....D7 10
Bullas, Sp., 8,936....C5 8
Bullitt, co., Ky., 26,090...C4 62
Bulloch, co., Ga., 31,585...D5 55
Bullock, co., Ala., 11,824...C4 46
Bulun, Sov. Un., 800....B15 13
Bunbury, Austl., 17,762....F2 25
Buncombe, co., N.C., 145,056....f10 76
Bundaberg, Austl., 27,394..D9 25
Bunia, Zaire, 5,000....H4 23
Bunker Hill, Ill., 1,465....D4 58
Bunker Hill, Ind., 956....C5 59
Bunker Hill, Oreg., 1,549....*D2 80
Bunker Hill, Tex., 3,977..*E5 84
Bunkie, La., 5,395....D3 63
Bunnell, Fla., 1,687....C5 54
Bunny Run, Mich., 1,391....*F7 66
Buo Ha, Viet., 10,000....*G5 17
Burao, Som., 10,000....G7 23
Buras, La., 2,500....E6 63
Buraydah, Sau. Ar., 50,000....D3 15
Burbank, Calif., 88,871....E4, m12 50
Burdur, Tur., 32,746....D8 14
Burdwān, India, 143,318..D8 20
Bureau, co., Ill., 38,541....B4 58
Bureya, Sov. Un., 5,000....B4 18
Burgas, Bul., 108,200....D8 10
Burgas, pol. div., Bul., 380,817....*D8 10
Burgaw, N.C., 1,744....C5 76
Burgdorf, Switz., 15,600 (*18,600)....E3 6
Burgeo, Newf., Can., 2,226....E3 44
Burgettstown, Pa., 2,118...F1 81
Burgos, Sp., 116,797....A4 8
Burgos, prov., Sp., 364,600....*A4 8
Burgundy (Bourgogne), former prov., Fr....D6 5
Burhānpur, India, 105,246 (*105,335)....D6 20
Burien, Wash., 15,000....*B3 86
Burin, Newf., Can., 2,586..E4 44
Buriram, Thai., 12,579...*C2 19
Burkburnett, Tex., 9,230...B3 84
Burke, co., Ga., 18,255....C4 55
Burke, co., N.C., 60,364...B1 76
Burke, co., N. Dak., 4,739..B3 77
Burke City, Mo., 1,800....f13 69
Burks Falls, Ont., Can., 926....B5 41
Burleigh, co., N. Dak., 40,714....D5 77
Burleson, Tex., 7,713....n9 84
Burleson, co., Tex., 9,999....D4 84
Burlingame, Calif., 27,320..h8 50
Burlingame, Kans., 999....D8 61
Burlington, Ont., Can., 87,023....D5 41
Burlington, Colo., 2,828....B8 51
Burlington, Iowa, 32,366..D6 60
Burlington, Kans., 2,099...D8 61
Burlington, Mass., 21,980..f11 65
Burlington, N.J., 12,010...C3 74
Burlington, N.C., 35,930 (*88,900)....A3 76
Burlington, Vt., 38,633 (*92,200)....C1 73
Burlington, Wash., 3,138...A3 86
Burlington, Wis., 7,479....F5, n11 88
Burlington, co., N.J., 323,132....D3 74
Burma, country, Asia, 29,695,000....D10 20
Burnet, Tex., 2,864....D3 84
Burnet, co., Tex., 11,420...D3 84
Burnett, co., Wis., 9,276...C1 88
Burney, Calif., 1,294....B3 50
Burnham, Ill., 3,634....*B6 58
Burnham, Pa., 2,607....E6 81
Burnie, Austl., 20,088....o15 25

Burnley, Eng., 76,130
  (*166,000)............D5   4
Burns, Oreg., 3,293......D7 80
Burns Flat, Okla., 988....B2 79
Burns Lake, B.C., Can.,
  1,259................B5 37
Burnsville, N.C., 1,348....f10 76
Burnwell, Ala., 200......f6 46
Burr Oak, Mich., 873....G5 66
Bursa, Tur., 275,953......B7 14
Burt, co., Nebr., 9,247....C9 71
Burton, Mich., 32,540....F7 66
Burton, Ohio, 1,214......A4 78
Burton-on-Trent, Eng.,
  50,540...............D6 4
Burundi, country, Afr.,
  3,825,000.............I3 23
Būshehr, Iran, 23,547....G8 16
Buskerud, co., Nor.,
  194,500.............*H4 11

Busko, Pol., 11,100.......C6 7
Bussum, Neth., 40,219....A6 5
Busto Arsizio, It., 75,600..B2 9
Buta, Zaire, 11,200......H2 23
Bute, co., Scot., 12,555...*C4 4
Butler, Ala., 2,064......C1 46
Butler, Ga., 1,589......D2 55
Butler, Ind., 2,394......B8 59
Butler, Mo., 3,984......C3 69
Butler, N.J., 7,051......B4 74
Butler, Ohio, 1,052......B3 78
Butler, Pa., 18,691......E2 81
Butler, Wis., 2,261......m11 88
Butler, co., Ala., 22,007...D3 46
Butler, co., Iowa, 16,953..B5 60
Butler, co., Kans., 38,658..E7 61
Butler, co., Ky., 9,723....C3 62
Butler, co., Mo., 33,529...E7 69
Butler, co., Nebr., 9,461...C8 71
Butler, co., Ohio, 226,207..C1 78

Butler, co., Pa., 127,941...E2 81
Butner, N.C., 3,538......*A4 76
Butte, Mont., 23,368
  (*40,000)..............D4 70
Butte, co., Calif., 101,969..C3 50
Butte, co., Idaho, 2,925....F5 57
Butte, co., S. Dak., 7,825..F2 77
Butterworth, Mala.,
  61,187...............D2 19
Buttonwillow, Calif., 950...E4 50
Butts, co., Ga., 10,560.....C3 55
Butuan, Phil., 48,470
  (131,094 ▲)..........D7 19
Buturlinovka, Sov. Un.,
  22,000...............F13 12
Bützow, Ger. Dem. Rep.,
  10,900...............B5 6
Buxtehude, Ger., Fed.
  Rep. of, 29,611........B4 6

Buxton, Guy., 3,800......C5 27
Büyük Ağrı Dağı (Mt.
  Ararat), mtn., Tur.....C15 14
Buzău, Rom., 56,400.....C8 10
Buzet, Yugo., 444........C1 10
Buzzards Bay, Mass.,
  2,422................C6 65
Byala Slatina, Bul., 14,951.D6 10
Bydgoszcz, Pol., 280,400..B5 7
Byelorussia (S.S.R.), rep.,
  Sov. Un., 9,320,000....E5 12
Byesville, Ohio, 2,097....C4 78
Byfield, Mass., 850......A6 65
Bykovo, Sov. Un., 10,000.G15 12
Byron, Ga., 1,368......D3 55
Byron, Ill., 1,749......A4 58
Bystrzyca, Pol., 7,929....C4 7
Bytom, Pol., 186,900...C5, g9 7
Bytosh, Sov. Un., 10,000..E10 12

C

Caacupé, Par., 7,278......E4 29
Caaguazú, dept., Par.,
  125,138.............D4 29
Caapucú, Par., 6,608......E4 29
Caazapá, Par., 16,588.....E4 29
Caazapá, dept., Par.,
  92,401...............E4 29
Cabaceiras, Braz., 581....*D4 27
Cabana, Peru, 2,560.....C2 31
Cabanatuan, Phil.,
  24,313 (99,890 ▲)......o13 19
Cabano, Que., Can.,
  3,063................B9 42
Cabarrus, co., N.C.,
  74,629..............B2 76
Cabedelo, Braz., 12,811..*D7 27
Cabell, co., W. Vir.,
  106,918.............C2 87
Cabeza del Buey, Sp.,
  11,737..............C3 8
Cabimas, Ven., 118,037...A3 32
Cabinda, Ang., 1,554.....B2 24
Cabinda, dist., Ang.,
  58,453..............B2 24
Cabin John, Md.,
  2,500..............C3, f8 53
Cabo, Braz., 6,029......*D7 27
Cabo Frio, Braz., 25,211..C4 30
Cabool, Mo., 1,848......D5 69
Caboolture, Austl., 3,240..*E9 25
Caborca, Mex., 20,771...A2 34
Cabo Rojo, P.R., 7,181
  (26,060 ▲)..........*G11 35
Cabo San Lucas, Mex.,
  1,534...............C3 34
Cabot, Ark., 2,903......C3 49
Cacak, Yugo., 38,170....D5 10
Caçapava, Braz., 24,626..C3 30
Cacequi, Braz., 9,976.....D2 30
Cáceres, Sp., 55,341.....C2 8
Cáceres, prov., Sp.,
  499,100.............C2 8
Cachan, Fr., 26,187......G10 5
Cache, Okla., 1,106......C3 79
Cache, co., Utah, 42,331..A6 72
Cache, peak, Idaho.....G5 57
Cache Bay, Ont.,
  Can., 810............A5 41
Cachi, Arg., 491........E2 29
Cachoeira, Braz., 11,464..*E7 27
Cachoeira do Sul, Braz.,
  50,001..............E2 30
Cachoeiro do Itapemirim,
  Braz., 58,968........C4 30
Cacouna, Que., Can.,
  1,001...............B8 42
Caddo, Okla., 886......C5 79
Caddo, co., Okla., 28,931..B3 79
Caddo, par., La., 230,184..B2 63
Cadillac, Mich., 9,990....D5 66
Cadillac, mtn., Maine....D4 64
Cadiz, Ky., 1,987......D2 62
Cadiz, Ohio, 3,060......B4 78
Cádiz, Sp., 134,342.....D2 8
Cádiz, prov., Sp.,
  893,500............*D2 8
Cadott, Wis., 977......D2 88
Cadyville, N.Y., 800......f11 75
Caen, Fr., 110,262
  (*155,000)............C3 5
Caernarvon, Wales, 9,370.D4 4
Caernarvon, co., Wales,
  122,410............*D4 4

Cagayan de Oro, Phil.,
  26,465 (128,319 ▲).....D6 19
Cagayan, prov., Phil.,
  445,289.............*B6 19
Cagli, It., 3,235.........C4 9
Cagliari, It., 219,900
  (*260,000)............E2 9
Cagnes-sur-Mer, Fr.,
  15,392..............F7 5
Caguas, P.R., 63,215
  (95,661).............G12 35
Cahaba Heights, Ala.,
  3,800..............*B3 46
Cahokia, Ill., 20,649.....E3 58
Cahors, Fr., 19,203......E4 5
Caibarién, Cuba, 27,000
  (31,200 ▲)..........C4 35
Caicedonia, Col., 16,327..C2 32
Caicó, Braz., 24,594.....*D7 27
Cailloma, Peru, 923......C3 31
Cairnbrook, Pa., 1,100....F4 81
Cairns, Austl., 30,059....C8 25
Cairo, Ga., 8,061......F2 55
Cairo, Ill., 6,277......F4 58
Cairo, Eg., 4,500,000
  (*5,900,000)..........B4 23
Caithness, co., Scot.,
  27,779.............*A5 4
Cajabamba, Peru, 10,500..C2 31
Cajacay, Peru, 1,094.....D2 31
Cajamarca, Peru, 37,608..C2 31
Cajamarca, dept., Peru,
  786,599.............C2 31
Cajatambo, Peru, 2,561....D2 31
Cajázeiras, Braz., 24,079..*D7 27
Cakovec, Yugo., 11,736...B3 10
Calabar, Nig., 76,418.....H6 22
Calabria, pol. dist., It.,
  2,045,047...........*E5 9
Calabria, reg., It.,
  2,067,013............E6 9
Calafat, Rom., 8,069......D6 10
Calahorra, Sp., 14,462....A5 8
Calais, Fr., 74,624
  (*94,000)............B4 5
Calais, Maine, 4,044.....C5 64
Calamar, Col., 6,055......A3 32
Calamba, Phil., 11,868....C6 19
Calañas, Sp., 4,059......D2 8
Calapan, Phil., 11,376....C6 19
Călărasi, Rom., 35,700....C8 10
Calarcá, Col., 30,342....C2 32
Calasparra, Sp., 8,155....C5 8
Calauag, Phil., 3,981....P14 19
Calaveras, co., Calif.,
  13,585..............C3 50
Calca, Peru, 3,037......D3 31
Calcasieu, par., La.,
  145,415.............D2 63
Calceta, Ec., 4,946......B1 31
Calcutta, India, 3,148,746
  (*9,100,000)..........D8 20
Calcutta, Ohio, 1,500....B5 78
Caldas, dept., Col.,
  775,400.............B2 32
Caldas da Rainha, Port.,
  10,635..............C1 8
Caldwell, Idaho, 14,219...F2 57
Caldwell, Kans., 1,540....E6 61
Caldwell, N.J., 8,677.....B4 74
Caldwell, Ohio, 2,082....C4 78
Caldwell, Tex., 2,308.....D4 84
Caldwell, co., Ky., 13,179..C2 62

Caldwell, co., Mo., 8,351..B3 69
Caldwell, co., N.C.,
  56,699..............B1 76
Caldwell, co., Tex., 21,178.E4 84
Caldwell, par., La., 9,354..B3 63
Caledonia, Ont., Can.,
  3,183...............D5 41
Caledonia, Minn., 2,619...G7 67
Caledonia, N.Y., 2,327....C3 75
Caledonia, Ohio, 792.....B3 78
Caledonia, co., Vt.,
  22,789..............C3 73
Calella, Sp., 7,947......B7 8
Calera, Ala., 1,655......B3 46
Calera, Chile, 13,047.....A2 28
Calexico, Calif., 10,625...F6 50
Calgary, Alta., Can.,
  403,319.............D3, g8 38
Calhoun, Ga., 4,748......B2 55
Calhoun, co., Ala.,
  103,092.............B4 46
Calhoun, co., Ark., 5,573..D3 49
Calhoun, co., Fla., 7,624..B1 54
Calhoun, co., Ga., 6,606..E2 55
Calhoun, co., Ill., 5,675..D3 58
Calhoun, co., Iowa,
  14,287..............B4 60
Calhoun, co., Mich.,
  141,963.............F5 66
Calhoun, co., Miss.,
  14,623..............B4 68
Calhoun, co., S.C., 10,780.D6 82
Calhoun, co., Tex.,
  17,831..............E4 84
Calhoun, co., W. Va.,
  7,046...............C3 87
Calhoun City, Miss.,
  1,847...............B4 68
Calhoun Falls, S.C., 2,234..C2 82
Cali, Col., 772,000......C2 32
Calico Rock, Ark., 723....A3 49
Calicut, India, 333,979...F6 20
Caliente, Nev., 916......C4 72
California, Mo., 3,105....C5 69
California, Pa., 6,635.....F2 81
California, state, U.S.,
  20,853,000...........C2 50
Calipatria, Calif., 1,824...F6 50
Calispell, peak, Wash....A8 86
Calistoga, Calif., 1,882...C2 50
Callahan, co., Tex., 8,205..C3 84
Callander, Ont., Can.,
  1,236...............A5 41
Callander, Scot., 1,750....B4 4
Callao, Peru, 196,919.....D2 31
Callao, prov., Peru,
  219,420.............D2 31
Callaway, co., Mo.,
  25,950..............C6 69
Callicoon, N.Y., 800.....D5 75
Calloway, co., Ky.,
  27,692..............f9 62
Calmar, Alta., Can., 700..C4 38
Calmar, Iowa, 1,053.....A6 60
Caloundra, Austl., 6,091..C9 26
Caltagirone, It., 37,000...F5 9
Caltanissetta, It., 52,800..F5 9
Caluire [-et-Cuire], Fr.,
  37,603..............E6 5
Calumet, Que., Can.,
  889.................D3 42
Calumet, Mich., 1,007....A2 66
Calumet, Pa., 800......*F2 81

Calumet, co., Wis., 27,604..D5 88
Calumet City, Ill.,
  33,107............B6, k9 58
Calumet Park, Ill.,
  10,069.............*B6 58
Calvados, dept., Fr.,
  519,695............*C3 5
Calvert, Tex., 2,072......D4 84
Calvert, co., Md., 20,682..C4 53
Calvert City, Ky., 2,104...e9 62
Calverton Park, Mo.,
  2,025...............A8 69
Calvillo, Mex., 6,453.....m12 34
Calwa, Calif., 8,000......*D4 50
Camacho, Mex., 1,672....C4 34
Camagüey, Cuba,
  196,900.............D5 35
Camagüey, prov., Cuba,
  813,200.............D5 35
Camaná, Peru, 5,100.....E2 31
Camanche, Iowa, 3,470...C7 60
Camargo, see Ciudad
  Camargo, Mex.
Camarillo, Calif., 19,219..*E4 50
Camarines Norte, prov.,
  Phil., 188,091.......*C6 19
Camarines Sur, prov.,
  Phil., 819,565.......*C6 19
Camas, Wash., 5,790.....D3 86
Camas, co., Idaho, 728...F4 57
Cambay, India, 62,133...*D5 20
Cambodia, country, Asia,
  7,535,000...........C2 19
Camborne [-Redruth],
  Eng., 41,930.........E4 4
Cambrai, Fr., 37,532
  (*48,000)............B5 5
Cambria, Calif., 700......E3 50
Cambria, co., Pa.,
  186,785.............E4 81
Cambrian Park, Calif.,
  4,000..............*D3 50
Cambridge, Eng., 99,600..D7 4
Cambridge, Ill., 2,095....B3 58
Cambridge, Md., 11,595..C5 53
Cambridge, Mass.,
  100,361...........B5, g11 65
Cambridge, Minn., 2,720..E5 67
Cambridge, Nebr., 1,145..D5 71
Cambridge, N.J., 1,000...*C3 74
Cambridge, N.Y., 1,769...B7 75
Cambridge, Ohio, 13,656..B4 78
Cambridge & Isle of Ely,
  co., Eng., 304,570....*D7 4
Cambridge City, Ind.,
  2,481...............E7 59
Cambridge Springs, Pa.,
  1,998...............C1 81
Camden, Ala., 1,742.....D2 46
Camden, Ark., 15,147....D3 49
Camden, Del., 1,241.....B6 53
Camden, Maine, 3,492
  (4,115 ▲)...........D3 64
Camden, N.J., 102,551...D2 74
Camden, N.Y., 2,936.....B5 75
Camden, Ohio, 1,507....C1 78
Camden, S.C., 8,532.....C6 82
Camden, Tenn., 3,052....A3 83
Camden, Tex., 350......D5 84
Camden, co., Ga., 11,334..F5 55
Camden, co., Mo., 13,315..C5 69
Camden, co., N.J.,
  456,291.............D3 74

Camden, co., N.C., 5,453..A6 76
Camdenton, Mo., 1,636...D5 69
Camerino, It., 4,000......C4 9
Cameron, La., 950........E2 63
Cameron, Mo., 3,960......B3 69
Cameron, Tex., 5,546.....D4 84
Cameron, W. Va.,
1,537..............B4, g8 87
Cameron, Wis., 893.......C2 88
Cameron, co., Pa., 7,096...D5 81
Cameron, co., Tex.,
140,368................F4 84
Cameron, par., La., 8,194..E2 63
Cameroon, country, Afr.,
6,250,000..............G7 22
Cameroun, Mont, mtn.,
Cam..................H6 22
Camiling, Phil., 9,799.....o13 19
Camilla, Ga., 4,987.......E2 55
Camillus, N.Y., 1,534.....*B4 75
Camino, Calif., 900.......C3 50
Cammack Village, Ark.,
1,165..............C3, h10 49
Camocim, Braz., 12,068..*D6 27
Camp, co., Tex., 8,005....C5 84
Campagna di Roma, reg.,
It......................h9 9
Campana, Arg., 35,000...g7 28
Campanario, Sp., 9,660....C3 8
Campania, pol. dist., It.,
4,760,759.............*D5 9
Campania, reg., It.,
5,132,900..............D5 9
Campbell, Calif., 24,770....k8 50
Campbell, Mo., 1,979......E7 69
Campbell, Ohio, 12,577...A5 78
Campbell, co., Ky.,
88,561.................B5 62
Campbell, co., S. Dak.,
2,866..................E5 77
Campbell, co., Tenn.,
26,045.................C9 83
Campbell, co., Va.,
43,319.................C3 85
Campbell, co., Wyo.,
12,957.................B7 89
Campbell, hill, Ohio B2 78
Campbellford, Ont., Can.,
3,522..................C7 41
Campbellpore, Pak.,
14,892 (*19,041)........B5 20
Campbell River, B.C.,
Can., 9,770...........D5 37
Campbells Bay, Que., Can.,
1,024..................B8 41
Campbellsport, Wis.,
1,681..................E5 88
Campbellsville, Ky.,
7,598..................C4 62
Campbellton, N.B., Can.,
10,335 (*12,443)........A3 43
Campbelltown, Pa.,
1,355.................*F9 81
Campbeltown, Scot.,
6,045..................C4 4
Campeche, Mex., 69,506...D6 34
Camp Hill, Ala., 1,554....C4 46
Camp Hill, Pa., 9,931.....F8 81
Campiglia Marittima, It.,
2,716..................C3 9
Campina Grande, Braz.,
163,206................D7 27
Campinas, Braz.,
328,629............C3, m8 30
Campoalegre, Col.,
9,768..................C2 32
Campobasso, It., 34,700...D5 9
Campo Belo, Braz.,
20,174.................C3 30
Campo de Criptana, Sp.,
14,608.................C4 8
Campo Grande, Braz.,
130,792................C2 30
Campo Maior, Braz.,
18,413................*D6 27
Campo Maior, Port.,
8,086..................C2 8
Campos, Braz., 153,310....C4 30
Camp Point, Ill., 1,143....C2 58
Camp Springs, Md.,
2,800...................f9 53
Campti, La., 1,078........C2 63
Campton Heights, Calif.,
1,500.................*B1 50
Camrose, Alta., Can.,
8,673..................C4 38
Canaan, Conn., 1,083.....A3 52
Canada, country, N.A.,
22,245,000.............D10 33
Cañada de Gómez, Arg.,
23,000.................A4 28
Canadensis, Pa., 800.....D11 81
Canadian, Tex., 2,292.....B2 84
Canadian, co., Okla.,
32,245.................B3 79
Canadian, riv., U.S.......C6 45
Canajoharie, N.Y., 2,686..C6 75
Çanakkale, Tur., 27,042...B6 14
Canal Fulton, Ohio,
2,367..................B4 78
Canal Point, Fla., 900.....F6 54
Canal Winchester, Ohio,
2,412.............C3, m11 78
Canal Zone, U.S. dep.,
N.A., 45,000...........B2 32
Canandaigua, N.Y.,
10,488.................C3 75
Cananea, Mex., 17,518....A2 34
Cañar, prov., Ec.,
128,700................B2 31
Canary Islands, reg., Sp.,
1,290,000..............C1 22
Cañas, C.R., 2,991.......*E7 75
Canastota, N.Y., 5,033.....B5 34
Canavieiras, Braz.,
11,680................*E7 27
Canberra, Austl., 141,575
(*158,594).............G8 25
Canby, Minn., 2,147......F2 67
Canby, Oreg.,
3,813..............B4, h12 80
Candeleda, Sp., 6,983.....B3 8
Candia, see Iraklion, Grc.
Candiac, Que., Can.,
5,185..................q19 42
Candler, co., Ga., 6,412...D4 55
Cando, N. Dak., 1,512.....B6 77
Candor, N.Y., 939........C4 75
Canea, see Khaniá, Grc.
Canelones, Ur., 14,028....E1 30
Canelones, dept., Ur.,
256,200...............*E1 30
Cañete, Peru, 7,100.......D2 31
Caney, Kans., 2,192.......E8 61
Canfield, Ohio, 4,997......A5 78
Cangallo, Peru, 902.......D3 31
Cangas, Sp., 4,008........A1 8
Cangas de Onís, Sp.,
9,936..................A3 8
Canicatti, It., 31,500......F4 9
Caniles, Sp., 8,040........D4 8
Canisteo, N.Y., 2,772......C3 75
Çankiri (Changra), Tur.,
26,124.................B9 14
Canmore, Alta, Can.,
1,736..................D3 38
Cannelton, Ind., 2,280.....I4 59
Cannes, Fr., 67,152
(*175,000).............F7 5
Canning, N.S., Can.,
850....................D5 43
Cannington, Ont., Can.,
1,083..................C5 41
Cannon, co., Tenn., 8,467..B5 83
Cannon Falls, Minn.,
2,072..................F6 67
Canoas, Braz., 148,798 ...*D2 30
Canoinhas, Braz., 13,864...D2 30
Canon City, Colo., 9,206...C5 51
Canonsburg, Pa., 11,439...F1 81
Canora, Sask., Can.,
2,603..................F4 39
Canosa [di Puglia], It.,
33,100.................D6 9
Canso, N.S., Can., 1,209...D8 43
Cantal, dept., Fr.,
169,330...............*E5 5
Canterbury, Eng., 35,530..E7 4
Can Tho, Viet., 61,100...*C3 19
Cantilan, Phil., 2,048.....*D7 19
Canton, China, 2,250,000..G7 17
Canton, Ga., 3,654........B2 55
Canton, Ill., 14,217.......C3 58
Canton, Mass.,
17,100............B5, h11 65
Canton, Miss., 10,503.....C3 68
Canton, Mo., 2,680........A6 69
Canton, N.Y., 6,398.......F9 75
Canton, N.C., 5,158.......D3 76
Canton, Ohio, 110,053
(*311,100).............B4 78
Canton, Okla., 844........A3 79
Canton, Pa., 2,037.........C8 81
Canton, S. Dak., 2,665....G9 77
Canton, Tex., 2,283........C5 84
Cantonment, Fla., 2,600..u14 54
Cantwell, Mo., 950.......D7 69
Canutillo, Tex., 1,588.....o11 84
Canyon, Tex., 8,333.......B2 84
Canyon, co., Idaho,
61,288.................F2 57
Canyonville, Oreg.,
940....................E3 80
Cao Bang, Viet., 25,000...G6 17
Capac, Mich., 1,279........F8 66
Cap Chat, Que., Can.,
3,868..................G20 36
Cap-de-la-Madeleine,
Que., Can., 31,463......C5 42
Cape Breton, Can.,.......G21 36
Cape Breton, co., N.S.,
Can., 131,507...........D9 43
Cape Canaveral, Fla.,
4,258..................D6 54
Cape Charles, Va., 1,689...C6 85
Cape Coast, Ghana,
41,200.................G4 22
Cape Coral, Fla., 10,193...F5 54
Cape Elizabeth, Maine,
7,873..............E2, g7 64
Cape Girardeau, Mo.,
31,282.................D8 69
Cape Girardeau, co., Mo.,
49,350.................D8 69
Cape Horn, mtn., Idaho...E3 57
Capels, W. Va., 300.......D3 87
Cape May, N.J., 4,392.....F3 74
Cape May, co., N.J.,
59,554.................E3 74
Cape May Court House,
N.J., 2,062.............E3 74
Cape of Good Hope, prov.,
S. Afr., 6,375,000.......G4 24
Capesterre, Guad., 6,790..H14 35
Cape Town (Kaapstad),
S. Afr., 691,296
(*1,125,000)...........G3 24
Cape Verde, country, Afr.,
285,000................o12 22
Cape Vincent, N.Y., 820...A4 75
Cap-Haïtien, Hai., 46,217..E7 35
Capiata, Par., 1,900......*E4 29
Capistrano Beach, Calif.,
2,026.................*F5 50
Capitan, N. Mex., 439.....C6 48
Capitola, Calif., 5,080....*D2 50
Capitol Heights, Md.,
3,835...............C4, f9 53
Capivarí, Braz., 12,905....m8 30
Capiz, prov., Phil.,
315,079...............*C6 19
Capoompeta, mtn., Austl..E9 25
Cap-Pelé, N.B., Can.,
2,081..................C5 43
Capreol, Ont., Can.,
3,470..................p19 41
Cap-St. Ignace, Que.,
Can., 1,247............B7 42
Captain Cook, Haw.,
1,263..................D6 56
Capua, It., 16,400........D5 9
Caquetá, intendencia, Col.,
136,900................C3 32
Carabobo, state, Ven.,
381,636................A4 32
Caracal, Rom., 19,082.....C7 10
Caracas, Ven., 1,625,000
(*2,375,000)...........A4 32
Caraguatay, Par., 1,900....E4 29
Carangola, Braz., 14,924...C4 30
Caransebes, Rom., 15,195..C6 10
Carapeguá, Par., 23,675...E4 29
Caraquet, N.B., Can.,
3,441..................B5 43
Caratinga, Braz., 28,119...B4 30
Caravelí, Peru, 1,177......E3 31
Caraway, Ark., 952.......B5 49
Caraz, Peru, 3,065........C2 31
Caràzinho, Braz., 28,363...D2 30
Carballino, Sp., 9,639.....A1 8
Carballo, Sp., 3,110.......A1 8
Carberry, Man., Can.,
1,113..................E2 40
Carbó, Mex., 2,804........B2 34
Carbon, co., Mont., 7,080..E7 70
Carbon, co., Pa., 50,573..E10 81
Carbon, co., Utah, 15,647..B6 72
Carbon, co., Wyo., 13,354..E5 89
Carbondale, Ill., 22,816....F4 58
Carbondale, Pa., 12,808..C10 81
Carbonear, Newf., Can.,
4,732 (*7,503)..........E5 44
Carbon Hill, Ala., 1,929...B2 46
Carbonia, It., 32,700......E2 9
Carcagente, Sp., 17,937....C5 8
Carcar, Phil., 6,657......*C6 19
Carcassonne, Fr., 43,616...F5 5
Carchi, prov., Ec., 111,600.A2 31
Cardale, Pa., 500.........*G2 81
Cárdenas, Cuba, 55,200
(55,700 ^)..............C3 35
Cárdenas, Mex., 15,643...D6 34
Cárdenas, Mex., 12,020...m14 34
Cardiff, Wales, 276,790
(*615,000).............E5 4
Cardiff-by-the-Sea, Calif.,
1,500.................*F5 50
Cardigan, Wales, 3,810....D4 4
Cardigan, co., Wales,
56,160................*D4 4
Cardinal, Ont., Can.,
1,865..................C9 41
Cardington, Ohio, 1,730...B3 78
Cardston, Alta., Can.,
2,685..................E4 38
Cardwell, Mo., 859........E7 69
Carei, Rom., 16,780.......B6 10
Carencro, La., 2,302.......D3 63
Carenero, Ven., 312.......A4 32
Caretta, W. Va., 950.......D3 87
Carey, Ohio, 3,523........B2 78
Carhuaz, Peru, 2,359......C2 31
Cariati, It., 5,204.........E6 9
Caribbean, sea, N.A......H13 33
Cariboo mts., B.C.,
Can....................C7 37
Caribou, Maine, 10,419....B5 64
Caribou, co., Idaho, 6,534 .F6 57
Caribou, mtn, Idaho,......F7 57
Caribou, mtn., Maine.....C2 64
Carichic, Mex., 1,520......B3 34
Carini, It., 16,723.........E4 9
Carinthia, reg., Aus.,
2,178,141..............E6 6
Caripito, Ven., 20,674.....A5 32
Carle Place, N.Y., 7,300..*G2 52
Carleton, Mich., 1,503.....F7 66
Carleton, co., N.B., Can.,
23,507.................C2 43
Carleton, mtn., N.B.,
Can....................B3 43
Carleton Place, Ont., Can.,
5,020..................B8 41
Carletonville, S. Afr.,
40,641................*F5 24
Carlin, Nev., 1,313........A3 72
Carlinville, Ill., 5,675.....D4 58
Carlisle, Ark., 2,048.......C4 49
Carlisle, Eng., 71,820......C5 4
Carlisle, Iowa, 2,246......C4 60
Carlisle, Ky., 1,579........B5 62
Carlisle, Pa., 18,079.......F7 81
Carlisle, co., Ky., 5,354.....f8 62
Carl Junction, Mo., 1,661..D3 69
Carloforte, It., 7,275......E2 9
Carlos Casares, Arg.,
9,218..................B4 28
Carlow, Ire., 9,588
(*10,399)..............D3 4
Carlow, co., Ire., 33,593..*D3 4
Carlsbad, Calif., 14,944....F5 50
Carlsbad, N. Mex.,
21,297.................C6 48
Carlstadt, N.J., 6,724......h8 74
Carlton, Oreg., 1,126.B3, h11 80
Carlton, co., Minn.,
28,072.................D6 67
Carlyle, Sask., Can.,
982....................H4 39
Carlyle, Ill., 3,139........E4 58
Carmagnola, It., 4,800.....B1 9
Carman, Man., Can.,
2,030..................E2 40
Carman, hill, Pa..........C6 81
Carmanville, Newf., Can.,
855....................D4 44
Carmarthen, Wales,
13,430.................E4 4
Carmarthen, co., Wales,
163,170...............*E4 4
Carmaux, Fr., 14,755
(*24,500)..............E5 5
Carmel, Calif., 4,525......D3 50
Carmel, Ind., 6,568........E5 59
Carmel, N.Y., 3,395.......D7 75
Carmel, mtn., Isr..........B3 15
Carmelo, Ur., 11,800......E1 30
Carmel Valley, Calif.,
1,143.................*D3 50
Carmel Woods, Calif.,
2,200.................*D3 50
Carmen, Par., 10,699......E4 29
Carmen de Patagones,
Arg., 7,478............C4 28
Carmi, Ill., 6,033.........E5 58
Carmichael, Calif.,
40,500................*C3 50
Carmichaels, Pa., 608.....G2 81
Carmona, Sp., 28,216.....D3 8
Carnarvon, Austl.,
4,222..................D1 25
Carnduff, Sask., Can.,
957....................H5 39
Carnegie, Okla., 1,723.....B3 79
Carnegie, Pa., 10,864..F1, k13 81
Carneys Point, N.J.,
2,500..................D2 74
Caro, Mich., 3,701........E7 66
Carol City, Fla., 27,361...s13 54
Caroleen, N.C., 950...B1, f11 76
Carolina, P.R., 94,271...*G11 35
Carolina Beach, N.C.,
1,663..................C5 76
Caroline, co., Md.,
19,781.................C6 53
Caroline, co., Va., 13,925..C5 85
Caroline, arch., Pac. O. ...F6 2
Carora, Ven., 36,115.......A3 32
Carouge, Switz., 13,500....E3 6
Carpentersville, Ill.,
24,059.............A5, h8 58
Carpentras, Fr., 14,169....E6 5
Carpi, It., 34,100.........B3 9
Carpinteria, Calif., 6,982...E4 50
Carrabelle, Fla., 1,044.....C2 54
Carrantuohill, mtn., Ire....D1 4
Carrara, It., 66,800.......B3 9
Carrboro, N.C., 5,058......B3 76
Carrickfergus, N. Ire.,
15,162.................C4 4
Carrie, mtn., Wash.........B2 86

Carriers Mills, Ill., 2,013...F5 58
Carrington, N. Dak., 2,491...C6 77
Carrizo, see El Carrizo, Mex.
Carrizo Springs, Tex., 5,374...E3 84
Carrizozo, N. Mex., 1,123..C6 48
Carroll, Iowa, 8,716...B3 60
Carroll, co., Ark., 12,301...A2 49
Carroll, co., Ga., 45,404...C1 55
Carroll, co., Ill., 19,276...A4 58
Carroll, co., Ind., 17,734...C4 59
Carroll, co., Iowa, 22,912..B3 60
Carroll, co., Ky., 8,523...B4 62
Carroll, co., Md., 69,006...A3 53
Carroll, co., Miss., 9,397...B4 68
Carroll, co., Mo., 12,545...B4 69
Carroll, co., N.H., 18,548..D5 73
Carroll, co., Ohio, 21,579..B4 78
Carroll, co., Tenn., 25,741..B3 83
Carroll, co., Va., 23,092...D2 85
Carrollton, Ga., 13,520...C1 55
Carrollton, Ill., 2,866...D3 58
Carrollton, Ky., 3,884...B4 62
Carrollton, Md., 40...A4 53
Carrollton, Mich., 8,526...E7 66
Carrollton, Mo., 4,847...B4 69
Carrollton, Ohio, 2,817...B4 78
Carrollton, Tex., 13,855..*C4 84
Carrolltown, Pa., 1,507...E4 81
Carrot River, Sask., Can., 930...D4 39
Carrville, Ala., 895...C4 46
Çarşamba, Tur., 20,463...B11 14
Carson, Calif., 72,358...*n12 50
Carson, Iowa, 756...C10 71
Carson, co., Tex., 6,358...B2 84
Carson City, Mich., 1,217..E6 66
Carson City, Nev., 15,468..B2 72
Carsonville, Mo., 650...*C7 69
Cartagena, Col., 285,100...A2 32
Cartagena, Sp., 118,000 (143,466 ▲)...D5 8
Cartago, Col., 60,500...C2 32
Cartago, C.R., 20,900...F8 34
Cartago, prov., C.R., 182,200...*I12 33
Cartaxo, Port., 5,920...C1 8
Cartaya, Sp., 9,002...D2 8
Carter, co., Ky., 19,850...B6 62
Carter, co., Mo., 3,878...E7 69
Carter, co., Mont., 1,956..E12 70
Carter, co., Okla., 37,349..C4 79
Carter, co., Tenn., 43,259...C11 83
Carteret, N.J., 23,137..B4, k8 74
Carteret, co., N.C., 31,603...C6 76
Carter Lake, Iowa, 3,268..C2 60
Cartersville, Ga., 10,138...B2 55
Carterville, Ill., 3,061...F4 58
Carterville, Mo., 1,716...D3 69
Carthage, Ill., 3,350...C2 58
Carthage, Ind., 946...E6 59
Carthage, Miss., 3,031...C4 68
Carthage, Mo., 11,035...D3 69
Carthage, N.Y., 3,889...B5 75
Carthage, N.C., 1,034...B3 76
Carthage, Tenn., 2,491...C8 83
Carthage, Tex., 5,392...C5 84
Caruaru, Braz., 101,006...D7 27
Carúpano, Ven., 50,935...A5 32
Caruthersville, Mo., 7,350..E8 69
Carver, Minn., 669...F5 67
Carver, co., Minn., 28,310...F5 67
Carville, La., 950...h9 63
Cary, Ill., 4,358...A5, h8 58
Cary, N.C., 7,435...B4 76
Caryville, Tenn., 648...C9 83
Casablanca, Mor., 1,506,373 (*1,575,000)...B3 22
Casa Branca, Braz., 11,660...C3, k8 30
Casa Grande, Ariz., 10,536...C3 48
Casale Monferrato, It., 38,000...B2 9
Casarano, It., 14,744...D7 9
Casas Adobes, Ariz., 4,800...*C3 48
Cascade, Idaho, 833...E2 57
Cascade, Iowa, 1,744...B6 60
Cascade, co., Mont., 81,804...C5 70
Cascade, range, Can., U.S..B2 45
Cascais, Port., 10,861...C1, f9 8
Caseros (Tres de Febrero), Arg., 313,460...*A5 28
Caserta, It., 52,800...D5 9
Casey, Ill., 2,994...D6 58
Casey, co., Ky., 12,930...C4 62
Casey, mtn., Idaho...A2 57
Caseyville, Ill., 3,411...*E3 58
Cashion, Ariz., 2,705...D1 48
Cashmere, Wash., 1,976...B5 86
Cashton, Wis., 824...E3 88
Casilda, Arg., 17,216...A4 28
Casino, Austl., 8,091...D9 26
Čáslav, Czech., 10,100...D3 7
Casma, Peru, 5,300...C2 31
Caspe, Sp., 9,033...B5 8
Casper, Wyo., 39,361 (*47,500)...D6 89
Caspian, Mich., 1,165...B2 66
Caspian, sea, Asia...E7 13
Cassadaga, N.Y. 905...C1 75
Cass, co., Ill., 14,219...D3 58
Cass, co., Ind., 40,456...C5 59
Cass, co., Iowa, 17,007...C3 60
Cass, co., Mich., 43,312...G4 66
Cass, co., Minn., 17,323...D4 67
Cass, co., Mo., 39,448...C3 69
Cass, co., Nebr., 18,076...D9 71
Cass, co., N. Dak., 73,653..C8 77
Cass, co., Tex., 24,133...C5 84
Cass City, Mich., 1,974...E7 66
Casselberry, Fla., 9,438...*D5 54
Casselman, Ont., Can., 1,337...B9 41
Casselton, N. Dak., 1,485..D8 77
Cassia, co., Idaho, 17,017..G5 57
Cassino, It., 19,400...D4 9
Cass Lake, Minn., 1,317...C4 67
Cassopolis, Mich., 2,108...G4 66
Cassville, Mo., 1,910...E4 69
Cassville, Wis., 1,343...F3 88
Castalia, Ohio, 1,045...A3 78
Castanea, Pa., 1,279...D7 81
Castaños, Mex., 8,996...B4 34
Castellammare di Stabia, It., 70,300...*D5 9
Castellón (Castellón de la Plana), prov., Sp., 379,700...*C5 8
Castellón de la Plana, Sp., 92,777...C5 8
Castelnaudary, Fr., 8,587..F4 5
Castelo Branco, Port., 14,838...C2 8
Castelvetrano, It., 31,100...F4 9
Castile, N.Y., 1,330...C2 75
Castilla, Peru, 29,541...C1 31
Castle, peak, Idaho...E4 57
Castle Douglas, Scot., 3,336...C5 4
Castlegar, B.C., Can., 3,072 (*5,918)...E9 37
Castle Hills, Tex., 5,311...*E3 84
Castlemaine, Austl., 7,547...H5 26
Castle Park, Calif., 2,500..*F5 50
Castle Rock, Colo., 1,531...B6 51
Castle Rock, Wash., 1,647.C3 86
Castle Rock, mtn., Oreg...C8 80
Castle Rock, mtn., Va...C4 85
Castle Shannon, Pa., 12,036...k13 81
Castleton-on-Hudson, N.Y., 1,730...C7 75
Castor, Alta., Can., 1,025..C5 38
Castres, Fr., 40,457...F5 5
Castries, St. Lucia, 39,132.J14 35
Castro, Braz., 11,887...C3 30
Castro, Sp., 11,842...D3 8
Castro, co., Tex., 10,394...B1 84
Castro Alves, Braz., 9,618...*E7 27
Castropol, Sp., 7,368...A2 8
Castro Valley, Calif., 46,500...h8 50
Castrovillari, It., 12,500...E6 9
Castroville, Calif., 3,000...D3 50
Castroville, Tex., 1,893...E3 84
Castrovirreyna, Peru, 872..D2 31
Castuera, Sp., 10,166...C3 8
Caswell, co., N.C., 19,055..A3 76
Catacaos, Peru, 8,526...C1 31
Catacocha, Ec., 3,796...B2 31
Cataguases, Braz., 32,515...C4, g6 30
Catahoula, par., La., 11,769...C4 63
Cataiñgan, Phil., 2,669...*C6 19
Catalao, Braz., 15,223...B3 30
Çatalca, Tur., 6,884...B7 14
Catalina, Newf., Can., 1,110...D5 44
Catamarca, Arg., 55,000...E2 29
Catamarca, prov., Arg., 172,323...E2 29
Catanduva, Braz., 48,446..C3 30
Catania, It., 409,100...F5 9
Cataño, P.R., 26,459...*G11 35
Catanzaro, It., 81,500...E6 9
Catarman, Phil, 13,018...C6 19
Catarroja, Sp., 11,680...C5 8
Catasauqua, Pa., 5,702...E11 81
Catawba, co., N.C., 90,873...B1 76
Catawissa, Pa., 1,701...E9 81
Catbalogan, Phil., 18,413..C6 19
Cathedral, mtn., Tex...o13 84
Cathedral City, Calif., 3,640...F5 50
Catlettsburg, Ky., 3,420...B7 62
Catlin, Ill., 2,093...C6 58
Catonsville, Md., 42,000...B4, g10 53
Catoosa, co., Ga., 28,271...B1 55
Catron, co., N. Mex., 2,198...C4 48
Catskill, N.Y., 5,317...C7 75
Catskill, mtns., N.Y...C6 75
Catt, mtn., B.C., Can...B3 37
Cattaraugus, N.Y., 1,200...C2 75
Cattaraugus, co., N.Y., 81,666...C2 75
Cattolica, It., 15,300...C4 9
Cauca, dept., Col., 664,000...C2 32
Caucasia, Col., 5,616...B2 32
Caudebec [-lès-Elbeuf], Fr., 9,595...C4 5
Caudete, Sp., 7,544...C5 8
Caudry, Fr., 13,328...B5 5
Caughnawaga, Que., Can...D4, q19 42
Cauquenes, Chile, 17,836..B2 28
Causapscal, Que., Can., 2,965...*h14 42
Cautín, prov., Chile, 444,200...B2 28
Cavadas, Mex., 24,377...m12 34
Cavaillon, Fr., 14,815...F6 5
Cavalier, N. Dak., 1,381...B8 77
Cavalier, co., N. Dak., 8,213...B7 77
Cavan, co., Ire., 54,022...*D3 4
Cavarzere, It., 5,600...B4 9
Cave, It., 5,856...h9 9
Cave City, Ky., 1,818...C4 62
Cave Junction, Oreg., 415...E3 80
Cave Spring, Ga., 1,305...B1 55
Cavite, Phil., 75,739...o13 19
Cavite, prov., Phil., 378,138...*C6 19
Cawnpore, see Kanpur, India
Cawood, Ky., 800...D6 62
Caxias, Braz., 31,089...*D6 27
Caxias do Sul., Braz., 107,487...D2 30
Caxito, Ang., 8,690...B2 24
Cayambe, Ec., 8,101...A2 31
Cayce, S.C., 9,967...D5 82
Cayenne, Fr. Gu., 24,518..C5 27
Cayey, P.R., 21,562 (38,432 ▲)...G11 35
Cayman Islands, Br. dep., N.A., 12,000...F3 35
Cayuga, Ont., Can., 1,084.E5 41
Cayuga, Ind., 1,090...E3 59
Cayuga, co., N.Y., 77,439..C4 75
Cayuga Heights, N.Y., 3,130...*C4 75
Cazalla de la Sierra, Sp., 9,284...D3 8
Cazenovia, N.Y., 3,031...C5 75
Cazorla, Sp., 8,699...D4 8
Ceará, state, Braz., 4,491,590...*D7 27
Ceará Mirim, Braz., 12,880...*D7 27
Cebu, Phil., 347,116...C6 19
Cebu, prov., Phil., 1,332,847...*C6 19
Cecil, Pa., 900...F1 81
Cecil, co., Md., 53,291...A6 53
Cecina, It., 6,741...C3 9
Cedar, co., Iowa, 17,655...C6 60
Cedar, co., Mo., 9,424...D4 69
Cedar, co., Nebr., 12,192...B8 71
Cedar, mtn., Cal...B3 50
Cedar Bluff, Va., 1,050...e10 85
Cedarburg, Wis., 7,697...E5, m12 88
Cedar City, Utah, 8,946...C5 72
Cedar Falls, Iowa, 29,597..B5 60
Cedar Grove, N.J., 15,582...*B4 74
Cedar Grove, W. Va., 1,275...C3, m13 87
Cedar Grove, Wis., 1,276..E6 88
Cedar Hammock, Fla., 3,089...*E4 54
Cedar Heights, Md., 2,200...*C4 53
Cedar Hill, Tex., 2,610...n10 84
Cedar Hills, Oreg., 7,500...*B4 80
Cedarhurst, N.Y., 6,941...k13 75
Cedar Key, Fla., 714...C3 54
Cedar Knolls, N.J., 3,000..B4 74
Cedar Lake, Ind., 7,589...B3 59
Cedar Rapids, Iowa, 110,642 (*150,100)...C6 60
Cedar Springs, Mich., 1,807...E5 66
Cedar Terrace, S.C., 3,500...*D5 82
Cedartown, Ga., 9,253...B1 55
Cedar Vale, Kans., 665...E7 61
Cedarville, Calif., 800...B3 50
Cedarville, N.J., 990...E2 74
Cedarville, Ohio, 2,342...C2 78
Cedarwood Park, N.J., 1,600...*C4 74
Ceduna, Austl., 2,056...F5 25
Cefalù, It., 11,100...E5 9
Cegléd, Hung., 30,933 (38,082 ▲)...B4 10
Ceglie Messapico, It., 16,500...D6 9
Celákovice, Czech., 6,041..n18 7
Celaya, Mex., 79,977...m13 34
Celebes (Sulawesi), isl., Indon...F6 19
Celendín, Peru, 5,800...C2 31
Celina, Ohio, 8,072...B1 78
Celina, Tenn., 1,370...C8 83
Celina, Tex., 1,272...C4 84
Celje, Yugo., 31,788...B2 10
Celle, Ger., Fed. Rep. of, 75,178...B5 6
Celoron, N.Y., 1,456...C1 75
Cement, Okla., 892...C3 79
Cementon, Pa., 1,200...E10 81
Cenon, Fr., 17,713...E3 5
Centennial, mts., Mont...F4 70
Center, Colo., 1,470...D4 51
Center, Tex., 4,989...D5 84
Centerburg, Ohio, 1,038...B3 78
Centereach, N.Y., 26,500...E3 75
Center Line, Mich., 10,379...*F8 66
Center Moriches, N.Y., 3,802...n16 75
Center Point, Ala., 15,000..f7 46
Center Point, Iowa, 1,456..B6 60
Centerport, N.Y., 5,000..*n15 75
Centerville, Ind., 2,380...E8 59
Centerville, Iowa, 6,531...D5 60
Centerville, Mont., 1,200..D4 70
Centerville, Ohio, 10,333..C1 78
Centerville, Pa., 4,175...F2 81
Centerville, S. Dak., 910...G9 77
Centerville, Tenn., 2,592...B4 83
Centerville, Tex., 831...D5 84
Centerville, Utah, 3,268...A6, C2 72
Central, N. Mex., 1,864...C4 48
Central, S.C., 1,550...B2 82
Central, mts., Dom. Rep...E8 35
Central African Empire, country, Afr., 1,715,000..G2 23
Central America, reg., N.A., 18,405,000...E6 34
Central Avenue Park, Ohio, 2,500...*A2 78
Central City, Ill., 1,377...E4 58
Central City, Iowa, 1,116...B6 60
Central City, Ky., 5,450...C2 62
Central City, Nebr., 2,803...C7 71
Central City, Pa., 1,547...F4 81
Central Falls, R.I., 18,716...B11 52
Central Heights, Ariz., 1,300...*C3 48
Central Heights, Iowa, 900...A4 60
Centralia, Ill., 15,217...E4 58
Centralia, Mo., 3,623...B5 69
Centralia, Pa., 1,165...*D8 81
Centralia, Wash., 10,054...C3 86
Central Islip, N.Y., 28,000...E7, n15 75
Central Nyack, N.Y., 1,300...*D7 75
Central Park, Ill., 1,500...*C6 58
Central Park, Wash., 2,720...*C2 86
Central Point, Oreg., 4,004...E4 80
Central Square, N.Y., 1,298...B4 75
Central Valley, Calif., 2,000...B2 50
Central Valley, N.Y., 950...D6, m14 75
Centre, Ala., 2,418...A4 46
Centre, co., Pa., 99,267...E6 81
Centre, mtn., Idaho...D3 57
Centre, peak, B.C., Can...B4 37
Centre Hall, Pa., 1,282...E6 81
Centreville, Ala., 2,233...C2 46
Centreville, Ill., 11,378...E3 58
Centreville, Md., 1,853...B5 53
Centreville, Mich., 1,044..G5 66
Centreville, Miss., 1,819...D2 68
Century, Fla., 2,046...u14 54
Ceram, isl., Indon...F7 19
Ceredo, W. Va., 1,583...C2 87
Ceres, Calif., 6,029...D3 50
Cereté, Col., 11,849...B2 32
Cerignola, It., 42,000...D5 9
Cernavoda, Rom., 8,802...C9 10
Cerralvo, Mex., 5,506...B5 34

Cerritos, Calif., 15,856....*F4 50
Cerritos, Mex., 10,421....C4 34
Cerro Alto, mtn., Tex....o12 84
Cerro Azul, Peru, 1,372..D2 31
Cerro de Pasco, Peru,
  35,975.................D2 31
Cerro Gordo, Ill., 1,368..D5 58
Cerro Gordo, co., Iowa,
  49,335.................A4 60
Cerro Largo, dept., Ur.,
  71,441................*E2 30
Cervantes, Sp., 7,011....A2 8
Cervera del Río Alhama,
  Sp., 7,101.............A2 8
Cesena, It., 53,200......B4 9
Cesenatico, It., 5,935....B4 9
Česká Lípa, Czech., 16,597.C3 7
Česká Třebová, Czech.,
  14,627.................D4 7
České Budějovice, Czech.,
  76,945.................D3 7
Český Brod, Czech., 5,754..n8 7
Český Krumlov, Czech.,
  10,265.................D3 7
Cessnock, Austl., 16,141
  (35,003 ▲)............F9 25
Cetinje, Yugo., 11,892...D4 10
Cetraro, It., 9,366......E5 9
Ceuta, Sp. dep., Afr.,
  83,300.................A3 22
Ceylon, see Sri Lanka,
  country, Asia
Chacabuco, Arg.,
  22,544............A4, m9 28
Chachapoyas, Peru, 10,418.C2 31
Chaco, prov., Arg.,
  543,331................E3 29
Chad, country, Afr.,
  3,915,000..............F1 23
Chad, lake, Cam., Nig....E7 22
Chadbourn, N.C., 2,213...C4 76
Chadron, Nebr., 5,921....B3 71
Chadwicks, N.Y., 1,200...*B5 75
Chaffee, Mo., 2,793......D8 69
Chaffee, co., Colo., 10,162.C4 51
Chaffins, Mass., 3,000...*B4 65
Chagrin Falls, Ohio,
  4,848..................A4 78
Chahar Burjak, Afg.,
  5,000..................B3 20
Chaibāsā, India, 35,386..D8 20
Chakradharpur, India,
  22,709 (*34,967)......D8 20
Chakwāl, Pak., 16,843....B5 20
Chalchuapa, Sal., 19,631..*E7 34
Chalfant, Pa., 1,370....*E1 81
Chalhuanca, Peru, 2,538..D3 31
Chalk River, Ont., Can.,
  1,135..................A7 41
Chalkville, Ala., 630....*E4 46
Chalmette, La.,
  23,200............E6, k11 63
Châlons-sur-Marne, Fr.,
  50,764.................C6 5
Chalon-sur-Saône, Fr.,
  50,589.................D6 5
Chama, N. Mex., 899.....A5 48
Chamalières, Fr., 17,638..E5 5
Chaman, Pak., 7,161.....B4 20
Chamberlain, S. Dak.,
  2,626..................G6 77
Chamberlayne Heights,
  Va., 1,000............*C5 85
Chambers, co., Ala.,
  36,356.................C4 46
Chambers, co., Tex.,
  12,187.................E5 84
Chambersburg, Pa.,
  17,315.................G6 81
Chambéry, Fr., 51,066
  (*76,000).............E6 5
Chamblee, Ga., 9,127....h8 55
Chambly, Que., Can.,
  11,469.................D4 42
Chambly, co., Que., Can.,
  190,464................D4 42
Chambord, Que., Can.,
  1,106..................A5 42
Chamdo, see Changtu, China
Champaign, Ill., 56,837
  (*119,400)............C5 58
Champaign, co., Ill.,
  163,281................C5 58
Champaign, co., Ohio,
  30,491.................B2 78
Champigny-sur-Marne,
  Fr., 70,419...........g11 5
Champion, Ohio, 5,000...A5 78
Champlain, N.Y., 1,426..f11 75
Champlain, co., Que.,
  Can., 112,341.........B4 42
Champlin, Minn., 2,275..m12 67
Champotán, Mex., 6,606..D6 34
Chañaral, Chile, 5,200...F3 27
Chancay, Peru, 2,761....D2 31
Chanchelulla, peak, Calif.B2 50
Chanchiang (Tsamkong),
  China, 170,000........G7 17

Chandīgarh, India
  218,743 (*232,940)....B6 20
Chandīgarh, ter., India
  257,251...............*B6 20
Chandler, Ariz.,
  13,763.............C3, D2 48
Chandler, Que., Can.,
  3,843................k14 42
Chandler, Ind., 2,032...H3 59
Chandler, Okla., 2,529..B5 79
Chāndpur, Bngl., 34,837..D9 20
Chandrapur, India, 75,134.E6 20
Changchiakou (Kalgan),
  China, 350,000........C7 17
Changchih, China,
  180,000..............*D7 17
Changchou, China,
  300,000...............E8 17
Changchou, China, 81,200.G8 17
Changchun (Hsinking),
  China, 1,200,000......C10 17
Changhua,Taiwan,
  70,000 (*119,900).....*G9 17
Changjin, Kor., 5,000...F3 18
Changsha, China, 750,000..F7 17
Changshu, China,
  101,400..............*E9 17
Changte, China, 94,800...F7 17
Changting, China, 27,000..F8 17
Changtu (Chamdo),
  China................B10 20
Changyon, Kor., 18,072..G2 18
Channel, is., Eur.......F5 4
Channel Lake, Ill., 600..H8 58
Channel-Port-aux-Basques,
  Newf., Can., 5,942....E2 44
Channelview, Tex.,
  12,000...............r14 84
Chantada, Sp., 2,262....A2 8
Chanthaburi, Thai.,
  10,795................C2 19
Chantilly, Fr., 10,246...C5 5
Chanute, Kans., 10,341..E8 61
Chaoan (Chaochow),
  China, 101,300........G8 17
Chaoching, China, 49,000.G7 17
Chaochou, China, 5,000...D2 18
Chaoyang, China, 16,000..*G8 17
Chaoyang, China, 66,000..C9 17
Chapala, Mex., 10,520..m12 34
Chaparral, Col., 13,261...C2 32
Chapayevsk, Sov. Un.,
  86,000...............*D7 13
Chapel Hill, N.C., 25,537..B3 76
Chapleau, Ont., Can.,
  3,365................p19 41
Chaplygin, Sov. Un.,
  10,000...............E12 12
Chapman, Ala., 350.....D3 46
Chapman, Kans., 1,132...D7 61
Chapmanville, W. Va.,
  1,175.................D2 87
Chappaqua, N.Y., 6,500..*D7 75
Chappell, Nebr., 1,204...C3 71
Chāpra, India, 83,101
  (*98,401).............C7 20
Charalá, Col., 5,458....B2 32
Charcas, Mex., 10,491...C4 34
Chardon, Ohio, 3,991....A4 78
Chardzhou, Sov. Un.,
  96,000................F9 13
Charente, dept., Fr.,
  331,016..............*E4 5
Charente-Maritime, dept.,
  Fr., 483,622..........*D3 5
Charenton-le-Pont, Fr.,
  22,300...............g10 5
Charikar, Afg., 21,070...A4 20
Chariton, Iowa, 5,009...C4 60
Chariton, co., Mo., 11,084.B4 69
Charlack, Mo., 1,872...*C7 69
Charlemagne, Que., Can.,
  4,111.............D4, p19 42
Charleroi, Bel., 23,296
  (*375,000)............B6 5
Charleroi, Pa., 6,723...F2 81
Charleroix West, co., Que.,
  Can., 16,450..........B7 42
Charles, co., Md., 47,678..C3 53
Charlesbourg, Que., Can.,
  33,443...............n17 42
Charles City, Iowa, 9,268.A5 60
Charles City, co., Va.,
  6,158.................C5 85
Charles Mix, co., S. Dak.,
  9,994.................G7 77
Charleston, Ark., 1,497..B1 49
Charleston, Ill., 16,421..D5 58
Charleston, Miss., 2,821..A3 68
Charleston, Mo., 5,131...E8 69
Charleston, S.C., 66,945
  (*280,000)........F8, k12 82
Charleston, W. Va.,
  71,505 (*238,800)..C3, m12 87
Charleston, Utah, 196...C4 72
Charleston, co., S.C.,
  247,650...............F8 82
Charlestown, Ind., 5,933..H6 59

Charlestown, N.H., 1,285..E3 73
Charlestown, St. Kitts-
  Nevis-Anguilla, 1,180..H13 35
Charles Town, W. Va.,
  3,023.................B7 87
Charleville, Austl., 3,939..E8 25
Charlevoix, Mich., 3,519..C5 66
Charlevoix, co., Mich.,
  16,541................C5 66
Charlieu, Fr., 4,911....D6 5
Charlotte, Mich., 8,244..F6 66
Charlotte, N.C., 241,299
  (*416,800)............B2 76
Charlotte, Tex., 1,329...E3 84
Charlotte, co., N.B., Can.,
  23,285................D3 43
Charlotte, co., Fla.,
  27,559................F5 54
Charlotte, co., Va.,
  12,366................D4 85
Charlotte Amalie, Vir. Is.
  (U.S.), 12,880........G12 35
Charlotte Harbor, Fla.,
  1,000.................F4 54
Charlottesville
  (Independent City), Va.,
  38,880 (*53,700)......B4 85
Charlottetown, P.E.I., Can.,
  19,133................C6 43
Charlton City, Mass.,
  1,000.................B4 65
Charlton, co., Ga., 5,680..F4 55
Charmco, W. Va., 700...*D4 87
Charny, Que., Can.,
  5,175.............C6, o17 42
Charter Oak, Calif.,
  4,500................*E4 50
Charters Towers, Austl.,
  7,529.................D8 25
Chartres, Fr., 34,469
  (*59,000).............C4 5
Chascomús, Arg., 10,521..B5 28
Chase, B.C., Can., 990...D8 37
Chase, Kans., 800......D5 61
Chase, co., Kans., 3,408..D7 61
Chase, co., Nebr., 4,129..D4 71
Chase City, Va., 2,909...D4 85
Chase, mtn., Maine.....B4 64
Chaska, Minn.,
  4,352.............F5, n11 67
Chasong, Kor., 5,000....F3 18
Chasov Yar, Sov. Un.,
  24,000...............q20 12
Chataignier, La., 365....D3 63
Châteaubriant, Fr.,
  11,986................D3 5
Châteaudun, Fr., 14,450..C4 5
Chateaugay, N.Y., 976...f11 10
Château-Gontier, Fr.,
  7,888.................D3 5
Châteauguay, Que., Can.,
  15,797...........D4, q19 42
Châteauguay, co., Que.,
  Can., 46,968..........D4 42
Châteauguay Heights,
  Que., Can., 1,231.....q19 42
Château-Richer, Que.,
  Can., 3,111...........C6 42
Châteauroux, Fr., 49,138..D4 5
Château-Theirry, Fr.,
  11,049................C5 5
Châtellerault, Fr., 35,337..D4 5
Chatfield, Minn., 1,885...G6 67
Chatham, N.B., Can.,
  7,833.................B4 43
Chatham, Ont., Can.,
  35,317................E2 41
Chatham, Eng., 57,760
  (*235,000)...........*E7 4
Chatham, Ill., 2,788....D4 58
Chatham, Mass., 1,652...C8 65
Chatham, N.J., 9,566....B4 74
Chatham, N.Y., 2,239....C7 75
Chatham, Va., 1,801....D3 85
Chatham, co., Ga.,
  187,767...............E5 55
Chatham, co., N.C.,
  29,554................B3 76
Chatom, Ala., 1,059....D1 46
Chatsworth, Ga., 2,706...B2 55
Chatsworth, Ill., 1,255...C5 58
Chattahoochee, Fla.,
  7,944.................B2 54
Chattahoochee, co., Ga.,
  25,813................D2 55
Chattanooga, Tenn.,
  119,932 (*311,100).D8, h11 83
Chattaroy, W. Va., 1,145..D2 87
Chattooga, co., Ga.,
  20,541................B1 55
Chatwood, Pa., 3,621...*G10 81
Chau Doc, Viet., 5,000...*C3 19
Chauk, Bur., 24,466....D9 20
Chaumont, Fr., 25,779...C6 5
Chauncey, Ohio, 1,117...C3 78
Chauny, Fr., 13,920
  (*20,000).............C5 5

Chautauqua, co., Kans.,
  4,642.................E7 61
Chautauqua, co., N.Y.,
  147,305...............C1 75
Chauvin, La., 800......E5 63
Chaves, Port., 13,156...B2 8
Chaves, co., N. Mex.,
  43,335................C6 48
Chavinda, Mex., 7,920..m12 34
Chazelles [sur-Lyon], Fr.,
  5,076.................E6 5
Chazy, N.Y., 800......f11 75
Cheatham, co., Tenn.,
  13,199................A4 83
Cheb, Czech., 26,098....C2 7
Chebanse, Ill., 1,185....C6 58
Cheboksary, Sov. Un.,
  216,000..............C16 12
Cheboygan, Mich., 5,553..C6 66
Cheboygan, co., Mich.,
  16,573................C6 66
Chechaouene, Mor.,
  15,362................A3 22
Checotah, Okla., 3,074...B6 79
Cheddar, S.C., 200.....B3 82
Cheektowaga, N.Y.,
  93,200................C2 75
Chehalis, Wash., 5,727..C3 86
Cheju, Kor., 58,000
  (106,456 ▲)..........J3 18
Chekhov, Sov. Un.,
  38,000...............C10 18
Chekiang, prov., China,
  25,280,000...........F9 17
Chelan, Wash., 2,837...B5 86
Chelan, co., Wash., 41,355.B4 86
Chelan, mts., Wash......A5 86
Chelkar, Sov. Un., 19,000.E3 13
Chełm [Lubelski], Pol.,
  38,700................C7 7
Chełmno, Pol., 17,900...B5 7
Chelmsford, Ont., Can.,
  7,501................*A3 41
Chelmsford, Eng., 58,050..E7 4
Chelmsford, Mass.,
  4,000............A5, f10 65
Chełmża, Pol., 14,200...B5 7
Chelsea, Mass.,
  30,625...........B5, g11 65
Chelsea, Mich., 3,858...F6 66
Chelsea, Okla., 1,622...A6 79
Cheltenham, Eng., 75,500..E5 4
Cheltenham, Md., 150...C4 53
Cheltenham, Pa., 7,700..*F11 81
Chelyabinsk, Sov. Un.,
  875,000 (*1,050,000)..D9 13
Chemainus, B.C., Can.,
  2,129............E6, g12 37
Chemnitz, see Karl-Marx-
  Stadt, Ger. Dem. Rep.
Chemung, co., N.Y.,
  101,537...............C4 75
Chenango, co., N.Y.,
  46,368................C5 75
Chenango Bridge, N.Y.,
  2,500................*C5 75
Chenchiang, China,
  190,000...............E8 17
Cheney, Kans.,
  1,160............E6, g11 61
Cheney, Wash., 6,358.B8, h13 86
Cheneyville, La., 1,082...C3 63
Chengchou, China,
  900,000...............E7 17
Chengte (Jehol), China,
  120,000...............C8 17
Chengtu, China,
  1,450,000.............E5 17
Chenoa, Ill., 1,860.....C5 58
Chepén, Peru, 8,214....C2 31
Chepstow, Wales, 8,340..E5 4
Cher, dept., Fr.,
  304,601..............*D5 5
Cheraw, S.C., 5,627....B8 82
Cherbourg, Fr., 38,243
  (*79,000).............C3 5
Cherchen, see Chiehmo,
  China
Cheremkhovo, Sov. Un.,
  99,000...............D13 13
Cherepovets, Sov. Un.,
  188,000..............B11 12
Cherkassy, Sov. Un.,
  158,000...............G9 12
Chernigov, Sov. Un.,
  159,000...............F8 12
Chernobay, Sov. Un.,
  25,000................G9 12
Chernobyl, Sov. Un.,
  10,000................F8 12
Chernovtsy, Sov. Un.,
  187,000...............G5 12
Chernyakhovsk
  (Insterburg),
  Sov. Un., 33,000......D3 12
Cherokee, Ala., 1,484...A2 46
Cherokee, Iowa, 7,272...B2 60
Cherokee, Kans., 790...E9 61

Cherokee, Okla., 2,119....A3 79
Cherokee, co., Ala.,
15,606.................A4 46
Cherokee, co., Ga., 31,059..B2 55
Cherokee, co., Iowa,
17,269.................B2 60
Cherokee, co., Kans.,
21,549.................E9 61
Cherokee, co., N.C.,
16,330.................f8 76
Cherokee, co., Okla.,
23,174.................B6 79
Cherokee, co., S.C.,
36,791.................A4 82
Cherokee, co., Tex.,
32,008.................D5 84
Cherokee Forest, S.C.,
2,000.................*B3 82
Cherokee Ranch, Pa.,
1,200.................*F9 81
Cherry, co., Nebr., 6,846..B4 71
Cherry Grove, Ohio,
2,500.................*C1 78
Cherry Hill, N.J., 64,395..D2 74
Cherry Hills Village,
Colo., 4,605..........*B6 51
Cherryvale, Kans., 2,609..E8 61
Cherry Valley, Ill., 952..A5 58
Cherry Valley, Mass.,
2,300.................B4 65
Cherryville, N.C., 5,258..B1 76
Chesaning, Mich., 2,876..E6 66
Chesapeake, Ohio, 1,364..D3 78
Chesapeake (Independent
City), Va., 89,580..D6, k15 85
Chesapeake, W. Va.,
2,428.................C3 87
Chesapeake City, Md.,
1,031.................A6 53
Chesham, Eng., 20,480...k11 4
Cheshire, Conn., 10,300..D5 52
Cheshire, Mass., 1,021...A1 65
Cheshire, co., Eng.,
1,551,350.............*D5 4
Cheshire, co., N.H.,
52,364.................F3 73
Cheshunt, Eng., 44,930...k12 4
Chesley, Ont., Can.,
1,697.................C3 41
Chesnee, S.C., 1,069.....A4 82
Chester, Calif., 1,553...B3 50
Chester, N.S., Can., 990..E5 43
Chester, Conn., 1,569....D7 52
Chester, Eng., 62,700....C3 4
Chester, Ill., 5,310.....F4 58
Chester, Md., 400........C5 53
Chester, Mass., 750......B2 65
Chester, Mont., 936......B6 70
Chester, N.J., 1,299.....B3 74
Chester, N.S., Can., 990..E5 43
Chester, N.Y.,
1,627.............D6, m14 75
Chester, Pa., 56,331..G11, p20 81
Chester, S.C., 7,045.....B5 82
Chester, Vt., 470........E3 73
Chester, Va., 5,556...C5, n18 85
Chester, W. Va.,
3,614.................A4, e8 87
Chester, co., Pa.,
277,746...............G10 81
Chester, co., S.C., 29,811..B5 82
Chester, co., Tenn., 9,927..B3 83
Chesterfield, Eng., 69,960
(*128,000)...........D6 4
Chesterfield, Ind., 3,001..D6 59
Chesterfield, S.C., 1,667..B7 82
Chesterfield, co., S.C.,
33,667.................B7 82
Chesterfield, co., Va.,
77,046.................C5 85
Chesterhill, Ohio, 361...C4 78
Chesterton, Ind., 6,177..A3 59
Chestertown, Md., 3,476..B5 53
Chesterville, Ont., Can.,
1,248.................B9 41
Cheswick, Pa., 2,563....h14 81
Chetek, Wis., 1,630.....C2 88
Chii-san, mtn., Korea....I3 18
Cheticamp, N.S., Can.,
1,223.................C8 43
Chetopa, Kans., 1,596....E8 61
Chetumal, see Ciudad
Chetumal, Mex..
Chetwynd, B.C., Can.,
1,020.................B7 37
Cheverly, Md., 6,808....*C4 53
Cheviot, Ohio, 11,135..C1, o12 78
Chevy Chase, Md.,
2,265.............C3, f8 53
Chevy Chase Heights, Pa.,
1,185.................*E3 81
Chevy Chase Section
Four, Md., 2,266.....*C3 53
Chevy Chase View, Md.,
1,200.................*C3 53
Chewelah, Wash., 1,365..A8 86
Chews (Chews Landing),
N.J., 600.............*C4 74
Cheyenne, Okla., 892.....B2 79

Cheyenne, Wyo., 40,914
(*51,500).............E8 89
Cheyenne, co., Colo., 2,396.C8 51
Cheyenne, co., Kans.,
4,256.................C2 61
Cheyenne, co., Nebr.,
10,778.................C2 71
Cheyenne Wells, Colo.,
982...................C8 51
Chiahsing, China, 132,000..E9 17
Chiai, Taiwan, 170,000
(208,500 ▲).........*G9 17
Chiamussu, China,232,000.C5 18
Chian, China, 52,800.....F3 18
Chiang Khong, Thai.,
3,320.................A2 19
Chiangling, China, 15,000..E7 17
Chiang Mai, Thai., 83,729.B1 19
Chiangmen, China,
110,000...............G7 17
Chiang Rai, Thai., 11,659.B1 19
Chiangtzu (Gyangtse),
China, 20,000.........C8 20
Chiaotso, China, 250,000..*D7 17
Chiapa de Corzo, Mex.,
8,571.................D6 34
Chiapas, state, Mex.,
1,381,500.............D6 34
Chiari, It., 9,000......B2 9
Chiautla de Tapia, Mex.,
5,847.................n14 34
Chiavari, It., 28,000....B2 9
Chiba, Jap., 482,133..I10, n19 18
Chiba, pref., Jap.,
3,369,357.............*I10 18
Chicago, Ill., 3,369,357
(*7,582,700).......B6, k9 58
Chicago Heights, Ill.,
40,900..............B6, k9 58
Chicago Ridge, Ill., 9,187.*B6 58
Chichester, Eng., 20,830..E6 4
Chichibu, Jap., 60,867...m18 18
Chichihaerh (Tsitsihar),
China, 825,000........B9 17
Chickamauga, Ga., 1,842..B1 55
Chickasaw, Ala., 8,447...E1 46
Chickasaw, co., Iowa,
14,969.................A5 60
Chickasaw, co., Miss.,
16,805.................B5 68
Chickasha, Okla., 14,194..B4 79
Chiclana, Sp., 21,524....D2 8
Chiclayo, Peru, 148,932..C2 31
Chico, Calif., 19,580....C3 50
Chico, Tex., 723........C4 84
Chico, Wash., 700.......B3 86
Chicontepec, Mex., 2,821.m14 34
Chicopee, Ga., 900......B3 55
Chicopee, Mass., 66,676..B2 65
Chicora, Pa., 1,166.....E2 81
Chicot, co., Ark., 18,164..D4 49
Chicoutimi, Que., Can.,
33,893 (*133,703)..A6, k12 42
Chicoutimi-Nord, Que.,
Can., 14,086..........A6 42
Chicoutimi, co., Que.,
Can., 161,773.........A6 42
Chico Vecino, Calif.,
4,787.................*C3 50
Chiefland, Fla., 1,965...C4 54
Chiehmo (Cherchen),
China.................A8 20
Chiehyang, China, 55,000.G8 17
Chieri, It., 22,800.....B1 9
Chieti, It., 45,700.....C5 9
Chigasaki, Jap., 129,621..*I9 18
Chigirin, Sov. Un., 10,000.G9 12
Chignahuapan, Mex.,
3,805.................n14 34
Chigwell, Eng., 54,620...k13 4
Chihfeng, China, 49,000..C8 17
Chihsi, China, 253,000...B11 17
Chihuahua, Mex., 257,027.B3 34
Chihuahua, state, Mex.,
1,462,400.............B3 34
Chilapa de Alvarez, Mex.,
9,204.............D5, o14 34
Childersburg, Ala., 4,831.B3 46
Chilca, Peru, 1,341.....D2 31
Childress, Tex., 5,408...B2 84
Childress, co., Tex., 6,605.B2 84
Chile, country, S.A.,
9,315,000.............E2 29
Chilecito, Arg., 9,809...E2 29
Chilhowie, Va., 1,317...f10 85
Chilin (Kirin), China,
583,000...............E3 18
Chillán, Chile, 65,121...B2 28
Chillicothe, Ill., 6,052..C4 58
Chillicothe, Mo., 9,519..B4 69
Chillicothe, Ohio, 24,842.C3 78
Chillicothe, Tex., 1,116..B3 84
Chilliwack, B.C., Can.,
9,135 (*33,322)....E7, f14 37
Chillum, Md., 13,800....*C3 53

Chiloé, prov., Chile,
109,400...............C2 28
Chiloquin, Oreg., 826....E5 80
Chilpancingo [de los
Bravos], Mex.,
36,193...............D5, o14 34
Chilton, Tex., 400......D4 84
Chilton, Wis., 3,030..D5, h10 88
Chilton, co., Ala., 25,180..C3 46
Chilung, Taiwan,
240,000 (306,000 ▲)....F9 17
Chimalhuacán, Mex.,
5,930.................h10 34
Chimayo, N. Mex., 600...B6 48
Chimbay, Sov. Un., 19,000.E8 13
Chimborazo, prov., Ec.,
342,300...............B2 31
Chimborazo, vol., Ec.....B2 31
Chimbote, Peru, 159,045..C2 31
Chimkent, Sov. Un.,
247,000...............E19 13
China (excl. Taiwan),
country, Asia,
821,010,000...........E4 17
China Grove, N.C., 1,788.B2 76
Chinan, see Tsinan, China
Chinandega, Nic., 34,500.E7 34
Chinati, peak, Tex.......p12 84
Chincha Alta, Peru, 20,817.D2 31
Chincheros, Peru, 1,300..D3 31
Chinchilla, Austl., 3,011..E9 25
Chinchilla, Pa., 1,100...*D10 81
Chinchou, China, 400,000.C9 17
Chincoteague, Va., 1,867..C7 85
Chindo, China, 6,900
(12,425 ▲)...........I3 18
Chingchiang (Huaiyin),
China, 77,000.........E8 17
Chingford, Eng., 46,200..k13 4
Chingola, Zam., 55,800...*C5 24
Chingtechen, China,
260,000...............F8 17
Chinhae, Kor., 91,947...I4 18
Chinhuangtao, China,
210,000...............D8 17
Chining, China, 100,000..D8 17
Chiniot, Pak., 47,099...B5 20
Chinju, Kor., 95,000
(121,622 ▲).........I4 18
Chinnampo (Nampo),
Kor., 82,162..........G2 18
Chino, Calif., 20,411..F5, m13 50
Chinook, Mont., 1,813...B7 70
Chinquapin, N.C., 270...C5 76
Chinú, Col., 7,552......B3 32
Chioggia, It., 25,700...B4 9
Chipley, Fla., 3,347....u16 54
Chipman, N.B., Can.,
1,977.................C4 43
Chippewa, co., Mich.,
32,412.................B6 66
Chippewa, co., Minn.,
15,109.................E3 67
Chippewa, co., Wis.,
47,717.................C2 88
Chippewa Falls, Wis.,
12,351.................D2 88
Chiquimula, Guat., 16,181.E7 34
Chiquinquira, Col., 16,926.B3 32
Chiriqui Grande, Pan., 98..B1 32
Chirpan, Bul., 17,863....D7 10
Chisago, co., Minn.,
17,492.................E6 67
Chisholm, Maine, 1,530..D2 64
Chisholm, Minn., 5,913...C6 67
Chișineu-Criș, Rom.,
6,124.................B5 10
Chisos, mts., Tex........p13 84
Chita, Sov. Un., 241,000.D14 13
Chitai (Kuchêng), China,
25,000.................C2 17
Chitradurga, India, 50,254.F6 20
Chitré, Pan., 12,379....B1 32
Chittagong, Bngl., 180,000
(*364,205)...........D9 20
Chittenango, N.Y., 3,605.*B5 75
Chittenden, co., Vt.,
99,131.................C1 73
Chittoor, India, 63,035..F6 20
Chiuchiang, China, 64,600.F8 17
Chiusi, It., 8,498......C3 9
Chivasso, It., 8,800....B1 9
Chivay, Peru, 2,027.....E3 31
Chivilcoy, Arg.,
35,000.............A4, g6 28
Chochiwŏn, Kor., 20,000
(27,996 ▲)..........H3 18
Chocó, dept., Col.,
199,700...............C2 32
Chocontá, Col., 3,379...B3 32
Choctaw, co., Ala.,
16,589.................C1 46
Choctaw, co., Miss., 8,440.B4 68
Choctaw, co., Okla.,
15,141.................C6 79
Chodziez, Pol., 14,100...B4 7
Choisy-le-Roi, Fr., 41,440.g10 5

Choix, Mex., 2,503......B3 34
Chojna, Pol., 4,038.....B3 7
Chojnice, Pol., 23,500..B4 7
Chojnów, Pol., 11,000...C3 7
Chokai-zan, mtn., Jap....G10 18
Cholet, Fr., 41,766.....D3 5
Cholula [de Rivadabia],
Mex., 15,399.........n14 34
Choluteca, Hond., 11,483.E7 34
Chomutov, Czech., 40,078.C2 7
Chŏnan, Kor., 55,000
(78,316 ▲)..........H3 18
Chon Buri, Thai., 39,376..C2 19
Chone, Ec., 12,832......B1 31
Chŏngjin, Kor., 184,301..F4 18
Chŏngju, Kor., 143,944..H3 18
Chonju, Kor., 262,816...I3 18
Chorrillos, Peru, 31,703.D2 31
Chŏrwŏn, Kor., 1,500
(6,805 ▲)...........G3 18
Chorzów, Pol., 151,300...g9 7
Chosen, Fla., 1,858.....F6 54
Chosen, see Korea, Asia
Choshi, Jap., 90,415..I10, n19 18
Chosica, Peru, 25,248...D2 31
Chota, Peru, 2,705......C2 31
Choteau, Mont., 1,586...C4 70
Chouchiakou, China,
85,500...............*E7 17
Choum, Maur.............D2 22
Chouteau, Okla., 1,046..A6 79
Chouteau, co., Mont.,
6,473.................C6 70
Chowan, co., N.C., 10,764.A6 76
Chowchilla, Calif., 4,349.D3 50
Chrisman, Ill., 1,285...D6 58
Christchurch, N.Z.,
166,800 (*289,000)...O14 26
Christian, co., Ill., 35,948.D4 58
Christian, co., Ky., 56,224.D2 62
Christian, co., Mo., 15,124.E4 69
Christiana, Pa., 1,132...C9 81
Christiansburg, Va., 7,857.C2 85
Christiansted, Vir. Is.
(U.S.), 3,020.........H12 35
Christmas Island, Austl.
dep., Oceania, 2,300...G4 2
Christopher, Ill., 2,910..F4 58
Chrudim, Czech., 17,214..D3 7
Chrzanów, Pol., 28,500...g10 7
Chüanchou (Chinchiang),
China, 110,000........G8 17
Chubbuck, Idaho, 2,924..G6 57
Chubut, prov., Arg.,
142,412...............C3 28
Chuchou, China, 190,000..*F7 17
Chugiak, Alsk.,
1,500.............C10, g17 47
Chuguyev, Sov. Un.,
25,000................G11 12
Chuho, China, 5,000.....D3 18
Chuhsien, China, 32,000..F8 17
Chuius, mtn., B.C., Can..B5 37
Chula Vista, Calif.,
67,901.............F5, o15 50
Chulucanas, Peru, 19,714..B1 31
Chumikan, Sov. Un.,
1,100.................D16 13
Chunchŏn, Kor., 122,672.H3 18
Chungju, Kor., 61,000
(87,727 ▲)..........H3 18
Chungking (Chungching),
China, 2,600,000......F6 17
Chungpa, China.........C7 20
Chungshan, China,
93,000...............*G7 17
Chupaca, Peru, 4,482....D2 31
Chuquibamba, Peru,
2,480.................E3 31
Chuquisaca, dept., Bol.,
309,600...............D3 29
Chur, Switz., 31,500....E4 6
Church, mtn., B.C., Can..f14 37
Church Hill, Tenn.,
2,822................C11 83
Churchill, Man., Can.,
973...................f9 40
Churchill, Pa., 4,690...*E1 81
Churchill, co., Nev.,
10,513.................B2 72
Churchill, mtn., B.C., Can.E6 37
Churchill, riv., Man.,
Sask., Can............B2 39
Church Point, La., 3,865.D3 63
Churchs Ferry, N. Dak.,
139...................B6 77
Churchville, Pa., 2,900..*F11 81
Churubusco, Ind., 1,528..B7 59
Churumuco, Mex.,
2,030.................n13 34
Chusovoy, Sov. Un.,
58,000...............*D8 13
Cicero, Ill., 67,058....B6, k9 58
Cicero, Ind., 1,378.....D5 59
Ciechanów, Pol., 23,200..B6 7
Ciego de Avila, Cuba,
60,900 (70,200 ▲)...D4 35

Ciénaga, Col., 57,200 (135,600 ▲)....A3 32
Ciénaga de Oro, Col., 8,047....B2 32
Cienfuegos, Cuba, 85,200 (90,700 ▲)....C3 35
Cieszyn, Pol., 25,200....D5 7
Cihuatlán, Mex., 9,451....n11 34
Cilacap, Indon., 82,043....G3 19
Cimarron, Kans., 1,373....E3 61
Cimarron, N. Mex., 927....A6 48
Cimarron, co., Okla., 4,145....e8 79
Cimarron, riv., U.S....C7 45
Cîmpina, Rom., 20,700....C7 10
Cîmpulung, Rom., 21,500....C7 10
Cîmpulung Moldovenesc, Rom....B7 10
Cincinnati, Ohio, 451,455 (*1,421,600)....C1, o12 78
Cinnaminson, N.J., 17,400....D3 74
Cinnaminson Township, N.J., 16,962....*C2 74
Cintalapa [de Figueroa], Mex., 12,036....D6 34
Cinto, mtn., Fr....C2 9
Circle, Mont., 964....C11 70
Circle Pines, Minn., 3,902....*E5 67
Circleville, Ohio, 11,687....C3 78
Cirencester, Eng., 13,420....E6 4
Cisco, Tex., 4,160....C3 84
Cisneros, Col., 7,554....B2 32
Cissna Park, Ill., 773....C6 58
Cisterna di Latina, It., 8,000....h9 9
Citac, mtn., Peru....D2 31
Citlaltépet (Pico de Orizaba), vol., Mex....n15 34
Citronelle, Ala., 1,935....D1 46
Citrus, co., Fla., 19,196....D4 54
Citrus Heights, Calif., 24,500....*C3 50
Cittadella, It., 6,300....B3 9
Città di Castello, It., 15,100....C4 9
City View, S.C., 2,497....B3 82
Ciudad Acuña, Mex., 30,276....B4 34
Ciudad Allende, Mex., 11,076....B4 34
Ciudad Altamirano, Mex., 8,694....n13 34
Ciudad Bolívar, Ven., 103,728....B5 32
Ciudad Camargo, Mex., 24,030....B3 34
Ciudad Chetumal, Mex., 23,685....D7 34
Ciudad del Carmen, Mex., 34,656....D6 34
Ciudad del Maíz, Mex., 5,241....C5 34
Ciudad de Naucalpan de Juárez, Mex., 9,425....h9 34
Ciudad de Valles, Mex., 47,587....C5, m14 34
Ciudad de Villaldama, Mex., 2,350....B4 34
Ciudad Dr. Hernández Alvarez, Mex., 8,553....*m13 34
Ciudad Guzmán, Mex., 48,166....D4, n12 34
Ciudad Hidalgo, Mex., 24,692....n13 34
Ciudad Ixtepec, Mex., 14,025....D5 34
Ciudad Jiménez, Mex., 18,095....B4 34
Ciudad Juárez, Mex., 407,370....A3 34
Ciudad Lerdo, Mex., 19,803....B4 34
Ciudad Madero, Mex., 90,830....C5 34
Ciudad Mante, Mex., 51,247....C5 34
Ciudad Melchor Múzquiz, Mex., 18,868....B4 34
Ciudad Mendoza, Mex., 18,696....n15 34
Ciudad Obregón, Mex., 114,407....B3 34
Ciudad Ojeda, Ven., 83,083....A3 32
Ciudad Real, Sp., 41,036....C4 8
Ciudad Real, prov., Sp., 540,200....*C4 8
Ciudad Serdán, Mex., 9,581....n15 34
Ciudad Victoria, Mex., 83,897....C5 34
Cividale de Friuli, It., 7,074....A4 9
Civitanova Marche, It., 23,700....C4 9
Civitavecchia, It., 42,600....C3 9
Cizre, Tur., 11,137....D14 14
Clackamas, Oreg., 1,500....h12 80
Clackamas, co., Oreg., 166,088....B4 80
Clackmannan, co., Scot., 45,566....*B5 4
Claflin, Kans., 887....D5 61
Claiborne, co., Miss., 10,086....D3 68
Claiborne, co., Tenn., 19,420....C10 83
Claiborne, par., La., 17,024....B2 63
Clairfield, Tenn., 150....C10 83
Clairton, Pa., 15,051....F2 81
Clallam, co., Wash., 34,770....A1 86
Clamart, Fr., 47,991....g10 5
Clamecy, Fr., 5,520....D5 5
Clanton, Ala., 5,868....C3 46
Clara City, Minn., 1,491....F3 67
Clare, Austl., 2,105....F6 25
Clare, Mich., 2,639....E6 66
Clare, co., Ire., 73,597....D2 4
Clare, co., Mich., 16,695....E6 66
Claremont, Calif., 23,998....m13 50
Claremont, N.H., 14,221....E3 73
Claremont, mtn., Cal....C3 50
Claremore, Okla., 9,084....A6 79
Clarence, Iowa, 915....C6 60
Clarence, Mo., 1,050....B5 69
Clarence, N.Y., 2,014 (18,168 ▲)....*C2 75
Clarendon, Ark., 2,563....C4 49
Clarendon, Tex., 1,974....B2 84
Clarendon, co., S.C., 25,604....D7 82
Clarendon Hills, Ill., 6,750....k9 58
Clarenville, Newf., Can., 2,193....D4 44
Claresholm, Alta., Can., 2,935....D4 38
Claridge, Pa., 600....F2 81
Clarinda, Iowa, 5,420....D2 60
Clarion, Iowa, 2,972....B4 60
Clarion, Pa., 6,095....D3 81
Clarion, co., Pa., 38,414....D2 81
Clark, N.J., 18,829....B4 74
Clark, S. Dak., 1,356....F8 77
Clark, co., Ark., 21,537....C2 49
Clark, co., Idaho, 741....E6 57
Clark, co., Ill., 16,216....D6 58
Clark, co., Ind., 75,876....H6 59
Clark, co., Kans., 2,896....E4 61
Clark, co., Ky., 24,090....C5 62
Clark, co., Mo., 8,260....A6 69
Clark, co., Nev., 273,288....C4 72
Clark, co., Ohio, 157,115....C2 78
Clark, co., S. Dak., 5,515....F8 77
Clark, co., Wash., 128,454....D3 86
Clark, co., Wis., 30,361....D3 88
Clark, mtn., Mo....D7 69
Clarkdale, Ariz., 892....B2 48
Clarke, co., Ala., 26,724....D2 46
Clarke, co., Ga., 65,177....C3 55
Clarke, co., Iowa, 7,581....D4 60
Clarke, co., Miss., 15,049....C5 68
Clarke, co., Va., 8,102....A4 85
Clarkes Harbour, N.S., Can., 945....F4 43
Clarkfield, Minn., 1,084....F3 67
Clark Mills, N.Y., 1,206....*B5 75
Clarks, La., 889....B3 63
Clarksburg, W. Va., 24,864 (*51,500)....B4, k10 87
Clarksdale, Miss., 21,673....A3 68
Clarks Green, Pa., 1,674....*D10 75
Clarks Harbour, N.S., Can., 945....F4 43
Clarks Summit, Pa., 5,376....m18 81
Clarkston, Ga., 3,127....h8 55
Clarkston, Wash., 6,312....C8 86
Clarksville, Ark., 4,616....B2 49
Clarksville, Ind., 13,806....H6 59
Clarksville, Iowa, 1,360....B5 60
Clarksville, Tenn., 31,719 (*64,500)....A4 83
Clarksville, Tex., 3,346....C5 84
Clarksville, Va., 1,641....D4 85
Clarkton, Mo., 1,177....E8 69
Clatskanie, Oreg., 1,286....A3 80
Clatsop, co., Oreg., 28,473....A3 80
Claude, Tex., 992....B2 84
Clausthal-Zellerfeld, Ger., Fed. Rep. of, 16,234....C5 6
Clawson, Mich., 17,617....o15 66
Claxton, Ga., 2,669....D5 55
Clay, Ky., 1,426....C2 62
Clay, co., Ala., 12,636....B4 46
Clay, co., Ark., 18,771....A5 49
Clay, co., Fla., 32,059....B5 54
Clay, co., Ga., 3,636....E2 55
Clay, co., Ill., 14,735....E5 58
Clay, co., Ind., 23,933....F3 59
Clay, co., Iowa, 18,464....A2 60
Clay, co., Kans., 9,890....C6 61
Clay, co., Ky., 18,481....C6 62
Clay, co., Minn., 46,585....D2 67
Clay, co., Miss., 18,840....B5 68
Clay, co., Mo., 123,644....B3 69
Clay, co., Nebr., 8,266....D7 71
Clay, co., N.C., 5,180....f9 76
Clay, co., S. Dak., 12,923....H9 77
Clay, co., Tenn., 6,624....C8 83
Clay, co., Tex., 8,079....C3 84
Clay, co., W. Va., 9,330....C3 87
Clay Center, Kans., 4,963....C6 61
Clay City, Ill., 1,049....E5 58
Clay City, Ind., 900....F3 59
Claycomo, Mo., 1,841....*B3 69
Claymont, Del., 15,000....A7 53
Claypool, Ariz., 2,000....C3, D3 48
Claysburg, Pa., 1,439....F5 81
Claysville, Pa., 951....F1 81
Clayton, Ala., 1,626....D4 46
Clayton, Del., 1,015....B6 53
Clayton, Ga., 1,569....B3 55
Clayton, Ill., 727....C3 58
Clayton, La., 1,103....C4 63
Clayton, Mo., 16,222....C7, f13 69
Clayton, N.J., 5,193....D2 74
Clayton, N. Mex., 2,931....A7 48
Clayton, N.Y., 1,970....A4, f8 75
Clayton, N.C., 3,103....B4 76
Clayton, Okla., 718....C6 79
Clayton, co., Ga., 98,043....C2 55
Clayton, co., Iowa, 20,606....B6 60
Clear Brook, B.C., Can., 3,653....f13 37
Clear Creek, co., Colo., 4,819....B5 51
Clearfield, Pa., 8,176....D5 81
Clearfield, Utah, 13,316....A5 72
Clearfield, co., Pa., 74,619....D4 81
Clear Lake, Iowa, 6,430....A4 60
Clear Lake, S. Dak., 1,157....F9 77
Clearlake Highlands, Calif., 800....C2 50
Clear Lake Shores, Tex., 721....r14 84
Clearwater, Fla., 52,074....E4, p10 54
Clearwater, Kans., 1,435....E6 61
Clearwater, S. C., 4,000....E4 82
Clearwater, co., Idaho, 10,871....C3 57
Clearwater, co., Minn., 8,013....C3 67
Clearwater, mts., Idaho....C2 57
Cleburne, Tex., 16,015....C4, n9 84
Cleburne, co., Ala., 10,996....B4 46
Cleburne, co., Ark., 10,349....B3 49
Cle Elum, Wash., 1,725....B5 86
Clementon, N.J., 4,492....D3 74
Clemmons, N.C., 1,500....A2 76
Clemson, S.C., 5,578....B2 82
Clemson College, S.C., 8,400....*B2 82
Clendenin, W. Va., 1,438....C3, m13 87
Cleona, Pa., 2,040....F9 81
Clermont, Austl., 1,674....D8 25
Clermont, Que., Can., 3,386....B7 42
Clermont, Fla., 3,661....D5 54
Clermont, co., Ohio, 95,887....C1 78
Clermont-Ferrand, Fr., 148,896 (*205,000)....E5 5
Clermont-l'Hérault, Fr., 5,538....F5 5
Cleveland, Miss., 13,327....B3 68
Cleveland, Ohio, 750,879 (*2,361,100)....A4, h9 78
Cleveland, Okla., 2,573....A5 79
Cleveland, Tenn., 20,651....D9 83
Cleveland, Tex., 5,627....D5 84
Cleveland, co., Ark., 6,605....D3 49
Cleveland, co., N.C., 72,556....B1 76
Cleveland, co., Okla., 81,839....B4 79
Cleveland, mtn., Mont....B3 70
Cleveland Heights, Ohio, 60,767....A4, g9 78
Cleves, Ohio, 2,044....o12 78
Clewiston, Fla., 3,896....F6 54
Clichy [-la-Garenne], Fr., 52,477....C5, g10 5
Cliffside, N.C., 500....B1, f11 76
Cliffside Park, N.J., 18,891....h9 74
Cliffwood, N.J., 3,500....*C4 74
Cliffwood Beach, N.J., 6,200....*C4 74
Clifton, Ariz., 5,087....C4 48
Clifton, Ill., 1,339....C6 58
Clifton, N.J., 82,437....B4, h8 74
Clifton, S.C., 8,138....B4 82
Clifton, Tex., 2,578....D4 84
Clifton Forge (Independent City), Va., 5,501....C3 85
Clifton Heights, Pa., 8,348....p20 81
Clifton Springs, N.Y., 2,058....C3 75
Climax, Colo., 150....B4 51
Clinch, co., Ga., 6,405....F4 55
Clinch, mtn., Va....f9 85
Clinchco, Va., 975....e9 85
Clinchfield, N.C., 400....*F10 76
Clingmans Dome, mtn., N. Car....f9 76
Clint, Tex., 900....o11 84
Clinton, Ark., 1,029....B3 49
Clinton, B.C., Can., 905....D7 37
Clinton, Ont., Can., 3,154....D3 41
Clinton, Conn., 10,267....D6 52
Clinton, Ill., 7,570....C5 58
Clinton, Ind., 5,340....E3 59
Clinton, Iowa, 34,719....C7 60
Clinton, Ky., 1,618....f9 62
Clinton, La., 1,884....D4 63
Clinton, Maine, 1,124 (1,971 ▲)....D3 64
Clinton, Md., 4,700....C4 53
Clinton, Mass., 13,383....B4 65
Clinton, Mich., 1,677....F7 66
Clinton, Miss., 7,289....C3 68
Clinton, Mo., 7,504....C4 69
Clinton, N.J., 1,742....B3 74
Clinton, N.Y., 2,271....B5 75
Clinton, N.C., 7,157....C4 76
Clinton, Ohio, 1,335....*A4 78
Clinton, Okla., 8,513....B3 79
Clinton, S.C., 8,138....C4 82
Clinton, Tenn., 4,794....C9, m13 83
Clinton, Utah, 1,768....B3 72
Clinton, Wash., 800....B3 86
Clinton, Wis., 1,333....F5 88
Clinton, co., Ill., 28,315....E4 58
Clinton, co., Ind., 30,547....D4 59
Clinton, co., Iowa, 56,749....C7 60
Clinton, co., Ky., 8,174....D4 62
Clinton, co., Mich., 48,492....F6 66
Clinton, co., Mo., 12,462....B3 69
Clinton, co., N.Y., 72,934....f11 75
Clinton, co., Ohio, 31,464....C2 78
Clinton, co., Pa., 37,721....D6 81
Clintonville, Wis., 4,600....D5 88
Clintwood, Va., 1,320....e9 85
Clio, Ala., 1,065....D4 46
Clio, Mich., 2,357....E7 66
Clio, S.C., 936....B8 82
Cloncurry, Austl., 2,190....D7 25
Clonmel, Ire., 11,622....D3 4
Cloquet, Minn., 8,699....D6 67
Closter, N.J., 8,604....B5, h9 74
Clothier, W. Va., 500....n12 87
Cloud, co., Kans., 13,466....C6 61
Cloud, peak, Wyo....A5 89
Clover, S.C., 3,506....A5 82
Cloverdale, Calif., 3,251....C2 50
Cloverdale, B.C., Can., 650....f13 37
Cloverleaf, Tex., 4,000....*E5 84
Cloverport, Ky., 1,388....C3 62
Clovis, Calif., 13,856....D4 50
Clovis, N. Mex., 28,495....B7 48
Cluj, Rom., 185,800 (222,700 ▲)....B6 10
Clute, Tex., 6,023....r14 84
Clyde, Kans., 946....C6 61
Clyde, N.Y., 2,828....B4 75
Clyde, Ohio, 5,503....A3 78
Clyde, Tex., 1,635....C3 84
Clydebank, Scot., 48,170....C4 4
Clyde Hill, Wash., 2,987....*B3 86
Clymer, Pa., 2,054....E3 81
Coachella, Calif., 8,353....F5 50
Coahoma, Tex., 1,158....C2 84
Coahoma, co., Miss., 40,447....A3 68
Coahuila, state, Mex., 1,005,900....B4 34
Coal, co., Okla., 5,525....C5 79
Coal City, Ill., 3,040....B5 58
Coalcomán [de Matamoros], Mex., 4,875....D4, n12 34
Coaldale, Alta., Can., 2,798....E4 38
Coaldale, Pa., 3,023....E10 81
Coal Fork, W. Va., 900....C3, m12 87
Coalgate, Okla., 1,859....C5 79

Coalgood, Ky., 400......D6 62
Coal Grove, Ohio, 2,759..D3 78
Coal Hill, Ark., 733......B2 49
Coalinga, Calif., 6,161...D3 50
Coalport, Pa., 796.......E4 81
Coaltown, Pa., 900......*E1 81
Coalville, Utah, 864...A6, C2 72
Coalwood, W. Va., 950...*D3 87
Coast, mts., B.C., Can.......B3, m16 37
Coast, ranges, Cal.......B2 50
Coamo, P.R., 12,077 (26,468▲)......*G11 35
Coatbridge, Scot., 51,985..C5 4
Coatepec, Mex., 21,542..n15 34
Coatepeque, Guat., 13,657......*E6 34
Coatesville, Pa., 12,331..G10 81
Coaticook, Que., Can., 6,569......D6 42
Coats, N.C., 1,051......B4 76
Coatzacoalcos (Puerto México), Mex., 69,753......D6 34
Cobalt, Ont., Can., 2,197..p19 41
Cobán, Guat., 11,880......D6 34
Cobb, co., Ga., 196,793...C2 55
Cobden, Ont., Can., 942..B8 41
Cobden, Ill., 1,114......F4 58
Cobequid, mts., N.S., Can......D5 43
Cobh, Ire., 6,076......E2 4
Cobija, Bol., 1,726......E4 27
Cobleskill, N.Y., 4,368...C6 75
Cobourg, Ont., Can., 11,282 (*18,316)......D6 41
Coburg, Ger., Fed. Rep. of, 47,070......C5 6
Coburn, mtn., Maine......C2 64
Cocentaina, Sp., 8,108....C5 8
Cochabamba, Bol., 135,300......C2 29
Cochabamba, dept., Bol., 555,400......C2 29
Cochin, India, 439,066....G6 20
Cochin China, reg., Viet., 6,500,000......*D3 19
Cochise, co., Ariz., 55,039.D4 48
Cochituate, Mass., 5,000..g10 65
Cochran, Ga., 5,161......D3 55
Cochran, co., Tex., 5,326..C1 84
Cochrane, Alta., Can., 857.D3 38
Cochrane, Ont., Can., 4,965......o19 41
Cochrane, dist., Ont., Can., 4,521......e9 41
Cochranton, Pa., 1,229...C1 81
Cocke, co., Tenn., 25,283......D10 83
Cockeysville, Md., 4,500..B4 53
Cockrell Hill, Tex., 3,515......n10 84
Cocoa, Fla., 16,110 (*93,200)......D6 54
Cocoa Beach, Fla., 9,952..D6 54
Cocoa West, Fla., 5,779..*D6 54
Coconino, co., Ariz., 48,326......B2 48
Cocula, Mex., 9,880......C4, m12 34
Codington, co., S. Dak., 19,140......F8 77
Codogno, It., 10,500......B2 9
Cody, Wyo., 5,161......B3 89
Coeburn, Va., 2,362......f9 85
Coesfeld, Ger., Fed. Rep. of, 26,481......C3 6
Coeur d'Alene, Idaho, 16,228......B2 57
Coeur d'Alene, mts., Idaho......B2 57
Coffee, co., Ala., 34,872..D3 46
Coffee, co., Ga., 22,828...E4 55
Coffee, co., Tenn., 32,572..B5 83
Coffey, co., Kans., 7,397..D8 61
Coffeyville, Kans., 15,116..E8 61
Coffs Harbour, Austl., 10,107......E9 26
Cognac, Fr., 22,062......E3 5
Cohasset, Mass., 3,000......B6, h12 65
Cohocton, N.Y., 897......C3 75
Cohoes, N.Y., 18,653......C7 75
Coimbatore, India, 356,368 (*750,000)......F6 20
Coimbra, Port., 46,313...B1 8
Coín, Sp., 11,828......D3 8
Cojedes, state, Ven., 72,652......B4 32
Cojutepeque, Sal., 20,615......*E7 34
Cokato, Minn., 1,735......E4 67
Coke, co., Tex., 3,087......D2 84
Cokeburg, Pa., 845......*F1 81
Colac, Austl., 10,418......I4 26
Colbert, co., Ala., 49,632..A2 46
Colborne, Ont., Can., 1,588......C7 41

Colby, Kans., 4,658......C2 61
Colby, Wis., 1,178......D3 88
Colchagua, prov., Chile, 182,800......A2 28
Colchester, Conn., 3,529..C7 52
Colchester, Eng., 76,710..E7 4
Colchester, Ill., 1,747......C3 58
Colchester, co., N.S., Can., 34,307......D6 43
Cold Lake, Alta., Can., 1,307......B5 38
Cold Spring, Ky., 1,406......A5, h14 62
Cold Spring, Minn., 2,006..E4 67
Cold Spring, N.Y., 2,800..*D7 75
Cold Spring Harbor, N.Y., 2,800......F3 52
Coldwater, Kans., 1,016...E4 61
Coldwater, Mich., 9,099...G5 66
Coldwater, Miss., 1,450...A4 68
Coldwater, Ohio, 3,533...B1 78
Cole, co., Mo., 46,228....C5 69
Colebrook, N.H., 1,070...B5 73
Cole Camp, Mo., 1,038...C4 69
Coleman, Alta., Can., 1,713......E3 38
Coleman, Fla., 614......D4 54
Coleman, Mich., 1,295....E6 66
Coleman, Tex., 5,608.....D3 84
Coleman, co., Tex., 10,288......D3 84
Coleraine, Minn., 1,086...C5 67
Coleraine, N. Ire., 14,871..C3 4
Coles, co., Ill., 47,815....D5 58
Colfax, Calif., 798......C3 50
Colfax, Ill., 935......C5 58
Colfax, Iowa, 2,293......C4 60
Colfax, La., 1,892......C3 63
Colfax, Wash., 2,664.....C8 86
Colfax, Wis., 1,026......D1 88
Colfax, co., Nebr., 9,498..C8 71
Colfax, co., N. Mex., 12,170......A6 48
Colima, Mex., 43,518......D4, n12 34
Colima, state, Mex., 197,200......D4, n12 34
College, Alsk., 3,434.....C10 47
Collegedale, Tenn., 3,031......h11 83
College Heights, S.C., 900......C7 82
College Park, Ga., 18,203......C2, h8 55
College Park, Md., 26,156..f9 53
College Place, Wash., 4,510......C7 86
College Station, Tex., 17,676......D4 84
Collegeville, Ind., 900....C3 59
Collegeville (P.O.), Minn., 1,600......*E4 67
Collegeville, Pa., 3,191...F11 81
Colleton, co., S.C., 27,622.F6 82
Colleyville, Tex., 3,368...*C4 84
Collie, Austl., 6,802......F2 25
Collier, co., Fla., 38,040..F5 54
Collierville, Tenn., 3,651..B2 83
Collin, co., Tex., 66,920...C4 84
Collingdale, Pa., 10,605..p20 81
Collingswood, N.J., 17,422......D2 74
Collingsworth, co., Tex., 4,755......B2 84
Collingwood, Ont., Can., 9,775......C4 41
Collins, Miss., 1,934......D4 68
Collins Park, Del., 2,600..*A6 53
Collinsville, Ala., 1,300...A4 46
Collinsville, Conn., 2,897..B5 52
Collinsville, Ill., 17,992...E4 58
Collinsville, Okla., 3,009..A6 79
Collinsville, Va., 6,015...*D3 85
Collister, Idaho, 2,700....F2 57
Colmar, Fr., 59,550......C7 5
Colmar Manor, Md., 1,715......f9 53
Colmenar Viejo, Sp., 8,375......B4, o17 8
Cologne (Köln), Ger., Fed. Rep. of, 840,328 (*1,700,000)......C3 6
Coloma, Mich., 1,814......F4 66
Colomb-Bechar, see Bechar, Alg.
Colombes, Fr., 8,357......g10 5
Colombia, Col., 1,599......C3 32
Colombia, country, S.A., 23,550,000......C3 32
Colombo, Sri Lanka, 562,160 (*1,400,000)...G6 20
Colón, Arg., 6,813......A5 28
Colón, Cuba, 26,000 (40,800▲)......C3 35
Colon, Mich., 1,172......G5 66
Colón, Pan., 67,695 (*76,000)......B2 32

Colón, Archipiélago de, (Galápagos Islands), is., Ec......g5 31
Colonia, N.J., 23,200......*k7 74
Colonia, dept., Ur., 149,467......*E1 30
Colonia del Sacramento, Ur., 12,846......E1 30
Colonia Gustavo A. Madero, Mex., 102,602......h9 34
Colonial Beach, Va., 2,058..B6 85
Colonial Heights, (Independent City), Va., 15,097......C5, n18 85
Colonial Manor, N.J., 1,000......*D2 74
Colonial Park, Pa., 10,000......*F8 81
Colonia Suiza, Ur., 4,307..g8 28
Colonie, N.Y., 8,701......*C7 75
Colorado, co., Tex., 17,638......E4 84
Colorado, state, U.S., 2,486,000......51
Colorado, riv., Mex., U.S..C5 45
Colorado, riv., Tex......D3 84
Colorado City, Tex., 5,227......C2 84
Colorado Springs, Colo., 135,060 (*229,300)...C6 51
Colored Hill, W. Va., 1,031......*D3 87
Colotlán, Mex., 6,135......C4, k12 34
Colquitt, Ga., 2,026......E2 55
Colquitt, co., Ga., 32,200..E3 55
Colton, Calif., 20,016....*E5 50
Columbia, Ill., 4,188......E3 58
Columbia, Ky., 3,234......C4 62
Columbia, La., 1,000......B3 63
Columbia, Miss., 7,587...D4 68
Columbia, Mo., 58,812 (*64,700)......C5 69
Columbia, N.C., 902......B6 76
Columbia, Pa., 11,237....F9 81
Columbia, S.C., 113,000 (*298,000)......C5 82
Columbia, Tenn., 21,471..B4 83
Columbia, co., Ark., 25,952......D2 49
Columbia, co., Fla., 25,250......B4 54
Columbia, co., Ga., 22,327......C4 55
Columbia, co., N.Y., 51,519......C7 75
Columbia, co., Oreg., 28,790......B3 80
Columbia, co., Pa., 55,114......D8 81
Columbia, co., Wash., 4,439......C7 86
Columbia, co., Wis., 40,150......E4 88
Columbia, mtn., Alta., Can......C2 38
Columbia, riv., Can., U.S..G9 36
Columbia City, Ind., 4,911......B7 59
Columbia Falls, Mont., 2,652......B2 70
Columbia Heights, Minn., 23,997......m12 67
Columbia Heights, Wash., 1,572......*C3 86
Columbiana, Ala., 2,248...B3 46
Columbiana, Ohio, 4,959..B5 78
Columbiana, co., Ohio, 108,310......B5 78
Columbia Station, Ohio, 400......*A3 78
Columbiaville, Mich., 935.E7 66
Columbus, Ga., 155,028 (*232,500)......D2 55
Columbus, Ind., 26,457....F6 59
Columbus, Kans., 3,356...E9 61
Columbus, Miss., 25,795..B5 68
Columbus, Mont., 1,173...E7 70
Columbus, Nebr., 15,471..C8 71
Columbus, Ohio, 540,025 (*886,500)......C3, m11 78
Columbus, Tex., 3,342....E4 84
Columbus, Wis., 3,789....E4 88
Columbus, co., Ga., 167,377......D2 55
Columbus, co., N.C., 46,937......C4 76
Columbus Grove, Ohio, 2,290......B1 78
Columbus Junction, Iowa, 1,205......C6 60
Colusa, Calif., 3,842......C2 50
Colusa, co., Calif., 12,430..C2 50
Colver, Pa., 1,175......E4 81
Colville, Wash., 3,742.....A8 86
Colwood, B.C., Can., 863......h12 37

Colwyn, Pa., 3,169......*G11 81
Comacchio, It., 10,200....B4 9
Comal, co., Tex., 24,165...E3 84
Comalapa, Guat., 7,404...E6 34
Comalcalco, Mex., 14,963.D6 34
Comanche, Okla., 1,862...C4 79
Comanche, Tex., 3,933....D3 84
Comanche, co., Kans., 2,702......E4 61
Comanche, co., Okla., 108,144......C3 79
Comanche, co., Tex., 11,898......D3 84
Combined Locks, Wis., 2,771......h9 88
Combs, Ky., 3,500......C6 62
Comerío, P.R., 6,297 (18,819▲)......*G11 35
Comfort, Tex., 950......E3 84
Comilla, Pak., 54,504....D9 20
Comiso, It., 26,900......F5 9
Comitán [de Domínguez], Mex., 21,249......D6 34
Commack, N.Y., 24,200..*n15 75
Commentry, Fr., 9,711...D5 5
Commerce, Calif., 10,635.*E4 50
Commerce, Ga., 3,702....B3 55
Commerce, Mich., 3,500......*F7 66
Commerce, Okla., 2,593..A7 79
Commerce, Tex., 9,534...C5 84
Commerce City, Colo., 17,407......B6 51
Commercy, Fr., 7,164.....C6 5
Communism, peak Sov. Un......F10 13
Como, Que., Can., 807...q18 42
Como, Colo., 25......e11 86
Como, It., 93,200 (*142,000)......B2 9
Comodoro Rivadavia, Arg., 55,000......D3 28
Comoros, country, Afr., 295,000......C8 24
Comox, B.C., Can., 3,980.E5 37
Compiègne, Fr., 29,700 (*48,000)......C5 5
Compostela, Mex., 9,801......m11 34
Compton, Calif., 78,547..n12 50
Compton, Que., Can., 22,459......D6 42
Comstock, Mich., 3,650...F5 66
Comstock Park, Mich., 3,370......*E5 66
Conakry, Guinea, 197,267.G2 22
Concarneau, Fr., 17,801..D2 5
Concepción, Arg., 15,832..E2 29
Concepción, Chile, 191,700 (*400,000)......B2 28
Concepción, prov., Chile, 638,118......B2 28
Concepción, Par., 19,392..D4 29
Concepción, dept., Par., 85,690......D4 29
Concepción del Oro, Mex., 8,144......C4 34
Concepción del Uruguay, Arg., 38,000......A5 28
Concho, co., Tex., 2,937...D3 84
Concord, Calif., 85,423...D4 50
Concord, Mass., 6,000 (16,148▲)....B5, g10 65
Concord, Mich., 983......F6 66
Concord, N.H., 30,022....E4 73
Concord, N.C., 18,464....B2 76
Concordia, Arg., 65,000...A5 28
Concordia, Col., 5,187....B2 32
Concordia, Kans., 7,221...C6 61
Concordia, Mo., 1,854.....C4 69
Concordia, par., La., 22,578......C4 63
Concrete, Wash., 573......A4 86
Condobolin, Austl., 3,214..F8 25
Condon, Oreg., 973......B6 80
Conecuh, co., Ala., 15,645......D2 46
Conegliano, It., 23,300....B4 9
Conejos, co., Colo., 7,846..D4 51
Conemaugh, Pa., 2,710...F4 81
Conflans-Ste. Honorine, Fr., 26,304......g9 5
Confluence, Pa., 954......G3 81
Congamond, Mass., 800...B2 65
Congers, N.Y., 5,928.....*D7 75
Congo, country, Afr., 1,115,000......I7 22
Congo, The (Republic of the Congo), see Zaire, country, Afr.
Congo (Zaire), riv., Afr...H2 21
Conil, Sp., 9,002......D2 8
Coniston, Ont., Can., 2,907......A4, p19 41
Conjeeveram, see Kānchipuram, India

124 *Con-Cra*

Connacht, prov., Ire., 401,950....*D2 4
Conneaut, Ohio, 14,552...A5 78
Conneautville, Pa., 1,032..C1 81
Connecticut, state, U.S., 3,102,000.... 52
Connell, Wash., 1,161.....C7 86
Connellsville, Pa., 11,643..F2 81
Connersville, Ind., 17,604..E7 59
Conning Towers, Conn., 1,500....*D8 52
Conover, N.C., 3,355......B1 76
Conrad, Iowa, 932........B5 60
Conrad, Mont., 2,770.....B5 70
Conroe, Tex., 11,969......D5 84
Conselheiro Lafaiete, Braz., 44,894....C4 30
Conshohocken, Pa., 10,195....F11, o20 81
Consolación del Sur, Cuba, 15,100 (42,000 ▲).......C2 35
Constanța, Rom., 150,400 (*199,400)......C9 10
Constantia, N.Y., 900.....B5 75
Constantina, Sp., 11,910...D3 8
Constantine, Alg., 253,649....A6 22
Constantine, Mich., 1,733..G5 66
Constantinople, see İstanbul, Tur.
Continental, peak, Wyo....D4 89
Constitución, Chile, 9,500..B2 28
Consuegra, Sp., 10,572....C4 8
Contamana, Peru, 2,860...C2 31
Continental, Ohio, 1,185...A1 78
Contra Costa, co., Calif., 555,805....D2 50
Contratación, Col., 3,117....B3 32
Contrecoeur, Que., Can., 2,694....D4 42
Contreras, Mex., 10,112....h9 34
Contumaza, Peru, 1,911...C2 31
Convent, La., 375....D5, h10 63
Converse, Ind., 1,163......C6 59
Converse, S.C., 900.......B4 82
Converse, co., Wyo., 5,938....C7 89
Convoy, Ohio, 991........B1 78
Conway, Ark., 15,510.....B3 49
Conway, Fla., 3,000......*D5 54
Conway, N.H., 1,489 .....D5 73
Conway, Pa., 2,822 ....E1 81
Conway, S.C., 8,151 ......D9 82
Conway, co., Ark., 16,805..B3 49
Conway Springs, Kans., 1,153....E6 61
Conyers, Ga., 4,890....C2, h8 55
Conyngham, Pa., 1,850 ..*D9 81
Cooch Behār, India, 53,684 (*62,664)........C8 20
Cook, co., Ga., 12,129 ....E3 55
Cook, co., Ill., 5,492,369...B6 58
Cook, co., Minn., 3,423....C8 67
Cooke, co., Tex., 23,471...C4 84
Cook, mtn., N.Z.........O13 26
Cookeville, Tenn., 14,270..C8 83
Cookshire, Que., Can., 1,484....D6 42
Cookstown, Ont., Can., 1,025....C5 41
Cooleemee, N.C., 1,800...B2 76
Coolidge, Ariz., 5,314..C3, E2 48
Coolidge, Tex., 786.......D4 84
Cool Ridge, W. Va., 400 ..D3 87
Cool Valley, Mo., 2,059...*C7 69
Cooma, Austl., 7,784......G8 25
Coonabarabran, Austl., 3,045....F8 25
Coonamble, Austl., 3,152....F8 25
Coon Rapids, Iowa, 1,381..C3 60
Coon Rapids, Minn., 30,505....m12 67
Cooper, Tex., 2,258.......C5 84
Cooper, co., Mo., 14,732...C5 69
Coopersburg, Pa., 2,326..E11 81
Cooperstown, N.Y., 2,403..C6 75
Cooperstown, N. Dak., 1,485....C7 77
Coopersville, Mich., 2,129..E5 66
Coos, co., N.H., 34,291....B5 73
Coos, co., Oreg., 56,515...D2 80
Coosa, co., Ala., 10,662 ...C3 46
Coos Bay, Oreg., 13,466...D2 80
Cootamundra, Austl., 6,530....G7 26
Copainalá, Mex., 3,087....D6 34
Copenhagen (København), Den., 643,300 (*1,460,000)....J5 11
Copiague, N.Y., 20,600....G3 52
Copiah, co., Miss., 24,749..D3 68
Copiapó, Chile, 30,123....E1 29
Coplay, Pa., 3,642......*E10 81
Copley, Ohio, 7,000......*A4 78
Copparo, It., 5,800........B3 9
Copper, mtn., Wyo........C5 89
Copperas Cove, Tex., 10,818....D4 84
Copper Cliff, Ont., Can., 4,089....A3 41
Copperhill, Tenn., 563.....D9 83
Coquille, Oreg., 4,437....D2 80
Coquimbo, Chile, 33,749...E1 29
Coquimbo, prov., Chile, 372,900....A2 28
Corabia, Rom., 11,502.....D7 10
Coracora, Peru, 6,500.....E3 31
Coral Gables, Fla., 42,494....G6, s13 54
Coralville, Iowa, 6,130....C6 60
Coram, N.Y., 3,300......n15 75
Coraopolis, Pa., 8,435....E1, h13 81
Corato, It., 39,300........D6 9
Corbeil, Fr., 32,192.......C5 5
Corbin, Ky., 7,317........D5 62
Corcoran, Calif., 5,249....D4 50
Corcoran, Minn., 1,656...*E5 67
Cordele, Ga., 10,733......E3 55
Cordell, Okla., 3,261......B3 79
Cordillera, dept., Par., 188,313....D4 29
Córdoba, Arg., 798,663 (*825,000)....A4 28
Córdoba, Mex., 78,495....n15 34
Córdoba, Sp., 232,343.....D3 8
Córdoba, prov., Sp., 768,200....*D3 8
Córdoba, prov., Arg., 1,753,840....A4 28
Cordova, Ala., 2,750......B2 46
Cordova, Alsk., 1,164....C10, g19 47
Cordova, N.C., 900.......C3 76
Córdova, Peru, 534.......D2 31
Cori, It., 9,681...........h9 9
Corigliano, It., 16,300.....E6 9
Corinna, Maine, 900 (1,700 ▲)....D3 64
Corinne, W. Va., 475.....D3 87
Corinth, Miss., 11,581.....A5 68
Corinth, N.Y., 15,792.....B7 75
Corinth, see Kórinthos, Grc.
Corinto, Braz., 15,554.....B4 30
Corinto, Nic., 12,200.....H12 33
Cork, Ire., 128,645 (*134,430)....E2 4
Cork, co., Ire., 339,703....E3 4
Corleone, It., 14,682......F4 9
Çorlu, Tur., 32,018.......B6 14
Cormeilles-en-Parisis, Fr., 11,486....g9 5
Cornelia, Ga., 3,014.......B3 55
Cornelius, N.C., 1,296.....B2 76
Cornelius, Oreg., 1,903...g11 80
Cornell, Wis., 1,616.......C2 88
Corner Brook, Newf., Can., 26,309....D3 44
Corning, Ark., 2,705.......A5 49
Corning, Calif., 3,573.....C2 50
Corning, Iowa, 2,095......D3 60
Corning, N.Y., 15,792.....C3 75
Corning, Ohio, 838.......C3 78
Corno, mtn., It..........C4 9
Cornwall, Ont., Can., 47,116....B10 41
Cornwall, N.Y., 2,032.....D6 75
Cornwall, Pa., 2,111.......F9 81
Cornwall, see Cornwall-on the-Hudson, N.Y.
Cornwall, co., Eng., 379,480....*E4 4
Cornwall-on-the-Hudson, N.Y., 3,131....D6 75
Cornwells Heights, Pa., 8,700....o22 81
Coro, Ven., 67,701........A4 32
Corona, Calif., 27,519....F5, n13 50
Coronado, Calif., 20,020....F5, o15 50
Coronation, Alta., Can., 864....C5 38
Coronel, Chile, 33,870.....B2 28
Coronel Dorrego, Arg., 9,154....B4 28
Coronel Oviedo, Par., 13,786....E4 29
Coronel Pringles, Arg., 14,180....B4 28
Coronel Suárez, Arg., 8,878....B4 28
Coropuna, mtn., Peru.....E3 31
Corozal, Col., 14,000......B2 32
Corpus Christi, Tex., 204,525 (*244,600)....F4 84
Corral de Almaguer, Sp., 8,261....C4 8
Corrales, Col., 1,378.......B3 32
Corralillo, Cuba, 4,000 (12,600 ▲)....C3 35
Correctionville, Iowa, 870..B2 60
Corrèze, dept., Fr., 237,858....*E4 5
Corrientes, Arg., 128,000...E4 29
Corrigan, Tex., 1,304.....D5 84
Corry, Pa., 7,435.........C2 81
Corse, dept., Fr., 205,000....*C2 9
Corsica, isl., Eur.........C2 9
Corsicana, Tex., 19,972....C4 84
Corson, co., S.Dak., 4,994....E4 77
Cortazar, Mex., 25,794....C4, m13 34
Cortegana, Sp., 7,179.....D2 8
Corte Madera, Calif., 8,464....*C2 50
Cortez, Colo., 6,032.......D1 51
Cortez, Fla., 900.........q10 54
Cortland, N.Y., 19,621....C4 75
Cortland, Ohio, 2,525.....A5 78
Cortland, co., N.Y., 45,894....C4 75
Cortona, It., 3,300........C3 9
Corumbá, Braz., 48,607....B1 30
Çorum (Chorum), Tur., 54,576....B10 14
Corunna, Ont., Can., 3,052....E2 41
Corunna, Mich., 2,829.....F6 66
Corvallis, Oreg., 35,056....C3, k11 80
Corydon, Ind., 2,719......H5 59
Corydon, Iowa, 1,745.....D4 60
Coryell, co., Tex., 35,311..D4 84
Cosalá, Mex., 2,279.......C3 34
Cosamaloapan [de Carpio], Mex., 19,766....D5 34
Coscomatepec [de Bravo], Mex., 6,023....n15 34
Cosenza, It., 94,800.......E6 9
Coshocton, Ohio, 13,747...B4 78
Coshocton, co., Ohio, 33,486....B3 78
Cosmopolis, Wash., 1,599..C2 86
Cosne [-sur-Loire], Fr., 9,601....D5 5
Costa Mesa, Calif., 72,660....n13 50
Costa Rica, country, N.A., 1,900,000....E8 34
Costilla, N. Mex., 200.....A6 48
Costilla, co., Colo., 3,091..D5 51
Cotabato, Phil., 51,425....D6 19
Cotabato, prov., Phil., 1,029,119....*D6 19
Cotahuasi, Peru, 1,354....D2 31
Cotati, Calif., 1,368......*C2 50
Coteaux, Hai., 1,426......E6 35
Côte-d'or, dept., Fr., 421,192....*D6 5
Côtes-du-Nord, dept., Fr., 506,102....*C2 5
Côte-St. Luc., Que., Can., 24,375....*D4 42
Cotija de la Paz, Mex., 9,178....n12 34
Cotonou, Benin, 109,300...G5 22
Cotopaxi, prov., Ec., 223,600....B2 31
Cotopaxi, vol., Ec.........A2 31
Cottage City, Md., 993...*C4 53
Cottage Grove, Oreg., 6,004....D3 80
Cottage Grove, Wis., 478....*E4 88
Cottage Hills, Ill., 1,261..*E3 58
Cottbus, Ger. Dem. Rep., 90,561....C7 6
Cotter, Ark., 858.........A3 49
Cottle, co., Tex., 3,204....B2 84
Cotton, co., Okla., 6,832...C3 79
Cottondale, Fla., 765....B1, u16 54
Cotton Plant, Ark., 1,657..B4 49
Cottonport, La., 1,862.....D3 63
Cotton Valley, La., 1,261..B2 63
Cottonwood, Ala., 1,149...D4 46
Cottonwood, Ariz., 2,815...B3 48
Cottonwood, Calif., 1,000..B2 50
Cottonwood, Idaho, 867....C2 57
Cottonwood, co., Minn., 14,887....F3 67
Cottonwood Falls, Kans., 987....D7 61
Cottonwood Heights, Utah, 9,300....*D2 72
Cotuit, Mass., 900........C7 65
Cotulla, Tex., 3,415.......E3 84
Coudekerque-Branche, Fr., 23,039....B5 5
Coudersport, Pa., 2,831....C5 81
Coulee City, Wash., 558...B6 86
Coulee Dam, Wash., 1,425....B7 86
Coulommiers, Fr., 11,263..C5 5
Coulterville, Ill., 1,186.....E4 58
Council, Idaho, 899.......E2 57
Council, mtn., Idaho......E2 57
Council Bluffs, Iowa, 60,348....C2 60
Council Grove, Kans., 2,403....D7 61
Country Club Hills, Ill., 6,920....*B6 58
Country Club Hills, Mo., 1,644....*C7 69
Country Homes, Wash., 4,000....*B8 86
Coupar Angus, Scot., 1,996....B5 4
Courbevoie, Fr., 58,118...g10 5
Courtdale, Pa., 1,027....*D9 81
Courtenay, B.C., Can., 7,125 (*16,166).........E5 37
Courtland, Calif., 400....*C3 50
Courtland, Va., 899.......D5 85
Courtrai, see Kortrijk, Bel.
Courville, Que., Can., 6,222....n17 42
Coushatta, La., 1,492......B2 63
Coutances, Fr., 9,061......C3 5
Coutras, Fr., 3,688........E3 5
Covedale, Ohio, 6,639....o12 78
Covelo, Calif., 950........C2 50
Coventry, Conn., 3,735 (8,140 ▲)....B7 52
Coventry, Eng., 333,000 (*640,000)....D6 4
Coventry, R.I., 6,500 (22,947 ▲)....C10 52
Covilhã, Port., 23,091.....B2 8
Covina, Calif., 30,395.....m13 50
Covington, Ga., 10,267....C3 55
Covington, Ind., 2,641....D3 59
Covington, Ky., 52,535....A5, h13 62
Covington, La., 7,170....D5, h11 63
Covington, Ohio, 2,575....B1 78
Covington, Tenn., 5,801...B2 83
Covington (Independent City), Va., 10,060......C3 85
Covington, co., Ala., 34,079....D3 46
Covington, co., Miss., 14,002....D4 68
Cowan, Tenn., 1,772......B5 83
Cowansville, Que., Can., 11,920....D5 42
Cowansville, Pa., 350......E2 81
Cowen, mtn., Mont.......E6 70
Cowes, Eng., 18,970.......E6 4
Coweta, Okla., 2,457......B6 79
Coweta, co., Ga., 32,310...C2 55
Cowley, co., Kans., 35,012....E7 61
Cowlitz, co., Wash., 68,616....C3 86
Cowpens, S.C., 2,109......A4 82
Cowra, Austl., 7,282.......F7 26
Coxsackie, N.Y., 2,399....C7 75
Coyame, Mex., 1,007.......B3 34
Coyoacán, Mex., 31,045....H9, n14 34
Coyuca de Catalán, Mex., 2,926....n13 34
Cozad, Nebr., 4,225.......D6 71
Cozumel, Mex., 5,858......C7 34
Crab Orchard, W. Va., 1,953....n13 87
Crabtree, Pa., 1,021.......F3 81
Crabtree Mills, Que., Can., 1,706....D4 42
Cradock, S. Afr., 20,522...G5 24
Crafton, Pa., 8,233.......k13 81
Craig, Colo., 4,205........A3 51
Craig, co., Okla., 14,722...A6 79
Craig, co., Va., 3,524......C2 85
Craig Beach, Ohio, 1,451....*B5 78
Craighead, co., Ark., 52,068....B5 49
Craigsville, Va., 988.......B3 85
Crailsheim, Ger., Fed. Rep. of, 23,126.........D5 6
Craiova, Rom., 148,800 (173,300 ▲)....C6 10
Cramerton, N.C., 2,142....B1 76
Cranberry Portage, Man., Can., 838....B10 40
Cranbrook, B.C., Can., 12,000....E10 37
Cranbury, N.J., 1,253.....C3 74
Crandon, Wis., 1,582......C5 88
Crane, Mo., 1,003.........E4 69
Crane, Tex., 3,427.........D1 84
Crane, co., Tex., 4,172....D1 84
Crane, mtn., Oreg.........E6 80
Cranford, N.J., 27,391.....B4 74
Cranston, R.I., 74,287....B11 52
Crateús, Braz., 25,022....*D6 27
Crato, Braz., 36,836......*D7 27
Craven, co., N.C., 62,554..B5 76
Crawford, Nebr., 1,291....B2 71
Crawford, co., Ark., 25,677....B1 49

Crawford, co., Ga., 5,748..D2 55
Crawford, co., Ill., 19,824..D6 58
Crawford, co., Ind., 8,033...........H4 59
Crawford, co., Iowa, 19,116...........B2 60
Crawford, co., Kans., 37,850..........E9 61
Crawford, co., Mich., 6,482...........D6 66
Crawford, co., Mo., 14,828...........D6 69
Crawford, co., Ohio, 50,364...........B2 78
Crawford, co., Pa., 81,342...........C1 81
Crawford, co., Wis., 15,252...........E3 88
Crawfordsville, Ind., 13,842...........D4 59
Crawfordville, Ga., 735...C4 55
Crazy, peak, Mont......D6 70
Creedmoor, N.C., 1,405...A4 76
Creek, co., Okla., 45,532...B5 79
Creemore, Ont., Can., 850............C4 41
Creighton, Sask., Can., 1,857.........C5 39
Creighton, Nebr., 1,461..B8 71
Creighton, Pa., 2,081...h14 81
Creighton Mine, Ont., Can., 1,294........A3, p19 41
Creil, Fr., 32,544 (*67,000)........C5 5
Crema, It., 28,600.....B2 9
Cremona, It., 80,800....B3 9
Crenshaw, Miss., 1,271..A3 68
Crenshaw, co., Ala., 13,188...........D3 46
Cresaptown, Md., 1,731..k13 53
Crescent, Okla., 1,568..B4 79
Crescent City, Calif., 2,586..........B1 50
Crescent City, Fla., 1,734..C5 54
Crescent City Northwest, Calif., 3,086.....*B1 50
Crescent Springs, Ky., 1,662.........h13 62
Cresco, Iowa, 3,927.....A5 60
Cresskill, N.J., 8,298......h9 74
Cresson, Pa., 2,446.....F4 81
Cressona, Pa., 1,814....E9 81
Crest, Fr., 4,494......E6 5
Crest Hill, Ill., 7,460..*B5 58
Crestline, Calif., 3,509...*E5 50
Crestline, Ohio, 5,947...B3 78
Crestmont, Pa., 2,000...*F11 81
Creston, B.C., Can., 3,204..E9 37
Creston, Newf., Can., 837............E4 44
Creston, Iowa, 8,234.....C3 60
Creston, Ohio, 1,792....B4 78
Crestview, Fla., 7,952....u15 54
Crestwood, Ill., 5,770....*B6 58
Crestwood, Mo., 15,123..*C7 69
Crete, Ill., 4,656......B6, m9 58
Crete, Nebr., 4,444.....D9 71
Crete, isl., Grc.........E5 14
Crete, sea, Grc.........E5 14
Creuse, dept., Fr., 156,876..........*D4 5
Creutzwald, Fr., 14,471...C7 5
Creve Coeur, Ill., 6,440...C4 58
Creve Coeur, Mo., 8,967..*C7 69
Crevillente, Sp., 14,047...C5 8
Crewe, Eng., 51,250.....D5 4
Crewe, Va., 1,797......C4 85
Cricket, N.C., 950......A1 76
Cridersville, Ohio, 1,103..B1 78
Crieff, Scot., 5,709.....B5 4
Crimmitschau, Ger. Dem. Rep., 28,750.......C6 6
Crisana, reg., Rom., 852,000..........B6 10

Crisfield, Md., 3,078.....E6 53
Crisp, co., Ga., 18,087....E3 55
Cristóbal Colón, mtn., Col..A3 32
Crittenden, co., Ark., 48,106..........B5 49
Crittenden, co., Ky., 8,493............e9 62
Croatia, reg., Yugo...*C2 10
Croatia, rep., Yugo., 4,159,696........C2 10
Crocker, Mo., 814......D5 69
Crockett, Calif., 3,300...g8 50
Crockett, Tex., 6,616...D5 84
Crockett, co., Tenn., 14,402..........B2 83
Crockett, co., Tex., 3,885..D2 84
Croghan, N.Y., 765.....B5 75
Cromona, Ky., 700.....C7 62
Cromwell, Conn., 7,400...C6 52
Crook, co., Oreg., 9,985...C6 80
Crook, co., Wyo., 4,535....B8 89
Crookston, Minn., 8,312...C2 67
Crooksville, Ohio, 2,828...C3 78
Crosby, Minn., 2,241.....D5 67
Crosby, Miss., 491......D2 68
Crosby, N. Dak., 1,545....A2 77
Crosby, Tex., 1,118.....r14 84
Crosby, co., Tex., 9,085...C2 84
Crosby, mtn., Wyo........C3 89
Crosbyton, Tex., 2,251...C2 84
Cross, co., Ark., 19,783...B5 49
Cross City, Fla., 2,268....C3 54
Crossett, Ark., 6,191....D4 49
Cross Mill, N.C., 1,000....f10 76
Cross Plains, Tex., 1,192...C3 84
Cross Plains, Wis., 1,478...E4 88
Crossville, Ill., 860......E5 58
Crossville, Tenn., 5,381...D8 83
Croswell, Mich., 1,954....E8 66
Crothersville, Ind., 1,663..G6 59
Crotone, It., 42,000.....E6 9
Croton-on-Hudson, N.Y., 7,523..........D7, m15 75
Crouse, N.C., 600......B1 76
Crow, peak, Mont.......D5 70
Crow Agency, Mont., 600..E9 70
Crowell, Tex., 1,399.....C3 84
Crowley, La., 16,104.....D3 63
Crowley, co., Colo., 3,086..C7 51
Crown Point, Ind., 10,931..B3 59
Crown Point, N.Y., 1,857..B7 75
Crow Wing, co., Minn., 34,826..........D4 67
Croydon, Pa., 9,800.....F12 81
Crozet, Va., 1,433......B4 85
Cruces, Cuba, 19,100 (32,100 ▲).........C3 35
Crucible, Pa., 900......G1 81
Cruden Bay, Scot., 489...B6 4
Crum Lynne, Pa., 2,200..*E1 81
Cruz Alta, Braz., 43,568...D2 30
Cruz del Eje, Arg., 24,000...........A4 28
Cruzeiro, Braz., 42,366....C4 30
Crystal, Minn., 30,925...m12 67
Crystal Beach, Fla., 700...D4 54
Crystal City, Mo., 3,898..........C7, g13 69
Crystal City, Tex., 8,104...E3 84
Crystal Falls, Mich., 2,000..B2 66
Crystal Lake, Fla., 150....u16 54
Crystal Lake, Ill., 14,541..........A5, h8 58
Crystal Lakes, Ohio, 2,000............C1 78
Crystal River, Fla., 1,696..D4 54
Crystal Springs, Miss., 4,195..........D3 68
Csongrád, Hung., 17,678 (20,331 ▲)........B5 10
Csongrád, co., Hung., 323,229.........*B5 10
Csorna, Hung., 9,208.....B3 10

Cuajimalpa, Mex., 13,239..h9 34
Cuauhtémoc, Mex., 26,598..........B3 34
Cuautepec, Mex., 19,923...........g9 34
Cuautla, Mex., 13,946...n14 34
Cuba, Ill., 1,581.......C3 58
Cuba, Mo., 2,070......C6 69
Cuba, N.Y., 1,735......C2 75
Cuba, country, N.A., 8,970,000.........C3 35
Cuba City, Wis., 1,993...F3 88
Cucamonga, Calif., 2,500............*E5 50
Cúcuta, Col., 199,400....B3 32
Cudahy, Calif., 16,998...*F4 50
Cudahy, Wis., 22,078.........F6, n12 88
Cuddalore, India, 101,335..........F6 20
Cuddapah, India, 66,195...F6 20
Cuddy, Pa., 12,000.....*B5 81
Cuenca, Ec., 71,500....B2 31
Cuenca, Sp., 33,571....B4 8
Cuenca, prov., Sp., 264,700..........*B4 8
Cuencamé [de Ceniceros], Mex., 3,774........C4 34
Cuernavaca, Mex., 134,117.......D5, n14 34
Cuero, Tex., 6,956......E4 84
Cuetzalan, Mex., 2,701...m15 34
Cuevas, Sp., 9,530.....D5 8
Cuiabá, Braz., 83,621...B1 30
Cuicatlán, Mex., 2,733...o15 34
Culberson, co., Tex., 3,429............o12 84
Culbertson, Mont., 821...B12 70
Culbertson, Nebr., 801...D5 71
Culhuacán, Mex., 8,698..h9 34
Culiacán, Mex., 167,956...C3 34
Cúllar de Baza, Sp., 9,502...........D4 8
Cullen, La., 1,956.....B2 63
Cullera, Sp., 14,103....C5 8
Cullman, Ala., 12,601...A3 46
Cullman, co., Ala., 52,445..........A3 46
Culloden, W. Va., 1,033..*C2 87
Cullowhee, N.C., 2,000...f9 76
Culmore, Va., 2,900....*B5 85
Culpeper, Va., 6,056.....B4 85
Culpeper, co., Va., 18,218..B5 85
Culver, Ind., 1,783.....B5 59
Culver City, Calif., 34,451..........m12 50
Cumaná, Ven., 119,751...A5 32
Cumberland, B.C., Can., 1,718...........E5 37
Cumberland, Ind., 479..........E6, k11 59
Cumberland, Ky., 3,380..D7 62
Cumberland, Md., 29,724...........k13 53
Cumberland, Wis., 1,839...C2 88
Cumberland, co., N.S., Can., 37,767..........D5 43
Cumberland, co., Eng., 291,090.........*C5 4
Cumberland, co., Ill., 9,772...........D5 58
Cumberland, co., Ky., 6,850...........D4 62
Cumberland, co., Maine, 192,528.........E2 64
Cumberland, co., N.J., 121,374.........E2 74
Cumberland, co., N.C., 212,042.........C4 76
Cumberland, co., Pa., 158,177.........F7 81
Cumberland, co., Tenn., 20,733.........D8 83
Cumberland, co., Va., 6,179...........C4 85

Cumberland, mtn., Ky., Tenn............C9 83
Cumberland, riv., U.S....C10 45
Cuming, co., Nebr., 12,034...........C9 71
Cumming, Ga., 2,031....B2 55
Cumpas, Mex., 2,395....A3 34
Çumra, Tur., 15,965.....D9 14
Cundinamarca, dept., Col., 3,313,500.........C3 32
Cuneo, It., 41,200.....B1 9
Cunnamulla, Austl., 1,806..E8 25
Cupertino, Calif., 18,216..*D2 50
Curaçao, isl., Neth. Antilles..........A4 32
Curacautín, Chile, 9,600...B2 28
Curicó, Chile, 32,562....A2 28
Curicó, prov., Chile, 113,710..........A2 28
Curitiba, Braz., 483,038 (*680,000).........D3 30
Currais Novos, Braz., 15,858.........*D7 27
Currituck, co., N.C., 6,976...........A6 76
Curry, co., N. Mex., 39,517..........B7 48
Curry, co., Oreg., 13,006..E2 80
Curtea-de-Arges, Rom., 10,764..........C7 10
Curtici, Rom., 8,050....B5 10
Curtis, Nebr., 1,166....D5 71
Curtisville, Pa., 1,376..........E1, h14 81
Curug, Yugo., 9,457.....C5 10
Curuzú Cuatia, Arg., 16,567..........E4 29
Curvelo, Braz., 30,225...B4 30
Curwensville, Pa., 3,189..E4 81
Cushing, Okla., 7,529....B5 79
Cusset, Fr., 13,117.....D5 5
Custer, S. Dak., 1,597...G2 77
Custer, co., Colo., 1,120...C5 51
Custer, co., Idaho, 2,967...........E4 57
Custer, co., Mont., 12,174..........D11 70
Custer, co., Nebr., 14,092..C6 79
Custer, co., Okla., 22,665..B2 71
Custer, co., S. Dak., 4,698...........G2 77
Cut Bank, Mont., 4,004..B4 70
Cutchogue, N.Y., 350...m16 75
Cutervo, Peru, 3,481....C2 31
Cuthbert, Ga., 3,972....E2 55
Cutler, Calif., 2,191....*D4 50
Cutler Ridge, Fla., 17,441..........*G6 54
Cutten, Calif., 1,572....*B1 50
Cuxhaven, Ger., Fed. Rep. of, 60,203....B4 6
Cuyahoga, co., Ohio, 1,720,835.........A4 78
Cuyahoga Falls, Ohio, 49,678..........A4 78
Cuzco, Peru, 67,658....D3 31
Cuzco, dept., Peru, 648,168..........D3 31
Cynthiana, Ky., 6,356....B5 62
Cypress, Calif., 31,026...*F4 50
Cypress Quarters, Fla., 1,310...........E6 54
Cyprus, country, Asia, 655,000.........E9 14
Cyprus, isl., Asia.......E9 14
Cyrenaica, prov., Libya, 291,328.........B2 23
Cyril, Okla., 1,302.....C3 79
Czechoslovakia, country, Eur., 14,590,000......D4 7
Czersk, Pol., 7,235.....B4 7
Częstochowa, Pol., 187,600..........C5 7

D

Dab, Pol., (part of Katowice)...........g9 7
Dab, Pol., (part of Szczecin)..........B3 7
Dabeiba, Col., 4,218.....B2 32
Dablice, Czech., 5,378...n18 7
Dąbrowa, Pol., 4,520.....C6 7
Dąbrowa Górnicza, Pol., 61,600...........C5, g10 7

Dacca, Bngl., 425,000 (*1,050,000).........D9 20
Dachau, Ger., Fed. Rep. of, 33,643...........D5 6
Dade, co., Fla., 1,267,792..G6 54
Dade, co., Ga., 9,910....B1 55
Dade, co., Mo., 6,850....D4 69
Dade City, Fla., 4,241...D4 54
Dadeville, Ala., 2,847....C4 46

Dadra and Nagar Haveli, ter., India, 74,170...*D5 20
Dādu, Pak., 19,142...........C4 20
Daet, Phil., 23,739...........*C6 19
Daggett, co., Utah, 666............A7 72
Dagupan, Phil., 83,582...n13 19

Dahlgren, Va., 500......B5 85
Dahlonega, Ga., 2,656...B3 55
Dailey, W. Va., 800....C5 87
Daimiel, Sp., 19,625....C4 8
Daingerfield, Tex., 2,630..C5 84
Daio, Jap., 5,622......o15 18
Dairen, see Lüta, China
Dairy Valley, Calif., 3,508...........*F4 50

Daisetta, Tex., 1,084......D5 84
Daisytown, Pa., 371......*F1 81
Dajabón, Dom. Rep., 6,000......E8 35
Dakar, Sen., 581,000 (*650,000)......F1 22
Dakota, co., Minn., 139,808......F5 67
Dakota, co., Nebr., 13,137......B9 71
Dakota City, Nebr., 1,057..B9 71
Da Lat, Viet., 83,700......C3 19
D'Albertis Dome, mtn., Pap. N. Gui......h11 25
Dalby, Austl., 8,890......E9 25
Dale, Ind., 1,113......H4 59
Dale, Pa., 2,274......*E4 81
Dale, co., Ala., 52,938......D4 46
Daleville, Ind., 1,548......D6 59
Dalhart, Tex., 5,705......A1 84
Dalhousie, N.B., Can., 6,255......A3 43
Dall, mtn., Alsk......f15 47
Dallam, co., Tex., 6,012...A1 84
Dallas, Ga., 2,133......C2 55
Dallas, N.C., 4,059......B1 76
Dallas, Oreg., 6,361......C3 80
Dallas, Pa., 2,398...D10, m17 81
Dallas, Tex., 844,401 (*1,580,600)......C4, n10 84
Dallas, co., Ala., 55,296......C2 46
Dallas, co., Ark., 10,022...D3 49
Dallas, co., Iowa, 26,085...C3 60
Dallas, co., Mo., 10,054...D4 69
Dallas, co., Tex., 1,327,321......C4 84
Dallas Center, Iowa, 1,128......C4 60
Dallas City, Ill., 1,284......C2 58
Dallastown, Pa., 3,560......G8 81
Dalmatia, reg., Yugo......D3 10
Dalmellington, Scot., 2,130......C4 4
Dalnerechensk, Sov. Un., 28,000......E16 13
Dalnyaya, Sov. Un., 10,000......D11 18
Dalrymple, mtn., Austl......D8 25
Dalton, Ga., 18,872......B2 55
Dalton, Mass., 7,505......B1 65
Dalton, Ohio, 1,177......B4 78
Dalton, Pa., 1,282......C10 81
Daltonganj, India, 32,367..D7 20
Dalton Gardens, Idaho, 1,559......B2 57
Daly City, Calif., 66,400...h8 50
Damān, India, 17,317......D5 20
Damanhūr, Eg., 146,079...G8 14
Damariscotta, Maine, 720, (1,264▲)......D3 64
Damascus, Md., 2,638......B3 53
Damascus, Va., 13,857......f10 85
Damascus (Dimashq), Syr., 836,179......F11 14
Da Nang, Viet.,334,200......B3 19
Dana Point, Calif., 1,186..*F5 50
Danbury, Conn., 50,781 (*79,900)......D3 52
Dane, co., Wis., 290,272...E4 88
Dania, Fla., 9,013......F6, r13 54
Daniels, co., Mont., 3,083......B11 70
Danielson, Conn., 4,580...B9 52
Dannemora, N.Y., 3,735...f11 75
Dannevirke, N.Z., 5,610..N16 26
Dans, mtn., Md......k13 53
Dansalan, Phil., 4,882......*D6 19
Dansville, N.Y., 5,436......C3 75
Dante, Som......F8 23
Dante, Va., 1,153......f9 85
Danube, riv., Eur......F10 3
Danubyu, Bur., 10,000...*E10 20
Danvers, Mass., 26,151......A6, f12 65
Danville, Ark., 1,362......B2 49
Danville, Calif., 7,000......h9 50
Danville, Que., Can., 2,566......D5 42
Danville, Ill., 42,570......C6 58
Danville, Ind., 3,771......E4 59
Danville, Ky., 11,542......C5 62
Danville, Ohio, 1,025......B3 78
Danville, Pa., 6,176......E8 81
Danville (Independent City), Va., 46,391......D3 85
Danville East, Pa., 2,046..*D8 81
Danzig see Gdańsk, Pol.
Daphne, Ala., 2,382......E2 46
Dar'ā, Syr., 27,673......F11 14
Darabani, Rom., 11,379...A8 10
Darasun, Sov. Un., 18,000......D14 13
Darbhanga, India, 132,059......C8 20
Darby, Pa., 13,729..G11, p20 81
Dardanelle, Ark., 3,297...B2 49
Dare, co., N.C., 6,995......B7 76
Darenbe, Tur., 7,929......C11 14
Dar-es-Salaam, Tan., 272,821......B7 24
Darien, Conn., 20,336......E3 52
Darien, Ga., 1,826......E5 55
Darien, Wis., 839......F5 88
Darjeeling, India, 42,873...C8 20
Dark Cove, Newf., Can., 955......*D4 44
Darke, co., Ohio, 49,141...B1 78
Darling Range, mts., Austl......F2 25
Darling, riv., Austl......E5 26
Darlington, Eng., 85,900...C6 4
Darlington, S.C., 6,990...C8 82
Darlington, Wis., 2,351....F3 88
Darlington, co., S.C., 53,442......C7 82
Darłowo, Pol., 11,200......A4 7
Darmstadt, Ger., Fed. Rep. of, 140,865 (*265,000)...D4 6
Darnah (Derna), Libya, 21,400......B2 23
Darrah, mtn., Alta., Can.,......E3 38
Darrington, Wash., 1,094......A4 86
Darrow, La., 450......h10 63
Dartmouth, N.S., Can., 64,770......E6 43
Dartmouth, Eng., 6,570....E5 4
Daruvar, Yugo., 6,280......C3 10
Darwin, Austl., 31,687 (*36,828)......B5 25
Dassel, Minn., 1,058......E4 67
Daugavpils, Sov. Un., 100,000......D6 12
Dauphin, Man., Can 8,891......D1, g7 40
Dauphin, co., Pa., 223,713......F8 81
Dauphiné, former prov., Fr......E6 5
Davao, Phil., 148,424 (392,473▲)......D7 19
Davao, prov., Phil., 893,023......*D7 19
Davenport, Fla., 1,303......D5 54
Davenport, Iowa, 98,469 (*310,900)......C7, g10 60
Davenport, Okla., 831......B5 79
Davenport, Wash., 1,363...B7 86
David, Pan., 35,677......B1 32
David City, Nebr., 2,380...C8 71
Davidson, Sask., Can., 928......F3 39
Davidson, N.C., 2,931......B2 76
Davidson, co., N.C., 95,627......B2 76
Davidson, co., Tenn., 447,877......A5 83
Davie, Fla., 5,859......F6, r13 54
Davie, co., N.C., 18,855...B2 76
Daviess, co., Ind., 26,602..G3 59
Daviess, co., Ky., 79,486...C2 62
Daviess, co., Mo., 8,420...B3 69
Davis, Calif., 23,448......C3 50
Davis, Okla., 2,223......C4 79
Davis, W. Va., 868......B5 87
Davis, co., Iowa, 8,207...D4 60
Davis, co., Utah, 99,028...A5 72
Davis, mtn., Pa......G3 81
Davison, Mich., 5,259......E7 66
Davison, co., S. Dak., 17,319......G7 77
Davisville, R.I., 400......C11 52
Davos, Switz., 11,800......E4 6
Davy, W. Va., 993......D3 87
Dawes, co., Nebr., 9,761...B2 71
Dawson, Yukon, Can., 762......D6 36
Dawson, Ga., 5,383......E2 55
Dawson, Minn., 1,699......F2 67
Dawson, Tex., 848......D4 84
Dawson, co., Ga., 3,639...B2 55
Dawson, co., Mont., 11,269......C11 70
Dawson, co., Nebr., 19,771......D6 71
Dawson, co., Tex., 16,604......C1 84
Dawson, mtn., B.C., Can......D9 37
Dawson Creek, B.C., Can., 11,885......B7, m8 37
Dawson Springs, Ky., 3,009......C2 62
Dax, Fr., 19,348 (*26,000)......F3 5
Day, co., S. Dak., 8,713....E8 77
Dayrūt, Eg., 27,646......C4 23
Dayton, Ky., 8,751......h14 62
Dayton, Ohio, 242,917 (*934,000)......C1 78
Dayton, Tenn., 4,361......D8 83
Dayton, Tex., 3,804..D5, q15 84
Dayton, Va., 978......B4 85
Dayton, Wash., 2,596......C8 86
Daytona Beach, Fla., 45,327 (*103,000)......C5 54
Daytona Beach Shores, Fla., 768......*C6 54
Dayville, Conn., 800......B9 52
De Aar, S. Afr., 17,823....G4 24
Dead Indian, peak, Wyo...B3 89
Dead Knoll, mtn., Wyo....D2 89
Deadwood, S. Dak., 2,409..F2 77
Deaf Smith, co., Tex., 18,999......B1 84
Deal, N.J., 2,401......C4 74
Deale, Md., 1,059......C4 53
Deán Funes, Arg., 16,280..A4 28
Dearborn, Mich., 104,199......F7, p15 66
Dearborn, co., Ind., 29,430......F8 59
Dearborn Heights, Mich., 80,069......p15 66
Death, valley, Calif......D5 50
Deauville, Fr., 5,232......C4 5
De Baca, co., N. Mex., 2,547......B6 48
Debaltsevo, Sov. Un., 35,000......q21 12
Debar, Yugo., 6,341......E5 10
De Bary, Fla., 3,154......D5 54
Dębica, Pol., 22,900......C6 7
Dębno, Pol., 10,700......B3 7
Deboullie, mtn., Maine....B4 64
Debrecen, Hung., 155,122..B5 10
Decatur, Ala., 38,044......A3 46
Decatur, Ga., 21,943...C2, h8 55
Decatur, Ill., 90,397 (*115,900)......D5 58
Decatur, Ind., 8,445......C8 59
Decatur, Mich., 1,764......F5 66
Decatur, Miss., 1,311......C4 68
Decatur, Tex., 3,240......C4 84
Decatur, co., Ga., 22,310...F2 55
Decatur, co., Ind., 22,738..F6 59
Decatur, co., Iowa, 9,737......D5 60
Decatur, co., Kans., 4,988..C3 61
Decatur, co., Tenn., 9,457..B3 83
Decazeville, Fr., 10,532 (*26,000)......E5 5
Deccan, reg., India......E6 20
Deception, mtn., Wash......B2 86
Decherd, Tenn., 2,148......B5 83
Děčín, Czech., 44,228......C3 7
Decorah, Iowa, 7,458......A6 60
Dededo, Guam, 2,247....*F6 2
Dedham, Mass., 26,938......B5, h11 65
Dedinovo, Sov. Un., 5,000......n19 12
Deephaven, Minn., 3,853......F5, n11 67
Deep River, Ont., Can., 5,671......A7 41
Deep River, Conn., 2,333..D7 52
Deepwater, N.J., 650......D2 74
Deer, mtn., Maine......C2 64
Deerfield, Ill., 18,876......h9 58
Deerfield, Mich., 834......G7 66
Deerfield Beach, Fla., 16,662......F6 54
Deer Lake, Newf., Can., 4,421......D3 44
Deer Lodge, Mont., 4,306..D4 70
Deer Lodge, co., Mont., 15,652......D3 70
Deer Park, N.Y., 32,000...*F3 75
Deer Park, Ohio, 7,415...o13 78
Deer Park, Tex., 12,773...*E5 84
Deer Park, Wash., 1,295...B8 86
Deer River, Minn., 815....C5 67
Defense Highway, Md., 1,000......*C4 53
Defiance, Ohio, 16,281....A1 78
Defiance, co., Ohio 36,949......A1 78
Defiance, mtn., Oreg......B5 80
De Forest, Wis., 1,911......E4 88
De Funiak Springs, Fla., 4,966......u15 54
Deggendorf, Ger., Fed. Rep. of, 22,426......D6 6
De Graff, Ohio, 1,117......B2 78
Dehiwala-Mount Lavinia, Sri Lanka, 154,785......*G7 20
Dehra Dūn, India, 166,073 (*203,464)......B6 20
Dej, Rom., 19,281......B6 10
De Kalb, Ill., 32,949......B5 58
De Kalb, Miss., 1,072......C5 68
De Kalb, Tex., 2,197......C5 84
De Kalb, co., Ala., 41,981......A4 46
De Kalb, co., Ga., 415,387......C2 55
De Kalb, co., Ill., 71,654...B5 58
De Kalb, co., Ind., 30,837......B7 59
De Kalb, co., Mo., 7,305...B3 69
De Kalb, co., Tenn., 11,151......D8 83
Delafield, Wis., 3,182......*E5 88
Del Aire, Calif., 5,000....*F4 50
Delanco, N.J., 4,011......C3 74
De Land, Fla., 11,641......C5 54
Delano, Calif., 14,559......E4 50
Delano, Minn., 1,851......E5 67
Delavan, Ill., 1,844......C4 58
Delavan, Wis., 5,526......F5 88
Delaware, Ohio, 15,008....B2 78
Delaware, co., Ind., 129,219......D7 59
Delaware, co., Iowa, 18,770......B6 60
Delaware, co., N.Y., 44,718......C5 75
Delaware, co., Ohio, 42,908......B2 78
Delaware, co., Okla., 17,767......A7 79
Delaware, co., Pa., 601,715......G11 81
Delaware, state, U.S., 573,000......C11 45
Delaware, bay, Del.,......B7 53
Delaware City, Del., 2,024......A6 53
Delbarton, W. Va., 903......D2 87
Delcambre, La., 1,975......E4 63
Del City, Okla., 27,133....B4 79
Delémont, Switz., 11,300...E3 6
De Leon, Tex., 2,170......C3 84
De Leon Springs, Fla., 900......C5 54
Delft, Neth., 87,777......A6 5
Delfzijl, Neth., 22,771......A7 5
Delhi, Calif., 1,175......*D3 50
Delhi, Ont., Can., 3,894...E4 41
Delhi, India, 3,706,558 (*4,500,000)......C6 20
Delhi, ter., India, 4,065,698......*C6 20
Delhi, La., 2,887......B4 63
Delhi, N.Y., 3,017......C6 75
Delhi Hills, Ohio, 9,000...*C1 78
Delisle, Que., Can., 1,302..A6 42
Delitzsch, Ger. Dem. Rep., 24,300......C6 6
Dellenbaugh, mtn., Ariz......A2 48
Dell Rapids, S. Dak., 1,991......G9 77
Dellwood, Mo., 7,137....*C7 69
Del Mar, Calif., 3,956....o15 50
Delmar, Del., 943......D6 53
Delmar, Md., 1,191......D6 53
Delmar, N.Y., 8,900......C7 75
Delmenhorst, Ger., Fed. Rep. of, 66,052......B4 6
Delmont, Pa., 1,934......*F2 81
Del Monte Park, Calif., 1,500......*D3 50
Del Norte, Colo., 1,569....D4 51
Del Norte, co., Calif., 14,580......B2 50
Deloraine, Man., Can., 916......E1 40
Delphi, Ind., 2,582......C4 59
Delphos, Ohio, 7,608......B1 78
Delran, N.J., 10,065......C3 74
Delray Beach, Fla., 19,915..F6 54
Del Rey Oaks, Calif., 1,823......*D3 50
Del Rio, Tex., 21,330......E2 84
Delson, Que., Can., 2,941.q19 42
Delta, Colo., 3,694......C2 51
Delta, Ohio, 2,544......A2 78
Delta, Pa., 778......G9 81
Delta, Utah, 1,610......B5 72
Delta, co., Colo., 15,286....C3 51
Delta, co., Mich., 35,924...G3 66
Delta, co., Tex., 4,927......C5 84
Delta, peak, B.C., Can......A3 37
Delta Amacuro, ter., Ven., 33,979......B5 32
Deltaville, Va., 500......C6 85
Demarest, N.J., 5,133......h9 74
Demavend, mtn., Iran,.....F8 16
Demidov, Sov., Un., 10,000......D8 12
Deming, N. Mex., 8,343....C5 48
Demirci, Tur., 13,007......C7 14
Demmin, Ger. Dem. Rep., 16,400......B6 6
Demopolis, Ala., 7,651....C2 46
Demorest, Ga., 1,070......B3 55
Demotte, Ind., 1,697......B3 59
Dempo, mtn., Indon......F2 19
Denain, Fr., 27,973 (*130,000)......B5 5
Denbigh, Wales, 8,340....D5 4
Denbigh, co., Wales, 184,830......*D5 4
Denham Springs, La., 6,752......D5, h10 63

Den Helder, Neth., 61,457............A6 5
Denia, Sp., 7,876.........C6 8
Deniliquin, Austl., 6,604...G7 25
Denison, Iowa, 5,882.....B2 60
Denison, Tex., 24,923....C4 84
Denizli, Tur., 82,372....D7 14
Denmark, S.C., 3,571.....E5 82
Denmark, Wis., 1,364............D6, h10 88
Denmark, country, Eur., 5,035,000......I3 11
Dennison, Ohio, 3,506....B4 78
Dennis Port, Mass., 1,410..C7 65
Denny Terrace, S.C., 2,000...........C5 82
Denpasar, Indon., 88,142..G5 19
Dent, co., Mo., 11,457...D6 69
Denton, Ga., 244........E4 55
Denton, Md., 1,561......C6 53
Denton, N.C., 1,017.....B2 76
Denton, Tex., 39,874.....C4 84
Denton, co., Tex., 75,633...C4 84
Dentsville, S.C., 2,700...C6 82
Denver, Colo., 514,678 (*1,105,400)...........B6 51
Denver, Iowa, 1,169.....B5 60
Denver, Pa., 2,248.......F9 81
Denver, co., Colo., 514,678 (*1,105,400)...B6 51
Denver City, Tex., 4,133..C1 84
Denville, N.J., 14,045....B4 74
Departure Bay, B.C., Can., 3,744...........f12 37
De Pere, Wis., 13,309........D5, h9 88
Depew, N.Y., 22,158....C2 75
Deposit, N.Y., 2,061....C5 75
Depue, Ill., 1,919.......B4 58
De Queen, Ark., 3,863...C1 49
De Quincy, La., 3,448...D2 63
Dera Ghazi Khan, Pak., 47,105..........B5 20
Dera Ismail Khan, Pak., 44,319 (*46,140)..B5 20
Derby, Austl., 2,521.....C3 25
Derby, Colo., 10,124.....*B6 51
Derby, Conn., 12,599....D4 52
Derby, Eng., 219,320 (*270,000)..........D6 4
Derby, Kans., 7,947.....E6 61
Derby, N.Y., 3,000......C2 75
Derby, co., Eng., 884,950..*D6 4
Derecske, Hung., 9,970...B5 10
De Ridder, La., 8,030....D2 63
Derita, N.C., 4,400......B2 76
Dermott, Ark., 4,250....D4 49
Derry, N.H., 11,712.....F5 73
Derry, Pa., 3,338.......F3 81
Derventa, Yugo., 11,830..C3 10
Derzhavinskoye, Sov. Un.,......D9 16
Des Allemands, La., 2,318..........E5, k11 63
Des Arc, Ark., 1,714......C4 49
Desbiens, Que., Can., 1,813.............A6 42
Deschaillons sur St. Laurent, Que., Can., 1,283...........*C5 42
Deschambault, Que., Can. 1,056.............C6 42
Deschênes, Que., Can., 2,090.............D2 42
Deschutes, co., Oreg., 30,442............D5 80
Dese, Eth., 45,731......F5 23
Deseronto, Ont., Can., 1,797.............C7 41
Desert Hot Springs, Calif., 2,738............*F5 50
Desha, co., Ark., 18,761..D4 49
Deshler, Nebr., 937......D8 71
Deshler, Ohio, 1,938....A2 78
Desloge, Mo., 2,818.....D7 69
De Smet, S. Dak., 1,336..F8 77
Des Moines, Iowa, 201,404 (*300,700).........C4, e8 60
Des Moines, Wash., 3,951...........B3, f11 86
Des Moines, co., Iowa 46,982............D6 60
De Soto, Kans., 1,839...........D9, m16 61
De Soto, Mo., 5,984......C7 69
De Soto, Tex., 6,617....*C4 84
De Soto, co., Fla., 13,060............E5 54
De Soto, co., Miss., 35,885............A3 68
De Soto, par., La., 22,764..B2 63
Des Peres, Mo., 5,333...f13 69
Des Plaines, Ill., 57,239...........A6, h9 58
Dessau, Ger. Dem. Rep., 100,441 (*135,000).....C6 6
Destin, Fla., 900........u15 54

Detmold, Ger., Fed. Rep. of, 65,316..........C4 6
Detroit, Mich., 1,513,601 (*4,720,000).......F7, p15 66
Detroit Beach, Mich., 2,053...............*G7 66
Detroit Lakes, Minn., 5,797...............D3 67
Detva, Czech., 11,032....D5 7
Deuel, co., Nebr., 2,717..C3 71
Deuel, co., S. Dak., 5,686..F9 77
Deurne, Bel., 81,507....B6 5
Deux-Montagnes, Que., Can., 8,631...........p19 42
Deux-Sèvres, dept., Fr., 326,462............*D3 5
Deva, Rom., 16,879......C6 10
Dévaványa, Hung., 10,828.B5 10
Deventer, Neth., 63,979...A7 5
Devils Lake, N. Dak., 7,078...............B7 77
Devine, Tex., 3,311......E3 84
De Vola, Ohio, 1,989.....C4 78
Devon, Alta., Can., 1,418..C4 38
Devon, Pa., 4,500.......*G10 81
Devon, co., Eng., 889,420............*E5 4
Devon, isl., Can.......*A15 36
Devonport, Austl., 18,150.............o15 25
Devonport, N.Z., 11,000..L15 26
Dewar, Okla., 933.......B6 79
Dewey, Okla., 3,958.....A6 79
Dewey, co., Okla., 5,656..B2 79
Dewey, co., S. Dak., 5,170...............E5 77
De Witt, Ark., 3,728.....C4 49
De Witt, Iowa, 3,647....C7 60
De Witt, Mich., 1,829.....F6 66
De Witt, N.Y., 10,032....*B4 75
De Witt, co., Ill., 16,975............C5 58
De Witt, co., Tex., 18,660..E4 84
Dewsbury, Eng., 51,600...A6 4
Dexter, Maine, 2,732, (3,725▲)..........C3 64
Dexter, Mich., 1,729....F7 66
Dexter, Mo., 6,024......E8 69
Dexter, N.Y., 1,061.....A4 75
Dezful, Iran, 84,499......C4 15
Dhahran (Az Zahran), Sau. Ar., 12,500........D5 15
Dhamar, Yemen, 20,000...G3 15
Dhanbad, India, 79,545 (*600,000)............*D8 20
Dharamjaygarh, India D7 20
Dharmapuri, India, 40,086............F6 20
Dharmsāla, India, 10,939..B6 20
Dhārwār, India, 110,000..E6 20
Dhaulāgiri, peak, Nep....C7 20
Dhidhimótikhon, Grc., 8,388..............E8 10
Dhule, India, 137,129....D5 20
Diablo, Calif., 2,096.....*D2 50
Diablo, mtn., Calif.......h9 50
Diablo Heights, C.Z., 1,178...............*B2 32
Diamante, Arg., 13,600...A4 28
Diamantina, Braz., 17,551.............E6 27
Diamantina, Braz., 14,252..B4 30
Diamond, peak, Oreg.....D4 80
Diamond Springs, Calif., 900................C3 50
Diber (Dibra), pref., Alb., 96,000.............*E5 10
D'Iberville, Miss., 3,005...........E5, f8 68
Diboll, Tex., 3,557......D5 84
Dickens, co., Tex., 3,737...C2 84
Dickenson, co., Va., 16,077..............e9 85
Dickey, co., N. Dak., 6,976...............D7 77
Dickinson, N. Dak., 12,405.D3 77
Dickinson, Tex., 4,715....*E5 84
Dickinson, co., Iowa 12,565.............A2 60
Dickinson, co., Kans., 19,993.............D6 61
Dickinson, co., Mich., 23,753.............*B3 66
Dickson, Tenn., 5,665....A4 83
Dickson, co., Tenn., 21,977.............A4 83
Dickson City, Pa., 7,698...........D10, m18 81
Didsbury, Alta., Can., 1,254.............D3 38
Diégo-Suarez (Antsirane), Mad., 44,000.........C9 24
Dien Bien Phu, Viet *A2 19
Diepholz, Ger., Fed. Rep. of, 11,515..........B4 6
Dieppe, N.B., Can., 4,277..C5 43
Dieppe, Fr., 29,970 (*40,000).............C4 5

Dierks, Ark., 1,159........C1 49
Digboi, India, 16,538 (*32,388)...........C10 20
Digby, N.S., Can., 2,363..E4 43
Digby, co., N.S., Can., 19,827.............E4 43
Dighton, Kans., 1,540....D3 61
Digne, Fr., 12,478......E7 5
Digoin, Fr., 10,050.....D5 5
Dijon, Fr., 145,357 (*185,000)...........D6 5
Dikson, Sov. Un., 10,000..B11 16
Dili, Indon., 29,312......G7 19
Dilley, Tex., 2,362......E3 84
Dillingen [an der Donau], Ger., Fed. Rep. of, 21,468............D5 6
Dillon, Mont., 4,548.....E4 70
Dillon, S.C., 6,391......C9 82
Dillon, co., S.C., 28,838...C9 82
Dillonvale, Ohio, 1,095...B5 78
Dillsburg, Pa., 1,441....F7 81
Dilworth, Minn., 2,321...D2 67
Dimitrovgrad, Bul., 41,816.............D7 10
Dimmit, co., Tex., 9,039..E3 84
Dimmitt, Tex., 4,327....B1 84
Dimona, Isr., 23,700....C3 15
Dimondale, Mich., 970...F6 66
Dinan, Fr., 13,137......C3 5
Dinant, Bel., 9,769.....B6 5
Dinard, Fr., 9,052......C2 5
Dindigul, India, 128,429..F6 20
Dingwall, Scot., 4,133....B4 4
Dinh Lap, Viet., 10,000..*G6 17
Dinuba, Calif., 7,917....D4 50
Dinwiddie, co., Va., 25,046............C5 85
Diourbel, Sen., 28,600....F1 22
Dipolog, Phil., 20,019...*D6 19
Dire Dawa, Eth., 66,570..G6 23
Diriamba, Nic., 15,100...E7 34
Dirranbandi, Austl., 708..E8 25
Dishman, Wash., 7,800...g14 86
Dismal, peak, Va.......C2 85
Disraëli, Que., Can., 3,384.............D6 42
District Heights, Md., 7,846.............*C4 53
District of Columbia, U.S., 740,000........C3, f8 53
Distrito Federal, fed. dist., Mex., 6,073,100.....D5 34
Distrito Federal, fed. dist., Ven., 1,257,515......A4 32
Disūq, Eg., 45,580......*G8 14
Diu, India, 6,214.......D5 20
Divernon, Ill., 1,010....D4 58
Dives-sur-Mer, Fr., 6,299 (*11,500)............C3 5
Divide, co., N. Dak., 4,564.............B2 77
Divide, peak, Wyo......E5 89
Divinópolis, Braz., 69,872..C4 30
Divnoye, Sov. Un., 17,300............I14 12
Dix, mtn., N.Y.........A7 75
Dixfield, Maine, 1,535...D2 64
Dixiana, Ala., 600......B3 46
Dixie, co., Fla., 5,480....C3 54
Dixmoor, Ill., 4,735.....*B6 58
Dixon, Calif., 4,432.....C3 50
Dixon, Ill., 18,147......B4 58
Dixon, Mo., 1,387......D5 69
Dixon, co., Nebr., 7,453..B9 71
Dixonville, Pa., 900.....E3 81
Diyarbakir, Tur., 149,566.D13 14
Djajapura, see Jayapura, Indon.
Djakarta, see Jakarta, Indon.
Djakovica, Yugo., 29,638..D5 10
Djakovo, Yugo., 15,958...C4 10
Djelfa, Alg., 25,472......B5 22
Djibouti, Dji., 41,200...F6 23
Djibouti, country, Afr., 95,000..........F6 23
Djombang, Indon., 45,450............*G4 19
Djurdjevac, Yugo., 6,408..B3 10
Djursholm, Swe., 7,400....t36 11
Dmitriyevka, Sov. Un., 10,000...........H12, r21 12
Dmitrov, Sov. Un., 44,000............C11 12
Dmitrovsk-Orlovskiy, Sov. Un., 10,000.....E10 12
Dnepr, riv., Sov. Un......H9 12
Dneprodzerzhinsk, Sov. Un., 227,000.....G10 12
Dnepropetrovsk, Sov. Un., 862,000 (*1,225,000)..G10 12
Dnestr, riv., Sov. Un......H7 12
Dno, Sov. Un., 10,000...C7 12
Dobbs Ferry, N.Y., 10,353............g13 75
Döbeln, Ger. Dem. Rep., 27,328.............C6 6

Doboj, Yugo., 18,108......C4 10
Dobrich, see Tolbukhin, Bul.
Dobrogea, reg., Rom., 510,500.............*C9 10
Dobruja, reg., Bul......C9 10
Dobruja, reg., Rom......C9 10
Docena, Ala., 1,100........f7 46
Doddridge, co., W. Va., 6,389.............B4 87
Dodge, co., Ga., 15,658...D3 55
Dodge, co., Minn., 13,037............G6 67
Dodge, co., Nebr., 34,782..C9 71
Dodge, co., Wis., 69,004...E5 88
Dodge Center, Minn., 1,603.............F6 67
Dodge City, Kans., 14,127............E3 61
Dodgeville, Wis., 3,255...F3 88
Dodoma, Tan., 13,435....B7 24
Doerun, Ga., 1,157......E3 55
Doe Run, Mo., 800......D7 69
Doha (Ad Dawḩah), Qatar, 95,000........D5 15
Doi Inthanon, mtn., Thai..............E10 20
Dolbeau, Que., Can., 7,633 (*11,234).......G19 36
Dôle, Fr., 27,188.......D6 5
Dolgeville, N.Y., 2,872...B6 75
Dolina, Sov. Un., 5,000...D8 7
Dolinsk (Ochiai), Sov. Un., 30,000......C11 18
Dolomite, Ala., 2,400...B3, g7 46
Dolores, Arg., 16,003....B5 28
Dolores, Ur., 13,300.....E1 30
Dolores, co., Colo., 1,641..D2 51
Dolores Hidalgo, Mex., 16,849............m13 34
Dolton, Ill., 25,937......k9 58
Dolzhanskaya, Sov. Un., 5,000.............q22 12
Domažlice, Czech., 8,451..D2 7
Dominguez, Calif., 6,000..*F4 50
Dominica, Br. dep., N.A., 74,000............I14 35
Dominican Republic, country, N.A., 4,470,000......E8 35
Dominion, N.S., Can., 2,879.................C9 43
Domodossola, It., 18,700..A2 9
Dom Pedrito, Braz., 20,522............E2 30
Don, riv., Sov. Un......H13 12
Dona Ana, co., N. Mex., 69,773............C5 48
Donaghadee, N. Ire., 3,687.............C4 4
Donaldsonville, La., 7,367...........D4, h10 63
Donalsonville, Ga., 2,907..E2 55
Don Benito, Sp., 25,248...C3 8
Doncaster, Eng., 81,060 (*158,000).........D6 4
Donegal, co., Ire., 108,549............*C2 4
Doneraile, S.C., 1,417....C8 82
Donets, riv., Sov. Un....G13 12
Donetsk, Sov. Un., 879,000 (*1,850,000).....H11, r20 12
Donggala, Indon., 3,821...F5 19
Dong Hoi, Viet., 10,000...B3 19
Doniphan, Mo., 1,850....E7 69
Doniphan, co., Kans., 9,107.............C8 61
Donkin, N.S., Can., 1,010.............C10 43
Donley, co., Tex., 3,641...B2 84
Donna, Tex., 7,365......F3 84
Donnacona, Que., Can., 5,940 (*7,898).....C6, o16 42
Donora, Pa., 8,825......F2 81
Donzère, Fr., 1,544.....E6 5
Doolittle, Mo., 509......D6 69
Dooly, co., Ga., 10,404...D3 55
Door, co., Wis., 20,106...D6 88
Dora, Ala., 1,862.......B2 46
Doraville, Ga., 9,157....h8 55
Dorchester, N.B., Can., 1,779.............D5 43
Dorchester, Eng., 13,720..E5 4
Dorchester, co., Que., Can., 33,669.........C7 42
Dorchester, co., Md., 29,405............D5 53
Dorchester, co., S.C., 32,421............E6 82
Dordogne, dept., Fr., 374,073............*E4 5
Dordrecht, Neth., 101,416 (*177,879).........B6 5
Dores do Indaiá, Braz., 12,511............B3 30
Dorgali, It., 7,189.......D2 9
Dorion-Vaudreuil, Que., Can., 6,209 ....q18 42

Dorking, Eng., 22,680....m12 4
Dormont, Pa., 12,856.....k13 81
Dornbirn, Aus., 34,772....E4 6
Dornoch, Scot., 833.......B4 4
Dorohoi, Rom., 14,771....B8 10
Dorris, Calif., 840.........B3 50
Dorset, co., Eng., 364,420...............*F5 4
Dortmund, Ger., Fed. Rep. of, 638,288........C3 6
Dorton, Ky., 700.........C7 62
Dörtyol, Tur., 12,947.....D11 14
Dorval, Que., Can., 20,469................q19 42
Dos Hermanas, Sp., 21,517 (27,696 ▲).......D3 8
Dos Palos, Calif., 2,496....D3 50
Dothan, Ala., 36,733......D4 46
Douai, Fr., 49,187 (*180,000).............B5 5
Douala, Cam., 200,000....H6 22
Douarnenez, Fr., 19,705...C1 5
Doubletop, peak, Wyo.....C2 89
Doubs, dept., Fr., 426,363..............*D7 5
Dougherty, co., Ga., 89,639.................E2 55
Douglas, Alsk., 1,243...........D13, k22 47
Douglas, Ariz., 12,462.....D4 48
Douglas, Ga., 10,159......E4 55
Douglas, I. of Man, 20,385 (*28,000).......C4 4
Douglas, Wyo., 2,677.....D7 89
Douglas, co., Colo., 8,407..B6 51
Douglas, co., Ga., 28,659..C2 55
Douglas, co., Ill., 18,997...D5 58
Douglas, co., Kans., 57,932................D8 61
Douglas, co., Minn., 22,892................E3 67
Douglas, co., Mo., 9,268...E5 69
Douglas, co., Nebr., 389,455...............C9 71
Douglas, co., Nev., 6,882...B2 72
Douglas, co., Oreg., 71,743................D3 80
Douglas, co., S. Dak., 4,569.................G7 77
Douglas, co., Wash., 16,787.................B6 86
Douglas, co., Wis., 44,657..B1 88
Douglass, Kans., 1,126.....E7 61
Douglasville, Ga., 5,472...C2 55
Doullens, Fr., 7,119.......B5 5
Douro Litoral, prov., Port., 1,240,149.............*B1 8
Dove Creek, Colo., 619....D2 51
Dover, Del., 17,488.......B6 53
Dover, Eng., 34,210.......E7 4
Dover, Fla., 800..........D4 54
Dover, Mass., 1,881......h10 65
Dover, N.H., 20,850 (*54,400).............E6 73
Dover, N.J., 15,039.......B3 74
Dover, Ohio, 11,516.......B4 78
Dover, Pa., 1,168.........F8 81
Dover, Tenn., 1,179.......A4 83
Dover-Foxcroft, Maine, 3,102 (4,178 ▲).........C3 64
Dover Plains, N.Y., 950...D7 75
Dowagiac, Mich., 6,583...G4 66
Down, co., N. Ire., 310,617..............*C4 4
Downers Grove, Ill., 32,751.............B5, k8 58
Downey, Calif., 88,442....n12 50
Downington, Pa., 7,437...F10 81
Downpatrick, N. Ire., 7,403..................C4 4
Downs, Kans., 1,268.......C5 61
Downs, mtn., Wyo.......C3 89
Downton, mtn., B.C., Can.C5 37
Dows, Iowa, 777..........B4 60
Doylestown, Ohio, 2,373...B4 78
Doylestown, Pa., 8,270....F11 81
Doyline, La., 716.........B2 63
Dracut, Mass., 18,214.....A5 65
Draganovo, Bul., 5,465....D7 10
Drăgășani, Rom., 9,963....C7 10
Dragerton, Utah, 1,614...*B6 72
Draguignan, Fr., 18,376...F7 5
Drain, Oreg., 1,204.......D3 80
Drake, peak, Oreg.........E6 80
Drakesboro, Ky., 907......C2 62
Drama, Grc., 29,692......B5 14
Drama, prov., Grc., 91,015................*B5 14
Drammen, Nor., 48,700 (*66,000).........H4, p28 11
Drancy, Fr., 69,444.......g10 5
Draper, Utah, 900....A6, D2 72
Dravosburg, Pa., 2,916...*E1 81
Drayton, N. Dak., 1,095...A8 77
Drayton, S.C., 1,400......B4 82
Drayton Plains, Mich., 16,462.................F7 66
Drayton Valley, Alta., Can., 3,900............C3 38
Drenthe, prov., Neth., 359,900...............*A7 5
Dresden, Ont., Can., 2,369.................E2 41
Dresden, Ger. Dem. Rep., 506,067 (*640,000)......C6 6
Dresden, Ohio, 1,516.......B3 78
Dresden, Tenn., 1,939.....A3 83
Dreux, Fr., 29,408........C4 5
Drew, Miss., 2,574........B3 68
Drew, co., Ark., 15,157....D4 49
Drexel, N.C., 1,431.......B1 76
Drexel, Ohio, 4,000.......C1 78
Drexel Hill, Pa., 32,200 .*G11 81
Drift, Ky., 600...........C7 62
Drifton, Pa., 600........D10 81
Driggs, Idaho, 727........F7 57
Driskill, mtn., La.........B3 63
Drissa, Sov. Un., 10,000...D6 12
Drogheda, Ire., 19,762....D3 4
Drogobych, Sov. Un., 56,000................G4 12
Druid Hills, N.C., 1,500..*f10 76
Drumheller, Alta., Can., 5,446.................D4 38
Drummond, co., Que., Can., 63,281............D5 42
Drummond Range, mts., Austl..................D8 25
Drummondville, Que., Can., 31,813 (*46,524).......D3 42
Drummondville Ouest, Que., Can., 2,057......*D5 42
Drumright, Okla., 2,931...B5 79
Druzhkovka, Sov. Un., 53,000................q20 12
Dryden, Ont., Can., 6,939..................o16 41
Dryden, N.Y., 1,490......C4 75
Duarte, Calif., 14,981....*E5 50
Duarte, peak, Dom. Rep...E8 35
Dubach, La., 1,096........B3 63
Dubai (Dubayy), U.A.E., 57,500...............D6 15
Dubawnt, lake, N.W. Ter., Can........D13 36
Dubbo, Austl., 17,767.....F8 25
Dublin, Ga., 15,143.......D4 55
Dublin, Ind., 1,021.......E7 59
Dublin (Baile Átha Cliath), Ire., 567,866 (*835,000)............D3 4
Dublin, Tex., 2,810.......C3 84
Dublin, Va., 1,653........C2 85
Dublin, co., Ire., 795,047..D3 4
Dubois, co., Ind., 30,934..H4 59
Du Bois, Pa., 10,112......D4 81
Duboistown, Pa., 1,468....D7 81
Dubossary, Sov. Un., 17,000................H7 12
Dubovka, Sov. Un., 11,700...............G15 12
Dubrovnik, Yugo., 31,106.................D4 10
Dubuque, Iowa, 62,309 (*76,900).............B7 60
Dubuque, co., Iowa, 90,609.................B7 60
Duchesne, co., Utah, 7,299..................A6 72
Duchov, Czech., 10,466....C2 7
Duck, mtn., Man., Can....D1 40
Ducktown, Tenn., 562.....D9 83
Dudinka, Sov. Un., 20,000...............C11 13
Dudley, Eng., 185,390.....D5 4
Dudley, Mass., 3,470 (8,087 ▲).............B4 65
Due West, S.C., 1,380.....C3 82
Dufferin, co., Ont., Can., 17,108................C4 41
Dugger, Ind., 1,150.......F3 59
Duisburg, Ger., Fed. Rep. of, 441,452........C3 6
Duitama, Col., 31,865 (52,537 ▲).............B3 32
Dukes, co., Mass., 6,117...D6 65
Dulawan, Phil., 16,376...*D6 19
Duluth, Ga., 1,810.....B2, g8 55
Duluth, Minn., 100,578 (*155,000)...............D6 67
Dumaguete, Phil., 13,924..D6 19
Dumas, Ark., 4,600.......D4 49
Dumas, Tex., 9,771.......B2 84
Dumfries, Scot., 28,963....C5 4
Dumfries, Va., 1,890......B5 85
Dumfries, co., Scot., 87,677................*C5 4
Dumont, N.J., 20,155..B5, h9 74
Dumyāṭ (Damietta), Eg., 86,327.................G8 14
Dunaföldvár, Hung., 11,251.................B4 10
Dunapataj, Hung., 4,846...B4 10
Dunaujváros, Hung., 44,200.................B4 10
Dunayevsty, Sov. Un., 10,000..................G6 12
Dunbar, Pa., 1,499.......G2 81
Dunbar, Scot., 4,576......B5 4
Dunbar, W. Va., 9,151............C3, m12 87
Dunbarton, co., Scot., 236,771...............*B4 4
Duncan, Ariz., 773........C4 48
Duncan, B.C., Can., 4,388.............E6, g12 37
Duncan, Okla., 19,718....C4 79
Duncan, S.C., 1,266.......B3 82
Duncannon, Pa., 1,739....F7 81
Duncansville, Pa., 1,427...F5 81
Duncanville, Tex., 14,105.n10 34
Dundalk, Ont., Can., 852..C4 41
Dundalk, Ire., 21,672.....C3 4
Dundalk, Md., 85,600...........B4, g11 53
Dundas, Ont., Can., 17,208.................D5 41
Dundas, co., Ont., Can., 17,106.................B9 41
Dundee, Ill., 3,295....A5, h6 58
Dundee, Fla., 1,660.......D5 54
Dundee, Mich., 2,472.....G7 66
Dundee, N.Y., 1,539......C4 75
Dundee, Scot., 182,930 (*205,000)......B5 4
Dundee, S. Afr., 15,614....F6 24
Dundy, co., Nebr., 2,926..D4 71
Dunean, S.C., 3,000......*B3 82
Dunedin, Fla., 17,639.D4, o10 54
Dunedin, N.Z., 82,700 (*112,000)............P13 26
Dunellen, N.J., 7,072......B4 74
Dunfermline, Scot., 51,738 (*127,000).......B5 4
Dungannon, N. Ire., 7,535..................C3 4
Dungarvan, Ire., 5,583....D3 4
Dungulah, Sud., 3,350.....E4 23
Dunkerque, Fr., 27,504 (*145,000)............B5 5
Dunkirk, Ind., 3,465......D7 59
Dunkirk, N.Y., 16,855.....C1 75
Dunkirk, Ohio, 1,036......B2 78
Dunkirk, see Dunkerque, Fr.
Dunklin, co., Mo., 33,742................E7 69
Dun Laoghaire, Ire., 53,171..................D3 4
Dunlap, Ind., 3,500.......A6 59
Dunlap, Iowa, 1,292......C2 60
Dunlap, Tenn., 1,672.....D8 83
Dunlo, Pa., 950..........F4 81
Dunmore, Pa., 18,168.........D10, m18 81
Dunn, N.C., 8,302........B4 76
Dunn, co., N. Dak., 4,895..C3 77
Dunn, co., Wis., 28,991...D2 88
Dunnellon, Fla., 1,146.....C4 54
Dunn Loring, Va., 1,100..*B5 85
Dunnville, Ont., Can., 5,576..................E5 41
Dunoon, Scot., 8,865......C4 4
Dunseith, N. Dak., 811...................A5 77
Dunsmuir, Calif., 2,214....B2 50
Dunville, Newf., Can., 1,742 (*4,365)..........E5 44
Du Page, co., Ill., 491,882.A5 58
Duparquet, Que., Can., 978...............*D3 42
Duplin, co., N.C., 38,015..C5 76
Dupnitsa, see Stanke Dimitrov, Bul.
Dupo, Ill., 2,842..........E3 58
Dupont, Pa., 3,431.......n18 81
Duque de Caxais, Braz., 173,077..............*C4 30
Duquesne, Pa., 11,410............F2, k14 81
Du Quoin, Ill., 6,691......E4 58
Dūrā, Jordan, 3,852.......C3 15
Durand, Mich., 3,678......F6 66
Durand, Wis., 2,103......D2 88
Durango, Colo., 10,333....D3 51
Durango, Mex., 150,541...C4 34
Durango, state, Mex., 826,100...............C4 34
Durant, Iowa, 1,472.......C7 60
Durant, Miss., 2,752......B4 68
Durant, Okla., 11,118.....D5 79
Durazno, Ur., 22,203......E1 30
Durazno, dept., Ur., 53,362................*E1 30
Durban, S. Afr., 495,458 (*1,040,000)...........F6 24
Düren, Ger., Fed. Rep. of, 89,277..................C3 6
Durg, India, 67,892 ......*D7 20
Durham, Calif., 950.......C3 50
Durham, Maine, (1,264 ▲)...............g7 64
Durham, Ont., Can., 2,448..................C4 41
Durham, Eng., 29,100.....C6 4
Durham, N.H., 7,221......E6 73
Durham, N.C., 95,438 (*170,000).............B4 76
Durham, co., Ont., Can., 44,549................C6 41
Durham, co., Eng., 1,413,590............*C6 4
Durham, co., N.C., 132,681..................A4 76
Durres, Alb., 53,200......*B2 14
Duryea, Pa., 5,264..D10, m17 81
Dushanbe, Sov. Un., 388,000..................F9 13
Duson, La., 1,190.........D3 63
Düsseldorf, Ger., Fed. Rep. of, 637,136 (*1,135,000).C3 6
Dutchess, co., N.Y., 222,295................D7 75
Dutton, Ont., Can., 815...E3 41
Duval, co., Fla., 528,865...B5 54
Duval, co., Tex., 11,722...F3 84
Duvergé, Dom. Rep., 8,000..................E8 35
Duxbury, Mass., 2,000 (7,636 ▲)..............B6 65
Düzce, Tur., 28,209.......B8 14
Dvůr Králové [nad Labem], Czech., 16,256.........C3 7
Dwight, Ill., 3,841........B5 58
Dyer, Ind., 4,906.........A2 59
Dyer, Tenn., 2,501........A3 83
Dyer, co., Tenn., 30,427...A2 83
Dyersburg, Tenn., 14,523..A2 83
Dyersville, Iowa, 3,437....B6 60
Dyrlow, see Darłowo, Pol.
Dysart, Iowa, 1,251.......B5 60
Dzaudzhikau, see Ordzhonikidze, Sov. Un.
Dzerzhinsk, Sov. Un., 47,000................q20 12
Dzerzhinsk, Sov. Un., 221,000...........C14, d7 12
Dzhambul, Sov. Un., 187,000..............E10 13
Dzhankoy, Sov. Un., 43,000................I1 12
Dzialdowo, Pol., 10,100....B6 7
Dzierzlow, see Darłowo, Pol.
Dzierżoniów, Pol., 32,800 (*73,000)........C4 7
Dzilam Gonzáles, Mex., 3,119..................C7 34
Dzitbalché, Mex., 4,393..................C6 34

E

Eads, Colo., 795.........C8 51
Eagan, Tenn., 140.......C10 83
Eagle, W. Va., 200...C3, m13 87
Eagle, co., Colo., 7,498....B4 51
Eagle, mtn., Tex........o12 84
Eagle, peak, Calif........B3 50
Eagle Grove, Iowa, 4,489..B4 60
Eagle Lake, Fla., 1,373...*E5 54
Eagle Lake, Maine, 839
  (1,138▲)..............A4 64
Eagle Lake, Tex., 3,587...E4 84
Eagle Pass., Tex., 15,364..E2 84
Eagle River, Wis., 1,326...C4 88
Eagleton Village, Tenn.,
  3,000.................*D10 83
Eagleville, Pa., 1,700...o20 81
Earle, Ark., 3,146........B5 49
Earlimart, Calif., 2,897...E4 50
Earlington, Ky., 2,321....C2 62
Earlville, Ill., 1,410.....B5 58
Earlville, N.Y., 1,050.....C5 75
Early, Iowa, 727.........B2 60
Early, co., Ga., 12,682...E2 55
Earth, Tex., 1,152.......B1 84
Easley, S.C., 11,175.....B2 82
East, div., Ice., 9,794...*n15 11
East Alamosa, Colo., 1,040.D5 51
East Alliance, Ohio,
  1,175.................*B5 78
East Alton, Ill., 7,309....E3 58
East Angus, Que., Can.,
  4,715..................D6 42
East Aurora, N.Y., 7,033..C2 75
East Bangor, Pa., 905....E11 81
East Bank, La., 15,713....k7 63
Eastbank, W. Va., 1,025..m13 87
East Bathurst, N.B., Can.,
  1,876..................B4 43
East Baton Rouge, par.,
  La., 285,167...........D4 63
East Berlin, Pa., 1,086...G8 81
East Bernstadt, Ky., 700...C5 62
East Berwick, Pa., 2,090..*D9 81
East Bethel, Minn.,
  2,586.................*E5 67
East Billerica, Mass., 1,500.f11 65
Eastborough, Kans.,
  1,141.................g12 61
Eastbourne, Eng. 68,810..E7 4
East Brady, Pa., 1,218....E2 81
East Brewton, Ala., 2,336..D2 46
East Bridgewater, Mass.,
  2,900 (8,34▲)..........B6 65
East Brookfield, Mass.,
  1,392 (1,800▲).........B3 65
East Brooklyn, Conn.,
  1,377.................*B9 52
East Broughton Station,
  Que., Can., 1,127
  (*2,515)...............C6 42
East Brunswick, N.J.,
  31,700.................C4 74
East Butler, Pa., 919.....E2 81
East Canon, Colo., 1,805..C5 51
East Canton, Ohio,
  1,631.................*B4 78
East Carroll, par., La.,
  12,884.................B4 63
East Chelmsford, Mass.,
  2,000.................f10 65
Eastchester, N.Y.,
  22,900................*E7 75
East Chicago, Ind.,
  46,982.................A3 59
East Chicago Heights, Ill.,
  5,000.................*B6 58
East China, sea, China....F9 17
East Cleveland, Ohio,
  39,600.................g9 78
East Conemaugh
  (Conemaugh)
  Pa., 2,710............*E4 81
East Coulée, Alta., Can.,
  683...................D4 38
East Detroit, Mich.,
  45,920................p16 66
East Douglas, Mass.,
  1,763..................B4 65
East Dubuque, Ill.,
  2,408..................A3 58
East Dundee, Ill., 2,920..*A5 58
East Ely, Nev., 1,992.....D7 72
Eastern, reg., Nig.,
  12,394,462.............G6 22
Eastern Valley, Ala.,
  1,600.................*f6 46
East Falmouth, Mass.,
  2,971..................C6 65
East Farmington Heights,
  Conn., 1,600..........*B6 52

East Faxon, Pa., 4,175...*D7 81
East Fayetteville, N.C.,
  3,500.................*B3 76
East Feliciana, par., La.,
  17,657.................D4 63
East Flanders, prov., Bel.,
  1,308,300.............*B5 5
East Flat Rock, N.C.,
  2,627.................f10 76
East Gaffney, S.C.,
  3,750..................A4 82
Eastgate, Wash., 5,000...*B3 86
East Glenville, N.Y.,
  11,800................*C7 75
East Grand Forks, Minn.,
  7,607..................C2 67
East Grand Rapids, Mich.,
  12,565.................F5 66
East Greenbush, N.Y.,
  1,325.................*C7 75
East Greenville, Pa.,
  2,003.................F10 81
East Greenwich, R.I.,
  9,577.................C11 52
East Hampden, Maine,
  950...................*D4 64
East Hampton, Conn.,
  3,497..................C6 52
Easthampton, Mass.,
  13,012.................B2 65
East Hampton, N.Y.,
  1,753.................m16 75
East Hartford, Conn.,
  57,583.................B6 52
East Haven, Conn.,
  25,120.................D5 52
East Hazelcrest, Ill.,
  1,885.................*B6 58
East Helena, Mont.,
  1,651..................D5 70
East Herkimer, N.Y.,
  1,135.................*B6 75
East Hickory, N.C.,
  3,274.................*B1 76
East Hills, N.Y., 8,624...*E7 75
East Islip, N.Y., 13,700...G4 52
East Jordan, Mich., 2,041..C5 66
East Keansburg, N.J.,
  3,100.................*C4 74
East Kingsford, Mich.,
  1,155.................*C2 66
Eastlake, Ohio, 19,690....A4 78
Eastland, Tex., 3,178.....C3 84
Eastland, co., Tex.,
  18,092.................C3 84
East Lansdowne, Pa.,
  3,186.................*G11 81
East Lansing, Mich.,
  47,540.................F6 66
East Liverpool, Ohio,
  20,020.................B5 78
East London, S. Afr.,
  118,298 (*190,000).....G5 24
East Longmeadow, Mass.,
  13,029.................B2 65
East Los Angeles, Calif.,
  100,000...............m12 50
East Lothian, co., Scot.,
  55,795................*C5 4
East McKeesport, Pa.,
  3,233.................*F2 81
Eastman, Ga., 5,416.....D3 55
East Marietta, Ga., 8,700..*A5 55
East Meadow, N.Y.,
  46,290................n15 75
East Millbury, Mass.,
  1,000.................*B4 65
East Millinocket, Maine
  2,567..................C4 64
East Moline, Ill., 20,832...B3 58
East Moriches, N.Y.,
  1,702..................F5 52
East Naples, Fla., 2,500...F5 54
East Newark, N.J., 1,922..k8 74
East Newnan, Ga., 500....C2 55
East Northport, N.Y.,
  21,500.................F3 52
East Norwich, N.Y.,
  3,600.................*F2 52
Easton, Calif., 2,500.....*D4 50
Easton, Maine, 100......B5 64
Easton, Md., 6,809.......C5 53
Easton, Pa., 29,450.....E11 81
East Orange, N.J.,
  75,471.............B4, h8 74
East Palatka, Fla., 1,133..C5 54
East Palestine, Ohio,
  5,604..................B5 78
East Palo Alto, Calif.,
  18,099................*D2 50

East Patchogue, N.Y.,
  8,092.................G5 52
East Peoria, Ill., 20,226....C4 58
East Pepperell, Mass.,
  1,500..................A4 65
East Petersburg, Pa.,
  3,407..................F9 81
East Pines, Md., 3,000....*C4 53
East Pittsburgh, Pa.,
  3,006.................*k14 81
East Point, Ga.,
  39,315.............C2, h8 55
Eastport, Newf., Can.,
  438...................D5 44
Eastport, Maine, 1,989...D6 64
Eastport, N.Y., 1,308.....n16 75
East Prairie, Mo., 3,275...E8 69
East Pryor, mtn., Mont....E8 70
East Providence, R.I.,
  48,207................B11 52
East Quincy, Calif.,
  1,500.................*C3 50
East Quogue, N.Y.,
  1,143.................*n16 75
East Richmond, Calif.,
  5,000.................*D2 50
East Ridge, Tenn.,
  21,799................h11 83
East Rochester, N.Y.,
  8,347..................B3 75
East Rochester, Pa.,
  920...................*E1 81
East Rockaway, N.Y.,
  11,795.................G2 52
East Rockingham, N.C.,
  2,858..................C3 76
East Rockwood, Mich.,
  400...................*F7 66
East Rutherford, N.J.,
  8,536..................h8 74
East St. John, N.B.,
  Can., 4,466...........D3 43
East St. Louis, Ill.,
  69,996.................E3 58
East Setauket, N.Y.,
  1,400..................F4 52
Eastside, Oreg., 1,331.....D2 80
East Sparta, Ohio, 959....B4 78
East Spencer, N.C., 2,217..B2 76
East Stroudsburg, Pa.,
  7,894.................D11 81
East Sudbury, Mass.,
  2,500.................g10 65
East Syracuse, N.Y.,
  4,333..................B4 75
East Tawas, Mich.,
  2,372..................D7 66
East Templeton, Mass.,
  900...................A3 65
East Troy, Wis., 1,711....F5 88
East Uniontown, Pa.,
  2,333.................*G2 81
East Vandergrift, Pa.,
  1,151.................*F2 81
East Walpole, Mass.,
  3,000..................D2 65
East Wareham, Mass.,
  900...................C6 65
East Washington, Pa.,
  2,198..................F1 81
East Wenatchee, Wash.,
  913...................B5 86
East Whittier, Calif.,
  19,884................*F4 50
East Williston, N.Y.,
  2,808..................G2 52
East Wilmington, N.C.,
  5,520.................*C5 76
Eastwood, Mich., 6,000..*E5 66
East York, Ont., Can.,
  104,784...............*m15 41
East York, Pa., 1,800....*G8 81
Eaton, Colo., 1,389.......A6 51
Eaton, Ind., 1,594........D7 59
Eaton, Ohio, 6,020........C1 78
Eaton, co., Mich., 68,892..F6 66
Eaton Rapids, Mich.,
  4,494..................F6 66
Eatonton, Ga., 4,125.....C3 55
Eatontown, N.J., 14,619...C4 74
Eatonville, Wash., 852....C3 86
Eau Claire, Wis., 44,619
  (*78,100).............D2 88
Eau Claire, co., Wis.,
  67,219.................D2 88
Ebensburg, Pa., 4,318....F4 81
Eberswalde, Ger. Dem.
  Rep., 47,037...........B6 6
Ebetsu, Jap., 63,762.....E10 18
Ebingen, Ger., Fed. Rep.
  of, 25,462.............D4 6

Eboli, It., 20,900.........D5 9
Eccles, W. Va.,
  1,145.............D3, n13 87
Eceabat (Maydos), Tur.,
  2,800.................*B6 14
Echigawa, Jap..........n15 18
Echols, co., Ga., 1,924....F3 55
Echuca, Austl., 7,510....G7 25
Écija, Sp., 31,000.......D3 8
Eckernförde, Ger., Fed.
  Rep. of, 21,301........A4 6
Eckert, Colo., 1,163......C3 51
Eckhart Mines, Md., 900..k13 53
Eckman, W. Va., 800....*D3 87
Eclectic, Ala., 1,184......C3 46
Economy, Pa., 7,176.....*E1 81
Ecorse, Mich., 17,515....p15 66
Ector, co., Tex., 91,805...D1 84
Ecuador, country, S.A.,
  6,825,000.............. 31
Edcouch, Tex., 2,656.....F4 84
Eddiceton, Miss., 130.....D3 68
Eddy, co., N. Mex.,
  41,119.................C6 48
Eddy, co., N. Dak., 4,103..C7 77
Eddystone, Pa., 2,706....p20 81
Eddyville, Iowa, 945......C5 60
Eddyville, Ky., 1,981......e9 62
Ede, Neth., 39,800........A4 5
Ede, Nig., 134,550.......*G5 22
Edea, Cam., 11,000......H7 22
Eden, N.Y., 2,962........C2 75
Eden, N. Car., 15,871.....A3 76
Eden, Tex., 1,291........D3 84
Edenborn, Pa., 500.......G2 81
Edenton, N.C., 4,956.....A6 76
Edgar, Wis., 928.........D4 88
Edgar, co., Ill., 21,591...D6 58
Edgartown, Mass., 1,006
  (1,481▲)..............D6 65
Edgecombe, co., N.C.,
  52,341.................B5 76
Edgefield, S.C., 2,750....D4 82
Edgefield, co., S.C.,
  15,692.................D3 82
Edgeley, N. Dak., 888....D7 77
Edgely, Pa., 530.........*F11 81
Edgemere, Md., 7,000....*B5 53
Edgemont, Calif., 3,500..*F5 50
Edgemont, S. Dak., 1,174..G2 77
Edgerton, Minn., 1,119...G2 67
Edgerton, Ohio, 2,126....A1 78
Edgerton, Wis., 4,118.....F4 88
Edgewater, Ala., 1,400....f7 46
Edgewater, Colo., 4,910...B5 51
Edgewater, Fla., 3,348....D6 54
Edgewater, Md., 500......C4 53
Edgewater, N.J., 4,987....h9 74
Edgewater Park, N.J.,
  7,412..................C3 74
Edgewood, Ind., 2,326....D6 59
Edgewood, Ky., 4,139.....A7 62
Edgewood, Md., 8,000....B5 53
Edgewood, Ohio, 3,437...A5 78
Edgewood, Pa., 5,138....k14 81
Edgewood, Pa., 3,399....*D8 81
Edgeworth, Pa., 2,200...h13 81
Edhessa, Grc., 13,967....B4 14
Edina, Minn., 44,046.....n12 67
Edina, Mo., 1,574........A5 69
Edinboro, Pa., 4,871......C1 81
Edinburg, Ill., 1,153......D4 58
Edinburg, Ind., 4,906.....F6 59
Edinburg, Miss., 500......C4 68
Edinburg, Tex., 17,163...F3 84
Edinburgh, Scot., 453,025
  (*645,000)............C5 4
Edirne, Tur., 53,806......B6 14
Edison, Ga., 1,210.......E2 55
Edison, N.J., 67,120......B4 74
Edisto Island, S.C.,
  30................F7, k11 82
Edith, mtn., Mont........D5 70
Edmeston, N.Y., 800.....C5 75
Edmond, Okla., 16,633...B4 79
Edmonds, Wash., 23,998..B3 86
Edmonson, co., Ky., 8,751.C3 62
Edmonston, Md., 1,441...*C4 53
Edmonton, Alta., Can.,
  438,152 (*495,702)..C4, g8 38
Edmonton, Eng., 90,800..K12 4
Edmore, Mich., 1,149.....E5 66
Edmunds, co., S. Dak.,
  5,548..................E6 77
Edmundson, Mo., 2,298..*C7 69
Edmundston, N.B., Can.,
  12,365.................B1 43
Edna, Tex., 5,332........E4 84
Edremit, Tur., 24,115....*C6 14

Edson, Alta., Can., 3,818 .... C7, g7 38
Edwards, Miss., 1,236 .... C3 68
Edwards, co., Ill., 7,090 .... E5 58
Edwards, co., Kans., 4,581 .... E4 61
Edwards, co., Tex., 2,107 .... E2 84
Edwardsburg, Mich., 1,107 .... G4 66
Edwardsville, Ill., 11,070 .... E4 58
Edwardsville, Pa., 5,633 .... n17 81
Eferding, Aus., 2,990 .... D7 6
Effinghan, Ill., 9,458 .... D5 58
Effingham, co., Ga., 13,632 .... D5 55
Effingham, co., Ill., 24,608 .... D5 58
Eganville, Ont., Can., 1,549 .... B7 41
Eger, Hung., 45,229 .... B5 10
Egg Harbor City, N.J., 4,304 .... D3 74
Egmont, mtn., N.Z., ... M15 26
Eğridir, Tur., 9,650 .... D8 14
Egypt, Mass., 1,500 .... B6, h12 65
Egypt, Pa., 1,200 .... E10 81
Egypt, country, Afr., 35,975,000 .... C3 23
Ehime, pref., Jap., 1,418,124 .... *J6 18
Ehrenfeld, Pa., 397 .... F4 81
Éibar, Sp., 31,725 .... A4 8
Eichstätt, Ger., Fed. Rep. of, 11,505 .... D5 6
Eidsberg, Nor., 233 .... H4, p29 11
Eidsvoll, Nor., 1,410 .... G4 11
Eilenburg, Ger. Dem. Rep., 19,400 .... C6 6
Einbeck, Ger., Fed. Rep. of, 19,747 .... C4 6
Eindhoven, Neth., 193,711 (*347,717) B6 5
Eire, see Ireland, country, Eur.
Eisenach, Ger. Dem. Rep., 50,236 .... C5 6
Eisenhüttenstadt, Ger. Dem. Rep., 46,478 .... B7 6
Eisenstadt, Aus., 10,073 .... E8 6
Eisleben, Ger. Dem. Rep., 29,852 .... C5 6
Ekalaka, Mont., 663 .... E12 70
Eksjö, Swe., 10,157 .... I6 11
El Aaiún, W. Sah., 5,500 .... C2 22
El Arahal, Sp., 17,361 .... D3 8
El Asnam (Orléansville), Alg., 49,109 .... A5 22
Elâziğ, Tur., 107,364 .... C12 14
Elba, Ala., 4,634 .... D3 46
El Banco, Col., 14,889 .... B3 32
El Barco, Sp., 7,041 .... A2 8
Elbasan, Alb., 33,900 .... B3 14
Elbasan, pref., Alb., 115,000 .... *B3 14
Elbe, (Labe), riv., Eur. B5 6
Elbert, Colo., 200 .... B6 51
Elbert, co., Colo., 3,903 .... B6 51
Elbert, co., Ga., 17,262 .... B4 55
Elberton, Ga., 6,438 .... B4 55
Elbeuf, Fr., 19,407 (*47,000) C4 5
Elbing, see Elblag, Pol.
Elbistan, Tur., 17,859 .... C11 14
Elbląg, Pol., 89,800 .... A5 7
El Bonillo, Sp., 5,286 .... C4 8
El Bordo, Col., 1,475 .... C2 32
Elbow Lake, Minn., 1,484 .... E3 67
Elbrus, mtn., Sov. Un. E7 13
Elburn, Ill., 1,122 .... B5 58
El Cajon, Calif., 52,273 .... F5, o16 50
El Campo, Tex., 9,332 .... E4 84
El Campo South, Tex., 1,880 .... *E4 84
El Capitan, mtn., Mont. D2 70
El Carmen de Bolivar, Col., 19,196 .... B2 32
El Carrizo, Mex., 127 .... B3 34
El Centro, Calif., 19,272 .... F6 50
El Cerrito, Calif., 25,190 .... h8 50
Elche, Sp., 90,000 (123,716 ▲) C5 8
El Cocuy, Col., 2,869 .... B3 32
Elda, Sp., 28,151 .... C5 8
Eldon, Iowa, 1,319 .... D5 60
Eldon, Mo., 3,520 .... C5 69
Eldora, Iowa, 3,223 .... B4 60
El Dorado, Ark., 25,283 .... D3 49
Eldorado, Ill., 3,876 .... F5 58
El Dorado, Kans., 12,308 .... E7, g13 61
Eldorado, Mex., 8,115 .... C3 34
Eldorado, Tex., 1,446 .... D2 84
El Dorado, co., Calif., 43,833 .... C3 50
Eldorado, peak, Wash. A4 86
El Dorado Springs, Mo., 3,300 .... D3 69
Eldoret, Ken., 19,605 .... H5 23
Eldred, Pa., 1,092 .... C5 81
Eldridge, Iowa, 1,535 .... C7, g10 60
Eleanor, W. Va., 1,035 .... C3 87
Electra, Tex., 3,895 .... C3 84
Electric, peak., Mont. D6 70
Eleele, Haw., 758 .... B2 56
Elektrostal, Sov. Un., 123,000 .... n18 12
Elephant, mtn., Maine D2 64
Elevsís (Eleusis), Grc., 18,535 .... g11 14
El Fasher, Sud., 40,500 .... F3 23
El Ferrol [del Caudillo], Sp., 80,194 (*106,000) A1 8
El Fuerte, Mex., 7,179 .... B3 34
Elgin, Ill., 55,691 .... A5, h8 58
Elgin, Iowa, 613 .... B6 60
Elgin, N. Dak., 839 .... D4 77
Elgin, Oreg., 1,375 .... B9 80
Elgin, Scot., 16,503 .... B5 4
Elgin, Tex., 3,832 .... D4 84
Elgin, co., Ont., Can., 61,912 .... E3 41
Elgon, mtn., Ken., Ug. H4 23
El Grullo, Mex., 10,538 .... n11 34
Elida, Ohio, 1,211 .... B1 78
Elim, Pa., 2,100 .... *E4 81
Eliot, Maine, 2,000 .... E2 64
Elizabeth, Austl., 33,363 .... F6 25
Elizabeth, Ga., 1,700 .... C2, h7 55
Elizabeth, La., 504 .... D3 63
Elizabeth, N.J., 112,654 .... B4, k8 74
Elizabeth, Pa., 2,273 .... *E1 81
Elizabeth City, N.C., 14,381 .... A6 76
Elizabeth Lake Estates, Mich., 3,000 .... *F7 66
Elizabethton, Tenn., 12,269 .... C11 83
Elizabethtown, Ky., 11,748 .... C4 62
Elizabethtown, N.C., 1,418 .... C4 76
Elizabethtown, Pa., 8,072 .... F8 81
Elizabethville, Pa., 1,629 .... E8 81
El Jadida, Mor., 55,501 .... B3 22
Elk, Pol., 27,100 .... B7 7
Elk, co., Kans., 3,858 .... E7 61
Elk, co., Pa., 37,770 .... D4 81
Elk, mtn., Wyo., 127 .... E6 89
Elk, peak, Mont. D6 70
Elkader, Iowa, 1,592 .... B6 60
El Kairouan, Tun., 46,199 .... A6 22
Elk City, Okla., 7,323 .... B2 79
El Kef, Tun., 23,244 .... A6 22
Elk Grove, Calif., 3,721 .... C3 50
Elk Grove Village, Ill., 21,907 .... h9 58
Elkhart, Ind., 43,152 .... A6 59
Elkhart, Kans., 2,089 .... E2 61
Elkhart, co., Ind., 126,529 .... A6 59
Elkhorn, W. Va., 900 .... *D3 87
Elkhorn, Wis., 3,992 .... F5 88
Elkhorn City, Ky., 1,081 .... C7 62
Elkhovo, Bul., 6,749 .... D8 10
Elkin N.C., 2,899 .... A2 76
Elkins, W. Va., 3,287 .... C5 87
Elkins Park, Pa., 14,000 .... o21 81
Elkland, Pa., 1,942 .... C7 81
Elk Mountain, N.C., 1,000 .... f10 76
Elko, Nev., 7,621 .... A4 72
Elko, co., Nev., 13,958 .... A4 72
Elk Point, S. Dak., 1,372 .... H9 77
Elk Rapids, Mich., 1,249 .... D5 66
Elkridge, Md., 2,000 .... B4, h10 53
Elkridge, W. Va., 400 .... m13 87
Elk River, Idaho, 383 .... C2 57
Elk River, Minn., 2,252 .... E5 67
Elk Run Heights, Iowa, 1,175 .... *B5 60
Elkton, Ky., 1,612 .... D2 62
Elkton, Md., 5,362 .... A6 53
Elkton, Mich., 973 .... E7 66
Elkton, Va., 1,511 .... B4 85
Elkville, Ill., 850 .... F4 58
Ellaville, Ga., 1,391 .... D2 55
Ellendale, N. Dak., 1,517 .... E7 77
Ellensburg, Wash., 13,568 .... C5 86
Ellenton, Fla., 950 .... E4, p10 54
Ellenville, N.Y., 4,482 .... D6 75
Ellerbe, N.C., 913 .... B3 76
Ellesmere, isl., N.W. Ter., Can. k34 36
Ellettsville, Ind., 1,627 .... F4 59
Ellicott City, Md., 2,000 .... B4 53
Ellicottville, N.Y., 955 .... C2 75
Ellijay, Ga., 1,326 .... B2 55
Ellington, Mo., 1,094 .... D7 69
Ellinwood, Kans., 2,416 .... D5 61
Elliott, co., Ky., 5,933 .... B6 62
Ellis, Kans., 2,137 .... D4 61
Ellis, co., Kans., 24,730 .... D4 61
Ellis, co., Okla., 5,129 .... A2 79
Ellis, co., Tex., 46,638 .... C4 84
Ellisville, Miss., 4,643 .... D4 68
Ellisville, Mo., 4,681 .... f12 69
Ellon, Scot., 2,349 .... B5 4
Elloree, S.C., 940 .... D6 82
Ellport, Pa., 1,350 .... E1 81
Ellsworth, Kans., 2,080 .... D5 61
Ellsworth, Maine, 4,603 .... D4 64
Ellsworth, Pa., 1,268 .... F1 81
Ellsworth, Wis., 1,983 .... D1 88
Ellsworth, co., Kans., 6,146 .... D5 61
Ellwangen, Ger., Fed. Rep. of, 22,427 .... D5 6
Ellwood City, Pa., 10,857 .... E1 81
Elma, N.Y., 2,784 .... *C2 75
Elma, Wash., 2,227 .... C2 86
El Mahdia, Tun., 15,900 .... A7 22
Elmali, Tur., 7,800 .... *D7 14
Elmer, N.J., 1,592 .... D2 74
Elm Grove, Wis., 7,201 .... *m11 88
Elmhurst, Ill., 48,887 .... B6, k9 58
Elmira, Ont., Can., 4,730 .... D4 41
Elmira, N.Y., 39,945 (*134,800) C4 75
El Mirage, Ariz., 3,258 .... D1 48
Elmira Heights, N.Y., 4,906 .... C4 75
Elmont, N.Y., 29,800 .... *G2 52
El Monte, Calif., 69,892 .... *E4 50
Elmora, Pa., 950 .... E4 81
Elmore, Minn., 910 .... G4 67
Elmore, Ohio, 1,316 .... A2 78
Elmore, co., Ala., 33,535 .... C3 46
Elmore, co., Idaho, 17,479 .... F3 57
Elmore City, Okla., 653 .... C4 79
Elmsford, N.Y., 3,911 .... g13 75
Elmshorn, Ger., Fed. Rep. of, 41,339 .... B4 6
Elmwood, Ill., 2,014 .... C4 58
Elmwood Park, Ill., 26,160 .... k9 58
Elmwood Park, N.J., 22,749 .... h8 74
Elmwood Place, Ohio, 3,525 .... o13 78
El Nevado, mtn., Col. C3 32
Elnora, Ind., 873 .... G3 59
El Obeid, Sud., 66,270 .... F4 23
Eloise, Fla., 3,256 .... E5 54
Elon College, N.C., 2,150 .... A3 76
Elora, Ont., Can., 1,486 .... D4 41
El Oro, prov., Ec., 208,700 .... B2 31
Eloy, Ariz., 5,381 .... C3 48
El Paso, Ill., 2,291 .... C4 58
El Paso, Tex., 322,261 (*780,000) o11 84
El Paso, co., Colo., 235,972 .... C6 51
El Paso, co., Tex., 359,291 .... o11 84
El Portal, Fla., 2,068 .... s13 54
El Porto Beach, Calif., 1,200 .... *F4 50
El Puerto de Santa María, Sp., 35,505 .... D2 8
Elrama, Pa., 800 .... F2 81
El Reno, Okla., 14,510 .... B4 79
El Rio, Calif., 7,800 .... E4 50
Elroy, Wis., 1,513 .... E3 88
Elsa, Tex., 4,400 .... F3 84
El Salto, Mex., 7,818 .... C3 34
El Salvador, country, N.A., 4,070,000 .... E7 34
Elsberry, Mo., 1,398 .... B6 69
El Segundo, Calif., 15,620 .... *F4 50
El Seibo, Dom. Rep., 9,000 .... E9 35
Elsie, Mich., 988 .... E6 66
Elsinore, Calif., 3,530 .... F5 50
Elsmere, Del., 8,415 .... A6 53
Elsmere, Ky., 5,161 .... B5, h13 62
El Sobrante, Calif., 11,500 .... *D2 50
Elsterwerda, Ger. Dem. Rep., 9,749 .... C6 6
El Tigre, Ven., 49,801 .... B5 32
El Tocuyo, Ven., 14,560 .... B4 32
Elton, La., 1,596 .... D3 63
Elūru, India, 127,023 .... E7 20
Elvas, Port., 11,742 .... C2 8
El Verano, Calif., 1,753 .... *C2 50
Elverum, Nor., 3,595 .... G4 11
El Viejo, mtn., Col. B3 32
Elvins, Mo., 1,660 .... D7 69
Elwood, Ind., 11,196 .... D6 59
Elwood, Kans., 1,283 .... C9 61
Elwood, N.Y., 15,031 .... n15 75
Elwyn, Pa., 1,500 .... *G11 81
Ely, Eng., 10,270 .... D7 4
Ely, Minn., 4,904 .... C7 67
Ely, Nev., 4,176 .... B4 72
Elyria, Ohio, 53,427 .... A3 78
Elysburg, Pa., 1,337 .... E8 81
Emanuel, co., Ga., 18,189 .... D4 55
Embetsu, Jap., 63,762 .... E10 18
Embrun, Ont., Can., 1,112 .... B9 41
Emden, Ger., Fed. Rep. of, 53,359 .... B3 6
Emerson, Man., Can., 830 .... E3 40
Emerson, Nebr., 850 .... B9 71
Emerson, N.J., 8,428 .... H8 74
Emery, co., Utah, 5,137 .... B6 72
Emeryville, Calif., 2,681 .... *D3 50
Emi Koussi, vol., Chad E1 23
Emilia, reg., It., ... B3 9
Emilia-Romagna, pol. dist., It., 3,815,300 .... B3 9
Emiliano Zapata, Mex., 6,422 .... D6 34
Eminence, Ky., 2,225 .... B4 62
Emirdağ, Tur., 12,559 .... C8 14
Emlenton, Pa., 854 .... D2 81
Emmaus, Pa., 11,511 .... E11 81
Emmen, Neth., 21,700 .... A7 5
Emerald, Austl., 2,188 .... D8 25
Emmerich, Ger., Fed. Rep. of, 24,772 .... C3 6
Emmet, co., Iowa, 14,009 .... A3 60
Emmet, co., Mich., 18,331 .... C6 66
Emmetsburg, Iowa, 4,150 .... A3 60
Emmett, Idaho, 3,945 .... F2 57
Emmitsburg, Md., 1,532 .... A3 53
Emmons, co., N. Dak., 7,200 .... D5 77
Empire, Calif., 1,635 .... *D3 50
Empire, La., 600 .... E6 63
Empire, Nev., 300 .... A2 72
Empoli, It., 33,500 .... C3 9
Emporia, Kans., 23,327 .... D7 61
Emporia, Va., 5,300 .... D5 85
Emporium, Pa., 3,074 .... D5 81
Emsdetten, Ger., Fed. Rep. of, 29,314 .... B3 6
Emsworth, Pa., 3,345 .... h13 81
Ena, Jap., 31,488 .... n16 18
Encarnación, Par., 23,343 .... E4 29
Encarnación de Díaz, Mex., 10,474 .... m12 34
Encinal, Tex., 700 .... E3 84
Encinitas, Calif., 5,000 .... F5 50
Ende, Indon., 26,843 .... G6 19
Enderby, B.C., Can., 1,075 .... D8 37
Enderlin, N. Dak., 1,343 .... D8 77
Endicott, N.Y., 16,556 .... C4 75
Endwell, N.Y., 15,999 .... *C4 75
Enfield, Conn., 3,500 .... B6 52
Enfield, Ill., 764 .... E5 58
Enfield, N.H., 1,408 .... D3 73
Enfield, N.C., 3,272 .... A5 76
Engaru, Jap., 14,595 .... D11 18
Engels, Sov. Un., 130,000 .... F16 12
Enghien, Fr., 12,152 .... g10 5
England, Ark., 3,075 .... C4, k11 49
England, reg., U.K., 46,745,000 .... D6 4
Englee, Newf., Can., 802 .... C3, h10 44
Englewood, Colo., 33,695 .... B6 51
Englewood, Fla., 5,108 .... *B5 54
Englewood, Fla., 5,182 .... F4 54
Englewood, Ind., 1,232 .... *G5 59
Englewood, N.J., 24,985 .... h9 74
Englewood, Ohio, 7,885 .... C1 78
Englewood, Oreg., 100 .... *D2 80
Englewood, Tenn., 1,878 .... D9 83
Englewood Cliffs, N.J., 5,938 .... *B5 74
Englishtown, N.J., 1,048 .... C4 74
Enguera, Sp., 5,663 .... C5 8
Enhaut, Pa., 950 .... *F8 81
Enid, Okla., 44,986 .... A4 79
Enka, N.C., 1,000 .... f10 76
Enköping, Swe., 23,736 (32,503 ▲) H7, t35 11
Enna, It., 28,700 .... F5 9
Ennis, Ire., 5,972 .... D2 4
Ennis, Tex., 11,046 .... C4, n10 84
Enniscorthy, Ire., 5,704 .... D3 4
Enniskillen, N. Ire., 6,553 .... C3 4
Enns, Aus., 9,624 .... D7 6
Enola, Pa., 3,600 .... F8 81
Enon, Ohio, 1,929 .... C2 78
Enoree, S.C., 700 .... B4 82
Enosberg Falls, Vt., 1,266 .... B2 73
Enriquillo, Dom. Rep., 4,100 .... F8 35
Enschede, Neth., 142,997 .... A7 5
Ensenada, Arg., 39,154 .... g8 28
Ensenada, Mex., 77,687 .... A1 34
Ensenada, P.R., 3,299 .... G11 35
Ensley, Fla., 2,200 .... u14 54
Entebbe, Ug., 10,941 .... H4 23
Enterprise, Ala., 15,591 .... D4 46
Enterprise, Calif., 4,946 .... *B2 50
Enterprise, Kans., 868 .... D6 61
Enterprise, Oreg., 1,680 .... B9 80
Entiat, mts., Wash., 355 .... B5 86
Entre Minho e Douro, reg., Port., 2,265,800 .... B1 8

Entre Ríos, prov., Arg.,
805,357......A5, f7 28
Enugu, Nig., 138,457......G6 22
Enumclaw, Wash.,
4,703............B4, f12 86
Enzan, Jap., 13,900
(26,723▲)............n17 18
Épernay, Fr., 26,583......C5 5
Ephraim, Utah, 2,127......B6 72
Ephrata, Pa., 9,662......F9 81
Ephrata, Wash., 5,255......B6 86
Épila, Sp., 5,072......B5 8
Épinal, Fr., 36,856
(*48,000)............C7 5
Épinay [-sur-Seine], Fr.,
41,774............g10 5
Epirus, reg., Grc.,......*C3 14
Epping, Eng., 11,720......k13 4
Epping, N.H., 1,097......E5 73
Epsom (& Ewell) Eng.,
72,120............m12 4
Epworth, Iowa, 1,132......B7 60
Equatorial Guinea, country,
Afr., 305,000............H6 22
Erath, La., 2,024......E3 63
Erath, co., Tex., 18,141...C3 84
Ercis, Tur., 19,532......C14 14
Erciyeş Dağı, mtn., Tur..C10 14
Érd, Hung., 23,177......B4 10
Erdek, Tur., 6,700......*B6 14
Erdenheim, Pa., 3,300...o21 81
Erding, Ger., Fed. Rep.
of, 11,006............D5 6
Ereğli, Tur., 28,904......B8 14
Ereğli, Tur., 46,727......D10 14
Erfurt, Ger. Dem. Rep.,
201,826............C5 6
Erice, It., 18,021......E4 9
Erick, Okla., 1,285......B2 79
Erickson, B.C., Can., 912..E9 37
Erie, Colo., 1,090......A5 51
Erie, Ill., 1,566......B3 58
Erie, Kans., 1,414......E8 61
Erie, Pa., 129,231
(*225,900)............B1 81
Erie, co., N.Y., 1,113,491..C2 75
Erie, co., Ohio, 75,909...A3 78
Erie, co., Pa., 263,654...C1 81
Erie, lake, N. Amer., U.S..B10 45
Erin, Tenn., 1,165......A4 83
Eritrea, prov., Eth.......E5 23
Erlangen, Ger., Fed. Rep.
of, 98,812 (*123,000)..D5 6
Erlanger, Ky., 12,676.A5, h13 62
Ermenak, Tur., 10,646...D9 14
Ermont, Fr., 19,263......g10 5
Ernakulam, India,
117,253............*G6 20
Ernest, Pa., 800............E3 81
Errigal, mtn., Ire.......C2 4
Errol Heights, Oreg.,
8,400............*B4 80
Erstein, Fr., 6,165......C7 5
Erwin, N.C., 2,852......B4 76
Erwin, Tenn., 4,715......C11 83
Erzincan, Tur., 58,352...C12 14
Erzurum, Tur., 133,444...C13 14
Esashi, Jap., 6,031......D11 18
Esashi, Jap., 10,048......F10 18

Esbjerg, Den., 57,400......J3 11
Escada, Braz., 19,994......*D7 27
Escalante, Utah, 638......C6 72
Escalón, Calif., 2,366......D3 50
Escalón, Mex., 2,998......B4 34
Escambia, co., Ala.,
34,906............D2 46
Escambia, co., Fla.,
205,334............u14 54
Escanaba, Mich., 15,368...C3 66
Escatawpa, Miss.,
1,579............E5, f8 68
Esch-sur-Alzette, Lux.,
27,575 (*96,000)......C7 5
Eschwege, Ger., Fed.
Rep. of, 24,912......C5 6
Eschweiler, Ger., Fed.
Rep. of, 54,440......C3 6
Escondido, Calif., 36,792...F5 50
Escoublac-La-Baule, Fr.,
13,336............D2 5
Escuinapa [de Hidalgo],
Mex., 16,442......C3 34
Escuintla, Guat., 37,180..*E6 34
Eşfahān (Isfahan), Iran,
424,045............C5 23
Esher, Eng., 64,760......m12 4
Eskdale, W. Va.,
400............C3, m13 87
Eskilstuna, Swe.,
92,656............H7, t34 11
Eskişehir, Tur., 216,373...C8 14
Esmeralda, co., Nev., 629..C3 72
Esmeraldas, Ec., 48,200...A2 31
Esmeraldas, prov., Ec.,
157,000............A2 31
Esmond, R.I., 4,500......B10 52
Espanola, Ont., Can.,
6,045............A3 41
Espanola, N. Mex., 4,136..B5 48
Esperanza, Arg., 10,035...A4 28
Espinal, Col., 22,791......C3 32
Espírito Santo, state, Braz.,
1,617,857............C4 30
Espita, Mex., 5,394......C7 34
Espy, Pa., 1,652......D9 81
Esquel, Arg., 14,000......C2 28
Esquimalt, B.C., Can.,
12,922............E6, h12 37
Essaouira, Mor., 30,061...B3 22
Essen, Ger., Fed. Rep. of,
682,336 (*5,375,000)...C3 6
Essendon, mtn., Austl....D3 25
Essex, Ont., Can., 4,002...E2 41
Essex, Conn., 2,473......D7 52
Essex, Md., 38,000......B5 52
Essex, co., Ont., Can.,
280,922............E2 41
Essex, co., Eng.,
1,359,260............*E7 41
Essex, co., Mass., 637,887..A5 65
Essex, co., N.J., 932,526...B4 74
Essex, co., N.Y., 34,631...B4 75
Essex, co., Vt., 5,416......B4 73
Essex, co., Va., 7,099......C6 85
Essex Fells, N.J., 2,541...*B4 74
Essex Junction, Vt., 6,511..C1 73
Essexville, Mich., 4,990...E7 66
Essington, Pa., 2,500......*G11 81
Esslingen, Ger., Fed. Rep.
of, 86,978............D4 6

Estacada, Oreg., 1,164......B4 80
Estância, Braz., 20,265...*E7 27
Estancia, N. Mex., 921......B5 48
Este, It., 11,800......B3 9
Estelí, Nic., 17,700......E7 34
Estepa, Sp., 9,476......D3 8
Esterhazy, Sask., Can.,
2,896............G4 39
Estes Park, Colo., 1,616...A5 51
Estevan, Sask., Can.,
9,150............H4 39
Esther, Mo., 1,040......*D7 69
Estherville, Iowa, 8,108...A3 60
Estill, S.C., 1,954......F5 82
Estill, co., Ky., 12,752...C5 62
Eston, Sask., Can., 1,695..F1 39
Estonia (S.S.R.), rep.,
Sov. Un., 1,415,000......B5 12
Estremadura, prov., Port.,
1,592,858............*C1 8
Estremadura, reg., Port.,
2,866,200............*C1 8
Estremoz, Port., 7,057......C2 8
Esztergom, Hung., 26,955..B4 10
Étampes Fr., 13,515......C5 5
Étaples, Fr., 9,095
(*19,000)............B4 5
Etāwah, India, 85,894......C6 20
Ethel, W. Va., 400......D5 87
Ethiopia (Abyssinia), country,
Afr., 26,465,000......G5 23
Etna, Pa., 5,819......k14 81
Etna, Monte, vol., It......F5 9
Etobicoke, Ont.,
282,686............D5, m14 41
Etowah, Tenn., 3,736......D9 83
Etowah, co., Ala., 94,144..A3 46
Ettrick, Va., 3,500......C5, n18 85
Etzatlan, Mex., 9,822......m11 34
Eu, Fr., 8,079 (*19,000)...B4 5
Euclid, Ohio, 71,552......A4, g9 78
Euclid Center, Mich.,
2,000............*F4 66
Eudora, Ark., 3,687......D4 49
Eudora, Kans.,
2,071............D8, m15 61
Eufaula, Ala., 9,102......D4 46
Eufaula, Okla., 2,355......B6 79
Eugene, Oreg., 79,028
(*171,100)............C3 80
Euless, Tex., 19,316......*C4 84
Eunice, La., 11,390......D3 63
Eunice, N. Mex., 2,641...C7 48
Eupen, Bel., 14,985......B7 5
Euphrates, see Firat, riv., Asia
Eupora, Miss., 1,792......B4 68
Eure, dept., Fr., 383,385..*C4 5
Eure-et-Loir, dept., Fr.,
302,207............*C4 5
Eureka, Calif., 24,337......B1 50
Eureka, Ill., 3,028......C4 58
Eureka, Kans., 3,576......E7 61
Eureka, Mo., 2,384......f12 69
Eureka, Mont., 1,195......B1 70
Eureka, S. Dak., 1,547...E6 77
Eureka, Utah, 753......B5 72
Eureka, co., Nev., 948......B3 72
Eureka Springs, Ark.,
1,670............A2 49

Europe, cont.,
642,200,000............3
Euskirchen, Ger., Fed.
Rep. of, 43,495......C3 6
Eustis, Fla., 6,722......D5 54
Eutaw, Ala., 2,805......C2 46
Evangeline, La., 800......D3 63
Evangeline, par., La.,
31,932............D3 63
Evans, Colo., 2,570......A6 51
Evans, co., Ga., 7,290......D5 55
Evans, mtn., Colo.......B5 51
Evans City (Evansburg),
Pa., 2,144............E1 81
Evansdale, Iowa, 5,038...B5 60
Evanston, Ill., 80,113..A6, h9 58
Evanston, Wyo., 4,462......E2 89
Evansville, Ill., 889......E4 58
Evansville, Ind., 138,764
(*204,200)............I2 59
Evansville, Wis., 2,992...F4 88
Evart, Mich., 1,707......E5 66
Evarts, Ky., 1,182......D6 62
Eveleth, Minn., 4,721......C6 67
Even Yehuda, Isr.,
52,49............*B2 15
Everard, mtn., B.C.,......D5 37
Everest, peak, China, Nep..C8 20
Everett, Mass., 42,485...g11 65
Everett, Pa., 2,243......F5 81
Everett, Wash., 53,622...B3 86
Everett, mtn., Mass.......B1 65
Everglades, Fla., 462......G5 54
Evergreen, Ala., 3,924......D3 46
Evergreen Park, Ill.,
25,921............k9 58
Everman, Tex., 4,570......*C4 84
Everson, Pa., 1,143......F2 81
Évora, Port., 24,144......C2 8
Évreux, Fr., 42,550......C4 5
Évros, prov., Grc.,
141,002............*B5 14
Evvoia (Euboea), prov.,
Grc., 165,822............*C4 14
Ewa, Haw., 2,906......B3, g9 56
Ewa Beach, Haw.,
7,765............g9 56
Ewing, N.J., 32,831......C3 74
Ewing, Va., 500......f8 85
Excelsior, Minn.,
2,563............F5, n11 67
Excelsior, mtn., Cal.......C4 50
Excelsior Springs, Mo.,
9,411............B3, h11 69
Exeter, Calif., 4,475......D4 50
Exeter, Ont., Can., 3,354..D3 41
Exeter, Eng., 93,800......E5 4
Exeter, N.H., 6,439......F6 73
Exeter, Pa., 4,670...D10, n17 81
Exira, Iowa, 966......C3 60
Exmore, Va., 1,421......C7 85
Exmouth, Austl., 2,638...D1 25
Exmouth, Eng., 25,470...E5 4
Experiment, Ga., 2,000...C2 55
Export, Pa., 1,402......F2 81
Eyemouth, Scot., 2,564...C5 4
Eylar, mtn., Calif.......D3 50
Eyre, lake, Austl.......E6 25
Ezine, Tur., 9,062......C6 14

F

Fabens, Tex., 3,200......o11 84
Fabriano, It., 19,200......C4 9
Facatativá Col., 20,742...C3 32
Factoryville, Pa., 922......C10 81
Fada Ngourma, Upper
Volta, 5,200............E6 21
Faenza, It., 31,700......B3 9
Faeroe Islands, Dan. dep.,
Eur., 40,000............C6 3
Fafe, Port., 5,855......B1 8
Făgăras, Rom., 17,256...C7 10
Fagatogo, Am. Sam.,
1,592............*G9 2
Fagersta, Swe., 16,495...C6 11
Faifo, Viet., 5,000......*B3 19
Fairbank, Iowa, 810......B5 60
Fairbanks, Alsk., 14,771..C10 47
Fair Bluff, N.C., 1,039...C3 76
Fairborn, Ohio, 32,267...C1 78
Fairburn, Ga., 3,143...C2, h7 55
Fairbury, Ill., 3,359......C5 58
Fairbury, Nebr., 5,265...D8 71

Fairchance, Pa., 1,906......G2 81
Fairdale, Ky., 4,100......g11 62
Fairfax, Ala., 3,107......C4 46
Fairfax, Calif., 7,661...C2, h7 50
Fairfax, Del., 4,000......*A6 53
Fairfax, Iowa, 635......C6 60
Fairfax, Minn., 1,432......F4 67
Fairfax, Mo., 835......A2 69
Fairfax, Ohio, 2,705......*C1 78
Fairfax, Okla., 1,889......A5 79
Fairfax, S.C., 1,937......F5 82
Fairfax (Independent City),
Va., 22,009............B5, g12 85
Fairfax, co., Va., 455,032...B5 85
Fairfield, Ala., 14,369...B3, f7 46
Fairfield, Calif., 44,146
(*71,700)............C2 50
Fairfield, Conn., 56,487...E3 52
Fairfield, Ill., 5,897......E5 58
Fairfield, Iowa, 8,715......D6 60
Fairfield, Maine, 3,694
(5,684▲)............D3 64

Fairfield, Mont., 638......C5 70
Fairfield, N.J., 6,884......*B4 74
Fairfield, Ohio, 14,680......n12 78
Fairfield, Tex., 2,074......D4 84
Fairfield, co., Conn.,
792,814............D3 52
Fairfield, co., Ohio,
73,301............C3 78
Fairfield, co., S.C., 19,999..C5 82
Fairgrove, Mich., 629......E7 66
Fair Grove, N.C., 1,100...*B2 76
Fairhaven, Mass., 16,332..C6 65
Fair Haven, Mich., 450...F8 66
Fair Haven, N.J. 6,142...C4 74
Fair Haven, N.Y., 859...B4 75
Fair Haven, Vt., 2,777...D1 73
Fairhope, Ala., 5,720......E2 46
Fairhope, Pa., 2,500......*G2 81
Fairland, Ind., 900......E6 59
Fairland, Okla., 958......A7 79
Fair Lawn, N.J., 37,975...h8 74
Fairlawn, Ohio, 6,102......*A4 78

Fairless Hills, Pa.,
12,500............*F11 81
Fairmont, Ill., 1,500......k8 58
Fairmont, Minn., 10,751...G4 67
Fairmont, N.C., 2,827......C3 76
Fairmont, Wash., 600......*B3 86
Fairmont, W. Va.,
26,093 (*51,600)...B4, k10 87
Fairmont City, Ill., 2,769..f13 69
Fairmount, Ill., 785......C6 58
Fairmount, Ind., 3,427...D6 59
Fairmount, N.Y., 15,317..*B4 75
Fairmount Heights, Md.,
1,972............f9 53
Fair Oaks, Calif., 15,500...C3 50
Fair Oaks, Calif., 1,622..*E3 50
Fair Oaks, Ga., 13,200......h7 55
Fairoaks, Pa., 1,646......h13 81
Fair Plain, Mich., 8,176...F4 66
Fairpoint, Ohio, 3,665...B5 78
Fairport, N.Y., 6,474......B3 75

Fairport Harbor, Ohio, 3,665 ... A4 78
Fairton, N.J., 800 ... E2 74
Fairvale, N.B., Can., 2,050 . D4 43
Fairview, Alta., Can., 2,109 ... A1 38
Fairview, Ill., 601 ... C3 58
Fairview, Mont., 956 ... C12 70
Fairview, N.J., 35 ... D3 74
Fairview, N.J., 10,698 ... h8 74
Fairview, N.Y., 8,517 ... *D7 75
Fairview, Ohio, 110 ... B4 78
Fairview, Okla., 2,894 ... A3 79
Fairview, Pa., 2,100 ... *D8 81
Fairview, Pa., 235 ... *E11 81
Fairview, Pa., 1,707 ... B1 81
Fairview, Tenn., 1,630 ... B4 83
Fairview, Utah, 696 ... B6 72
Fairview, Wash, 2,111 ... *C5 86
Fairview, peak, Oreg. ... D4 80
Fairview Park, Ind., 1,067 .. E3 59
Fairview Park, Ohio, 21,681 ... h9 78
Fairview Shores, Fla., 5,200 ... *D5 54
Fairvilla, Fla., 1,500 ... *D5 54
Fairway, Kans., 5,133 ... B9 61
Faison, N.C., 598 ... B4 76
Faizabad, Afg., 30,000 ... A5 20
Faizābād, India, 102,835 (*109,806) ... C7 20
Fajardo, P.R., 18,249 (23,032 ▲) ... G12 35
Fakfak, Indon., 1,800 ... F8 19
Fălciu, Rom., 5,124 ... B9 10
Falcón, state, Ven., 340,450 ... A3 32
Falconer, N.Y., 2,983 ... C1 75
Falcon Heights, Minn., 5,530 ... n12 67
Falconwood, N.Y., 2,100 .. *C2 75
Faleshty, Sov. Un., 5,000 ... B8 10
Falfurrias, Tex., 6,355 ... F3 84
Falher, Alta., Can., 741 ... B2 38
Falkirk, Scot., 37,489 (*139,000) ... C5 4
Falkland Islands, Br. dep., S.A., 2,000 ... I5 27
Falköping, Swe., 15,708 ... H5 11
Fall Branch, Tenn., 950 .. C11 83
Fallbrook, Calif., 5,100 ... F5 50
Fallon, Nev., 2,959 ... B2 72
Fallon, co., Mont., 4,050 . D12 70
Fall River, Mass., 96,898 (*150,400) ... C5 65
Fall River, co., S. Dak., 7,505 ... G2 77
Fall Rock, Ky., 50 ... C6 62
Falls, co., Tex., 17,300 ... D4 84
Falls Church (Independent City), Va., 10,772 ... g12 85
Falls City, Nebr., 5,444 .. D10 71
Falls City, Oreg., 745 ... C3 80
Falls Creek, Pa., 1,255 ... D4 81
Fallsington, Pa., 571 ... *F11 81
Falmouth, Eng., 17,960 ... E4 4
Falmouth, Jam., 3,900 ... E5 35
Falmouth, Ky., 2,593 ... B5 62
Falmouth, Maine, 6,291 ... E5 64
Falmouth, Mass., 4,000 ... C6 65
Falmouth, N.S., 831 ... E5 43
Falmouth, Va., 2,139 ... B5 85
Fălticeni, Rom., 13,305 ... B8 10
Falun, Swe., 37,379 ... G6 11
Fannin, co., Ga., 13,357 ... B2 55
Fannin, co., Tex., 22,705 ... C4 84
Fanny, mtn., Oreg. ... B9 80
Fano, It., 30,500 ... C4 9
Fanwood, N.J., 8,920 ... *B4 74
Farafangana, Mad., 9,500 ... E9 24
Farah, Afg., 12,000 ... B3 20
Faranah, Guinea, 2,250 ... F2 22
Fargo, N. Dak., 53,365 (*94,800) ... D9 77
Far Hills, N.J., 780 ... B3 74
Faribault, Minn., 16,595 ... F5 67
Faribault, co., Minn., 20,896 ... G5 67
Farina, Ill., 634 ... E5 58
Farley, Iowa, 1,096 ... B6 60
Farmer City, Ill., 2,217 ... C5 58
Farmers Branch, Tex., 27,492 ... n10 84
Farmersburg, Ind., 962 ... F3 59
Farmersville, Calif., 3,456 . *D4 50
Farmersville, Tex., 2,311 ... C4 84
Farmerville, La., 3,416 ... B3 63
Farmingdale, Maine, 1,832 (2,423 ▲) ... D3 64
Farmingdale, N.J., 1,148 ... C4 74
Farmingdale, N.Y., 9,297 .. G3 52
Farmington, Conn., 1,700 .. C5 52
Farmington, Ill., 2,959 ... C3 58
Farmington, Iowa, 800 ... D6 60
Farmington, Maine, 3,096, (5,657 ▲) ... D2 64
Farmington, Mich., 10,329 ... p15 66
Farmington, Minn., 3,104 ... F5 67
Farmington, Mo., 6,590 ... D7 69
Farmington, N.H., 2,884 (3,588 ▲) ... E5 73
Farmington, N. Mex., 21,979 ... A4 48
Farmington, Utah, 2,526 ... A6, C2 72
Farmington Hills, Mich., 48,694 ... o15 66
Farmingville, N.Y., 6,600 ... n16 75
Farmland, Ind., 1,262 ... D7 59
Farmville, N.C., 4,424 ... B5 76
Farmville, Va., 5,127 ... C4 85
Farnham, Que., Can., 6,496 ... D5 42
Farnham, mtn., B.C. ... D9 37
Faro, Port., 18,909 ... D2 8
Farrell, Pa., 11,022 ... D1 81
Farrukhābād, India, 102,768 (*110,835) ... C6 20
Farwell, Mich., 777 ... E6 66
Farwell, Tex., 1,185 ... B1 84
Fasano, It., 19,600 ... D6 9
Fastov, Sov. Un., 42,000 ... F7 12
Fatehpur, India, 54,665 ... C7 20
Fatsa, Tur., 14,266 ... B11 14
Faulk, co., S. Dak., 3,893 .. E6 77
Faulkner, co., Ark., 31,572 ... B3 49
Faulkton, S. Dak., 955 ... E6 77
Fauquier, co., Va., 26,375 ... B5 85
Faust, Alta., Can., 763 ... B3 38
Favara, It., 30,800 ... F4 9
Fawnie Nose, mtn., B.C., Can. ... C5 37
Faxon, Pa., 1,946 ... *D7 81
Fayette, Ala., 4,568 ... B2 46
Fayette, Iowa, 1,947 ... B6 60
Fayette, Miss., 1,725 ... D2 68
Fayette, Mo., 3,520 ... B5 69
Fayette, Ohio, 1,175 ... A1 78
Fayette, co., Ala., 16,252 .. B2 46
Fayette, co., Ga., 11,364 ... C2 55
Fayette, co., Ill., 20,752 ... D4 58
Fayette, co., Ind., 26,216 ... E7 59
Fayette, co., Iowa, 26,898 .. B6 60
Fayette, co., Ky., 174,323 .. B5 62
Fayette, co., Ohio, 25,461 .. C2 78
Fayette, co., Pa., 154,667 .. G2 81
Fayette, co., Tenn., 22,692 ... B2 83
Fayette, co., Tex., 17,650 .. E4 84
Fayette, co., W. Va., 49,332 ... C3 87
Fayette City, Pa., 968 ... *G2 81
Fayetteville, Ark., 30,729 (*63,900) ... A1 49
Fayetteville, Ga., 2,160 ... C2 55
Fayetteville, N.Y., 4,996 ... B5 75
Fayetteville, N.C., 53,510 (*202,700) ... B4 76
Fayetteville, Pa., 2,449 ... G6 81
Fayetteville, Tenn., 7,030 .. B5 83
Fayetteville, W. Va., 1,712 ... C3, m13 87
Fayville, Mass., 900 ... g9 65
Feasterville, Pa., 6,900 ... o21 81
Feather Falls, Calif., 560 ... C3 50
Fécamp, Fr., 21,406 ... C4 5
Federalsburg, Md., 1,917 .. C6 53
Federal Way, Wash., 18,500 ... *B3 86
Fedscreek, Ky., 400 ... C7 62
Feeding Hills, Mass., 6,000 ... B2 65
Feilding, N.Z., 9,880 ... N15 26
Feira de Santana, Braz., 127,105 ... *E7 27
Fejer, co., Hung., 390,000 ... *B4 10
Felanitx, Sp., 11,759 ... C7 8
Feldkirch, Aus., 21,776 ... E4 6
Felicity, Ohio, 786 ... D1 78
Felipe Carrillo Puerto, Mex., 2,052 ... D7 34
Fellsmere, Fla., 813 ... E6 54
Felton, Calif., 1,600 ... D2 50
Feltre, It., 18,800 ... A3 9
Fenelon Falls, Ont., Can., 1,359 ... C6 41
Fengshan, Taiwan, 5,000 ... *G9 17
Fennimore, Wis., 1,861 ... F3 88
Fennville, Mich., 811 ... F4 66
Fenton, Mich., 8,284 ... F7 66
Fenton, Mo., 2,275 ... f13 69
Fentress, co., Tenn., 12,593 ... C9 83
Fenyang, China, 30,000 ... D7 17
Feodosiya, Sov. Un., 65,000 ... I10 12
Ferdinand, Ind., 1,432 ... H4 59
Ferentino, It., 16,836 ... D4 9
Fergana, Sov. Un., 111,000 ... *E10 13
Fergus, Ont., Can., 5,433 (*9,775) ... D4 41
Fergus, co., Mont., 12,611 ... C7 70
Fergus Falls, Minn., 12,433 ... D2 67
Ferguson, Mo., 28,759 ... C7, f13 69
Fermanagh, co., N. Ire., 49,960 ... *C3 4
Ferme-Neuve, Que., Can., 1,990 ... C2 42
Fermo, It., 18,500 ... C4 9
Fernandina Beach, Fla., 6,955 ... B5, k9 54
Fern Creek, Ky., 6,000 ... g11 62
Ferndale, Calif., 1,352 ... B1 50
Ferndale, Md., 3,000 ... B4 53
Ferndale, Mich., 30,850 ... *F7 66
Ferndale, Pa. 2,482 ... F4 81
Ferndale, Wash., 2,164 ... A3 86
Fernie, B.C., Can., 4,422 .. E10 37
Fern Park, Fla., 1,200 ... D5 54
Fernwood, N.Y., 100 ... B4 75
Ferrara, It., 118,700 (156,600 ▲) ... B3 9
Ferreñafe, Peru, 12,112 ... C2 31
Ferriday, La., 5,239 ... C4 63
Ferris, Ont., Can., 4,338 .. *A5 41
Ferris, Tex., 2,180 ... C4, n10 84
Ferris, mts., Wyo ... D5 89
Ferry, co., Wash., 3,655 ... A7 86
Ferryland, Newf., Can., 713 ... E5 44
Ferrysburg, Mich., 2,196 .. *E4 66
Ferryville, Tun., 29,353 ... F2 9
Fertile, Minn., 955 ... C2 67
Fès, Mor., 325,327 ... B3 22
Fessenden, N. Dak., 815 ... C6 77
Festus, Mo., 7,530 ... C7, g13 69
Fetești, Rom., 15,383 ... C8 10
Fetters Hot Springs, Calif., 300 ... *C2 50
Ffestiniog, Wales, 5,680 ... D5 4
Fianarantsoa, Malag., 45,800 ... E9 24
Fidenza, It., 9,800 ... B3 9
Fieldale, Va., 1,337 ... D3 85
Fier, Alb., 11,000 ... *B2 14
Fierro Urco, vol., Peru ... B2 31
Fife, co., Sask., Can., 323,200 ... *B5 4
Fife, Wash., 1,458 ... *B3 86
Figeac, Fr., 6,933 ... E4 5
Figueira da Foz, Port., 10,855 ... B1 8
Figueras, Sp., 17,548 ... A7 8
Fiji, country, Oceania, 560,000 ... H8 2
Filer, Idaho., 1,173 ... G4 57
Filiatra, Grc., 5,919 ... D3 14
Fillmore, Calif., 6,285 ... E4 50
Fillmore, Utah, 1,411 ... B5 72
Fillmore, co., Minn., 21,916 ... G6 67
Fillmore, co., Nebr., 8,137 ... D8 71
Finderne, N.J., 4,500 ... *B3 74
Findlay, Ohio, 35,800 ... A2 78
Findlay, Ill., 809 ... D5 58
Findlay, mtn., B.C., Can ... D9 37
Finistère, dept., Fr., 768,929 ... *C2 5
Finland, country, Eur., 4,620,000 ... E12 11
Finney, co., Kans., 19,029 . D3 61
Finneytown, Ohio, 3,000 .. *C1 78
Finnmark, co., Nor., 76,500 ... *B13 11
Finspång, Swe., 19,052 ... u33 11
Finsterwalde, Ger. Dem. Rep., 22,500 ... C6 6
Firat (Euphrates), riv., Asia ... D12 14
Fircrest, Wash., 5,651 ... f10 86
Firebaugh, Calif., 2,517 ... D3 50
Firenze, see Florence, It.
Firenzuola, It., 743 ... B3 9
Firminy, Fr., 24,924 ... E6 5
Firozabad, India, 133,863 . *C6 20
Firozpur, India, 49,545 (*97,709) ... B5 20
Fisher, Ill., 1,525 ... C5 58
Fisher, co., Tex., 6,344 ... C2 84
Fisher, peak, Va. ... D2 85
Fishersville, Va., 700 ... B4 85
Fishguard, Wales, 4,960 ... E4 4
Fishing Creek, Md., 700 ... D5 53
Fishkill, N.Y., 913 ... D7 75
Fiskdale, Mass., 1,612 ... B3 65
Fitchburg, Mass., 43,343 (*100,100) ... A4 65
Fitzgerald, Ga., 8,187 ... E3 55
Fitz Roy, mtn., Arg ... D2 28
Fiume, see Rijeka, Yugo.
Five Points, N. Mex., 4,000 ... *B3 48
Flagler, co., Fla., 4,454 ... C5 54
Flagler Beach, Fla., 1,042 .. C5 54
Flagstaff, Ariz., 26,117 ... B3 48
Flagtown, N.J., 800 ... B3 74
Flanagan, Ill., 976 ... C5 58
Flanders, N.Y., 1,905 ... *n16 75
Flandreau, S. Dak., 2,027 .. F9 77
Flat Creek, Ala., 160 .. B2, f6 46
Flathead, co., Mont., 39,450 ... B2 70
Flathead, mts., Mont. ... B2 70
Flatonia, Tex., 1,108 ... E4 84
Flat River, Mo., 4,550 ... D7 69
Flat Rock, Newf., Can., 632 ... *E5 44
Flat Rock, Mich., 5,643 ... F7 66
Flat Rock, N.C., 1,688 ... f10 76
Flatwoods, Ky., 7,380 ... B7 62
Fleetwing Estates, Pa., 400 ... *F11 81
Fleetwood, Pa., 3,064 ... F10 81
Fleming, co., Ky., 11,366 .. B6 62
Flemingsburg, Ky., 2,483 .. B6 62
Flemington, N.J., 3,917 ... B3 74
Flemington, Pa., 1,519 ... D7 81
Flensburg, Ger., Fed. Rep. of, 94,113 (*112,000) ... A4 6
Flers, Fr., 17,683 ... C3 5
Fletcher, N.C., 1,164 ... f10 76
Fletcher, Okla., 950 ... C4 79
Flin Flon, Man., Can., 9,344 (*11,201) ... B1, g7 40
Flint, Mich., 193,317 (*523,300) ... F7 66
Flint, co., Wales, 176,830 . *D5 4
Flintridge, Calif., 2,650 ... *F4 50
Flomaton, Ala., 1,584 ... D2 46
Floodwood, Minn., 650 ... D6 67
Flora, Ill., 5,283 ... E5 58
Flora, Ind., 1,877 ... C4 59
Florala, Ala., 2,701 ... D3 46
Floral City, Fla., 950 ... D4 54
Floral Park, Mont., 5,113 ... *D4 70
Floral Park, N.Y., 18,466 .. k13 75
Flordell Hills, Mo., 989 ... *C7 69
Florence, Ala., 34,031 (*88,100) ... A2 46
Florence, Ariz., 2,173 .. C3, D2 48
Florence, Calif., 28,000 ... *E4 50
Florence, Colo., 2,846 ... C5 51
Florence (Firenze), It., 459,100 (*610,000) ... C3 9
Florence, Kans., 716 ... D7 61
Florence Ky., 11,661 .. B5, k13 62
Florence, N.J., 4,000 ... C3 74
Florence, Oreg., 2,246 ... D2 80
Florence, S.C., 25,997 (*47,500) ... C8 82
Florence, Wis., 575 ... C5 88
Florence, co., S.C., 89,636 . C8 82
Florence, co., Wis., 3,298 .. C5 88
Florence (Firenze), It., 460,944 (*620,000) ... C3 9
Florencia, Col., 17,709 ... C2 32
Flores, Guat., 1,596 ... H12 33
Flores, isl., Indon. ... G6 19
Flores, dept., Ur., 23,550 .. *E1 30
Floresville, Tex., 3,707 ... E3, k7 84
Florham Park, N.J., 8,094 .. B4 74
Floriano, Braz., 26,791 ... D6 27
Florianópolis, Braz., 115,665 ... D3 30
Florida, Cuba, 32,700 (37,500 ▲) ... D4 35
Florida, N.Y., 1,674 .. D6, m14 75
Florida, Ur., 23,035 ... E1 30
Florida, dept., Ur., 63,899 ... *E1 30
Florida, state, U.S., 7,881,000 ... E10 45
Florida, bay, Fla ... E10 54
Florida City, Fla., 5,133 ... G6, t13 54
Florida Keys, is., Fla ... H6 54
Florina, Grc., 11,164 ... E5 10
Flórina, prov., Grc., 52,213 ... *B3 14
Florissant, Mo., 65,908 ... f13 69
Flossmoor, Ill., 7,846 ... k9 58
Flourtown, Pa., 5,200 ... o21 81
Flower Hill, N.Y., 4,486 .. *E7 75
Floyd, co., Ga., 73,742 ... B1 55
Floyd, co., Ind., 55,622 ... H6 59
Floyd, co., Iowa, 19,860 ... A5 60
Floyd, co., Ky., 35,889 ... C7 62
Floyd, co., Tex., 11,044 ... B2 84
Floyd, co., Va., 9,775 ... D2 85
Floydada, Tex., 4,109 ... C2 84
Flushing, Mich., 7,190 ... E7 66
Flushing, Ohio, 1,207 ... B4 78
Fluvanna, co., Va., 7,621 .. C4 85
Foam Lake, Sask., Can., 933 ... F4 39
Foard, co., Tex., 2,211 ... B3 84

Focşani, Rom., 35,100.....C8 10
Foggia, It., 138,300.....D5 9
Fogo, Newf., Can., 1,152.....D4 44
Fohnsdorf, Aus., 11,165....E7 6
Foix, Fr., 9,331.......F4 5
Folcroft, Pa., 9,610.....*G11 81
Foley, Ala., 3,368.......E2 46
Foley, Minn., 1,271.....E5 67
Foligno, It., 33,600......C4 9
Folkestone, Eng., 44,810....E7 4
Folkston, Ga., 2,112......F4 55
Follansbee, W. Va., 3,883........A4, f8 87
Follonica, It., 7,147......C3 9
Folly Beach, S.C., 1,157............F8, k12 82
Folsom, Calif., 5,810.....C3 50
Folsom, Pa., 7,600........*G11 81
Fomento, Cuba, 12,900 (33,600 ▲).........C4 35
Fonda, Iowa, 980........B3 60
Fonda, N.Y., 1,120......C6 75
Fond du Lac, Wis., 35,515 (*47,700)....E5, k9 88
Fond du Lac, co., Wis., 84,567...........E5 88
Fondi, It., 13,700.......D4 9
Fonsagrada, Sp., 950....A2 8
Fontainebleau, Fr., 18,094 (*35,000).......C5 5
Fontana, Calif., 20,673...m14 50
Fontana, Wis., 1,464.....F5 88
Fontanelle, Iowa, 752....C3 60
Fontenay-le-Comte, Fr., 11,434............D3 5
Fontenay [-sous-Bois], Fr., 38,962...........g10 5
Foochow, see Fuchou, China
Footville, Wis., 698.......F4 88
Forbach, Fr., 23,120 (*58,000).......C7 5
Forbes, Austl., 7,467......F8 25
Forbes, mtn., Alta., Can...D2 38
Forchheim, Ger., Fed. Rep. of, 23,715.......D5 6
Ford, co., Ill., 16,382....C5 58
Ford, co., Kans., 22,587..E4 61
Ford City, Calif., 3,926...E4 50
Ford City, Pa., 4,749.....E2 81
Fords, N.J., 14,000......*B4 74
Fords Prairie, Wash., 2,250...........*C3 86
Fordyce, Ark., 4,837.....D3 49
Foreman, Ark., 1,173.....D1 49
Forest, Bel., 55,020......B6 5
Forest, Ont., Can., 2,355..D2 41
Forest, Miss., 4,085......C4 68
Forest, Ohio, 1,535......B2 78
Forest, co., Pa., 4,926.....C3 81
Forest, co., Wis., 7,691...C5 88
Forest Acres, S.C., 6,808..C6 82
Forestburg, Alta., Can., 677............C4 38
Forest City, Iowa, 3,841..A4 60
Forest City, N.C., 7,179............B1, f11 76
Forest City, Pa., 2,322...C11 81
Forest Grove, Oreg., 8,275...........B3, g11 80
Forest Heights, Md., 3,600............*C4 53
Forest Hill, N.B., Can., 715............*D4 43
Forest Hill, Tex., 8,236...*C4 84
Forest Hills, Pa., 9,561...k14 81
Forest Homes, Ill., 2,025............*E3 58
Forest Knolls, Calif., 500...g7 50
Forest Lake, Minn., 3,207............E6 67
Forest Park, Ga., 19,994..h8 55
Forest Park, Ill., 15,472..K9 58
Forestview, Ill., 927......*B6 58
Forestville, Md., 9,000...*C4 53
Forestville, N.Y., 908....C1 75
Forfar, Scot., 10,651.....B5 4
Forge Village, Mass., 1,600...........A5, f10 65
Forked River, N.J., 1,422..D4 74
Forks, Wash., 1,680......B1 86
Forli, It., 75,900 (103,200 ▲).......B4 9
Formiga, Braz., 28,719...C3 30
Formosa, Arg., 55,000....E4 29
Formosa, prov., Arg., 178,526...........E4 29
Formosa, see Taiwan, Asia
Forney, Tex., 1,745...C4, n10 84
Forres, Scot., 14,893.....B5 4
Forrest, Ill., 1,219.......C5 58
Forrest, co., Miss., 57,849..D4 68
Forrest City, Ark., 12,521..B5 49
Forreston, Ill., 1,227.....A4 58
Forst, Ger. Dem. Rep., 28,380...........C7 6
Forster-Tuncurry, Austl., 3,682............F9 26

Forsyth, Ga., 3,736......C3 55
Forsyth, Mont., 1,873......D10 70
Forsyth, co., Ga., 16,928..B2 55
Forsyth, co., N.C., 214,348...........A2 76
Fortaleza, Braz., 859,135 (*910,000).............D7 27
Fort Atkinson, Wis., 9,164..F5 88
Fort Bend, co., Tex., 52,314...........E5 84
Fort Benton, Mont., 1,863..C6 70
Fort Bragg, Calif., 4,455...C2 50
Fort Branch, Ind., 2,535.....H2 59
Fort Chipewyan, Alta., Can., 1,122.........f8 38
Fort Cobb, Okla., 722.....B3 79
Fort Collins, Colo., 43,337...........A5 51
Fort Collins West, Colo., 1,569...........*A5 51
Fort Coulonge, Que., Can., 1,823.........B8 41
Fort Covington, N.Y., 983.........f10 75
Fort-Dauphin, Mad., 11,200.........E9 24
Fort Davis, Tex., 850.....o13 84
Fort-de-France, Mart., 96,943 (*110,000).............I14 35
Fort Deposit, Ala., 1,438..D3 46
Fort Dodge, Iowa, 31,263..B3 60
Fort Edward, N.Y., 3,733..B7 75
Fort Erie, Ont., Can., 23,113..........E6 41
Fort Fairfield, Maine, 2,322, (4,859 ▲).............B7 64
Fort Frances, Ont., Can., 9,947.........o16 41
Fort Gaines, Ga., 1,255...E1 55
Fort-George, Que., Can., 1,280.........h11 42
Fort Gibson, Okla., 1,418...........B6 79
Fort Hall, Idaho, 600......F6 57
Fort Hancock, Tex., 600..o12 84
Fort Howard, Md., 500...B5 53
Fort Johnson, N.Y., 771..*C6 75
Fort Kent, Maine, 2,876, (4,575 ▲).............A4 64
Fort-Lamy, see Ndjamena, Chad
Fort Langley, B.C., Can., 962.........f13 37
Fort Lauderdale, Fla., 139,590........F6, r13 54
Fort Lee, N.J., 30,619.....h9 74
Fort Levenworth, Kans., 8,000......C8, k15 61
Fort-Liberté, Hai., 2,982...E8 35
Fort Loramie, Ohio, 744............B1 78
Fort Lupton, Colo., 2,489...........A6 51
Fort Macleod, Alta., Can., 2,715..........E4 38
Fort Madison, Iowa, 13,996..........D6 60
Fort McKinley, Ohio, 11,536..........*C1 78
Fort Meade, Fla., 4,374..E5 54
Fort Mill, S.C., 4,505....A6 82
Fort Morgan, Colo., 7,594...........A7 51
Fort Myers, Fla., 27,351 (*34,500).......F5 54
Fort Myers Beach, Fla., 2,463...........F5 54
Fort Nelson, B.C., Can., 2,289..........m18 37
Fort Oglethorpe, Ga., 3,869...........B1 55
Fort Payne, Ala., 8,435...A4 46
Fort Peck, Mont., 86.....B10 70
Fort Pierce, Fla., 29,721..E6 54
Fort Pierre, S. Dak., 1,448...........F5 77
Fort Plain, N.Y., 2,809...C6 75
Fort Qu'Appelle, Sask., Can., 1,606........G4 39
Fort Recovery, Ohio, 1,348...........B1 78
Fort Riley, Kans., 1,500..C7 61
Fort St. James, B.C., Can., 1,483.........B5 37
Fort St. John, B.C., Can., 8,264......A7, m18 37
Fort Saskatchewan, Alta., Can., 5,726........C4 38
Fort Scott, Kans., 8,967..E9 61
Fort Shawnee, Ohio, 3,436...........B1 78
Fort Smith, Ark., 62,802 (*85,300).........B1 49
Fort St. John, B.C., Can., 8,264......A7, m18 37
Fort Stockton, Tex., 8,283.................D1 84

Fort Sumner, N. Mex., 1,615.................B6 48
Fort Thomas, Ky., 16,338..h14 62
Fortuna, Calif., 4,203....B1 50
Fortune, Newf., Can., 2,164...........E4 44
Fort Valley, Ga., 9,251....D3 55
Fort Vermilion, Alta., Can., 740.........f7 38
Fort Victoria, Rh., 9,400...E6 24
Fortville, Ind., 2,460.....E6 59
Fort Walton Beach, Fla., 19,994.........u15 54
Fort Washington, Pa., 3,400...........o21 81
Fort Washington Forest, Md., 1,350........C4 53
Fort Wayne, Ind., 178,021 (*274,400).......B7 59
Fort William, Scot., 4,260..B4 4
Fort Worth, Tex., 393,476 (*674,000)....C4, n9 84
Fort Wright, Ky., 4,819...h13 62
Fort Yates, N. Dak., 1,153..D5 77
Forty Fort, Pa., 6,114............D10, n17 81
Fossano, It., 11,000.....B1 9
Fossil, Oreg., 511.......B6 80
Fossombrone, It., 4,659..C4 9
Fosston, Minn., 1,684....C3 67
Foster, co., N. Dak., 4,832...........C7 77
Foster Brook, Pa., 950...C4 81
Foster Village, Haw., 3,775...........g10 56
Fostoria, Ohio, 16,037...A2 78
Fougères, Fr., 26,045....C3 5
Fouhsin (Fusin), China, 290,000.........C9 17
Fouliang, China, 92,000..*E8 17
Fouling, China, 60,000..F6 17
Foumban, Cam., 18,000..G7 22
Fountain, Colo., 3,515...C6 51
Fountain, co., Ind., 18,257...........D3 59
Fountain, peak, Calif.....E6 50
Fountain City, Ind., 852..E8 59
Fountain City, Wis., 1,017..D2 88
Fountain Green, Utah, 467...........B6 72
Fountain Hill, Pa., 5,384..E11 81
Fountain Inn, S.C., 3,391..B3 82
Fountain Place, La., 4,000...........*D4 63
Fountain Valley, Calif., 31,886...........*F5 50
Four Corners, Oreg., 5,823...........*C4 80
Fourmies, Fr., 15,117....B6 5
Four Oaks, N.C., 1,057...B4 76
Fouyang, China, 65,000..E8 17
Fowler, Calif., 2,239......D4 50
Fowler, Colo., 1,241.....C6 51
Fowler, Ind., 2,643.......C3 59
Fowler, Kans., 588.......E3 61
Fowler, Mich., 1,020.....E6 66
Fowlerville, Mich., 1,978..F6 66
Foxboro, Mass., 4,090...B5 65
Fox Chapel, Pa., 4,684...*E1 81
Fox Farm, Wyo., 1,329...*E8 89
Fox Harbour, Newf., Can., 746........E5 44
Fox Lake, Ill., 3,886...A5, h8 58
Fox Lake, Wis., 1,242....E5 88
Fox Point, Wis., 7,939...........E5, m12 88
Fox River Grove, Ill., 2,245...........h8 58
Foxworth, Miss., 950....D4 68
Frackville, Pa., 5,445....E9 81
Fraga, Sp., 8,691.......B6 8
Framingham, Mass., 64,048.........B5, g10 65
Franca, Braz., 86,852....C3 30
Francavilla Fontana, It., 31,200...........D6 9
France, country, Eur., 52,430,000.............5
Francesville, Ind., 1,015..C4 59
Franche-Comté reg., Fr., 992,536..........D6 5
Francistown, Bots., 19,680..E5 24
Franconville, Fr., 11,185..g9 5
Frankenberg, Ger., Fed. Rep. of, 15,429........C4 6
Frankenmuth, Mich., 2,834...........E7 66
Frankenthal, Ger., Fed. Rep. of, 42,707......D4 6
Frankford, Ont., Can., 1,642...........C7 41
Frankfort, Ill., 2,325....m9 58
Frankfort, Ind., 14,956..D4 59
Frankfort, Kans., 960....C7 61
Frankfort, Ky., 21,902...B5 62
Frankfort, Mich., 1,660..D4 66
Frankfort, N.Y., 3,305...B5 75

Frankfurt [am Main], Ger., Fed. Rep. of, 667,451 (*1,675,000)....C4 6
Frankfurt [an der Oder], Ger. Dem. Rep., 67,451..B7 6
Franklin, Idaho, 402.....*F2 57
Franklin, Ind., 11,447...F5 59
Franklin, Kans., 600.....E9 61
Franklin, Ky., 6,553.....D3 62
Franklin, La., 9,325.....E4 63
Franklin, Mass., 17,830..B5 65
Franklin, Mich., 3,311...*F7 66
Franklin, Nebr., 1,193...D7 71
Franklin, N.H., 7,292....E4 73
Franklin, N.J., 4,236....A3 74
Franklin, N.C., 2,336....f9 76
Franklin, Ohio, 10,075...C1 78
Franklin, Pa., 864......*E4 81
Franklin, Pa., 8,629....D2 81
Franklin, Tenn., 9,494...B5 83
Franklin, Tex., 1,063.....D4 84
Franklin (Independent City) Va., 6,880.........D6 85
Franklin, Wis., 12,247...n11 88
Franklin, co., Ala., 23,933..A2 46
Franklin, co., Ark., 11,301...........B2 49
Franklin, co., Fla., 7,065..C2 54
Franklin, co., Ga., 12,784..B3 55
Franklin, co., Idaho, 7,373...........G7 57
Franklin, co., Ill., 38,329..E5 58
Franklin, co., Ind., 16,943..F7 59
Franklin, co., Iowa, 13,255..........B4 60
Franklin, co., Kans., 20,007..........D8 61
Franklin, co., Ky., 34,481..B5 62
Franklin, co., Maine, 22,444..........C2 64
Franklin, co., Mass., 59,210..........A2 65
Franklin, co., Miss., 8,011..D3 68
Franklin, co., Mo., 55,116..........C6 69
Franklin, co., Nebr., 4,566...........D7 71
Franklin, co., N.Y., 43,931..........A6 75
Franklin, co., N.C., 26,820..........A4 76
Franklin, co., Ohio, 833,249..........B2 78
Franklin, co., Pa., 100,833..G6 81
Franklin, co., Tenn., 27,244..........B5 83
Franklin, co., Tex., 5,291..C5 84
Franklin, co., Vt., 31,282..B2 73
Franklin, co., Va., 28,163..D3 85
Franklin, co., Wash., 25,816..........C6 86
Franklin, dist., N. W. Ter., Can., 9,500........B13 36
Franklin, par., La., 23,946..........B4 63
Franklin Furnace, Ohio, 800............D3 78
Franklin Grove, Ill., 968...B4 58
Franklin Lakes, N.J., 7,550...........*B4 74
Franklin Park, Ill., 20,348..k9 58
Franklin Park, N.J., 800...C3 74
Franklin Park, Va., 1,000...........*B5 85
Franklin Square, N.Y., 32,600..........G2 52
Franklinton, La., 3,562...D5 63
Franklinton, N.C., 1,459..A4 76
Franklinville, N.J., 900...D2 74
Franklinville, N.Y., 1,948..C2 75
Franklinville, N.C., 794...B3 76
Frankston, Tex., 1,056...C5 84
Frankton, Ind., 1,796....D6 59
Frascati, It., 14,300...D4, h9 9
Fraser, Mich., 11,868...*F8 66
Fraser, riv., B.C., Can...C6 37
Fraser, mtn., B.C., Can...........C8 37
Fraserburgh, Scot., 10,900..B6 4
Frauenfeld, Switz., 17,400..E4 6
Fray Bentos, Ur., 17,094..E1 30
Frazee, Minn., 1,015.....D3 67
Frazeyburg, Ohio, 941...B3 78
Frazier Park, Calif., 900..E4 50
Frederic, Wis., 908......C1 88
Fredericia, Den., 34,000..J3 11
Frederick, Md., 23,641...B3 53
Frederick, Okla., 6,132..C2 79
Frederick, co., Md., 84,927..........B3 53
Frederick, co., Va., 28,893..........A4 85
Fredericksburg, Iowa, 912............B5 60
Fredericksburg, Pa., 750..*F9 81
Fredericksburg, Tex., 5,326...........D3 84

Fredericksburg (Independent City), Va., 14,450.......B5 85
Fredericktown, Mo., 3,799.................D7 69
Fredericktown, Ohio, 1,935.................B3 78
Fredericktown, Pa., 1,067.................F1 81
Fredericton, N.B., Can., 24,254 (*37,684).......D3 43
Frederiksborg, co., Den., 236,800...............*J5 11
Frederikshavn, Den., 24,800.................I4 11
Frederiksted, Vir. Is., (U.S.), 277...........H12 35
Fredonia, Kans., 3,080....E8 61
Fredonia, N.Y., 10,326....C1 75
Fredonia, Pa., 731........D1 81
Fredonia, Wis., 1,045......E6 88
Fredrikstad, Nor., 30,200 (*48,000).........H4, p28 11
Freeborn, co., Minn., 38,064................G5 67
Freeburg, Ill., 2,495......E4 58
Freedom, Calif., 4,206....*D3 50
Freedom, Pa., 2,643.......E1 81
Freehold, N.J., 10,545.....C4 74
Freel, peak, Calif.........C4 50
Freeland, Mich., 1,303....E6 66
Freeland, Pa., 4,784......D10 81
Freelandville, Ind., 650....G3 59
Freeman, S. Dak., 1,357...G8 77
Freemansburg, Pa., 1,681.................E11 81
Freeport, Fla., 518.......u15 54
Freeport, Ill., 27,736......A4 58
Freeport, Maine, 1,822, (4,781▲)............E2, g7 64
Freeport, Minn., 593......E4 67
Freeport, N.Y., 40,374....G2 52
Freeport, Pa., 2,375.......E2 81
Freeport, Tex., 11,997.............E5, s14 84
Freer, Tex., 2,804.........F3 84
Freestone, co., Tex., 11,116................D4 84
Freetown, N.Y., 1,543...............*m16 75
Freetown, S.L., 170,600 (*215,000)............G2 22
Fregenal de la Sierra, Sp., 10,498................C2 8
Freiberg, Ger. Dem. Rep., 50,689................C6 8
Freiburg [im Breisgau], Ger., Fed. Rep. of, 171,453 (*215,000).....D3 6
Freising, Ger., Fed. Rep. of, 30,705............D5 6
Freistadt, Aus., 5,952......D7 6
Fréjus, Fr., 23,629 (*41,500)................F3 5
Fremantle, Austl., 25,990...F2 25
Fremont, Calif., 100,869...........D2, h9 50
Fremont, Ind., 1,043......A8 59
Fremont, Mich., 3,465.....E5 66
Fremont, Nebr., 22,962...........C9, g11 71
Fremont, N.C., 1,596......B5 76
Fremont, Ohio, 18,490....A2 78
Freemont, co., Colo., 21,942................C5 51
Fremont, co., Idaho, 8,710..................E7 57
Fremont, co., Iowa, 9,282..................D2 60
Fremont, co., Wyo., 28,352................C4 89
French Camp, Calif., 2,500................*D3 50
French Guiana, dep., S.A., 58,000................C5 27
French Lick, Ind., 2,059..................G4 59
French Polynesia, Fr. dep., Oceania, 132,000.............*H11 2
Frenchtown, N.J., 1,459..................B2 74
Frenchville, Maine, 700 (1,375▲).............A4 64
Freshfield, mtn., Alta., Can.....................D9 37
Freshwater, Newf., Can., 1,562.................*f9 44
Fresnillo [de González Echeverría], Mex., 44,475................C4 34
Fresno, Calif., 165,990 (*306,100)............D4 50
Fresno, co., Calif., 413,329...............D4 50
Freudenstadt, Ger., Fed. Rep. of, 14,811.........D4 6
Frewsburg, N.Y., 1,772....C1 75
Friant, Calif., 350.........D4 50
Friars Point, Miss., 1,177..A3 68
Frias, Arg., 11,862........E2 29
Fribourg, Switz., 40,200 (*52,000)........E3 6
Fribourg, canton, Switz., 178,000...............*E3 6
Friday Harbor, Wash., 803...................A2 86
Fridley, Minn., 29,233...m12 67
Friedberg, Ger., Fed. Rep. of, 24,919........C4 6
Friedens, Pa., 900.........F4 81
Friedland, Ger. Dem. Rep., 8,500..............B6 6
Friedrichshafen, Ger., Fed. Rep. of, 52,920.....E4 6
Friend, Nebr., 1,126.......D8 71
Friendship, N.Y., 1,285....C2 75
Friern Barnet, Eng., 28,300...................k12 4
Fries, Va., 885...........D2 85
Friesland, prov., Neth., 516,400..............*A6 5
Frio, co., Tex., 11,159.....E3 84
Friona, Tex., 3,111........B1 84
Frisco, Pa., 900..........*E1 81
Frisco, Tex., 1,845........*C4 84
Frisco City, Ala., 1,286....D2 46
Fritch, Tex., 1,778........B2 84
Fritzlar, Ger., Fed. Rep. of, 14,813.............C4 6
Friuli-Venezia Giulia, reg., It., 1,225,900..........*B4 9
Frontenac, Kans., 2,223...E9 61
Frontenac, Mo., 3,920....*C7 69
Frontenac, co., Ont., Can., 97,138................C8 41
Frontenac, co., Que., Can., 28,848...............D7 42
Frontera, Mex., 10,066....D6 34
Frontier, co., Nebr., 3,982.D5 71
Frontignan, Fr., 5,341.....F5 5
Frontino, peak, Col........B2 32
Front Royal, Va., 8,211...B4 85
Frosinone, It., 33,100.....D4 9
Frostburg, Md., 7,327.....k13 53
Frostproof, Fla., 2,814.....E5 54
Frouard, Fr., 7,419.......C7 5
Fruita, Colo., 1,822.......B2 51
Fruitdale, Oreg., 2,655...*E3 80
Fruitland, Idaho, 1,576....F2 57
Fruitland, Ill., 800.......*B3 58
Fruitland, Md., 2,315.....D6 53
Fruitland Park, Fla., 1,359.D5 54
Fruitport, Mich., 1,409....E4 66
Fruitvale, Wash., 3,275...*C5 86
Fruitville, Fla., 2,131..E4, q11 54
Frunze, Sov. Un., 442,000.E10 13
Frýdek-Místek, Czech., 37,025................D5 7
Fryeburg, Maine, 1,075 (2,208▲)..............D2 64
Fthiotis (Phthiotis), prov., Grc., 154,720.........*C4 14
Fuchin, China, 40,000....B11 17
Fuchou (Foochow), China, 700,000................F8 17
Fuchū, Jap., 163,173.....*I9 18
Fuente Álamo, Sp., 9,270..D5 8
Fuente de Cantos, Sp., 8,941.................C2 8
Fuenteovejuna, Sp., 5,914..C3 8
Fuhai (Bulun Tokhoi), China, 10,000..........B2 17
Fuji, Jap., 180,639 (*265,000)...........n17 18
Fuji, vol., Jap........I9, n17 18
Fujieda, Jap., 56,000, (78,750▲)............o17 18
Fujimi, Jap., 52,011......n17 18
Fujinomiya, Jap., 69,000 (88,880▲)............n17 18
Fujisawa, Jap., 228,978...*I9 18
Fuji-yoshida, Jap., 50,046.n17 18
Fukagawa, Jap., 22,000 (38,373▲)...........E10 18
Fukien, prov., China, 14,650,000............F8 17
Fukuchiyama, Jap., 41,000 (57,174▲)...I7, n14 18
Fukui, Jap., 200,509......H8 18
Fukui, pref., Jap., 744,230..............*H8 18
Fukuoka, Jap., 5,120.....F10 18
Fukuoka, Jap., 914,877 (*1,285,000).....J5 18
Fukuoka, pref., Jap., 4,027,416.............*J5 18
Fukushima, Jap., 6,675..............I8, n16 18
Fukushima, Jap., 227,451..............H10 18
Fukushima, pref., Jap., 1,946,077...........*H10 18
Fukuyama, Jap., 255,086...I6 18
Fulda, Ger., Fed. Rep. of, 60,293 (*92,000).....C4 6
Fulda, Minn., 1,226.......G3 67
Fullerton, Calif., 85,987...n13 50
Fullerton, Ky., 500........B7 62
Fullerton, Nebr., 1,444....C8 71
Fulton, Ill., 3,630.........B3 58
Fulton, Ky., 3,250.........f9 62
Fulton, Miss., 2,899.......A5 68
Fulton, Mo., 12,248........C6 69
Fulton, N.Y., 14,003......B4 75
Fulton, co., Ark., 7,699....A4 49
Fulton, co., Ga., 607,592...C2 55
Fulton, co., Ill., 41,890....C3 58
Fulton, co., Ind., 16,984...B5 59
Fulton, co., Ky., 10,183....B2 62
Fulton, co., N.Y., 52,637...B6 75
Fulton, co., Ohio, 33,071..A1 78
Fulton, co., Pa., 10,776....G5 81
Fultondale, Ala., 5,163.....f7 46
Fumay, Fr., 6,426........C6 5
Funabashi, Jap., 325,426...............n19 18
Funchal, Port., 43,301....h12 8
Fundación, Col., 14,128...A3 32
Funkstown, Md., 1,051....A2 53
Fuquay-Varina, N.C., 3,576..................*B4 76
Furano, Jap., 20,000 (30,876▲)............E11 18
Furman University, S.C., 239..................*B3 82
Furnas, co., Nebr., 6,897.................D6 71
Fürstenfeld, Aus., 6,071....E8 6
Fürstenwalde, Ger. Dem. Rep., 31,191...........B7 6
Fürth, Ger., Fed. Rep. of, 103,942...............D5 6
Furukawa, Jap., 30,000 (52,518▲)..H8, m16 18
Fusagasugá, Col., 18,755...C3 32
Fushun, China, 1,350,000..............C9 17
Füssen, Ger., Fed. Rep. of, 10,405.................E5 6
Fusung, China, 5,000.....E3 18
Fuyü, China, 45,000.......B9 17
Fuyuan, China, 5,000.....B7 18

G

Gabès, Tun., 32,330.......B7 22
Gabin, Pol., 3,339.........B5 7
Gabon (Gabun), country, Afr., 515,000...........I7 22
Gaborone, Bots., 17,698....E5 24
Gabrovo, Bul., 57,805.....D7 10
Gadag, India, 95,426......E6 20
Gadsden, Ala., 53,928 (*81,500)..............A3 46
Gadsden, co., Fla., 39,184..B2 54
Gadyach, Sov. Un., 10,000.F9 12
Găeşti, Rom., 7,179.......C7 10
Gaeta, It., 22,800.........D4 9
Gaffney, S.C., 13,253......A4 82
Gafsa, Tun., 24,345.......B6 22
Gage, co., Nebr., 25,731...D9 71
Gages Lake, Ill., 3,395...*A5 58
Gagnon, Que., Can., 3,787.h13 42
Gagny, Fr., 35,780.......g11 5
Gahanna, Ohio, 12,400...k11 78
Gaillac, Fr., 6,205........F4 5
Gaines, co., Tex., 11,593...C1 84
Gainesboro, Tenn., 1,101..C8 83
Gainesville, Fla., 64,510 (*82,100)..............C4 54
Gainesville, Ga., 15,459....B3 55
Gainesville, Tex., 13,830...C4 84
Gainsborough, Eng., 17,580.................D6 4
Gairdner, lake, Austl......F6 25
Gairloch, Scot., 104........B4 4
Gaithersburg, Md., 8,344..B3 53
Galacz, see Galati, Rom.
Galápagos, prov., Ec., 3,400..................g5 31
Galashiels, Scot., 12,560...C5 4
Galati, Rom., 151,300.....C8 10
Galatia, Ill., 792..........F5 58
Galatina, It., 20,900......D7 9
Galax (Independent City), Va., 6,278..............D2 85
Gáldar, Sp., 6,165.......m14 8
Galeana, Mex., 710.......A3 34
Galena, Ill., 3,930.........A3 58
Galena, Kans., 3,712......E9 61
Galena Park, Tex., 10,479..................r14 84
Gales, peak, Oreg........g11 80
Galesburg, Ill., 36,290.....C3 58
Galesburg, Mich., 1,355...F5 66
Galesville, Md., 625.......C4 53
Galesville, Wis., 1,162.....D2 88
Galeton, Pa., 1,552.......C6 81
Galeville, N.Y., 1,000.....*B4 75
Galicia, reg., Pol., Sov. Un...............D6 7
Galicia, reg., Sp., 2,692,100...............A1 8
Galien, Mich., 691........G4 66
Galion, Ohio, 13,123......B3 78
Gallarate, It., 41,200......B1 9
Gallatin, Mo., 1,833.......B4 69
Gallatin, Tenn., 13,253....A5 83
Gallatin, co., Ill., 7,418...F5 58
Gallatin, co., Ky., 4,134...B5 62
Gallatin, co., Mont., 32,505...................E5 70
Galle, Sri Lanka, 72,720...G7 20
Gallia, co., Ohio, 25,239...D3 78
Gallipoli, It., 17,700......D6 9
Gallipoli, see Gelibolu, Tur.
Gallipolis, Ohio, 7,490....D3 78
Gallitzin, Pa., 2,496.......F4 81
Gällivare, Swe., 22,119....D9 11
Galloway, W. Va., 300....B4 87
Gallup, N. Mex., 13,779...B4 48
Galt, Calif., 3,200.........C3 50
Galt, Ont., Can., 38,897...D4 41
Galty, mts., Ire...........D2 4
Galva, Ill., 3,061.........B3 58
Galveston, Ind., 1,284.....C5 59
Galveston, Tex., 61,809 (*132,500).........E5, r15 84
Galveston, co., Tex., 169,812................E5 84
Galway, Ire., 27,726......D2 4
Galway, co., Ire., 148,340...............*D2 4
Gamagori, Jap., 82,868...o16 18
Gamarra, Col., 4,664......B3 32
Gambia, country, Afr., 400,000................F1 22
Gambia, riv., Afr.........F2 22
Gambier, Ohio, 1,571......B3 78
Gamboa, C.Z., 2,102.....*B2 32
Gambrills, Md., 600........B4 53
Ganado, Tex., 1,640.......E4 84
Gananoque, Ont., Can., 5,212..................C8 41
Gand, see Gent, Bel.
Gander, Newf., Can., 7,748.................D4 44

Gandhinager, India,
24,055.............D5 20
Gandía, Sp., 15,812.......C5 8
Gangaw, Bur., 3,800......D9 20
Ganges, riv., Asia.........D8 20
Gangtok, Sikkim, 6,848...C8 20
Gannat, Fr., 5,376.........D5 5
Gannett, peak, Wyo......C3 89
Gantt, S.C., 900..........B3 82
Gao, Mali, 6,500...........E5 22
Gap, Fr., 23,994..........E7 5
Gap, Pa., 1,022...........G9 81
Garanhuns, Braz.,
49,579.............*D7 27
Garber, Okla., 1,011......A4 27
Garberville, Calif., 900....B2 50
Garça, Braz., 21,871......C3 30
Garciasville, Tex., 350....F3 84
Gard, dept., Fr., 478,544..*F6 5
Gardelegen, Ger. Dem.
Rep., 12,400..........B5 6
Garden, co., Nebr.,
2,929..............C3 71
Gardena, Calif., 41,021...n12 50
Garden City, Ga., 5,790...D5 55
Garden City, Idaho,
2,368..............*F2 57
Garden City, Kans.,
14,790.............E3 61
Garden City, Mich.,
41,864.............p15 66
Graden City, Mo., 633....C3 69
Garden City, N.Y.,
25,373.............G2 52
Garden City, Pa.,
745...............*G11 81
Garden City Park, N.Y.,
7,488.............*G2 52
Gardendale, Ala.,
6,537.............B3, f7 46
Garden Grove, Calif.,
122,524...........n13 50
Garden Home, Oreg.,
4,700.............*B4 80
Garden Lakes, Ga.,
2,500.............*B1 55
Garden View, Pa., 2,662..*D7 81
Gardez, Afg., 17,540.....B4 20
Gardiner, Maine, 6,685...D3 64
Gardiner, Mont., 650.....E6 70
Gardner, Ill., 1,212......B5 58
Gardner, Kans., 1,839....D9 61
Gardner, Mass., 19,748...A4 65
Garfield, N.J., 30,797....h8 74
Garfield, Wash., 610.....B8 86
Garfield, co., Colo.,
14,821.............B2 51
Garfield, co., Mont.,
1,796.............C9 70
Garfield, co., Nebr.,
2,411.............C6 71
Garfield, co., Okla.,
56,343.............A4 79
Garfield, co., Utah, 3,157..C6 72
Garfield, co., Wash.,
2,911.............C8 86
Garfield Heights, Ohio,
41,417.............h9 78
Garfield peak, Wyo......D5 89
Gargaliánoi, Grc., 5,888..D3 14
Garibaldi, Oreg., 1,083...B3 80
Garibaldi, mtn., B.C.,
Can..............E6 37
Garland, Md., 1,000.....*B4 53
Garland, N.C., 656.......C4 76
Garland, Tex., 81,437....n10 84
Garland, Utah, 1,187....A5 72
Garland, co., Ark., 54,131..C2 49
Garmisch-Partenkirchen,
Ger., Fed. Rep. of,
27,408.............E5 6
Garnavillo, Iowa, 634....B6 60
Garner, Iowa, 2,257......A4 60
Garner, N.C., 4,923......B4 76
Garnett, Kans., 3,169....D8 61
Garoua, Cam...........G7 22
Garrard, co., Ky., 9,457..C5 62
Garrett, Ind., 4,715.....B7 59
Garrett, Ky., 300........C7 62
Garrett, co., Md.,
21,476.............k12 53
Garrett Park, Md., 1,276..B3 53
Garrett Park Estates, Md.,
3,000.............*B3 53
Garrettsville, Ohio, 1,718..A4 78
Garrison, Md., 600......B4 53
Garrison, N. Dak., 1,614..C4 77
Garrison, Tex., 1,082....D5 84
Garrovillas, Sp., 5,764...C2 8
Garson, Ont., Can.,
4,447.............*p19 41
Gartok, see Kaerh, China
Garut, Indon., 81,234....G3 19
Garvin, co., Okla., 24,874..C4 79
Garwolin, Pol., 6,910....C6 7
Garwood, N.J., 5,260....*B4 74
Gary, Ind., 175,415......A3 59
Gary, W. Va., 2,800......D3 87

Garyville, La., 2,389..D5, h10 63
Garza, co., Tex., 5,289...C2 84
Garzón, Col., 11,999.....C2 32
Gas City, Ind., 5,742....D6 59
Gasconade, co., Mo.,
11,878.............C6 69
Gascony (Gascogne),
former prov., Fr......E3 5
Gaspé, Que., Can., 17,211.k14 42
Gaspe East, co., Que.,
Can., 41,250.......*k14 42
Gaspe West, co., Que.,
Can., 18,492......*k13 42
Gasport, N.Y., 900.......B2 75
Gassaway, W. Va., 1,253..C4 87
Gaston, Ind., 928........D7 59
Gaston, N.C., 1,105......A5 76
Gaston, co., N.C., 148,415..B1 76
Gastonia, N.C., 47,142
(*113,600)..........B1 76
Gatchina, Sov. Un.,
63,000..........H14, s31 11
Gate City, Va., 1,914....f9 85
Gates, N.Y., 26,442.....*B3 75
Gates, co., N.C., 8,524...A6 76
Gates Mills, Ohio, 2,378..*A4 78
Gatesville, Tex., 4,683...D4 84
Gatineau, Que., Can.,
22,321.............D2 42
Gatineau, co., Que., Can.,
50,979.............C2 42
Gatlinburg, Tenn.,
2,329.............D10 83
Gatton, Austl., 3,546....C9 26
Gatun, C.Z., 668........*B2 32
Gauhāti, India, 123,783
(*200,377)..........C9 20
Gauley Bridge, W. Va.,
950............C3, m13 87
Gävle, Swe., 84,537......G7 11
Gävleborg, co., Swe.,
294,100...........*G7 11
Gavrilovka, Sov. Un.,
10,000.............G11 12
Gawler, Austl., 6,953....G2 26
Gaya, India, 179,884.....D7 20
Gaylord, Mich., 3,012....C6 66
Gaylord, Minn., 1,720....F4 67
Gaysin, Sov. Un., 24,000..G7 12
Gays Mills, Wis., 623....E3 88
Gaza (Ghazzah), Gaza
Strip, 118,272........C2 15
Gaza Strip, Israeli occ.,
Asia, 360,000........C2 15
Gaziantep, Tur.,
227,652............D11 14
Gdańsk (Danzig), Pol.,
364,200 (*670,000)....A5 7
Gdynia, Pol., 190,100....A5 7
Gearhart, mtn., Oreg....E6 80
Geary, N.B., Can., 938...D3 43
Geary, Okla., 1,380......B3 79
Geary, co., Kans., 28,111..D7 61
Geauga, co., Ohio,
62,977.............A4 78
Gediz, Tur., 10,651......C7 14
Geelong, Austl., 17,775
(*121,966).......G7, n14 25
Geislingen, Ger., Fed.
Rep. of, 29,774.......D4 6
Geistown, Pa., 3,633.....F4 81
Gela, It., 65,300........F5 9
Gelderland, prov., Neth.,
1,479,800..........*A6 5
Gelibolu, Tur., 14,716....B6 14
Gelsenkirchen, Ger., Fed.
Rep. of, 339,845......C3 6
Gem, co., Idaho, 9,387...E2 57
Gemlik, Tur., 16,915.....B7 14
General Belgrano, Arg.,
6,994.............B5 28
General Madariaga, Arg.,
7,073.............B5 28
General Pico, Arg., 22,500..B4 28
General Roca, Arg.,
32,000.............B3 28
Genesee, Idaho, 619......C2 57
Genesee, Mich., 800......E7 66
Genesee, co., Mich.,
445,589............E7 66
Genesee, co., N.Y., 58,722..B2 75
Geneseo, Ill., 5,840.....B3 58
Geneseo, N.Y., 5,714....C3 75
Geneva, Ala., 4,398......D4 46
Geneva, Ill., 9,115......F1 58
Geneva, Ind., 1,100......C8 59
Geneva, Nebr., 2,275....D8 71
Geneva, N.Y., 16,793....C4 75
Geneva, Ohio, 6,449......A5 78
Geneva-on-the-Lake,
Ohio, 877..........A5 78
Geneva, co., Ala., 21,924..D4 46
Genève (Geneva), Switz.,
169,200 (*390,000)....E3 6
Genève, canton, Switz.,
329,400...........*E3 6
Genevia, Ark., 3,500..C3, k10 49

Genichesk, Sov. Un.,
20,000.............H10 12
Genk, Bel., 58,720.......B6 5
Gennevilliers, Fr., 46,074..g10 5
Genoa, Ill., 3,003.......A5 58
Genoa (Genova), It.,
841,800 (*890,000)....B2 9
Genoa, Nebr., 1,174......C8 71
Genoa, Ohio, 2,139....A2, e7 78
Genoa City, Wis.,
1,085..........F5, n11 88
Genova, see Genoa, It.
Gent (Ghent), Bel.,
148,166 (*320,000)....B5 5
Genthin, Ger. Dem. Rep.,
15,200.............B6 6
Gentilly, Fr., 19,211.....g10 5
Gentry, co., Mo., 8,060...A3 69
Genzano di Roma, It.,
12,727.............h9 9
George, Iowa, 1,194......A2 60
George, S. Afr., 24,395...G4 24
George, co., Miss.,
12,459.............E5 68
George, hill, Md.........k12 53
George Town, Austl.,
4,837.............o15 25
Georgetown, Ont., Can.,
17,053.............D5 41
Georgetown, P.E.I., Can.,
767...............C7 43
Georgetown, Conn., 1,600..D3 53
Georgetown, Del., 1,844...C7 53
Georgetown, Guy.,
66,070 (*190,000).....C5 27
Georgetown, Idaho, 421...G7 57
Georgetown, Ill., 3,984...D6 58
Georgetown, Ind., 1,273..H6 59
Georgetown, Ky., 8,629...B5 62
Georgetown, Mass., 2,300..A6 65
Georgetown, Ohio, 3,087..D2 78
Georgetown, S.C., 10,449..E9 82
Georgetown, Tex., 6,395..D4 84
George Town, see
Pinang, Mala.
Georgetown, co., S.C.,
33,500.............E9 82
George West, Tex., 2,022..E3 84
Georgia (Georgian S.S.R.),
rep., Sov. Un.,
4,880,000.........*A3 15
Georgia, state, U.S.,
4,808,000..........55
Georgiana, Ala., 2,148...D3 46
Gera, Ger. Dem. Rep.,
112,384............C6 6
Geraldton, Austl., 15,330..E1 25
Geraldton, Ont., Can.,
3,178.............o18 41
Gerber, Calif., 775......B2 50
Gering, Nebr., 5,639.....C2 71
Gerlachovka, mtn., Czech..D6 7
German Democratic
Republic, country, Eur.,
16,990,000.........E10 3
Germantown, Ill., 1,108...E4 58
Germantown, Ohio, 4,088..C1 78
Germantown, Tenn.,
3,474.............B2 83
Germantown, Wis.,
6,974..........E5, m11 88
Germany, East, see German
Democratic Republic,
country, Eur.
Germany, Federal Republic
of, country, Eur.,
62,115,000.........E9 3
Germany, West, see,
Germany, Federal
Republic of, country, Eur.
Germiston, S. Afr.,
210,298............F5 24
Gero, Jap............n16 18
Gerona, Sp., 47,747.....B7 8
Gerona, prov., Sp.,
400,300...........*B7 8
Gers, dept., Fr., 181,577..*F4 5
Gertrudis Sánchez, Mex.,
40,740.............h9 34
Getafe, Sp., 69,396....B4, p17 8
Gettysburg, Pa., 7,275...G7 81
Gettysburg, S. Dak.,
1,915.............E6 77
Geyserville, Calif., 750...C2 50
Ghana, country, Afr.,
9,430,000..........G4 22
Gharyan, Libya, 2,796....B7 22
Ghazni, Afg., 27,084.....B4 20
Ghazzah, see
Gaza, Gaza Strip
Ghent, see Gent, Bel.
Gheorgheni, Rom.,
11,969.............B7 10
Gherla, Rom., 7,617......B6 10
Gia Dinh, Viet. S.,
151,100............C3 19
Giant, mtn., N.Y.,........A7 75

Gibara, Cuba, 12,100
(29,800 ▲)...........D5 35
Gibbon, Minn., 877.......F4 67
Gibbon, Nebr., 1,388.....D7 71
Gibbsboro, N.J., 2,634...*D3 74
Gibbstown, N.J., 5,676...D2 74
Gibraleón, Sp., 8,865....D2 8
Gibraltar, Gib.,
25,300 (*102,000).....D3 8
Gibraltar, Mich., 3,842..*F7 66
Gibraltar, Br. dep., Eur.,
29,000............*D3 8
Gibsland, La., 1,380.....B2 63
Gibson, co., Ind., 30,444..H2 59
Gibson, co., Tenn.,
47,871.............A3 83
Gibsonburg, Ohio,
2,585..........A2, e7 78
Gibson City, Ill., 3,454...C5 58
Gibsonia, Pa., 2,065.....h14 81
Gibsons, B.C., Can.,
1,934.............E6 37
Gibsonton, Fla., 2,500...p11 54
Gibsonville, N.C., 2,019..A3 76
Giddings, Tex., 2,783....D4 84
Gideon, Mo., 1,112......E8 69
Gien, Fr., 8,812.........D5 5
Giessen, Ger., Fed. Rep. of,
77,537 (*155,000)......C4 6
Giffard, Que., Can.,
13,135.............N17 42
Gifford, Fla., 3,509......E6 54
Gifu, Jap., 385,727....I8, n15 18
Gifu, pref., Jap.,
1,758,954.........*I8 18
Gigante, Col., 4,594.....C2 32
Gig Harbor, Wash.,
1,657..........B3, f10 86
Gijon, Sp., 184,698.....A3 8
Gila, co., Ariz., 29,255...C3 48
Gila, riv., Ariz., N. Mex...D4 45
Gila Bend, Ariz., 1,795...C2 48
Gila River, Ariz., 1,971..C3, D2 48
Gilbert, Minn., 2,287....C6 67
Gilbert, peak, Wash......C4 86
Gilbert & Ellice Is., Br.
dep., Oceania, 60,000...*F8 2
Gilberton, Pa., 1,293....*E9 81
Gilbert Plains, Man.,
Can., 849..........D1 40
Gilbertsville, Pa., 900....F10 81
Gilbertville, Iowa, 665....B5 60
Gilbertville, Mass., 1,247..B3 65
Gilchrist, co., Fla., 3,551..C4 54
Giles, co., Tenn., 22,138..B4 83
Giles, co., Va., 16,741....C2 85
Gilford Park, N.J.,
3,200.............*D4 74
Gillespie, Ill., 3,457.....D4 58
Gillespie, co., Tex., 10,553.D3 84
Gillett, Wis., 1,288......D5 88
Gillette, Wyo., 7,194.....B7 89
Gilliam, co., Oreg., 2,342..B6 80
Gillingham, Eng., 90,800..E7 4
Gilly, Bel., 23,531.......B6 5
Gilman, Ill., 1,786......C5 58
Gilmer, Tex., 4,196.....C5 84
Gilmer, co., Ga., 8,956...B2 55
Gilmer, co., W. Va.,
7,782.............C4 87
Gilmore City, Iowa, 766..B3 60
Gilpin, co., Colo., 1,272...B5 51
Gilroy, Calif., 12,665....D3 50
Gimli, Man., Can., 2,041..D3 40
Ginosa, It., 17,800......D6 9
Ginzo, Sp., 9,130.......A2 8
Gioia del Colle, It.,
22,600.............D6 9
Gioiosa Ionica, It., 5,002..E6 9
Girard, Ill., 1,881......D4 58
Girard, Kans., 2,591.....E9 61
Girard, Ohio, 14,119....A5 78
Girard, Pa., 2,613.......B1 81
Girardot, Col., 71,200
(82,300 ▲)..........C3 32
Girardville, Pa., 2,450...E9 81
Giresun, Tur., 32,522....B12 14
Giridih, India, 40,308....D8 20
Girishk, Afg., 5,000......B3 20
Gironde, dept., Fr.,
1,009,390.........*E3 5
Girvan, Scot., 7,396......C4 4
Gisborne, N.Z., 28,700
(*30,700)..........M17 26
Giscome, B.C., Can., 646..B6 37
Gisors, Fr., 7,329.......C4 5
Gitega, Burundi, 2,800...I4 23
Giulianova, It., 9,100....C4 9
Giurgiu, Rom., 39,200...D7 10
Giv'atayim, Isr., 48,500..*B2 15
Givet, Fr., 7,865........B6 5
Givors, Fr., 19,048
(*34,000)...........E6 5
Gjinokaster, Alb., 15,600..B3 14
Gjinokaster, pref., Alb.,
168,000...........*B3 14
Gjövik, Nor., 23,700.....G4 11

Glace Bay, N.S., Can., 22,440...C10 43
Glacier, co., Mont., 10,783...B3 70
Glacier, peak, Wash...A4 86
Gladbrook, Iowa, 961...B5 60
Glades, co., Fla., 3,669...F5 54
Glade Spring, Va., 1,615...f10 85
Gladewater, Tex., 5,574...C5 84
Gladstone, Austl., 15,365...D9 25
Gladstone, Man., Can., 944...D2 40
Gladstone, Mich., 5,237...C4 66
Gladstone, Mo., 23,422...h10 69
Gladstone, N.J., 1,924...B3 74
Gladstone, Oreg., 6,254...B4, h12 80
Gladwin, Mich., 2,071...E6 66
Gladwin, co., Mich., 13,471...D6 66
Gladwyne, Pa., 4,000...*F11 81
Glamoč, Yugo., 986...C3 10
Glamorgan, co., Wales, 1,252,970...*E5 4
Glandorf, Ohio, 732...A1 78
Glarus, Switz., 6,189...E4 6
Glarus, canton Switz., 37,300...*E4 6
Glasco, Kans., 767...C6 61
Glasco, N.Y., 1,169...C7 75
Glascock, co., Ga., 2,280...C4 55
Glasford, Ill., 1,066...C4 58
Glasgow, Ky., 11,301...C4 62
Glasgow, Mo., 1,336...B5 69
Glasgow, Mont., 4,700...B10 70
Glasgow, Scot., 893,790 (*1,990,000)...C4 4
Glasgow, Va., 1,304...C3 85
Glasgow, W. Va., 904...m13 87
Glassboro, N.J., 12,938...D2 74
Glasscock, co., Tex., 1,155...D2 84
Glassport, Pa., 7,450...F2 81
Glastonbury, Conn., 9,500...C6 52
Glauchau, Ger. Dem. Rep., 31,138...C6 6
Gleason, Tenn., 1,314...A3 83
Gleasondale, Mass., 650...g9 65
Glenarden, Md., 4,447...*C4 53
Glen Allen, Va., 1,200...C5 85
Glen Alpine, N.C., 797...B1, f11 76
Glen Avon Heights, Calif., 5,759...*F5 50
Glenboro, Man., Can., 797...E2 40
Glen Burnie, Md., 34,500...B4 53
Glen Carbon, Ill., 1,897...E4 58
Glencoe, Ala., 2,901...B4 46
Glencoe, Ont., Can., 1,156...E3 41
Glencoe, Ill., 10,675...A6, h9 58
Glencoe, Minn., 4,217...F4 67
Glen Cove, N.Y., 25,770...h13 75
Glendale, Ariz., 36,228...C2, D1 48
Glendale, Calif., 132,664...m12 50
Glendale, Mo., 6,891...*C7 69
Glendale, Ohio, 2,690...C1, m13 78
Glendale, S.C., 800...B4 82
Glen Dale, W. Va., 2,150...B4 87
Glendale, Wis., 13,426...*E6 88
Glendive, Mont., 6,305...C12 70
Glendora, Calif., 31,380...m13 50
Glendora, N.J., 5,400...*D2 74
Glen Ellyn, Ill., 21,909...k8 58
Glen Gardner, N.J., 874...B3 74
Glengarry, co., Ont., Can., 18,181...B10 41
Glen Head, N.Y., 4,300...*F2 52
Glen Innes, Austl., 5,762...E9 25
Glen Jean, W. Va., 500...D3, n13 87
Glen Lake, B.C., Can., 663...E5 37
Glen Lyon, Pa., 3,408...D9 81
Glen Moore, Pa., 900...*G9 81
Glenmora, La., 1,651...D3 63
Glenn, co., Calif., 17,521...C2 50
Glenn Dale, Md., 600...C4 53
Glenns Ferry, Idaho, 1,386...G3 57
Glennville, Ga., 2,965...E5 55
Glenolden, Pa., 8,697...p20 81
Glenorchy, Austl., 42,620...o15 25
Glen Raven, N.C., 2,848...A3 76
Glen Riddle, Pa., 800...p20 81
Glen Rock, N.J., 13,001...D5, h8 74
Glen Rock, Pa., 1,600...G8 81
Glenrock, Wyo., 1,515...D7 89
Glen Rose, Tex., 1,554...C4 84
Glens Falls, N.Y., 17,222...B7 75
Glenshaw, Pa., 14,000...*E1 81
Glenside, Pa., 17,400...o21 81
Glen Ullin, N. Dak., 1,070...D4 77
Glenview, Ill., 24,880...h9 58
Glenview Countryside, Ill., 2,500...*E2 58
Glenville, Minn., 740...G5 67
Glenville, W. Va., 2,183...C4 87
Glenwillard, Pa., 2,000...*E1 81
Glenwood, Newf., Can., 1,130...D4 44
Glenwood, Iowa, 4,421...C2 60
Glenwood, Minn., 2,584...E3 67
Glenwood, Va., 1,295...*D3 85
Glenwood Landing, N.Y., 3,800...*F2 52
Glenwood Springs, Colo., 4,106...B3 51
Glidden, Iowa, 964...B3 60
Glidden, Wis., 700...B3 88
Gliwice, Pol., 170,900...C5, g9 7
Globe, Ariz., 7,333...C3, D3 48
Globino, Sov. Un., 10,000...G9 12
Gloucester, Eng., 89,980 (*111,000)...E5 4
Gloucester, Mass., 27,941...A6, f13 65
Gloucester, co., N.B., Can., 70,301...B4 43
Gloucester, co., Eng., 1,079,840...*E5 4
Gloucester, co., N.J., 172,681...D2 74
Gloucester, co., Va., 14,059...C6 85
Gloucester City, N.J., 14,707...D2 74
Glouster, Ohio, 2,121...C3 78
Gloversville, N.Y., 19,677...B6 75
Glovertown, Newf., Can., 1,915...D4 44
Glovertown South, Newf., Can., 663...*D5 44
Gloverville, S.C., 1,682...E4 82
Glubczyce, Pol., 11,300...C4 7
Glubokoye, Sov. Un., 25,000...D6 12
Głuchołazy, Pol., 13,200...C4 7
Gluck, S.C., 650...C2 82
Glukhov, Sov. Un., 27,000...F9 12
Glussk, Sov. Un., 10,000...E7 12
Glyndon, Md., 900...B4 53
Glynn, co., Ga., 50,528...E5 55
Gmunden, Aus., 12,211...E6 6
Gnadenhutten, Ohio, 1,466...B4 78
Gniezno, Pol., 50,600...B4 7
Goa, Daman and Diu, ter., India, 857,771...D5, E5 20
Goat, mtn., Mont...C3 70
Gobles, Mich., 801...F5 66
Gobo, Jap., 30,573...J7 18
Goch, Ger., Fed. Rep. of, 27,850...C3 6
Godāvari, riv., India...E6 20
Goderich, Ont., Can., 6,813...D3 41
Godfrey, Ill., 1,261...E3 58
Godwin Austen, peak, Pak...A6 20
Goffstown, N.H., 2,272...E4 73
Gogebic, co., Mich., 20,676...n12 66
Goiânia, Braz., 362,152...B3 30
Goiás, state, Braz., 2,997,570...B2 30
Gojo, Jap., 33,737...o14 18
Golan Heights, hills, Syria...*B3 15
Golchika, Sov. Un., 1,300...B11 13
Golconda, Ill., 922...F5 58
Gold Beach, Oreg., 1,554...E2 80
Gold Coast, see Ghana, country, Afr.
Gold Coast, see Southport, Austl.
Golden, B.C., Can., 3,010...D9 37
Golden, Colo., 9,817...B5 51
Golden City, Mo., 810...D3 69
Goldendale, Wash., 2,484...D5 86
Golden Hill, Minn., 800...*F6 67
Golden Hinde, mtn., B.C., Can...E5 37
Golden Meadow, La., 2,681...E5 63
Golden Valley, Minn., 24,246...n12 67
Golden Valley, co., Mont., 931...D7 70
Golden Valley, co., N. Dak., 2,611...D2 77
Gold Hill, Ore., 603...E3 80
Goldsboro, N.C., 26,960...B5 76
Goldsmith, Tex., 387...D1 84
Goldthwaite, Tex., 1,693...D3 84
Goleta, Calif., 22,700...E4 50
Golf Manor, Ohio, 5,170...o13 78
Goliad, Tex., 1,709...E4 84
Goliad, co., Tex., 4,869...E4 84
Golspie, Scot., 1,167...A5 4
Gomel, Sov. Un., 272,000...E8 12
Gómez Palacio, Mex., 79,650...B4 34
Gonaïves, Hai., 29,261...E7 35
Gonda, India, 52,662...C7 20
Gondar, Eth., 38,600...F5 23
Gönen, Tur., 13,815...B6 14
Gonesse, Fr., 8,517...g10 5
Gonzales, Calif., 2,575...D3 50
Gonzales, La., 4,512...D5, h10 63
Gonzales, Tex., 5,854...E4 84
Gonzales, co., Tex., 16,375...E4 84
Goochland, co., Va., 10,069...C5 85
Goodhue, co., Minn., 34,763...F6 67
Gooding, Idaho, 2,599...G4 57
Gooding, co., Idaho, 8,645...F4 57
Goodland, Ind., 1,176...C3 59
Goodland, Kans., 5,510...C2 61
Goodman, Miss., 1,194...C4 68
Good Pine, La., 420...C3 63
Goodsprings, Ala., 400...B2 46
Goodview, Minn., 1,829...F7 67
Goodwater, Ala., 2,172...B3 46
Goodwell, Okla., 1,467...e9 79
Goodyear, Ariz., 2,140...C3, D2 48
Goondiwindi, Austl., 3,731...E9 25
Goose Bay, Newf., Can., 496...B1, h9 44
Goose Creek, S.C., 3,656...F7, k11 82
Goppingen, Ger., Fed. Rep. of, 49,186 (*146,000)...D4 6
Gorakhpur, India, 230,911...C7 20
Gordo, Ala., 1,991...B2 46
Gordon, Ga., 2,553...D3 55
Gordon, Nebr., 2,106...B3 71
Gordon, Pa., 856...*E9 81
Gordon, co., Ga., 23,570...B1 55
Gordonsville, Va., 1,253...B4 85
Gore, Eth., 8,381...G5 23
Gore, N.Z., 8,780...Q10 26
Gore Bay, Ont., Can., 716...B2 41
Gorgan, Iran, 51,181...B5 15
Gorgas, Ala., 100...B2 46
Gorham, Maine, 3,337 (7,839 ▲)...E2, g7 64
Gorham, N.H., 2,020...C5 73
Gorham, N.Y., 800...C3 75
Gorizia, It., 43,400...B4 9
Gorki (Gorkiy), Sov. Un., 1,189,000 (*1,635,000)...D7 13
Gorlice, Pol., 15,200...D6 7
Görlitz, Ger. Dem. Rep., 85,789...C7 6
Gorlovka, Sov. Un., 335,000 (*690,000)...G12, q21 12
Gorman, Tex., 1,236...C3 84
Gorna-Dzhumaya, see Blagoevgrad, Bul.
Gorna Oryakhovitsa, Bul., 26,299...D7 10
Gorno-Altaysk, Sov. Un., 34,000...*D11 12
Gorodenka, Sov. Un., 10,000...G5 12
Gorodisehe, Sov. Un., 10,000...q22 12
Gorodnya, Sov. Un., 10,000...F8 12
Gorodok, Sov. Un., 10,000...D7 12
Gorodok, Sov. Un., 10,000...G4 12
Gorontalo, Indon., 82,328...E6 19
Gorzów [Wielkopolski], Pol., 74,200...B3 7
Gosainthan, peak, China...C8 20
Gosford, Austl., 38,093...F8 26
Goshen, Calif., 1,061...*D4 50
Goshen, Ind., 17,871...A6 59
Goshen, N.Y., 4,343...D6, m14 75
Goshen, Ohio, 1,174...C1 78
Goshen, co., Wyo., 10,885...D8 89
Goshogawara, Jap., 23,000 (47,567 ▲)...F10 18
Goslar, Ger., Fed. Rep. of, 52,759...C5 6
Gosper, co., Nebr., 2,178...D6 71
Gospic, Yugo., 6,857...C2 10
Gosport, Ind., 692...F4 59
Gostivar, Yugo., 19,282...E5 10
Gostyń, Pol., 13,000...C4 7
Gostynin, Pol., 12,000...B5 7
Goteborg, Swe., 441,522 (*660,000)...I4 11
Göteborg, och Bohus, co., Swe., 690,500...*I4 11
Gotemba, Jap., 44,000 (55,997 ▲)...n18 18
Gotha, Ger. Dem. Rep. 57,371...C5 6
Gothenburg, Nebr., 3,158...D5 71
Gotland, co., Swe., 54,000...*I8 11
Göttingen, Ger., Fed. Rep. of, 119,147...C4 6
Gottwaldov, (Zlín), Czech., 65,310...D4 7
Gouda, Neth., 47,920...A6 5
Goulburn, Austl., 21,568...F8 25
Gould, Ark., 1,683...D4 49
Goulding, Fla., 900...*u14 54
Goulds, Fla., 5,121...s13 54
Gournay-en-Bray, Fr., 3,195...C4 5
Gouverneur, N.Y., 4,574...f9 75
Gove, co., Kans., 3,940...D3 61
Governador Valadares, Braz., 125,174...B4 30
Gowanda, N.Y., 3,110...C2 75
Gowrie, Iowa, 1,225...B3 60
Goya, Arg., 34,000...E4 29
Graaff-Reinet, S. Afr., 22,065...G4 24
Gračanica, Yugo., 7,668...C4 10
Grace, Idaho, 826...G7 57
Grace, mtn., Mass...A3 65
Grace Park, Pa., 700...*G11 81
Graceville, Fla., 2,560...u16 54
Graceville, Minn., 735...E2 67
Gradacac, Yugo., 5,897...C4 10
Gradizhsk, Sov. Un., 10,000...G9 12
Grado, Sp., 3,671...A2 8
Grady, co., Ga., 17,826...F2 55
Grady, co., Okla., 29,354...C4 79
Graehl, Alsk, 349...*C10 47
Graettinger, Iowa, 907...A3 60
Grafton, Austl., 16,354...E9 25
Grafton, Ill., 1,018...E3 58
Grafton, Mass., 1,300...B4 65
Grafton, N. Dak., 5,946...B8 77
Grafton, Ohio, 1,771...A3 78
Grafton, Va., 900...h15 85
Grafton, W. Va., 6,433...B4, k10 87
Grafton, Wis., 5,998...E5, m12 88
Grafton, co., N.H., 54,914...D4 73
Graham, N.C., 8,172...A3 76
Graham, Tex., 7,477...C3 84
Graham, co., Ariz., 16,578...C3 48
Graham, co., Kans., 4,751...C4 61
Graham, co., N.C., 6,562...f9 76
Grahamstown, S. Afr., 41,086...G5 24
Grainger, co., Tenn., 13,948...C10 83
Grajewo, Pol., 11,200...B7 7
Gramalote, Col., 3,098...B3 32
Grambling, La., 4,407...B3 63
Gramercy, La., 2,567...h10 63
Grammichele, It., 14,486...F5 9
Granada, Nic., 34,976...E7 34
Granada, Sp., 186,160...D4 8
Granada, prov., Sp., 751,900...*D4 8
Granbury, Tex., 2,473...C4 84
Granby, Que., Can., 34,385 (*39,307)...D5 42
Granby, Mo., 1,678...E3 69
Grand, co., Colo., 4,107...A4 51
Grand, co., Utah, 6,688...B7 72
Grand, isl., La...E6 63
Grand Bank, Newf., Can., 3,476...E4 44
Grand Bassam, I.C., 22,994...G4 22
Grand Bay, N.B., Can., 725...D3 43
Grand Bend, Ont., Can., 928...D3 41
Grand Blanc, Mich., 5,132...F7 66
Grand-Bourg, Guad., 2,489...I14 35
Grand Centre, Alta., Can., 2,088...B5 38
Grand Coteau, La., 1,301...D3 63
Grand Coulee, Wash., 1,302...B6 86
Grande-Entrée, Que., Can., 715...B8 43
Grande Prairie, Alta., Can., 13,079...B1, f7 38
Grande Rivière, Que., Can., 1,176...*k14 42
Grandes-Bergeronnes, Que., Can., 779...A8 42

Grand Falls, N.B., Can., 4,516....B2 43
Grand Falls, Newf., Can., 7,677 (*14,321)....D4 44
Grandfalls, Tex., 622....D1 84
Grandfather, mtn., N.C....A1 76
Grandfield, Okla., 1,524....C3 79
Grand Forks, B.C., Can., 3,173....E8 37
Grand Forks, N. Dak., 39,008....C8 77
Grand Forks, co., N. Dak., 61,102....C8 77
Grand Gorge, N.Y., 600....C6 75
Grand Haven, Mich., 11,844....E4 66
Grand Island, Nebr., 31,269....D7 71
Grand Island, N.Y., 500....*B2 75
Grand Isle, La., 2,236....E6 63
Grand Isle, co., Vt., 3,574....B1 73
Grand Junction, Colo., 20,170....B2 51
Grand Junction, Iowa, 967....B3 60
Grand Ledge, Mich., 6,032....F6 66
Grand Marais, Minn., 1,301....k9 67
Grand Meadow, Minn., 869....G6 67
Grand' Mère, Que., Can., 17,137....C5 42
Grand Prairie, Tex., 50,904....n10 84
Grand Rapids, Man., Can., 986....C2 40
Grand Rapids, Mich., 197,649 (*444,300)....F5 66
Grand Rapids, Minn., 7,247....C5 67
Grand Rapids, Ohio, 976....A2, f6 78
Grand Saline, Tex., 2,257....C5 84
Grand Terrace, Calif., 5,901....*F5 50
Grand Teton, mtn., Wyo....C2 89
Grand Tower, Ill., 664....F4 58
Grand Traverse, co., Mich., 39,175....D5 66
Grand Valley, Ont., Can., 643....D4 41
Grandview, Man., Can., 1,057....D1 40
Grandview, Ill., 2,242....D6 58
Grand View, Ind., 696....I4 59
Grandview, Mo., 17,456....C3, k10 69
Grandview, Tex., 935....*C4 84
Grandview, Wash., 3,605....C6 86
Grandview Heights, Ohio, 8,460....m10 78
Grandview Heights, Pa., 2,400....*G9 81
Grandville, Mich., 10,764....F5 66
Granger, Tex., 1,256....D4 84
Granger, Utah., 13,000....*A5 72
Granger, Wash., 1,567....C5 86
Grangeville, Idaho, 3,636....D2 57
Grangeville, Pa., 1,100....*G8 81
Granite, Md., 700....B4 53
Granite, Okla., 1,808....C2 79
Granite, co., Mont., 2,737....D3 70
Granite, peak, Mont....E7 70
Granite, peak, Wyo....D4 89
Granite City, Ill., 40,440....E3 58
Granite Falls, Minn., 3,225....F3 67
Granite Falls, N.C., 2,388....B1 76
Granite Falls, Wash., 813....A4 86
Granite Quarry, N.C., 1,344....B2 76
Graniteville, Mass., 950....f10 65
Graniteville, S.C., 2,464....D4 82
Granja de Torrehermosa, Sp., 6,314....C3 8
Granollers, Sp., 20,194....B7 8
Grant, Mich., 772....E5 66
Grant, Nebr., 1,099....D4 71
Grant, co., Ark., 9,711....C3 49
Grant, co., Ind., 83,955....C6 59
Grant, co., Kans., 5,961....E2 61
Grant, co., Ky., 9,999....B5 62
Grant, co., Minn., 7,462....E2 67
Grant, co., Nebr., 1,019....C4 71
Grant, co., N. Mex., 22,030....C4 48
Grant, co., N. Dak., 5,009....D4 77
Grant, co., Okla., 7,117....A4 79
Grant, co., Oreg., 6,996....C7 80
Grant, co., S. Dak., 9,005....E9 77
Grant, co., Wash., 41,881....B6 86
Grant, co., W. Va., 8,607....B5 87
Grant, co., Wis., 48,398....F3 88
Grant, par., La., 13,671....C3 63
Grant City, Mo., 1,095....A3 69
Grantham, Eng., 27,890....D6 4
Grant Park, Ill., 914....B6 58
Grants, N. Mex., 8,768....B5 48
Grantsboro, N.C., 500....B6 76
Grantsburg, Wis., 930....C1 88
Grants Pass, Oreg., 12,455....E3 80
Grantsville, Utah, 2,931....A5, D1 72
Grantsville, W. Va., 795....C3 87
Grant Town, W. Va., 946....B4, h10 87
Grantville, Ga., 1,128....C2 55
Granville, Fr., 12,715....C3 5
Granville, Ill., 1,232....B4 58
Granville, N.Y., 2,784....B7 75
Granville, Ohio, 3,963....B3 78
Granville, W. Va., 1,027....h11 87
Granville, co., N.C., 32,762....A4 76
Grapeland, Tex., 1,211....D5 84
Grapeville, Pa., 1,000....*F2 81
Grapevine, Ky., 900....C2 62
Grapevine, Tex., 7,023....C4, n9 84
Grasonville, Md., 1,182....C5 53
Grasse, Fr., 30,907....F7 5
Grassflat, Pa., 750....D5 81
Grass Lake, Mich., 1,061....F6 66
Grass Valley, Calif., 5,149....C3 50
Gratiot, co., Mich., 39,246....E6 66
Graton, Calif., 900....*C2 50
Graubünden, canton, Switz., 163,600....*E4 6
Graulhet, Fr., 10,318....F5 5
Gravatá, Braz., 21,324....*D7 27
Grave, peak, Idaho....C4 57
Gravelbourg, Sask., Can., 1,428....H2 39
Gravenhurst, Ont., Can., 7,133....C5 41
Graves, co., Ky., 30,939....f9 62
Gravesend, Eng., 53,600....E7, m13 4
Gravina [in Puglia], It., 33,200....D6 9
Gray, Ga., 2,014....C3 55
Gray, Ky., 750....D5 62
Gray, co., Kans., 4,516....E3 61
Gray, co., Tex., 26,949....B2 84
Grayling, Mich., 2,143....D6 66
Grays, peak, Colo....B5 51
Grays Harbor, co., Wash., 59,553....B2 86
Grayslake, Ill., 4,907....A5, h8 58
Grayson, Ky., 2,184....B7 62
Grayson, co., Ky., 16,445....C3 62
Grayson, co., Tex., 83,225....C4 84
Grayson, co., Va., 15,439....D1 85
Graysville, Ala., 3,182....f7 46
Grayville, Ill., 2,035....E5 58
Graz, Aus., 249,211 (*270,000)....E7 6
Great Barrington, Mass., 3,203....B1 65
Great Bear, lake, Can....C9 36
Great Bend, Kans., 16,133....D5 61
Great Bend, Pa., 826....C10 81
Great Blue, hill, Mass....B5 65
Great Divide, basin, Wyo....E4 89
Greater Antilles, is., W.I....B3 27
Great Falls, Mont., 60,091 (*74,500)....G5 70
Great Falls, S.C., 2,727....B6 82
Greathouse, peak, Mont....D7 70
Great Neck, N.Y., 10,798....h13 75
Great Neck Estates, N.Y., 3,131....n15 75
Great Salt, lake, Utah....A5 72
Great Slave, lake, Can....D11 36
Great Yarmouth, Eng., 49,920....D7 4
Greece, N.Y., 53,200....*B3 75
Greece, country, Eur., 8,875,000....C4 14
Greeley, Colo., 38,902....A6 51
Greeley, Nebr., 580....C7 71
Greeley, co., Kans., 1,819....D2 61
Greeley, co., Nebr., 4,000....C7 71
Green, co., Ky., 10,350....C4 62
Green, co., Wis., 26,714....F4 88
Green, riv., U.S....B6 72
Greenacres, Calif., 1,000....*E4 50
Greenacres, Wash., 2,324....B8, g14 86
Greenacres City, Fla., 1,731....F6 54
Greenback, Tenn., 318....D9 83
Green Bay, Wis., 87,809 (*140,000)....D6, g10 88
Greenbelt, Md., 18,199....B4 53
Greenbrae, Calif., 3,500....*D2 50
Greenbrier, co., W. Va., 32,090....D4 87
Green Brook, N.J., 4,302....*B4 74
Greenbush, Mass., 600....h12 65
Greenbush, Minn., 787....B2 67
Greencastle, Ind., 8,852....E4 59
Greencastle, Pa., 3,293....G6 81
Green City, Mo., 632....A5 69
Green Cove Springs, Fla., 3,857....C5, n8 54
Greendale, Ind., 3,783....F8 59
Greendale, Wis., 15,089....F6, n12 88
Greene, Iowa, 1,363....B5 60
Greene, N.Y., 1,874....C5 75
Greene, co., Ala., 10,650....C1 46
Green, co., Ark., 24,765....A5 49
Greene, co., Ga., 10,212....C3 55
Greene, co., Ill., 17,014....D3 58
Greene, co., Ind., 26,894....F4 59
Greene, co., Iowa, 12,716....B3 60
Greene, co., Miss., 8,545....D5 68
Greene, co., Mo., 152,929....D4 69
Greene, co., N.Y., 33,136....C6 75
Greene, co., N.C., 14,967....B5 76
Greene, co., Ohio, 125,057....C2 78
Greene, co., Pa., 36,090....G1 81
Greene, co., Tenn., 47,630....C11 83
Greene, co., Va., 5,248....B4 85
Greeneville, Tenn., 13,722....C11 83
Greenfield, Calif., 2,608....D3 50
Greenfield, Ill., 1,179....D3 58
Greenfield, Ind., 9,986....E6 59
Greenfield, Iowa, 2,212....C3 60
Greenfield, Mass., 18,116....A2 65
Greenfield, Mo., 1,172....D4 69
Greenfield, Ohio, 4,780....C2 78
Greenfield, Tenn., 2,050....A3 83
Greenfield, Wis., 24,424....n12 88
Greenfield Park, Que., Can., 15,348....q20 42
Green Forest, Ark., 1,354....A2 49
Green Harbor, Mass., 900....B6 65
Green Haven, Md., 2,700....*B2 53
Greenhills, Ohio, 6,092....n12 78
Green Island, N.Y., 3,297....*C7 75
Green Lake, Sask., Can., 756....C2 39
Green Lake, Wis., 1,109....E5 88
Green Lake, co., Wis., 16,878....E4 88
Greenland, Dan. dep., N.A., 53,000....B16 33
Greenlawn, N.Y., 8,493....F3 52
Greenlee, co., Ariz., 10,330....C4 48
Green Lookout, mtn., Wash....D3 86
Green Manorville, Conn., 2,500....*B6 52
Green Meadows, Md., 1,500....*C4 53
Greenock, Pa., 2,800....*E1 81
Greenock, Scot., 69,171 (*104,000)....C4 4
Greenport, N.Y., 2,481....m16 75
Green Ridge, Pa., 3,400....*G11 81
Green River, Utah, 1,033....B6 72
Green River, Wyo., 4,196....E3 89
Greensboro, Ala., 3,371....C2 46
Greensboro, Fla., 716....B2 54
Greensboro, Ga., 2,583....C3 55
Greensboro, Md., 1,173....C6 53
Greensboro, N.C., 144,076 (*334,100)....A3 76
Greensburg, Ind., 8,620....F7 59
Greensburg, Kans., 1,907....E4 61
Greensburg, Ky., 1,990....C4 62
Greensburg, Pa., 17,077....F2 81
Green's Harbour, Newf., Can., 713....*E5 44
Greenspond, Newf., Can., 728....D5 44
Green Springs, Ohio, 1,279....A2 78
Greensville, co., Va., 9,604....D5 85
Greentown, Ind., 1,870....D6 59
Green Tree, Pa., 6,441....*E1 81
Greenup, Ill., 1,618....D5 58
Greenup, Ky., 1,284....B7 62
Greenup, co., Ky., 33,192....B6 62
Greenvale, N.Y., 1,050....*F2 52
Greenview, Ill., 740....C4 58
Greenville, Ala., 8,033....D3 46
Greenville, Calif., 1,073....B3 50
Greenville, Fla., 1,141....B3 54
Greenville, Ill., 4,631....E4 58
Greenville, Ky., 3,875....C2 62
Greenville, Maine, 1,320....C3 64
Greenville, Mich., 7,493....E5 66
Greenville, Miss., 39,648....B2 68
Greenville, N.H., 1,332....F4 73
Greenville, N.Y., 5,500....h13 75
Greenville, N.C., 29,063....B5 76
Greenville, Ohio, 12,380....B1 78
Greenville, Pa., 8,704....D1 81
Greenville, R.I., 3,000....B10 52
Greenville, S.C., 61,436 (*232,800)....B3 82
Greenville, Tex., 22,043....C4 84
Greenville, co., S.C., 240,546....A3 82
Greenville Junction, Maine, 600....C3 64
Greenwich, Conn., 59,755....E2 52
Greenwich, Eng., (part of London)....m13 4
Greenwich, N.Y., 2,092....B7 75
Greenwich, Ohio, 1,473....A3 78
Greenwood, Ark., 2,156....B1 49
Greenwood, B.C., Can., 932....E8 37
Greenwood, Ind., 11,408....E5, m10 59
Greenwood, Miss., 22,400....B3 68
Greenwood, Pa., 1,700....E5 81
Greenwood, S.C., 21,069....C3 82
Greenwood, Wis., 1,036....D3 88
Greenwood, co., Kans., 9,141....E7 61
Greenwood, co., S.C., 49,686....C3 82
Greenwood Lake, N.Y., 2,262....*D6 75
Greer, S.C., 10,642....B3 82
Greer, co., Okla., 7,979....C2 79
Gregg, co., Tex., 75,929....C5 84
Gregory, S. Dak., 1,756....G6 77
Gregory, Tex., 2,246....*F4 84
Gregory, co., S. Dak., 6,710....G6 77
Greifswald, Ger. Dem. Rep., 52,039....A6 6
Greilickville, Mich., 900....D5 66
Greiz, Ger. Dem. Rep., 37,864....C6 6
Grenada, Miss., 9,944....B4 68
Grenada, co., Miss., 19,854....B4 68
Grenada, country, N.A., 97,000....J14 35
Grenfell, Sask., Can., 1,256....G4 39
Grenloch, N.J., 850....D2 74
Grenoble, Fr., 161,616 (*335,000)....E6 5
Grenville, Que., Can., 1,495....D3 42
Grenville, co., Ont., Can., 23,429....C9 41
Gresham, Oreg., 10,030....B4 80
Gretna, Fla., 883....B2 54
Gretna, La., 24,875....E5, k11 63
Gretna, Nebr., 1,557....C9, g12 71
Gretna, Va., 986....D3 85
Grey, co., Ont., Can., 62,592....C4 41
Greybull, Wyo., 1,953....B4 89
Greylock, mtn., Mass....A1 65
Greymouth, N.Z., 8,881....O13 26
Gridley, Calif., 3,534....C3 50
Gridley, Ill., 1,007....C5 58
Griffin, Ga., 22,734....C2 55
Griffing Park, Tex., 2,075....*E5 84
Griffith, Austl., 11,015....F8 25
Griffith, Ind., 18,168....A3 59
Grifton, N.C., 1,860....B5 76
Griggs, co., N. Dak., 4,184....C7 77
Griggsville, Ill., 1,245....D3 58
Grimes, co., Tex., 11,855....D4 84
Grimma, Ger. Dem. Rep., 16,100....C6 6
Grimsby, Ont., Can., 15,770....D5 41
Grimsby, Eng., 95,610 (*149,000)....D6 4
Grimshaw, Alta., Can., 1,714....A2 38
Grindstone, Pa., 700....*G2 81
Grinnell, Iowa, 8,402....C5 60
Griswold, Iowa, 1,181....C2 60
Grodno, Sov. Un., 132,000....E4 12
Grodzisk, Pol., 6,015....B4 7
Grodzisk Mazowiecki, Pol., 20,400....m13 7
Groesbeck, Ohio, 6,000....*C1 78
Groesbeck, Tex., 2,396....D4 84
Grójec, Pol., 8,611....C6 7
Grombalia, Tun., 5,043....F3 9
Gronau, Ger., Fed. Rep. of, 27,084....B3 6
Groningen, Neth., 170,295 (*205,880)....A7 5

Groningen, prov., Neth., 514,000............*A7 5
Grosse Ile, Mich., 8,306...*B7 66
Grossenhain, Ger. Dem. Rep., 19,500............C6 6
Grosse Pointe, Mich., 6,637................p16 66
Grosse Pointe Farms, Mich., 11,701........*p16 66
Grosse Pointe Park, Mich., 15,641............p16 66
Grosse Pointe Shores, Mich., 3,042.........*F8 66
Grosse Pointe Woods, Mich., 21,878.......p16 66
Grosseto, It., 45,200......C3 9
Grossglockner, mtn., Aus..E6 6
Grossmont, Calif., 2,000...o16 50
Gros Ventre, range, Wyo..C2 89
Groton, Conn., 8,933 (38,244 ▲)............D8 52
Groton, Mass., 1,314..A4, f9 65
Groton, N.Y., 2,112......C4 75
Groton, S. Dak., 1,021....E7 77
Grottaferrata, It., 5,377...h9 9
Grottaglie, It., 24,800....D6 9
Grottoes, Va., 1,166......B4 85
Grove, Okla., 2,000......A7 79
Grove City, Ohio, 13,911.........C2, m10 78
Grove City, Pa., 8,312.....D1 81
Grove Hill, Ala., 1,825....D2 46
Groveland, Fla., 1,928....D5 54
Groveland, Mass., 2,500...A5 65
Groveport, Ohio, 2,490.........C2, m11 78
Grover City, Calif., 5,939..E3 50
Groves, Tex., 18,067......E6 84
Groveton, N.H., 1,597....B4 73
Groveton, Pa., 640.......*E1 81
Groveton, Tex., 1,219....D5 84
Groveton, Va., 11,750....g12 85
Grovetown, Ga., 3,169....C4 55
Groveville, N.J., 1,800....C3 74
Groznyy, Sov. Un., 341,000............E7 13
Grudziądz, Pol., 75,500...B5 7
Grulla, Tex., 1,500.......F3 84
Grundy, Va., 2,054.......e9 85
Grundy, co., Ill., 26,535...B5 58
Grundy, co., Iowa, 14,119..B5 60
Grundy, co., Mo., 11,819..A4 69
Grundy, co., Tenn., 10,631............D8 83
Grundy Center, Iowa, 2,712................B5 60
Gruver, Tex., 1,265......A2 84
Gruz, Yugo., 10,000......D4 10
Gryazi, Sov. Un., 41,000..E12 12
Guadalajara, Mex., 1,193,601 (*1,500,000)......C4, m12 34
Guadalajara, Sp., 31,640...B4 8

Guadalajara, prov., Sp., 159,000............*B4 8
Guadalcanal, Sp., 6,931...C3 8
Guadalupe, Ariz., 4,000...D2 48
Guadalupe, Calif., 3,145...E3 50
Guadalupe, co., N. Mex., 4,765................B6 48
Guadalupe, co., Tex., 33,554.............E4 84
Guadalupe, peak, Tex....o12 84
Guadeloupe, Fr. dep., N.A., 345,000............H14 35
Guaira, dept., Par., 114,949............E4 29
Gualeguay, Arg., 16,542...A5 28
Gualeguaychú, Arg., 31,000............A5 28
Guam, U.S., dep., Oceania, 92,000............*F6 2
Guanabacoa, Cuba, 69,700............C2 35
Guanacaste, prov., C.R., 171,700............*E8 34
Guanajay, Cuba, 18,800 (22,000 ▲)...........C2 35
Guanajuato, Mex., 36,809..........C4, m13 34
Guanajuato, state, Mex., 1,957,900...........C4 34
Guanare, Ven., 37,715....B4 32
Guane, Cuba, 8,300 (24,700 ▲)...........C1 35
Guánica, P.R., 8,979 (14,889 ▲)..........*G11 35
Guantánamo, Cuba, 130,100 (131,500 ▲)...D6 35
Guarabira, Braz., 22,627..*D7 27
Guaranda, Ec., 9,900......B2 31
Guarapuava, Braz., 14,419............D2 30
Guaratinguetá, Braz., 55,069.............C3 30
Guarda, Port., 9,094......B2 8
Guareña, Sp., 9,742......C2 8
Guárico, state, Ven., 244,966............B4 32
Guarujá, Braz., 30,741....n8 30
Guatemala, Guat., 717,322 (*945,000)......E6 34
Guatemala, country, N.A., 5,810,000...........D6 34
Guaxupé, Braz., 17,319..C3, k8 30
Guayabal, Cuba, 9,000....D5 35
Guayama, P.R., 20,318 (36,249 ▲)...........n13 36
Guayaquil, Ec., 738,600...B2 31
Guayas, prov., Ec., 1,238,800...........B1 31
Guaymas, Mex., 57,492...B2 34
Gubakha, Sov. Un., 33,000............*D8 13

Gubat, Phil., 8,392.......*C6 19
Gubbio, It., 9,200........C4 9
Gūdūr, India, 33,778.....F6 20
Guebwiller, Fr., 10,840 (*20,500)............D7 5
Guecho, Sp., 22,951......A4 8
Guelma, Alg., 39,817.....A6 22
Guelph, Ont., Can., 60,087 (*62,659)......D4 41
Güemes, Arg., 5,688.....D2 29
Guéret, Fr., 12,849.......D4 5
Guerneville, Calif., 900..*C2 50
Guernsey, Wyo., 793.....D8 89
Guernsey, Br. dep., Eur., 55,000............F5 4
Guernsey, co., Ohio, 37,665............B4 78
Guerrero, state, Mex., 1,331,000...........D5 34
Gueydan, La., 1,984......D3 63
Guiana, French, see French Guiana, dep., S.A.
Guiana, Netherlands, see Surinam, Neth. dep., S.A.
Guidonia, It., 22,205...D4, h9 9
Guildford, Eng., 58,090........E6, m11 4
Guilford, Conn., 3,632...D6 52
Guilford, Maine, 1,216...C3 64
Guilford, N.C., 61......*A3 76
Guilford, co., N.C., 288,590............A3 76
Guimarães, Port., 23,229..B1 8
Guin, Ala., 2,220........B2 46
Guinea, country, Afr., 4,260,000...........F2 22
Guinea-Bissau, country, Afr., 475,000........E4 21
Güines, Cuba, 41,400 (45,300 ▲)...........C2 35
Guingamp, Fr., 9,232....C2 5
Guipúzcoa, prov., Sp., 591,900...........*A4 8
Güira de Melena, Cuba, 19,900 (26,700 ▲)....C2 35
Güiria, Ven., 10,061.....A5 32
Guise, Fr., 6,805........C5 5
Gujarat, state, India, 26,697,475...........D5 20
Gujrānwāla, Pak., 366,000............B5 20
Gujrāt, Pak., 100,000....*B5 20
Gulbarga, India, 145,588..E6 20
Gulf, co., Fla., 10,096....C1 54
Gulf Hammock, Fla., 350..............C4 54
Gulfport, Fla., 9,976.........E4, p10 54
Gulfport, Miss., 40,791 (*151,300).........E4, f7 68
Gull Lake, Sask., Can., 1,038................G1 39

Gulyay-Pole, Sov. Un., 10,000............H11 12
Gumma, pref., Jap., 1,658,909..........*H9 18
Gummersbach, Ger., Fed. Rep. of, 45,361........*C3 6
Gunnedah, Austl., 8,219...E8 26
Gunnison, Colo., 4,613....C4 51
Gunnison, Utah, 1,073....B6 72
Gunnison, co., Colo., 7,578..C3 51
Guntersville, Ala., 6,491..A3 46
Guntūr, India, 269,991...E7 20
Gurabo, P.R., 6,290 (18,289 ▲)..........*G11 35
Gurdon, Ark., 2,075.....D2 49
Gurnee, Ill., 2,738.......E2 58
Guryev, Sov. Un., 114,000.E8 13
Gusav, Nig., 69,231......F6 22
Gusev, Sov. Un., 20,000...A7 7
Gusinje, Yugo., 2,757....D4 10
Gus-Khrustalnyy, Sov. Un., 65,000.....D13 12
Gustavo A. Madero, Mex., 11,773............h9 34
Gustine, Calif., 2,793....D3 50
Güstrow, Ger. Dem. Rep., 36,882............B6 6
Gütersloh, Ger., Fed. Rep. of, 77,599............C4 6
Guthrie, Ky., 1,200......D2 62
Guthrie, Okla., 9,575.....B4 79
Guthrie, co., Iowa, 12,243..C3 60
Guthrie Center, Iowa, 1,834................C3 60
Guttenberg, Iowa, 2,177...B6 60
Guttenberg, N.J., 5,754...h8 74
Guyana, country, S.A., 770,000............C5 27
Guyenne, former prov., Fr................E4 5
Guymon, Okla., 7,674................e9 79
Guysborough, co., N.S., Can., 12,830........D8 43
Gvardeysk, Sov. Un., 5,000................A6 7
Gwādar, Pak., 8,146.....C3 20
Gwalior, India, 384,772 (*406,140)..........C6 20
Gwelo, Rh., 34,000 (*41,000)............D5 24
Gwinn, Mich., 1,054.....B3 66
Gwinnett, co., Ga., 72,349............C2 55
Gyangtse, see Chiangtzu, China
Gympie, Austl., 11,131...E9 25
Gyöngyös, Hung., 33,149............B4 10
Győr, Hung., 100,065...B3 10
Gyor-Sopron, co., Hung., 404,698...........*B3 10
Gyula, Hung., 22,880 (26,266 ▲)..........B5 10

H

Haakon, co., S. Dak., 2,802.F4 77
Haapsalu, Sov. Un., 10,000.B4 12
Haarlem, Neth., 170,667..A6 5
Habersham, Ga., 200.....B3 55
Habersham., co., Ga., 20,691............B3 55
Haboru, Jap., 11,650....D10 18
Hachiman, Jap., 8,680...n15 18
Hachinohe, Jap., 208,801.F10 18
Hachiōji, Jap., 253,527.I9, n18 18
Hackberry, La., 800......E2 63
Hackensack, N.J., 36,008........B4, h8 74
Hackettstown, N.J., 9,472..B3 74
Haddonfield, N.J., 13,118..D2 74
Haddon Heights, N.J., 9,365................D2 74
Hadera, Isr., 31,900..B2, g5 15
Haderslev, co., Den., 74,600............J3 11
Ḥadramawt, reg., P.D.R. of Yem.........G4 15
Hadley, Mass., 800 (3,750 ▲)............B2 65
Haeju, Kor., 82,135......G2 18
Haerhpin (Harbin), China, 2,100,000..........E15 16
Hagaman, N.Y., 1,410...*C6 75

Hagar Shores (Lake Michigan Beach), Mich., 1,201.........*F4 66
Hagen, Ger., Fed. Rep. of, 197,870............C3 6
Hagerman, N. Mex., 953..C6 48
Hagerstown, Ind., 2,059..E7 59
Hagerstown, Md., 35,862 (*83,400)............A2 53
Hagersville, Ont., Can., 2,292................E4 41
Hagi, Jap., 42,000 (52,541 ▲)............I5 18
Ha Giang, Viet., 25,000...G6 17
Haguenau, Fr., 22,944....C7 5
Hague, The ('s Gravenhage), see The Hague, Neth.
Hahira, Ga., 1,326.......F3 55
Hahnville, La., 1,297..E5, k11 63
Haicheng, China, 80,000..*C9 17
Hai Duong, Viet., 24,752............*A3 19
Haifa (Hefa), Isr., 217,400 (*370,000).........B3, g5 15
Ḥā'il, Sau. Ar., 30,000....D3 15
Hailaerh (Hulun), China, 60,000............B8 17
Hailey, Idaho, 1,425......F4 57

Haileybury, Ont., Can., 5,280 (*12,965)......p20 41
Haileyville, Okla., 928....C6 79
Hailun, China, 48,000....C3 18
Hailung, China, 20,000...E2 18
Hainan, isl., China......B4 19
Hainaut, prov., Bel., 1,332,500...........*B5 5
Haines City, Fla., 8,956...D5 54
Haines Falls, N.Y., 700....C6 75
Hainesport, N.J., 900....D3 74
Haiphong, Viet., 182,496 (369,248 ▲).....A3 19
Haiti, country, N.A., 5,420,000...........E7 35
Hajdu-Bihar, co., Hung., 375,371...........*B5 10
Hajduhadház, Hung., 11,221............B5 10
Hajdunánás, Hung., 16,100 (17,824 ▲).....B5 10
Hajduszoboszló, Hung., 20,789 (21,793 ▲)....B5 10
Hakalau, Haw., 742.....D6 56
Hakodate, Jap., 241,663.F10 18
Halawa Heights, Haw., 5,809................g10 56

Halberstadt, Ger. Dem. Rep., 46,812...........C5 6
Halden, Nor., 26,700....H4 11
Haldensleben, Ger. Dem. Rep., 19,490..........B5 6
Haldimand, co., Ont., Can., 30,020..........E5 41
Hale, co., Ala., 15,888....C2 46
Hale, co., Tex., 34,137...B2 84
Haleakala, crater, Haw...C5 56
Hale Center, Tex., 1,964..B2 84
Haledon, N.J., 6,767....*B4 74
Haleiwa, Haw., 2,626..B3, f9 56
Hales Corners, Wis., 7,771............n11 88
Halesite, N.Y., 4,400...*n15 75
Halethorpe, Md., 24,000...........B4, h10 53
Haleyville, Ala., 4,190....A2 46
Half Moon Bay, Calif., 4,038................k8 50
Halfway, Md., 6,106.....A2 53
Haliburton, Ont., Can., 853................B6 41
Haliburton, co., Ont., Can., 7,768................B6 41
Halifax, N.S., Can., 122,035 (*222,637)..........E6 43

Halifax, Eng., 91,040
(*164,000)........D6 4
Halifax, N.C., 335......A5 76
Halifax, Mass., 600
(1,599▲)..........C6 65
Halifax, Pa., 907......F8 81
Halifax, Va., 899......D4 85
Halifax, co., N.C.,
53,884............A5 76
Halifax, co., N.S., Can.,
244,948..........E7 43
Halifax, co., Va., 30,076..D4 85
Hall, Aus., 10,016......E5 6
Hall, co., Ga., 59,405.....B3 55
Hall, co., Nebr., 42,851...D7 71
Hall, co., Tex., 6,015.....B2 84
Halland, co., Swe.,
189,300............I15 11
Hallandale, Fla.,
23,849..........G6, s13 54
Halle, Ger. Dem. Rep.,
245,681 (*470,000)......C5 6
Hallein, Aus., 14,090......E6 6
Hallettsville, Tex., 2,712..E4 84
Hallock, Minn., 1,477....B2 67
Hallowell, Maine, 2,814...D3 64
Halls, Tenn., 2,323......B2 83
Hallstead, Pa., 1,447....C10 81
Hallsville, Tex., 1,038....C5 84
Halmstad, Swe., 46,912
(*62,526)............I5 11
Halstad, Minn., 598......C2 67
Halstead, Kans.,
1,716..........E6, g11 61
Haltia, mtn., Fin.........C9 11
Haltom City, Tex.,
28,127............*C4 84
Halton, co., Ont., Can.,
140,800............D4 41
Hamada, Jap., 49,407....I6 18
Hamadān, Iran, 124,167..F7 16
Ḥamāh, Syr., 137,584...E11 14
Hamamatsu, Jap.,
432,221.........I8, o16 18
Hamar, Nor., 15,000....G4 11
Hama-tombetsu, Jap.....D11 18
Hambantota, Sri Lanka,
6,908.............G7 20
Hamblen, co., Tenn.,
38,696............C10 83
Hamburg, Ger.,
Fed. Rep. of,
1,766,214 (*2,300,000)...B5 6
Hamburg, Iowa, 1,649...D2 60
Hamburg, N.J., 1,820.....A3 74
Hamburg, N.Y., 10,215...C2 75
Hamburg, Pa., 3,909....E10 81
Hamburg, state, Ger. Fed.
Rep. of, 1,800,000......*B5 6
Hamburg, mts., N.J......A3 74
Hamden, Conn., 49,357..D6 52
Hamden, Ohio, 953......C3 78
Häme, prov., Fin.,
619,200............*G11 11
Hämeenlinna, Fin.,
38,380............G11 11
Hamel, Minn., 2,396.....*E5 67
Hameln, Ger., Fed. Rep.
of, 62,845 (*77,000)....B4 6
Hamhung, Kor., 112,184..G3 18
Hami (Kumul) (Qomul),
China, 30,000........C3 17
Hamilton, Ala., 3,088....A2 46
Hamilton, Austl., 9,662...G7 25
Hamilton, Bermuda,
2,060 (*13,757)......p20 35
Hamilton, Ont., Can.,
309,173 (*498,523)....D5 41
Hamilton, Ill., 2,764.....C2 58
Hamilton, Mass., 900
(6,373▲).........A6, f12 65
Hamilton, Mich., 700....F4 66
Hamilton, Mo., 1,645.....B3 69
Hamilton, Mont., 2,499...D2 70
Hamilton, N.Y., 3,636....C5 75
Hamilton, N.Z., 77,600
(*83,800)............L15 26
Hamilton, Ohio, 67,865..C1 78
Hamilton, Scot., 46,376...C4 4
Hamilton, Tex., 2,760....D3 84
Hamilton, co., Fla., 7,787..B3 54
Hamilton, co., Ill., 8,665..E5 58
Hamilton, co., Ind.,
54,532............D5 59
Hamilton, co., Iowa,
18,383............B4 60
Hamilton, co., Kans., 2,747.E2 61
Hamilton, co., Nebr.,
8,867.............D7 71
Hamilton, co., N.Y.,
4,714.............C5 75
Hamilton, co., Ohio,
923,205............C1 78
Hamilton, co., Tenn.,
254,236............D8 83
Hamilton, co., Tex., 7,198..D3 84
Hamilton, mtn., N.Y......B6 75

Hamilton Park, Pa.,
3,800............*G9 81
Hamilton Square, N.J.,
10,000............C3 74
Hamina, Fin., 9,800.....G12 11
Hamiota, Man., Can.,
779...............D1 40
Hamīrpur, India, 10,000...C7 20
Hamlet, N.C., 4,627.....C3 76
Hamlin, Tex., 3,325.....C2 84
Hamlin, co., S. Dak.,
5,520.............F8 77
Hamm [in Westfalen], Ger.,
Fed. Rep. of, 84,370
(*166,000)...........C3 6
Hammon, Okla., 677.....B2 79
Hammond, Ind., 107,885..A2 59
Hammond, La.,
12,487..........D5, h11 63
Hammond, Wis., 768.....D1 88
Hammond East, La.,
1,342............*D5 63
Hammondsport, N.Y.,
1,066.............C3 75
Hammonton, N.J., 11,464..D3 74
Hampden, Newf., Can.,
682..............D3 44
Hampden, Maine, 1,400
(4,693▲)..........*D4 64
Hampden, co., Mass.,
459,050............B2 65
Hampden Highlands,
Maine, 800.........D4 64
Hampshire, Ill., 1,611....A5 58
Hampshire, co., Eng.,
1,687,010..........*E6 4
Hampshire, co., Mass.,
123,981............B2 65
Hampshire, co., W. Va.,
11,710............B6 87
Hampstead, Que., Can.,
7,033............*D4 42
Hampton, Ark., 1,252.....D3 49
Hampton, Ga., 1,551.....C2 55
Hampton, Iowa, 4,376....B4 60
Hampton, N.H., 5,407....F6 73
Hampton, N.J., 1,380.....B3 74
Hampton, S.C., 2,845.....F5 82
Hampton, Tenn., 1,000...C11 83
Hampton
(Independent City)
Va., 120,779.....C6, h15 85
Hampton, co., S.C.,
15,878............F5 82
Hampton Bays, N.Y.,
1,862.............n16 75
Hamtramck, Mich.,
27,245............p15 66
Hana, Haw., 459........C6 56
Hanahan, S.C.,
8,376..........F7, k11 82
Hanamaki, Jap., 37,000
(63,753▲)..........G10 18
Hanamaulu, Haw., 2,461..B2 56
Hanapepe, Haw., 1,388...B2 56
Hanau, Ger., Fed. Rep.
of, 57,073..........C4 6
Hanceville, Ala., 2,027....A3 46
Hanchung, China,
70,000............E6 17
Hancock, Md., 1,832.....A1 53
Hancock, Mich., 4,820....A2 66
Hancock, Minn., 806.....E3 67
Hancock, N.Y., 1,688.....D5 75
Hancock, co., Ga., 9,019..C3 55
Hancock, co., Ill., 23,645..C2 58
Hancock, co., Ind.,
35,096............E6 59
Hancock, co., Iowa,
13,330............A4 60
Hancock, co., Ky., 7,080..C3 62
Hancock, co., Maine,
34,590............D4 64
Hancock, co., Miss.,
17,387............E4 68
Hancock, co., Ohio,
61,217............A2 78
Hancock, co., Tenn.,
6,719............C10 83
Hancock, co., W. Va.,
39,749............A4 87
Hand, co., S. Dak., 5,883..F6 77
Handa, Jap., 80,663.....o15 18
Handley, W. Va., 460....m13 87
Haney, B.C., Can.,
3,221..........E6, f13 37
Hanford, Calif., 15,179...D4 50
Hanford Northwest, Calif.,
1,364............*D4 50
Hangchou, China,
875,000............E9 17
Hangö, Fin., 8,200......H10 11
Hankinson, N. Dak.,
1,125.............D9 77
Hanley Hills, Mo.,
2,807............*C7 69
Hanna, Alta., Can.,
2,545.............D5 38

Hanna, Wyo., 460.......E6 89
Hanna City, Ill., 1,282....C4 58
Hannibal, Mo., 18,609....B6 69
Hannibal, N.Y., 686.....B4 75
Hannover (Hanover),
Ger., Fed. Rep. of,
511,298 (*845,000)......B4 6
Hanoi, Viet., 414,620
(*643,576)...........G6 17
Hanover, Ont., Can.,
5,063.............C3 41
Hanover, Ill., 1,243......A3 58
Hanover, Ind., 3,018.....G7 59
Hanover, Kan., 793......C7 61
Hanover, Mass., 1,500
(10,107▲)........B6, h12 65
Hanover, N.H., 6,147.....D3 73
Hanover, N.J., 7,734.....*B4 74
Hanover, Pa., 15,623.....G8 81
Hanover, co., Va., 37,479..C5 85
Hanover, reg., Ger.,
Fed. Rep. of..........B4 6
Hanover Green, Pa., 700..*D9 81
Hansford, co., Tex., 6,351..A2 84
Hanson, Mass., 800
(7,148▲)...........B6 65
Hanson, co., S. Dak.,
3,781.............G8 77
Hantan, China, 380,000...D7 17
Hants, co., N.S., Can.,
26,893............D6 43
Hantsport, N.S., Can.,
1,381.............D5 43
Haochong, China........C11 20
Haoli, China, 200,000....C5 18
Hapeville, Ga., 9,567...C2, h8 55
Happy Valley, Newf., Can.,
4,937 (*6,528)......B1, h9 44
Harahan, La., 13,037....k11 63
Haralson, co., Ga., 15,927..C1 55
Harar, Eth., 48,440......G6 23
Harbin, see Haehpin, China
Harbor Beach, Mich.,
2,134.............E8 66
Harborcreek, Pa., 800....B2 81
Harbor Isle, N.Y., 1,300..*E7 75
Harbor Springs, Mich.,
1,662.............C6 66
Harbour Breton, Newf.,
Can., 2,196........E4 44
Harbour Grace, Newf.,
Can., 2,771........E5 44
Harbour Main, Newf.,
Can., 469.........E5 44
Hardee, co., Fla., 14,889..E5 54
Hardeeville, S.C., 853....G5 82
Hardeman, co., Tenn.,
22,435............B2 83
Hardeman, co., Tex.,
6,795.............B3 84
Hardin, Ill., 1,035......D3 58
Hardin, Mo., 683.......B4 69
Hardin, co., Ill., 4,914....F5 58
Hardin, co., Iowa, 22,248..B4 60
Hardin, co., Ky., 78,421...C3 62
Hardin, co., Mont., 2,733..E9 70
Hardin, co., Ohio, 30,813..B2 78
Hardin, co., Tenn.,
18,212............B3 83
Hardin, co., Tex., 29,996..D5 84
Harding, co., N. Mex.,
1,348.............B7 48
Harding, co., S. Dak.,
1,855.............E2 77
Hardinsburg, Ky., 1,547..C3 62
Hardshell, Ky., 350.....C6 62
Hardwār, India, 77,864
(*79,277)...........C6 20
Hardwick, Ga., 6,000....C3 55
Hardwick, Vt., 1,503.....B3 73
Hardy, co., W. Va., 8,855..B6 87
Hare Bay, Newf., Can.,
1,467.............D4 44
Harfleur, Fr., 10,514....C4 5
Harford, co., Md.,
115,378............A5 53
Hargeisa, Som., 42,000...G6 23
Harihar, India, 33,888....F6 20
Harkers Island, N.C.,
1,633.............C6 76
Harlan, Iowa, 5,049......C2 60
Harlan, Ky., 3,318......D6 62
Harlan, co., Ky., 37,370..D6 62
Harlan, co., Nebr., 4,357..D6 71
Harlem, Fla., 1,256......F6 54
Harlem, Ga., 1,540......C4 55
Harlem, Mont., 1,094....B8 70
Harlingen, Neth., 13,853..A6 5
Harlingen, Tex., 33,503
(*56,800)...........F4 84
Harlow, Eng., 77,920....k13 4
Harlowton, Mont.,
1,375.............D7 70
Harmarville, Pa., 1,300...h14 81
Harmon, co., Okla.,
5,136.............C2 79
Harmony, Ind., 750.....E3 59
Harmony, Minn., 1,130..G6 67

Harmony, Pa., 1,207.....E1 81
Harnett, co., N.C., 49,667..B4 76
Harney, co., Oreg., 7,215..D7 80
Harney, peak, S. Dak.....F2 77
Harnösand, Swe., 24,128..F8 11
Haro, Sp., 8,554........A4 8
Harper, Kans., 1,665.....E5 61
Harper, Lib., 8,000......H3 22
Harper, co., Kans.,
7,871.............E5 61
Harper, co., Okla., 5,151..A2 79
Harper Woods, Mich.,
20,186............*F7 66
Harrah, Okla., 1,931.....B4 79
Harriman, Tenn., 8,734...D1 83
Harrington, Del., 2,407...C6 53
Harrington Park, N.J.,
4,841.............h9 74
Harris, co., Ga., 11,520...D1 55
Harris, hill, Mass.......A3 65
Harrisburg, Ark., 1,931...B5 49
Harrisburg, Ill., 9,535....F5 58
Harrisburg, Oreg., 1,311..C3 80
Harrisburg, Pa., 68,061
(*355,100)..........F8 81
Harris Hill, N.Y., 5,000..*C2 75
Harrison, Ark., 7,239.....A2 49
Harrison, Mich., 1,460...D6 66
Harrison, N.J., 11,811....k8 74
Harrison, N.Y.,
13,000.........D2, h13 75
Harrison, Ohio, 4,408....C3 78
Harrison, co., Ind.,
20,423............H5 59
Harrison, co., Iowa,
16,240............C2 60
Harrison, co., Ky.,
14,158............B5 62
Harrison, co., Miss.,
134,582............E4 68
Harrison, co., Mo.,
10,257............A3 69
Harrison, co., Ohio,
17,013............B4 78
Harrison, co., Tex.,
44,841............C5 84
Harrison, co., W. Va.,
73,028............B4 87
Harrisonburg, La., 626....C4 63
Harrisonburg (Independent
City), Va., 14,605.....B4 85
Harrisonville, Mo., 5,052..C3 69
Harriston, Ont., Can.,
1,631.............D4 41
Harrisville, Pa., 944.....D2 81
Harrisville, R.I., 1,053...B10 52
Harrisville, W. Va., 1,464..B3 87
Harrisville, N.Y., 836.....A5 75
Harrodsburg, Ky., 6,741..C5 62
Harrogate, Eng., 63,470..C6 4
Harrow, Ont., Can.,
1,787.............E2 41
Hart, Mich., 2,139......E4 66
Hart, co., Ga., 15,814....B3 55
Hart, co., Ky., 13,980....C4 62
Hart, mtn., Man., Can....C1 40
Hartford, Ala., 2,648....D4 46
Hartford, Conn.,
158,017 (*1,036,900)....B6 52
Hartford, Ill., 2,243.....E3 58
Hartford, Ky., 1,868.....C3 62
Hartford, Mich., 2,508...F4 66
Hartford, Wis.,
6,499............E5, m11 88
Hartford, co., Conn.,
816,737............B5 52
Hartford City, Ind.,
8,207.............D7 59
Hartington, Nebr., 1,581..B8 71
Hartland, N.B., Can.,
1,025.............C2 43
Hartland, Maine, 950
(1,414▲)...........D3 64
Hartland, Wis.,
2,763...........E5, m11 88
Hartlepool, Eng., 97,110..C6 4
Hartley, Iowa, 1,694.....A2 60
Hartley, co., Tex., 2,782..B1 84
Hartsdale, N.Y., 12,226..*D7 75
Hartselle, Ala., 7,355....A3 46
Hartshorne, Okla., 2,121..C6 79
Hartsville, S.C., 8,017....C7 82
Hartsville, Tenn., 2,243...A5 83
Hartville, Ohio, 1,752....B4 78
Hartwell, Ga., 4,865.....B4 55
Hartwick, N.Y., 600.....C5 75
Harvard, Ill., 5,177......A5 58
Harvard, Nebr., 1,230....D7 71
Harvard, mtn., Colo......C4 51
Harvey, Ill., 34,636....B6, k9 58
Harvey, La., 10,000...E5, k11 63
Harvey, Mich., 900......B3 66
Harvey, N. Dak., 2,361...C6 77
Harvey, co., Kans.,
27,236............D6 61
Harvey, mtn., Mass......B1 65

Harwich, Eng., 14,830.....E7 4
Harwich, Mass., 1,000 (5,892 ▲).............C7 65
Harwich Port, Mass., 1,700.................C7 65
Harwick, Pa., 1,200......*E1 81
Harwood Heights, Ill., 9,060.................*B6 58
Haryāna, state, India, 10,036,808.............C5 20
Hasbrouck Heights, N.J., 13,651.................h8 74
Hashimoto, Jap., 24,000 (33,334 ▲).............o14 18
Haskell, Okla., 2,063.......B6 79
Haskell, Tex., 3,655.......C3 84
Haskell, co., Kans., 3,672..E3 61
Haskell, co., Okla., 9,578..B6 79
Haskell, co., Tex., 8,512...C3 84
Haslett, Mich., 4,000......*F6 66
Hassan, India, 51,325......F6 20
Hasselt, Bel., 39,888.......B6 5
Hässleholm, Swe., 20,274...I5 11
Hastings, Ont., Can., 897..C7 41
Hastings, Eng., 72,770.....E7 4
Hastings, Fla., 628........C5 54
Hastings, Mich., 6,501.....F5 66
Hastings, Minn., 12,195....F6 67
Hastings, Nebr., 23,580....D7 71
Hastings, N.Z., 30,600...M16 26
Hastings, Pa., 1,791.......E4 81
Hastings, co., Ont., Can., 94,127................C7 41
Hastings-on-Hudson, N.Y., 13,957................h13 75
Hatboro, Pa., 8,880.......F11 81
Hatch, N. Mex., 867......C5 48
Hatfield, Mass., 1,300 (2,825 ▲)..............B2 65
Hatfield, Pa., 2,385.......F11 81
Hathras, India, 74,349...*C6 20
Ha Tien, Viet., 4,700.....C2 19
Hatteras, N.C., 700.......B7 76
Hattiesburg, Miss., 38,277.................D4 68
Hatton, N. Dak., 808......C8 77
Hatton Fields, Calif., 2,400................*D3 50
Hatvan, Hung., 21,958....B4 10
Hatzic, B.C., Can., 724....f13 37
Haubstadt, Ind., 1,171....H2 59
Haugesund, Nor., 27,300.................H1 11
Hauppauge, N.Y., 17,800...............*D3 75
Haute-Garonne, dept., Fr., 690,712...............*F4 5
Haute-Loire, dept., Fr., 208,337...............*E5 5
Haute-Marne, dept., Fr., 214,336..............*C6 5
Hauterive, Que., Can., 13,181................k13 42
Hautes-Alpes, dept., Fr., 91,790................*E7 5
Haute-Saône, dept., Fr., 214,176...............*D6 5
Haute-Savoie, dept., Fr., 378,550..............*D7 5
Hautes-Pyrénées, dept., Fr., 225,730...........*F4 5
Haute-Vienne, dept., Fr., 341,589..............*E4 5
Hautmont, Fr., 18,594.....B6 5
Haut-Rhin, dept., Fr., 585,018..............*C7 5
Hauula, Haw., 2,048..B4, f10 56
Havana (La Habana), Cuba, 1,755,400 (*1,800,000)...........C2 35
Havana, Fla., 2,022.......B2 54
Havana, Ill., 4,376........C3 58
Havelock, Ont., Can., 1,260.................C7 41
Havelock, N.C., 5,283.....C6 76
Haven, Kans., 1,146...E6, g11 61
Haverford, Pa., 5,800....*F10 81
Haverhill, Mass., 46,120...A5 65
Haverstraw, N.Y., 8,198...........D7, m15 75
Havertown, Pa., 36,800..*G10 81
Haviland, Kans., 705......E4 61
Havlíčkův Brod, Czech., 17,702................D3 7
Havre, Mont., 10,558......B7 70
Havre, see Le Havre, Fr.
Havre-Aubert, Que., Can., 494...................B8 43
Havre de Grace, Md., 9,791.................A5 53
Havza, Tur., 13,073......B10 14
Hawaii, co., Haw., 63,468.................D5 56
Hawaii, state, U.S., 842,000...............D5 56
Hawaii, isl., Haw.........D6 56
Hawaiian Gardens, Calif., 9,052.................*F4 50
Hawarden, Iowa, 2,789....A1 60
Hawera, N.Z., 8,150.....M15 26
Hawesville, Ky., 1,262.....C3 62
Hawi, Haw., 797.........C6 56
Hawick, Scot., 16,299.....C5 4
Hawkesbury, Ont., Can., 9,276 (*10,771)........B10 41
Hawkins, co., Tenn., 33,726..............C10 83
Hawkinsville, Ga., 4,077...D3 55
Hawk Run, Pa., 750.......E5 81
Hawks Bill, mtn., Va......B4 85
Hawley, Minn., 1,371.....D2 67
Hawley, Pa., 1,331.......D11 81
Haworth, N.J., 3,760.......h9 74
Haw River, N.C., 1,944....A3 76
Hawthorne, Calif., 53,304...............n12 50
Hawthorne, Fla., 1,126....C4 54
Hawthorne, Nev., 3,539....B2 72
Hawthorne, N.J., 19,173...B4 74
Hawthorne, N.Y., 5,000...g13 75
Haxtun, Colo., 899........A8 51
Hayange, Fr., 10,305 (*75,000).............C7 5
Hayden, Ariz., 1,283..C3, D3 48
Hayden, Idaho, 1,285......B2 57
Haydenville, Mass., 750....B2 65
Haydenville, Ohio, 500.....C3 78
Hayes, La., 800..........D3 63
Hayes, co., Nebr., 1,530...D4 71
Hayesville, Oreg., 5,518..*C4 80
Hayfield, Minn., 939......G6 67
Haynau, see Chojnow, Pol.
Haynesville, La., 3,055....B2 63
Hay River, N. W. Ter., Can., 2,406...........D10 36
Hays, Kans., 15,396.......D4 61
Hays, Mont., 600..........C8 70
Hays, co., Tex., 27,642....D3 84
Hay Springs, Nebr., 682...B3 71
Haysville, Kans., 6,483....B5 61
Hayti, Mo., 3,841.........E8 69
Hayward, Calif., 93,058....h8 50
Hayward, Wis., 1,457......B2 88
Haywood, N.C., 200.......B3 76
Haywood, co., N.C., 41,710..................f9 76
Haywood, co., Tenn., 19,596.................B2 83
Hazard, Ky., 5,459........C6 62
Hazardville, Conn., 10,000.B6 52
Hazebrouck, Fr., 17,446...B5 5
Hazel Crest, Ill., 10,329....k9 58
Hazel Dell, Wash., 3,500..*D3 86
Hazel Green, Wis., 982....F3 88
Hazel Park, Mich., 23,784................p15 66
Hazelwood, Mo., 14,082..*C7 69
Hazelwood, N.C., 2,057...f10 76
Hazen, Ark., 1,605........C4 49
Hazen, N. Dak., 1,204.....C4 77
Hazlehurst, Ga., 4,065.....E4 55
Hazlehurst, Miss., 4,577...D3 68
Hazlet, N.J., 18,000.......C4 74
Hazleton, Iowa, 626.......B6 60
Hazleton, Pa., 30,426 (*65,900).............E10 81
Hazelton, peak, Wyo......C3 89
Headland, Ala., 2,545.....D4 46
Healdsburg, Calif., 5,438..C2 50
Healdton, Okla., 2,324....C4 79
Heard, co., Ga., 5,354.....C1 55
Hearne, Tex., 4,982.......D4 84
Hearst, Ont., Can., 3,501..o19 41
Heart's Content, Newf., Can., 607..............E5 44
Heart's Delight, Newf., Can., 631.............*E5 44
Heath, Ohio, 6,768........B3 78
Heavener, Okla., 2,566....C7 79
Hebbronville, Tex., 4,000..F3 84
Heber, Utah, 3,245...A6, D2 72
Heber Springs, Ark., 2,497..................B3 49
Hébertville, Que., Can., 1,604.................A6 42
Hébertville Station, Que., Can., 1,163 (*3,409)...*A6 42
Hebrides, sea, Scot.......B3 4
Hebron, Ill., 781..........A5 58
Hebron, Ind., 1,624.......B3 59
Hebron, Nebr., 1,667.....D8 71
Hebron, N. Dak., 1,103...D3 77
Hebron, Ohio, 1,699.......C3 78
Hecelchakán, Mex., 4,279..C6 34
Hechingen, Ger., Fed. Rep. of, 16,239....D4 6
Hector, Minn., 1,178......F4 67
Hedemora, Swe., 10,664...G6 11
Hedmark, co., Nor., 177,900..............*G4 11
Hedrick, Iowa, 790........C5 60
Hedwig Village, Tex., 3,255.................*E5 84
Heerlen, Neth., 73,849 (*265,280)............B6 5
Heflin, Ala., 2,872........B4 46
Hegeler, Ill., 1,640.......*C6 58
Hegins, Pa., 800..........E8 81
Heide, Ger., Fed. Rep. of, 22,590................A4 6
Heidelberg, Ger., Fed. Rep. of, 122,668........D4 6
Heidelberg, Miss., 1,112...D5 68
Heidelberg, Pa., 2,034....*E1 81
Heidenheim, Ger., Fed. Rep. of, 50,008 (*98,000).......D5 6
Heidrick, Ky., 600........D6 62
Heilbronn, Ger., Fed. Rep. of, 105,458 (*225,000)...D4 6
Heiligenstadt, Ger. Dem. Rep., 12,500...........C5 6
Heilungkiang, prov., China, 14,860,000............B10 17
Heislerville, N.J., 600.....E3 74
Hejaz, pol. div., Sau. Ar., 2,000,000..............D2 15
Hekla, peak, Ice.........n23 11
Helena, Ark., 10,415......C5 49
Helena, Ga., 1,230........D4 55
Helena, Mont., 22,730.....D5 70
Helensburgh, Scot., 13,028.B4 4
Hellam, Pa., 1,825........G8 81
Hellertown, Pa., 6,615....E11 81
Hell-Ville, Mad., 7,497....C9 24
Helmetta, N.J., 955.......C4 74
Helmond, Neth., 58,784...B6 5
Helmstedt, Ger., Fed. Rep. of, 26,653..............B5 6
Helper, Utah, 1,964.......B6 72
Helsingborg, Swe., 101,176.................I5 11
Helsingfors, see Helsinki, Fin.
Helsingor, Den., 29,800 (*40,000)..............I5 11
Helsinki, Fin., 512,305 (*780,000)............G11 11
Hemel Hempstead, Eng., 69,720................k12 4
Hemet, Calif., 12,252......F5 50
Hemingford, Nebr., 734....B2 71
Hemingway, S.C., 1,026...D9 82
Hemlock, Mich., 900.......E6 66
Hemlock (Eureka), S.C., 1,524.................B5 82
Hemmingford, Que., Can., 778..............D4 42
Hemphill, Tex., 1,005.....D6 84
Hemphill, co., Tex., 3,084..................B2 84
Hempstead, N.Y., 39,411..................k13 75
Hempstead, Tex., 1,891...D4 84
Hempstead, co., Ark., 19,308.................D2 49
Hendaye, Fr., 8,006.......F3 5
Hendek, Tur., 12,627......B8 14
Henderson, Ky., 22,976....C2 62
Henderson, Minn., 730.....F5 67
Henderson, Nebr., 901....D8 71
Henderson, Nev., 16,395...C4 72
Henderson, N.C., 13,896...A4 76
Henderson, Tenn., 3,581...B3 83
Henderson, Tex., 10,187...C5 84
Henderson, co., Ill., 8,451..................C3 58
Henderson, co., Ky., 36,031.................C2 62
Henderson, co., N.C., 42,804.................f10 76
Henderson, co., Tenn., 17,291.................B3 83
Henderson, co., Tex., 26,466................C5 84
Hendersonville, N.C., 6,443.................f10 76
Hendersonville, Tenn., 262...............A5, g10 83
Hendricks, Minn., 712.....F2 67
Hendricks, co., Ind., 53,974.................E4 59
Hendry, co., Fla., 11,859...F5 54
Hengelo, Neth., 72,062....A7 5
Hengyang, China, 240,000..................F7 17
Henlawson, W. Va., 900..n12 87
Hennebont, Fr., 7,623.....D2 5
Hennepin, co., Minn., 960,080................E5 67
Hennessey, Okla., 2,181...A4 79
Henning, Minn., 850......D3 67
Henrico, co., Va., 154,364.................C5 85
Henrietta, N.Y., 600......B3 75
Henrietta, N.C., 1,200.B2, f11 76
Henrietta, Tex., 2,897.....C3 84
Henry, Ill., 2,610..........B4 58
Henry, co., Ala., 13,254...D4 46
Henry, co., Ga., 23,724....C2 55
Henry, co., Ill., 53,217.....B3 58
Henry, co., Ind., 52,603...E7 59
Henry, co., Iowa, 18,114...C6 60
Henry, co., Ky., 10,264....B4 62
Henry, co., Mo., 18,451...C4 69
Henry, co., Ohio, 27,058...A1 78
Henry, co., Tenn., 23,749..A3 83
Henry, co., Va., 50,901....D3 85
Henryetta, Okla., 6,430....B6 79
Hensall, Ont., Can., 926...D3 41
Henryville, Que., Can., 711...................D4 42
Henzada, Bur., 61,972....E10 20
Heppner, Oreg., 1,429.....B7 80
Herat, Afg., 100,000.......B3 20
Hérault, dept., Fr., 591,397...............*F5 5
Herbert, Sask., Can., 1,008.................G2 39
Herblay, Fr., 10,220.......g9 5
Hercegovina, reg., Yugo...D3 10
Herculaneum, Mo., 2,439.............C7, g13 69
Heredia, C.R., 22,300.....E8 34
Heredia, prov., C.R., 97,800................*E8 34
Hereford, Eng., 47,200....D5 4
Hereford, Tex., 13,414.....B1 84
Hereford, co., Eng., 142,100.............*D5 4
Herencia, Sp., 8,606......C4 8
Herford, Ger., Fed. Rep. of, 65,336 (*120,000)....B4 6
Herington, Kans., 3,165...D7 61
Herisau, Switz., 14,500....E4 6
Herkimer, N.Y., 8,960.....B6 75
Herkimer, co., N.Y., 67,633.................B5 75
Herman, Minn., 619.......E2 67
Hermann, Mo., 2,658.....C6 69
Hermansville, Mich., 700..C3 66
Hermantown, Minn., 900..D6 67
Herminie, Pa., 1,100......F2 81
Hermiston, Oreg., 4,893...B7 80
Hermon, N.Y., 521.........f9 75
Hermosa Beach, Calif., 17,412.................*F4 50
Hermosillo, Mex., 176,596..B2 34
Hernando, Miss., 2,499....A4 68
Hernando, co., Fla., 17,004................D4 54
Herndon, Va., 430....B5, g12 85
Herning, Den., 31,500.....I3 11
Heron Lake, Minn., 777...G3 67
Herrin, Ill., 9,623.........F4 58
Hershey, Pa., 9,000.......F8 81
Herstal, Bel., 29,571.......B6 5
Hertford, Eng., 20,770...........E6, k12 4
Hertford, N.C., 2,023.....A6 76
Hertford, co., Eng., 930,390...............*E6 4
Hertford, co., N.C., 23,529..................A5 76
Herzliyya, Isr., 41,200..B2, g5 15
Hesperia, Mich., 877......E4 66
Hesse, reg., Ger., Fed. Rep. of.................C4 6
Hessen, state, Ger., Fed. Rep. of, 5,590,000.....*C4 6
Hesston, Kans., 1,926.....D6 61
Hettinger, N. Dak., 1,655..D3 77
Hettinger, co., N. Dak., 5,075..................D3 77
Heuvelton, N.Y., 770......f9 75
Heves, Hung., 9,923.......B5 10
Heves, co., Hung., 348,395................*B5 10
Hewitt, N.J., 300.........A4 74
Hewlett, N.Y., 6,796.....*G2 52
Hewlett Harbor, N.Y., 1,512................*G2 52
Heyworth, Ill., 1,441......C5 58
Hialeah, Fla., 102,452...........G6, s13 54
Hiawatha, Iowa, 2,416...*C6 60
Hiawatha, Kans., 3,365....C8 61
Hiawatha, Utah, 166......B6 72
Hibbing, Minn., 16,104....C6 67
Hibernia, N.J., 300.......B4 74
Hickman, Ky., 3,048.......f8 62
Hickman, co., Ky., 6,264...f8 62
Hickman, co., Tenn., 12,096.................B4 83
Hickory, co., Mo., 4,481...D4 69
Hickory Hills, Ill., 13,176.*B6 58
Hicksville, N.Y., 49,820............E7, n15 75
Hicksville, Ohio, 3,461....A1 78
Hico, Tex., 975...........D3 84
Hidalgo, Tex., 1,289......F3 84
Hidalgo, co., N. Mex., 4,734..................D4 48
Hidalgo, co., Tex., 181,535.F3 84
Hidalgo, state, Mex., 1,064,000.........C5, m14 34

Hidalgo del Parral, Mex., 57,619 . . . B3 34
Higashiizu, Jap., 5,685 . . . o18 18
Higashiōsaka, Jap., 500,173 . . . I7, o14 18
Higbee, Mo., 641 . . . B5 69
Higgins, Tex., 582 . . . A2 84
Higginsville, Mo., 4,318 . . . B4 69
High Bridge, N.J., 2,606 . . . B3 74
Highgrove, Calif., 2,800 . . . *F5 50
High Knob, mtn., Va. . . . A4 85
Highland, Calif., 11,557 . . . *E5 50
Highland, Ill., 5,981 . . . E4 58
Highland, Ind., 24,947 . . . A3 59
Highland, Kans., 899 . . . C8 61
Highland, Mich., 700 . . . o14 66
Highland, N.Y., 2,184 . . . D7 75
Highland, Wis., 785 . . . E3 88
Highland, co., Ohio, 28,996 . . . C2 78
Highland, co., Va., 2,529 . . . B3 85
Highland City, Fla., 1,500 . . . *E5 54
Highland Creek, Ont., Can. . . . D5 41
Highland Crest, Kans . . . *B8 61
Highland Falls, N.Y., 4,638 . . . *D7 75
Highland Heights, Ky., 4,543 . . . *A5 62
Highland Heights, Ohio, 5,926 . . . *A4 78
Highland Park, Ill., 32,263 . . . A6, h9 58
Highland Park, Mich., 35,444 . . . p15 66
Highland Park, N.J., 14,385 . . . *C4 74
Highland Park, Pa., 1,704 . . . *F6 81
Highland Park, Tex., 10,133 . . . B5 84
Highlands, Fla., 29,507 . . . *B5 54
Highlands, N.J., 3,916 . . . C5 74
Highlands, Tex., 3,462 . . . r14 84
Highlands, co., Fla., 29,507 . . . E5 54
Highland Springs, Va., 7,345 . . . C5, m18 85
Highmore, S. Dak., 1,173 . . . F6 77
High Point, N.C., 63,204 . . . B3 76
High Point, mtn., N.J. . . . A3 74
High Prairie, Alta., Can., 2,354 . . . B2 38
High River, Alta., Can., 2,676 . . . D4 38
Highshoals, N.C., 800 . . . B1 76
High Spire, Pa., 2,947 . . . F8 81
High Springs, Fla., 2,787 . . . C4 54
Hightstown, N.J., 5,431 . . . C3 74
Highway City, Calif., 1,100 . . . *D4 50
Highway Village, Tex . . . *F4 84
Highwood, Ill., 4,973 . . . A6, h9 58
High Wycombe, Eng., 59,930 . . . E6 4
Higüey, Dom. Rep., 21,700 . . . E9 35
Hikone, Jap., 78,753 . . . n15 18
Hilbert, Wis., 896 . . . E3 88
Hildburghausen, Ger. Dem. Rep., 7,870 . . . C5 6
Hildesheim, Ger., Fed. Rep. of, 94,033 (*135,000) . . . B4 6
Hill, co., Mont., 17,358 . . . B6 70
Hill, co., Tex., 22,596 . . . D4 84
Hillburn, N.Y., 1,058 . . . *D6 75
Hill City, Kans., 2,071 . . . C4 61
Hillcrest, N.J. . . . *B2 74
Hillcrest, N.Y., 5,357 . . . *D6 75
Hillcrest Center, Calif., 29,200 . . . *E4 50
Hillcrest Heights, Md., 25,700 . . . *C3 53
Hillcrest Mines, Alta., Can., 618 . . . E3 38
Hiller, Pa., 1,688 . . . *G2 81
Hilliard, Fla., 1,205 . . . B5 54
Hilliard, Ohio, 8,369 . . . k10 78
Hillsboro, Ill., 4,267 . . . D4 58
Hillsboro, Kans., 2,730 . . . D6 61
Hillsboro, N.H., 1,784 . . . E4 73
Hillsboro, N. Dak., 1,309 . . . C8 77
Hillsboro, Ohio, 5,584 . . . C2 78
Hillsboro, Oreg., 14,675 . . . B3, g12 80
Hillsboro, Tenn., 200 . . . B6 83
Hillsboro, Tex., 7,224 . . . C4 84
Hillsboro, Wis., 1,231 . . . E3 88
Hillsboro, co., N.H., 223,941 . . . F4 73
Hillsborough, Calif., 8,753 . . . *D2 50
Hillsborough, N.B., Can., 679 . . . D5 43
Hillsborough, N.C., 1,444 . . . A3 76
Hillsborough, co., Fla., 490,265 . . . E4 54
Hillsborough Lower Village, N.H., 85 . . . E3 73
Hillsborough Upper Village, N.H., 135 . . . E4 73
Hillsdale, Mich., 7,728 . . . G6 66
Hillsdale, Mo., 2,599 . . . *C7 69
Hillsdale, N.J., 11,768 . . . g8 74
Hillsdale, co., Mich., 37,171 . . . G6 66
Hillside, Ill., 8,888 . . . *B6 58
Hillside, N.J., 21,636 . . . k8 74
Hillside Manor, N.Y., 4,300 . . . *G2 52
Hillsville, Pa., 915 . . . D1 81
Hillsville, Va., 1,149 . . . D2 85
Hilltop, N.J., 1,200 . . . *D2 74
Hillwood, Va., 1,500 . . . *B5 85
Hilo, Haw., 26,353 . . . D6, n16 56
Hilton, N.Y., 2,440 . . . B3 75
Hilversum, Neth., 96,841 . . . A6 5
Himachal Pradesh, state, India, 3,460,434 . . . *B6 20
Himalayas, mts., India . . . C7 20
Himeji, Jap., 408,353 . . . I7 18
Himi, Jap., 38,000 (60,883 ▲) . . . H8 18
Ḥimṣ (Homs), Syr., 215,526 . . . B5 23
Hinche, Hai., 8,462 . . . E7 35
Hinckley, Ill., 1,053 . . . B5 58
Hinckley, Minn., 885 . . . D6 67
Hindenburg, see Zabrze, Pol.
Hinds, co., Miss., 214,973 . . . C3 68
Hines, Oreg., 1,407 . . . D7 80
Hinesville, Ga., 4,115 . . . E5 55
Hingham, Mass., 13,500 . . . B6, h12 65
Hinojosa [del Duque], Sp., 14,767 . . . C3 8
Hinsdale, Ill., 15,918 . . . k9 58
Hinsdale, Mass., 900 (1,588 ▲) . . . B1 65
Hinsdale, N.H., 1,059 . . . F3 73
Hinsdale, co., Colo., 202 . . . D3 51
Hinton, Alta., Can., 4,911 . . . C2 38
Hinton, Okla., 889 . . . B3 79
Hinton, W. Va., 4,503 . . . D4 87
Hirakata, Jap., 217,369 . . . *I7 18
Hiram, Ohio, 1,484 . . . A4 78
Hiratsuka, Jap., 163,671 . . . n17 18
Hiroo, Jap., 7,966 . . . E11 18
Hirosaki, Jap., 102,000 (157,603 ▲) . . . F10 18
Hiroshima, Jap., 541,998 (*1,175,000) . . . I6 18
Hiroshima, pref., Jap., 2,436,135 . . . *I6 18
Hirson, Fr., 11,858 . . . C5 5
Hisār, India, 89,437 . . . C6 20
Hispaniola, isl., N.A. . . . D8 35
Hita, Jap. 48,000 (64,866 ▲) . . . *J5 18
Hitachi, Jap., 193,210 . . . H10 18
Hitchcock, Tex., 5,565 . . . r14 84
Hitchcock, co., Nebr., 4,051 . . . D4 71
Hitchins, Ky., 700 . . . B7 62
Hitoyoshi, Jap., 30,000 (42,196 ▲) . . . J5 18
Hixon, Tenn., 6,500 . . . D8, h11 83
Hjørring, Den., 15,038 . . . I3 11
Hjørring, co., Den., 184,600 . . . *I3 11
Hlohovec, Czech., 14,657 . . . D4 7
Hlomsak, Thai., 7,906 . . . *E11 20
Hoa Binh, Viet., 25,000 . . . *A3 19
Hobart, Austl., 52,425 (*153,024) . . . o15 25
Hobart, Ind., 21,485 . . . A3 59
Hobart, Okla., 4,638 . . . B2 79
Hobbs, N. Mex., 26,025 . . . C7 48
Hoboken, Bel., 34,273 . . . B6 5
Hoboken, N.J., 45,380 . . . k8 74
Ho Chi Minh City (Saigon), Viet., 1,640,000 (*2,250,000) . . . C3 19
Hocking, co., Ohio, 20,322 . . . C3 78
Hockley, co., Tex., 20,396 . . . C1 84
Hoddesdon, Eng., 26,310 . . . k13 4
Hodeida, Yemen, 90,000 . . . F6 23
Hodgeman, co., Kans., 2,662 . . . D4 61
Hodgenville, Ky., 2,562 . . . C4 62
Hodgkins, Ill., 2,270 . . . *B6 58
Hódmezővásárhely, Hung., 44,219 (52,797 ▲) . . . B5 10
Hodonín, Czech, 20,834 . . . D4 7
Hoeryong, Kor., 24,330 . . . E4 18
Hof, Ger., Fed. Rep of, 55,493 . . . C5 6
Hofei, China, 360,000 . . . E8 17
Hoffman, Minn., 627 . . . E3 67
Hoffman Estates, Ill., 22,238 . . . h8 58
Hofu, Jap., 76,000 (97,009 ▲) . . . I5 18
Hogansville, Ga., 3,075 . . . C2 55
Hogback, mtn., S.C. . . . A3 82
Hohenwald, Tenn., 3,385 . . . B4 83
Ho-Ho-Kus (Hohokus), N.J., 4,348 . . . h8 74
Hoihow, China, 402,000 . . . *A4 19
Hoisington, Kans., 4,248 . . . D5 61
Hokah, Minn., 697 . . . G7 67
Hoke, co., N.C., 16,436 . . . B3 76
Hokendauqua, Pa., 2,500 . . . *E10 81
Hokes Bluff, Ala., 2,133 . . . B4 46
Hokkaido, pref., Jap., 5,184,287 . . . *E10 18
Hokkaido, isl., Jap . . . E10 18
Holbaek, co., Den., 133,000 . . . *J4 11
Holbrook, Ariz., 4,759 . . . B3 48
Holbrook, Mass., 9,750 (11,775 ▲) . . . B5, h11 65
Holbrook, N.Y., 12,800 . . . *n15 75
Holden, Mass., 2,200 (12,564 ▲) . . . B4 65
Holden, Mo., 2,089 . . . C4 69
Holden, W. Va., 1,900 . . . D2 87
Holdenville, Okla., 5,181 . . . B5 79
Holdrege, Nebr., 5,635 . . . D6 71
Holgate, Ohio, 1,541 . . . A1 78
Holguín, Cuba, 131,500 (163,100 ▲) . . . D5 35
Hollabrunn, Aus., 6,671 . . . D8 6
Holladay, Utah, 26,000 . . . *C3 72
Holland, Mich., 26,479 (*55,900) . . . F4 66
Holland, N.Y., 950 . . . C2 75
Holland, Ohio, 1,108 . . . A2,e6 78
Hollandale, Miss., 3,260 . . . B3 68
Holley, N.Y., 1,868 . . . B2 75
Holliday, Tex., 1,048 . . . C3 84
Hollidaysburg, Pa., 6,262 . . . F5 81
Hollins, Va., 5,000 . . . C3 85
Hollis, Alsk . . . n23 47
Hollis, Okla., 3,150 . . . C2 79
Hollister, Calif., 7,663 . . . D3 50
Hollister, Mo., 906 . . . E4 69
Holliston, Mass., 12,069 . . . h10 65
Holloway Terrace, Del., 2,000 . . . *A6 53
Hollsopple, Pa., 900 . . . F4 81
Holly, Colo., 993 . . . C8 51
Holly, Mich., 4,355 . . . F7 66
Holly Hill, Fla., 8,191 . . . C5 54
Holly Hill, S.C., 1,178 . . . E7 82
Holly Oak, Del., 1,000 . . . A7 53
Holly Ridge, N.C., 415 . . . C5 76
Holly Springs, Miss., 5,728 . . . A4 68
Hollywood, Fla., 106,873 . . . F6, r13 54
Hollywood, La., 1,888 . . . *D2 63
Hollywood, Pa., 2,000 . . . *F11 81
Hollywood Heights, Ill, 950 . . . *E3 58
Holmdel Gardens, Kans., 1,436 . . . *D6 61
Holmen, Wis., 1,081 . . . E2 88
Holmes, Pa., 2,400 . . . *G11 81
Holmes, co., Fla., 10,720 . . . u16 54
Holmes, co., Miss., 23,120 . . . B3 68
Holmes, co., Ohio, 23,024 . . . B4 78
Holmes, mtn., Wyo . . . B2 89
Holmes Beach, Fla., 2,699 . . . *E4 54
Holmes Run Acres, Va., 1,400 . . . *B5 85
Holmes Run Park, Va., 650 . . . *B5 85
Ḥolon, Isr., 98,000 . . . B2 15
Holopaw, Fla., 150 . . . D5 54
Holstebro, Den., 23,300 . . . I3 11
Holstein, Iowa, 1,445 . . . B2 60
Holt, Ala., 4,300 . . . B2 46
Holt, Mich., 6,980 . . . F6 66
Holt, co., Mo., 6,654 . . . A2 69
Holt, co., Nebr., 12,933 . . . B7 71
Holton, Kans., 3,063 . . . C8 61
Holtville, Calif., 3,496 . . . F6 50
Holyhead, Wales, 10,860 . . . D4 4
Holyoke, Colo., 1,640 . . . A8 51
Holyoke, Mass., 50,112 . . . B2 65
Holyoke, range, Mass . . . B2 65
Holyrood, Kans., 593 . . . D5 61
Holzminden, Ger., Fed. Rep. of, 24,256 . . . C4 6
Homalin, Bur., 10,000 . . . D9 20
Homeacre, Pa., 2,500 . . . *E2 81
Home Corner, Ind., 300 . . . C6 59
Homécourt, Fr., 10,510 . . . C6 5
Homedale, Idaho, 1,411 . . . F2 57
Homedale, Ohio, 670 . . . *B2 78
Home Gardens, Calif., 1,541 . . . *F5 50
Home Hill, Austl., 3,062 . . . C8 25
Homer, Alsk., 1,083 . . . D6, h16 47
Homer, Ill., 1,354 . . . C6 58
Homer, La., 4,483 . . . B2 63
Homer, Mich., 1,617 . . . F6 66
Homer, N.Y., 4,143 . . . C4 75
Homer City, Pa., 2,465 . . . E3 81
Homerville, Ga., 3,025 . . . E4 55
Homestead, Fla., 13,674 . . . G6, t13 54
Homestead, Pa., 6,309 . . . k14 81
Homestead Valley, Calif., 1,500 . . . *C2 50
Hometown, Ill., 6,729 . . . *B6 58
Homewood, Ala., 21,137 . . . g7 46
Homewood, Calif., 500 . . . C3 50
Homewood, Ill., 18,871 . . . B6, k9 58
Homeworth, Ohio, 600 . . . B4 78
Hominy, Okla., 2,274 . . . A5 79
Honaker, Va., 911 . . . e10 85
Honan, prov., China, 48,670,000 . . . E7 17
Honda, Col., 19,945 . . . B3 32
Hondo, Tex., 5,487 . . . E3 84
Honduras, country, N.A., 2,765,000 . . . D7 34
Honea Path, S.C., 3,707 . . . C3 82
Honeoye Falls, N.Y., 2,248 . . . C3 75
Honesdale, Pa., 5,224 . . . C11 81
Honey Brook, Pa., 1,115 . . . F10 81
Honey Grove, Tex., 1,853 . . . C5 84
Honfleur, Fr., 9,121 . . . C4 5
Hon Gai, Viet., 35,412 . . . *A3 19
Hongwon, Kor., 25,663 . . . G3 18
Hong Kong, Br. dep., Asia, 4,225,000 . . . G7 17
Honokaa, Haw., 1,555 . . . C6 56
Honolulu, Haw., 324,871 (*621,400) . . . B4, g10 56
Honolulu, co., Haw., 630,528 . . . B3 56
Honshū, isl., Jap . . . H8 18
Honto, see Nevelsk, Sov. Un.
Hood, co., Tex., 6,368 . . . C4 84
Hood, mtn., Oreg . . . B5 80
Hoodoo, peak, Wash . . . A5 86
Hood River, Oreg., 3,991 . . . B5 80
Hood River, co., Oreg., 13,187 . . . B5 80
Hoodsport, Wash., 500 . . . B2 86
Hooghly-Chinsura, India, 105,241 . . . *D8 20
Hooker, Okla., 1,615 . . . e9 79
Hooker, co., Nebr., 939 . . . C4 71
Hooker, mtn., B.C., Can . . . C8 37
Hooks, Tex., 2,545 . . . *C5 84
Hooksett, N.H., 1,303 . . . E5 73
Hoolehua, Haw., 1,000 . . . B4 56
Hooper, Nebr., 895 . . . C9 71
Hooper, Utah, 250 . . . A5, C2 72
Hooper Bay, Alsk., 490 . . . C6 47
Hoopeston, Ill., 6,461 . . . C6 58
Hoorn, Neth., 20,475 . . . A6 5
Hoosac, range, Mass . . . A1 65
Hoosick Falls, N.Y., 3,897 . . . C7 75
Hooversville, Pa., 962 . . . F4 81
Hopatcong, N.J., 9,052 . . . B3 74
Hope, Ark., 8,830 . . . D2 49
Hope, B.C., Can., 3,153 . . . E7 37
Hope, Ind., 1,603 . . . F6 59
Hopedale, Ill., 923 . . . C4 58
Hopedale, La., 300 . . . E6 63
Hopedale, Mass., 4,292 . . . B4, h9 65
Hopedale, Ohio, 916 . . . B5 78
Hopeh (Hopei), prov., China, 42,500,000 . . . D8 17
Hopelawn, N.J., 2,300 . . . *B4 74
Hope Mills, N.C., 1,866 . . . C4 76
Hope Ranch, Calif., 2,500 . . . *E4 50
Hope Valley, R.I., 1,326 . . . C10 52
Hopewell, N.J., 2,271 . . . C3 74
Hopewell (Independent City), Va., 23,471 . . . C5, n18 85
Hopewell Junction, N.Y., 2,055 . . . D7 75
Hopkins, Minn., 13,428 . . . n12 67
Hopkins, Mo., 656 . . . A3 69
Hopkins, co., Ky., 38,167 . . . C2 62
Hopkins, co., Tex., 20,710 . . . C5 84
Hopkinsville, Ky., 21,250 . . . D2 62
Hopkinton, Iowa, 800 . . . B6 60
Hopkinton, Mass., 3,300 (5,981 ▲) . . . B4, h9 65
Hopland, Calif., 900 . . . C2 50
Hopu, China, 45,000 . . . G6 17
Hopwood, Pa., 2,190 . . . G2 81
Hoquiam, Wash., 10,466 . . . C2 86

Hordaland, co., Nor.,
250,900..............*G1 11
Horicon, Wis., 3,356......E5 88
Hornell, N.Y., 12,144....C3 75
Hornersville, Mo., 693.....E7 69
Horní Počernice, Czech.,
7,579...............n18 7
Hornsea, Eng., 7,140.....D6 4
Hornsey, Eng., 98,200...k12 4
Horqueta, Par., 17,389....D4 29
Horry, co., S.C., 69,992...D9 82
Horseback Knob, hill,
Ohio...............C2 78
Horse Cave, Ky., 2,068....C4 62
Horseheads, N.Y., 7,987...C4 75
Horsens, Den., 36,300....J3 11
Horsham, Austl., 11,046...G7 25
Horsham, Pa., 6,000.....*F11 81
Horta, Port. (Azores), 8,564.k9 22
Horten, Nor., 13,800..H4, p28 11
Horton, Kans., 2,177.....C8 61
Hortonville, Wis., 1,524...D5 88
Hoshiārpur, India, 57,691..B6 20
Hospers, Iowa, 646.......A2 60
Hospitalet, Sp., 240,630....B7 8
Hotien (Khotan), China,
15,000.............A6 20
Hot Springs, N.C., 653....f10 76
Hot Springs, S. Dak.,
4,434..............G2 77
Hot Spring, co., Ark.,
21,963.............C2 49
Hot Springs, co., Wyo.,
4,952..............C4 89
Hot Springs, see Truth or
Consequences, N. Mex.
Hot Springs
[National Park],
Ark., 35,631......C2, f7 49
Houghton, Mich., 6,067...A2 66
Houghton, N.Y., 1,620....C2 75
Houghton, Wash........e11 86
Houghton, co., Mich.,
34,652.............B2 66
Houghton Lake, Mich.,
800...............D6 66
Houghton Lake Heights,
Mich., 1,252........D6 66
Houilles, Fr., 29,338......g9 5
Houlton, Maine, 6,760
(8,111▲).............B5 64
Houma, La., 30,922...E5, k10 63
Housatonic, Mass., 1,344...B1 65
Houston, B.C., Can., 699..B4 37
Houston, Minn., 1,090....G7 67
Houston, Miss., 2,720....B4 68
Houston, Mo., 2,178......D6 69
Houston, Pa., 1,812......F1 81
Houston, Tex., 1,232,802
(*1,847,900).....E5, r14 84
Houston, co., Ala., 56,574..D4 46
Houston, co., Ga., 62,924..D3 55
Houston, co., Minn.,
17,556.............G7 67
Houston, co., Tenn.,
5,845..............A4 83
Houston, co., Tex.,
17,855.............D5 84
Houtzdale, Pa., 1,193.....E5 81
Hove, Eng., 72,010.......E6 4
Howard, Kans., 918......E7 61
Howard, S. Dak., 1,175....F8 77
Howard, Wis., 4,911...D5, g9 88
Howard, co., Ark., 11,412..C2 49
Howard, co., Ind., 83,198..C5 59
Howard, co., Iowa,
11,442.............A5 60
Howard, co., Md., 61,911..B4 53
Howard, co., Mo., 10,561..B5 69
Howard, co., Nebr.,
6,807..............C7 71
Howard, co., Tex., 37,796..C2 84
Howard City, Mich.,
1,060..............E5 66
Howard Lake, Minn.,
1,162..............E4 67
Howe, Ind., 500.........A7 59
Howell, Mich., 5,224.....F7 66
Howell, co., Mo., 23,521..E6 69
Howells, Nebr., 682......C8 71
Howick, Que., Can., 647..D4 42
Howland, Maine, 1,468...C4 64
Howley, mtn., Newf., Can..D2 44
Howrah, India, 737,877...D8 20
Howson, peak, B.C.,
Can..............B4, n17 37
Hoxie, Ark., 2,265.......A5 49
Hoxie, Kans., 1,419......C3 61
Hoya, Ger., Fed. Rep. of,
4,133..............B4 6

Hoyerswerda, Ger. Dem.
Rep., 62,758..........C7 6
Hoyt Lakes, Minn., 3,634..C6 67
Hradec Králové, Czech.,
68,160.............C3 7
Hranice, Czech., 12,364...D4 7
Hriňová, Czech., 6,831....D5 7
Hrubieszów, Pol., 14,900..C7 7
Hsi (Si), riv., China......G7 17
Hsiakuan, China, 26,200..C11 20
Hsian, see Sian, China
Hsiangtan, China, 247,000..F7 17
Hsichang (Sichang), China,
50,000.............F5 17
Hsinchu, Taiwan,
135,000 (178,400▲)....G9 17
Hsinghua, China, 85,000..*E8 17
Hsinhsiang, China, 203,000.D7 17
Hsining (Sining), China,
300,000............D5 17
Hsinkao, mtn., Taiwan....G9 17
Hsinmin, China, 35,000...C9 17
Hsipaw, Bur., 5,000.....*D10 20
Hsüanhua, China, 114,100.C8 17
Hsüchou (Süchow), China,
825,000............E8 17
Huacho, Peru, 22,806.....D2 31
Huaillay, Peru, 593.......D2 31
Huainan, China, 280,000..E8 17
Huaite (Kungchuling),
China, 60,000.......E2 18
Hualgayoc, Peru, 1,173...C2 31
Hualien, Taiwan, 65,000..G9 17
Huamachuco, Peru, 2,324..C2 31
Huamantla, Mex., 15,565.n15 34
Huambo, Ang., 38,745....C3 24
Huancabamba, Peru, 2,443.C2 31
Huancané, Peru, 2,236....E4 31
Huancavelica, Peru,
15,916.............D2 31
Huancavelica, dept., Peru,
315,730............D2 31
Huancayo, Peru, 64,777..D2 31
Huang Ho (Yellow), riv.,
China............F13 16
Huangshih, China, 110,000..E8 17
Huanta, Peru, 5,600......D3 31
Huánuco, Peru, 41,123....C2 31
Huánuco, dept., Peru.,
355,003............C2 31
Huaral, Peru, 5,012......D2 31
Huaráz, Peru, 29,719.....C2 31
Huariaca, Peru, 1,593....C2 31
Huascaran, mtn., Peru....C2 31
Huatabampo, Mex., 18,506.B3 34
Huatien, China, 35,000...C10 17
Huatusco [de Chicuellar],
Mex., 9,501.........n15 34
Huauchinango, Mex.,
16,826............m14 34
Huaytará, Peru, 718......D2 31
Hubbard, Iowa, 846......B4 60
Hubbard, Ohio, 8,583....A5 78
Hubbard, Tex., 1,572....D4 84
Hubbard, co., Minn.,
10,583............C3 67
Hubbell, Mich., 1,251....A2 66
Huberdeau, Que., Can.,
605...............D3 42
Huber Heights, Ohio,
18,943............*C1 78
Hubli, India, 265,000
(*379,166).........E6 20
Huddersfield, Eng.,
130,560 (*209,000)...D6 4
Hudiksvall, Swe., 17,139...G7 11
Hudson, Que., Can.,
4,345..........D3, q18 42
Hudson, Iowa, 1,535.....B5 60
Hudson, Mass., 16,084..B4, g9 65
Hudson, Mich., 2,618.....G6 66
Hudson, N.H., 5,500.....F5 73
Hudson, N.Y., 8,940.....C7 75
Hudson, N.C., 2,820......B1 76
Hudson, Ohio, 3,933.....A4 78
Hudson, Pa., 1,900.....*D9 81
Hudson, Wis., 5,049.....D1 88
Hudson, co., N.J., 607,839.B4 74
Hudson, bay, Can........D16 36
Hudson, mtn., Maine.....B3 64
Hudson Bay, Sask., Can.,
1,971.............E4 39
Hudson Falls, N.Y., 7,917..B7 75
Hudsonville, Mich., 3,523..F5 66
Hudspeth, co., Tex., 2,392.o12 84
Hue, Viet., 156,500......B3 19
Hueco, mts., Tex........o11 84
Huedin, Rom., 5,134.....B6 10
Huehuetenango, Guat.,
11,774............*D6 34

Huelma, Sp., 7,739......D4 8
Huelva, Sp., 96,347......D2 8
Huelva, prov., Sp.,
404,600.............*D2 8
Huércal-Overa, Sp.,
13,016.............D5 8
Huerfano, co., Colo.,
6,590..............C6 51
Huesca, Sp., 31,552......A5 8
Huesca, prov., Sp.,
229,600............*A5 8
Huéscar, Sp., 5,499......D4 8
Hueytown, Ala., 8,174.....g6 46
Hughes, Ark., 1,872......C5 49
Hughes, co., Okla.,
13,228.............B5 79
Hughes, co., S. Dak.,
11,632.............F6 77
Hughes Springs, Tex.,
1,701..............*C5 84
Hughestown, Pa., 1,407..*D9 81
Hughesville, Pa., 2,249...D8 81
Hughson, Calif., 1,898...*D3 50
Hugo, Colo., 759........B7 51
Hugo, Okla., 6,585......C6 79
Hugoton, Kans., 2,739....E2 61
Huguley, Ala., 1,000.....*C4 46
Huhohaote (Huhehot),
China, 320,000.....C7 17
Huichon, Kor., 14,619....F3 18
Huila, dept., Col., 460,000.C2 32
Huixtla, Mex., 15,737....D6 34
Hukou, China, 5,000.....F8 17
Hulan, China, 60,000....B10 17
Hulen, Ky., 400.........D6 62
Hull, Iowa, 1,523........A1 60
Hull, Mass., 9,961.....B6, g12 65
Hull, Que., Can., 63,580..D2 42
Hull, Eng., 284,680
(*355,000)..........D6 4
Hull, co., Que., Can.,
95,415.............D2 42
Hulmeville, Pa., 906....*F11 81
Humacao, P.R., 12,411
(36,023▲)..........*G12 35
Humansville, Mo., 825...D4 69
Humble, Tex., 3,278..E5, q14 84
Humboldt, Sask., Can.,
3,881..............E3 39
Humboldt, Iowa, 4,665...B3 60
Humboldt, Kans., 2,249..E8 61
Humboldt, Nebr., 1,194..D10 71
Humboldt, Tenn., 10,066..B3 83
Humboldt, co., Calif.,
99,692.............B2 50
Humboldt, co., Iowa,
12,519.............B3 60
Humboldt, co., Nev.,
6,375..............A2 72
Humenné, Czech., 16,068.D6 7
Humeston, Iowa, 673....D4 60
Hummelstown, Pa.,
4,723..............*F8 81
Humphrey, Nebr., 862....C8 71
Humphreys, co., Miss.,
14,601.............B3 68
Humphreys, co., Tenn.,
13,560.............A4 83
Humphreys, peak, Ariz...B2 48
Humpolec, Czech., 5,083..D3 7
Hunan, prov., China,
36,220,000.........F7 17
Hunchiang, China.......C10 17
Hunchun, China, 25,000..C11 17
Hunedoara, Rom.,
68,300 (101,000▲)....C6 10
Hungary, country, Eur.,
10,470,000.........B4 10
Hungnam, Kor., 143,600..G3 18
Hunt, mtn., Wyo.........B5 89
Hunt, co., Tex., 47,948....C4 84
Hunterdon, co., N.J., 69,718..B3 74
Huntersville, N.C., 1,538..B2 76
Huntingburg, Ind., 4,794.H4 59
Huntingdon, Que., Can.,
3,087..............D3 42
Huntingdon, Pa., 1,264...F6 81
Huntingdon, Tenn.,
3,661..............A3 83
Huntingdon, co., Que., Can.,
15,421.............D3 42
Huntingdon, co., Pa.,
39,108.............F5 81
Huntingdon
& Peterborough,
co., Eng., 205,780......*D7 4
Huntington, Ind., 16,217..C7 59
Huntington, Mass., 850
(1,593▲).............B2 65

Huntington, N.J., 700.....B2 74
Huntington, N.Y.,
12,601............E7, n15 75
Huntington, Oreg., 507...C9 80
Huntington, Tex., 1,192...D5 84
Huntington, Utah, 857....B6 72
Huntington, W. Va.,
74,315 (*248,200).......C2 87
Huntington, co., Ind.,
34,970.............C6 59
Huntington Bay, N.Y.,
1,789..............*G3 52
Huntington Beach, Calif.,
115,960............n13 50
Huntington Beach, N.Y.,
2,000..............*D3 75
Huntington Park, Calif.,
33,744.............F4 50
Huntington Station, N.Y.,
29,600.............F3 52
Huntington Woods, Mich.,
8,536..............p15 66
Huntingtown, Md., 200...C4 53
Huntley, Ill., 1,432......A5 58
Huntly, Scot., 3,782......B5 4
Huntsville, Ala., 139,282
(*206,800)..........A3 46
Huntsville, Ark., 1,287...A2 49
Huntsville, Ont., Can.,
9,784..............B5 41
Huntsville, Mo., 1,442....B5 69
Huntsville, Tex., 17,610..D5 84
Hupeh (Hupei), prov.,
China, 30,790,000....E7 17
Hurley, N. Mex., 1,796...C4 48
Hurley, N.Y., 4,081......D6 75
Hurley, Wis., 2,418......B3 88
Hurleyville, N.Y., 750....D6 75
Hurlock, Md., 1,056......C5 53
Huron, Calif., 1,525.....*D4 50
Huron, Ohio, 6,896......A3 78
Huron, S. Dak., 14,299...F7 77
Huron, co., Ont., Can.,
54,446.............D3 41
Huron, co., Mich., 34,083..E7 66
Huron, co., Ohio, 49,587..A3 78
Huron, lake, Can., U.S...B10 45
Hurricane, Utah, 1,408...C5 72
Hurricane, W. Va., 3,491..C2 87
Hurst, Ill., 934.........F4 58
Hurst, Tex., 27,215.....*C4 84
Hurtsboro, Ala., 937.....C4 46
Huși, Rom., 18,055......B9 10
Hustisford, Wis., 789.....E5 88
Husum, Ger., Fed. Rep.
of, 25,300...........A4 6
Hutchins, Tex., 1,755....n10 84
Hutchinson, Kans.,
36,885 (*46,600)....D6, f11 61
Hutchinson, Minn.,
8,032..............F4 67
Hutchinson, co., S. Dak.,
10,379.............G8 77
Hutchinson, co., Tex.,
24,443.............B2 84
Huttig, Ark., 822........D3 49
Huxley, Iowa, 937....C4, e8 60
Huy, Bel., 12,654.......B6 5
Hvannadalshnúkur, mtn.,
Ice...............o24 11
Hvittingfoss, Nor., 576....p28 11
Hyannis, Mass., 7,800....C7 65
Hyannis Port, Mass., 400..C7 65
Hyattsville, Md.,
14,998............C4, f9 53
Hybla Valley, Va., 4,000..*B5 85
Hyde, Pa., 850.........D5 81
Hyde, co., N.C., 5,571...B6 76
Hyde, co., S. Dak., 2,515..F6 77
Hyde Park, N.Y., 2,805...D7 75
Hyde Park, Pa., 729.....*F9 81
Hyde Villa, Pa.........*F9 81
Hydro, Okla., 805.......B3 79
Hyères, Fr., 34,875......F7 5
Hymera, Ind., 970.......F3 59
Hyndman, Pa., 1,151....G4 81
Hyogo, pref., Jap.,
4,667,928...........*I7 18
Hyopchon, Kor., 5,900
(16,132▲)...........I4 18
Hyrum, Utah, 2,340.....A6 72
Hyrynsalmi, Fin., 1,300..E13 11
Hythe, Alta., Can., 487...B1 38
Hythe, Eng., 11,700.....E7 4

Iaeger, W. Va., 822......D3 87
Iasi, Rom., 160,900
　(194,800 ▲)........B8 10
Iba, Phil., 4,241......*B5 19
Ibadan, Nig., 627,379.....G5 22
Ibagué, Col., 131,700
　(172,100 ▲).........C2 32
Ibaraki, Jap., 163,903.....*o14 18
Ibaraki, pref., Jap.,
　2,143,551.........*H10 18
Ibarra, Ec., 32,800......A2 31
Ibb, Yemen, 25,000....G3 15
Iberia, Mo., 741........C5 69
Iberia, par., La., 57,397...E4 63
Iberville, Que., Can.,
　9,331.............D4 42
Iberville, co., Que., Can.,
　19,538............D4 42
Iberville, par., La.,
　30,746.........D4, h9 63
Iberville, mtn., Newf.,
　Can..............f9 44
Ibitinga, Braz., 14,667....C3 30
Ibiza, Sp., 11,259.......C6 8
Ica, Peru, 73,883........D2 31
Ica, dept., Peru, 261,126..D2 31
Ice, mtn., B.C., Can......B7 37
Iceland, country, Eur.,
　210,000...........n23 11
Ichang, China, 85,000.....E7 17
Ichihara, Jap., 116,000
　(156,016 ▲).......*n19 18
Ichikawa, Jap., 261,055...n18 18
Ichinomiya, Jap., 219,274.n15 18
Ichinoseki, Jap., 34,000
　(55,830 ▲)........G10 18
Ichnya, Sov. Un., 10,000..F9 12
Ichun, China, 200,000.....C4 18
Ida, Mich., 800.........G7 66
Ida, co., Iowa, 9,190......B2 60
Idabel, Okla., 5,946......D7 79
Ida Grove, Iowa, 2,261....B2 60
Idaho, co., Idaho, 12,891..D3 57
Idaho, state, U.S., 742,000... 57
Idaho Falls, Idaho, 35,776
　(*45,500).........F6 67
Idaho Springs, Colo.,
　2,003............B5 51
Idalou, Tex., 1,729......C2 84
Idamay, W. Va., 800....k10 87
Idanha-a-Nova, Port.,
　4,459............C2 8
Idaville, Ind., 600.......C4 59
Idrija, Yugo., 6,030......B2 10
Ieper (Ypres), Bel., 20,835.B5 5
Ierápetra, Grc., 7,055....E5 14
Iesi, It., 28,100.........C4 9
Ife, Nig., 130,053........G5 22
Igarapava, Braz., 12,398..C3 30
Igarka, Sov. Un.,
　16,000...........C11 13
Iğdir, Tur., 21,420......C15 14
Ighil Izane, Alg., 43,547...A5 22
Iglesias, It., 28,300......E2 9
Igloo, S. Dak........G2 77
Igualada, Sp., 19,866.....B6 8
Iguatu, Braz., 27,851....*D7 27
Ihsing, China, 93,000....*E8 17
Iida, Jap., 52,000
　(77,261▲).....I8, n16 18
Iide-san, mtn., Jap.......H9 18
Iijima, Jap............n16 18
Iisalmi, Fin., 20,516.....F12 11
Iizuka, Jap., 75,643
　(*100,000)........J5 18
Ijebu Ode, Nig., 68,543...G5 22
Ijuí, Braz., 31,879.......D2 30
Ikeda, Jap., 94,333.....D14 18
Ikerre, Nig., 107,216....*G6 22
Ikhtiman, Bul., 9,063....D6 10
Ila, Nig., 114,688.......E5 22
Ilagan, Phil., 11,494.....B6 19
Ilan, China, 40,000.....B10 17
Ilan, Taiwan, 40,000....*G9 17
Ilawe, Nig., 80,833.....*E6 22
Ile-a-la-Cross, Sask.,
　Can., 570.........m7 39
Ilebo (Port-Francqui),
　Zaire............I2 23
Ile-de-France, former
　prov., Fr..........C5 5
Ile-Perrot, Que., Can.,
　4,021............q19 42
Ilesha, Nig., 165,822.....G5 22
Ilford, Eng., 176,600....k13 4
Ilfracombe, Eng., 8,960...E4 4
Ilgin, Tur., 11,118.......C8 14
Ilhavo, Port., 6,346......B1 8
Ilhéus, Braz., 58,529.....E7 27
Ilia (Elis), prov., Grc.,
　188,861.........*D3 14
Iliang, China.........D11 20

Ilinskaya, Sov. Un.,
　10,000...........I13 12
Ilion, N.Y., 9,808.......B5 75
Illampu, mtn., Bol.......C2 29
Illapel, Chile, 10,400.....A2 28
Ille-et-Vilaine, dept., Fr.,
　652,722.........*C3 5
Illinois, state, U.S.,
　11,273,000.......... 58
Illinois, peak, Idaho......B3 57
Illinois, peak, Mont......C1 70
Illiopolis, Ill., 1,122......D4 58
Illmo, Mo., 1,232.......D8 69
Illora, Sp., 13,458.......D4 8
Ilmenau, Ger. Dem. Rep.,
　17,700...........C5 6
Ilo, Peru, 1,043........E3 31
Ilocos Norte, prov., Phil.,
　287,333.........*B6 19
Ilocos Sur, prov., Phil.,
　338,058..........C6 19
Iloilo, Phil., 209,738.....C6 19
Iloilo, prov., Phil.,
　966,266.........*C6 19
Ilorin, Nig., 208,546.....G5 22
Ilovaysk, Sov. Un.,
　20,000...........r21 12
Imabari, Jap., 111,125....I6 18
Imabetsu, Jap.........F10 18
Imari, Jap., 37,000
　(61,561▲)........*J4 18
Imazu, Jap...........n15 18
Imbābah, Eg., 225,988...*G8 14
Imbabura, prov., Ec.,
　200,900..........A2 31
Imlay City, Mich., 1,980..E7 66
Immenstadt, Ger., Fed.
　Rep. of, 14,105......E5 6
Immokalee, Fla., 3,224...F5 54
Imola, It., 34,900.......B3 9
Imperia, It., 39,300.....C2 9
Imperial, Calif., 3,094....F6 50
Imperial, Sask., Can., 557.F3 39
Imperial, Mo., 500....C7, g13 69
Imperial, Nebr., 1,589....D4 71
Imperial, Pa., 2,385....k13 81
Imperial, co., Calif.,
　74,492...........F6 50
Imperial Beach, Calif.,
　20,244..........o15 50
Imperoyal, N.S., Can.,
　490.............E6 43
Imphāl, India, 100,366....D9 20
Ina, Jap., 31,000
　(51,922▲).........n16 18
Inca, Sp., 13,816.......C7 8
Inchŏn, Kor., 646,013....H3 18
Indaw, Bur., 2,138.....D10 20
Independence, Calif., 950.D4 50
Independence, Iowa,
　5,910...........B6 60
Independence, Kans.,
　10,347..........E8 61
Independence, La., 1,770..D5 63
Independence, Minn.,
　1,993...........*F5 67
Independence, Mo.,
　111,630........B3, h11 69
Independence, Ohio,
　7,034...........h9 78
Independence, Oreg.,
　2,594.........C3, k11 80
Independence, Wis., 1,036.D2 88
Independence, co., Ark.,
　22,723..........B4 49
Independence Hill, Ind.,
　900............*B3 59
India, country, Asia,
　581,200,000.......D6 20
Indialantic, Fla., 2,685...*D6 54
Indian, ocean........G2 2
Indiana, Pa., 16,100.....E3 81
Indiana, co., Pa., 79,451..E3 81
Indiana, state, U.S.,
　5,344,000.......... 59
Indianapolis, Ind., 746,302
　(*978,200)....E5, k10 59
Indian Head, Sask., Can.,
　1,810...........G4 39
Indian Head, Md., 1,350..C3 53
Indian Hill, Ohio,
　5,651...........o13 78
Indian Lake, N.Y., 500...B6 75
Indian Mound Beach,
　Mass., 300.......*C6 65
Indianola, Iowa, 8,852....C4 60
Indianola, Miss., 8,947...B3 68
Indianola, Nebr., 672....D5 71
Indianola, Pa., 600......*E1 81
Indian, peak, Wyo......B3 89
Indian River, co., Fla.,
　35,992..........E6 54

Indian Rocks Beach, Fla.,
　2,666...........p10 54
Indiantown, Fla., 2,500...E6 54
Indio, Calif., 14,459......F5 50
Indochina, reg., Asia.....B3 19
Indonesia, country, Asia,
　128,395,000.......F6 19
Indore, India, 543,381
　(*560,936)........D6 20
Indramaju, Indon.,
　25,710..........G3 19
Indre, dept., Fr., 247,178.*D4 5
Indre-et-Loire, dept., Fr.,
　437,870.........*D4 5
Indus, riv., Asia........C4 20
Industrial, S.C., 900.....B6 82
Industry, Pa., 2,442....*E1 81
Ine, Jap...........n14 18
Infantes, Sp., 9,909......C4 8
Infiesto, Sp., 1,650......A3 8
Ingalls, Ind., 888.......E6 59
Ingalls Park, Ill., 4,000...B5 58
Ingersoll, Ont., Can.,
　7,783...........D4 41
Ingham, Austl., 5,797....C8 25
Ingham, co., Mich.,
　261,039..........F6 66
Ingleside, Nebr.........D7 71
Ingleside, Tex., 3,763....F4 84
Inglewood, Calif., 89,985..n12 50
Inglewood, Nebr.,
　275...........C9, g11 71
Ingolstadt, Ger., Fed. Rep.
　of, 88,799 (*120,000)...D5 6
Ingomar, Pa., 1,100.....h13 81
Ingonish Beach, N.S.,
　Can............C9 43
Ingram, Pa., 4,902.....k13 81
Inhambane, Moz.......E7 24
Inharrime, Moz........E7 24
Inishbofin, isl., U.K......D1 4
Inishtrahull, isl., U.K.....C3 4
Inishturk, isl., U.K......D1 4
Inkerman, Pa., 900.....*D9 81
Inkom, Idaho, 522......G6 57
Inkster, Mich., 38,595...p15 66
Inman, Kans., 836......D6 61
Inman, S.C., 1,661......A3 82
Inman Mills, S.C., 1,811..*A3 82
Inner Mongolia, prov.,
　China, 9,200,000.....C8 17
Innisfail, Alta., Can.,
　2,474...........C4 38
Innisfail, Austl., 7,475....C8 25
Innsbruck, Aus., 115,293
　(*140,000)........E5 6
Ino, Jap., 7,769........J6 18
Inowrocław, Pol.,
　54,800..........B5 7
Insein, Bur., 27,030.....E10 20
Institute, W. Va., 2,000...C3 87
Intercession City, Fla.,
　500............D5 54
Intercity, Wash........*B3 86
Interlaken, N.J., 1,182...*C4 74
International Falls, Minn.,
　6,439...........B5 67
Intersection, mtn., B.C.,
　Can............C7 37
Invercargill, N.Z., 47,900
　(*51,500)........Q12 26
Inverell, Austl., 9,700.....E9 25
Invermere, B.C., Can.,
　744............D9 37
Inverness, Calif., 600.....C2 50
Inverness, N.S., Can.,
　1,846...........C8 43
Inverness, Fla., 2,299....D4 54
Inverness, Ill., 4,059....*B6 58
Inverness, Miss., 1,119...B3 68
Inverness, Scot., 34,426..B4 4
Inverness, co., N.S., Can.,
　18,152..........C8 43
Inverness, co., Scot.,
　88,062.........*B4 4
Invisible, mtn., Idaho....F5 57
Inwood, Iowa, 644.....A1 60
Inwood, N.Y., 8,200....k13 75
Inyan Kara, mtn., Wyo...B8 89
Inyo, co., Calif., 15,571...D5 50
Inyokern, Calif., 800.....E5 50
Ioánnina, Grc., 40,130...C3 14
Ioannina, prov., Grc.,
　134,536.........*C3 14
Iola, Kans., 6,493......E8 61
Iola, Wis., 900........D4 88
Iona, Idaho, 890........F7 57
Ione, Calif., 2,369......C3 50
Ionia, Mich., 6,361......F5 66
Ionia, co., Mich., 45,848..F5 66
Iosco, co., Mich., 24,905..D7 66
Iota, La., 1,271........D3 63

Iowa, La., 1,944........D2 63
Iowa, co., Iowa, 15,419...C5 60
Iowa, co., Wis., 19,306...E3 88
Iowa, state, U.S.,
　2,891,000.......... 60
Iowa City, Iowa, 46,850
　(*61,300)........C6 60
Iowa Falls, Iowa, 6,454...B4 60
Iowa Park, Tex., 5,796...C3 84
Ipameri, Braz., 11,572...B3 30
Ipava, Ill., 608........C3 58
Ipiales, Col., 23,320....C2 32
Ipin, China, 190,000.....F5 17
Ipoh, Mala., 247,969....E2 19
Ipswich, Austl., 61,514...E9 25
Ipswich, Eng., 122,700...D7 4
Ipswich, Mass., 5,022....A6 65
Ipswich, S. Dak., 1,187...E6 77
Iquique, Chile, 50,655....D2 29
Iquitos, Peru, 111,327....B3 31
Iraklion (Candia), Grc.,
　77,506 (*84,710)......E5 14
Iraklion, prov., Grc.,
　209,652.........*E5 14
Iran (Persia), country,
　Asia, 31,830,000.....F8 16
Irapuato, Mex.,
　116,651.......C4, m13 34
Iraq, country, Asia,
　10,410,000.......C3 15
Irbid, Jordan, 110,000..B3, g5 15
Irbīl, Iraq, 90,320.....D15 14
Iredell, co., N.C., 72,197..B2 76
Ireland (Eire), country,
　Eur., 3,045,000......D3 4
Ireton, Iowa, 582......B1 60
Iri, Kor., 72,000 (86,770 ▲).I3 18
Iringa, Tan., 9,587......B7 24
Irion, co., Tex., 1,070....D2 84
Irkutsk, Sov. Un.,
　451,000.........D13 13
Iron, co., Mich., 13,813...B2 66
Iron, co., Mo., 9,529.....D7 69
Iron, co., Utah, 12,177...C5 72
Iron, co., Wis., 6,533....B3 88
Iron, mts., Va.........f10 85
Irondale, Ala., 3,166.....f7 46
Irondale, Ohio, 602......B5 78
Irondequoit, N.Y., 63,675.B3 75
Ironia, N.J., 900........B3 74
Iron Mountain, Mich.,
　8,702...........C2 66
Iron River, Mich., 2,684..B2 66
Iron River, Wis., 650....B2 88
Ironton, Minn., 562.....D5 67
Ironton, Mo., 1,452.....D7 69
Ironton, Ohio, 13,000....D3 78
Ironwood, Mich., 8,711..n11 66
Iroquois, N.B., Can., 818..*B1 43
Iroquois, Ont., Can.,
　1,136...........C9 41
Iroquois, co., Ill., 33,532..C6 58
Iroquois Falls, Ont., Can.,
　7,271...........*o19 41
Irosin, Phil., 8,031.....*C6 19
Irrawaddy, riv., Bur....D10 20
Irtysh, riv., Sov.
　Un.............D10 13
Irún, Sp., 29,814......A5 8
Irvine, Ky., 2,918......C6 62
Irvine, Scot., 23,145
　(*80,000)........C4 4
Irving, Tex., 97,260....n10 84
Irvington, Ky., 1,300....C3 62
Irvington, N.J., 59,743...k8 74
Irvington, N.Y., 5,878...g13 75
Irvona, Pa., 714.......E4 81
Irwin, Pa., 4,059.......F2 81
Irwin, S.C., 1,424.....*B6 82
Irwin, co., Ga., 8,036....E3 55
Irwindale, Calif., 784...*E4 50
Isabel, mtn., Wyo......D2 89
Isabela, P.R., 9,515
　(30,430 ▲).......*G11 35
Isabela, prov., Phil.,
　442,062.........*D6 19
Isabella, Pa., 700.......G2 81
Isabella, Tenn., 300.....D9 83
Isabella, co., Mich.,
　44,594..........E6 66
Isahaya, Jap., 44,000
　(65,261▲)........J5 18
Isanti, Minn., 672......E5 67
Isanti, co., Minn., 16,560..E5 67
Ise (Uji-yamada), Jap.,
　103,576......I8, o15 18
Iselin, N.J., 18,400.....B4 74
Iselin, Pa., 400........E3 81
Isère, dept., Fr.,
　768,450.........*E6 5

Iserlohn, Ger., Fed. Rep. of, 57,078 (*97,000) *C3 6
Isernia, It., 8,600 D5 9
Isesaki, Jap., 91,277 H9, m18 18
Iseyin, Nig., 95,220 G5 22
Ishikawa, pref., Jap., 1,002,420 *H8 18
Ishim, Sov. Un., 56,000 D9 13
Ishimbay, Sov. Un., 54,000 *D8 13
Ishinomaki, Jap., 106,681 G10 18
Ishioka, Jap., 27,500 (39,508*) m19 18
Ishpeming, Mich., 8,245 B3 66
Isigny-sur-Mer, Fr., 2,391 C3 5
Isiro (Paulis), Zaire, 9,700 H3 23
İskenderun (Alexandretta), Tur., 79,297 D11 14
İskilip, Tur., 16,129 B10 14
Isla Cristina, Sp., 8,276 D2 8
Islāmābād, Pak., 77,000 B5 20
Islamorado, Fla., 700 H6 54
Island, co., Wash., 27,011 A3 86
Island Falls, Maine, 800 (913 ▲) B4 64
Island Heights, N.J., 1,397 D4 74
Island Lake, Ill., 1,973 *E2 58
Island Park, N.Y., 5,396 *E7 75
Island Pond, Vt., 1,123 B4 73
Islav, isl., U.K. C3 4
Isle, Minn., 551 D5 67
Isle-aux-Morts, Newf., Can., 884 E2 44
Isle of Ely, co., Eng., 89,112 *D7 4
Isle of Man, Br. dep; Eur., 58,000 *C4 4
Isle of Man, isl., U.K. C4 4
Isle of Palms, S.C., 2,657 k12 82
Isle of Wight, co., Eng., 102,100 *E6 4
Isle of Wight, co., Va., 18,285 D6 85
Isle of Wight, isl., U.K. E6 4
Isle Royale, isl., Mich. h9 66
Isleton, Calif., 909 C3 50
Isle-Verte, Que., Can., 1,360 A8 42
Islington, Mass., 4,500 h11 65
Islip, N.Y., 12,100 n15 75
Islip Terrace, N.Y., 5,100 *n15 75
Isola Capo Rizzuto, It., 9,218 E6 9
Isparta, Tur., 50,905 D8 14
Israel, country, Asia, 3,195,000 C2 15
Issaquah, Wash., 4,313 e11 86
Issaquena, co., Miss., 2,737 C2 68
Issoire, Fr., 11,886 E5 5
Issoudun, Fr., 13,900 D4 5
Issyk-kul, lake, Sov. Un. E10 13
Issy [les-Moulineaux], Fr., 50,442 g10 5
İstanbul (Constantinople), Tur., 2,132,407 (*2,825,000) B7 14
Istmina, Col., 3,996 B2 32
Itá, Par., 18,777 E4 29
Itabaiana, Braz., 16,425 *E7 27
Itabaiana, Braz., 14,148 *D7 27
Itaberaba, Braz., 16,003 *E6 27
Itabira, Braz., 40,143 B4 30
Itabuna, Braz., 89,928 E7 27
Itajaí, Braz., 54,135 D3 30
Itajubá, Braz., 42,485 C3 30
Italy, Tex., 1,309 C4 84
Italy, country, Eur., 54,980,000 9
Itami, Jap., 153,763 o14 18
Itaperuna, Braz., 26,508 C4 30
Itapetininga, Braz., 42,331 C3, m7 30
Itapeva, Braz., 24,220 C3 30
Itápolis, Braz., 9,372 k7 30
Itapúa, dept., Par., 149,821 E4 29
Itaqui, Braz., 17,262 D1 30
Itararé, Braz., 15,696 C3 30
Itasca, Ill., 4,638 k8 58
Itasca, Tex., 1,483 C4 84
Itasca, co., Minn., 35,530 C5 67
Itatiba, Braz., 20,765 m8 30
Itaúna, Braz., 32,731 C4 30
Itawamba, co., Miss., 16,847 A5 68
Ithaca, Mich., 2,749 E6 66
Ithaca, N.Y., 26,226 C4 75
Itō, Jap., 63,003 o18 18
Itoigawa, Jap., 22,000 (38,395 ▲) H8 18
Itta Bena, Miss., 2,489 B3 68
Itu, Braz., 35,907 C3, m8 30
Ituango, Col., 3,466 B2 32
Ituiutaba, Braz., 46,784 B3 30
Ituna, Sask., Can., 837 F4 39
Itzehoe, Ger., Fed. Rep. of, 36,178 B4 6
Iuka, Miss., 2,389 A5 68
Iva, S.C., 1,114 C2 82
Ivanhoe, Calif., 1,595 *D4 50
Ivanhoe, Minn., 738 F2 67
Ivanhoe, Va., 500 D2 85
Ivano-Frankovsk, Sov. Un., 105,000 G5 12
Ivanovka, Sov. Un., 5,000 q21 12
Ivanovo, Sov. Un., 420,000 C13 12
Ivanteyevka, Sov. Un., 36,000 n17 12
Ivory Coast, country, Afr., 4,695,000 G3 22
Ivoryton, Conn., 950 D7 52
Ivrea, It., 28,600 B1 9
Ivry-sur-Seine, Fr., 60,455 g10 5
Ivywild, Colo., 4,000 C6 51
Iwaki (Tairi), Jap., 260,000 (327,164 ▲) H10 18
Iwaki-yama, mtn., Jap. F10 18
Iwakuni, Jap., 106,116 I6 18
Iwamizawa, Jap., 54,000 (68,712▲) E10 18
Iwanai, Jap., 25,799 E10 18
Iwate, pref., Jap., 1,371,383 *G10 18
Iwate-yama, mtn., Jap. G10 18
Iwo, Nig., 158,583 G5 22
Ixmiquilpan, Mex., 6,048 m14 34
Ixtacalco, Mex., 48,954 h9 34
Ixtacihuatl, mtn., Mex. n14 34
Ixtapalapa, Mex., 41,243 h9 34
Ixtlán de Juárez, Mex., 1,396 o15 34
Ixtlán del Río, Mex., 10,986 C4, m11 34
Izamal, Mex., 9,749 C7 34
Izard, co., Ark., 7,381 A4 49
Izhevsk, Sov. Un., 422,000 D8 13
Izmail, Sov. Un., 70,000 I7 12
İzmir (Smyrna), Tur., 520,832 (*760,000) C6 14
İzmit (Kocaeli), Tur., 120,694 B7 14
Izúcar de Matamoros, Mex., 21,164 n14 34
Izuhara, Jap., 9,131 I4 18
Izumo, Jap., 46,000 (69,078▲) I6 18
Izyum, Sov. Un., 52,000 G11 12

J

Jabalpur (Jubbulpore), India, 426,224 (*534,845) D6 20
Jaboatão, Braz., 52,537 *D7 27
Jaboticabal, Braz., 29,019 C3, k7 30
Jaca, Sp., 9,856 A5 8
Jacala de Ledesma, Mex., 2,160 m14 34
Jacareí, Braz., 48,684 m9 30
Jacarèzinho, Braz., 19,161 C3 30
Jáchymov, Czech., 6,806 C2 7
Jacinto City, Tex., 9,563 r14 84
Jack, co., Tex., 6,711 C3 84
Jack, mtn., Mont. D4 70
Jack, mtn., Va. B3 85
Jackfork, mtn., Okla. C6 79
Jacks, mtn., Pa. E6 81
Jacksboro, Tex., 3,554 C3 84
Jackson, Ala., 5,957 D2 46
Jackson, Calif., 1,924 C3 50
Jackson, Ga., 3,778 C3 55
Jackson, Ky., 1,887 C6 62
Jackson, La., 4,697 D4 63
Jackson, Mich., 45,484 (*131,100) F6 66
Jackson, Minn., 3,550 G3 67
Jackson, Miss., 153,968 (*239,100) C3 68
Jackson, Mo., 5,896 D8 69
Jackson, N.C., 762 A5 76
Jackson, Ohio, 6,843 C3 78
Jackson, S.C., 1,928 E4 82
Jackson, Tenn., 39,996 (*52,300) B3 83
Jackson, Wyo., 2,688 C2 89
Jackson, co., Ala., 39,202 A3 46
Jackson, co., Ark., 20,452 B4 49
Jackson, co., Colo., 1,811 A4 51
Jackson, co., Fla., 34,434 B1 54
Jackson, co., Ga., 21,093 B3 55
Jackson, co., Ill., 55,008 F4 58
Jackson, co., Ind., 33,187 G5 59
Jackson, co., Iowa, 20,839 B7 60
Jackson, co., Kans., 10,342 C8 61
Jackson, co., Ky., 10,005 C5 62
Jackson, co., Mich., 143,274 F6 66
Jackson, co., Minn., 14,352 G3 67
Jackson, co., Miss., 87,975 E5 68
Jackson, co., Mo., 654,558 C3 69
Jackson, co., N.C., 21,593 f9 76
Jackson, co., Ohio, 27,174 C3 78
Jackson, co., Okla., 30,902 C2 79
Jackson, co., Oreg., 94,533 E3 80
Jackson, co., S. Dak., 1,531 G4 77
Jackson, co., Tenn., 8,141 C8 83
Jackson, co., Tex., 12,975 E4 84
Jackson, co., W. Va., 20,903 C3 87
Jackson, co., Wis., 15,325 D3 88
Jackson, par., La., 15,963 B3 63
Jackson, mtn., Maine D2 64
Jackson Center, Ohio, 1,119 B1 78
Jacksonville, Ala., 7,715 B4 46
Jacksonville, Ark., 19,832 C3, h10 49
Jacksonville, Fla., 528,865 (*548,500) B5, m8 54
Jacksonville, Ill., 20,553 D3 58
Jacksonville, N.C., 16,289 C5 76
Jacksonville, Oreg., 1,611 E4 80
Jacksonville, Tex., 9,734 D5 84
Jacksonville Beach, Fla. B5, m9 54
Jacmel, Hai., 11,391 E7 35
Jacobābād, Pak., 35,278 C4 20
Jacobina, Braz., 18,892 *E6 27
Jacomino, Cuba, 6,121 *C2 35
Jacques Cartier, mtn., Que. k13 42
Jaén, Sp., 77,317 D4 8
Jaén, prov., Sp., 702,900 *D4 8
Jaffna, Sri Lanka, 107,663 G7 20
Jaffrey, N.H., 1,922 (3,353▲) F3 73
Jaguarão, Braz., 16,541 E2 30
Jagüey Grande, Cuba, 8,700 (17,100 ▲) C3 35
Jaipur, India, 615,258 C6 20
Jaisalmer, India, 16,578 C5 20
Jajce, Yugo., 6,853 C3 10
Jājpur, India, 16,707 D8 20
Jakarta (Djakarta), Indon., 4,576,009 G3 19
Jakobstad (Pietersaari), Fin., 19,333 F10 11
Jal, N. Mex., 2,602 C7 48
Jalalabad, Afg., 14,756 B5 20
Jalapa, Guat., 13,819 *F6 34
Jalapa Enríquez, Mex., 122,377 D5, n15 34
Jalca Grande, Peru, 1,189 C2 31
Jālgaon, India, 106,711 D6 20
Jalisco, state, Mex., 2,857,200 C4, m12 34
Jālna, India, 91,099 E6 20
Jalpa, Mex., 9,904 C4, m12 34
Jalpan, Mex., 1,878 C5, m14 34
Jamaica, country, N.A., 1,960,000 E5 35
Jambi, Indon., 158,559 F2 19
James, riv., S. Dak. F7 77
Jamesburg, N.J., 4,584 C4 74
James City, N.C., 500 B5 76
James City, co., Va., 17,853 C6 85
Jamesport, Mo., 614 B4 69
Jamestown, Calif., 950 D3 50
Jamestown, Ind., 938 E4 59
Jamestown, Ky., 1,027 D4 62
Jamestown, N.Y., 39,795 C1 75
Jamestown, N.C., 1,297 B3 76
Jamestown, N. Dak., 15,385 D7 77
Jamestown, Ohio, 1,790 C2 78
Jamestown, Pa., 937 D1 81
Jamestown, R.I., 2,911 D11 52
Jamestown, Tenn., 1,899 C9 83
Jamesville, N.Y., 1,000 *C4 75
Jamiltepec, Mex., 5,280 D5 34
Jammu, India, 155,338 (*164,207) B5 20
Jammu and Kashmir, Disputed reg., India, Pak., 4,616,632 B6 20
Jāmnagar, India, 199,709 (*277,640) D5 20
Jamshedpur, India, 341,576 (*456,146) D8 20
Jämtland, co., Swe., 127,900 *F6 11
Janesville, Iowa., 741 B5 60
Janesville, Minn., 1,557 F5 67
Janesville, Wis., 46,426 (*59,200) F4 88
Janīn, Jordan, 13,365 B3 15
Janos, Mex., 1,178 A3 34
Jánoshalma, Hung., 10,767 B4 10
Janów Lubelski, Pol., 4,708 C7 7
Januária, Braz., 13,605 B4 30
Jaoho (Tuanshantzu), China, 30,000 B11 17
Japan, country, Asia., 108,960,000 I6 18
Japan, sea, Asia F6 18
Jaral [del Progreso], Mex., 8,689 m13 34
Jarales, N. Mex., 300 B5 48
Jarocin, Pol., 18,100 C4 7
Jarosław, Pol., 26,500 C7 7
Jarvis, Ont., Can., 783 E4 41
Jarvisburg, N.C., 150 A7 76
Jasonville, Ind., 2,335 F3 59
Jasper, Ala., 10,798 B2 46
Jasper, Alta., Can., 2,932 C1 38
Jasper, Fla., 2,221 B4 54
Jasper, Ga., 1,202 B2 55
Jasper, Ind., 8,641 H4 59
Jasper, Minn., 754 G2 67
Jasper, Mo., 796 D3 69
Jasper, Tenn., 1,839 D8 83
Jasper, Tex., 6,251 D6 84
Jasper, co., Ga., 5,760 C3 55
Jasper, co., Ill., 10,741 D5 58
Jasper, co., Ind., 20,429 B3 59
Jasper, co., Iowa, 35,425 C4 60
Jasper, co., Miss., 15,994 C4 68
Jasper, co., Mo., 79,852 D3 69
Jasper, co., S.C., 11,885 G5 82
Jasper, co., Tex., 24,692 D5 84

Jászapáti, Hung., 9,423....B5 10
Jászbereny, Hung.,
　23,996 (29,785 ▲)........B4 10
Jatibonico, Cuba, 5,700...D4 35
Játiva, Sp., 19,896........C5 8
Jaú, Braz., 40,989....C3, m7 30
Jauja, Peru, 12,751........D2 31
Jaumave, Mex., 3,072.....C5 34
Jaunpur, India, 80,737...C7 20
Java, isl., Indon.........G3 19
Javellanos, Cuba, 12,400...C3 35
Jawor, Pol., 15,600.......C4 7
Jaworzno, Pol., 63,200....g10 7
Jay, Fla., 646...........u14 54
Jay, N.Y., 500...........f11 75
Jay, Okla., 1,594........A7 79
Jay, co., Ind., 23,575....D7 59
Jayanca, Peru, 3,413......C2 31
Jayapura (Sukarnapura),
　Indon, 45,786.........F10 19
Jeanerette, La., 6,322....E4 63
Jeannette, Pa., 15,209....F2 81
Jeberos, Peru, 981.......C2 31
Jedburgh, Scot., 3,880....C5 4
Jędrzejów, Pol., 13,200...C6 7
Jeff, Ky., 200...........C6 62
Jeff Davis, co., Ga., 9,425..E4 55
Jeff Davis, co., Tex.,
　1,527................o12 84
Jefferson, Ga., 1,647.....B3 55
Jefferson, Iowa, 4,735....B3 60
Jefferson, La., 16,489....k11 63
Jefferson, Mass., 700.....B4 65
Jefferson, N.C., 943......A1 76
Jefferson, Ohio, 2,472....A5 78
Jefferson, Oreg., 936..C3, k11 80
Jefferson, Pa., 8,512.....*E1 81
Jefferson, Tex., 2,866....C5 84
Jefferson, Wis., 5,429....E5 88
Jefferson, co., Ala.,
　644,991..............B3 46
Jefferson, co., Ark.,
　85,329...............C3 49
Jefferson, co., Colo.,
　233,031..............B5 51
Jefferson, co., Fla., 8,778...B3 54
Jefferson, co., Ga., 17,174..C4 55
Jefferson, co., Idaho,
　11,740...............F6 57
Jefferson, co., Ill., 31,446..E5 58
Jefferson, co., Ind.,
　27,006...............G7 59
Jefferson, co., Iowa,
　15,774...............C6 60
Jefferson, co., Kans.,
　11,945...............C8 61
Jefferson, co., Ky.,
　695,055..............B4 62
Jefferson, co., Miss.,
　9,295................D2 68
Jefferson, co., Mo.,
　105,248..............C7 69
Jefferson, co., Mont.,
　5,238................D4 70
Jefferson, co., Nebr.,
　10,436...............D8 71
Jefferson, co., N.Y.,
　88,508...............A5 75
Jefferson, co., Ohio,
　96,193...............B5 78
Jefferson, co., Okla.,
　7,125................C4 79
Jefferson, co., Oreg.,
　8,548................C5 80
Jefferson, co., Pa., 43,695..D3 81
Jefferson, co., Tenn.,
　24,940...............C10 83
Jefferson, co., Tex.,
　244,773..............E5 84
Jefferson, co., Wash.,
　10,661...............B2 86
Jefferson, co., W. Va.,
　21,280...............B7 87
Jefferson, co., Wis.,
　60,060...............E5 88
Jefferson, par., La.,
　338,229..............E5 63
Jefferson City, Mo.,
　32,407...............*C5 69
Jefferson City, Tenn.,
　5,124................C10 83
Jefferson Davis, co., Miss.,
　12,936...............D4 68
Jefferson Davis, par., La.,
　29,554...............D3 63
Jeffersontown, Ky.,
　9,701.............B4, g11 62
Jefferson Village, Va.,
　2,500................*B5 85
Jeffersonville, Ga., 1,302..D3 55
Jeffersonville, Ind.,
　20,008...............H6 59
Jeffersonville, Ky., 775...C6 62
Jeffersonville, Ohio, 1,031..C2 78
Jeffrey City, Wyo., 700...*D4 89
Jehossee, isl., S.C........k11 82

Jekabpils, Sov. Un.,
　22,500...............C5 12
Jelenia Góra, Pol., 55,700
　(*82,000)............C3 7
Jelgava, Sov. Un., 55,000..C4 12
Jellico, Tenn., 2,235.....C9 83
Jelm, mtn., Wyo..........E7 89
Jember, Indon., 122,712...G4 19
Jemison, Ala., 1,423......C3 46
Jena, Ger. Dem. Rep.,
　97,463...............C5 6
Jena, La., 2,431.........C3 63
Jenison, Mich., 11,266....*F4 66
Jenkins, Ky., 2,552......C7 62
Jenkins, co., Ga., 8,332..D4 55
Jenkinsville, S.C., 500...C5 82
Jenkintown, Pa.,
　5,404.............F11, o21 81
Jenks, Okla., 1,997......A6 79
Jenners, Pa., 800........F3 81
Jennings, Fla., 582......B3 54
Jennings, La., 11,783....D3 63
Jennings, Mo., 19,379....f13 69
Jennings, co., Ind., 19,454..G6 59
Jennings Lodge, Oreg.,
　3,000...............*B4 80
Jensen Beach, Fla., 900..E6 54
Jenny Jump, mtn., N.J...B3 74
Jequié, Braz., 62,341....*E6 27
Jerauld, co., S. Dak.,
　3,310................F7 77
Jérémie, Hai., 17,624....E6 35
Jerez de García Salinas,
　Mex., 20,325.........C4 34
Jerez, de la Frontera, Sp.,
　110,000 (149,337 ▲)...D2 8
Jericho, N.Y., 14,200....*E7 75
Jericho, Va.............*D6 85
Jermyn, Pa., 2,435......C10 81
Jerome, Idaho, 4,183.....G4 57
Jerome, Ill., 1,673......*D4 58
Jerome, Pa., 1,158......F4 81
Jerome, co., Idaho,
　10,253...............G4 57
Jersey, Br. dep., Eur.,
　75,000...............F5 4
Jersey, co., Ill., 18,492...D3 58
Jersey City, N.J.,
　260,350............B4, k8 74
Jersey Shore, Pa., 5,322...D7 81
Jerseyside, Newf., Can.,
　923................*E5 44
Jerseyville, Ill., 7,446...D3 58
Jerusalem (Yerushalayim),
　Isr., 304,500
　(*315,000).......C3, h5 15
Jerusalem, Jordan,
　60,488...........C3, h5 15
Jesenik, Czech., 5,873....C4 7
Jessamine, co., Ky.,
　17,430...............C5 62
Jessup, Md., 1,000.......B4 53
Jessup, Pa., 4,948......m18 81
Jesup, Ga., 9,091.......E5 55
Jesup, Iowa, 1,662......B5 60
Jesús Carranza, Mex.,
　2,441................D6 34
Jesús María, Arg., 6,284...A4 28
Jetmore, Kans., 936......D4 61
Jever, Ger., Fed. Rep. of,
　12,054...............B3 6
Jewell, Iowa, 1,152......B4 60
Jewell, Kans., 569.......C5 61
Jewell, co., Kans., 6,099..C5 61
Jewell Ridge, Va., 600...e10 85
Jewett, Ohio, 901........B4 78
Jewett City, Conn., 3,372..C9 52
Jeypore, India, 34,319....E7 20
Jhang Maghiana, Pak.,
　94,971...............*B5 20
Jhālrapātan, India,
　12,456...............D6 20
Jhānsi, India, 173,292
　(*198,135)............C6 20
Jhelum, Pak., 41,160
　(*52,585).............B5 20
Jibhalanta (Uliassutai),
　Mong., 5,000.........B4 17
Jičín, Czech., 12,923.....C3 7
Jihkatse (Shigatse), China,
　26,000...............C8 20
Jihlava, Czech., 40,463...D3 7
Jima, Eth., 47,360.......G5 23
Jimbolia, Rom., 11,281...C5 10
Jimena, Sp., 10,123......D3 8
Jim Hogg, co., Tex., 4,654..F3 84
Jim Thorpe, Pa., 5,456...E10 81
Jim Wells, co., Tex.,
　33,032...............F3 84
Jindřichův Hradec, Czech.,
　12,483...............D3 7
Jinja, Ug., 29,741.......H4 23
Jinotepe, Nic., 15,900....E7 34
Jipijapa, Ec., 13,367....B1 31
Jiquilpan de Juárez, Mex.,
　15,960...............n12 34

Jirgalanta (Kobdo), Mong.,
　5,800................B3 17
Joanna, S.C., 1,631......C4 82
João Pessoa, Braz.,
　197,398 (*310,000)....D7 27
Jocobus, Pa............*G8 81
Jocotepec, Mex., 7,736...m12 34
Jódar, Sp., 14,424......D4 8
Jo Daviess, co., Ill.,
　21,766...............A3 58
Jodhpur, India, 317,612...C5 20
Joe Batt's Arm, Newf.,
　Can., 1,058..........D4 44
Joensuu, Fin., 37,682....F13 11
Joeuf, Fr., 12,305
　(*31,000)............C6 5
Joffre, mtn., Alta., Can...D3 38
Joffre, mtn., B.C., Can...D10 37
Joggins, N.S., Can.,
　909.................D5 43
Jogjakarta, see
　Yogyakarta, Indon.
Johannesburg, S. Afr.,
　654,682 (*2,550,000)...F5 24
John Day, Oreg., 1,566...C8 80
Johns Island, S.C.,
　200................F7, k11 82
Johnson, Kans.,
　1,038................E2 61
Johnson, Vt., 1,296
　(1,927 ▲)............B2 73
Johnson, co., Ark., 13,630..B2 49
Johnson, co., Ga., 7,727..D4 55
Johnson, co., Ill., 7,550..F5 58
Johnson, co., Ind., 61,138..F5 59
Johnson, co., Iowa,
　72,127...............C6 60
Johnson, co., Kans.,
　220,073..............D9 61
Johnson, co., Ky., 17,539..C7 62
Johnson, co., Mo., 34,172..C4 69
Johnson, co., Nebr.,
　5,743................D9 71
Johnson, co., Tenn.,
　11,569...............C12 83
Johnson, co., Tex., 45,769..C4 84
Johnson, co., Wyo., 5,587..B6 89
Johnsonburg, Pa., 4,304...D4 81
Johnson City, N.Y.,
　18,025...............C5 75
Johnson City, Tenn.,
　33,770 (*93,500)......C11 83
Johnson City, Tex., 767...D3 84
Johnson Creek, Wis., 790..E5 88
Johnsonville, S.C., 1,267..D9 82
Johnston, Iowa, 222......e8 60
Johnston, R.I., 22,037....B10 52
Johnston, S.C., 2,552.....D4 82
Johnston, co., N.C.,
　61,737...............B4 76
Johnston, co., Okla.,
　7,870................C5 79
Johnston City, Ill., 3,928..F5 58
Johnstown, Colo., 1,191..A6 51
Johnstown, N.Y., 10,045...B6 75
Johnstown, Ohio, 3,208...B3 78
Johnstown, Pa., 42,476
　(*112,300)...........F4 81
Johor, state, Mala.,
　1,179,200............*E2 19
Johor Baharu, Mala.,
　136,229..............E2 19
Joigny, Fr., 9,698......D5 5
Joinville, Braz., 77,760...D3 30
Jojutla, Mex., 14,438....n14 34
Joliet, Ill., 78,887.....B5, k8 58
Joliette, Que., Can.,
　20,127 (*29,350)......C4 42
Joliette, co., Que., Can.,
　48,920...............C3 42
Jolo, Phil., 46,586......D6 19
Jonava, Sov. Un., 14,400..A8 7
Jones, Okla., 1,666......B4 79
Jones, co., Ga., 12,218..C3 55
Jones, co., Iowa, 19,868..B6 60
Jones, co., Miss., 56,357..D4 68
Jones, co., N.C., 9,779...B5 76
Jones, co., S. Dak., 1,882..G5 77
Jones, co., Tex., 16,106..C3 84
Jonesboro, Ark., 27,050...B5 49
Jonesboro, Ga., 4,105....C2 55
Jonesboro, Ill., 1,676....F4 58
Jonesboro, Ind., 2,466...D6 59
Jonesboro, La., 5,072....B3 63
Jonesboro, Tenn., 1,510..C11 83
Jones Mill, Ark., 850...C3, g8 49
Jonesport, Maine, 1,073..D5 64
Jonesville, La., 2,761....C4 63
Jonesville, Mich., 2,081..G6 66
Jonesville, N.C., 1,659...A2 76
Jonesville, S.C., 1,447...B4 82
Jonesville, Va., 700......f8 85
Jönköping, Swe., 88,761
　108,429 ▲)...........I6 11
Jönköping, co., Swe.,
　301,800..............*I5 11

Jonquière, Que., Can.,
　28,430...............A6 42
Jonuta, Mex., 2,746......D6 34
Joplin, Mo., 39,256......D3 69
Joppa, Ill., 531.........F5 58
Jordan, Minn., 1,836.....F5 67
Jordan, N.Y., 1,493......B4 75
Jordan, country, Asia,
　2,555,000............C3 15
Jorhāt, India, 30,247
　(*70,674)............C9 20
Jos, Nig., 90,402.......G6 22
José Batlle y Ordóñez, Ur.,
　1,781................E1 30
Joseph, Oreg., 839.......B9 80
Josephine, Oreg., 35,746..E3 80
Joshua Tree, Calif., 1,211..E5 50
Jourdanton, Tex., 1,841..E3 84
Jovellanos, Cuba, 16,500
　(23,900 ▲)..........C3 35
Juab, co., Utah, 4,574....B5 72
Juana Díaz, P.R.,
　8,765 (36,270 ▲).....*G11 35
Juan Aldama, Mex.,
　9,667................C4 34
Juanita, Wash., 3,000....*B3 86
Juanjui, Peru, 5,200.....C2 31
Juárez, Arg., 9,535......B5 28
Juarez, Mex., 731.......B4 34
Juàzeiro, Braz., 36,273...D6 27
Juazeiro do Norte, Braz.,
　79,796..............*D7 27
Jūbā, Sud., 10,660......H4 23
Júcaro, Cuba, 1,411.....D4 35
Juchipila, Mex., 6,328...m12 34
Juchitán [de Zaragoza],
　Mex., 30,218.........D6 34
Juddah (Jidda), Sau. Ar.,
　194,000.............E2 15
Jude, isl., Newf., Can.....E4 44
Judenburg, Aus., 11,361..E7 6
Judith Basin, co., Mont.,
　2,667................C6 70
Judith, mtn., Mont.......C7 70
Judith, peak, Mont.......C7 70
Judson, S.C., 4,000.....*B3 82
Judsonia, Ark., 1,667....B4 49
Juiz de Fora, Braz.,
　218,832...........C4, g6 30
Jujuy, Arg., 31,091......D2 29
Jujuy, prov., Arg.,
　241,462.............D2 29
Jukao, China, 40,000....*E9 17
Julesburg, Colo., 1,578..A8 51
Juliaca, Peru, 20,351....E3 31
Julian, Calif., 500......F5 50
Julianehåb, Grnld.,
　2,198...............C16 33
Jullundur, India, 296,106
　(*329,830)...........B6 20
Julimes, Mex., 1,540....B3 34
Jumet, Bel., 28,206.....B6 5
Jumilla, Sp., 16,199.....C5 8
Junāgadh, India, 95,485...D5 20
Juncos, P.R., 7,985
　(21,814 ▲)..........*G12 35
Junction, Tex., 2,654....D3 84
Junction City, Ark., 763..D3 49
Junction City, Kans.,
　19,018...............C7 61
Junction City, Ky., 1,046..C5 62
Junction City, Ohio, 732..C3 78
Junction City, Oreg.,
　2,373................C3 80
Jundiaí, Braz.,
　145,785............C3, m8 30
Juneau, Alsk.,
　6,050...........D13, k22 47
Juneau, Wis., 2,043......E5 88
Juneau, co., Wis., 18,455..E3 88
Junee, Austl., 3,765.....F8 25
Jungfrau, mtn., Switz....E3 6
Juniata, co., Pa., 16,712..F6 81
Juniata Terrace, Pa.,
　733.................E6 81
Junín, Arg., 56,000......A4 28
Junín, Peru, 5,100......D2 31
Junín, dept., Peru,
　546,662.............D2 31
Juniper, N.B., Can., 691..C2 43
Junipero Serra, peak,
　Calif................D3 50
Jupiter, Fla., 3,136.....F6 54
Jura, dept., Fr.,
　233,547.............*D6 5
Jura, isl., Scot.........C4 4
Jurbarkas, Sov. Un.,
　5,000...............A7 7
Juruá, riv.............C4 31
Justice, Ill., 9,473.....*B6 58
Jüterbog, Ger. Dem. Rep.,
　13,500...............C6 6
Jutiapa, Guat., 10,086...E7 34
Juwain, Afg., 5,000.....B3 20
Jyvaskylä, Fin., 58,848...F11 11

K

Kaala, peak, Haw.,........f9 56
Kaalaea, Haw., 150......g10 56
Kabaena, isl., Mala.......G6 19
Kabong, Mala., 1,957.....E4 19
Kabul, Afg., 299,800 (*472,300)............B4 20
Kachuga, Sov. Un., 53,500...............D13 13
Kadinhani, Tur., 10,721...C9 14
Kadiri, India, 33,810......F6 20
Kadiyevka, Sov. Un., 137,000 (*585,000).......G12, o21 12
Kaduna, Nig., 149,910.....F6 22
Kaédi, Maur., 10,000.....E2 22
Kaerh (Gartok), China, 5,000.................B7 20
Kaeryong, Kor., 6,000 (14,282 ▲)............H4 18
Kaesong, Kor., 100,000 (139,900 ▲).....G3 18
Kāf, Sau. Ar.,............C2 15
Kafr az Zayyāt, Eg., 25,100...............D2 14
Kagawa, pref., Jap., 907,897...............*I7 18
Kağizman, Tur., 10,236..B14 14
Kagoshima, Jap., 403,340..K5 18
Kagoshima, pref., Jap., 1,729,150............*K5 18
Kagul, Sov. Un., 26,000...C9 10
Kahoka, Mo., 2,207.......*A6 69
Kahoolawe, isl., Haw......C5 56
Kahuka, Haw., 917...B4, f10 56
Kahului, Haw., 8,280.....C5 56
Kaifeng, China, 299,100...E7 17
Kaihsien, China, 40,000...C9 17
Kailua, Haw., 33,783.....g11 56
Kaimana, Indon., 800.....F8 19
Kainan, Jap., 53,370.......I7 18
Kaiserslautern, Ger., Fed. Rep. of, 101,616 (*131,000)............D3 6
Kaiyuan, China, 25,000...E2 18
Kaizuka, Jap., 73,366.....o14 18
Kajaani, Fin., 19,763.....E12 11
Kajikazawa, Jap.........n17 18
Kakegawa, Jap., 37,000 (59,153 ▲)............o17 18
Kākināda, India., 164,200...............E7 20
Kakogawa, Jap., 127,112..............*I7 18
Kālābagh, Pak., 9,073.....B5 20
Kalach, Sov. Un., 18,000..F13 12
Kalaheo, Haw., 1,514.....B2 56
Kalama, Wash., 1,106.....C3 86
Kalamai (Kalamata), Grc., 39,133 (*40,402).......D4 14
Kalamazoo, Mich., 85,555 (*208,800)............F5 66
Kalamazoo, co., Mich., 201,550...............F5 66
Kalaotoa, isl., Indon......G6 19
Kalapana, Haw., 60.......D7 56
Kalemi, Zaire, 29,500.....B5 24
Kalgan, see Changchiakou, China
Kalgoorlie, Austl., 9,170 (*20,784)............F3 25
Kálimnos, Grc., 9,492....*D6 14
Kalinin, Sov. Un., 345,000..............C10 12
Kaliningrad, Sov. Un., 106,000..............n17 12
Kaliningrad (Königsberg), Sov. Un., 297,000.......D3 12
Kalinkovichi, Sov. Un., 24,000.................E7 12
Kalispell, Mont., 10,526...B2 70
Kalisz, Pol., 81,200.......C5 7
Kalkaska, Mich., 1,475....D5 66
Kalkaska, co., Mich., 5,372.................D5 66
Kallithéa, Grc., 82,438...*D4 14
Kalmar, Swe., 44,505......I7 11
Kalmar, co., Swe., 241,400.*I7 11
Kalocsa, Hung., 16,004...B4 10
Kalona, Iowa, 1,488......C6 60
Kalone, peak, B.C., Can...C4 37
Kaluga, Sov. Un., 211,000...............D11 12
Kalush, Sov. Un., 41,000..G5 12
Kama, riv., Sov. Un......D8 13
Kamaishi, Jap., 72,923...G10 18
Kamakura, Jap., 139,249..n18 18
Kamarhati, India, 169,404..............*D8 20
Kamenets-Podolskiy, Sov. Un., 57,000.......G6 12
Kamen-na-Obi, Sov. Un., 36,000...............D11 13
Kamensk-Shakhtinskiy, Sov. Un., 68,000......G13 12
Kamensk-Uralskiy, Sov. Un., 169,000......D9 13
Kamenz, Ger. Dem. Rep., 14,900...............C7 6
Kameoka, Jap., 29,500 (47,151 ▲)............o14 18
Kamiah, Idaho, 1,307.....C2 57
Kamioka, Jap., 10,455...m16 18
Kamloops, B.C., Can., 26,168 (*43,790)...D7, n18 37
Kammuri-Yama, mtn., Jap.I6 18
Kamouraska, co., Que., Can., 26,593...........B8 42
Kampala, Ug., 46,735 (*123,332)............H4 23
Kampen, Neth., 29,163....A6 5
Kampot, Camb., 12,600...C2 19
Kamsack, Sask., Can., 2,783.................F5 39
Kamuela, Haw., 800......C6 56
Kamyshin, Sov. Un., 97,000...............F15 12
Kanab, Utah, 1,381.......C5 72
Kanabec, co., Minn., 9,775.................E5 67
Kanagawa, pref., Jap., 5,472,247...............*I9 18
Kananga (Luluabourg), Zaire, 140,900..........B4 24
Kanash, Sov. Un., 41,000.D16 12
Kanawha, Iowa, 822......B4 60
Kanawha, co., W. Va., 229,515...............C3 87
Kanayama, Jap..........n16 18
Kanazawa, Jap., 361,379..H8 18
Kanchanaburi, Thai., 12,957...............C1 19
Kānchenjunga, peak, Nep., Sikkim...............C8 20
Kānchipuram, India, 110,657 (*119,693)......F7 20
Kanchou, China, 98,600...F7 17
Kandahar, Afg., 127,000...B4 20
Kandalaksha, Sov. Un., 43,000...............C6 13
Kandangan, Indon., 26,112................F5 19
Kandira, Tur., 6,717......B8 14
Kandiyohi, co., Minn., 30,548...............E3 67
Kandy, Sri Lanka, 93,602..G7 20
Kane, Pa., 5,001.........C4 81
Kane, co., Ill., 251,005....B5 58
Kane, co., Utah, 2,421....C5 72
Kaneohe, Haw., 29,903...........B4, g10 56
Kanggye, Kor., 30,013.....F3 18
Kangnung, Kor., 49,000 (74,489 ▲)............H4 18
Kangting, China, 30,000...E5 17
Kanjiža, Yugo., 11,261....B5 10
Kankakee, Ill., 30,944 (*74,900)..............B6 58
Kankakee, co., Ill., 97,250..B6 58
Kankan, Guinea, 29,000...F3 22
Kānker, India, 6,437......D7 20
Kanku, China..........B12 20
Kannan, China, 5,000.....C1 18
Kannapolis, N.C., 36,293 (*87,500)..............B2 76
Kano, Nig., 295,432.......F6 22
Kanopolis, Kan., 626.....D5 61
Kanoya, Jap., 38,000 (66,995 ▲)............K5 18
Kānpur, India, 1,154,388 (*1,320,000)..........C7 20
Kansas, Ill., 779..........D6 58
Kansas, state, U.S., 2,255,000............... 61
Kansas, riv., Kans.........C7 61
Kansas City, Kans., 168,213..........C9, k16 61
Kansas City, Mo., 507,330 (*1,222,700).......B3, h10 69
Kansk, Sov. Un., 95,000..D12 13
Kansong, Kor., 5,000.....G4 18
Kansu, prov., China, 12,800,000............D5 17
Kantunilkín, Mex., 1,970..C7 34
Kanye, Bots., 34,045......E5 24
Kaohsiung, Taiwan, 580,000 (727,300 ▲).....G9 17
Kaolack, Sen., 69,600.....F1 22
Kapaa, Haw., 3,794.......A2 56
Kapanga, Zaire...........B4 24
Kapfenberg, Aus., 26,006..E7 6
Kapit, Mala., 1,834.......E4 19
Kaplan, La., 5,540........D3 63
Kaposvár, Hung., 58,099..B3 10
Kapuskasing, Ont., Can., 12,834................o19 41
Kapuvár, Hung., 10,500...B3 10
Karachev, Sov., Un. 16,000...............E10 12
Karāchi, Pak., 2,850,000 (*3,500,000)..........D4 20
Karaga, Sov. Un., 10,000...............D19 13
Karaganda, Sov. Un., 523,000..............E10 13
Karaköse, Tur., 29,577...C14 14
Karaman, Tur., 35,056....D9 14
Karapinar, Tur., 16,065...D9 14
Karatsu, Jap., 74,233......J4 18
Karbalā', Iraq, 83,301.....C3 15
Karcag, Hung., 22,286 (24,631 ▲)............B5 10
Kardhitsa, Grc., 25,685....C3 14
Karelia (Kerelo-Finnish S.S.R), former rep., Sov. Un.............*C6 16
Kargil, India, 5,000.......B6 20
Kargopol, Sov. Un., 5,000...............A12 12
Kariba, Rh., 5,950........D5 24
Kārikal, India, 26,080.....F6 20
Karkaralinsk, Sov. Un., 12,200..............E10 13
Karl-Marx-Stadt (Chemnitz), Ger. Dem. Rep., 302,409 (*460,000)............C6 6
Karlovac, Yugo., 47,532...C2 10
Karlóvasi, Grc., 4,401.....D6 14
Karlovy Vary, Czech., 45,102 (*58,000)........C2 7
Karlshamn, Swe., 14,828...I6 11
Karlskoga, Swe., 38,536...H6 11
Karlskrona, Swe., 36,797 (*49,904).............I6 11
Karlsruhe, Ger., Fed. Rep. of, 263,456 (*460,000)...D4 6
Karlstad, Minn., 727......B2 67
Karlstad, Swe., 72,488....H5 11
Karmutzen, mtn., B.C., Can.....................D4 37
Karnak, Ill., 641..........F5 58
Karnataka, state, India, 29,299,014..............F6 20
Karnes, co., Tex., 13,462..E4 84
Karnes City, Tex., 2,926...E4 84
Kars, Tur., 53,338.......B14 14
Karsakpay, Sov. Un., 12,000................E9 13
Karshi, Sov. Un., 71,000...F9 13
Kartal, Tur., 10,800......*B7 14
Kartaly, Sov. Un., 43,000...............D9 13
Kartuzy, Pol., 10,500......A5 7
Karviná, Czech., 77,117...D5 7
Kārwār, India, 27,770.....F5 20
Kāsaragod, India, 34,984..F6 20
Kasba Tadla, Mor., 15,776................B3 22
Kāshān, Iran, 58,468......B8 23
Kashih (Kashgar), China, 100,000..............F10 16
Kashima, Jap............n19 18
Kashira, Sov. Un., 39,000...............D12 12
Kashiwa, Jap., 150,635..*n18 18
Kashiwazaki, Jap., 49,000 (73,569 ▲).......H9 18
Kasimov, Sov. Un., 33,000...............D13 12
Kaslo, B.C., Can., 646.....E9 37
Kasota, Minn., 732.......F5 67
Kassalā, Sud., 68,100......E5 23
Kassel, Ger., Fed. Rep. of, 212,974 (*345,000).....C4 6
Kasson, Minn., 1,883......F6 67
Kastamonu, Tur., 29,338...B9 14
Kastoria, Grc., 15,407.....B3 14
Kasugai, Jap., 161,835...*n15 18
Kasukabe, Jap., 84,919...n18 18
Kasumi, Jap., 6,934.......I7 18
Kasūr, Pak., 103,000......B5 20
Katahdin, mtn., Maine....C4 64
Katanga, prov., Zaire, 1,664,200..............C5 24
Katanning, Austl., 3,603...F2 25
Katata, Jap. (part of Otsu).........n14 18
Kateríni, Grc., 28,808 (*30,512)...............B4 14
Katherine, Austl., 2,520....B5 25
Kathleen, Fla., 800.......D4 54
Kathwood, S.C., 2,000....*D4 82
Katiola, I.C., 7,900.......G4 22
Kātmāndu, Nep., 153,405...............C8 20
Katonah, N.Y., 3,000.....A5 75
Katoomba-Wentworth Falls, Austl., 11,593.....F8 26
Katowice (Stalinogród), Pol., 303,200 (*2,060,000)......C5, g10 7
Katrīnah, Jabal, mtn., Eg..C4 23
Katrineholm, Swe., 24,941...........H7, u34 11
Katsina, Nig., 90,538......F6 22
Katsuyama, Jap., 25,000 (32,691 ▲)......m15 18
Katy, Tex., 2,923........r14 84
Kauai, isl., Haw..........A2 56
Kauai, co., Haw., 29,761..B2 56
Kaufbeuren, Ger., Fed. Rep. of, 42,995.........E5 6
Kaufman, Tex., 4,012.....C4 84
Kaufman, co., Tex., 32,392................C4 84
Kaukauna, Wis., 11,308.............D5, h9 88
Kaumakani, Haw., 1,014..B2 56
Kaunakakai, Haw., 1,070..B4 56
Kaunas, Sov. Un., 305,000.D4 12
Kavaje, Alb., 13,700.....*B2 14
Kavála, Grc., 46,234......B5 14
Kavála, prov., Grc., 121,491..............*B5 14
Kavarna, Bul., 5,625......D9 10
Kawagoe, Jap., 171,038...n18 18
Kawaguchi, Jap., 305,886...............n18 18
Kawaikini, peak, Haw.....A2 56
Kawasaki, Jap., 1,001,368..........I9, n18 18
Kawkareik, Bur., 10,000..*B1 19
Kawkawlin, Mich., 650....E7 66
Kawn Umbū, Eg., 27,227..D4 23
Kay, co., Okla., 48,791....A4 79
Kayes, Mali, 28,000.......F2 22
Kayford, W. Va., 150..............C3, m13 87
Kayseri, Tur., 160,985....C10 14
Kaysville, Utah, 6,192..............A6, C2 72
Kazachye, Sov. Un., 900..B16 13
Kazakh S.S.R., rep., Sov. Un., 13,720,000...*E9 16
Kazan, Sov. Un., 869,000..D7 13
Kazanluk, Bul., 44,384....D7 10
Keaau, Haw., 950........D6 56
Keansburg, N.J., 9,720....C4 74
Kearney, Nebr., 19,181....D6 71
Kearney, Mo., 984....B3, h11 69
Kearney, co., Nebr., 6,707.................D7 71
Kearns, Utah, 17,071....*A5 72
Kearny, N.J., 37,585......h8 74
Kearny, co., Kans., 3,047..D2 61
Kearsarge, Mich., 500.....A2 66
Keasbey, N.J., 700.......*B4 74
Kebnekaise, mtn., Swe.....D8 11
Kecskemét, Hung., 61,784 (77,484 ▲).......B4 10
Kedah, state, Mala., 849,900..............*D2 19
Kedainiai, Sov. Un., 19,700................A7 7
Kedgwick, N.B., Can., 1,095.................B2 43
Kediri, Indon., 178,865...*G4 19
Keegan, Maine, 800.......A5 64
Keego Harbor, Mich., 3,092.................o15 66
Keene, N.H., 20,467......F3 73
Keene, Tex., 2,440........n9 84
Keeseville, N.Y., 2,122....f11 75
Keewatin, Ont., Can., 2,112.................E4 40
Keewatin, Minn., 1,382....C5 67
Keewatin, dist., N.W., Ter., Can., 4,000......D15 36
Kefallinia, prov., Grc., 36,657..............*C3 14
Kefar Ata, Isr., 27,000.....B3 15
Kefar Sava, Isr., 26,500...B2 15
Keighley, Eng., 55,720....D6 4
Keith, Scot., 4,208........B5 4
Keith, co., Nebr., 8,487...C4 71
Keithsburg, Ill., 836.......B3 58
Keizer, Oreg., 11,405....*C4 80
Kekaha, Haw., 2,404......B2 56
Kelang, Mala., 113,607...K4 19
Kelantan, state, Mala., 618,900...............D2 19
Keller, Tex., 1,474........n9 84
Kellerman, Ala., 50.......B2 46
Kellogg, Idaho, 3,811.....B2 57
Kellogg, Iowa, 607.......C5 60
Kelly Brook, mtn., Maine..A3 64
Kelly Lake, Minn., 900....C5 67

Kelowna, B.C., Can., 19,412 (*36,956) E8 37
Kelseyville, Calif., 900 C2 50
Kelso, Mo., 401 D8 69
Kelso, Scot., 4,855 C5 4
Kelso, Wash., 10,296 C3 86
Keltys, Tex *D5 84
Keluang, Mala., 43,272 E2 19
Kelvington, Sask., Can., 885 E4 39
Kem, Sov. Un., 10,000 E16 11
Kemah, Tex., 1,144 *E5 84
Kemerovo, Sov. Un., 385,000 D11 13
Kemi, Fin., 27,717 E11 11
Kemmerer, Wyo., 2,292 E2 89
Kemp, Tex., 999 C4 84
Kemper, co., Miss., 10,233 C5 68
Kempsey, Austl., 8,867 F9 25
Kempshall, mtn., N.Y. A6 75
Kempten, Ger., Fed. Rep. of, 57,135 E5 6
Kemptville, Ont., Can., 2,413 B9 41
Kenansville, N.C., 762 C4 76
Kenbridge, Va., 1,223 D4 85
Kendal, Eng., 21,410 C5 4
Kendall, Fla., 37,700 s13 54
Kendall, co., Ill., 26,374 B5 58
Kendall, co., Tex., 6,964 E3 84
Kendall Park, N.J., 7,412 C3 74
Kendallville, Ind., 6,838 B7 59
Kendari, Indon, 11,672 F6 19
Kendrāpāra, India, 20,079 D8 20
Kendrick, Fla., 300 C4 54
Kenedy, Tex., 4,156 E4 84
Kenedy, co., Tex., 678 F4 84
Kenhorst, Pa., 3,482 *F9 81
Kenilworth, Ill., 2,980 H9 58
Kenilworth, N.J., 9,165 *B4 74
Kenitra, Mor., 139,206 B3 22
Kenly, N.C., 1,370 B4 76
Kenmare, N. Dak., 1,515 B3 77
Kenmawr, Pa., 5,100 *E1 81
Kenmore, N.Y., 20,980 C2 75
Kenmore, Wash., 7,500 *B3 86
Kennaday, peak, Wyo E6 89
Kennebec, co., Maine, 95,247 D3 64
Kennebunk, Maine, 2,764 (5,646▲) E2 64
Kennebunkport, Maine, 1,097 (2,160 ▲) E2 64
Kennedale, Tex., 3,076 n9 84
Kennedy, N.Y., 600 C1 75
Kenner, La., 29,858 k11 63
Kennesaw, Ga., 3,548 B2, g7 55
Kenneth City, Fla., 3,862 *E4 54
Kennett, Mo., 10,090 E7 69
Kennett Square, Pa., 4,876 G10 81
Kennewick, Wash., 15,212 C6 86
Kennydale, Wash., 900 e11 86
Kénogami, Que., Can., 10,970 A6 42
Kenora, Ont., Can., 10,952 (*13,064) o16 41
Kenora, dist., Ont., Can., 53,995 o16 41
Kenosha, Wis., 78,805 (*104,500) F6, n12 88
Kenosha, co., Wis., 117,917 F5 88
Kenova, W. Va., 4,860 C2 87
Kensington, Calif., 5,823 *D3 50
Kensington, Conn., 7,500 C5 52
Kensington, Kans., 653 C4 61
Kensington, Md., 2,322 B3 53
Kensington, N.Y., 1,402 *G2 52
Kensington Estates, Md., 2,500 *B3 53
Kensington Park, Fla., 3,138 *E4 54
Kent, Conn., 500 C2 52
Kent, Ohio, 28,183 A4 78
Kent, Wash., 16,596 B3, f11 86
Kent, co., N.B., Can., 24,736 C4 43
Kent, co., Ont., Can., 96,406 E2 41
Kent, co., Del., 81,892 B6 53
Kent, co., Eng., 1,408,820 *E7 4
Kent, co., Md., 16,146 B5 53
Kent, co., Mich., 411,044 E5 66
Kent, co., R.I., 142,382 C10 52
Kent, co., Tex., 1,434 C2 84
Kent City, Mich., 686 E5 66
Kentfield, Calif., 5,500 *C2 50
Kentland, Ind., 1,864 C3 59
Kentland, Md., 2,500 *C4 53
Kenton, Ohio, 8,315 B2 78
Kenton, Tenn., 1,439 A2 83
Kenton, co., Ky., 129,440 B5 62
Kentucky, state, U.S., 3,322,000 62
Kent Village, Md., 1,500 *C4 53
Kentville, N.S., Can., 5,198 (*11,571) D5 43
Kentwood, La., 2,736 D5 63
Kentwood, Mich., 20,310 F5 66
Kenvil, N.J., 1,700 B3 74
Kenvir, Ky., 950 D6 62
Kenwood, Ohio, 15789 *C1 78
Kenya, country, Afr., 12,690,000 H5 23
Kenya, mtn., Ken I5 23
Kenyon, Minn., 1,575 F6 67
Keokuk, Iowa, 14,631 D6 60
Keokuk, co., Iowa, 13,943 C5 60
Keosauqua, Iowa, 1,018 D6 60
Keota, Iowa, 1,112 C6 60
Keota, Okla., 685 B7 79
Kepno, Pol., 9,177 C5 7
Kerala, state, India, 21,347,375 F6 20
Kerang, Austl., 4,120 G7 25
Kerby, Oreg., 250 E3 80
Kerch, Sov. Un., 128,000 I11 12
Keremeos, B.C., Can., 563 E8 37
Kerens, Tex., 1,446 C4 84
Kerhonkson, N.Y., 1,243 D6 75
Kerintji, mtn., Indon F2 19
Kerkhoven, Minn., 641 E3 67
Kérkira, Grc., 28,630 C2 14
Kerkira, prov., Grc., 92,261 *C2 14
Kerkrade, Neth., 47,301 B7 5
Kerman, Calif., 2,667 *D4 50
Kermān, Iran, 85,404 C6 15
Kermānshāh, Iran, 187,930 B7 23
Kermit, Tex., 7,884 D1 84
Kermit, W. Va., 716 D2 87
Kermode, mtn., B.C., Can C2 37
Kern, co., Calif., 330,234 E4 50
Kernersville, N.C., 4,815 A2 76
Kernville, Calif., 900 E4 50
Kerr, co., Tex., 19,454 D3 84
Kerrobert, Sask., Can., 1,220 F1 39
Kerrville, Tex., 12,672 D3 84
Kerry, co., Ire., 112,785 *D2 4
Kershaw, S.C., 1,818 B6 82
Kershaw, co., S.C., 34,727 C6 82
Keşan, Tur., 23,801 B6 14
Kesennuma, Jap., 63,265 G10 18
Keski-Suomi, prov., Fin., 248,000 *K5 11
Keswick, Ont., Can., 699 C5 41
Keszthely, Hung., 16,731 B3 10
Keta, Ghana, 16,700 G5 22
Ketapang, Indon., 3,279 F3 19
Ketchikan, Alsk., 6,994 D13, n24 47
Ketchum, Idaho, 1,454 F4 57
Ketona, Ala., 600 f7 46
Ketrzyn Mazowiecki, Pol., 19,300 A6 7
Kettering, Eng., 42,530 D6 4
Kettering, Ohio, 71,864 C1 78
Kettle Falls, Wash., 893 A7 86
Kęty, Pol., 11,500 D5, h10 7
Kewanee, Ill., 15,762 B4 58
Kewaskum, Wis., 1,926 E5 88
Kewaunee, Wis., 2,901 D6 88
Kewanna, Ind., 614 B5 59
Kewaunee, co., Wis., 18,961 D6 88
Keweenaw, co., Mich., 2,264 A2 66
Keya Paha, co., Nebr., 1,340 B6 71
Key Biscayne, Fla., 4,500 *G6 54
Keyes, Calif., 1,875 *D4 50
Keyes, Okla., 569 e8 79
Keyport, N.J., 7,205 C4 74
Keyser, W. Va., 6,586 B6 87
Keystone, Iowa, 549 C5 60
Keystone, W. Va., 1,008 D3 87
Keysville, Fla., 50 E2 54
Keysville, Va., 818 C4 85
Keytesville, Mo., 730 B5 69
Key West, Fla., 29,312 H5 54
Kezar Falls, Maine, 900 E2 64
Kezhma, Sov. Un., 3,000 D13 13
Kežmarok, Czech., 10,676 D6 7
Khabarovsk, Sov. Un., 436,000 E16 13
Khairpur, Pak., 18,186 C4 20
Khalkidhikí (Chalcidice), prov., Grc., 73,851 *B4 14
Khalkis, Grc., 36,300 C4 14
Khalūf, Om E6 15
Khambhāliya, India, 19,973 D4 20
Khanabad, Afg., 30,000 A4 20
Khānaqīn, Iraq, 23,522 E15 15
Khandwa, India, 84,517 D6 20
Khaniá (Canea), Grc., 40,564 (*53,026) E5 14
Khaniá, prov., Grc., 119,595 *E4 14
Khānpur, Pak., 31,465 C5 20
Khān Yūnus, Gaza Strip, 52,997 C2, h5 15
Kharagpur, India, 61,783 D8 20
Kharkov, Sov. Un., 1,248,000 (*1,480,000) G11 12
Kharmanli, Bul., 15,502 E7 10
Kharovsk, Sov. Un., 5,000 B13 12
Khartoum (Al Khurtum), Sud., 194,000 (*515,000) E4 23
Khartoum North, Sud., 127,672 E4 23
Khartsyzsk, Sov. Un., 51,000 q21 12
Khash, Afg., 5,000 B3 20
Khaskovo, Bul., 57,681 E7 10
Khatanga, Sov. Un., 10,000 B13 16
Khenifra, Mor., 25,526 B3 22
Kherson, Sov. Un., 261,000 H9 12
Khilok, Sov. Un., 15,000 D14 13
Khimki, Sov. Un., 87,000 n17 12
Khíos, Grc., 24,084 (*30,021) C6 14
Khíos, (Chios), prov., Grc., 53,942 *C6 14
Khmelnik, Sov. Un., 18,000 G6 12
Khmelnitskiy, Sov. Un., 113,000 G6 12
Kholm, Sov. Un., 10,000 C8 12
Khong, Laos, 10,000 C3 19
Khong Sedone, Laos, 10,000 *B3 19
Khorog, Sov. Un., 12,000 F10 13
Khorol, Sov. Un., 10,000 G9 12
Khorramābād, Iran, 59,578 C4 15
Khorramshahr, Iran, 88,536 C4 15
Khotin, Sov. Un., 10,000 G6 12
Khulna, Bngl., 80,917 (*127,970) D8 20
Khust, Sov. Un., 24,000 G4 12
Kiamichi, mtn., Okla C6 79
Kiangsi, prov., China, 18,610,000 F9 17
Kiangsu, prov., China, 42,630,000 E8 17
Kiaohsien, China, 40,000 D9 17
Kičevo, Yugo., 15,378 E5 10
Kidder, co., N. Dak., 4,362 C6 77
Kidderminster, Eng., 47,640 D5 4
Kiel, Ger., Fed. Rep. of, 268,840 (*347,000) A5 6
Kiel, Wis., 2,848 E5, k9 88
Kielce, Pol., 125,900 C6 7
Kiester, Minn., 681 G5 67
Kiev (Kiyev), Sov. Un., 1,632,000 (*1,775,000) F8 12
Kifisiá, Grc., 20,082 g11 14
Kigali, Rwanda, 15,000 I4 23
Kikinda, Yugo., 37,487 C5 10
Kikladhes (Cyclades), prov., Grc., 86,084 *D5 14
Kikwit, Zaire, 11,000 B3 24
Kilauea, crater, Haw D6 56
Kilbride, Newf., Can., 2,148 *E5 44
Kilchu, Kor., 30,026 F4 18
Kildare, co., Ire., 66,404 *D3 4
Kilgore, Tex., 9,495 C5 84
Kilimanjaro, mtn., Tan I5 23
Kilis, Tur., 43,438 D11 14
Kiliya, Sov., Un., 24,000 I7 12
Kilkenny, Ire., 9,838 D3 4
Kilkenny, co., Ire., 60,463 *D3 4
Kilkís, Grc., 10,538 E6 10
Kilkís, prov., Grc., 84,539 *B4 14
Killaloe Station, Ont., Can., 932 B7 41
Killarney, Man., Can., 2,074 E2 40
Killarney, Ire., 7,184 D2 4
Killbuck, Ohio, 893 B4 78
Killeen, Tex., 35,507 D4 84
Killian, S.C., 800 C6 82
Killona, La., 650 h11 63
Kilmallie, Scot., 5,049 B4 4
Kilmarnock, Scot., 48,992 (*79,000) C4 4
Kilmarnock, Va., 841 C6 85
Kimchaek, (Songjin), Kor., 67,778 F4 18
Kimball, Minn., 567 E4 67
Kimball, Nebr., 3,680 C2 71
Kimball, S. Dak., 825 G7 77
Kimball, co., Nebr., 6,009 C2 71
Kimberly, B.C., Can., 7,641 E9 37
Kimberly, S. Afr., 103,789 (*105,000) F4 24
Kimberly, Ala., 847 B3 46
Kimberly, Idaho, 1,557 G4 57
Kimberly, W. Va., 900 D6 87
Kimberly, Wis., 6,131 h9 88
Kimble, co., Tex., 3,904 D3 84
Kimry, Sov. Un., 53,000 C11 12
Kinabalu, mtn., Mala D5 19
Kincaid, Ill., 1,424 D4 58
Kincardine, Ont., Can., 3,239 C3 41
Kincardine, co., Scot., 26,393 *B5 4
Kinde, Mich., 618 E8 66
Kinder, La., 2,307 D3 63
Kinderhook, N.Y., 1,233 C7 75
Kindersley, Sask., Can., 3,451 F1 39
Kindia, Guinea, 25,000 F2 22
Kineo, mtn., Maine C3 64
Kineshma, Sov. Un., 96,000 C14 12
King, N.C., 1,033 A2 76
King, Wis., 750 D4 88
King, co., Tex., 464 C2 84
King, co., Wash., 1,156,633 B4 86
King, mtn., Oreg., 1,427 D8 80
King, mtn., Oreg E3 80
King and Queen, co., Va., 5,491 C6 85
Kingaroy, Austl., 4,931 E9 25
King City, Calif., 3,717 D3 50
King City, Ont., Can., 2,091 k14 41
King City, Mo., 1,023 A3 69
Kingfield, Maine, 700 (877▲) D2 64
Kingfisher, Okla., 4,042 B4 79
Kingfisher, co., Okla., 12,857 B3 79
King George, co., Va., 8,039 B5 85
King George, mtn., B.C., Can D10 37
Kingman, Ariz., 7,312 B1 48
Kingman, Kans., 3,622 E5, g10 61
Kingman, co., Kans., 8,886 E5 61
King of Prussia, Pa., 18,200 *F11 81
Kings, co., Calif., 66,717 D3 50
Kings, co., N.B., Can., 28,548 D4 43
Kings, co., N.S., Can., 43,249 E5 43
Kings, co., P.E.I., Can., 18,015 C7 43
Kings (Brooklyn Borough), co., N.Y., 2,602,012 E7 75
Kings, peak, Calif B1 50
Kings, peak, Utah A6 72
Kingsburg, Calif., 3,843 D4 50
Kingsbury, co., S. Dak., 7,657 F7 77
Kingscote, Austl., 1,007 G6 25
Kingsford, Mich., 5,276 C2 66
Kingsford Heights, Ind., 1,200 *A4 59
Kings Gardens, Kans., 400 A4 61
Kingsley, Iowa, 1,097 B2 60
Kingsley, Mich., 632 D5 66
King's Lynn, Eng., 30,200 D7 4
Kings Mills, Ohio, 500 C1, n13 78
Kings Mountain, N.C., 8,465 B1 76
Kings Park, N.Y., 5,555 n15 75
King's Point, Newf., Can., 542 D3 44
Kings Point, N.Y., 5,614 F1 52
Kingsport, Tenn., 31,938 (*100,900) C11 83
Kingston, Austl., 1,173 G6 25
Kingston, Ont., Can., 59,047 (*85,877) C8 41
Kingston, Idaho, 500 B2 57
Kingston, Jam., 550,100 F5 35
Kingston, Mass., 3,772 (5,999▲) C6 65
Kingston, N.H., 600 (2,882▲) F6 73
Kingston, N.J., 900 C3 74
Kingston, N.Y., 25,544 D6 75

Kingston, Ohio, 1,157.....C3 78
Kingston, Okla., 710......D5 79
Kingston, Pa., 18,325..........D10, n17 81
Kingston, R.I., 5,601.....D10 52
Kingston, Tenn., 4,142....D9 83
Kingston, W. Va., 400..............D3, n13 87
Kingstree, S.C., 3,381.....D8 82
Kingsville, Ont., Can., 4,076.................E2 41
Kingsville, Ohio, 1,129....A5 78
Kingsville, Tex., 28,915....F4 84
King William, co., Va., 7,497.................C5 85
King William's Town, S. Afr., 15,429.........G5 24
Kingwood, W. Va., 2,550..B5 87
Kinistino, Sask., Can., 764..................E3 39
Kinloch, Mo., 5,629......f13 69
Kinmundy, Ill., 759.......E5 58
Kinnaird, B.C., Can., 2,846..................E9 37
Kinnelon, N.J., 7,600.....B4 74
Kinney, co., Tex., 2,006...E2 84
Kinomoto, Jap..........n15 18
Kinross, co., Scot., 6,371..*B5 4
Kinshasa (Leopoldville), Zaire, 901,500..........A3 24
Kinsley, Kans., 2,212......E4 61
Kinsman, Ohio, 700.......A5 78
Kinston, N.C., 23,020.....B5 76
Kinwood, Tex., 1,800....*E5 84
Kiowa, Kans., 1,414.......E5 61
Kiowa, Okla., 754.........C6 79
Kiowa, co., Colo., 2,029...C8 51
Kiowa, co., Kans., 4,088...E4 61
Kiowa, co., Okla., 12,532.................C2 79
Kiparissia, Grc., 3,882.....D3 14
Kipling, Sask., Can., 773..G4 39
Kippens, Newf., Can., 1,079................*D2 44
Kipushi, Zaire, 15,100.....C5 24
Kirbyville, Tex., 1,869....D6 84
Kirensk, Sov. Un., 14,500...............D13 13
Kirghiz, S.S.R., rep., Sov. Un., 3,130,000....E10 16
Kırıkkale, Tur., 91,658...*C9 14
Kirin, prov., China, 12,550,000............C9 17
Kirkağaç, Tur., 14,072....C6 14
Kirkcaldy, Scot., 50,091 (*138,000).............B5 4
Kirkcudbright, co., Scot., 27,448................*C4 4
Kirkland, Ill., 1,138.......A5 58
Kirkland, Wash., 14,970...........B3, e11 86
Kirkland Lake, Ont., Can., 13,599...............o19 41
Kirklareli, Tur., 27,431....B6 14
Kirklin, Ind., 736.........D5 59
Kirksville, Mo., 15,560....A5 69
Kirkūk, Iraq, 167,413...E15 14
Kirkwood, Md., 2,500....*C3 53
Kirkwood, Mo., 31,890....f13 69
Kirn, Ger., Fed. Rep. of, 10,545................D3 6
Kirov, Sov. Un., 333,000..D7 13
Kirovabad, Sov. Un., 190,000...............E7 13
Kirovograd, Sov. Un., 189,000...............G9 12
Kirovsk, Sov. Un., 45,000.................C6 13
Kirsanov, Sov. Un., 22,000...............E14 12
Kirşehir, Tur., 33,173....C10 14
Kirtland, Ohio, 5,530....*A4 78
Kiruna, Swe., 26,160......D9 11
Kiryū, Jap., 132,000.........H9, m18 18
Kisangani (Stanleyville), Zaire, 149,900..........H3 23
Kisarazu, Jap., 73,319....n18 18
Kiselevsk, Sov. Un., 127,000..............*D11 13
Kishangarh, India, 37,405................C5 20
Kishinev, Sov. Un., 374,000...............H7 12
Kishiwada, Jap., 162,022...............o14 18
Kishorganj, Bngl., 19,067..D9 20
Kiskoros, Hung., 9,972....B4 10
Kiskundorozsma, Hung., 8,705..................B5 10
Kiskunfelegyháza, Hung., 25,871 (34,127 ▲).......B4 10
Kiskunhalas, Hung., 20,787 (28,447 ▲).......B4 10
Kiskunmajsa, Hung., 7,611.................B4 10
Kislovodsk, Sov. Un., 90,000................*E7 13
Kiso-sammyaku, mts., Jap...................n16 18
Kissimmee, Fla., 7,119....D5 54
Kistler, W. Va., 500...D3, D5 87
Kisújszállás, Hung., 11,802 (13,391 ▲).......B5 10
Kisumu, Ken., 23,526......I4 23
Kisvárda, Hung., 13,759...A6 10
Kita-dake, mtn., Jap.......I9 18
Kitakyūshū, Jap., 1,051,076 (*1,470,000)...J5 18
Kitale, Ken., 9,342.......H4 23
Kitami, Jap., 66,000 (82,727 ▲)...........E11 18
Kit Carson, co., Colo., 7,530..................B8 51
Kitchener, Ont., Can., 111,804 (*226,846)......D4 41
Kitimat, B.C., Can., 11,824.................B3 37
Kitsap, co., Wash., 101,732.................B3 86
Kittanning, Pa., 6,231.....E2 81
Kittery, Maine, 7,363 (11,028▲).............E2 64
Kittery Point, Maine, 1,172..................E2 64
Kittitas, co., Wash., 25,039...................B5 86
Kitts, Ky., 500...........D6 62
Kittson, co., Minn., 6,853..................B2 67
Kitwe, Zam., 146,000....*C5 24
Kitzbühel, Aus., 8,003.....E6 6
Kitzingen, Ger., Fed. Rep. of, 17,775.........D5 6
Kitzmiller, Md., 443.....m12 53
Kizel, Sov. Un., 46,000...*D8 13
Kizyl-Arvat, Sov. Un., 22,000.................F8 13
Kladno, Czech., 56,935 (*73,000)...C3, n17 7
Klagenfurt, Aus., 82,512...E7 6
Klaipeda (Memel), Sov. Un., 140,000......D3 12
Klamath, co., Oreg., 50,021..................E4 80
Klamath, mts., Calif.......B2 50
Klamath Falls, Oreg., 15,775..................E5 80
Klamath Glen, Calif., 600....................B2 50
Klatovy, Czech., 16,852...D2 7
Kleberg, Tex., 4,768.....*C4 84
Kleberg, co., Tex., 33,166..................F4 84
Klemme, Iowa, 554.......A4 60
Kletnya, Sov. Un., 10,000..................E9 12
Kletsk, Sov. Un., 10,000...E6 12
Kleve, Ger., Fed. Rep. of, 43,481..................C3 6
Klickitat, Wash., 700......D4 86
Klickitat, co., Wash., 12,138..................D5 86
Klintsy, Sov. Un., 58,000..E9 12
Ključ, Yugo., 2,322........C3 10
Kłobuck, Pol., 12,600.....C5 7
Kłodzko, Pol., 26,000.....C4 7
Klosterneuburg, Aus., 21,989..................D8 6
Kluczbork, Pol., 18,000....C5 7
Klyuchevskaya, vol., Sov. Un..................D19 13
Knezha, Bul., 14,049......D7 10
Knightdale, N.C., 815.....B4 76
Knights Landing, Calif., 900.....................C3 50
Knightstown, Ind., 2,456..E6 59
Knightsville, Ind., 788.....E3 59
Knittlefeld, Aus., 14,494...E7 6
Knob Noster, Mo., 2,264..C4 69
Knockmealdown, mts., Ire.D2 4
Knollwood, Ohio, 5,353..*C2 78
Knoolwood Park, Mich., 350....................*F6 66
Knott, co., Ky., 14,698....C6 62
Knox, Ind., 3,519.........B4 59
Knox, Pa., 1,306........*E1 81
Knox, co., Ill., 61,280....B3 58
Knox, co., Ind., 41,546....G3 59
Knox, co., Ky., 23,689....D6 62
Knox, co., Maine, 29,013..D4 64
Knox, co., Mo., 5,692......A5 69
Knox, co., Nebr., 11,723...B8 71
Knox, co., Ohio, 41,795...B3 78
Knox, co., Tenn., 276,293 ....C10 83
Knox, co., Tex., 5,972.....C3 84
Knox City, Tex., 1,536....C3 84
Knoxville, Ill., 2,930......C3 58
Knoxville, Iowa 7,755.....C4 60
Knoxville, Tenn., 174,587 (*415,800).......D10, n14 83
Knysna, S. Afr., 13,304....G4 24
Kōbe, Jap., 1,338,705.....o14 18
Kobelyaki, Sov. Un., 10,000..............G10 12
København (Copenhagen), co., Den., 1,467,200....*J5 11
Koblenz, Ger., Fed. Rep. of, 119,781 (*172,000)...C3 6
Kobrin, Sov. Un., 25,000..E5 12
Kočani, Yugo., 17,237.....E6 10
Koch, mtn., Mont.........E5 70
Kochi, Jap., 240,481.......J6 18
Kochi, pref., Jap., 786,882.*J6 18
Kochiu, China, 180,000...G5 17
Kodaira, Jap., 137,373..*n18 18
Kodak, Ky., 90...........C6 62
Kodiak, Alsk., 3,798......D9 47
Kodiak, isl., Alsk.........D9 47
Koforidua, Ghana, 34,900.G4 22
Kofu, Jap., 182,669...I9, n17 18
Koga, Jap., 54,173.......m18 18
Kohala, Haw., 237........C6 56
Kohāt, Pak., 36,016 (*49,854).............B5 20
Kohler, Wis., 1,738...E5, k10 88
Kokand, Sov. Un., 133,000..............E10 13
Kokchetav, Sov. Un., 81,000.................D9 13
Kokkola, Fin., 21,347....F10 11
Kokomo, Ind., 44,042 (*81,200)..............D5 59
Kokonor, lake, China.....D4 17
Kokstad, S. Afr., 9,268....G5 24
Kolār Gold Fields, India 76,112 (*118,861).......F6 20
Kolarovo, Bul., 31,169....D8 10
Kolárovo, Czech., 10,829..E4 7
Kolhāpur, India, 259,050 (*267,513).............E5 20
Kolín, Czech., 26,519.....C3 7
Köln, see Cologne, Ger.
Koło, Pol., 13,100.........B5 7
Koloa, Haw., 1,368.......B2 56
Kolomna, Sov. Un., 136,000..........D12, n18 12
Kolomyya, Sov. Un., 41,000................G5 12
Kolonodale, Indon.........F6 19
Kolpino, Sov. Un., 62,000................s31 11
Kolwezi, Zaire, 48,000....C5 24
Kolyberovo, Sov. Un., 10,000.................n18 12
Kolyma, riv., Sov. Un....C18 16
Komádi, Hung., 7,362.....B5 10
Komandorski Village, Calif., 900............*D2 50
Komárno, Czech., 27,282..E5 7
Komarno, Sov. Un., 5,000.D7 7
Komárom, Hung., 11,271..B4 10
Komárom, co., Hung., 301,853................*B4 10
Komatsu, Jap., 95,684....H8 18
Komatsushima, Jap., 31,000 (40,507 ▲).......I7 18
Kommunarsk, Sov. Un., 123,000..........G12, q21 12
Komotiní, Grc., 28,896....B5 14
Kompong Cham, Camb., 28,000.................*C2 19
Kompong Chhnang, Camb., 12,900.........*C2 19
Kompong Kleang, Camb., 10,000.................*C2 19
Kompong Speu, Camb., 7,500..................*C2 19
Kompong Thom, Camb., 9,600...................C2 19
Komrat, Sov. Un., 21,400.H7 12
Komsomolsk [-na Amure], Sov. Un., 218,000......D16 13
Konawa, Okla., 1,719......C5 79
Kondoa, Tan., 2,816......A7 24
Kondopoga, Sov. Un., 5,000..................F16 11
Kong, reg., I.C...........G4 22
Kongju, Kor., 27,500 (33,210 ▲).......H3 18
Kongsberg, Nor., 18,100...H3 11
Konin, Pol., 40,600.......B5 7
Konosha, Sov. Un., 10,000.................A13 12
Konotop, Sov. Un., 68,000.................F9 12
Końskie, Pol., 13,100......C6 7
Konstantinovka, Sov. Un., 105,000...............q20 12
Konstanz, Ger., Fed. Rep. of, 65,203..................E4 6
Kontum, Viet., 8,760......C3 19
Konya, Tur., 200,464.....D9 14
Konyang, Kor., 2,300 (10,760 ▲)...............I3 18
Koochiching, co., Minn., 17,131..................B4 67
Koontz Lake, Ind., 900....B5 59
Kooskia, Idaho, 809.......C3 57
Kootenai, co., Idaho, 35,332.................B2 57
Kopeysk, Sov. Un., 156,000..............*D9 13
Köping, Swe., 22,155..H6, t33 11
Kopparberg, co., Swe., 280,000..............*G6 11
Koppel, Pa., 1,312........E1 81
Koprivnica, Yugo., 16,469..B3 10
Kopychintsy, Sov. Un., 10,000.................G5 12
Korçë, Alb., 45,900.......B3 14
Korçë, pref., Alb., 175,000................*B3 14
Korea, North, country, Asia, 15,275,000........F4 18
Korea, South, country, Asia, 34,170,000........H4 18
Korets, Sov. Un., 10,000...F6 12
Korhogo, I.C., 14,000.....G3 22
Kórinthos (Corinth), Grc., 20,773..................D4 14
Kóriyama, Jap., 165,000 (241,673▲)...........H10 18
Korkino, Sov. Un., 71,000.*D9 13
Korla, see Kuerhlo, China
Körmend, Hung., 7,581....B3 10
Korneuburg, Aus., 8,751...D8 6
Koropí, Grc., 9,367.......h11 14
Korosten, Sov. Un., 56,000.................F7 12
Korsakov, Sov., Un., 38,000...............E17 13
Kortrijk, Bel., 45,040 (*168,000).............B5 5
Kos, Grc., 7,828..........D6 14
Kościan, Pol., 18,700......B4 7
Kościerzyna, Pol., 14,900...A4 7
Kosciusko, Miss., 6,800....B4 68
Kosciusko, co., Ind., 48,127.................B6 59
Kosciusko, mtn., Austl. ...G8 25
Koshan, China, 25,000...B10 17
Košice, Czech., 142,233...D6 7
Kosong, Kor., 14,842.....G4 18
Kosove (Kosovo), pref., Alb., 53,000...........*A3 14
Kosovska Mitrovica, Yugo., 42,241..................D5 10
Kossuth, co., Iowa, 22,937.................A3 60
Kostroma, Sov. Un., 223,000..............C13 12
Kostrzyn, Pol., 11,200.....B3 7
Koszalin, Pol., 64,400.....A4 7
Koszeg, Hung., 10,164.....B3 10
Kota, India, 212,991......C6 20
Kota Baharu, Mala., 55,124 (*69,812).......D2 19
Kotabaru, Indon., 330.....F5 19
Kota Kinabalu, Mala., 40,939.................I14 19
Kotelnikovskiy, Sov. Un., 17,605...............H14 12
Köthen, Ger. Dem. Rep., 35,723...................C5 6
Kotka, Fin., 33,862......G12 11
Kotlas, Sov. Un., 56,000...C7 13
Kotor, Yugo., 4,833.......D4 10
Kotovsk, Sov. Un., 33,000.................H7 12
Kotung, China, 5,000.....B7 18
Kotzebue, Alsk., 1,696....*B7 47
Koudougou, Upper Volta, 8,000....................F4 22
Kountze, Tex., 2,173......D5 84
Kouts, Ind., 1,388.........B3 59
Kouvola, Fin., 27,148....G12 11
Kovel, Sov. Un., 33,000...F5 12
Kovrov, Sov. Un., 123,000..............C13 12
Kowa, Jap., 10,300.......o15 18
Kowloon, Hong Kong, 715,440................G7 17
Kowon, Kor., 5,000.......G3 18
Kozan, Tur., 26,097.....D10 14
Kozáni, Grc., 23,240......B3 14
Kozáni, prov., Grc., 135,619.................*B3 14
Kozienice, Pol., 6,109.....C6 7
Koźle, Pol., 13,100.......C5 7
Kozloduy, Bul., 7,422.....D6 10
Kożuchów, Pol., 7,419.....C3 7
Kragujevac, Yugo., 71,180..................D5 10
Kraków, Pol., 583,400.....C5 7
Kraljevo, Yugo., 27,817...D5 10
Kralupy [nad Vltavou], Czech., 14,777.........n17 7
Kramatorsk, Sov. Un., 150,000 (*375,000).......G11, q20 12
Kranj, Yugo., 27,209......B2 10
Kraslice, Czech., 6,294....C2 7
Kraśnik Lubelski, Pol., 14,600..................C7 7
Krasnoarmeysk, Sov. Un., 55,000 (*135,000)......F15 12
Krasnodar, Sov. Un., 464,000...............I12 12
Krasnograd, Sov. Un., 18,000...............G10 12

Krasnoselye, Sov. Un., 10,000................G9 12
Krasnoslobodsk, Sov. Un., 5,000................D14 12
Krasnovodsk, Sov. Un., 49,000................E8 13
Krasnoyarsk, Sov. Un., 648,000................D12 13
Krasnystaw, Pol., 12,400...C7 7
Krasnyy Liman, Sov. Un., 30,000................q20 12
Krasnyy Luch, Sov. Un., 103,000 (*210,000)...q21 12
Krasnyy Sulin, Sov. Un., 42,000................H13 12
Krasnyy Yar, Sov. Un., 10,000................F15 12
Kratie, Camb., 11,900....C3 19
Krebs, Okla., 1,515.....C6 79
Krefeld, Ger., Fed. Rep. of, 221,574........C3 6
Kremenchug, Sov. Un., 148,000................G9 12
Kremenets, Sov. Un., 20,000................F5 12
Kremennaya, Sov. Un., 25,000................p21 12
Krems, Aus., 23,409.....D7 6
Krichev, Sov. Un., 26,000................E8 12
Krishnagiri, India, 35,383..F6 20
Kristiansand, Nor., 54,900................H2 11
Kristianstad, Swe., 43,532..I6 11
Kristianstad, co., Swe., 264,700................*I5 11
Kristiansund, Nor., 18,600................F2 11
Krivoy Rog, Sov. Un., 573,000................H9 12
Križevci, Yugo., 6,498...B3 10
Krnov, Czech., 23,054....C4 7
Kroměříž, Czech., 22,132................D4 7
Kromy, Sov. Un., 10,000................E10 12
Kronoberg, co., Swe., 163,600................*I6 11
Kronshtadt, Sov. Un., 40,000................B7 12
Kroonstad, S. Afr., 50,898..F5 24
Kropotkin, Sov. Un., 68,000................I13 12
Krosno, Pol., 26,500.....D6 7
Krosno Odrzańskie, Pol., 6,611................B3 7
Krotoszyn, Pol., 22,000....C4 7

Krotz Springs, La., 1,435..D4 63
Krsko, Yugo., 629.......C2 10
Krugersdorp, S. Afr., 91,202................F5 24
Krumroy, Ohio, 1,600....*A4 78
Kruševac, Yugo., 29,469...D5 10
Krusevo, Yugo., 4,099....E6 10
Krymskaya, Sov. Un., 41,000................I11 12
Krynki, Pol............B7 7
Ksar el Kebir, Mor., 48,262................B3 22
Ksar es Souk, Mor., 16,775.B4 22
Kuala Lipis, Mala., 9,270..E2 19
Kuala Lumpur, Mala., 451,810 (*708,191)....E2 19
Kuala Terengganu, Mala., 53,320 (*58,920)......D2 19
Kuantan, Mala., 43,358...E2 19
Kubokawa, Jap.........J6 19
Kuching, Mala., 63,535...E4 19
Kudat, Mala., 3,660.....D5 19
Kudus, Indon., 87,767....G4 19
Kueilin, China, 170,000...F7 17
Kueiyang, China, 530,000..F6 17
Kuerhlo (Korla), China, 10,000................C2 17
Kufstein, Aus., 12,503....E6 6
Kuji, Jap., 23,000 (37,533) ▲..........F10 18
Kuju-San, mtn., Jap......J5 18
Kuki, Jap., 34,028......m18 18
Kula, Bul., 5,566.......D6 10
Kula, Tur., 9,180......*C7 14
Kula, Yugo., 17,260.....C4 10
Kula Kangri, peak, Bhutan, China................C9 20
Kulebaki, Sov. Un., 46,000................D14 12
Kulmbach, Ger., Fed. Rep. of, 25,613........C5 6
Kulpmont, Pa., 4,026.....E9 81
Kumagaya, Jap., 120,841.m18 18
Kumamoto, Jap., 440,020..J5 18
Kumamoto, pref., Jap., 1,700,229...........*J5 18
Kumanovo, Yugo., 46,406................D5 10
Kumasi, Ghana, 281,600 (340,200 ▲).........G4 22
Kumbakonam, India, 113,130 (*119,655)......F6 20
Kŭmch'ŏn, Kor., 47,000 (62,157▲)...........H4 18
Kumha, Kor., 1,400......G3 18
Kumihama, Jap.........n14 19
Kumla, Swe., 10,800..H6, t33 11

Kumo, Nig., 64,878.......D7 22
Kuna, Idaho, 593........F2 57
Kuneitra (Al Qunayţirah), Syr., 17,080.........F10 14
Kungchuling, see Huaite, China
Kunming (Yunnanfu), China, 1,100,000.....F5 17
Kunsan, Kor., 112,453....I3 18
Kunszentmárton, Hung., 8,783................B5 10
Kuolayarvi, Sov. Un., 10,000................D13 11
Kuopio, Fin., 65,082....F12 11
Kuopio, prov., Fin., 266,000................*F12 11
Kupang, Indon., 52,698...H6 19
Kupyansk, Sov. Un., 30,000................G11 12
Kurashiki, Jap., 339,799..I6 18
Kuraymah, Sud., 5,989....E4 23
Kurdzhali, Bul., 33,271...E7 10
Kure, Jap., 235,193.....I6 18
Kuressaare, Sov. Un., 10,000................B4 12
Kurgan, Sov. Un., 244,000................D9 13
Kurnool, India, 136,710...E6 20
Kurri Kurri-Weston, Austl., 11,624.......F8 26
Kursk, Sov. Un., 284,000................F11 12
Kurthwood, La., 70......C2 63
Kurtistown, Haw., 1,025...D6 56
Kurume, Jap., 194,178....J5 18
Kurunegala, Sri Lanka, 25,189...............G7 20
Kusatsu, Jap., 46,409....n14 18
Kushchevskaya, Sov. Un., 10,000................H12 12
Kushevat, Sov. Un., 1,000................C9 13
Kushimoto, Jap., 6,220...J7 18
Kushiro, Jap., 191,948...E12 18
Kushka, Sov. Un., 4,600...F9 13
Kustanay, Sov. Un., 124,000................D9 13
Küstī, Sud., 22,688......F4 23
Küstrin, see Kostrzyn, Pol.
Kütahya (Kutaiah), Tur., 62,222................C7 14
Kutaisi, Sov. Un., 161,000................A14 14
Kutná Hora, Czech., 17,720................D3 7
Kutno, Pol., 30,300......B5 7

Kutztown, Pa., 4,166....E10 81
Kuwait, Kuw., 99,609 (*295,273)..........D4 15
Kuwait, country, Asia, 1,035,000...........D4 15
Kuwana, Jap., 81,015........I8, n18 18
Kuybyshev, Sov. Un., 1,069,000 (*1,250,000)..D8 13
Kuybyshev, Sov. Un., 40,000...............*D10 13
Kuznetsk, Sov. Un., 84,000................E16 12
Kwangju, Kor., 502,753....I3 18
Kwangsi Chuang, auton. reg., China, 19,390,000..G6 17
Kwangtung, prov., China, 37,960,000...........G7 17
Kweichow, prov., China, 16,890,000...........F6 17
Kwidzyń, Pol., 23,100....B5 7
Kyabram, Austl., 5,086...H5 26
Kyaiklat, Bur., 15,781...E10 20
Kyaikto, Bur., 10,000...*B1 19
Kyakhta, Sov. Un., 15,000................D13 13
Kyaukse, Bur., 8,659...D10 20
Kybartai, Sov. Un., 7,274................A7 7
Kyje, Czech., 5,836....n18 7
Kyle, Sask., Can., 535...G1 39
Kyle, Tex., 1,629.......E4 84
Kylestrome, Scot......*A4 4
Kyllburg, Ger., Fed. Rep. of, 1,250..........*C3 6
Kymi, prov., Fin., 348,600...........*G12 11
Kynlyn, Del., 1,600....*A6 53
Kyomipo, see Songnim, Kor.
Kyongju, Kor., 55,000 (92,093▲)............I4 18
Kyongsong, Kor., 25,925..F4 18
Kyōto, Jap., 1,435,254........I7, n14 18
Kyoto, pref., Jap., 2,250,087............*I7 18
Kyritz, Ger. Dem. Rep., 8,679................B6 6
Kyshtym, Sov. Un., 36,000...............*D9 13
Kyūshū, isl., Jap.......J5 18
Kyustendil, Bul., 37,707..D6 10
Kyzyl, Sov. Un., 52,000................D12 13
Kzyl-Orda, Sov. Un., 122,000................E9 13

L

Labadieville, La., 650............E5, k10 63
La Barca, Mex., 18,055..........C4, m12 34
La Barge, Wyo., 204.....D2 89
Labe, Guinea, 12,500.....F2 22
Labelle, Que., Can., 1,492................C3 42
La Belle, Fla., 1,823....F5 54
La Belle, Mo., 848......A6 69
Labelle, co., Que., Can., 30,167................C2 42
Labette, co., Kans., 25,775................E8 61
Labin, Yugo., 6,152.....C2 10
La Boca, C.Z., 448....*B2 32
Laboulaye, Arg., 11,265...A4 28
Labrador, reg., Newf., Can.................g9 44
Laburnum Manor, Va., 2,500...............*C5 85
La Canada, Calif., 18,400...............m12 50
La Carlota, Phil., 19,283..*C6 19
La Carolina, Sp., 12,138...C4 8
Lac au Saumon, Que., Can., 1,548...........*k13 42
Lac-aux-Sables, Que., Can., 857.............C5 42
Lac-Beauport, Que., Can., 9,192................C9 42
Lac-Bouchette, Que., Can., 911.............A5 42
Lac-Brome, Que., Can., 4,063................D5 42
Laccadive, is., India......F5 20

Lac-Carre, Que., Can., 687.............C3 42
Lac-du-Bonnet, Man., Can., 569............D3 40
Lac du Flambeau, Wis., 700................B4 88
La Ceiba, Hond., 24,863...D7 34
La Ceja, Col., 9,424.....B2 32
Lac-Etchemin, Que., Can., 2,789................C7 42
Lacey, Wash., 9,696.....B3 86
Lacey Park, Pa........*F11 81
La Chaux-de-Fonds, Switz., 42,300...............E3 6
Lachine, Que., Can., 44,423............D4, q19 42
La Chorrera, Pan., 25,873................B2 32
Lachute, Que., Can., 11,813 (*15,294)......D3 42
La Ciotat, Fr., 18,827....F6 5
Lackawanna, N.Y., 28,657................C2 75
Lackawanna, co., Pa., 234,107.............D10 81
Lac la Biche, Alta, Can., 1,791................B5 38
Lac la Hache, B.C., Can., 775................D7 37
Laclede, co., Mo., 19,944..D5 69
Lac-Mégantic, Que., Can., 6,770................D7 42
Lacolle, Que., Can., 1,254................D4 42
Lacombe, Alta., Can., 3,436................C4 38

Lacombe, La., 1,100..D6, h12 63
Lacon, Ill., 2,147.......B4 58
Laconia, N.H., 14,888....D5 73
La Conner, Wash., 639...A3 86
Lacoochee, Fla., 1,380...D4 54
La Coruña, Sp., 189,467..A1 8
La Coruña, prov., Sp., 1,027,600...........*A1 8
La Courneuve, Fr., 43,318...............g10 5
Lac Qui Parle, co., Minn., 11,164................F2 67
La Crescent, Minn., 3,296..G7 67
La Crescenta, Calif., 14,900...............*F4 50
La Cresta Village, Calif...*E4 50
La Crosse, Ind., 696.....B4 59
La Crosse, Kans., 1,583...D4 61
La Crosse, Va., 674.....D4 85
La Crosse, Wis., 51,153 (*74,800)...........E2 88
La Crosse, co., Wis., 80,468................E2 88
La Cruz, Col., 4,014.....C2 32
La Cruz, Mex., 45,662....C3 34
Lac-St.-Jean-Est, co., Que., Can., 45,662......A6 42
Lac-St.-Jean-Ouest, co., Que., Can., 60,247......A5 42
La Cygne, Kans., 989....D9 61
Lacy-Lakeview, Tex., 2,558...............*D4 84
Ladd, Ill., 1,328.......B4 58
Ladera Heights, Calif., 6,535...............*F4 50

Ladner, B.C., Can., 5,000.............E6, f12 37
Ladoga, Ind., 1,099.....E4 59
Ladoga, lake, Sov. Un....A8 12
Ladonia, Tex., 757......C5 84
La Dorado, Col., 26,168...B3 32
Ladue, Mo., 10,491....*C7 69
Lady Laurier, mtn., B.C., Can...........A6 37
Ladysmith, B.C., Can., 3,664.............E6, g12 37
Ladysmith, S. Afr., 28,554..F5 24
Ladysmith, Wis., 3,674...C2 88
Lae, Pap. N. Gui., 16,500.k12 25
La Esperanza, Cuba, 3,500 (9,800 ▲).......C2 35
La Estrada, Sp., 2,540...A1 8
La Farge, Wis., 748.....E3 88
Lafayette, Ala., 3,530...C4 46
Lafayette, Calif., 20,484..*D2 50
Lafayette, Colo., 3,498...B5 51
La Fayette, Ga., 6,044...B1 55
Lafayette, Ind., 44,955 (*101,000).........D4 59
Lafayette, La., 68,908 (*116,400).........D3 63
Lafayette, N.J., 250....A3 74
Lafayette, Oreg., 786..B3, h11 80
Lafayette, Tenn., 2,583..C7 83
Lafayette, co., Ark., 10,018................D2 49
Lafayette, co., Fla., 2,892..C3 54
Lafayette, co., Miss., 24,181................A4 68
Lafayette, co., Mo., 26,624.C4 69

Lafayette, co., Wis., 17,456 ... F3 88
Lafayette, par., La., 111,745 ... D3 63
Lafayette Hill, Pa., 6,600 ... *F11 81
La Feria, Tex., 2,642 ... F4 84
La Ferté-Bernard, Fr., 5,979 ... C4 5
Lafferty, Ohio, 600 ... B4 78
Lafitte, La., 1,223 ... k11 63
Laflèche (Mackayville), Que., Can., 13,433 ... *D4 42
Laflèche, Sask., Can., 749 ... H2 39
La Flèche, Fr., 9,439 ... D3 5
La Follette, Tenn., 6,902 .. C9 83
La Fontaine, Ind., 793 ... C6 59
Lafourche, par., La., 68,941 ... E5 63
La France, S.C., 700 ... B2 82
Laghouat, Alg., 26,553 ... B5 22
La Gloria, Col., 2,915 ... B3 52
Lagny, Fr., 15,743 ... C5 5
Lagos, Nig., 665,246 (*950,000) ... G5 22
Lagos, Port., 7,143 ... D1 8
Lagos de Moreno, Mex., 33,782 ... C4, m13 34
La Grand' Combe, Fr., 13,240 (*20,000) ... E5 5
La Grande, Oreg., 9,645 ... B8 80
La Grange, Ga., 23,301 ... C1 55
La Grange, Ill., 17,814 ... B6, k9 58
Lagrange, Ind., 2,053 ... A7 59
La Grange, Ky., 1,713 ... B4 62
La Grange, Mo., 1,237 ... A6 69
La Grange, N.C., 2,679 ... B5 76
Lagrange, Ohio, 1,074 ... A3 78
La Grange, Tex., 3,092 ... E4 84
Lagrange, co., Ind., 20,890 ... A7 59
La Grange Highlands, Ill., 6,920 ... *B6 58
La Grange Park, Ill., 15,459 ... k9 58
Lagro, Ind., 552 ... C6 59
La Guadeloupe, Que., Can., 1,934 ... D7 42
La Guaira, Ven., 20,344 ... A4 32
La Guajira, intendencia, Col., 201,300 ... A3 32
La Guardia, Sp., 9,311 ... B1 8
Laguna, Braz., 16,916 ... D3 30
Laguna, prov., Phil., 472,064 ... *C6 19
Laguna Beach, Calif., 14,550 ... F5, n13 50
Lagunas, Peru, 1,548 ... C2 31
Laguna Shores, Tex., 1,500 ... *F4 84
La Habra, Calif., 41,350 .. n13 50
La Habra Heights, Calif., 4,500 ... *F4 50
Lahad Datu, Mala., 1,544 ... D5 19
Lahaina, Haw., 3,718 ... C5 56
La Harpe, Ill., 1,240 ... C3 58
Lahij, P.D.R. of Yem., 10,000 ... G3 15
Lahore, Pak., 1,575,000 (*1,675,000) ... B5 20
Lahr, Ger., Fed. Rep. of, 35,781 ... D3 6
Lahti, Fin., .90,780 ... G11 11
La Huaca, Peru, 2,012 ... B1 31
Laie, Haw., 3,009 ... B4, f10 56
Laigle, Fr., 5,520 ... C4 5
Laingsburg, Mich., 1,159 .. F6 66
Lairg, Scot., 538 ... A4 4
La Jara, Colo., 768 ... D5 51
Lajes, Braz., 82,325 ... D2 30
Lajosmizse, Hung., 4,735 ... B4 10
La Joya, Mex., 20,586 ... h9 34
La Junta, Colo., 7,938 ... D7 51
Lake, co., Calif., 19,548 ... C2 50
Lake, co., Colo., 8,282 ... B4 51
Lake, co., Fla., 69,305 ... D5 54
Lake, co., Ill., 382,638 ... A6 58
Lake, co., Ind., 546,253 ... B3 59
Lake, co., Mich., 5,661 ... E5 66
Lake, co., Minn., 13,351 ... C7 67
Lake, co., Mont., 14,445 ... C2 70
Lake, co., Ohio, 197,200 ... A4 78
Lake, co., Oreg., 6,343 ... E6 80
Lake, co., S. Dak., 11,456 .. F8 77
Lake, co., Tenn., 7,896 ... A2 83
Lake, mtn., Wyo ... E6 89
Lake Alfred, Fla., 2,847 ... D5 54
Lake Andes, S. Dak., 948 .. G7 77
Lake Arrowhead, Calif., 400 ... E5 50
Lake Arthur, La., 3,551 ... D3 63
Lake Barcroft, Va., 3,000 ... *B5 85
Lake Benton, Minn., 759 ... F2 67
Lake Bluff, Ill., 5,008 .. A6, h9 58
Lake Butler, Fla., 1,598 ... B4 54
Lake Charles, La., 77,998 (*124,100) ... D2 63
Lake City, Fla., 10,575 ... B4 54
Lake City, Iowa, 1,910 ... B3 60
Lake City, Mich., 704 ... D5 66
Lake City, Minn., 3,594 ... F6 67
Lake City, Pa., 2,117 ... B1 81
Lake City, S.C., 6,247 ... D8 82
Lake City, Tenn., 1,923 ... C9 83
Lake Cowichan, B.C., Can., 2,364 ... g11 37
Lake Crystal, Minn., 1,807 ... F4 67
Lake Delton, Wis., 1,059 ... E4 88
Lake Erie Beach, N.Y., 3,467 ... *C1 75
Lake Fenton, Mich., 2,101 ... *F7 66
Lakefield, Ont., Can., 2,245 ... C6 41
Lakefield, Minn., 1,820 ... G3 67
Lake Forest, Ill., 15,642 ... A6, h9 58
Lake Forest, S.C., 1,200 .. *B3 82
Lake Forest Park, Wash., 2,530 ... *B3 86
Lake Geneva, Wis., 4,890 .. F5 88
Lake George, N.Y., 1,046 ... B7 75
Lake Hamilton, Fla., 1,165 ... *D5 54
Lake Harbor, Fla., 600 ... *F6 54
Lake Helen, Fla., 1,303 ... D5 54
Lake Hiawatha, N.J., 11,389 ... B4 74
Lake Hills, Wash ... *B3 86
Lake Hopatcong, N.J., 1,941 ... *B3 74
Lakehurst, N.J., 2,641 ... C4 74
Lake in the Hills, Ill., 3,240 ... *A5 58
Lake Jackson, Tex., 13,376 ... E5, r14 84
Lake James, Ind ... A7 59
Lakeland, Fla., 42,803 ... D5 54
Lakeland, Ga., 2,569 ... E3 55
Lakeland Village, Calif., 1,724 ... *F5 50
Lake Linden, Mich., 1,214 ... A2 66
Lake Lotawana, Mo., 1,786 ... *C3 69
Lake Luzerne, N.Y., 900 ... B7 75
Lake Mary, Fla., 1,300 ... D5 54
Lake Mills, Iowa, 2,124 ... A4 60
Lake Mills, Wis., 3,556 ... E5 88
Lake Mohawk, N.J ... A3 74
Lakemont, Pa., 1,800 ... F5 81
Lakemore, Ohio, 2,708 ... A4 78
Lake Odessa, Mich., 1,924 ... F5 66
Lake of the Woods, lake, Can., U.S ... A4 67
Lake of the Woods, co., Minn., 3,987 ... B3 67
Lake Orion, Mich., 2,921 .. F7 66
Lake Orion Heights, Mich., 2,552 ... *F7 66
Lake Oswego, Oreg., 14,615 ... B4, h12 80
Lake Ozark, Mo., 507 ... C5 69
Lake Park, Fla., 6,993 ... F6 54
Lake Park, Iowa, 918 ... A2 60
Lake Park, Minn., 658 ... D2 67
Lake Placid, Fla., 656 ... E5 54
Lake Placid, N.Y., 2,731 ... A7, f10 75
Lakeport, Calif., 3,005 ... C2 50
Lake Preston, S. Dak., 812. F8 77
Lake Providence, La., 6,183 ... B4 63
Lake Ronkonkoma, N.Y., 8,250 ... F4 52
Lakeside, Calif., 12,800 ... F5, o16 50
Lakeside, N.S., Can., 1,687 ... E6 43
Lakeside, La., 600 ... *C3 63
Lakeside, Ohio, 800 ... A3 78
Lakeside, Oreg., 900 ... D2 80
Lakeside, Va., 11,137 ... *C5 85
Lakeside Park, Ky., 2,511 ... h13 62
Lake Station, Ind., 9,858 .. A3 59
Lake Stevens, Wash., 1,283 ... A3 86
Lake Success, N.Y., 3,254 .. h13 75
Lake Telemark, N.J., 1,086 ... *B3 74
Lake Toxaway, N.C., 700 .. f10 76
Lake View, Iowa, 1,249 ... B2 60
Lakeview, Mich., 16,222 .. *F5 66
Lakeview, Mich., 1,118 ... E5 66
Lake View, N.Y., 1,500 ... *C2 75
Lakeview, Ohio, 1,026 ... B2 78
Lakeview, Oreg., 2,705 ... E6 80
Lake View, S.C., 949 ... C9 82
Lakeview, Tex., 3,567 ... *E6 84
Lake Villa, Ill., 1,090 ... h8 58
Lake Village, Ark., 3,310 .. D4 49
Lakeville, Conn., 900 ... B3 52
Lakeville, Ind., 712 ... A5 59
Lakeville, Minn., 7,556 ... F5 67
Lakeville, N.Y., 800 ... C3 75
Lakeville, Ohio, 225 ... A5 78
Lake Waccamaw, N.C., 924 ... C4 76
Lake Wales, Fla., 8,240 ... E5 54
Lakewood, Calif., 83,025 .. n12 50
Lakewood, N.B., Can., 836 ... *C2 43
Lakewood, Colo., 92,743 ... B5 51
Lakewood, N.J., 25,223 ... C4 74
Lakewood, N.Y., 3,864 ... C1 75
Lakewood, Ohio, 70,173 ... A4, h9 78
Lakewood, Tex ... *E5 84
Lakewood Center, Wash., 51,000 ... *B3 86
Lake Worth, Fla., 23,714 .. F6 54
Lake Zurich, Ill., 4,082 ... h8 58
Lakhīmpur, India, 43,752 .. C7 20
Lakin, Kans., 1,570 ... E2 61
Lakonia (Laconia), prov., Grc., 95,800 ... *D4 14
Lakota, N. Dak., 964 ... B7 77
Lakshadweep, ter., India, 31,810 ... *F5 20
La Laguna, Sp., 19,000 ... m13 8
La Libertad, dept., Peru, 609,105 ... C2 31
Lalín, Sp., 1,353 ... A1 8
La Línea, Sp., 52,749 ... D3 8
Lalitpur, India, 34,462 ... D6 20
La Loche, Sask., Can., 1,136 ... m7 39
La Maddalena, It., 11,169. D2 9
La Malbaie, Que., Can., 4,036 (*5,267) ... B7 42
Lamar, Colo., 7,797 ... C8 51
Lamar, Mo., 3,760 ... D3 69
Lamar, S.C., 1,250 ... C7 82
Lamar, co., Ala., 14,335 ... B1 46
Lamar, co., Ga., 10,688 ... C2 55
Lamar, co., Tex., 36,062 ... C5 84
Lamar, co., Miss., 15,209 .. D4 68
La Marque, Tex., 16,131 .. r15 84
Lamartine, Que., Can., 40 . B7 42
Lamas, Peru., 7,300 ... C2 31
Lamb, co., Tex., 17,770 ... B1 84
Lamballe, Fr., 5,075 ... C2 5
Lambayeque, Peru, 10,629 ... C2 31
Lambayeque, dept., Peru, 353,657 ... C2 31
Lambert, Miss., 1,511 ... A3 68
Lamberton, Minn., 962 ... F3 67
Lambertville, Mich., 5,721 ... *G7 66
Lambertville, N.J., 4,359 .. C3 74
Lambeth, Ont., Can., 3,023 ... E3 41
Lambton, Que., Can., 699 ... D6 42
Lambton, co., Ont., Can., 108,236 ... E2 41
Lamego, Port ... B2 8
Lamèque, N.B., Can., 1,082 ... B5 43
La Mesa, Calif., 39,178 ... o15 50
Lamesa, Tex., 11,559 ... C2 84
Lamía, Grc., 37,872 ... C4 14
La Mirada, Calif., 30,808 . *F4 50
La Moille, Ill., 669 ... B4 58
Lamoille, co., Vt., 13,309 .. B2 73
Lamoni, Iowa, 2,540 ... D4 60
Lamont, Calif., 7,007 ... E4 50
Lamont, Alta., Can., 705 .. C4 38
Lamont, Okla., 478 ... A4 79
La Monte, Mo., 814 ... C4 69
La Moure, N. Dak., 951 ... D7 77
La Moure, co., N. Dak., 7,117 ... D7 77
Lampa, Peru, 2,619 ... E3 31
Lampang, Thai., 40,500 .. *B1 19
Lampasas, Tex., 5,922 ... D3 84
Lampasas, co., Tex., 9,323 ... D3 84
Lamphun, Thai., 10,600 .. *B1 19
Lampman, Sask., Can., 637 ... H4 39
Lanai City, Haw., 2,122 ... C5 56
Lanao del Norte, prov., Phil., 270,603 ... *D6 19
Lanark, Ont., Can., 918 ... C8 41
Lanark, Ill., 1,495 ... A4 58
Lanark, Scot., 8,572 ... C5 4
Lanark, co., Ont., Can., 41,212 ... C8 41
Lanark, co., Scot., 1,519,241 ... *C5 4
Lanark Village, Fla., 600 .. C2 54
Lancashire, co., Eng., 5,109,800 ... *C5 4
Lancaster, Calif., 34,500 ... E4 50
Lancaster, N.B., Can., 15,836 ... D3 43
Lancaster, Ont., Can., 584 ... B10 41
Lancaster, Eng., 49,300 (*99,000) ... C5 4
Lancaster, Ky., 3,230 ... C5 62
Lancaster, Mass., 750 (6,095▲) ... B4 65
Lancaster, Mo., 821 ... A5 69
Lancaster, N.H., 2,120 (3,166▲) ... C4 73
Lancaster, N.Y., 13,365 ... C2 75
Lancaster, Ohio, 32,911 ... G3 78
Lancaster, Pa., 57,690 (*171,600) ... F9 81
Lancaster, S.C., 9,186 ... B6 82
Lancaster, Tex., 10,522 ... n10 84
Lancaster, Wis., 3,756 ... F3 88
Lancaster, co., Nebr., 167,972 ... D9 71
Lancaster, co., Pa., 320,079 ... G9 81
Lancaster, co., S.C., 43,328 ... B6 82
Lancaster, co., Va., 9,126 .. C6 85
Lancaster Mills, S.C ... *B6 82
Lancer, Ky., 400 ... C7 62
Lanchou, China, 875,000 .. D5 17
Lanciano, It., 22,300 ... C5 9
Łańcut, Pol., 12,000 ... C7 7
Landau [an der Isar], Ger., Fed. Rep. of, 6,000 ... D6 6
Landau [in der Pfalz], Ger., Fed. Rep. of, 38,438 ... D4 6
Landeck, Aus., 7,248 ... E5 6
Lander, Wyo., 7,125 ... D4 89
Lander, co., Nev., 2,666 ... A3 72
Landerneau, Fr., 12,781 ... C1 5
Landes, dept., Fr., 277,381 ... *F3 5
Landing, N.J., 3,064 ... *B3 74
Landis, N.C., 2,297 ... B2 76
Landisville, Pa., 1,690 ... *F11 81
Landivisiau, Fr., 4,121 ... C1 5
Lando, S.C., 850 ... B5 82
Landover Hills, Md., 2,409 ... *C4 53
Landrum, S.C., 1,859 ... A3 82
Landsberg, Ger., Fed. Rep. of, 15,501 ... D5 6
Landshut, Ger., Fed. Rep. of, 55,650 ... D6 6
Landskrona, Swe., 34,690 .. J5 11
Lane, co., Kans., 2,707 ... D3 61
Lane, co., Oreg., 215,401 .. D4 80
Lanesboro, Mass., 900 (2,972▲) ... A1 65
Lanesboro, Minn., 850 ... G7 67
Lanett, Ala., 6,908 ... C4 46
Langadhas, Grc., 6,707 ... *B4 14
Langdale, Ala., 2,235 ... C4 46
Langdon, N. Dak., 2,182 ... B7 77
L'Ange-Gardien, Que., Can., 1,543 ... n17 42
Langeloth, Pa., 950 ... F1 81
Langenburg, Sask., Can., 757 ... G5 39
Langenthal, Switz., 13,100 (*21,400) ... E3 6
Langesund, Nor., 2,200 ... H3, p27 11
Langford, B.C., Can., 1,024 ... h12 37
Langhorne, Pa., 1,673 ... F12 81
Langlade, co., Wis., 19,220 ... C4 88
Langley, B.C., Can., 4,684 ... f13 37
Langley, Ky., 600 ... C7 62
Langley, S.C., 1,400 ... D4 82
Langley Park, Md., 11,564 ... *C3 53
Langnau in Emmental, Switz., 9,201 ... E3 6
Langon, Fr., 4,197 ... E3 5
Langreo, Sp., 11,000 (59,465▲) ... A3 8
Langres, Fr., 8,954 ... D6 5
Langsa, Indon., 55,016 ... E1, m11 19
Lang Son, Viet., 25,000 ... *G13 16
Langstaff, Ont., Can., 1,153 ... k15 41
Languedoc, former prov., Fr ... F5 5
Lanham, Md., 6,700 ... C4 53
Lanhsi, China, 5,000 ... C3 18
Lanier, co., Ga., 5,031 ... E3 55
Lannion, Fr., 6,497 ... C2 5
Lannon, Wis., 1,056 ... m11 88
L'Annonciation, Que., Can., 2,162 ... C3 42
Lanoraie, Que., Can., 1,151 ... D4 42
Lansdale, Pa., 18,451 ... F11 81
Lansdowne, Md., 10,100 ... B4 53

Lansdowne, Pa., 14,090 G11, p20 81
Lansdowne House, Ont., Can., 612 n18 41
L'Anse, Mich., 2,538 B2 66
Lansford, Pa., 5,168 E10 81
Lansing, Ill., 25,805 B6, k9 58
Lansing, Iowa, 1,227 A6 60
Lansing, Kans., 3,797 B8 61
Lansing, Mich., 131,403 (*303,200) F6 66
Lansing, Ohio, 1,200 *C4 78
Lantana, Fla., 7,126 F6 54
Lanús, Arg., 449,824 *A5 28
Laoag, Phil., 30,938 B6 19
Laoighis, co., Ire., 44,595 *D3 4
Lao Kay, Viet., 25,000 *G13 16
Laon, Fr., 26,316 C5 5
Laona, Wis., 700 C5 88
La Oroya, Peru, 24,724 D2 31
Laos, country, Asia, 3,215,000 B2 19
Lapa, Braz., 9,502 D3 30
La Palma, Sp., 8,669 D2 8
La Pampa, prov., Arg., 158,746 B3 28
La Paz, Arg., 11,028 A5 28
La Paz, Bol., 525,000 C2 29
La Paz, Col., 4,278 A3 32
La Paz, Mex., 46,011 C2 34
La Paz, Mex., 3,735 C4 34
La Paz, dept., Bol., 1,176,300 C2 29
Lapeer, Mich., 6,314 E7 66
Lapeer, co., Mich., 52,361 E7 56
Lapel, Ind., 1,796 D6 59
La Piedad [Cavadas], Mex., 34,963 m12 34
Laplace, La., 5,953 h11 63
Lapland, reg., Eur. C12 11
La Plata, Arg., 408,300 (*510,000) A5, g8 28
La Plata, Col., 5,863 C2 32
La Plata, Md., 1,561 C4 53
La Plata, Mo., 1,377 A5 69
La Plata, co., Colo., 19,199 D3 51
La Pocatière, Que., Can., 4,256 B7 42
La Pola, Sp., 5,430 A3 8
La Porte, Ind., 22,140 A4 59
La Porte, Tex., 7,149 r14 84
La Porte, co., Ind., 105,342 A4 59
La Porte City, Iowa, 2,256 B5 60
Lappeenranta, Fin., 51,203 G13 11
Lappi, prov., Fin., 221,200 *D11 11
La Prairie, Que., Can., 8,309 D4, q20 42
Laprairie, co., Que., Can., 44,980 D4, q20 42
La Presa, Calif *F5 50
La Providence, Que., Can., 4,709 *D5 42
La Pryor, Tex., 900 E3 84
La Puebla, Sp., 9,931 C7 8
La Puebla de Montalbán, Sp., 7,700 C3 8
La Puente, Calif., 31,092 *F4 50
La Purisima, Mex., 377 B2 34
La Quiaca, Arg., 6,290 D2 29
L'Aquila, It., 46,500 C4 9
Lara, state, Ven., 489,140 A3 32
Larache, Mor., 45,710 A3 22
Laramie, Wyo., 23,143 E7 89
Laramie, co., Wyo., 56,360 E8 89
Laramie, peak, Wyo D7 89
Larchmont, N.Y., 7,203 h13 75
Laredo, Sp., 6,206 A4 8
Laredo, Tex., 69,024 (*220,000) F3 84
Largo, Fla., 22,031 E4, p10 54
Lariat, Colo D4 51
La Ricamarie, Fr., 11,902 E6 5
Larimer, Pa., 550 *F2 81
Larimer, co., Colo., 89,900 A5 51
Larimore, N. Dak., 1,469 C8 77
Larino, It., 8,678 D5 9
La Rioja, Arg., 43,000 E2 29
La Rioja, prov., Arg., 136,237 E2 29
La Rioja, Cuba, 1,818 D5 35
Lárisa (Larissa), Grc., 72,336 C4 14
Lárisa (Larissa), prov., Grc., 232,157 *C4 14
Lārkāna, Pak., 48,008 C4 20
Larkspur, Calif., 10,487 h7 50
Larksville, Pa., 3,937 n17 81
Larne, N. Ire., 18,242 C4 4
Larned, Kans., 4,567 D4 61
La Rochelle, Fr., 73,347 (*88,000) D3 5
La Roche-sur-Yon, Fr., 36,067 D3 5
La Roda, Sp., 12,190 C4 8
La Romana, Dom. Rep., 36,700 E9 35
La Ronge, Sask., Can., 707 B3 39
Larose, La., 4,267 E5 63
La Rue, Ohio, 867 B2 78
Larue, co., Ky., 10,672 C4 62
Larvik, Nor., 10,500 (*18,000) H4, p28 11
Larwill, Ind., 324 B6 59
Lasa, see Lhasa, China
La Salle, Que., Can., 72,912 q19 42
La Salle, Colo., 1,227 A6 51
La Salle, Ill., 10,736 B4 58
La Salle, co., Ill., 111,409 B5 58
La Salle, co., Tex., 5,014 E3 84
La Salle, par., La., 13,295 C3 63
Las Animas, Colo., 3,148 C7 51
Las Animas, co., Colo., 15,744 D6 51
La Sarre, Que., Can., 5,185 o20 41
Lascahobas, Hai., 3,132 E8 35
L'Ascension, Que., Can., 1,197 A6 42
La Scie, Newf., Can., 939 D4 44
Las conchas, Arg., 24,809 g7 28
Las Cruces, N. Mex., 37,857 (*48,000) C5 48
La Selle, peak, Hai E8 37
La Serena, Chile, 40,854 E1 29
La Seyne [-sur-Mer], Fr., 43,783 F6 5
Las Flores, Arg., 14,838 B5 28
La Sierra, Calif n14 50
Lasithi (Lasithion), prov., Grc., 66,105 *E5 14
Las Matas de Farfan, Dom. Rep., 3,585 *E8 35
La Solana, Sp., 14,948 C4 8
Las Palmas [de Gran Canaria], Sp., 254,800 m14 8
Las Palmas, prov., Sp., 554,200 m14 8
La Spezia, It., 129,200 (*196,000) B2 9
Las Piedras, Ur., 40,658 E1 30
Lassen, co., Calif., 16,796 B3 50
Lassen, peak, Calif B3 50
L'Assomption, Que., Can., 4,915 D4 42
L'Assomption, co., Que., Can., 49,839 D4 42
Las Varillas, Arg., 7,405 A4 28
Las Vegas, Nev., 125,787 (*261,900) C4 72
Las Vegas, N. Mex., 6,307 B6, D7 48
Las Villas, prov., Cuba, 1,362,200 C3 35
Latacunga, Ec., 16,400 B2 31
Latah, co., Idaho, 24,891 C2 57
Latakia (Al Lādhiqīyah), Syr., 125,657 E10 14
Laterrière, Que., Can., 651 A6 42
La Teste-de-Buch, Fr., 11,842 E3 5
Latham, N.Y., 9,661 *C7 75
Lathrop, Calif., 2,137 *D3 50
Lathrop, Mo., 1,268 B3 69
Lathrup Village, Mich., 4,676 *F7 66
Latimer, co., Okla., 8,601 C6 79
Latina, It., 47,800 D4, k9 9
Latium, reg., It C4 9
Laton, Calif., 1,071 D4 50
Latour, peak, Idaho B2 57
La Trinité, Mart., 3,631 I14 35
Latrobe, Pa., 11,749 F3 81
Latta, S.C., 1,764 C9 82
Lattimer Mines, Pa., 650 E10 81
Lattingtown, N.Y., 1,773 *E7 75
La Tuque, Que., Can., 13,009 B5 42
Latvia (S.S.R.), rep., Sov. Un., 2,455,000 C4 12
Lauderdale, Minn., 2,530 n12 67
Lauderdale, co., Ala., 68,111 A2 46
Lauderdale, co., Miss., 67,087 C5 68
Lauderdale, co., Tenn., 20,271 B2 83
Lauderdale-by-the-Sea, Fla., 2,879 *F6 54
Launceston, Austl., 35,001 (*62,181) o15 25
Launceston, Eng., 4,780 E4 4
La Unión, Chile, 11,600 C5 28
La Unión, Col., 3,875 C2 32
La Unión, Mex., 1,385 D4, o13 34
La Unión, Peru, 1,672 C2 31
La Unión, Sal., 17,207 E7 34
La Unión, Sp., 11,687 D5 8
La Union, prov., Phil., 293,300 *B6 19
Laupheim, Ger., Fed. Rep. of, 13,592 D4 6
Laurel, Del., 2,408 C6 53
Laurel, Fla., 1,200 E4 54
Laurel, Ind., 753 F7 59
Laurel, Md., 10,525 B4 53
Laurel, Miss., 24,145 D4 68
Laurel, Mont., 4,454 E8 70
Laurel, Nebr., 1,009 B8 71
Laurel, Va., 900 C5 85
Laurel, co., Ky., 27,386 C5 62
Laurel Bay, S.C., 4,490 G6 82
Laureldale, Pa., 4,519 F10 81
Laurel Gardens, Pa., 1,800 *E1 81
Laurel Heights, Wash *B3 86
Laurel Hill, N.C., 1,215 C3 76
Laurel Run, Pa., 327 n17 81
Laurel Springs, N.J., 2,566 *D3 74
Laurence Harbor, N.J., 3,500 C4 74
Laurens, Iowa, 1,792 B3 60
Laurens, S.C., 10,298 B3 82
Laurens, co., Ga., 32,738 D3 55
Laurens, co., S.C., 49,713 C3 82
Laurentides, Que., Can., 1,746 D4 42
Laurier, Que., Can., 653 C6 42
Laurierville, Que., Can., 872 C6 42
Laurinburg, N.C., 8,859 C3 76
Laurium, Mich., 2,868 A2 66
Lausanne, Switz., 134,900 (*225,800) E3 6
Lautaro, Chile, 10,400 B2 28
Lauzon, Que., Can., 12,809 C6, n17 42
Lavaca, co., Tex., 17,903 E4 84
Lava Hot Springs, Idaho, 516 G6 57
Laval, Fr., 45,674 C3 5
Laval, Que., Can., 228,010 D4 42
Laval-des-Rapides, Que., Can., 19,227 *D4 42
La Vale, Md., 3,971 k13 53
Lavalleja, dept., Ur., 65,525 *E1 30
Lavallette, N.J., 1,509 D4 74
Laval-Ouest, Que., Can., 5,440 *p19 42
Lavaltrie, Que., Can., 1,261 D4 42
Lavaur, Fr., 4,137 F4 5
La Vega, Dom. Rep., 31,100 E8 35
Lavello, It., 13,745 D5 9
La Verne, Calif., 12,965 m13 50
Laverne, Okla., 1,373 A2 79
Laviana, Sp., 12,455 A3 8
La Victoria, Ven., 41,889 A4 32
La Villa, Tex., 1,255 *F4 84
La Vista, Ga., 5,200 C2 55
La Vista, Nebr., 4,807 g13 71
La Viuda, mtn., Peru C2 31
Lavonia, Ga., 2,044 B3 55
Lavras da Mangabeira, Braz., 4,111 *D7 27
Lawn, Newf., Can., 716 E4 44
Lawndale, Calif., 24,825 *F4 50
Lawndale, N.C., 544 B1 76
Lawnside, N.J., 2,757 *D2 74
Lawnton, Pa., 1,500 *F8 81
Lawrence, Ind., 16,917 E5, k10 59
Lawrence, Kans., 45,698 (*46,500) D9, m15 61
Lawrence, Mass., 66,915 A5 65
Lawrence, Mich., 790 F4 66
Lawrence, N.Y., 6,566 G2 52
Lawrence, Pa., 970 F1 81
Lawrence, co., Ala., 27,281 A2 46
Lawrence, co., Ark., 16,320 A4 49
Lawrence, co., Ill., 17,522 E6 58
Lawrence, co., Ind., 38,038 G4 59
Lawrence, co., Ky., 10,726 B7 62
Lawrence, co., Miss., 11,137 D3 68
Lawrence, co., Mo., 24,585 D4 69
Lawrence, co., Ohio, 56,868 D3 78
Lawrence, co., Pa., 107,374 E1 81
Lawrence, co., S. Dak., 17,453 F2 77
Lawrence, co., Tenn., 29,097 B4 83
Lawrenceburg, Ind., 4,636 F8 59
Lawrenceburg, Ky., 3,579 B5 62
Lawrenceburg, Tenn., 8,899 B4 83
Lawrence Park, Pa., 4,517 B1 81
Lawrenceville, Ga., 5,115 C3, h9 55
Lawrenceville, Ill., 5,863 E6 58
Lawrenceville, N.J., 1,800 C3 74
Lawrenceville, Va., 1,636 D5 85
Lawson, Mo., 1,034 B3 69
Lawtey, Fla., 636 B4 54
Lawton, Mich., 1,358 F5 66
Lawton, Okla., 74,470 (*96,500) C3 79
Layland, W. Va., 400 n14 87
Layton, Utah, 13,603 C2 72
Laytonville, Calif., 900 C2 50
Lazio, reg., It., 4,565,400 *D4 9
Lea, co., N. Mex., 49,554 C7 48
Leachville, Ark., 1,582 B5 49
Lead, S. Dak., 5,420 F2 77
Lead, mtn., Maine D4 64
Leader, Sask., Can., 1,211 G1 39
Leadville, Colo., 4,314 B4 51
Leadwood, Mo., 1,397 D7 69
League City, Tex., 10,818 *E5 84
Leake, co., Miss., 17,085 C4 68
Leakesville, Miss., 1,090 D5 68
Leakey, Tex., 393 E3 84
Leaksville, N.C A3 76
Lealman, Fla., 16,000 p10 54
Leamington, Ont., Can., 10,435 E2 41
Leamington, Eng., 45,010 D6 4
Leaside, Ont., Can., 21,250 m15 41
Leatherhead, Eng., 41,050 m12 4
Leatherwood, Ky., 250 C6 62
Leavenworth, Kans., 25,147 (*42,400) C9, k16 61
Leavenworth, Wash., 1,322 B5 86
Leavenworth, co., Kans., 53,340 C8 61
Leavittsburg, Ohio, 3,000 A5 78
Leawood, Kans., 10,349 D9 61
Lebanon, Ill., 3,564 E4 58
Lebanon, Ind., 9,766 D5 59
Lebanon, Ky., 5,528 C4 62
Lebanon, Mo., 8,616 D5 69
Lebanon, N.H., 9,725 D3 73
Lebanon, N.J., 885 B3 74
Lebanon, Ohio, 7,934 G1 78
Lebanon, Oreg., 6,636 C4, k12 80
Lebanon, Pa., 28,572 F9 81
Lebanon, Tenn., 12,492 A5 83
Lebanon, Va., 2,272 f9 85
Lebanon, co., Pa., 99,665 F9 81
Lebanon, country, Asia, 3,115,000 F10 14
Lebanon Junction, Ky., 1,571 C4 62
Lebedyan, Sov. Un., 10,000 E12 12
Le Blanc, Fr., 5,279 D4 5
Le Blanc-Mesnil, Fr., 48,487 g10 5
Lębork, Pol., 25,000 A4 7
Le Bourget, Fr., 9,648 g10 5
Le Bouscat, Fr., 22,550 E3 5
Lebrija, Sp., 12,297 D2 8
Le Cateau, Fr., 9,114 B5 5
Lecce, It., 81,000 D7 9
Lecco, It., 52,000 B2 9
Le Center, Minn., 1,890 F5 67
Le Chambon-Feugerolles, Fr., 21,937 E6 5
Le Chesnay, Fr., 13,249 g9 5
Le Claire, Iowa, 2,520 C7, g11 60
Lecompte, La., 1,518 C3 63
Le Coteau, Fr., 6,571 D6 5
Le Creusot, Fr., 34,102 D6 5
Łęczyca, Pol., 12,600 B5 7
Ledgewood, N.J., 1,100 B3 74
Ledo, India C10 20
Leduc, Alta., Can., 4,000 C4 38
Lee, Mass., 3,389 (6,426 ▲) B1 65
Lee, co., Ala., 61,268 C4 46
Lee, co., Ark., 18,884 C5 49
Lee, co., Fla., 105,216 F5 54

152 *Lee-Lim*

Lee, co., Ga., 7,044 E2 55
Lee, co., Ill., 37,947 B4 58
Lee, co., Iowa, 42,996 D6 60
Lee, co., Ky., 6,587 C6 62
Lee, co., Miss., 46,148 A5 68
Lee, co., N.C., 30,467 B3 76
Lee, co., S.C., 18,323 C7 82
Lee, co., Tex., 8,048 D4 84
Lee, co., Va., 20,321 f8 85
Leechburg, Pa., 2,999 E2 81
Leedon, Estates, Pa., 1,600 *G11 81
Leeds, Ala., 6,991 B3, f7 46
Leeds, Eng., 501,080 (*1,550,000) D6 4
Leeds, co., Ont., Can., 49,129 C8 41
Leelanau, co., Mich., 10,872 D5 66
Lee Park, Pa., 3,900 n17 81
Leer, Ger., Fed. Rep. of, 33,647 B3 6
Leesburg, Fla., 11,869 D5 54
Leesburg, N.J., 700 E3 74
Leesburg, Ohio, 984 C2 78
Leesburg, Va., 4,821 A5 85
Lee's Summit, Mo., 16,230 C3, k11 69
Leesville, La., 8,928 C2 63
Leesville, S.C., 1,907 D4 82
Leetes Island, Conn., 400 D6 52
Leeton, Austl., 6,638 G6 26
Leetonia, Ohio, 2,342 B5 78
Leetsdale, Pa., 1,862 h13 81
Leeuwarden, Neth., 86,339 A6 5
Leeward, is., see Antigua, Montserrat, St. Kitts-Nevis-Anguilla, and Virgin Islands, (Br.), Br. dep., N.A.
Leflore, co., Miss., 42,111 B3 68
Le Flore, co., Okla., 32,137 C7 79
Lefors, Tex., 816 B2 84
Le François, Mart., 2,849 I14 37
Leganés, Sp., 56,279 p17 8
Legaspi, Phil., 35,476 C6 19
Legion, Tex *E3 84
Legnano, It., 46,400 B2 9
Legnica, Pol., 75,800 C4 7
Lago, mtn., Wash A5 86
Le Grand, Calif., 900 D3 50
Le Havre, Fr., 199,509 (*250,000) C3 5
Lehi, Utah, 4,659 A6, D2 72
Lehigh, Iowa, 739 B3 60
Lehigh, co., Pa., 255,304 E10 81
Lehigh Acres, Fla., 4,394 F5 54
Lehighton, Pa., 6,095 E10 81
Lehrte, Ger., Fed. Rep. of, 21,282 B4 6
Leiah, Pak., 14,914 B5 20
Leicester, Eng., 282,000 (*475,000) D6 4
Leicester, Mass., 1,850 (8,177▲) B4 65
Leicester, co., Eng., 771,900 *D6 4
Leiden, Neth., 98,060 (*164,887) A6 5
Leigh Creek, Austl., 943 F6 25
Leighton, Ala., 1,231 A2 46
Leinster, prov., Ire., 1,414,415 *D3 4
Leipsic, Ohio, 2,072 A2 78
Leipzig, Ger. Dem. Rep., 574,432 (*730,000) C6 6
Leiria, Port., 7,477 C1 8
Leisure City, Fla., 5,600 s13 54
Leitchfield, Ky., 2,983 C3 62
Leith, Pa., 800 *G2 81
Leitrim, co., Ire., 30,572 *D3 4
Leiva, mtn., Col C3 32
Lejunior, Ky., 600 D6 62
Leksand, Swe., 4,200 G6 11
Leland, Miss., 6,000 B3 68
Leland Grove, Ill., 1,624 *D4 58
Le Locle, Switz., 14,200 E3 6
Le Mans, Fr., 143,246 D4 5
Le Marin, Mart., 2,004 I14 35
Le Mars, Iowa, 8,159 B1 60
Lemay (Luxemburg), Mo., 25,700 *C7 69
Leme, Braz., 11,785 m8 30
Lemeta, Alsk., 1,318 *C10 47
Lemgo, Ger., Fed. Rep. of, 39,563 B4 6
Lemhi, co., Idaho, 5,566 E4 57
Lemmon, S. Dak., 1,997 E3 77
Lemon Grove, Calif., 20,300 F5, o15 50
Lemont, Ill., 5,080 B6, k9 58
Lemont, Pa., 2,547 E6 81
Lemoore, Calif., 4,219 D4 50
Le Moule, Guad., 8,189 H14 35
Le Moyen, La., 150 D3 63
Lemoyne, Pa., 4,625 *F8 81
Le Moyne, Que., Can., 8,194 *D4 42
Lena, Ill., 1,722 A4 58
Lena, Sp., 2,252 A3 8
Lena, riv., Sov. Un C15 13
Lenawee, co., Mich., 81,951 G6 66
Lenexa, Kans., 5,242 D9 61
Leninabad, Sov. Un., 103,000 E9 13
Leninakan, Sov. Un., 165,000 B14 14
Leningrad, Sov. Un., 3,560,000 (*4,675,000) H14, s31 11
Leninogorsk, Sov. Un., 72,000 D11 13
Leninsk, Sov. Un., 5,000 G15 12
Leninsk-Kuznetskiy, Sov. Un., 128,000 D11 13
Lenkoran, Sov. Un., 36,000 F7 13
Lennox, Calif., 16,121 *E4 50
Lennox, S. Dak., 1,487 G9 77
Lennox & Addington, co., Ont., Can., 23,717 C7 41
Lennoxville, Que., Can., 3,859 D6 42
Lenoir, N.C., 14,705 B1 76
Lenoir, co., N.C., 55,204 B5 76
Lenoir City, Tenn., 5,324 D9 83
Lenox, Iowa, 1,215 D3 60
Lenox, Mass., 2,208 B1 65
Lenox Avenue, N.Y *C4 75
Lennox & Addington co., Ont., Can., 25,202 C7 41
Lennoxville, Que., Can., 3,699 D6 42
Lens, Fr., 41,874 (*330,000) B5 5
Lenwood, Calif., 3,834 *E5 50
Leo, Ind., 600 B7 59
Leoben, Aus., 35,122 (*48,000) E7 6
Léogâne, Hai., 4,603 E7 35
Leominster, Mass., 32,939 A4 65
Leon, Iowa, 2,142 D4 60
León (de los Aldamas), Mex., 364,990 C4, m13 34
León, Nic., 58,900 E7 34
León, Sp., 105,243 (*126,000) A3 8
Leon, co., Fla., 103,047 B2 54
Leon, co., Tex., 8,738 D5 84
León, prov., Sp., 574,800 *A3 8
León, reg., Sp., 1,231,200 B3 8
Leonard, Tex., 1,423 C4 84
Leonardo, N.J., 3,600 C4 74
Leonardtown, Md., 1,406 D4 53
Leonforte, It., 17,927 F5 9
Leonia, N.J., 8,847 h9 74
Leonora, Austl., 594 E3 25
Leopoldina, Braz., 21,142 C4, g6 30
Leoti, Kans., 1,916 D2 61
Leovo, Sov. Un., 10,000 H7 12
Lepanto, Ark., 1,846 B5 49
Lepe, Sp., 10,038 D2 8
Lepel, Sov. Un., 10,000 D7 12
Le Petit-Quevilly, Fr., 22,876 C4 5
L'Épiphanie, Que., Can., 2,752 D4 42
Le Puy [-en-Velay], Fr., 26,389 (*39,000) E5 5
Le Raincy, Fr., 14,908 g11 5
Lercara Friddi, It., 11,872 F4 9
Lérida, Sp., 73,000 (88,897 ▲) B6 8
Lérida, prov., Sp., 344,800 *B6 8
Le Roy, Ill., 2,435 C5 58
Le Roy, Kans., 551 D8 61
Le Roy, Minn., 870 G6 67
Le Roy, N.Y., 5,118 C3 75
Lerwick, Scot., 6,179 g10 4
Léry, Que., Can., 2,247 q19 42
Les Cayes, Hai., 22,065 E7 35
Les Éboulements, Que., Can., 619 B7 42
Lesh, Alb., 1,609 B2 14
Leskovac, Yugo., 44,255 D5 10
Leslie, Mich., 1,894 F6 66
Leslie, co., Ky., 11,623 C6 62
Les Lilas, Fr., 17,721 g10 5
Lesotho, country, Afr., 1,110,000 F5 24
Les Sables-d'Olonne, Fr., 18,093 (*28,000) D3 5
Lesser Antilles, is., W.I B4 27
Lester, Pa., 2,300 *G11 81
Lester, W. Va., 507 n13 87
Lester Prairie, Minn., 1,162 F4 67
Le Sueur, Minn., 3,745 F5 67
Le Sueur, co., Minn., 21,332 F5 67
Lesvos (Lesbos), prov., Grc., 114,504 *C6 14
Leszno, Pol., 33,800 C4 7
Letcher, co., Ky., 23,165 C7 62
Le Teil, Fr., 8,236 E6 5
Lethbridge, Alta., Can., 41,217 E4, h8 38
Leticia, Col., 4,013 D4 32
Letpadan, Bur., 15,896 *H12 16
Le Tréport, Fr., 6,328 B4 5
Leucadia, Calif., 5,600 *F5 50
Leuser mtn., Indon m11 19
Leuven, Bel., 31,273 (*110,000) B6 5
Levack, Ont., Can., 2,948 *A3 41
Levadhia, Grc., 15,445 C4 14
Levallois-Perret, Fr., 58,941 C4, g10 5
Level Green, Pa., 3,000 *F2 81
Levelland, Tex., 11,445 C1 84
Level Park, Mich., 3,080 *F5 66
Leven, Scot., 9,544 B5 4
Leverkusen, Ger., Fed. Rep. of, 109,037 *C3 6
Levice, Czech., 16,413 D5 7
Levin, N.Z., 13,400 N15 26
Lévis, Que., Can., 16,597 C6, n17 42
Lévis, co., Que., Can., 58,375 C6 42
Levittown, N.Y., 65,600 *G2 52
Levittown, Pa., 79,000 *F12 81
Levkas, Grc., 6,818 C3 14
Levoča, Czech., 9,410 D6 7
Levy, co., Fla., 12,756 C4 54
Lewes, Del., 2,563 C7 53
Lewes, Eng., 14,080 E7 4
Lewis, co., Idaho, 3,867 C2 57
Lewis, co., Ky., 12,355 B6 62
Lewis, co., Mo., 10,993 A6 69
Lewis, co., N.Y., 23,644 B5 75
Lewis, co., Tenn., 6,761 B4 83
Lewis, co., Wash., 45,467 C3 86
Lewis, co., W. Va., 17,847 C4 87
Lewis and Clark, co., Mont., 33,281 C4 70
Lewisburg, Ohio, 1,553 C1 78
Lewisburg, Pa., 6,376 E8 81
Lewisburg, Tenn., 7,207 B5 83
Lewisburg, W. Va., 2,407 D4 87
Lewisdale, Md., 5,000 *C3 53
Lewis Gardens, Va., 1,450 *C5 85
Lewisporte, Newf., Can., 3,175 D4 44
Lewis Run, Pa., 756 C4 81
Lewiston, Idaho, 26,068 C1 57
Lewiston, Maine, 41,779 (*75,900) D2, f7 64
Lewiston, Mich., 600 D6 66
Lewiston, Minn., 1,000 G7 67
Lewiston, N.Y., 3,292 B1 75
Lewiston, Utah, 1,244 A6 72
Lewiston Orchards, Idaho C1 57
Lewistown, Ill., 2,706 C3 58
Lewistown, Mont., 6,437 C7 70
Lewistown, Pa., 11,098 E6 81
Lewisville, Ark., 1,653 D2 49
Lewisville, Ind., 530 F7 59
Lewisville, N.B., Can., 3,710 C5 43
Lewisville, Tex., 9,264 C4, m10 84
Lexington, Ill., 1,615 C5 58
Lexington, Ky., 108,137 (*217,900) B5 62
Lexington, Mass., 31,886 B5, g11 65
Lexington, Mich., 834 E8 66
Lexington, Minn., 2,165 *E5 67
Lexington, Miss., 2,756 B3 68
Lexington, Mo., 5,388 B4 69
Lexington, Nebr., 5,654 D6 71
Lexington, N.C., 17,205 B2 76
Lexington, Ohio, 2,972 B3 78
Lexington, Okla., 1,516 B4 79
Lexington, S.C., 969 D5 82
Lexington, Tenn., 5,024 B3 83
Lexington (Independent City), Va., 7,597 C3 85
Lexington, co., S.C., 89,012 D5 82
Lexington Park, Md., 9,136 *D5 53
Leyte, prov., Phil., 963,364 *C6 19
Leyte, isl., Phil C6 19
Leyton, Eng., 92,600 k12 4
Lézignan, Fr., 7,558 F5 5
Lezirias, reg., Port f10 8
Lgov, Sov. Un., 25,000 F10 12
Lhasa (Lasa), China, 70,000 F3 17
L' Hay-les-Roses, Fr., 17,968 g10 5
Liaoning, prov., China, 24,090,000 C9 17
Liaoyang, China, 169,000 C9 17
Líbano, Col., 18,640 C3 32
Libby, Mont., 3,286 B1 70
Liberal, Kans., 13,789 E3 61
Liberal, Mo., 644 D3 69
Liberec, Czech, 73,444 (*87,000) C3 7
Liberia, country, Afr., 1,695,000 G3 22
Liberty, Ind., 1,831 E8 59
Liberty, Ky., 1,765 C5 62
Liberty, Mo., 13,704 B3, h11 69
Liberty, N.Y., 4,514 D6 75
Liberty, N.C., 2,167 B3 76
Liberty, Pa., 3,594 *E1 81
Liberty, S.C., 2,860 B2 82
Liberty, Tex., 5,591 D5, q15 84
Liberty, co., Fla., 3,379 B2 54
Liberty, co., Ga., 17,569 E5 55
Liberty, co., Mont., 2,359 B5 70
Liberty, co., Tex., 33,014 D5 84
Liberty Acres, Calif., 6,500 *E4 50
Liberty Center, Ohio, 1,007 A1 78
Liberty Corner, N.J., 800 B3 74
Liberty Lake, Wash., 800 g14 86
Liberty Plain, Mass h12 65
Libertyville, Ill., 11,684 A6, h9 58
Libourne, Fr., 22,123 E3 5
Library, Pa., 4,200 *E1 81
Libreville, Gabon, 57,000 H6 22
Libya, country, Afr., 2,195,000 C2 23
Licata, It., 40,400 F4 9
Lice, Tur., 8,093 C13 14
Licking, Mo., 1,002 D6 69
Licking, co., Ohio, 107,799 B3 78
Lida, Sov. Un., 48,000 E5 12
Lidgerwood, N. Dak., 1,000 D8 77
Lidice, Czech C3, n17 7
Lidingö, Swe., 35,485 H8, t36 11
Lidköping, Swe., 26,473 H5 11
Liechtenstein, country, Eur., 23,000 E4 6
Liège, Bel., 144,875 (*550,000) B6 5
Liège, prov., Bel., 1,017,700 B6 5
Lienz, Aus., 11,713 E6 6
Liepāja, Sov. Un., 93,000 C3 12
Lier, Bel., 28,248 B6 5
Liestal, Switz., 13,000 E3 6
Lighthouse Point, Fla., 9,071 *F6 54
Lighthouse, point, Fla C2 80
Lighthouse, point, Mich C5 66
Ligonier, Ind., 3,034 B6 59
Ligonier, Pa., 2,258 F3 81
Liguria, pol. dist., It., 1,735,349 *B2 9
Liguria, reg., It., 1,866,200 B2 9
Lihue, Haw., 3,124 B2 56
Likasi, Zaire, 102,200 C5 24
Likhoslavl, Sov. Un., 5,000 C10 12
Likino-Dulevo, Sov. Un., 28,000 n18 12
Lilbourn, Mo., 1,152 E8 69
Lilesville, N.C., 641 C2 76
Lille, Fr., 190,546 (*950,000) B5 5
Lillehammer, Nor., 20,400 G4 11
Lillestrom, Nor., 10,547 H4, p29 11
Lillington, N.C., 1,155 B4 76
Lillooet, B.C., Can., 1,514 D7 37
Lillooet, range, B.C., Can E7 37
Lilongwe, Malawi, 102,000 C6 24
Lima, N.Y., 1,686 C3 75
Lima, Ohio, 53,734 (*100,300) B1 78
Lima, Peru, 340,339 (*3,350,000) D2 31
Lima, dept., Peru, 2,093,435 D2 31
Limbé, Hai., 6,502 E7 35
Limburg, Ger., Fed. Rep. of, 20,715 C4 6
Limburg, prov., Bel., 644,200 *B6 5
Limburg, prov., Neth., 990,600 *B6 5
Limeil-Brévannes, Fr., 8,377 h10 5
Limeira, Braz., 77,243 m8 30
Limerick, Ire., 57,161 D2 4
Limerick, co., Ire., 137,357 *D2 4

Limestone, Maine, 1,572...B5 64
Limestone, co., Ala., 41,699..............A2 46
Limestone, co., Tex., 18,100..............D4 84
Limoeiro do Norte, Braz., 6,179...............*D7 27
Limoges, Fr., 132,935.....E4 5
Limon, Colo., 1,814.......B7 51
Limón, C.R., 22,000.......F8 34
Limón, prov., C.R., 79,300...............*I12 33
Limousin, former prov., Fr....................E4 5
Limoux, Fr., 9,603........F5 5
Linares, Chile, 27,568.....B2 28
Linares, Col., 1,344.......C2 32
Linares, Mex., 24,456.....C5 34
Linares, Sp., 43,000 (51,883 ▲)............C4 8
Linares, prov., Chile, 197,500...............B2 28
Linch, Wyo., 300........*C6 89
Linchuan, China, 10,000...F8 17
Lincoln, Arg., 15,477......A4 28
Lincoln, Calif., 3,176......C3 50
Lincoln, Ont., Can., 14,247..............D5 41
Lincoln, Eng., 74,090.....D6 4
Lincoln, Ill., 17,582.......C4 58
Lincoln, Kans., 1,582.....C5 61
Lincoln, Maine, 3,482.....C4 64
Lincoln, Mass., 2,400.....g10 65
Lincoln, Nebr., 149,518 (*158,100).D9, h11 71
Lincoln, N.H., 800 (1,341 ▲)............*C4 73
Lincoln, Pa., 1,885.......*E1 81
Lincoln, R.I............B11 52
Lincoln, co., Ark., 12,913..D4 49
Lincoln, co., Colo., 4,836..C7 51
Lincoln, co., Eng., 812,310..............*D6 4
Lincoln, co., Ga., 5,895...C4 55
Lincoln, co., Idaho, 3,057..G4 57
Lincoln, co., Kans., 4,582..C5 61
Lincoln, co., Ky., 16,663...C5 62
Lincoln, co., Maine, 20,537..............D3 64
Lincoln, co., Minn., 8,143..F2 67
Lincoln, co., Miss., 26,198..D3 68
Lincoln, co., Mo., 18,041..B6 69
Lincoln, co., Mont., 18,063...............B1 70
Lincoln, co., Nebr., 29,538.D5 71
Lincoln, co., Nev., 2,557...C4 72
Lincoln, co., N. Mex., 7,560...............C6 48
Lincoln, co., N.C., 32,682..B1 76
Lincoln, co., Okla., 19,482.B5 79
Lincoln, co., Oreg., 25,755...............C3 80
Lincoln, co., S.Dak., 11,761..............G9 77
Lincoln, co., Tenn., 24,318...............B5 83
Lincoln, co., Wash., 9,572................B7 86
Lincoln, co., W. Va., 18,912...............C2 87
Lincoln, co., Wis., 23,499..C4 88
Lincoln, co., Wyo., 8,640..D2 89
Lincoln, par., La., 33,800..B3 63
Lincoln Acres, Calif., 1,000...............o15 50
Lincoln City, Oreg., 4,198...............C3 80
Lincoln Heights, Ohio, 6,099...............o13 78
Lincoln Highway, Nebr..*C5 71
Lincoln Park, Colo., 2,984...............*C5 51
Lincoln Park, Ga., 1,852...D2 55
Lincoln Park, Mich., 52,984...............p15 66
Lincoln Park, N.J., 9,034..B4 74
Lincoln Park, N.Y., 1,100...............*D6 75
Lincoln Park, Pa., 1,500..*F9 81
Lincolnton, Ga., 1,442....C4 55
Lincolnton, N.C., 5,293....B1 76
Lincoln Village, Calif., 6,112...............*D3 50
Lincoln Village, Ohio, 11,215...............*C3 78
Lincolnwood, Ill., 12,929..h9 58
Lincroft, N.J., 4,100......C4 74
Lind, Wash., 622.........C7 86
Linda, Calif., 7,731.......*C3 50
Lindale, Ga., 2,768........B1 55
Lindale, Tex., 1,631.......C5 84
Lindau, Ger., Fed. Rep. of, 25,395...............E4 6
Linden, Ala., 2,697........C2 46
Linden, Ind., 713.........D4 59
Linden, Mich., 1,546.......F7 66
Linden, N.J., 41,409.......k8 74
Linden, Tenn., 1,062......B4 83
Linden, Tex., 2,264.......C5 84
Lindenhurst, Ill., 3,141....h8 58
Lindenhurst, N.Y., 28,359...............G3 52
Lindenwold, N.J., 12,199..D3 74
Lindesberg, Swe., 10,749..H6 11
Lindi, Tan, 10,315........B7 24
Lindon, Utah, 1,644.....*A6 72
Lindsay, Calif., 5,206......D4 50
Lindsay, Ont., Can., 12,746...............C6 41
Lindsay, Okla., 3,705......C4 79
Lindsborg, Kans., 2,764....D6 61
Lindstrom, Minn., 1,260...E6 67
Linesville, Pa., 1,265......C1 81
Lineville, Ala., 1,984......B4 46
Lingayen, Phil., 8,221......B6 19
Lingen, Ger., Fed. Rep. of, 31,984...............B3 6
Linglestown, Pa., 3,000....F8 81
Lingyuan, China, 20,000..C8 17
Linhai, China, 26,000.....F9 17
Lini, China, 40,000.......D8 17
Linière, Que., Can., 1,269..C7 42
Linköping, Swe., 106,628..H6 11
Linn, Mo., 1,289.........C6 69
Linn, co., Iowa, 163,213...B6 60
Linn, co., Kans., 7,770....D9 61
Linn, co., Mo., 15,125.....B4 69
Linn, co., Oreg., 71,914....C4 80
Linntown, Pa., 1,851.....*E7 81
Lino Lakes, Minn., 3,692..*E5 67
Lins, Braz., 38,080........C3 30
Linthicum Heights, Md., 12,700........B4, h11 53
Linton, Ind., 5,450........F3 59
Linton, N. Dak., 1,695....D5 77
Linwood, Mass., 1,100.....B4 65
Linwood, Mich., 650.......E7 66
Linwood, N.J., 6,159.......E3 74
Linwood, Pa., 4,009......*G11 81
Linworth, Ohio, 500......k10 78
Linz, Aus., 204,627 (*275,000)..............D7 6
Lipa, Phil., 16,006..C6, p13 19
Lipari, It., 3,731..........E5 9
Lipetsk, Sov. Un., 289,000...............E12 12
Lipkany, Sov. Un., 10,000................A8 10
Lipno, Pol., 10,900........B5 7
Lipova, Rom., 10,064.....B5 10
Lippstadt, Ger., Fed. Rep. of, 42,191..............C4 6
Lipscomb, Ala., 3,225..B3, g7 46
Lipscomb, co., Tex., 3,486...............A2 84
Liria, Sp., 9,723..........C5 8
Lisboa, see Lisbon, Port.
Lisbon, Iowa, 1,329......C6 60
Lisbon, Maine, 1,100...D2, f7 64
Lisbon, N.H., 1,247 (1,480 ▲)...............C4 73
Lisbon, N. Dak., 2,090....D8 77
Lisbon, Ohio, 3,521........B5 78
Lisbon (Lisboa), Port., 757,700 (*1,735,000).........C1, f9 8
Lisbon Falls, Maine, 3,257..............D5, f7 64
Lisburn, N. Ire., 27,405...C3 4
Lishu, China, 5,000.......E2 18
Lisichansk, Sov. Un., 118,000 (*320,000).....q21 12
Lisieux, Fr., 23,830.......C4 5
Lisle, Ill., 5,329..........k8 58
L'Islet, co., Que., Can., 24,382...............B7 42
L'Islet-sur-Mer, Que., 1,195...............B7 42
L'Isletville, Que., Can., 1,184...............B7 42
Lisman, Ala., 628.........C1 46
Lismore, Austl., 20,901....E9 25
Listowel, Ont., Can., 4,677...............D4 41
Litchfield, Conn., 1,559 (6,264▲)...............B4 52
Litchfield, Ill., 7,190......D4 58
Litchfield, Mich., 1,167....F6 66
Litchfield, Minn., 5,262...E4 67
Litchfield, co., Conn., 144,091...............B3 52
Litchfield Park, Ariz., 1,664...............D1 48
Lithgow, Austl., 13,135....F9 25
Lithonia, Ga., 2,270...C2, h8 55
Lithuania (S.S.R), rep., Sov. Un., 3,280,000.....D4 12
Lititz, Pa., 7,072..........F9 81
Litókhoron, Grc., 5,561...*B4 14
Litoměřice, Czech., 19,713...............C3 7
Litomyšl, Czech., 6,384....D7 7
Little, mtn., Wyo..........E5 89
Little Belt, mtn., Mont.....D6 70
Little Canada, Minn., 3,481...............*E5 67
Little Catalina, Newf., Can., 752...............D5 44
Little Chute, Wis., 5,522..............D5, h9 88
Little Current, Ont., Can., 1,527...............B3 41
Little Falls, Minn., 7,467..E4 67
Little Falls, N.J., 11,727...B4 74
Little Falls, N.Y., 7,629....B6 75
Little Ferry, N.J., 9,064...h8 74
Littlefield, Tex., 6,738....C1 84
Littlefork, Minn., 824......B5 67
Little River, co., Ark., 11,194...............D1 49
Little Rock, Ark., 132,483 (*293,700).........C3, k10 49
Little Rock, river, Iowa....A1 70
Little Silver, N.J., 6,010...C4 74
Littlestown, Pa., 3,026....G7 81
Littleton, Colo., 26,466....B6 51
Littleton, Mass., 2,764 (6,380 ▲)...............f9 65
Littleton, N.H., 4,180 (5,290 ▲)...............C4 73
Littleton, N.C., 903.......A5 76
Littleton Common, Mass..f10 65
Little Valley, N.Y., 1,340..C2 75
Liuho, China., 5,000......E2 18
Lively, Ont., Can., 3,000..A3 41
Live Oak, Calif., 2,654....C3 50
Live Oak, Fla., 6,830.....B4 54
Live Oak, co., Tex., 6,697..E3 84
Livermore, Calif., 37,703..h9 50
Livermore, Ky., 1,594....C2 62
Livermore, peak, Tex.....o12 84
Livermore Falls, Maine, 2,378...............D2 64
Liverpool, N.S., Can., 3,654...............E5 43
Liverpool, Eng., 603,210 (*1,615,000)..........D5 4
Liverpool, N.Y., 3,307.....B4 75
Liverpool, Pa., 847........E7 81
Livingston, Ala., 2,358....C1 46
Livingston, Calif., 2,588...D3 50
Livingston, Guat., 2,606...D7 34
Livingston, Ill., 916.......E4 58
Livingston, La., 1,398..............D5, g10 63
Livingston, Mont., 6,883...E6 70
Livingston, N.J., 30,127....B4 74
Livingston, Tenn., 3,050...C8 83
Livingston, Tex., 3,965....D5 84
Livingstone, Zambia, 33,600...............D5 24
Livingston, co., Ill., 40,690...............C5 58
Livingston, co., Ky., 7,596...............e9 62
Livingston, co., Mich., 58,967...............F6 66
Livingston, co., Mo., 15,368...............B4 69
Livingston, co., N.Y., 54,041...............C3 75
Livingston, par., La., 36,511...............D5 63
Livingston Manor, N.Y., 1,522...............D6 75
Livno, Yugo., 5,170.......D3 10
Livny, Sov. Un., 37,000...E11 12
Livonia, Mich., 110,109...F7 66
Livonia, N.Y., 1,278......C3 75
Livorno (Leghorn), It., 172,800...............C3 9
Livry-Gargan, Fr., 32,063...............g11 5
Lizard Head, peak, Wyo...............D3 89
Ljubljana, Yugo., 173,662...............B2 10
Ljungby, Swe., 14,535.....I5 11
Llandrindod Wells, Wales, 3,360...............D5 4
Llandudno, Wales, 17,360...............D5 4
Llanelli, Wales, 26,260....E4 4
Llanes, Sp., 20,421........A3 8
Llano, Tex., 2,608........D3 84
Llano, co., Tex., 6,979.....D3 84
Llanquihue, prov., Chile, 201,800...............C2 28
Lloyd, Ky., 400...........B7 62
Lloyd Harbor, N.Y., 3,371...............*G3 52
Lloydminster, Alta., Sask., Can., 8,691...............D1 39
Lloyd Place, Va...........*D6 85
Lluchmayor, Sp., 10,664...C7 8
Llullaillaco, vol., Chile....D2 29
Löbau, Ger. Dem. Rep., 16,800...............C7 6
Lobería, Arg., 8,455.......B5 28
Lobito, Ang., 50,164......C2 24
Lobos, Arg., 10,352....B5, g7 28
Locarno, Switz., 14,700 (*38,500)...............E4 6
Lochdale, B.C., Can......f12 37
Lochearn, Md., 5,000.....*B4 53
Loches, Fr., 6,359........D4 5
Loch Raven, Md.........*B4 53
Lockeport, N.S., Can., 1,231...............F4 43
Lockhart, Tex., 6,489..............E4, h8 84
Lock Haven, Pa., 11,427...D7 81
Lockland, Ohio, 5,288....o13 78
Lockney, Tex., 2,094.......B2 84
Lockport, Ill., 9,985....B5, k8 58
Lockport, La., 2,398..E5, k10 63
Lockport, N.Y., 25,399....B2 75
Lockwood, Mo., 887.......D4 69
Locumba, Peru, 634.......E3 31
Locust, N.J., 700.........C4 74
Locust Grove, Okla., 1,090...............A6 79
Locust Valley, N.Y., 3,900...............F2 52
Lod (Lydda), Isr., 30,500.............C2, h5 15
Lodève, Fr., 7,556........F5 5
Lodeynoye Pole, Sov. Un., 20,000...............A9 12
Lodge Grass, Mont., 806...E9 70
Lodhrān, Pak., 6,663......C5 20
Lodi, Calif., 28,691........C3 50
Lodi, N.J., 25,163.........h8 74
Lodi, Ohio, 2,399.........A3 78
Lodi, Wis., 1,831.........E4 88
Łódź, Pol., 761,700 (*930,000)...............C5 7
Loei, Thai., 7,268........*B2 19
Logan, Iowa, 1,526.......C2 60
Logan, Kans., 760.........C4 61
Logan, Ohio, 6,269........C3 78
Logan, Utah, 22,333......A6 72
Logan, W. Va., 3,311..D3, n12 87
Logan, co., Ark., 16,789...B2 49
Logan, co., Colo., 18,852..A7 51
Logan, co., Ill., 33,538....C4 58
Logan, co., Kans., 3,814...D2 61
Logan, co., Ky., 21,793....D3 62
Logan, co., Nebr., 991.....C5 71
Logan, co., N. Dak., 4,245...............D6 77
Logan, co., Ohio, 35,072...B2 78
Logan, co., Okla., 19,645..B4 79
Logan, co., W. Va., 46,269...............D3 87
Logan, mtn., Yukon, Can..D6 36
Logansport, Ind., 19,255...C5 59
Logansport, La., 1,330....C2 63
Loganville, Ga., 1,318.....C3 55
Loggieville, N.B., Can., 691...............B4 43
Logroño, Sp., 82,821.......A4 8
Logroño, prov., Sp., 234,600...............*A4 8
Logrosán, Sp., 6,595.......C3 8
Lohārdaga, India, 17,087..D7 20
Lohrville, Iowa, 553.......B3 60
Loire, dept., Fr., 722,383...............*E6 5
Loire, riv., Fr............D3 5
Loire-Atlantique, dept., Fr., 861,452...........*D3 5
Loiret, dept., Fr., 430,629...............*D4 5
Loir-et-Cher, dept., Fr., 267,896...............*D4 5
Loja, Ec., 33,900..........B2 31
Loja, Sp., 11,441 (25,976 ▲)...............D3 8
Loja, prov., Ec., 345,500...B2 31
Lokhvitsa, Sov. Un., 10,000...............F9 12
Lom, Bul., 28,196.........D6 10
Loma Linda, Calif., 10,100...............*E5 50
Lomas de Zamora, Arg., 410,806.............A5, g7 28
Lombard, Ill., 34,043......k8 58
Lombardia, reg., It., 8,231,700...............*B2 9
Lombardy, reg., It.........B2 9
Lomé, Togo, 90,600.......G5 22
Lometa, Tex., 633.........D3 84
Lomira, Wis., 1,084.......E5 88
Lomita, Calif., 19,784....*E4 50
Lomonosov, Sov. Un., 40,000...............s30 11
Lompoc, Calif., 25,284....E3 50
Łomża, Pol., 25,500.......B7 7
Lonaconing, Md., 1,572...k13 53
London, Ont., Can., 223,222 (*286,011)......E3 41
London, Eng., 7,418,020 (*10,700,000)......E6, k12 4
London, Ky., 4,337.......C5 62
London, Ohio, 6,481.......C2 78
London, Greater, co., Eng., 7,418,020...............*E6 4
Londonderry, N. Ire., 51,850 (*85,000)........C3 4

154 Lon-Lyk

Londonderry, co., N. Ire., 130,296.....*C3 4
London Mills, Ill., 610.....C3 58
Londrina, Braz., 156,670.....C2 30
Lone Oak, Ky., 3,759.....e9 62
Lone Pine, Calif., 1,800.....D4 50
Lone Star, Tex., 1,760.....*C5 84
Lone Wolf, Okla., 584.....C2 79
Lone Tree, Iowa, 834.....C6 60
Long, co., Ga., 3,746.....E5 55
Long Beach, Calif., 358,633.....F4, n12 50
Long Beach, Ind., 2,740.....A4 59
Long Beach, Miss., 6,170.....E4, f7 68
Long Beach, N.Y., 33,127.....E7, n15 75
Long Beach, Wash., 968.....C1 86
Longboat Key, Fla., 2,850.....q10 54
Long Branch, Ont., Can., 12,980.....m14 41
Long Branch, N.J., 31,774.....C5 74
Long Creek, mtn., Wyo.....D4 89
Longford, co., Ire., 28,989.....*D3 4
Longhurst, N.C., 1,485.....A4 76
Long Island, isl., N.Y.....n15 75
Long Lake, Ill., 1,500.....h8 58
Long Lake, Minn., 1,506.....*F5 67
Long Lake, N.Y., 400.....B6 75
Longleaf, La., 400.....C3 63
Long Leaf Park, N.C.....*C5 76
Longmeadow, Mass., 15,630.....B2 65
Longmont, Colo., 23,209.....A5 51
Long Pond, Newf., Can., 1,758.....E5 44
Longport, N.J., 1,225.....E13 74
Long Prairie, Minn., 2,416.....E4 67
Longreach, Austl., 3,453.....D7 25
Longs, peak, Colo.....A5 51
Long Range, mts., Newf., Can.....E2, k10 44
Longueuil, Que., Can., 97,590.....D4, p19 42
Long Valley, N.J., 1,645.....B3 74
Longview, Alta., Can., 189.....D3 38
Long View, Ky., 650.....C4 62
Long View, N.C., 3,360.....B1 76
Longview, Tex., 45,547.....C5 84
Longview, Wash., 28,373.....C3 86
Longwood, Fla., 3,203.....*D5 54
Longwood Park, N.C., 1,284.....*B3 76
Longwy, Fr., 21,087 (*82,000).....C6 5
Long Xuyen, Viet., 23,300.....*C3 19
Lonoke, Ark., 3,140.....C4, h11 49
Lonoke, co., Ark., 26,249.....C4 49
Lons-le-Saunier, Fr., 18,769.....D6 5
Loogootee, Ind., 2,953.....G4 59
Lookout, Ky., 550.....C7 62
Lookout Mountain, Tenn., 1,741.....h11 83
Loon Lake, mtn., N.Y.....f10 75
Lopei, China, 5,000.....C5 18
Lora, Sp., 11,864.....D3 8
Lorado, W. Va., 500.....D3, n12 87
Lorain, Ohio, 78,185.....A3 78
Lorain, Pa., 972.....*E4 81
Lorain, co., Ohio, 256,843.....A3 78
Loraine, Tex., 700.....C2 84
Lorca, Sp., 21,000 (60,286 ▲).....D5 8
Lordsburg, N. Mex., 3,429.....C4 48
Loreauville, La., 728.....D4 63
Lorena, Braz., 39,655.....G3 30
Lorenzo, Tex., 1,206.....C2 84
Loreto, Mex., 2,570.....B2 34
Loreto, Par., 11,321.....D4 29
Loreto, dept., Peru, 411,340.....C3 31
Loretteville, Que., Can., 11,644.....C6, n17 42
Loretto, Pa., 1,661.....F4 81
Loretto, Tenn., 1,375.....B4 83
Lorica, Col., 12,880.....B2 32
Lorient, Fr., 66,444 (*98,000).....D2 5
L'Orignal, Ont., Can., 1,189.....B10 41
Loris, S.C., 1,741.....C10 82
Lorne, N.B., Can., 890.....B3 43
Lorneville, N.B., Can., 666.....D3 43
Lörrach, Ger., Fed. Rep. of, 34,119.....E3 6
Lorraine, former prov., Fr.....C6 5
Los Alamitos, Calif., 11,346.....*F5 50
Los Alamos, N. Mex., 15,198.....B5 48
Los Alamos, co., N. Mex., 15,198.....B5 48
Los Altos, Calif., 24,726.....k8 50
Los Altos Hills, Calif., 6,865.....*D2 50
Los Andes, Chile, 20,448.....A2 28
Los Angeles, Calif., 2,809,813 (*8,716,700).....E4, m12 50
Los Angeles, Chile, 35,511.....B2 28
Los Angeles, co., Calif., 7,040,679.....E4 50
Los Banos, Calif., 9,188.....D3 50
Los Barrios, Sp., 3,583.....D3 8
Los Fresnos, Tex., 1,297.....F4 84
Los Gatos, Calif., 23,735.....D2 50
Loshan, China, 60,000.....F5 17
Los Mochis, Mex., 67,953.....B3 34
Los Nietos, Calif., 7,100.....*E4 50
Los Palacios, Cuba, 10,200 (22,900 ▲).....C2 35
Los Reyes [de Salgado], Mex., 19,452.....D4, n12 34
Los Ríos, prov., Ec., 314,800.....B2 31
Los Teques, Ven., 62,747.....A4 32
Lost Nation, Iowa, 547.....C7 60
Lot, dept., Fr., 151,198.....*E4 5
Lota, Chile, 48,693.....B2 28
Lotbinière, co., Que., Can., 28,765.....C6 42
Lot-et-Garonne, dept., Fr., 290,592.....*E4 5
Lothair, Ky., 600.....C6 62
Lott, Tex., 799.....D4 84
Loudon, Tenn., 3,728.....D9 83
Loudon, co., Tenn., 24,266.....D9 83
Loudonville, N.Y., 9,299.....*C6 75
Loudonville, Ohio, 2,865.....B3 78
Loudoun, co., Va., 37,150.....B5 85
Loudun, Fr., 5,587.....D4 5
Loughborough, Eng., 48,180.....D6 4
Louisa, Ky., 1,781.....B7 62
Louisa, co., Iowa, 10,682.....C6 60
Louisa, co., Va., 14,004.....C5 85
Louisbourg, N.S., Can., 1,582.....D10 43
Louisburg, Kans., 1,033.....D9 61
Louisburg, N.C., 2,941.....A4 76
Louisdale, N.S., 793.....D8 43
Louisiana, Mo., 4,533.....B6 69
Louisiana, state, U.S., 3,799,000..... 63
Louis Trichardt, S. Afr., 8,816.....E5 24
Louisville, Que., Can., 4,042.....C5 42
Louisville, Colo., 2,409.....B5 51
Louisville, Ga., 2,691.....C4 55
Louisville, Ill., 1,020.....E5 58
Louisville, Ky., 361,706 (*840,000).....B4, g11 62
Louisville, Miss., 6,626.....B4 68
Louisville, Nebr., 1,036.....D9, h12 71
Louisville, Ohio, 6,298.....B4 78
Loulé, Port., 6,479.....D1 8
Louny, Czech., 13,447.....C2 7
Loup, co., Nebr., 854.....C6 71
Loup, riv., Nebr.....C8 71
Loup City, Nebr., 1,456.....C7 71
Lourdes, Newf., Can., 975.....D2 44
Lourdes, Fr., 17,939.....F4 5
Lourenço Marques, see Maputo, Moz.
Loures, Port., 6,089.....f9 8
Louth, Eng., 11,710.....D7 4
Louth, co., Ire., 69,519.....*C3 4
Loutrá Aidhipsoú, Grc., 2,195.....C4 14
Louvain, see Leuven, Bel.
Louviers, Fr., 13,160.....C4 5
Love, co., Okla., 5,637.....D4 79
Lovech, Bul., 30,879.....D7 10
Lovejoy, Ill., 1,702.....*E3 58
Loveland, Colo., 16,220.....A5 51
Loveland, Ohio, 7,144.....C1, n12 78
Loveland Park, Ohio, 1,000.....C1, n13 78
Lovell, Wyo., 2,371.....B4 89
Lovelock, Nev., 1,571.....A2 72
Lovely, Ky., 700.....C7 62
Loves Park, Ill., 12,390.....A4 58
Lovilia, Iowa, 640.....C5 60
Loving, N. Mex., 1,192.....C6 48
Loving, co., Tex., 164.....o13 84
Lovington, Ill., 1,303.....D5 58
Lovington, Iowa, 800.....e8 60
Lovington, N. Mex., 8,915.....C7 48
Lowden, Iowa, 667.....C7 60
Lowell, Ind., 3,839.....B3 59
Lowell, Mass., 94,239.....A5, f10 65
Lowell, Mich., 3,068.....F5 66
Lowell, N.C., 3,307.....B1 76
Lowell, Ohio, 852.....C4 78
Lowell, Wash., 1,086.....*B3 86
Lowellville, Ohio, 1,836.....A5 78
Lower Burrell, Pa., 13,654.....*F2 81
Lower Caraquet, N.B., Can., 807.....*B5 43
Lower Hutt, N.Z., 58,800.....*N15 26
Lower Paia, Haw., 1,105.....C5 56
Lower West Pubnico, N.S., Can., 618.....F4 43
Lowestoft, Eng., 52,120.....D7 4
Łowicz, Pol., 20,400.....B5 7
Lowmoor, Va., 600.....C3 85
Lowndes, co., Ala., 12,897.....C3 46
Lowndes, co., Ga., 55,112.....F3 55
Lowndes, co., Miss., 49,700.....B5 68
Lowville, N.Y., 3,671.....B5 75
Loxton, Austl., 2,321.....G3 26
Loyal, Wis., 1,126.....D3 88
Loyalhanna, Pa., 900.....*F2 81
Loyall, Ky., 1,212.....D6 62
Loyalton, Calif., 945.....C3 50
Loyalty, is., Pac. O.....H8 2
Loyang, China, 500,000.....E7 17
Lozere, dept., Fr., 77,258.....*E5 5
Loznica, Yugo., 13,891.....C4 10
Lozovatka, Sov. Un., 10,000.....G9 12
Luanda, Ang., 224,540.....B2 24
Luang Prabang, Laos, 22,200.....B2 19
Luanshya, Zambia, 72,100.....C5 24
Lubań, Pol., 17,200.....C3 7
Lubango, Ang., 13,867.....C2 24
Lubartów, Pol., 10,100.....C7 7
Lübben, Ger., 9,433.....C6 6
Lubbock, Tex., 149,101 (*164,300).....C2 84
Lubbock, co., Tex., 179,295.....C2 84
Lubec, Maine, 950.....D6 64
Lubeck, Ger., Fed. Rep. of, 237,698 (*284,000).....B5 6
Lublin, Pol., 235,900.....C7 7
Lubliniec, Pol., 19,800.....C5 7
Lubny, Sov. Un., 40,000.....F9 12
Lubrín, Sp., 5,417.....D4 8
Lubumbashi (Elisabethville), Zaire, 233,100.....C5 24
Lubutu, Zaire.....I3 23
Lucan, Ont., Can., 986.....D3 41
Lucas, Ohio, 771.....B3 78
Lucas, co., Iowa, 10,163.....C4 60
Lucas, co., Ohio, 483,594.....A2 78
Lucasville, Ohio, 900.....D3 78
Lucca, It., 74,200.....C3 9
Luce, co., Mich., 6,789.....B5 66
Lucedale, Miss., 2,083.....E5 68
Lucena, Phil., 77,006.....C6, p13 19
Lucenec, Czech., 20,427.....D5 7
Lucera, It., 25,300.....D5 9
Lucerne, see Luzern, Switz.
Lucernemines, Pa., 1,380.....E3 81
Luceville, Que., Can., 1,411.....A9 42
Luchou (Luhsien), China, 130,000.....F6 17
Luck, Wis., 848.....C1 88
Luckau, Ger., 6,145.....C6 6
Luckenwalde, Ger. Dem. Rep., 28,691.....B6 6
Luckey, Ohio, 996.....A2, f7 78
Lucknow, Ont., Can., 1,031.....D3 41
Lucknow, India, 749,239 (*840,000).....C7 20
Lucknow, Pa., 1,300.....*F8 81
Luçon, Fr., 8,243.....D3 5
Lucy, La., 400.....h10 63
Lüdenscheid, Ger., Fed. Rep. of, 78,938.....C3 6
Ludhiāna, India, 397,850.....B6 20
Ludington, Mich., 9,021.....E4 66
Ludlam, Fla.....*G6 54
Ludlow, Eng., 6,796.....D5 4
Ludlow, Ky., 5,815.....h13 62
Ludlow, Mass., 17,580.....B3 65
Ludlow, Pa., 800.....C4 81
Ludlow, Vt., 1,508 (2,386▲).....E2 73
Ludowici, Ga., 1,419.....E5 55
Ludvika, Swe., 21,809.....G6 11
Ludwigsburg, Ger., Fed. Rep. of, 77,824.....D4 6
Ludwigshafen, Ger., Fed. Rep. of, 174,337.....D4 6
Ludwigslust, Ger. Dem. Rep., 12,000.....B5 6
Lueders, Tex., 511.....C3 84
Lufkin, Tex., 23,049.....D5 84
Luga, Sov. Un. 32,000.....B7 12
Lugano, Switz., 23,600 (*63,300).....E4 6
Lugansk, see Voroshilovgrad, Sov. Un.
Lugo, It., 20,500.....B3 9
Lugo, Sp., 50,000 (63,604 ▲).....A2 8
Lugo, prov., Sp., 458,800.....*A2 8
Lugoff, S.C., 1,500.....C6 82
Lugoj, Rom., 35,400.....C5 10
Luichou, China, 190,000.....G6 17
Luján, Arg., 33,500.....g7 28
Lukovit, Bul., 7,755.....D7 10
Łuków, Pol., 15,500.....C7 7
Lukoyanov, Sov. Un., 5,000.....D15 12
Luleå, Swe., 60,455.....E10 11
Luling, La., 3,255.....k11 63
Luling, Tex., 4,719.....E4, h8 84
Luluabourg, see Kananga, Zaire
Lumber City, Ga., 1,377.....E4 55
Lumberport, W. Va., 957.....B4, k10 87
Lumberton, Miss., 2,084.....D4 68
Lumberton, N.J., 700.....D3 74
Lumberton, N.C., 19,961.....C4 76
Lumby, B.C., Can., 1,842.....D8 37
Lumpkin, Ga., 1,431.....D2 55
Lumpkin, co., Ga., 8,728.....B2 55
Lumsden, Sask., Can., 685.....G3 39
Luna, co., N. Mex., 11,706.....C5 48
Luna Pier (Lakewood), Mich., 1,418.....G7 66
Lund, Swe., 58,808 (*69,224).....J5 11
Lundale, W. Va., 500.....D3, n12 87
Lundar, Man., Can., 713.....D2 40
Lüneburg, Ger., Fed. Rep. of, 60,301.....B5 6
Lunel, Fr., 7,758.....F6 5
Lunenburg, N.S., Can., 3,215.....E5 43
Lunenburg, Mass., 950.....A4 65
Lunenburg, co., N.S., Can., 36,114.....E5 43
Lunenburg, co., Va., 11,687.....D4 85
Lunéville, Fr., 23,177.....C7 5
Lunino, Sov. Un., 10,000.....E15 12
Lupeni, Rom., 21,888.....C6 10
Lupin, see Manchouli, China
Luque, Par., 13,921.....E4 29
Luray, Va., 3,612.....B4 85
Lure, Fr., 6,408.....D7 5
Lurgan, N. Ire., 24,055 (*59,000).....C3 4
Lusaka, Zambia, 238,200.....D5 24
Lusambo, Zaire, 9,800.....I2 23
Luseland, Sask., Can., 665.....E1 39
Lushan, China, 5,000.....F8 17
Lüshun (Port Arthur), China, 126,000.....D9 17
Lusk, Wyo., 1,495.....D8 89
Lüta (Dairen), China, 1,150,000 (*1,200,000).....D9 17
Lutcher, La., 3,911.....D5, h10 63
Lutesville, Mo., 626.....D8 69
Lutherville-Timonium, Md., 27,000.....B4 53
Luton, Eng., 160,730 (*205,000).....E6 4
Lutsk, Sov. Un., 94,000.....F5 12
Lutugino, Sov. Un., 5,000.....q22 12
Lutz, Fla., 720.....D4 54
Luverne, Ala., 2,440.....D3 46
Luverne, Minn., 4,703.....G2 67
Luwuk, Indon., 6,069.....F6 19
Luxembourg, Lux., 76,143 (*100,000).....C7 5
Luxembourg, country, Eur., 350,000.....C7 5
Luxembourg, prov., Bel., 219,300.....*C6 5
Luxemburg, Wis., 853.....D6 88
Luxeuil-les-Bains, Fr., 9,216.....D7 5
Luxor, see Al Uqsur, Eg.
Luxora, Ark., 1,566.....B6 49
Luzern, Switz., 68,500 (*156,800).....E4 6
Luzern, canton, Switz., 288,000.....*E4 6
Luzerne, Pa., 4,504.....n17 81
Luzerne, co., Pa., 342,329.....D9 81
Luzon, isl., Phil.....B6 19
Lvov, Sov. Un., 553,000.....G5 12
Lyallpur, Pak., 425,248.....B5 20
Lyaskovets, Bul., 5,560.....D7 10
Lycoming, co., Pa., 113,296.....D7 81
Lydia Mills, S.C., 950.....*C4 82
Lydick, Ind., 1,341.....*A5 59
Lyell, mtn., B.C., Can.....D9 37
Lyford, Tex., 1,425.....F4 84
Lykens, Pa., 2,506.....E8 81

Lyle, Minn., 522........G6 67
Lyman, Nebr., 561......C1 71
Lyman, S.C., 1,159......B3 82
Lyman, co., S. Dak., 4,060.G6 77
Lynbrook, N.Y., 23,151...G2 52
Lynch, Ky., 1,517......D7 62
Lynchburg, Ohio, 1,186...C2 78
Lynchburg (Independent
  City), Va., 54,083
  (*96,600)..........C3 85
Lynden, Wash., 2,808.....A3 86
Lyndhurst, N.J., 22,729...h8 74
Lyndhurst, Ohio, 19,749...g9 78
Lyndon, Kans., 958......D8 61
Lyndon, Ky., 460.......g11 62

Lyndonville, N.Y., 888....B2 75
Lyndonville, Vt., 1,415....B3 73
Lyndora, Pa., 5,700......E2 81
Lynn, Ind., 1,360.......D8 59
Lynn, Mass., 90,294...B6, g12 65
Lynn, co., Tex., 9,107.....C2 84
Lynnfield, Mass., 10,826...f11 65
Lynn Garden, Tenn.,
  7,000.............C11 83
Lynn Haven, Fal., 4,044...u16 54
Lynn Lake, Man.,
  Can., 2,931......A1, f7 40
Lynnville, Ky., 1,165......f9 62
Lynnwood, Pa., 1,800....*D9 81
Lynnwood, Wash., 16,919.*B3 86

Lynwood, Calif., 43,354...n12 50
Lyon, Fr., 527,800
  (*1,100,000)..........E6 5
Lyon, co., Iowa, 13,340....A1 60
Lyon, co., Kans., 32,071...D7 61
Lyon, co., Ky., 5,562.....C1 62
Lyon, co., Minn., 24,273...F3 67
Lyon, co., Nev., 8,221.....B2 72
Lyon Mountain, N.Y.,
  950.............f11 75
Lyonnais, former prov., Fr..E6 5
Lyons, Ga., 3,739.......D4 55
Lyons, Ill., 11,124.......k9 58
Lyons, Ind., 702........G3 59
Lyons, Kans., 4,355......D5 61

Lyons, Mich., 758.......F6 66
Lyons, Nebr., 1,177......C9 71
Lyons, N.Y., 4,496......B4 75
Lyons Falls, N.Y., 852....B5 75
Lysá, Czech., 10,281......n18 7
Lysaya Gora, Sov. Un.,
  10,000............G8 12
Lysekil, Swe., 6,783......H4 11
Lyster Station, Que.,
  Can., 912........C6 42
Lysva, Sov. Un., 73,000...D8 13
Lytle, Tex., 1,271.......E3 84
Lyubar, Sov. Un., 10,000..G6 12
Lyubertsy, Sov. Un.,
  139,000...........N17 12

M

Ma'alot Tarshiha, Isr.,
  5,100.............A3 15
Maastricht, Neth.,
  111,931 (*145,277)......B6 5
Mabank, Tex., 1,239......C4 84
Mabel, Minn., 888.......G7 67
Mableton, Ga., 12,900....h7 55
Mabscott, W. Va.,
  1,254..........D3, n13 87
Mabton, Wash., 926....C5 86
McAdam, N.B., Can.,
  2,224.............D2 43
McAdenville, N.C., 950...*B1 76
McAdoo, Pa., 3,326......E9 81
Macaé, Braz., 29,348......C4 30
McAlester, Okla., 18,802...C6 79
McAllen, Tex., 37,636
  (*86,700).............F3 84
Macamic, Que., Can.,
  1,614..........*o20 41
Macao, Port. dep., Asia,
  285,000............G7 17
Macapá, Braz., 51,563....C5 27
McArthur, Ohio, 1,543...C3 78
Macas Ec., 1,355.......D3 27
Macau, Braz., 18,853.....D7 27
McBee, S.C., 592.......C7 82
McBride, B.C., Can., 658..C7 37
McCall, Idaho, 1,758.....E2 57
McCamey, Tex., 2,647....D1 84
McCarthy, mtn., Mont.....E4 70
McCaysville, Ga., 1,619...B2 55
McChesneytown, Pa., 400.*F2 81
McClain, co., Okla.,
  14,157.............C4 79
McCleary, Wash., 1,265...B2 86
MacClenny, Fla., 2,733...B4 54
Macclesfield, Eng.,
  44,030.............D5 4
McCloud, Calif., 1,643...B2 50
McClure, Ohio, 699......A2 78
McClure, Pa., 1,094......E7 81
McColl, S.C., 2,524......B8 82
McComas, W. Va., 900...D3 87
McComb, Miss., 11,969...D3 68
McComb, Ohio, 1,329....A2 78
McCone, co., Mont.,
  2,875.............C11 70
McConnellsburg, Pa.,
  1,228.............G6 81
McConnelsville, Ohio,
  2,107.............C4 78
McCook, Nebr., 8,285....D5 71
McCook, Co., S. Dak.,
  7,246.............G8 77
McCormick, S.C., 1,864..D3 82
McCormick, co., S.C.,
  7,955.............D3 82
McCracken, co., Ky.,
  58,281.............e9 62
McCreary, Man., Can.,
  597..............D2 40
McCreary, co., Ky.,
  12,548.............D5 62
McCrory, Ark., 1,378.....B4 49
McCulloch, co., Tex.,
  8,571.............D3 84
McCurtain, Okla., 575....B7 79
McCurtain, co., Okla.,
  28,642.............C7 79
McDermott, Ohio, 900....D2 78
McDonald, Ohio, 3,177...A5 78
McDonald, Pa., 2,879....k13 81
MacDonald, W. Va.,
  300...........D3, D7 87
McDonald, co., Mo.,
  12,357.............E3 69

McDonough, Ga., 2,675...C2 55
McDonough, co., Ill.,
  36,653.............C3 58
McDowell, co., N.C.,
  30,648.............f10 76
McDowell, co., W. Va.,
  50,606.............D3 87
McDuffie, co., Ga.,
  15,276.............C4 55
Macedon, N.Y., 1,168....B3 75
Macedonia, reg., Eur.....*B4 14
Macedonia, rep., Yugo.,
  1,406,003..........*D5 10
Maceió, Braz., 242,867....D7 27
Macerata, It., 32,500....C4 9
McEwen, Tenn., 1,237....A4 83
McFarland, Calif., 4,177...E4 50
McFarland, Wis., 2,386...E4 88
McGehee, Ark., 4,683....D4 49
McGill, Nev., 2,164......B4 72
MacGillicuddy's Reeks,
  mts., Ire............E2 4
McGrann, Pa., 500.....*E2 81
McGraw, N.Y., 1,319....C4 75
MacGregor, Man., Can.,
  642..............E2 40
McGregor, Iowa, 990....A6 60
McGregor, Tex., 4,365....D4 84
McGuffey, Ohio, 704.....B2 78
McGuire, mtn., Idaho....D4 57
Machado, Braz.,
  11,119............C3, k9 30
Machala, Ec., 46,100......B2 31
McHenry, Ill., 6,772...A5, h8 58
McHenry, co., Ill.,
  111,555.............A5 58
McHenry, co., N. Dak.,
  8,977.............B5 77
Machias, Maine, 1,368,
  (2,441 ▲)...........D5 64
Machida, Jap., 202,801..*n18 18
Machilipatnam (Bandar),
  India, 112,612.......E7 20
Macías Nguema Biyoga,
  reg., Equat. Gui.,
  83,000...........*H6 22
Măcin, Rom., 6,533......C9 10
McIntoch, Minn., 753....C3 67
McIntosh, co., Ga., 7,371..E5 55
McIntosh, co., N. Dak.,
  5,545.............D6 77
McIntosh, co., Okla.,
  12,472.............B6 79
Mack, Ohio, 6,000......*D2 78
Mackay, Austl., 19,101
  (*28,416)...........D8 25
Mackay, Idaho, 539......F5 57
McKean, co., Pa., 51,915..C4 81
McKeesport, Pa.,
  37,977..........F4, r14 81
McKees Rocks, Pa.,
  11,901..........F1, k13 81
McKenney, Va., 489.....D5 85
McKenzie, Tenn., 4,873...A3 83
McKenzie, co., N. Dak.,
  6,127.............C2 77
Mackenzie, dist., N.W.
  Ter., Can., 26,500....D11 36
Mackenzie, mts., Can.....C7 33
McKenzie, riv.,
  N. W. Ter., Can.....C8 36
Mackinac, co., Mich.,
  9,660.............B5 66
Mackinac Island, Mich.,
  517..............C6 66
Mackinaw, Ill., 1,293....C4 58
Mackinaw City, Mich.,
  810..............C6 66

McKinley, Minn., 317.....C6 67
McKinley, co., N. Mex.,
  43,391.............B4 48
McKinley, mtn., Alsk.....C9 47
McKinley Heights, Ohio,
  1,700.............*A5 78
McKinleyville, Calif.,
  2,000.............B1 50
McKinney, Tex., 15,193...C4 84
McKittrick Summit, mtn.,
  Calif..............E4 50
Macklin, Sask., Can., 829..E1 39
McKnight, Pa..........*E1 81
McKnownville, N.Y.,
  3,500.............*C7 75
McLaughlin, S. Dak.,
  863..............E5 77
McLean, Tex., 1,183.....B2 84
McLean, Va., 17,698.....g12 85
McLean, co., Ill., 104,389..C5 58
McLean, co., Ky., 9,062...C2 62
McLean, co., N. Dak.,
  11,252.............C4 77
McLean, mtn., Maine.....A4 64
McLeansboro, Ill., 2,630...E5 58
McLennan, Alta., Can.,
  1,090.............B2 38
McLennan, co., Tex.,
  147,553............D4 84
McLeod, co., Minn.,
  27,662............F4 67
McLeod Lake, B.C., Can.,
  123............B6, n18 37
McLoud, Okla., 2,159....B4 79
McLoughlin, mtn., Oreg...E4 80
McLouth, Kans.,
  623............C8, k15 61
McMasterville, Que.,
  Can., 2,518........*D4 42
McMechen, W. Va.,
  2,808............B4, g8 87
McMillan Manor, Calif.,
  1,000.............*E4 50
McMinn, co., Tenn.,
  35,462............D9 83
McMinnville, Oreg.,
  10,125..........B3, h11 80
McMinnville, Tenn.,
  10,662.............D8 83
McMullen, co., Tex.,
  1,095.............E3 84
McMurray, Alta., Can.,
  1,186...........A5, f8 38
McNair, Tex., 2,039.....E5 84
McNairy, co., Tenn.,
  18,369.............B3 83
McNary, Ariz., 900......B4 48
McNeill, mtn., B.C., Can..B2 37
Macomb, Ill., 19,643.....C3 58
Macomb, co., Mich.,
  625,309............F8 66
Macon, Fr., 33,445......D6 5
Macon, Ga., 122,423
  (*212,800)..........D3 55
Macon, Ill., 1,249.......D5 58
Macon, Miss., 2,614.....B5 68
Macon, Mo., 15,432.....B5 69
Macon, co., Ala., 24,841..C4 46
Macon, co., Ga., 12,933...D2 55
Macon, co., Ill., 125,010...D5 58
Macon, co., Mo., 5,301...B5 69
Macon, co., N.C., 15,788...f9 76
Macon, co., Tenn., 12,315..C7 83
Macoupin, co., Ill.,
  44,557.............D4 58
McPherson, Kans., 10,851.D6 61
McPherson, co., Kans.,
  24,778............D6 61

McPherson, co., Nebr.,
  623..............C4 71
McPherson, co., S. Dak.,
  5,022.............E6 77
McRae, Ga., 3,151......D4 55
McRoberts, Ky., 1,037...C7 62
McSherrystown, Pa.,
  2,773.............G7 81
Macksville, Kans., 484...E5 61
MacTier, Ont., Can., 851..B5 41
Macungie, Pa., 1,414....E10 81
McVeigh, Ky., 800......C7 62
Ma'dabā, Jordan, 11,224..C3 15
Madagascar, country, Afr.,
  7,290,000..........E9 24
Madawaska, Maine,
  4,452 (5,585 ▲)........A4 64
Madawaska, co., N.B.,
  Can., 37,306........B1 43
Madeira, Ohio, 6,713.....o13 78
Madeira Beach, Fla.,
  4,177.............*E4 54
Madeira Is., reg., Port.
  245,000............B1 22
Madelia, Minn., 2,316....F4 67
Madera, Calif., 16,044....D3 50
Madera, Mex., 9,759.....B3 34
Madera, co., Calif.,
  41,519.............D4 50
Madgaon, India, 41,655
  (*48,593)...........E5 20
Madhya Pradesh, state,
  India, 41,654,119......D6 20
Madill, Okla., 2,875......C5 79
Madīnat ash Sha'b,
  P.D.R. of Yem., 10,000..G4 15
Madison, Ala., 3,086.....A3 46
Madison, Ala., 900......C3 46
Madison, Conn., 4,310...D6 52
Madison, Fla., 3,737.....B3 54
Madison, Ga., 2,890.....C3 55
Madison, Ill., 7,042......E3 58
Madison, Ind., 13,081....G7 59
Madison, Kans., 1,061...D7 61
Madison, Maine, 2,920
  (4,278 ▲)...........D3 64
Madison, Minn., 2,242...E2 67
Madison, Mo., 540......B5 69
Madison, Nebr., 1,595....C8 71
Madison, N.J., 16,710....B4 74
Madison, N.C., 2,018....A3 76
Madison, Ohio, 1,678....A4 78
Madison, S. Dak., 6,315...G9 77
Madison, W. Va.,
  2,342...........C3, m12 87
Madison, Wis., 171,769
  (*248,100)..........E4 88
Madison, co., Ala.,
  186,540............A3 46
Madison, co., Ark., 9,453..B2 49
Madison, co., Fla., 13,481..B3 54
Madison, co., Ga., 13,517..B3 55
Madison, co., Idaho,
  13,452............F7 57
Madison, co., Ill., 250,934..E4 58
Madison, co., Ind.,
  138,451............D6 59
Madison, co., Iowa,
  11,558............C3 60
Madison, co., Ky., 42,730.C5 62
Madison, co., Miss.,
  29,737............C3 68
Madison, co., Mo., 8,641..D7 69
Madison, co., Mont.,
  5,014.............E4 70
Madison, co., Nebr.,
  27,402............C8 71

Madison, co., N.Y., 62,864 . . . . C5 75
Madison, co., N.C., 16,003 . . . . f10 76
Madison, co., Ohio, 28,318 . . . . C2 78
Madison, co., Tenn., 65,727 . . . . B3 83
Madison, co., Tex., 7,693 . . D5 84
Madison, co., Va., 8,638 . . B4 85
Madison, par., La., 15,065 . . B4 63
Madison Heights, Mich., 38,599 . . . . o15 66
Madison Heights, Va., 3,000 . . . . C3 85
Madisonville, Ky., 15,332 . . C2 62
Madisonville, La., 801 . . . . D5, h11 63
Madisonville, Tenn., 2,614 . . . . D9 83
Madisonville, Tex., 2,881 . . D5 84
Madium, Indon., 136,147 . . . . *G4 19
Madoc, Ont., Can., 1,347 . . C7 41
Madras, India, 2,469,449 (*3,200,000) F7 20
Madras, Oreg., 1,689 . . . . . . C5 80
Madre de Dios, dept, Peru, 25,269 . . . . D3 31
Madrid, Iowa, 2,448 . . C4, e8 60
Madrid, N.Y., 700 . . . . f9 75
Madrid, Sp., 3,120,941 (*3,525,000) B4, p17 8
Madrid, prov., Sp., 3,379,800 . . . . *B4 8
Madridejos, Phil., 3,041 . . *C6 19
Madridejos, Sp., 9,795 . . . . C4 8
Madurai, India, 549,114 (*725,000) G6 20
Maebashi, Jap., 233,632 . . . . H9, m18 18
Maeser, Utah, 1,248 . . . . . . A7 72
Mafeking, S. Afr., 6,493 . . . F5 24
Mafra, Braz., 19,312 . . . . . . D3 30
Magadan, Sov. Un., 92,000 . . . . D18 13
Magallanes, prov., Chile, 85,300 . . . . E2, h11 28
Magangué, Col., 27,354 (64,651▲) B3 32
Magdalena, Mex., 10,281 . . A2 34
Magdalena, N. Mex., 652 . . . . B5 48
Magdalena, dept., Col., 627,000 . . . . A3 32
Magdalena, riv., Col. C3 27
Magdalena Contreras, Mex., 2,952 . . . . h9 34
Magdalen Islands, co., Que., Can., 12,479 . . . . . B8 43
Magdeburg, Ger. Dem. Rep., 274,146 (*385,000) . B5 6
Magé, Braz., 10,712 . . . . h6 30
Magee, Miss., 2,973 . . . . D4 68
Magelang, Indon., 110,308 . G4 19
Magenta, It., 22,100 . . . . . . B2 9
Maglie, It., 13,028 . . . . D7 9
Magna, Utah, 8,400 . . A5, C2 72
Magnitogorsk, Sov. Un., 364,000 . . . . D8 13
Magnolia, Ark., 11,303 . . . . D2 49
Magnolia, Miss., 1,970 . . . . D3 68
Magnolia, N.J., 5,893 . . . . . D2 74
Magnolia, N.C., 614 . . . . . . C4 76
Magnolia, Ohio, 1,064 . . . . B4 78
Magoffin, co., Ky., 10,443 . . C6 62
Magog, Que., Can., 13,281 (*14,383) D5 42
Magrath, Alta., Can., 1,215 . . . . E4 38
Magwe, Bur., 13,270 . . . . . . D9 20
Mahameru, mtn., Indon. . . . G4 19
Mahanoy City, Pa., 7,257 . . E9 81
Maharashtra, state, India, 50,412,235 . . . . D5 20
Mahaska, co., Iowa, 22,177 . . . . C5 60
Mahbubnagar, India, 51,756 . . . . E6 20
Mahe, India, 8,972 . . . . F6 20
Mahnomen, Minn., 1,313 . . C3 67
Mahnomen, co., Minn., 5,638 . . . . C2 67
Mahoganny, mtn., Oreg. D9 80
Mahomet, Ill., 1,296 . . . . . . C5 58
Mahón, Sp., 16,619 . . . . C8 8
Mahone Bay, N.S., Can., 1,333 . . . . E5 43
Mahoning, co., Ohio, 304,545 . . . . B5 78
Mahopac, N.Y., 5,265 . . . . D7, m15 75
Mahtomedi, Minn., 2,640 . . E7 67
Mahwah, N.J., 7,500 . . . . . . A4 74
Maiden, N.C., 2,416 . . . . . . B1 76
Maidstone, Sask., Can., 577 . . . . D1 39
Maidstone, Eng., 71,250 . . . E7 4

Maiduguri, Nig., 139,965 . . F7 22
Maimana, Afg., 30,000 . . . . A3 20
Maine, former prov., Fr . . . C3 5
Maine, state, U.S., 1,045,000 64
Maine-et-Loire, dept., Fr., 584,709 . . . . *D3 5
Maintirano, Mad., 3,100 . . . . D8 24
Main Topsail, mtn., Newf., Can. D3 44
Mainz, Ger., Fed. Rep. of, 181,112 . . . . C4 6
Maipú, Arg., 18,000 . . . . . . B5 28
Maiquetía, Ven., 59,238 . . A4 32
Maisonette, N.B., Can., 627 . . . . B4 43
Maisons-Alfort, Fr., 53,149 . . . . g10 5
Maisons-Laffitte, Fr., 24,223 . . . . g9 5
Maitland, Austl., 30,963 . . F9 25
Maitland (Lake Maitland), Fla., 7,157 . . *D5 54
Maize, Kans., 785 . . . . . . g12 61
Maizuru, Jap., 81,000 (95,895▲) I7, n14 18
Majagual, Col., 2,197 . . . . . B3 32
Majestic, Ky., 400 . . . . C7 62
Major, co., Okla., 7,529 . . A3 79
Majunga, Mad., 47,700 . . . . D9 24
Makaha, Haw., 4,644 . . . . g9 56
Makarov Shirutoru, Sov. Un., 5,000 . . . . B11 18
Makarska, Yugo., 3,637 . . D3 10
Makasar, see Ujung Pandang, Indon.
Makati, Phil., 264,918 . . . *o3 19
Makawao, Haw., 1,066 . . . C5 56
Makaweli, Haw., 500 . . . . B2 56
Makeyevka, Sov. Un., 392,000 . . . . G11, q20 12
Makhachkala, Sov. Un., 186,000 . . . . E7 13
Makhlata, Bul., 6,537 . . . . D7 10
Makurazaki, Jap., 30,084 . . . . K5 18
Makurdi, Nig., 53,967 . . . . G6 22
Malabar, Fla., 634 . . . . D6 54
Malabo, Equat. Gui., 17,500 (37,152 ▲) H6 22
Malacca, state, Mala., 372,100 . . . . E2 19
Malad City, Idaho, 1,848 . . G6 57
Málaga, Col., 9,674 . . . . . . B3 32
Malaga, N.J., 950 . . . . D2 74
Málaga, Sp., 361,282 . . . . . D3 8
Málaga, prov., Sp., 830,900 . . . . *D3 8
Malagasy Republic, see Madagascar, country, Afr.
Malakāl, Sud., 9,680 . . . . . . G4 23
Malakoff, Fr., 36,198 . . . . g10 5
Malakoff, Tex., 2,045 . . . . C4 84
Malang, Indon., 422,428 . . G4 19
Malanje, Ang., 4,779 . . . . . B3 24
Malartic, Que., Can., 5,347 . . . . k11 42
Malatya, Tur., 128,841 . . C12 14
Malawi, country, Afr., 4,845,000 . . . . C6 24
Malaya Vishera, Sov. Un., 25,000 . . . . B9 12
Malaybalay, Phil., 10,193 . D7 19
Malaysia, country, Asia, 11,295,000 . . . . E4 19
Malbork, Pol., 30,900 . . . . A5 7
Malchin, Ger. Dem. Rep., 6,825 . . . . B6 6
Malden, Mass., 56,127 . . . . B5, g11 65
Malden, Mo., 5,374 . . . . . . E8 69
Malden, W. Va., 400 . . . . m12 87
Maldives, country, Asia, 126,000 . . . . G5 20
Maldonado, Ur., 15,005 . . E2 30
Maldonado, dept., Ur., 62,344 . . . . *E2 30
Malegaon, India, 191,847 . . . . *D5 20
Māler Kotla, India, 48,536 (*48,859) B6 20
Malheur, co., Oreg., 23,169 . . . . D9 80
Mali, country, Afr., 5,425,000 . . . . F3 22
Malibu, Calif., 7,000 . . . m11 50
Malin, Oreg., 486 . . . . E5 80
Malinec, Czech., 6,551 . . . . D5 7
Malita, Phil., 5,947 . . . . . . *D7 19
Malkara, Tur., 13,108 . . . . B6 14
Mallawī, Eg., 59,938 . . . . . C4 23
Malleco, prov., Chile, 193,200 . . . . B2 28
Mallory, W. Va., 800 . . . . *D3 87
Mallow, Ire., 5,901 . . . . . . D2 4

Malmédy, Bel., 6,376 . . . . . . B7 5
Malmö, Swe., 258,830 (*315,000) J5 11
Malmöhus, co., Swe., 697,500 . . . . *J5 11
Maloarkhangelsk, Sov. Un., 10,000 . . . . E11 12
Malolos, Phil., 73,996 . . . o13 19
Malone, Fla., 667 . . . . B1 54
Malone, N.Y., 8,048 . . . . . f10 75
Maloyaroslavets, Sov. Un., 21,000 . . . . D11 12
Malta, Mont., 2,195 . . . . . . B9 70
Malta, Ohio, 1,017 . . . . C4 78
Malta, country, Eur., 340,000 . . . . A7 22
Malton, Eng., 4,000 . . . . . . C6 4
Malvern, Ark., 8,739 . . C3, g8 49
Malvern, Iowa, 1,158 . . . . D2 60
Malvern, Ohio, 1,256 . . . . B4 78
Malvern, Pa., 2,583 . F10, o19 81
Malverne, N.Y., 10,036 . . *G2 52
Mamanguape, Braz., 12,138 . . . . *D7 27
Mamaroneck, N.Y., 18,909 . . . . h13 75
Mamba, Jap. m17 18
Mamers, Fr., 4,869 . . . . C4 5
Mammoth, Ariz., 1,953 . . . C3 48
Mammoth, W. Va., 700 . . . . C3, m13 87
Mamou, Guinea, 9,000 . . . F2 22
Mamou, La., 3,275 . . . . . . D3 63
Man, W. Va., 1,201 . . D3, n12 87
Man, Isle of, see Isle of Man, Br. dep., Eur.
Manabi, prov., Ec., 743,200 . . . . B1 31
Manacor, Sp., 19,224 . . . . . C7 8
Manado, Indon., 169,684 . . E6 19
Managua, Nic., 398,514 . . . E7 34
Manahawkin, N.J., 1,278 . . D4 74
Manakara, Mad., 12,000 . . . . E9 24
Manama, Bahrain, 89,112 (*145,000) D5 15
Mananjary, Mad., 15,600 . . E9 24
Manasquan, N.J., 4,971 . . . C4 74
Manassas, Va., 9,164 . . B5, g12 85
Manassas Park, Va., 6,844 . . . . *B5 85
Manatee, co., Fla., 97,115 . E4 54
Manatí, P.R., 13,483 (30,559 ▲) *G11 35
Manaus, Braz., 284,118 . . D4 27
Manawa, Wis., 1,105 . . . . D5 88
Mancelona, Mich., 1,255 . . D5 66
Mancha, reg., Sp. C4 8
Mancha Real, Sp., 7,855 . . D4 8
Manchaug, Mass., 900 . . . B4 65
Manche, dept., Fr., 451,939 . . . . *C3 5
Manchester, Conn., 47,994 . . . . B6 52
Manchester, Eng., 542,430 (*2,875,000) . . . D5 4
Manchester, Ga., 4,779 . . . D2 55
Manchester, Iowa, 4,641 . . B6 60
Manchester, Ky., 1,664 . . . C6 62
Manchester, Md., 1,466 . . . A4 53
Manchester, Mass., 5,151 . . . . A6, f12 65
Manchester, Mich., 1,650 . F6 66
Manchester, Mo., 5,031 . . f12 69
Manchester, N.H., 87,754 (*137,800) F5 73
Manchester, N.Y., 1,305 . . C3 75
Manchester, Ohio, 2,195 . . D2 78
Manchester, Pa., 2,391 . . . F8 81
Manchester, Tenn., 6,208 . . B5 83
Manchester Depot, Vt., 500 . . . . E1 73
Manchouli (Lupin), China, 30,000 . . . . B8 17
Manchuria, reg., China . . . B10 17
Mandalay, Bur., 195,300 . D10 20
Mandan, N. Dak., 11,093 . . D5 77
Mandasor, India, 52,347 . . D6 20
Manderson, Wyo., 117 . . . . B5 89
Mandeville, Jam., 13,100 . . E5 35
Mandeville, La., 2,571 . . . . D5, h11 63
Mandurah, Austl., 5,039 . . F2 25
Manduria, It., 27,800 . . . . . D6 9
Māndvi, India, 27,849 . . . . D4 20
Manfalūṭ, Eg., 34,132 . . . . C4 23
Manfredonia, It., 40,200 . . D5 9
Mangalore, India, 165,174 (*215,122) F5 20
Mangham, La., 544 . . . . . . B4 63
Mangum, Okla., 4,066 . . . . C2 79
Manhasset, N.Y., 8,530 . . F2 52
Manhattan, Ill., 1,530 . . . *B6 58
Manhattan, N.Y., 1,539,233 . . . . *B5 75
Manhattan Beach, Calif., 35,352 . . . . n12 50

Manheim, Pa., 5,434 . . . . . . F9 81
Manhuaçu, Braz., 15,300 . . C4 30
Manila, Ark., 1,961 . . . . . . B5 49
Manila, Phil., 1,330,788 (*4,350,000) o13 19
Manilla, Iowa, 943 . . . . C2 60
Manipur, state, India, 1,072,753 . . . . D9 20
Manisa, Tur., 72,276 . . . . . C6 14
Manistee, Mich., 7,723 . . . D4 66
Manistee, co., Mich., 20,393 . . . . D4 66
Manistique, Mich., 4,324 . . C4 66
Manito, Ill., 1,334 . . . . C4 58
Manitoba, prov., Can., 1,010,000 40
Manitoba, lake, Man., Can. D2 40
Manitou, Man., Can., 863 . . . . E2 40
Manitou Beach, Mich., 1,800 . . . . *G6 66
Manitoulin, dist., Ont., Can., 10,544 . . . . B2 41
Manitou Springs, Colo., 4,278 . . . . C6 51
Manitowoc, Wis., 33,430 (*57,300) . . D6, h10 88
Manitowoc, co., Wis., 82,294 . . . . D6 88
Maniwaki, Que., Can., 6,689 . . . . C2 42
Manizales, Col., 256,300 . . B2 32
Manjimup, Austl., 3,523 . . F2 25
Mankato, Kans., 1,287 . . . C5 61
Mankato, Minn., 30,895 . . F5 67
Manlius, N.Y., 4,295 . . . . . C5 75
Manlléu, Sp., 9,410 . . . . . . A7 8
Manly, Iowa, 1,294 . . . . . . A4 60
Mannar, Sri Lanka, 11,157 . . . . G6 20
Mannheim, Ger., Fed. Rep. of, 328,411 (*1,265,000) . D4 6
Manning, Alta., Can., 896 . . . . A2 38
Manning, Iowa, 1,656 . . . . C2 60
Manning, S.C., 4,025 . . . . . D7 82
Mannington, W. Va., 2,747 . . . . B4, h10 87
Mannum, Austl., 2,036 . . . G2 26
Mannville, Alta., Can., 632 . . . . C5 38
Manomet, Mass., 500 . . . . C6 65
Manomet, hill, Mass. C6 65
Manono, Zaire, 19,500 . . . B5 24
Manor, Pa., 2,276 . . . . *F2 81
Manorhaven, N.Y., 5,488 . . . . *E7 75
Manosque, Fr., 7,454 . . . . . F6 5
Manresa, Sp., 58,110 . . . . . B6 8
Manseau, Que., Can., 837 . . . . C5 42
Mansfield, Eng., 57,820 (*197,000) D6 4
Mansfield, Ill., 870 . . . . C5 58
Mansfield, La., 6,432 . . . . . B2 63
Mansfield, Mass., 4,778 (9,939 ▲) B5 65
Mansfield, Ohio, 55,047 (*112,100) B3 78
Mansfield, Pa., 4,114 . . . . . C7 81
Mansfield, Tex., 3,658 . . . . n9 84
Mansfield, mtn., Vt. B2 73
Mansfield Southeast, Ohio *B3 78
Manson, Iowa, 1,993 . . . . . B3 60
Mansura, La., 1,699 . . . . . . C3 63
Manta, Ec., 33,622 . . . . . . B1 31
Manteca, Calif., 13,845 . . . D3 50
Manteno, Ill., 2,864 . . . . . B6 58
Mantes [la-Jolie], Fr., 26,058 (*58,000) C4 5
Manti, Utah, 1,803 . . . . . . D4 72
Manton, Mich., 1,107 . . . . D5 66
Mantova, It., 66,100 . . . . . B3 9
Mantua, N.J., 1,900 . . . . . . D2 74
Mantua, Ohio, 1,199 . . . . . A4 78
Manuel Benavides, Mex., 1,314 . . . . B4 34
Manuels, Newf., Can., 724 . . . . *E5 44
Manukau, N.Z., 111,200 . . . . *L15 26
Manville, N.J., 13,029 . . . . B3 74
Manville, R.I., 3,500 . . . . B11 52
Many, La., 3,112 . . . . C2 63
Manzanares, Sp., 17,847 . . C4 8
Manzanillo, Cuba, 77,900 (88,900 ▲) D5 35
Manzanillo, Mex., 20,777 . . . . D4, n11 34
Mapastepec, Mex., 5,907 . . . . D6 34
Maple, Ont., Can., 1,552 . . . . k14 41
Maple Bluff, Wis., 1,974 . . E4 88
Maple Creek, Sask., Can., 2,268 . . . . H1 39

Maple Heights, Ohio, 34,093....h9 78
Maple Lake, Minn., 1,124..E4 67
Maple Lane, Ind........*A5 59
Maple Mount, Ky., 500...C2 62
Maple Plain, Minn., 1,169............m11 67
Maple Rapids, Mich., 683.............E6 66
Maple Shade, N.J., 16,464............D2 74
Mapleton, Iowa, 1,647..B2 60
Mapleton, Maine, 500 (1,598 ▲).........B4 64
Mapleton, Minn., 1,307..G5 67
Mapleton, Oreg., 900....C3 80
Mapleton, Utah, 1,980..D2 72
Maplewood, La., 470....D2 63
Maplewood, Minn., 25,000...........m12 67
Maplewood, Mo., 12,785..f13 69
Maplewood, N.J., 24,932..B4 74
Maplewood, N.Y., 650...*C7 75
Maplewood Park, Pa., 2,000............*G11 81
Maputo, Moz. 90,000 (*250,000)......F6 24
Maquoketa, Iowa, 5,677..B7 60
Marabá, Braz., 14,593...D6 27
Maracaibo, Ven., 650,002..A3 32
Maracaju, Braz., 3,410...F5 27
Maracay, Ven., 255,134..A4 32
Maradi, Niger, 10,100...F6 22
Marāgheh, Iran, 54,106..B4 15
Maragogipe, Braz., 12,769...........*E7 27
Marana, Ariz., 500......C3 48
Maranguape, Braz., 8,715............*D7 27
Maranhão, state, Braz., 3,037,135.........*D6 27
Marañón, riv., Peru....B2 31
Maraş, Tur., 110,761....D11 14
Marathon, Ont., Can., 2,409............o18 41
Marathon, Fla., 4,397....H5 54
Marathon, Iowa, 447....B3 60
Marathon, N.Y., 1,053...C4 75
Marathon, Tex., 750..D1, o13 84
Marathon, Wis., 1,214...D4 88
Marathon, co., Wis., 97,457...........D4 88
Maravatío de Ocampo, Mex., 5,732.......n13 34
Mara Vista, Mass.......C6 65
Marawī, Sud., 1,620.....E4 23
Marbella, Sp., 8,982....D3 8
Marble, Minn., 682.....C5 67
Marble Cliff, Ohio, 715..m10 78
Marble Falls, Tex., 2,209..D3 84
Marblehead, Mass., 21,295........B6, f12 65
Marblehead, Ohio, 726...A3 78
Marbleton, Que., Can., 661.............D6 42
Marburg, Ger., Fed. Rep. of, 48,031.......C4 6
Marbury, Md., 500......C3 53
Marceline, Mo., 2,622...B5 69
Marcellus, Mich., 1,139..F5 66
Marcellus, N.Y., 2,017..C4 75
Marche, former prov., Fr..D4 5
Marche, pol. dist., It., 1,347,489........*C4 9
Marchena, Sp., 17,030...D3 8
Marches, reg., It., 1,358,100.........C4 9
Marcola, Oreg., 500.....C4 80
Marcos Juarez, Arg., 12,897...........A4 28
Marcus, Iowa, 1,272....B2 60
Marcus Hook, Pa., 3,041.G11 81
Marcy, mtn., N.Y......A7 75
Mardān, Pak., 109,000..B5 20
Mar Del Plata, Arg., 302,000...........B5 28
Mardin, Tur., 33,740...D13 14
Marechal Deodoro, Braz., 5,508............*D7 27
Marengo, Ill., 4,235.....A5 58
Marengo, Ind., 767......H5 59
Marengo, Iowa, 2,235...C5 60
Marengo, co., Ala., 23,819...........C2 46
Marenisco, Mich., 700...n12 66
Marfa, Tex., 2,647.....o12 84
Margaret, Ala., 685.....B3 46
Margaretville, N.Y., 816..C6 75
Margate, Eng., 49,680...E7 4
Margate, Fla., 8,867....*F6 54
Margate City, N.J., 10,576.E3 74
Margelan, Sov. Un., 95,000...........E10 13
Margherita, mtn., Ug., Zaire..............H3 23
Maria la Baja, Col., 5,739............A2 32
Mariana, is., Pac. O.....E6 2

Marianna, Ark., 6,196...C5 49
Marianna, Fla., 6,741....B1 54
Marianna, Pa., 875.....*F1 81
Mariánské Lázně, Czech., 13,581............D2 7
Maribo, co., Den., 127,700.........*J4 11
Maribor, Yugo., 97,167..B2 10
Maricopa, Calif., 740...E4 50
Maricopa, co., Ariz., 968,487..........C2 48
Mariemont, Ohio, 4,540..o13 78
Marienville, Pa., 900....D3 81
Maries, co., Mo., 6,851..C6 69
Mariestad, Swe., 20,379..H5 11
Marietta, Ga., 27,216..C2, h7 55
Marietta, Ohio, 16,861..C4 78
Marietta, Okla., 2,013...D4 79
Marietta, Pa., 2,838.....F8 81
Marietta, S.C., 1,000....A2 82
Marieville, Que., Can., 4,563............D4 42
Marília, Braz., 73,165.....C3 30
Marín, Sp., 7,261......A1 8
Marin, co., Calif., 206,758..C2 50
Marin City, Calif., 1,650..*C2 50
Marinduque, prov., Phil., 114,586..........*C6 19
Marine, Ill., 882.......E4 58
Marine City, Mich., 4,567..F8 66
Marinette, Wis., 12,696...C6 88
Marinette, co., Wis., 35,810............C5 88
Maringouin, La., 1,365...D4 63
Marinha Grande, Port., 4,698............C1 8
Marino, It., 33,700......H9 9
Marion, Ala., 4,289......C2 46
Marion, Ill., 11,724......F5 58
Marion, Ind., 39,607.....C6 59
Marion, Iowa, 18,028.....B6 60
Marion, Kans., 2,052.....D6 61
Marion, Ky., 3,008.......e9 62
Marion, La., 796.......B3 63
Marion, Mass., 1,262 (3,466 ▲)..........C6 65
Marion, Mich., 891......D5 66
Marion, N.Y., 850......B3 75
Marion, N.C., 3,335...B1, f10 76
Marion, Ohio, 38,646....B2 78
Marion, S.C., 7,435......C9 82
Marion, Va., 8,158......f10 85
Marion, Wis., 1,218.....D5 88
Marion, co., Ala., 23,788..A2 46
Marion, co., Ark., 7,000..A3 49
Marion, co., Fla., 69,030..C4 54
Marion, co., Ga., 5,099..D2 55
Marion, co., Ill., 38,986..E5 58
Marion, co., Ind., 792,299..E5 59
Marion, co., Iowa, 26,352..C4 60
Marion, co., Kans., 13 935..............D6 61
Marion, co., Ky., 16,714..C4 62
Marion, co., Miss., 22,871..D4 68
Marion, co., Mo., 28,121..B6 69
Marion, co., Ohio, 64,724..B2 78
Marion, co., Oreg., 151,309...........C4 80
Marion, co., S.C., 30,270..C9 82
Marion, co., Tenn., 20,577...........D8 83
Marion, co., Tex., 8,517..C5 84
Marion, co., W. Va., 61,356............B4 87
Marion Heights, Pa., 958..*D8 81
Marionville, Mo., 1,496..D4 69
Mariposa, Calif., 900....D4 50
Mariposa, co., Calif., 6,015............D3 50
Marissa, Ill., 2,004......E4 58
Maris Town, Miss......C3 68
Mariupol, see Zhdanov, Sov. Un.
Marka, Som., 17,700....H6 23
Markdale, Ont., Can., 1,090............C4 41
Marked Tree, Ark., 3,229..B5 49
Markesan, Wis., 1,285...E5 88
Markham, Ont., Can., 36,684.........D5, k15 41
Markham, Ill., 15,987.....k9 58
Markham, mtn., Ant....L7 2
Markle, Ind., 963.......C7 59
Markovka, Sov. Un., 5,000............G12 12
Marks, Miss., 2,609.....A3 68
Marksville, La., 4,519....C3 63
Marktredwitz, Ger., Fed. Rep. of, 16,209.......C6 6
Marlbank, Ont., Can., 237.............C7 41
Marlboro, Mass., 27,936.........B4, g9 65
Marlboro, N.J., 900.....C4 74
Marlboro, N.Y., 1,580...D6 75
Marlboro, co., S.C., 27,151............B8 82
Marlborough, N.H., 1,231.F3 73

Marlene Village, Oreg., 1,000............*B3 80
Marlette, Mich., 1,706...E7 66
Marley, Md., 2,500.....B4 53
Marlin, Tex., 6,351......D4 84
Marlinton, W. Va., 1,286..C4 87
Marlow, Okla., 4,027....C4 79
Marlowe, W. Va., 700...B7 87
Marlton, N.J., 10,180...D3 74
Marmande, Fr., 10,199..E4 5
Marmet, W. Va., 2,339..........C3, m12 87
Marmora, Ont., Can., 1,381............C7 41
Marmora, N.J., 500.....E3 74
Marmora, peak, It......D2 9
Marne, Mich., 500.....E5 66
Marne, dept., Fr., 485,388..........*C6 5
Maroa, Ill., 1,467......C5 58
Maroantsetra, Mad., 5,300............D9 24
Maromokotro, mtn., Mad..............C9 24
Maroochydore-Mooloolaba, Austl., 6,360........C9 26
Maroua, Cam.........F7 22
Marovoay, Mad., 14,000...........D9 24
Marquesas, is., Fr. Polynesia.......G11 2
Marquette, Kans., 578...D6 61
Marquette, Mich., 21,967..B3 66
Marquette, co., Mich., 64,686............B3 66
Marquette, co., Wis., 8,865............E4 88
Marquette Heights, Ill., 2,758............C4 58
Marrakech, Mor., 332,741..B3 22
Marrero, La., 35,000...k11 63
Marromeu, Moz.......D7 24
Mars, Pa., 1,488.......E1 81
Mars, hill, Maine......g7 64
Marsala, It., 42,100.....F4 9
Marseille, Fr., 889,029 (1,015,000).....F6 5
Marseilles, Ill., 4,320....B5 58
Marshall, Ark., 1,397....B3 49
Marshall, Ill., 3,468.....D6 58
Marshall, Mich., 7,253...F6 66
Marshall, Minn., 9,886...F3 67
Marshall, Mo., 12,051...B4 69
Marshall, N.C., 982....F10 76
Marshall, Tex., 22,937...C5 84
Marshall, Va., 500......B5 85
Marshall, Wis., 1,034...E4 88
Marshall, co., Ala., 54,211..A3 46
Marshall, co., Ill., 13,302..B4 58
Marshall, co., Ind., 34,986..B5 59
Marshall, co., Iowa, 41,076...........C4 60
Marshall, co., Kans., 13,139............C7 61
Marshall, co., Ky., 20,381..f9 62
Marshall, co., Minn., 13,060............B2 67
Marshall, co., Miss., 24,027............A4 68
Marshall, co., Okla., 7,682............C5 79
Marshall co., S. Dak., 5,965............E8 77
Marshall, co., Tenn., 17,319............B5 83
Marshall, co., W. Va., 37,598............B4 87
Marshallberg, N.C., 600..C6 76
Marshall Northeast, Tex..*C5 84
Marshallton, Del., 9,000..A6 35
Marshallton, Pa., 1,802..*D8 81
Marshalltown, Iowa, 26,219...........B5 60
Marshallville, Ga., 1,376..D3 55
Marshallville, Ohio, 693..B4 78
Marshfield, Mass., 2,562 (15,223 ▲)....B6, h13 65
Marshfield, Mo., 2,961...D5 69
Marshfield, Wis., 15,619...D3 88
Marshfield Hills, Mass., 1,350.........B6, h13 65
Mars Hill, Ind........E5, m10 59
Mars Hill, Maine, 1,384 (1,875 ▲).........B5 64
Mars Hill, N.C., 1,623...f10 76
Marshville, N.C., 1,405..C2 76
Marsing, Idaho, 610....F2 57
Marston, Mo., 666.....E8 69
Mart, Tex., 2,183.......D4 84
Martel, Que., Can., 1,009..A6 42
Martí, Cuba........D5 35
Martigues, Fr., 17,826...F6 5
Martin, Ky., 786.......C7 62
Martin, Mich., 502.....F5 66
Martin, S. Dak., 1,248...G4 77
Martin, Tenn., 7,781....A3 83
Martin, co., Fla., 28,035..E6 54
Martin, co., Ind., 10,909..G4 59

Martin, co., Ky., 9,377....C7 62
Martin, co., Minn., 24,316............G4 67
Martin, co., N.C., 24,730..B5 76
Martin, co., Tex., 4,774...C2 84
Martina [Franca], It., 28,500...........D6 9
Martinez, Calif., 16,506......C2, h8 50
Martinez, Ga., 7,300....C4 55
Martinique, Fr. dep., N.A., 355,000.......I14 35
Martinsburg, Pa., 2,088..F5 81
Martinsburg, W. Va., 14,626............B7 87
Martins Creek, Pa., 850..B2 81
Martins Ferry, Ohio, 10,757............B5 78
Martinsville, Ill., 1,374...D6 58
Martinsville, Ind., 9,723..F5 59
Martinsville, N.J., 900...B3 74
Martinsville (Independent City), Va., 19,653...........D3 85
Martos, Sp., 16,442 (23,990 ▲)........D4 8
Marudi, Mala., 2,663...E5 19
Maruf, Afg., 5,000.....B4 20
Marugame, Jap., 59,214...I6 18
Marvell, Ark., 1,980....C5 49
Mary, Sov. Un., 62,000..F9 13
Maryborough, Austl., 19,304............E9 25
Maryborough, Austl., 7,469............G7 25
Maryfield, Sask., Can., 476............H5 39
Maryland, state, U.S., 4,113,000............ 53
Maryland Heights, Mo., 6,000............f13 69
Maryport, Eng., 11,660..C5 4
Marys, peak, Oreg......C3 80
Mary's Harbour, Newf., Can., 264........B4 44
Marystown, Newf., Can., 4,960............E4 44
Marysville, Calif., 9,353...C3 50
Marysville, B.C., Can., 1,057............E10 37
Marysville, N. B., Can., 3,872............D3 43
Marysville, Kans., 3,588..C7 61
Marysville, Mich., 5,610..F8 66
Marysville, Ohio, 5,744..B2 78
Marysville, Pa., 2,328...F8 81
Marysville, Wash., 4,343..A3 86
Maryvale, Ariz......*C2 48
Maryville, Mo., 9,970....A3 69
Maryville, Tenn., 13,808.........D10, n14 83
Masan, Kor., 190,992....I4 18
Masaya, Nic., 30,753.....E7 34
Masbate, Phil., 17,749...C6 19
Masbate, prov., Phil., 335,971..........*H7 19
Mascara, Alg., 36,930....A5 22
Mascot, Tenn., 900..C10, m14 83
Mascota, Mex., 5,674...m11 34
Mascouche, Que., Can., 8,812............D4 42
Mascoutah, Ill., 5,045...E4 58
Mashhad (Meshed), Iran, 409,616..........B6 15
Masindi, Ug., 1,571....H4 23
Masisea, Peru, 1,742....C3 31
Masjed, Soleymān, Iran, 64,488...........C4 15
Maskinongé, Que., Can., 893............C4 42
Maskinongé, co., Que., Can., 21,466.......C4 42
Mason, Mich., 5,468....F6 66
Mason, Ohio, 5,677...C1, n13 78
Mason, Tex., 1,806.....D3 84
Mason, W. Va., 1,319...B2 87
Mason, co., Ill., 16,161..C4 58
Mason, co., Ky., 17,273..B6 62
Mason, co., Mich., 22,612..D4 66
Mason, co., Tex., 3,356..D3 84
Mason, co., Wash., 20,918..B2 86
Mason, co., W. Va., 24,306............C3 87
Mason City, Ill., 2,611...C4 58
Mason City, Iowa, 30,379..A4 60
Masontown, Pa., 4,226..G2 81
Masontown, W. Va., 868..B5 87
Mass, Mich., 500...B1, m12 66
Massa, It., 62,400 (*137,000)..........B3 9
Massac, co., Ill., 13,889..F5 58
Massachusetts, state, U.S., 5,822,000............ 65
Massaemett, mtn., Mass..A2 65
Massafra, It., 22,500....D6 9
Massa Marittima, It., 5,700............C3 9
Massanutten, mtn., Va....B4 85

Massapequa, N.Y., 26,821................G3 52
Massapequa Park, N.Y., 22,112................*E7 75
Massawa, Eth., 18,490....E5 23
Massena, N.Y., 14,042...f10 75
Masset, B.C., Can., 975....C1 37
Massey, Ont., Can., 1,324..A2 41
Massillon, Ohio, 32,539....B4 78
Massive, mtn., Colo....B4 51
Masson, Que., Can., 2,336................D2 42
Masterton, N.Z., 18,700..N15 26
Mastic, N.Y., 4,700......*n15 75
Mastic Beach, N.Y., 4,870................*F4 52
Mastung, Pak., 2,792....C4 20
Masuda, Jap., 34,000 (50,071▲)................I5 18
Masuria, reg., Pol........B6 7
Masury, Ohio, 5,180....A5 78
Matachewan, Ont., Can., 923................p19 41
Matadi, Zaire, 59,000....B2 24
Matador, Tex., 1,091....C2 84
Matagalpa, Nic., 23,500..E7 34
Matagorda, co., Tex., 27,913................E5 84
Matamoras, Pa., 2,244...D12 81
Matamoros, Mex., 137,749................B5 34
Matamoros [de la Laguna], Mex., 15,125................B4 34
Matane, Que., Can., 11,841................G20 36
Matane, co., Que., Can., 31,794................*G20 36
Matanzas, Cuba, 85,400...C3 35
Matanzas, prov., Cuba, 395,780................C3 35
Matapedia, co., Que., Can., 31,433................*G20 36
Matara, Sri Lanka .36,641................G7 20
Mataram, Indon., 17,601..G5 19
Mataró, Sp., 73,125......B7 8
Matawan, N.J., 9,136....C4 74
Matehuala, Mex., 28,799................C4 34
Matera, It., 44,300......D6 9
Mátészalka, Hung., 12,325................B6 10
Mateur, Tun., 12,714....F2 9
Matewan, W. Va., 651....D2 87
Matfield, Mass., 900......B6 65
Mather, Pa., 950.......G1 81
Mather, peak, Wyo.....B5 89
Mathews, co., Va., 7,168..C6 85
Mathis, Tex., 5,351.....E4 84
Mathura, India, 132,028 (*140,150)................C6 20
Matoaca, Va., 1,500....n18 85
Matoaka, W. Va., 608....D3 87
Mato Grosso, state, Braz., 1,623,618................B1 30
Matozinhos, Port., 37,694..B1 8
Matrah, Om., 14,000....E6 15
Matruh, Eg., 11,039....B3 23
Matsudo, Jap., 253,591...*I9 18
Matsue, Jap., 118,005....I6 18
Matsuida, Jap......m17 18
Matsumae, Jap......F10 18
Matsumoto, Jap., 162,931.......H9, m16 18
Matsuyama, Jap., 322,902..J6 18
Matsuzaka, Jap., 74,000 (102,138▲)..I8, o15 18
Matsuzaki, Jap......o17 18
Mattapoisett, Mass., 2,188 (4,500▲)................C6 65
Mattawa, Ont., Can., 2,881................A6, p20 41
Mattawamkeag, Maine, 700 (988▲)................C4 64
Matterhorn, mtn., Switz...E3 6
Matteson, Ill., 4,741....k9 58
Matthews, Ind., 728.....D7 59
Matthews, N.C., 783.....B2 76
Matthews, mtn., Mo.....D7 69
Matthew Town, Ba., 995................D7 35
Mattituck, N.Y., 1,995...n16 75
Mattoon, Ill., 19,681....D5 58
Mattydale, N.Y., 8,292...*B4 75
Matucana, Peru, 1,746...D2 31
Matun, Afg., 5,000......B4 20
Maturín, Ven., 121,662..B5 32
Maubeuge, Fr., 32,028 (*99,000)................B5 5
Maubin, Bur., 22,130....*E10 20
Mauch Chunk, see Jim Thorpe, Pa.
Maud, Ohio, 700.....C1, n13 78
Maud, Okla., 1,143.....B5 79
Maud, Tex., 1,107......C5 84
Maugansville, Md., 1,069..A2 53
Maugerville, N.B., Can., 631................D3 43

Maui (incl. Kalawao), co., Haw., 46,156......B4 56
Maui, isl., Haw.......C6 56
Mauldin, S.C., 3,797....*B3 82
Maule, prov., Chile, 94,300................B2 28
Maumee, Ohio, 15,937................A2, e6 78
Mauna Kea, vol., Haw...D6 56
Maunaloa, Haw., 872....B4 56
Mauna Loa, vol., Haw...D6 56
Mauritania, country, Afr., 1,275,000................E2 22
Mauritius, country, Afr., 875,000................*H24 2
Maury, co., Tenn., 44,028..B4 83
Mauston, Wis., 3,466....E3 88
Maverick, co., Tex., 18,093.E2 84
Maxcanú, Mex., 6,505....C7 34
Max Meadows, Va., 400..D2 85
Maxton, N.C., 1,885....C3 76
Maxwell, Iowa, 758....C4, e9 60
May, mtn., Alta., Can....B1 38
Mayagüez, P.R., 68,872 (85,857▲)......G11 35
Mayarí, Cuba, 17,600 (34,000▲)................D6 35
Maybee, Mich., 485.....F7 66
Maybeury, W. Va., 700..*D3 87
Maybole, Scot., 4,530....C4 4
Maybrook, N.Y., 1,536...D6 75
Mayen, Ger., Fed. Rep. of, 20,784................C3 6
Mayenne, Fr., 11,382....C5 5
Mayenne, dept., Fr., 252,762................*C3 5
Mayer, Ariz., 650.......B2 48
Mayerthorpe, Alta., Can., 663................C3 38
Mayes, co., Okla., 23,302..A6 79
Mayesville, S.C., 757....D7 82
Mayfield, Ky., 10,724....f9 62
Mayfield, N.Y., 981......B6 75
Mayfield, Ohio, 3,548...*A4 78
Mayfield, Pa., 2,176....C11 81
Mayfield Heights, Ohio, 22,139................A4 78
Mayking, Ky., 170......C7 62
Maykop, Sov. Un., 110,000................*E7 13
Maymyo, Bur., 22,287...D10 20
Maynard, Iowa, 503.....B6 60
Maynard, Mass., 9,710................B5, g10 65
Mayo, Yukon, Can.; 462..D6 36
Mayo, Fla., 793........B3 54
Mayo, Md., 2,154......C4 53
Mayo, S.C., 300.......A4 82
Mayo, co., Ire., 115,547..*D2 4
Mayodan, N.C., 2,875....A3 76
Mayon, vol., Phil.......C6 19
Mayotte, Fr. ter., Afr., 21,000................C9 24
May Pen, Jam., 26,200....F5 35
Mays Landing, N.J., 1,272................E3 74
Maysville, Ky., 7,411....B6 62
Maysville, Mo., 1,045...B3 69
Maysville, N.C., 912.....C5 76
Maysville, Okla., 1,380...C4 79
Mayville, Mich., 872....E7 66
Mayville, N.J........E3 74
Mayville, N.Y., 1,567...C1 75
Mayville, N. Dak., 2,554..C8 77
Mayville, Wis., 4,139....E5 88
Maywood, Calif., 16,996..*F4 50
Maywood, Ill., 29,019...k9 58
Maywood, N.J., 11,087...h8 74
Maywood, N.Y., 3,000...*C7 75
Mazamet, Fr., 16,171 (*28,000)................F5 5
Mazapil, Mex., 1,072....C4 34
Mazara Del Vallo, It., 40,000................F4 9
Mazar-I-Sharif, Afg., 70,000................A4 20
Mazarrón, Sp., 11,569....D5 8
Mazatenango, Guat., 24,156................E6 34
Mazatlán, Mex., 119,553..C3 34
Mazomanie, Wis., 1,217..E4 88
Mazon, Ill., 727........B5 58
Mazzarino, It., 17,789...F5 9
Mbabane, Swaz., 13,803..F6 24
Mbala, Zambia.........B6 24
Mbalmayo, Cam.......H7 22
Mbandaka, Zaire, 37,500..H1 23
Mbanza-Ngungu, Zaire, 11,600................B2 24
Mbeya, Tan., 6,932.....B6 24
Mead, Wash., 1,099..B8, g14 86
Meade, Kans., 1,899....E3 61
Meade, co., Kans., 4,912..E3 61
Meade, co., Ky., 18,796..C3 62
Meade, co., S. Dak., 17,020................F3 77
Meade, peak, Idaho....G7 57
Meaderville, Mont., 600..*D4 70

Meadowbrook, Ind., 3,400................*B7 59
Meadowbrook, W. Va., 500................k10 87
Meadow Lake, Sask., Can., 3,435................n7 39
Meadow Lands, Pa., 1,200................F1 81
Meadow Park, Fla., 700...F6 54
Meadowview, Va., 600...f10 85
Meadville, Pa., 16,573...C1 81
Meaford, Ont., Can., 4,045................C4 41
Meagher, co., Mont., 2,122................D6 70
Meath, co., Ire., 67,323..*D3 4
Meaux, Fr., 30,167......C5 5
Mebane, N.C., 2,433....A3 76
Mecca, Ind., 453........E3 59
Mecca (Makkah), Sau. Ar., 185,000................E2 15
Mechanic Falls, Maine, 2,193................D2 64
Mechanicsburg, Ohio, 1,686................B2 78
Mechanicsburg, Pa., 9,385..F7 81
Mechanicsville, Iowa, 989................C6 60
Mechanicsville, Va., 5,189..C5 85
Mechanicville, N.Y., 6,247................C7 75
Mechelen, Bel., 65,136...B6 5
Mecklenburg, co., N.C., 354,656................B2 76
Mecklenburg, co., Va., 29,426................D4 85
Mecklenburg, state, Ger. Dem. Rep., 2,139,640..*B6 6
Mecosta, co., Mich., 27,992................E5 66
Medan, Indon., 635,562......E1, m11 19
Medaryville, Ind., 732....B4 59
Medea, Alg., 36,992....A5 22
Medellín, Col., 913,000 (*1,240,000)................B2 32
Medfield, Mass., 5,300 (9,821▲)................h10 65
Medford, Mass., 64,397.......B5, g11 65
Medford, N.J., 1,448....D3 74
Medford, Okla., 1,304....A4 79
Medford, Oreg., 28,454 (*63,300)................E4 80
Medford, Wis., 3,454....C3 88
Medford Lakes, N.J., 4,792................D3 74
Medgidia, Rom., 17,943..C9 10
Media, Pa., 6,444..C11, p20 81
Mediapolis, Iowa, 1,242..C6 60
Medias, Rom., 46,400....B7 10
Medical Lake, Wash., 3,529.......B8, g13 86
Medicine Bow, peak, Wyo..E6 89
Medicine Hat, Alta., Can., 26,518 (*28,773)....D5, g8 38
Medicine Lodge, Kans., 2,545................E5 61
Medicine Park, Okla., 483..C3 79
Medina, N.Y., 6,415....B2 75
Medina, Ohio, 10,913....A4 78
Medina (Al Madīnah), Sau. Ar., 60,000................E2 15
Medina, Wash., 3,455...e11 86
Medina, co., Ohio, 82,717..A4 78
Medina, co., Tex., 20,249..E3 84
Medina del Campo, Sp., 14,327................B3 8
Medina Sidonia, Sp., 8,704................D3 8
Mediterranean, sea....D21 2
Medora, Ind., 788......G5 59
Medvezhegorsk, Sov. Un., 17,000................F16 11
Medway, Mass., 3,716 (7,938▲)....B5, h10 65
Medzhibozh, Sov. Un., 10,000................G6 12
Meekatharra, Austl., 921..E2 25
Meeker, Colo., 1,597....A3 51
Meeker, Okla., 683.....B5 79
Meeker, co., Minn., 18,810................E4 67
Meerane, Ger. Dem. Rep., 24,757................C6 6
Meerut, India, 270,993 (*367,754)................C6 20
Mégantic, co., Que., Can., 57,504................C6 42
Mégantic, mtn., Que., Can .D6 42
Megara, Grc., 17,294....C4 14
Meggett, S.C., 180....F7, k11 82
Meghalaya, state, India, 1,011,699................C9 20
Megunticook, mtn., Maine................D3 64
Mehun-sur-Yèvre, Fr., 4,735................D5 5

Meigs, Ga., 1,226......E2 55
Meigs, co., Ohio, 19,799..C3 78
Meigs, co., Tenn., 5,219..D9 83
Meihsien, China, 45,000...G8 17
Meiktila, Bur., 25,180....D10 20
Meiners Oaks, Calif., 5,000................*E4 50
Meiningen, Ger. Dem. Rep., 25,934.......C5 6
Meissen, Ger. Dem. Rep., 43,879................C6 6
Mejillones, Chile, 3,363...F3 27
Meknès, Mor., 248,369...B3 22
Mekong, riv., Asia......B2 19
Melaka (Malacca), Mala., 87,160 (*99,169)....E2 19
Melbourne, Austl., 74,877 (*2,497,993)....G8, n15 25
Melbourne, Fla., 40,236 (*93,600)................D6 54
Melbourne, Iowa, 661....C4 60
Melbourne Beach, Fla., 2,262................D6 54
Melcher, Iowa, 913.....C4 60
Melfi, It., 18,208.......D5 9
Melfort, Sask., Can., 4,725................E3 39
Melilla, Sp. dep., Afr., 77,700................A4 22
Melipilla, Chile, 15,593...A2 28
Melita, Man., Can., 1,038..E1 40
Melito di Porto Salvo, It., 8,880................F5 9
Melitopol, Sov. Un., 137,000................H10 12
Mellen, Wis., 1,168....B3 88
Mellette, co., S. Dak., 2,420................G5 77
Mělník, Czech., 15,283...n18 7
Melo, Ur., 33,741......E2 30
Melocheville, Que., Can., 1,666................q19 42
Melouprey, Camb., 10,000................*C3 19
Melrose, Fla., 800......C4 54
Melrose, Mass., 33,180................B5, g11 65
Melrose, Minn., 2,273...E4 67
Melrose, N. Mex., 636...B7 48
Melrose, Wis., 505.....D3 88
Melrose Park, Fla., 6,111..*F6 54
Melrose Park, Ill., 22,716..F2 58
Melrose Park, N.Y......*C4 75
Melrose Park, Pa., 3,700..*F11 81
Melun, Fr., 34,518 (*60,000)................C5 5
Melville, Sask., Can., 5,375................G4 39
Melville, La., 2,076....D4 63
Melville, isl., N.W. Ter., Can.........A11 36
Melvin, Ky., 700.......C7 62
Melvindale, Mich., 13,862................*F7 66
Memel, see Klaipeda, Sov. Un.
Memmingen, Ger., Fed. Rep. of, 35,301......E5 6
Memphis, Fla., 3,207....p10 54
Memphis, Mich., 1,121...F8 66
Memphis, Mo., 2,081...A5 69
Memphis, Tenn., 623,530 (*770,700)......B1, e9 83
Memphis, Tex., 3,227...B2 84
Memramcook, N.B., Can., 402................C5 43
Memramcook East, N.B., Can., 720......*C5 43
Mena, Ark., 4,530......C1 49
Menahga, Minn., 835....D3 67
Menands, N.Y., 3,449...C7 75
Menard, Tex., 1,740....D3 84
Menard, co., Ill., 9,685...C4 58
Menard, co., Tex., 2,646..D3 84
Menasha, Wis., 14,836.D5, h9 88
Mende, Fr., 9,713......E5 5
Mendenhall, Miss., 2,402..D4 68
Mendham, N.J., 3,729...B3 74
Mendocino, Calif., 950...C2 50
Mendocino, co., Calif., 51,101................C2 50
Mendon, Ill., 883.......C2 58
Mendon, Mass., 900 (2,524▲)................h9 65
Mendon, Mich., 949....F5 66
Mendon, Ohio, 672.....B1 78
Mendota, Calif., 2,705...D3 50
Mendota, Ill., 6,902....B4 58
Mendota Heights, Minn., 6,565................*F5 67
Mendoza, Arg., 118,568 (*400,000)................A3 28
Mendoza, prov., Arg., 824,036................A3 28
Menemen, Tur., 16,734................*C6 14
Menfi, It., 12,492......F4 9
Mengtzu, China, 9,000...G5 17

Menifee, co., Ky., 4,050...C6	62		
Menindee, Austl., 474.....F7	25		
Menlo Park, Calif., 26,826..k8	50		
Menlo Park, N.J.........B4	74		
Menlo Park Terrace, N. J., 4,300.........*B4	74		
Menominee, Mich., 10,748............C3	66		
Menominee, co., Mich., 24,587...........C3	66		
Menominee, co., Wis., 2,607.............C5	88		
Menominee, riv., Mich...C3	66		
Menomonee Falls, Wis., 31,697.............E5, m11	88		
Menomonie, Wis., 11,112..D2	88		
Mentana, It., 5,489.....g9	9		
Menton, Fr., 25,040 (*34,000)..........F7	5		
Mentone, Calif., 3,800...*E5	50		
Mentone, Ind., 830.....B5	59		
Mentor, Ohio, 36,912....A4	78		
Mentor Headlands, Ohio. *A4	78		
Mentor-on-the-Lake, Ohio, 6,517.........A4	78		
Meoqui, Mex., 12,308....B3	34		
Meppel, Neth., 19,847....A7	5		
Meppen, Ger., Fed. Rep. of, 19,383........B3	6		
Mequon, Wis., 12,150.........E6, m12	88		
Merano, It., 31,400.....A3	9		
Merauke, Indon., 3,600............G10	19		
Mercāra, India, 19,357.....F6	20		
Merced, Calif., 22,670.....D3	50		
Merced, co., Calif., 104,629...........D3	50		
Mercedes, Arg., 13,368....E4	29		
Mercedes, Arg., 25,778...........A5, g7	28		
Mercedes, Arg., 42,000...A3	28		
Mercedes, Tex.,9,355....F4	84		
Mercedes, Ur., 31,225....E1	30		
Mercer, Pa., 2,773.....D1	81		
Mercer, Wis., 750.......B3	88		
Mercer, co., Ill., 17,294...B3	58		
Mercer, co., Ky., 15,960..C5	62		
Mercer, co., Mo., 4,910...A4	69		
Mercer, co., N.J., 304,116...C3	74		
Mercer, co., N. Dak., 6,175.............C4	77		
Mercer, co., Ohio, 35,558..B1	78		
Mercer, co., Pa., 127,225..D1	81		
Mercer, co., W. Va., 63,206............D3	87		
Mercer Island, Wash., 19,047..........B3, e11	86		
Mercersburg, Pa., 1,727...G6	81		
Mercerville, N.J., 15,000..C3	74		
Merchantville, N.J., 4,425............*D2	74		
Meredith, N.H., 1,017 (2,904 ▲)............D4	73		
Meredosia, Ill., 1,178....D3	58		
Merefa, Sov. Un., 30,000..G11	12		
Mergui, Bur., 33,697.....F10	20		
Mérida, Mex., 212,097....C7	34		
Mérida, Sp., 34,297.....C2	8		
Mérida, Ven., 74,214......B3	32		
Mérida, state, Ven., 270,668...........B3	32		
Meriden, Conn., 55,959...C5	52		
Meridian, Idaho, 2,616...F2	57		
Meridian, Miss., 45,083....C5	68		
Meridian, Pa., 2,234....*E2	81		
Meridian, Tex., 1,162....D4	84		
Merioneth, co., Wales, 34,810..........*D5	4		
Merion Park, Pa.......*F11	81		
Merion Station, Pa., 7,400............*F11	81		
Meriwether, co., Ga., 19,461............C2	55		
Merkel, Tex., 2,163.......C3	84		
Merksem, Bel., 39,964...B6	5		
Merlin, Ont., Can., 595...E2	41		
Merlo, Arg., 188,868.....g7	28		
Mermentau, La., 756.....D3	63		
Mermentau, riv., La......E2	63		
Merredin, Austl., 3,596..F2	25		
Merriam, Kans., 10,851..B8	61		
Merrick, N.Y., 26,100....G2	52		
Merrick, co., Nebr., 8,751..C7	71		
Merrickville, Ont., Can., 947.............C9	41		
Merrill, Iowa, 790.......B1	60		
Merrill, Mich., 961......E6	66		
Merrill, Oreg., 722......E5	80		
Merrill, Wis., 9,502......C4	88		
Merrillan, Wis., 612.....D3	88		
Merrillville, Ind., 24,075..B3	59		
Merrimac, Mass., 2,400 (4,245 ▲)........A5	65		
Merrimack, N.H., 400....F5	73		
Merrimack, co., N.H., 80,925............E4	73		
Merrionette Park, Ill., 2,303............*B6	58		
Merritt, B.C., Can., 5,289..D7	37		
Merritt Island, Fla., 29,000............D6	54		
Mer Rouge, La., 819......B4	63		
Merryville, La., 1,286....D2	63		
Merseburg, Ger. Dem. Rep., 54,908.........C4	6		
Mersey, riv., Eng........D5	4		
Mersin, Tur., 112,982....D10	14		
Mersing, Mala., 7,228....E2	19		
Merthyr Tydfil, Wales, 55,100............E5	4		
Meru, mtn., Tan........I5	23		
Merzifon, Tur., 28,034...B10	14		
Mesa, Ariz., 62,853...C3, D2	48		
Mesa, co., Colo., 54,374..C2	51		
Mesa de Tijuana, Mex., 50,094...........*A1	34		
Mesagne, It., 28,600.....D6	9		
Meshkovskaya, Sov. Un...G13	12		
Mesilla, N. Mex., 1,713..E3	48		
Mesilla Park, N. Mex....E3	48		
Mesolongion, Grc., 11,614..C3	14		
Mesquite, Tex., 55,131....n10	84		
Messina, It., 270,200....E5	9		
Messina, S. Afr., 11,914..E6	24		
Messini, Grc., 6,625.....D3	14		
Messinia (Messenia), prov., Grc., 172,850..*D4	14		
Mestre, It., 73,435......B4	9		
Meta, dept., Col., 216,000..C3	32		
Meta, riv., Col.........B4	32		
Métabetchouan, Que., Can.,1,910.........A6	42		
Metairie, La., 155,000....k11	63		
Metamora, Ill., 2,176....C4	58		
Metamora, Ohio, 594.....A2	78		
Metán, Arg., 12,849.....E3	29		
Metcalfe, co., Ky., 8,177..C4	62		
Meteghan, N.S., Can., 925.E3	43		
Methuen, Mass., 35,456..A5	65		
Metkovic, Yugo., 4,488...D3	10		
Metropolis, Ill., 6,940....F5	58		
Metter, Ga., 2,912......D4	55		
Metuchen, N.J., 16,031....B4	74		
Metz, Fr., 107,537 (*165,000)..........C7	5		
Metzger, Oreg., 4,200...h12	80		
Meudon, Fr., 50,623.....g9	5		
Meulaboh, Indon., 7,619.m11	19		
Meurthe-et-Moselle, dept., Fr., 705,413.........*C7	5		
Meuse, dept., Fr., 209,513...........*C6	5		
Mexia, Tex., 5,943........D4	84		
Mexicali, Mex., 263,498..A1	34		
Mexico, Ind., 750.......C5	59		
Mexico, Maine, 3,325....D2	64		
Mexico, Mo., 11,807.....B6	69		
Mexico, N.Y., 1,555.....B4	75		
Mexico, country, N.A., 55,310,000........G10	33		
México, state, Mex., 2,188,800.......D5, n14	34		
Mexico, gulf, N.A.......G11	33		
Mexico City, Mex., 2,902,969 (*9,000,000).........n14	34		
Meyersdale, Pa., 2,648...G3	81		
Mezen, Sov. Un., 7,300...C7	13		
Mezőkövesd, Hung., 18,640...........B5	10		
Mezőtúr, Hung., 17,888 (21,788 ▲)........B5	10		
Mglin, Sov. Un., 10,000..E9	12		
Miajadas, Sp., 8,632.....C3	8		
Miami, Ariz., 3,394...C3, D3	48		
Miami, Fla., 334,859 (*1,864,200)......G6, s13	54		
Miami, Okla., 13,880.....A7	79		
Miami, W. Va., 500.....m13	87		
Miami, co., Ind., 39,246..C5	59		
Miami, co., Kans., 19,254..D9	61		
Miami, co., Ohio, 84,342..B1	78		
Miami Beach, Fla., 87,072...........G6, s13	54		
Miamisburg, Ohio, 14,797..C1	78		
Miami Shores, Fla., 9,425...........G6, s13	54		
Miami Shores, Ohio.....*C1	78		
Miami Springs, Fla., 13,279...........G6, s13	54		
Miamitown, Ohio, 700...o12	78		
Miānwāli, Pak., 31,398..B5	20		
Miaoli, Taiwan, 5,000....*G9	17		
Miass, Sov. Un., 131,000............*D9	13		
Micanopy, Fla., 759......C4	54		
Michalovce, Czech., 19,061............D6	7		
Michigan, lake, U.S.....E12	33		
Michigan, state, U.S., 9,101,000............	66		
Michigan Center, Mich., 5,000.............F6	66		
Michigan City, Ind., 39,369............A4	59		
Michoacán, state, Mex., 2,085,900.......D4, n13	34		
Michurinsk, Sov. Un., 94,000............E13	12		
Mickleyville, Ind.......m10	59		
Micoud, St. Lucia, 2,040..J14	35		
Middelburg, Neth., 33,470..B5	5		
Middelburg, S. Afr., 10,818............G5	24		
Middleboro, Mass., 6,259 (13,607 ▲).......C6	65		
Middlebranch, Ohio, 600..B4	78		
Middle Brook, Newf., Can., 744..........D4	44		
Middleburg, Fla., 900....B5	54		
Middleburg, N.Y., 1,410..C6	75		
Middleburg, Pa., 1,369...E7	81		
Middleburg, Va., 885....B5	85		
Middleburgh Heights, Ohio, 12,367........h9	78		
Middlebury, Conn., 1,200..C4	52		
Middlebury, Ind., 1,055...A6	59		
Middlebury, Vt., 4,000...C1	73		
Middle Caraquet, N.B., Can., 895.........*B5	43		
Middlefield, Conn., 600 (4,132 ▲)........C5	52		
Middlefield, Ohio, 1,726..A4	78		
Middle Granville, N.Y., 600............B7	75		
Middle Haddam, Conn., 500.............C5	52		
Middle Musquodoboit, N.S., Can., 741....D6	43		
Middleport, N.Y., 2,132..B2	75		
Middleport, Ohio, 2,784..C3	78		
Middleport, Pa., 609....*E9	81		
Middle River, Md., 22,000............*B5	53		
Middlesboro, Ky., 11,878..D6	62		
Middlesbrough (Teesside), Eng., 395,530 (*580,000).C6	4		
Middlesex, N.J., 15,038...B4	74		
Middlesex, N.C., 729.....B4	76		
Middlesex, co., Ont., Can., 249,403..........D3	41		
Middlesex, co., Conn., 115,018...........D6	52		
Middlesex, co., Eng., 2,230,093.........*E6	4		
Middlesex, co., Mass., 1,398,355.........A5	65		
Middlesex, co., N.J., 583,813...........C4	74		
Middlesex, co., Va., 6,295..C6	85		
Middleton, Conn., 36,924..C6	52		
Middleton, N.S., Can., 1,870...........E4	43		
Middleton, Idaho, 739....F2	57		
Middleton, Mass., 4,044............A5, f11	65		
Middleton, Wis., 8,286...E4	88		
Middletown, Calif., 900..C2	50		
Middletown, Del., 2,644..B6	53		
Middletown, Ind., 2,046..D6	59		
Middletown, Ky., 3,900..g11	62		
Middletown, Md., 1,262..B2	53		
Middletown, N.J., 16,000 (58,000 ▲).......C4	74		
Middletown, N.Y., 22,607..D6	75		
Middletown, Ohio, 48,767 (*101,900).......C1	78		
Middletown, Pa., 9,080...F8	81		
Middletown, R.I., 29,290...........C11	52		
Middletown Heights, Pa., 700............*G11	81		
Middleville, Mich., 1,865..F5	66		
Middleville, N.Y., 725....B6	75		
Midfield, Ala., 6,340.....g7	46		
Midland, Calif.........F6	50		
Midland, Ont., Can., 10,992 (*23,503)....C5	41		
Midland, La., 600.......D3	63		
Midland, Md., 665......K13	53		
Midland, Mich., 35,176...E6	66		
Midland, N.C., 400.....B2	76		
Midland, Pa., 5,271.....E1	81		
Midland, Tex., 59,463 (*63,300)..........D1	84		
Midland, Wash., 3,000...*D3	86		
Midland, co., Mich., 63,769............E6	66		
Midland, co., Tex., 65,433............D1	84		
Midland Park, Kans., 400..B5	61		
Midland Park, N.J., 8,159............B4	74		
Midland Park, S.C., 1,300............K11	82		
Midleton, Ire., 3,075....E2	4		
Midlothian, Ill., 15,939...k9	58		
Midlothian, Tex., 2,322............C4, n10	84		
Midlothian, co., Scot., 596,620..........*C5	4		
Midnapore, India, 71,326............D8	20		
Midvale, Ohio, 636......B4	78		
Midvale, Utah, 7,840....D2	72		
Midway, Ky., 1,278.....B5	62		
Midway, Oreg.........*B4	80		
Midway, Pa., 1,188.....G7	81		
Midway City, Calif., 5,200............*F5	50		
Midway Park, N.C......C5	76		
Midway Is., U.S. dep., Oceania, 2,200.......E9	2		
Midwest, Wyo., 825.....C6	89		
Midwest City, Okla., 48,212............B4	79		
Mid-Western, reg., Nig., 2,535,839.........G6	22		
Midyat, Tur., 12,987....D13	14		
Mie, pref., Jap., 1,543,083..........*I8	18		
Miechów, Pol., 6,907....C6	7		
Miechowice, Pol........g9	7		
Miedzyrzec, Pol., 13,500..C7	7		
Mielec, Pol., 26,800.....C6	7		
Mieres, Sp., 19,000 (65,923 ▲)........A3	8		
Mifflin, co., Pa., 45,268...F6	81		
Mifflinburg, Pa., 2,607...E7	81		
Mifflintown, Pa., 828....E7	81		
Mifflinville, Pa., 1,074...D9	81		
Migennes, Fr., 6,352....D5	5		
Mignon, Ala., 1,726.....B3	46		
Mihama, Jap.........o15	18		
Mihara, Jap., 82,621....*I6	18		
Mikhaylovgrad, Bul., 26,985............D6	10		
Mikhaylovka, Sov. Un., 50,000............H10	12		
Mikhaylovka, Sov. Un., 31,000............F14	12		
Mikindani, Tan., 4,807...C8	24		
Mikkeli, Fin., 26,301....G12	11		
Mikkeli, prov., Fin., 226,900..........*G12	11		
Mikołów, Pol., 21,300...g9	7		
Mikulczyce, Pol........g9	7		
Mikulov, Czech., 5,220...D4	7		
Milaca, Minn., 1,940....E5	67		
Milam, co., Tex., 20,028..D4	84		
Milan, Ill., 4,873......B3	58		
Milan, Ind., 1,260......F7	59		
Milan (Milano), It., 1,701,600 (*3,495,000)...B2	9		
Milan, Mich., 3,997.....F7	66		
Milan, Mo., 1,794......A4	69		
Milan, N. Mex., 2,222...*B2	48		
Milan, Ohio, 1,862......A3	78		
Milan, Tenn., 7,313.....B3	83		
Milano, see Milan, It.			
Milas, Tur., 11,700.....*D6	14		
Milazzo, It., 17,200.....E5	9		
Milbank, S. Dak., 3,727..E9	77		
Milbridge, Maine, 500 (1,154 ▲)........D5	64		
Mildmay, Ont., Can., 847..C3	41		
Mildred, Pa., 800.......D9	81		
Mildura, Austl., 13,190...*F7	25		
Miles, Austl., 1,431.....*E9	25		
Miles, Tex., 631.......D2	84		
Miles City, Mont., 9,023..D11	70		
Milford, Conn., 50,858...E4	52		
Milford, Del., 5,314.....C7	53		
Milford, Ill., 1,656......C6	58		
Milford, Ind., 1,264.....B6	59		
Milford, Iowa, 1,668.....A2	60		
Milford, Maine, 1,519 (1,828 ▲)........D4	64		
Milford, Mass., 19,352..B4, h9	65		
Milford, Mich., 4,699..F7, o14	66		
Milford, Nebr., 1,846....D8	71		
Milford, N.H., 4,997.....F4	73		
Milford, N.J., 1,230.....B2	74		
Milford, N.Y., 527......C6	75		
Milford, Ohio, 4,828....C1	78		
Milford, Pa., 1,190.....D12	81		
Milford, Utah, 1,304....B5	72		
Milford Center, Ohio, 753..B2	78		
Milford Haven, Wales, 13,840............E4	4		
Milford Station, N.S., Can., 528..........D6	43		
Miliana, Alg., 16,735....A5	22		
Milk, riv., Alta., Can.....E5	38		
Milk River, Alta., Can., 801............E4	38		
Mill, riv., Mass........h9	65		
Millard, Nebr., 7,460....g12	71		
Millard, co., Utah, 6,988..B5	72		
Millau, Fr., 22,595.....E5	5		
Millbourne, Pa., 637....*G11	81		
Millbrae, Calif., 20,781..h8	50		
Millbrook, Ala., 3,034...C3	46		
Millbrook, Ont., Can., 891............C6	41		
Millbrook, N.J 600....*B3	74		
Millbrook, N.Y., 1,735...D7	75		
Millburn, N.J., 21,089...B4	74		
Millbury, Mass., 6,500....B4	65		

Millbury, Ohio, 771.......e7 78
Mill City, Oreg., 1,451....C4 80
Milldale, Conn., 900......C4 52
Milledgeville, Ga., 11,601..C3 55
Milledgeville, Ill., 1,130....B4 58
Mille Lacs, co., Minn., 15,703.........E5 67
Mille Lacs, lake, Minn.....D5 67
Millen, Ga., 3,713........D5 55
Miller, S. Dak., 2,148.....F7 77
Miller, co., Ark., 33,385...D2 49
Miller, co., Ga., 6,397.....E2 55
Miller, co., Mo., 15,026...C5 69
Millerovo, Sov. Un., 35,000.........G13 12
Millersburg, Ky., 788......B5 62
Millersburg, Ohio, 2,979...B4 78
Millersburg, Pa., 3,074.....E8 81
Millers Falls, Mass., 1,186..A3 65
Millersport, Ohio, 777.....C3 78
Millersville, Pa., 6,396.....F9 81
Millerton, N.Y., 1,042.....D7 75
Mill Hall, Pa., 1,838.......D7 81
Millicent, Austl., 5,075....G7 25
Milligan, Fla., 900.......u15 54
Millington, Mich., 1,099...E7 66
Millington, N.J., 2,200...*B3 74
Millington, Tenn., 21,177..B2 83
Millinocket, Maine, 7,742..C4 64
Millis, Mass., 3,217 (5,686 ▲)..........B5, h10 65
Millport, Ala., 1,070......B1 46
Mills, Wyo., 1,724........D6 89
Mills, co., Iowa, 11,832....C2 60
Mills, co., Tex., 4,212.....D3 84
Millsboro, Del., 1,073......C2 53
Millsboro, Pa., 900.......G1 81
Millside, Del..............*A6 53
Millstadt, Ill., 2,168.......E3 58
Milltown, N.B., Can., 1,892.........D2 43
Milltown, Ind., 829.......H5 59
Milltown, Mont., 700......D3 70
Milltown, N.J., 6,470.....C4 74
Milltown, Wis., 634.......C1 88
Millvale, Pa., 5,815.......k14 81
Mill Valley, Calif., 12,942.........D2, h7 50
Millville, Mass., 1,764.....B4 65
Millville, N.J., 21,366.....E2 74
Millville, Ohio, 697......n12 78
Millville, Pa., 896........D9 81
Millwood, Wash., 1,770...g14 86
Milmont Park, Pa., 2,000.........*G11 81
Milo, Maine, 1,514.......C4 64
Milpitas, Calif., 27,149...*D3 50
Milroy, Ind., 800.........F7 59
Milroy, Pa., 1,575........E6 81
Milstead, Ga., 1,157...C3, h8 55
Milton, N.S., Can., 1,854..E5 43
Milton, Ont., Can., 7,018..D5 41
Milton, Del., 1,490........C7 53
Milton, Fla., 5,360.......u14 54
Milton, Ind., 694.........E7 59
Milton, Iowa, 567.........D5 60
Milton, Mass., 27,190..B5, g11 65
Milton, N.H., 1,164 (4,495▲).........D5 73
Milton, N.J., 500..........A3 74
Milton, N.Y., 800.........D7 75
Milton, Pa., 7,723.........D8 81
Milton, Wash., 2,607......f11 86
Milton, W. Va., 1,597.....C2 87
Milton, Wis., 3,699........F5 88
Milton-Freewater, Oreg., 4,105.........B8 80
Milton Junction, Wis......F5 88
Miltonvale, Kans., 718....C6 61
Milverton, Ont., Can., 1,111.........D4 41
Milwaukee, Wis., 717,372 (*1,379,000).......E6, m12 88
Milwaukee, co., Wis., 1,054,249.........E6 88
Milwaukie, Oreg., 16,379.........B4, h12 80
Mims, Fla., 8,309.........D6 54
Minamata, Jap., 28,500 (38,109▲).........J5 18
Minas, Ur., 31,256.......E1 30
Minas de Riotinto, Sp., 9,060.........D2 8
Minas Gerais, state, Braz., 11,645,095.........B4 30
Minatare, Nebr., 939.......C2 71
Minatitlán, Mex., 68,397..D6 34
Minato, Jap., 7,100......m19 18
Minbu, Bur., 9,096.......D9 20
Minco, Okla., 1,129.......B4 79
Mindanao, isl., Phil.......D6 19
Minden, Ont., Can., 658..C6 41
Minden, Ger., Fed. Rep. of, 80,026 (*100,000).......B4 6
Minden, La., 13,996.......B2 63
Minden, Nebr., 2,669...... D7 71
Minden, W. Va., 700.D3, n13 87
Mindoro, isl., Phil.........C6 19
Minechoag, mtn., Mass....B3 65
Minehead, Eng., 8,080.....E5 4
Mine Hill, N.J., 3,557....*B3 74
Mineola, N.Y., 21,845.........E7, n15 75
Mineola, Tex., 3,926......C5 84
Miner, Mo., 640..........E8 69
Miner, co., S. Dak., 4,454.........G8 77
Mineral, co., Colo., 786...D4 51
Mineral, co., Mont., 2,958..C1 70
Mineral, co., Nev., 7,051...B2 72
Mineral, co., W. Va., 23,109.........B6 87
Mineral City, Ohio, 860...B4 78
Mineral del Oro, Mex., 2,310.........n13 34
Mineral Point, Wis., 2,305..F3 88
Mineral Ridge, Ohio 2,100.........*A5 78
Mineral Wells, Tex., 18,411.........C3 84
Minersville, Pa., 6,012.....E9 81
Minerva, Ohio, 4,359......B4 78
Minerva Park, Ohio, 1,402.........*C3 78
Minervino Murge, It., 18,427.........D6 9
Minetto, N.Y., 800........B4 75
Mineville, N.Y., 1,000.....A7 75
Mingenew, Austl., 555.....E2 25
Mingo, co., W. Va., 32,780.........D2 87
Mingo Junction, Ohio, 5,278.........B5 78
Mingshui, China, 5,000....C2 18
Minho, prov., Port., 825,788.........*B1 8
Minhow, see Foochou, China
Minidoka, co., Idaho, 15,731.........G5 57
Minier, Ill., 986..........C4 58
Minitonas, Man., Can., 606.........C1 40
Minna, Nig., 59,988.......G6 22
Minneapolis, Kans., 1,971..C6 61
Minneapolis, Minn., 434,400 (*1,875,000).......F5, n12 67
Minnedosa, Man., Can., 2,621.........D2 40
Minnehaha, Wash., 2,000.........*D3 86
Minnehaha, co., S. Dak., 95,209.........G9 77
Minneola, Kans., 630.....E3 61
Minneota, Minn., 1,320....F3 67
Minnesota, state, U.S., 3,947,000......... 67
Minnesota, riv., Minn.....F3 67
Minnesota Lake, Minn., 738.........G5 67
Minnetonka, Minn., 35,776.........*F5 67
Minnetrista, Minn., 2,878.........*E5 67
Mino, Jap., 57,414.......n15 18
Minoa, N.Y., 2,245.......*B4 75
Minocqua, Wis., 800......C4 88
Minokamo, Jap., 35,075..n15 18
Minonk, Ill., 2,267........C4 58
Minot, N. Dak., 32,290....B4 77
Minquadale, Del., 1,300..*A6 53
Minsk, Sov. Un., 945,000 (*970,000).........E6 12
Minster, Ohio, 2,405......B1 78
Minturno, It., 3,125......D4 9
Minûf, Eg., 48,256.......*G8 14
Minusinsk, Sov. Un., 41,000.........D12 13
Minya Konka, peak, China.........F5 17
Miraflores, Col., 3,257.....C3 32
Miraflores, Peru, 88,446...A3 31
Miraj, India, 77,606.......E5 20
Mira Loma, Calif., 8,482..*E5 50
Miramar, Fla., 23,997......s13 54
Miranda, state, Ven., 492,349.........A4 32
Miranda de Ebro, Sp., 27,881.........A4 8
Mirassol, Braz., 16,559....C3 30
Mirebalais, Hai., 3,952....E7 35
Mirecourt, Fr., 8,572......C7 5
Mirgorod, Sov. Un., 28,000.........G9 12
Miri, Mala., 35,702.......E4 19
Mirpur-Khas, Pak., 60,861.........*C4 20
Mirror, Alta., Can., 577...C4 38
Mirzāpur, India, 105,939..C7 20
Misakubo, Jap...........n16 18
Misamis Occidental, prov., Phil., 248,371.........*D6 19
Misamis Oriental, prov., Phil., 388,615.........*D7 19
Misantla, Mex., 8,799.........D5, h15 34
Misenheimer, N.C., 1,250..B2 76
Mishan, China, 5,000.....D6 18
Mishawaka, Ind., 35,517...A5 59
Mishicot, Wis., 938...D6, h10 88
Mishima, Jap., 78,141..I9, n17 18
Misiones, dept., Par., 59,441.........E4 29
Misiones, prov., Arg., 361,440.........E4 29
Miskolc, Hung., 172,952...A5 10
Misrātah, Libya, 12,000...B8 22
Missaukee, co., Mich., 7,126.........D5 66
Mission, Kans., 8,376.....*B9 61
Mission, Tex., 13,043......F3 84
Mission City, B.C., Can., 3,649........E6, f13 37
Mission Hills, Kans., 4,177..B9 61
Missisquoi, co., Que., Can., 32,609.........D4 42
Mississauga, Ont., Can., 156,070.........D5, m14 41
Mississippi, co., Ark., 62,060.........B5 49
Mississippi, co., Mo., 16,647.........E8 69
Mississippi, state, U.S., 2,288,000......... 68
Mississippi, riv., U.S......D8 45
Mississippi City, Miss...E4, f7 68
Missoula, Mont., 29,497 (*51,700).........D2 70
Missoula, co., Mont., 58,263.........D2 70
Missoula Southwest, Mont., 4,000.........*D2 70
Missouri, state, U.S., 4,764,000......... 69
Missouri, riv., U.S.........B7 45
Missouri Valley, Iowa, 3,519.........C2 60
Mistelbach [an der Zaya], Aus., 6,306.........D8 6
Misti, vol., Peru..........E3 31
Mistretta, It., 9,979.......F5 9
Mitaka, Jap., 155,693.....*I9 18
Mitake, Jap..........I8, n16 18
Mitchell, Austl., 1,441.....E8 25
Mitchell, Ont., Can., 2,545.........D3 41
Mitchell, Ind., 4,092......G5 59
Mitchell, Nebr., 1,842......C2 71
Mitchell, S. Dak., 13,425..G7 77
Mitchell, co., Ga., 18,956..E2 55
Mitchell, co., Iowa, 13,108.........A5 60
Mitchell, co., Kans., 8,010.........C5 61
Mitchell, co., N.C., 13,447.........e10 76
Mitchell, co., Tex., 9,073...C2 84
Mitchell, mtn., N.C.......f10 76
Mitchellsburg, Ky., 300...C5 62
Mitchellville, Iowa, 1,341..C4 60
Mitilíni (Mytilene), Grc., 23,426.........C6 14
Mito, Jap., 173,789..H10, m19 18
Mittagong, Austl., 3,620..*F9 25
Mitterteich, Ger., Fed. Rep. of, 6,500.........D6 6
Mittweida, Ger. Dem. Rep., 19,800.........C6 6
Mitú, Col., 1,623.........C3 32
Miura, Jap., 45,532.......n18 18
Mixquiahuala, Mex., 10,887.........m13 34
Miyagi, pref., Jap., 1,819,223.........*G10 18
Miyako, Jap., 59,063.....G10 18
Miyakonojo, Jap., 74,000 (114,802▲).........K5 18
Miyazaki, Jap., 202,862...K5 18
Miyazaki, pref., Jap., 1,051,105.........*K5 18
Miyazu, Jap., 25,000 (31,603 ▲).......n14 18
Mizil, Rom., 7,460........C8 10
Mizoram, ter., India, 332,390.........D9 20
Mjölby, Swe., 13,987......H6 11
Mlada Boleslav, Czech., 29,687.........C3, n18 7
Mława, Pol., 20,000.......B6 7
Moab, Utah, 4,793........B7 72
Mobara, Jap., 48,495......n19 18
Moberly, Mo., 12,988.....B5 69
Mobile, Ala., 190,026 (*303,500).........E1 46
Mobile, co., Ala., 317,308..E1 46
Mobridge, S. Dak., 4,545..E5 77
Moca, mun., P.R., 21,990..E8 35
Moçambique, Moz., 12,166.........D8 24
Moçâmedes, Ang., 7,185...D2 24
Mocanaqua, Pa., 990......D9 81
Mochudi, Bots., 17,712....E5 24
Mocksville, N.C., 2,529....B2 76
Moclips, Wash., 600.......B1 86
Mocoa, Col., 2,571........C2 32
Mococa, Braz., 21,082..C3, k8 30
Mocorito, Mex., 3,993.....B3 34
Moctezuma, Mex., 2,700...B3 34
Modena, It., 164,800.......B3 9
Modesto, Calif., 61,712 (*136,700).........D3 50
Modica, It., 29,300........F5 9
Modjokerto, Indon., 60,013.........*G4 19
Modlin, Pol.........B6, k13 7
Mödling, Aus., 18,792.....D8 6
Modoc, co., Calif., 7,469....B3 50
Modřany, Czech., 10,004..o17 7
Moe-Yallourn, Austl., 20,764.........I6 26
Moffat, co., Colo., 6,525...A2 51
Mogadisho, Som., 200,000.H7 23
Mogadore, Ohio, 4,825.....A4 78
Mogaung, Bur., 2,940.....C10 20
Mogi das Cruzes, Braz., 90,330.........C3, m8 30
Mogilev, Sov. Un., 202,000.........E8 12
Mogilev-Podolskiy, Sov. Un., 26,000.......G6 12
Mogilno, Pol., 7,125.......B4 7
Mogí Mirim, Braz., 28,408.........C3, m8 30
Mogocha, Sov. Un., 18,000.........D14 13
Mogok, Bur., 8,369......D10 20
Moguer, Sp., 7,222.......D2 8
Mohács, Hung., 16,522 (19,583 ▲).......C4 10
Mohall, N. Dak., 950......B4 77
Mohammedia, Mor., 70,392.B3 22
Mohave, co., Ariz., 25,857.B1 48
Mohawk, Mich., 750......A2 66
Mohawk, N.Y., 3,301......C5 75
Mohnton, Pa., 2,153.....F10 81
Moinesti, Rom., 12,934....B8 10
Moissac, Fr., 4,770........E4 5
Mojave, Calif., 2,573......E4 50
Mokelumne Hill, Calif., 560.........C3 50
Mokena, Ill., 1,643........k9 58
Mokpo, Kor., 177,801......I3 18
Mol, Yugo., 8,079.........C5 10
Mola [di Bari], It., 23,900.D6 9
Molalla, Oreg., 2,005......B4 80
Mold, Wales, 8,000......*D5 4
Moldavia, reg., Rom.......B8 10
Moldavia (S.S.R.), rep., Sov. Un., 3,750,000.....H7 12
Molepolole, Bots., 29,625..E5 24
Molfetta, It., 65,200......D6 9
Molina, Chile, 7,600......B2 28
Molina de Segura, Sp., 8,578.........C5 8
Moline, Ill., 46,237........B3 58
Moline, Kans., 555.........E7 61
Moline, Mich., 550........F5 66
Moline Acres, Mo., 3,722.........*C7 69
Molino, Fla., 900.........u14 54
Molino de Rosas, Mex., 13,310.........h9 34
Moliterno, It., 5,657......D5 9
Mollendo, Peru., 12,483...E3 31
Mölndal, Swe., 46,288.....I5 11
Molodechno, Sov. Un., 50,000.........D6 12
Molotovsk, Sov. Un., 145,000.........E18 11
Molotovskoye, Sov. Un., 10,000.........I13 12
Molus, Ky., 190..........D6 62
Mombasa, Ken., 179,575...I5 23
Mombetsu, Jap., 30,000 (40,389▲).........D11 18
Momence, Ill., 2,836......B6 58
Momostenango, Guat., 5,002.........*D6 34
Mompós, Col., 10,965.....B3 32
Monaca, Pa., 7,486........E1 81
Monaco, country, Eur., 26,000.........F7 5
Monagas, state, Ven., 246,217.........B5 32
Monaghan, S.C., 750......B3 82
Monaghan, co., Ire., 45,732.........*C3 4
Monahans, Tex., 8,333....D1 84
Monarch, S.C., 1,726......B4 82
Monarch, mtn., B.C., Can.........D5, n17 37
Monashee, mts., B.C., Can.........D8 37
Monastir, Tur., 12,596....A7 22
Monchegorsk, Sov. Un., 46,000.........D15 11
Mönchengladbach, Ger., Fed. Rep. of, 151,125 (*370,000).........C3 6
Moncks Corner, S.C., 2,314.........E7 82
Monclova, Mex., 78,134...B4 34

Moncton, N.B., Can., 47,891 (*71,416)......C5 43
Mondoñedo, Sp., 9,153....A2 8
Mondoví, It., 8,800........B1 9
Mondovi, Wis., 2,338......D2 88
Monessen, Pa., 15,216....F2 81
Monett, Mo., 5,937........E4 69
Monette, Ark., 1,076......B5 49
Monfalcone, It., 27,900....B4 9
Monforte de Lemos, Sp., 13,502...............A2 8
Monfort Heights, Ohio, 8,000.................*C1 78
Monghyr, India, 102,474 (*164,205)............C8 20
Mong Mit, Bur., 5,000....D10 20
Mongolia, country, Asia, 1,375,000.............B4 17
Moniquirá, Col., 4,882....B3 32
Moniteau, co., Mo., 10,742................C5 69
Monmouth, Ill., 11,022....C3 58
Monmouth, Oreg., 5,237.............C3, k11 80
Monmouth, co., N.J., 461,849...............C4 74
Monmouth, co., Wales, 461,670..............*E5 4
Monmouth, mtn., B.C., Can................D6 37
Monmouth Beach, N.J., 2,042................C5 74
Monmouth Junction, N.J., 950.............C3 74
Mono, co., Calif., 4,016..D4 50
Monon, Ind., 1,548........C4 59
Monona, Iowa, 1,395.....A6 60
Monona, Wis., 10,420.....E4 88
Monona, co., Iowa, 12,069..B1 60
Monongah, W. Va., 1,194...............B4, k10 87
Monongahela, Pa., 7,113...F2 81
Monongahela, riv., Pa....G2 81
Monongalia, co., W. Va., 63,714.................B4 87
Monopoli, It., 27,000.....D6 9
Monor, Hung., 14,830.....B4 10
Monóvar, Sp., 9,933......C5 8
Monponsett, Mass., 600...B9 65
Monreale, It., 20,500......E4 9
Monroe, Conn., 760......D3 52
Monroe, Ga., 8,071.......C3 55
Monroe, Iowa, 1,389......C4 60
Monroe, La., 56,374 (*105,000)............B3 63
Monroe, Mich., 23,894 (*56,100)............G7 66
Monroe, N.Y., 4,439..........D6, m14 75
Monroe, N.C., 11,282....C2 76
Monroe, Ohio, 3,492.....*C1 78
Monroe, Utah, 918.......B5 72
Monroe, Va., 800.........C3 85
Monroe, Wash., 2,687.....B4 86
Monroe, Wis., 8,654......F4 88
Monroe, co., Ala., 20,883..D2 46
Monroe, co., Ark., 15,657..C4 49
Monroe, co., Fla., 52,586..G5 54
Monroe, co., Ga., 10,991..D3 55
Monroe, co., Ill., 18,831...E3 58
Monroe, co., Ind., 84,849..F4 59
Monroe, co., Iowa, 9,357..D5 60
Monroe, co., Ky., 11,642..D4 62
Monroe, co., Mich., 119,172..............G7 66
Monroe, co., Miss., 34,043..B5 68
Monroe, co., Mo., 9,542..B5 69
Monroe, co., N.Y., 711,917..B3 75
Monroe, co., Ohio, 15,739..C4 78
Monroe, co., Pa., 45,422..D11 81
Monroe, co., Tenn., 23,475................D9 83
Monroe, co., W. Va., 11,272................D4 87
Monroe, co., Wis., 31,610..E3 88
Monroe City, Mo., 2,456..B6 69
Monroeville, Ala., 4,846...D2 46
Monroeville, Ind., 1,353..C8 59
Monroeville, Ohio, 1,455..A3 78
Monroeville, Pa., 29,011..*E1 81
Monrovia, Calif., 30,562..m13 50
Monrovia, Lib., 80,992....G2 22
Mons, Bel., 28,877 (*169,000)............B5 5
Monson, Maine, 500 (669 ▲)...............C3 64
Monson, Mass., 1,110 (7,355 ▲)............B2 65
Montague, Calif., 890....B2 50
Montague, P.E.I., Can., 1,608................C7 43
Montague, Mass., 600 (8,451 ▲)............A2 65
Montague, Mich., 2,396..E4 66
Montague, co., Tex., 15,326...............C4 84
Montague City, Mass., 700.................A2 65

Mont Alto, Pa., 1,532......G6 81
Montalvo, Calif........*E4 50
Montana, state, U.S., 726,000................70
Montánchez, Sp., 4,190....C2 8
Montargis, Fr., 18,225 (*45,000)............D5 5
Montauban, Que., Can., 623.................C5 42
Montauban, Fr., 34,513...E4 5
Montauk, N.Y., 600......m17 75
Monta Vista, Calif., 1,000................*D3 50
Monta Vista, Wash., 1,500................*B3 86
Montbeliard, Fr., 23,908 (*115,000)..........D7 5
Mont Belvieu, Tex., 1,144...........E5, r15 84
Montbrison, Fr., 9,449....E6 5
Montcalm, co., Que., Can., 19,260.......C3 42
Montcalm, co., Mich., 39,660...............E5 66
Mont-Carmel, Que., Can., 895...........B8 42
Montceau-les-Mines, Fr., 27,421 (*50,000)......D6 5
Montchanin [-les-Mines], Fr., 6,408..........D6 5
Montclair (Monte Vista), Calif., 22,546......m13 50
Montclair, N.J., 44,043....B4 74
Mont Clare, Pa., 1,274....o19 81
Montcoal, W. Va., 275............D3, n12 87
Mont-De-Marsan, Fr., 24,458...............F3 5
Montebello, Calif., 42,807..............m12 50
Montebello, Que., Can., 1,486...............D3 42
Monte Caseros, Arg., 12,930...............A5 28
Montecelio, It., 5,000.....g9 9
Montecristi, Dom. Rep., 8,300................E8 35
Montefrio, Sp., 5,137.....D3 8
Montego Bay, Jam., 42,800...............E5 35
Montegut, La., 700.......E5 63
Monteith, mtn., B.C., Can................B6 38
Montélimar, Fr., 26,748...E6 5
Montellano, Sp., 9,334....D3 8
Montello, Wis., 1,082....E4 88
Montemorelos, Mex., 18,642...............B5 34
Montemor-o-Novo, Port., 5,047................C1 8
Montenegro, Braz., 21,497...............D2 30
Montenegro (Crna Gora), rep., Yugo., 471,894...*D4 10
Monte Plata, Dom. Rep., 3,600................E9 35
Montepulciano, It., 3,400................C3 9
Montereau, Fr., 14,121...C5 5
Monterey, Calif., 26,302 (*127,100)..........D3 50
Monterey, Ohio, 1,500....*C1 78
Monterey, Tenn., 2,351....C8 83
Monterey, co., Calif., 247,450.............D3 50
Monterey Park, Calif., 49,166.............m12 50
Montería, Col., 90,000 (161,300▲)..........B2 32
Monteros, Arg., 11,968...E2 29
Monterotondo, It., 9,340...g9 9
Monterrey, Mex., 858,107 (*1,200,000)........B4 34
Montesano, Wash., 2,847..C2 86
Monte Sant' Angelo, It., 20,100...............D5 9
Montes Claros, Braz., 81,572...............B4 30
Monte Sereno, Calif., 3,089................*D3 50
Montevallo, Ala., 3,719...B3 46
Montevarchi, It., 9,100....C3 9
Montevideo, Minn., 5,661..F3 67
Montevideo, Ur., 1,325,000 (*1,525,000)...E1 30
Montevideo, dept., Ur., 1,158,632............*E1 30
Monte Vista, Colo., 3,909..D4 51
Montezuma, Ga., 4,125....D2 55
Montezuma, Ind., 1,192....E3 59
Montezuma, Iowa, 1,353...C5 60
Montezuma, co., Colo., 12,952..............D2 51
Montfort, Wis., 518.......F3 88
Montgomery, Ala., 133,386 (*188,000)..........C3 46
Montgomery, Ill., 3,278.............B5, k8 58

Montgomery, La., 923.....C3 63
Montgomery, Minn., 2,281................F5 67
Montgomery, N.Y., 1,533..D6 75
Montgomery, Ohio, 5,683................*C1 78
Montgomery, Pa., 1,902...D8 81
Montgomery, W. Va., 2,525...........C3, m13 87
Montgomery, co., Ala., 167,790.............C3 46
Montgomery, co., Ark., 5,821................C2 49
Montgomery, co., Ga., 6,099................D4 55
Montgomery, co., Ill., 30,260...............D4 58
Montgomery, co., Ind., 33,930...............D4 59
Montgomery, co., Iowa, 12,781...............C2 60
Montgomery, co., Kans., 39,949...............E8 61
Montgomery, co., Ky., 15,364...............B6 62
Montgomery, co., Md., 522,809.............B3 53
Montgomery, co., Miss., 12,918...............B4 68
Montgomery, co., Mo., 11,000...............C6 69
Montgomery, co., N.Y., 55,883...............C6 75
Montgomery, co., N.C., 19,267...............B3 76
Montgomery, co., Ohio, 608,413.............C1 78
Montgomery, co., Pa., 623,956.............F11 81
Montgomery, co., Tenn., 62,721..............A4 83
Montgomery, co., Tex., 49,479..............D5 84
Montgomery, co., Va., 47,157..............C2 85
Montgomery, co., Wales, 43,110.............*D5 4
Montgomery City, Mo., 2,187...............C6 69
Monticello, Ark., 5,085...D4 49
Monticello, Fla., 2,473....B3 54
Monticello, Ga., 2,132....C3 55
Monticello, Ill., 4,130.....C5 58
Monticello, Ind., 4,869....C4 59
Monticello, Iowa, 3,509...B6 60
Monticello, Ky., 3,618....D5 62
Monticello, Maine, 600 (1,072 ▲)............B5 64
Monticello, Minn., 1,636..E5 67
Monticello, Miss., 1,790...D3 68
Monticello, N.Y., 5,991...D6 75
Monticello, Utah, 1,431...C7 72
Monticello, Wis., 870.....F4 88
Montigny [-lès-Metz], Fr., 24,520.............C7 5
Montijo, Port., 17,751...C1, f10 8
Montijo, Sp., 14,961.....C2 8
Montilla, Sp., 19,755.....D3 8
Montivilliers, Fr., 8,910...C4 5
Mont-Joli, Que., Can., 6,698...............G20 36
Mont-Laurier, Que., Can., 8,240.............C2 42
Montluçon, Fr., 57,871....D5 5
Montmagny, Que., Can., 12,432.............C7 42
Montmagny, co., Que., Can., 26,751.......C7 42
Montmartre, Sask., Can., 482................G4 39
Montmorenci, S.C., 900...D4 82
Montmorency, Que., Can., 4,949........C6, n17 42
Montmorency, Fr., 18,691..............g10 5
Montmorency, co., Mich., 5,247................C6 66
Montmorency No. 1, co., Que., Can., 20,680...B6 42
Montmorency No. 2, co., Que., Can., 5,268....C7 42
Montmorillon, Fr., 4,766..D4 5
Montoro, Sp., 14,950.....C3 8
Montour, co., Pa., 16,508..D8 81
Montour Falls, N.Y., 1,534................C4 75
Montoursville, Pa., 5,985..D8 81
Montpelier, Idaho, 2,604..G7 57
Montpelier, Ind., 2,093...C7 59
Montpelier, Ohio, 4,184...A1 78
Montpelier, Vt., 8,609....C3 73
Montpellier, Fr., 161,910..F5 5
Montréal, Que., Can., 1,214,352 (*2,743,208)......D4, q19 42
Montréal West, Que., Can., 6,368..........*D4 42

Montreuil-sous-Bois, Fr., 95,714..............C5 5
Montreux, Switz., 20,700..E3 6
Mont-Rolland, Que., Can., 1,503..............D3 42
Montrose, Ala., 500......E2 46
Montrose, Calif., 6,000..*E4 50
Montrose, B.C., Can., 862..E9 37
Montrose, Colo., 6,496...C3 51
Montrose, Iowa, 735.....D6 60
Montrose, Mich., 1,789...E7 66
Montrose, Pa., 1,100....*F10 81
Montrose, Pa., 2,058....C10 81
Montrose, Scot., 10,091...B5 4
Montrose, co., Colo., 18,366...............C2 51
Montrose Hill, Pa., 2,400..*E1 81
Montrouge, Fr., 44,922...g10 5
Mont-Royal, Que., Can., 21,561.............p19 42
Montserrat, Br. dep., N.A., 14,800.......H13 35
Montvale, N.J., 7,327....g8 74
Montville, Conn., 1,688...D8 52
Montville, N.J., 2,500....B4 74
Monument, peak, Idaho...G4 57
Monument Beach, Mass., 1,000................C6 65
Monywa, Bur., 26,172....D10 20
Monza, It., 105,400.....B2 9
Monzón, Peru, 514......C2 31
Moodus, Conn., 1,352....D7 52
Moody, Tex., 1,286......D4 84
Moody, co., S. Dak., 7,622..F9 77
Mooers, N.Y., 536......f11 75
Moonachie, N.J., 2,951...*B4 74
Moon Crest, Pa., 1,000...*E1 81
Moon Run, Pa., 700.....k13 81
Moonta, Austl., 1,578....F6 25
Moora, Austl., 1,423.....F2 25
Moorcraft, Wyo., 981....B8 89
Moore, Okla., 18,761.....B4 79
Moore, co., N.C., 39,048..B3 76
Moore, co., Tenn., 3,568..B5 83
Moore, co., Tex., 14,060..B2 84
Moorefield, W. Va., 2,124..B6 87
Moore Haven, Fla., 974...F5 54
Mooreland, Okla., 1,196..A2 79
Moorestown, N.J., 15,577..D3 74
Mooresville, Ind., 5,800...E5 59
Mooresville, N.C., 8,808..B2 76
Moorhead, Minn., 29,687..D2 67
Moorhead, Miss., 2,284...B3 68
Mooringsport, La., 830....B2 63
Moorpark, Calif., 3,380...E4 50
Moose, mtn., Sask., Can...H4 39
Mooseheart, Ill., 1,200..B5, k8 58
Moose Jaw, Sask., Can., 31,854.............G3, n7 39
Moose Lake, Minn., 1,400................D6 67
Moosic, Pa., 4,273......m18 81
Moosic, mts., Pa.........m18 81
Moosomin, Sask., Can., 2,407...............G5 39
Moosonee, Ont., Can., 1,793...............o19 41
Moosup, Conn., 3,376....C9 52
Mopti, Mali, 32,000.....F4 22
Moquegua, Peru, 7,700...E3 31
Moquegua, dept., Peru, 41,072..............E3 31
Mor, Hung., 11,482.....B4 10
Mora, Minn., 2,582......E5 67
Mora, N. Mex., 400......B6 48
Mora, Sp., 10,657......C4 8
Mora, Swe., 17,462.....G6 11
Mora, co., N. Mex., 4,673..A6 48
Morada, Calif., 2,936....*D3 50
Morādābād, India, 258,590, (*272,652)..........C6 20
Moraine, Ohio, 4,898....*C1 78
Moramanga, Mad., 5,700................D9 24
Moran, Kans., 550.......E8 61
Morant Bay, Jam., 7,800..F5 35
Moratalla, Sp., 5,879....C5 8
Moratuwa, Sri Lanka, 77,600..............*G6 20
Moravia, Iowa, 699......D5 60
Moravia, N.Y., 1,642....C4 75
Moravia (Morava), reg., Czech., 3,738,035.....D4 7
Moray, co., Scot., 52,329..*B5 4
Morbihan, dept., Fr., 540,474.............*D2 5
Morden, Man., Can., 3,266................E2 40
Moreauville, La., 807....C4 63
Moree, Austl., 9,114.....E8 25
Morehead, Ky., 7,191....B6 62
Morehead City, N.C., 5,233................C6 76
Morehouse, par., La., 32,463...............B4 63
Morehouse, Mo., 1,332...E8 69
Moreland Hills, Ohio, 2,952................*A4 78

Morelia, Mex., 161,040..........D4, n13 34
Morelos, state, Mex., 454,700..........D5, n14 34
Morenci, Ariz., 900..........C4 48
Morenci, Mich., 2,132.....G6 66
Møre og Romsdal, co., Nor., 222,200..........*F2 11
Morez, Fr., 6,408..........D7 5
Morgan, Minn., 972.....F4 67
Morgan, Utah, 1,586.....A6 72
Morgan, co., Ala., 77,306...A3 46
Morgan, co., Colo., 20,105..........A7 51
Morgan, co., Ga., 9,904...C3 55
Morgan, co., Ill., 36,174...D3 58
Morgan, co., Ind., 44,176..F5 59
Morgan, co., Ky., 10,019...C6 62
Morgan, co., Mo., 10,068...C5 69
Morgan, co., Ohio, 12,375..C4 78
Morgan, co., Tenn., 13,619..........C9 83
Morgan, co., Utah, 3,983..A6 72
Morgan, co., W. Va., 8,547..........B6 87
Morgan City, La., 16,586..........E4, k9 63
Morganfield, Ky., 3,563...C2 62
Morgan Hill, Calif., 6,485..D3 50
Morganton, N.C., 13,625..B1 76
Morgantown, Ind., 1,134..F5 59
Morgantown, Ky., 1,394...C3 62
Morgantown, W. Va., 29,431 (*59,200)...B5, h11 87
Morganza, La., 836......D4 63
Mori, Jap., 6,011.........E10 18
Moriguchi, Jap., 184,466..........*I7 18
Morinville, Alta., Can., 935..........C4 38
Morioka, Jap., 196,036...G10 18
Morlaix, Fr., 19,919.....C2 5
Morningdale, Mass., 900...B4 65
Morningside, Md..........*C4 53
Morningside, Minn., 1,981..........*F5 67
Morning Sun, Iowa, 906...C6 60
Morocco, Ind., 1,285......C3 59
Morocco, country, Afr., 16,495,000..........B4 22
Morococha, Peru, 1,522...D2 31
Morogoro, Tan., 14,507...B7 24
Moroléon, Mex., 25,620..m13 34
Morón, Arg., 485,983......g7 28
Moron, Cuba, 29,000 (31,100 ▲)..........C4 35
Morona-Santiago, prov., Ec., 34,700..........B2 31
Morondava, Mad., 10,700..........E8 24
Moroni, Utah, 894.......B6 72
Morozovsk, Sov. Un., 27,000..........G13 12
Morrill, Nebr., 937......C2 71
Morrill, co., Nebr., 5,813..C2 71
Morrilton, Ark., 6,814....B3 49
Morris, Ala., 519.........B3 46
Morris, Man., Can., 1,399..........E3 40
Morris, Ill., 8,194.......B5 58
Morris, Minn., 5,366.....E3 67
Morris, N.Y., 675.......C5 75
Morris, Okla., 1,119......B6 79
Morris, co., Kans., 6,432..D7 61
Morris, co., N.J., 383,454..B3 74
Morris, co., Tex., 12,310...C5 84
Morris, mtn., N.Y........A6 75
Morrisburg, Ont., Can., 2,055..........C9 41
Morrisdale, Pa., 600.....E5 81
Morrison, Ill., 4,387......B4 58
Morrison, Tenn., 379....D8 83
Morrison, co., Minn., 26,949..........D4 67
Morrisonville, Ill., 1,178...D4 58
Morris Plains, N.J., 5,540..B4 74
Morristown, Ind., 838....E6 59
Morristown, Minn., 659...F5 67
Morristown, N.J., 17,662..B4 74
Morristown, N.Y., 532....f9 75
Morristown, Tenn., 20,318..........C10 83
Morrisville, N.Y., 2,296...C5 75
Morrisville, Vt., 2,116....B2 73
Morro Bay, Calif., 7,109...E3 50
Morro do Chapéu, Braz., 3,560..........E6 27
Morropón, Peru, 3,909....C2 31
Morrow, Ohio, 1,486.....C1 78
Morrow, co., Ohio, 21,348..B3 78
Morrow, co., Oreg., 4,465..B7 80
Morse, La., 759.........D3 63
Morshansk, Sov. Un., 44,000..........E13 12
Mortara, It., 10,500......B2 9
Morteros, Arg., 7,351....A4 28
Morton, Ill., 10,419.....C4 58
Morton, Minn., 591......F4 67

Morton, Miss., 2,672......C4 68
Morton, Pa., 2,602......*G11 81
Morton, Tex., 2,738......C1 84
Morton, Wash., 1,134.....C3 86
Morton, co., Kans., 3,576..E2 61
Morton, co., N. Dak., 20,310..........D4 77
Morton Grove, Ill., 26,369..h9 58
Mortons Gap, Ky., 1,169..C2 62
Moruya, Austl., 1,181....G8 26
Morven, N.C., 562.......C2 76
Morwell, Austl., 16,827..........G8, n15 25
Moscow, Idaho, 14,146....C2 57
Moscow, Pa., 1,430......m18 81
Moscow (Moskva), Sov. Un., 7,040,000 (*10,000,000).....D11, n17 12
Moselle, dept., Fr., 971,314..........*C7 5
Moses Lake, Wash., 10,310..........B6 86
Moshi, Tan., 13,726......I5 23
Mosinee, Wis., 2,395.....D4 88
Mosjoen, Nor., 4,600.....E5 11
Moskva, see Moscow, Sov. Un.
Mosonmagyaróvár, Hung., 24,452........B3 10
Mosquera, Col., 766......C2 32
Moss, Nor., 24,300......H4, p28 11
Mossbank, Sask., Can., 568..........H3 39
Mosselbaai, S. Afr., 17,359..........G4 24
Mossman, Austl., 1,585....C8 25
Mossoro, Braz., 38,833...*D7 27
Moss Point, Miss., 19,321..........E5, f8 68
Moss Vale, Austl., 3,233..*F9 25
Most, Czech., 55,364.....C2 7
Mostaganem, Alg., 75,332..A5 22
Mostar, Yugo., 47,606....D3 10
Mosul (Al Mawşil), Iraq, 293,100..........D14 14
Motala, Swe., 31,980.....H6 11
Motherwell [& Wishaw], Scot., 74,038.......C5 4
Motley, co., Tex., 2,178...B2 84
Motomachi, Jap........o18 18
Motril, Sp., 18,624.......D4 8
Mott, N. Dak., 1,368.....D3 77
Motul [de Felipe Carrillo Puerto], Mex., 12,949...C7 34
Motupe, Peru, 4,396......C2 31
Moulins, Fr., 25,979 (*40,000)..........D5 5
Moulmein, Bur., 108,000..E10 20
Moulton, Ala., 2,470.....A2 46
Moulton, Iowa, 763......D5 60
Moultrie, Ga., 14,400....E3 55
Moultrie, co., Ill., 13,263..D5 58
Mound, Minn., 7,572.....n11 67
Mound Bayou, Miss., 2,134..........B3 68
Mound City, Ill., 1,177...F4 58
Mound City, Kans., 714...D9 61
Mound City, Mo., 1,202...A2 69
Moundridge, Kans., 1,271..D6 61
Mounds, Ill., 1,718......F4 58
Mounds, Okla., 766......B5 79
Mounds View, Minn., 10,599..........*F5 67
Moundsville, W. Va., 13,560..........B4, g8 87
Moundville, Ala., 996.....C2 46
Mountain, prov., Phil., 435,839..........*B6 19
Mountainair, N. Mex., 1,022..........B5 48
Mountain Brook, Ala., 19,509..........g7 46
Mountain City, Tenn., 1,883..........C12 83
Mountain Dale, N.Y., 900..........D6 75
Mountain Grove, Mo., 3,377..........D5 69
Mountain Home, Ark., 3,936..........A3 49
Mountain Home, Idaho, 6,451..........F3 57
Mountain Iron, Minn., 1,698..........C6 67
Mountain Lake, Minn., 1,986..........G4 67
Mountain Lake Park, Mo., 1,263.......m12 53
Mountain Lakes, N.J., 4,739..........B4 74
Mountain Pine, Ark., 1,127..........C2, f7 49
Mountainside, N.J., 7,520..........B4 74
Mountain View, Ark., 1,866..........B3 49
Mountain View, Calif., 54,304..........k8 50

Mountainview, Haw., 419..D6 56
Mountain View, Idaho...*F2 57
Mountain View, Mo., 1,320..........D6 69
Mountain View, Okla., 1,110..........B3 79
Mountain View, Wyo., 500..........E3 89
Mount Airy, Md., 1,825...B3 53
Mount Airy, N.C., 7,325...A2 76
Mount Angel, Oreg., 1,973..........B4, h12 80
Mount Arlington, N.J., 3,590..........B3 74
Mount Ayr, Iowa, 1,762...D3 60
Mount Berry, Ga., 712...B1 55
Mount Bethel, N.J.......B3 74
Mount Brydges, Ont., Can., 1,016..........E3 41
Mount Carmel, Newf., Can., 673..........E5 44
Mount Carmel, Ill., 8,096..E6 58
Mount Carmel, Ohio, 680.o13 78
Mount Carmel, Pa., 9,317..E9 81
Mount Carroll, Ill., 2,143..A4 58
Mount Clare, W. Va., 800.B4 87
Mount Clemens, Mich., 20,476..........F8, o16 66
Mount Dora, Fla., 4,543...D5 54
Mount Edgecumbe, Alsk., 835..........m22 47
Mount Ephraim, N.J., 5,625..........*D2 74
Mount Forest, Ont., Can., 3,037..........D4 41
Mount Gambier, Austl., 17,867..........G7 25
Mount Gilead, N.C., 1,286..........B3 76
Mount Gilead, Ohio, 2,971..........B3 78
Mount Healthy, Ohio, 7,446..........o12 78
Mount Hermon, Mass., 600..........A3 65
Mount Holly, N.J., 12,713..........C3 74
Mount Holly, N.C., 5,107..B1 76
Mount Holly Springs, Pa., 2,009..........F7 81
Mount Hope, Ont., Can., 807..........D5 42
Mount Hope, Kans., 665..........E6, g11 61
Mount Hope, N.J., 700...B3 74
Mount Hope, W. Va., 1,829..........D3, n13 87
Mount Horeb, Wis., 2,402..E4 88
Mount Houston, Tex., 2,000..........*E5 84
Mount Isa, Austl., 26,213..D6 25
Mount Jackson, Va., 681..B4 85
Mount Jewett, Pa., 1,060..C4 81
Mount Joy, Pa., 5,041....F9 81
Mount Kisco, N.Y., 8,172..........D7, m15 75
Mountlake, Terrace, Wash., 16,600......*B3 86
Mount Lebanon, Pa., 39,157..........F1 81
Mount Magnet, Austl., 632..........E2 25
Mount Morgan, Austl., 3,733..........D9 25
Mount Moriah, Newf., Can., 716.......*D2 44
Mount Morris, Ill., 3,173..A4 58
Mount Morris, Mich., 3,778..........E7 66
Mount Morris, N.Y., 3,417..........C3 75
Mount Olive, Ala., 1,900..........B3, f7 46
Mount Olive, Ill., 2,288...D4 58
Mount Olive, N.C., 4,914..B4 76
Mount Oliver, Pa., 5,509..k14 81
Mount Orab, Ohio, 1,306..C2 78
Mount Pearl Park, Newf., Can., 7,211........f9 44
Mount Penn, Pa., 3,465..*F10 81
Mount Pleasant, Iowa, 7,007..........D6 60
Mount Pleasant, Mich., 20,524..........E6 66
Mount Pleasant, N.C., 1,174..........B2 76
Mount Pleasant, Pa., 5,895..........F2 81
Mount Pleasant, S.C., 6,879..........F8, k12 82
Mount Pleasant, Tenn., 3,530..........B4 83
Mount Pleasant, Tex., 9,459..........C5 84
Mount Pleasant, Utah, 1,516..........B6 72
Mount Pocono, Pa., 1,019..........D11 81

Mount Prospect, Ill., 34,995..........A6, h9 58
Mount Pulaski, Ill., 1,677..C4 58
Mountrail, co., N. Dak., 8,437..........B3 77
Mount Rainier, Md., 8,180..........f9 53
Mount Royal, N.J., 750..D2 74
Mount Savage, Md., 1,413..........k13 53
Mount Shasta, Calif., 2,256..........B2 50
Mount Sterling, Ill., 2,182.D3 58
Mount Sterling, Ky., 5,083..........B6 62
Mount Sterling, Ohio, 1,536..........C2 78
Mount Union, Pa., 3,662..F6 81
Mount Vernon, Ala., 1,079..........D1 46
Mount Vernon, Ga., 1,579.D4 55
Mount Vernon, Ill., 16,382..........E5 58
Mount Vernon, Ind., 6,770..........I2 59
Mount Vernon, Iowa 3,018..........C6 60
Mount Vernon, Ky., 1,639..........C5 62
Mount Vernon, Md., 500..D6 53
Mount Vernon, Mo., 2,600..........D4 69
Mount Vernon, N.Y., 3,200..........*C2 75
Mount Vernon, N.Y., 72,778..........h13 75
Mount Vernon, Ohio, 13,373..........B3 78
Mount Vernon, Tex., 1,806..........C5 84
Mount Vernon, Wash., 8,804..........A3 86
Mount Victory, Ohio, 633..B2 78
Mountville, Pa., 1,454...*G9 81
Mount Washington, Ky., 2,020..........B4, g11 62
Mount Wolf, Pa., 1,811...F8 81
Mount Zion, Ill., 2,343...D5 58
Moura, Port., 9,509......C2 8
Mourne, mts., N. Ire.....C3 4
Mouscron, Bel., 37,433...B5 5
Mousie, Ky., 300.......C7 62
Moville, Iowa, 1,198.....B1 60
Moweaqua, Ill., 1,687....D4 58
Mower, co., Minn., 43,783..........G6 67
Moyeuvre [-Grande], Fr., 14,568 (*78,000)..C7 5
Moyobamba, Peru, 8,850..C2 31
Mozambique, country, Afr., 8,720,000....D7 24
Mozhaysk, Sov. Un., 10,000..........D11 12
Mozyr, Sov. Un., 49,000..E7 12
Mtsensk, Sov. Un., 28,000..........E11 12
Muang Hot, Thai........*B1 19
Muang Nan, Thai., 13,802..........*B2 19
Muar (Bandar Maharani), Mala., 61,218.......*E2 19
Muchkap, Sov. Un., 10,000..........F14 12
Mucuri, Braz., 603.......E7 27
Mudanya, Tur., 5,900....*B7 14
Mudgee, Austl., 5,583....F7 26
Muenster, Tex., 1,411....C4 84
Mufulira, Zambia, 75,900..C5 24
Mugía, Sp., 7,061.......A1 8
Muğla, Tur., 18,624......D7 14
Mühldorf, [Ger., Fed. Rep. of], 12,885..........D6 6
Muhlenberg, co., Ky., 27,537..........C2 62
Muhlenberg Park, Pa., 1,200..........*F9 81
Mühlhausen, Ger. Dem. Rep., 44,277........C5 6
Muir, Mich., 617........E6 66
Mukachevo, Sov. Un., 57,000..........G4 12
Mukden, see Shenyang, China
Mukilteo, Wash., 1,369...B3 86
Mukwonago, Wis., 2,367..........F5, n11 88
Mula, Sp., 14,312......C5 8
Mulberry, Ark., 1,340....B1 49
Mulberry, Fla., 2,701....E5 54
Mulberry, Ind., 1,075....D4 59
Mulberry, Kans., 622....E9 61
Mulchén, Chile, 10,700...B2 28
Muldraugh, Ky., 1,773...C4 26
Muldrow, Okla., 1,680...B7 79
Mulege, Mex., 597......B2 34
Muleng, China, 5,000...D5 18
Muleshoe, Tex., 4,525...B1 84
Mulga, Ala., 582......B3, f7 46

Mulgrave, N.S., Can.,
1,145...............D8 43
Mulhacén, mtn., Sp.,.....D4 8
Mülheim an der Ruhr,
Ger., Fed. Rep. of,
191,807...............C3 6
Mulhouse, Fr., 116,336
(*200,000)............D7 5
Mullan, Idaho, 1,279.....B3 57
Mullens, W. Va., 2,967...D3 87
Mullewa, Austl., 874.....E2 25
Mullica Hill, N.J., 550...D2 74
Mullingar, Ire., 6,790....D3 4
Mullins, S.C., 6,006......C9 82
Multán, Pak., 520,000
(*544,000).............B5 20
Multnomah, co., Oreg.,
554,668...............B4 80
Mulvane, Kans., 3,185....E6 61
Muna, Mex., 5,491........C7 34
München, see Munich, Ger.,
Fed. Rep. of
Munchŏn, Kor., 12,005...G3 18
Muncie, Ind., 69,082
(*122,300)............D7 59
Muncy, Pa., 2,872.......D8 81
Mundare, Alta., Can., 603.C4 38
Munday, Tex., 1,726.....C3 84
Mundelein, Ill., 16,128.A5, h9 58
Münden, Ger., Fed. Rep.
of, 27,497............C4 6
Munford, Tenn., 1,281...B2 83
Munfordville, Ky., 1,233.C4 62
Mungindi, Austl., 848...E8 25
Munhall, Pa., 16,574....k14 81
Munich (München), Ger.,
Fed. Rep. of, 1,338,924
(*1,885,000)..........D5 6
Munising, Mich., 3,677...B4 66
Munroe Falls, Ohio,
3,794................*A4 78
Munsan, Kor., 5,000.....H3 18
Munsey Park, N.Y.,
2,980................*E7 75
Munster, Fr., 4,888......C7 5
Munster, Ind., 16,514....A2 59
Münster [in Westfalen],
Ger., Fed. Rep. of,
200,509 (*255,000)......C3 6

Munster, prov., Ire.,
859,334..............*D2 4
Muntenia, prov., Rom.,
4,991,289.............*C8 10
Muntenia, reg., Rom......C7 10
Muntok, Indon., 6,929....F3 19
Muong Hou Nua, Laos,
10,000...............*D11 20
Muong Sing, Laos,
10,000................D11 20
Murakami, Jap., 32,549...G9 18
Murcia, Sp., 160,000
(243,687 ▲)...........C5 8
Murcia, reg., Sp.,
1,200,100.............C5 8
Murfreesboro, Ark., 1,350..C2 49
Murfreesboro, N.C.,
3,508................A5 76
Murfreesboro, Tenn.,
26,360...............B5 83
Murgon, Austl., 2,479....E9 25
Muriae, Braz., 34,118.....C4 30
Murmansk, Sov. Un.,
309,000...............C15 11
Murom, Sov. Un.,
99,000................D13 12
Muroran, Jap., 162,059
(*210,000)............E10 18
Muroto, Jap., 27,445.....J7 18
Murphy, Mo., 800.......g13 69
Murphy, N.C., 2,082......F8 76
Murphysboro, Ill., 10,013..F4 58
Murray, Iowa, 600........C4 60
Murray, Ky., 13,537......f9 62
Murray, Utah,
21,206.............A6, C2 72
Murray, co., Ga., 12,986..B2 55
Murray, co., Minn.,
12,508...............F3 67
Murray, co., Okla., 10,669.C4 79
Murray, riv., Austl......G7 25
Murray Bridge, Austl.,
7,400................G6 25
Murray City, Ohio, 562...C3 78
Murrells Inlet, S.C., 700..D9 82
Murrysville, Pa., 2,600...k15 81
Murud, India, 9,744......E5 20
Murwāra, India, 54,864
(*86,535).............D7 20

Murwillumbah, Austl.,
7,374................D9 26
Mürzzuschlag, Aus.,
11,494...............E7 6
Muş, Tur., 23,058.......C13 14
Musala, peak, Bul........D6 10
Musan, Kor., 20,717.....E4 18
Musashino, Jap.,
136,959..............*I9 18
Muscat, Om., 6,000......D2 20
Muscat & Oman, see Oman,
country, Asia
Muscatine, Iowa,
22,405...............C6 60
Muscatine, co., Iowa,
37,181...............C6 60
Muscle Shoals, Ala.,
6,907................A2 46
Musclow, mtn., B.C.,
Can..................C4 37
Muscoda, Wis., 1,099....E3 88
Musconetcong, mtn.,
N.J..................B2 74
Muse, Pa., 1,358.........F1 81
Musgravetown, Newf.,
Can., 597............D5 44
Mushin, Nig., 145,976....*G5 22
Mushketovo, Sov. Un.,
10,000................r20 12
Muskego, Wis.,
11,573............F5, n11 88
Muskegon, Mich., 44,631
(*178,400)............E4 66
Muskegon, co., Mich.,
157,426..............E4 66
Muskegon Heights, Mich.,
17,304...............E4 66
Muskingum, co., Ohio,
77,826...............B3 78
Muskö, Swe............u36 11
Muskogee, Okla., 37,331..B6 79
Muskogee, co., Okla.,
59,542...............B6 79
Muskoka, dist., Ont.,
Can., 27,691.........B5 41
Musquash, mtn., Maine...C5 64
Musquodoboit Harbour,
N.S., Can., 654........E6 43

Musselburgh, Scot.,
16,903...............C5 4
Musselshell, co., Mont.,
3,734................D8 70
Mustafakemalpaşa, Tur.,
25,684...............B7 14
Muswellbrook, Austl.,
8,082................F9 25
Mutanchiang, China,
251,000..............C10 17
Mutsu, Jap., 41,134......F10 18
Mutton, mts., Oreg......C5 80
Muttontown, N.Y.,
2,081................*E7 75
Muzaffarnagar, India,
114,783..............*C6 20
Muzaffarpur, India,
126,379..............C8 20
Muzambinho, Braz.,
6,731................k8 30
Muztagh Ata, mtn.,
China................A7 20
Mwanza, Tan., 19,877....I4 23
Myaungmya, Bur.,
20,770...............*E9 20
Myers, S.C., 950........k12 82
Myerstown, Pa., 3,645....F9 81
Myingyan, Bur., 36,536...D10 20
Myitkyina, Bur., 12,833..C10 20
Myjava, Czech., 9,935....D4 7
Myrtle Beach, S.C.,
9,035................D10 82
Myrtle Creek, Oreg.,
2,733................D3 80
Myrtle Grove, Fla.,
16,186...............u14 54
Myrtle Point, Oreg.,
2,511................D2 80
Mysen, Nor., 2,525......p29 11
Myślenice, Pol., 12,100...D5 7
Mysłowice, Pol., 44,700..g10 7
Mysore, India, 355,685...F6 20
Mysore, see Karnataka,
state, India
Mystic, Conn., 4,850.....D9 52
Mystic, Iowa, 696........D5 60
My Tho, Viet, 62,700....C3 19
Mytishchi, Sov. Un.,
119,000..............n17 12

N

Naalehu, Haw., 1,014.....D6 56
Nabadwip, India, 94,204...*D8 20
Nabeul, Tun., 14,047.....A7 22
Nabnasset, Mass., 2,700...A5 65
Nābulus, Jordan,
44,223.............B3, g5 15
Naches, Wash., 666......C5 86
Náchod, Czech., 19,019...C4 7
Nacogdoches, Tex.,
22,544...............D5 84
Nacogdoches, co., Tex.,
36,362...............D5 84
Nacozari [de García],
Mex., 2,976..........A3 34
Nadiād, India, 108,269...*D5 20
Nădlac, Rom., 12,284.....B5 10
Nadvornaya, Sov. Un.,
16,000...............G5 12
Naesong, Kor., 5,000.....H4 18
Naestved, Den., 22,900
(*33,000).............J4 11
Naga, Phil., 79,846......C6 19
Nagaland, state, India,
516,449..............*C9 20
Nagano, Jap., 215,000
(285,355 ▲)..........H9 18
Nagano, pref., Jap.,
1,956,917............*H9 18
Nagaoka, Jap., 162,262...H9 18
Nāgappattinam, India,
68,026 (*74,019).....F6 20
Nagasaki, Jap., 421,114...J4 18
Nagasaki, pref., Jap.,
1,570,245............*J4 18
Nāgercoil, India,
141,288..............G6 20
Nagoya, Jap., 2,075,249
(*3,450,000)......J8, n15 18
Nāgpur, India, 866,076
(*950,000)...........D6 20
Nags Head, N.C., 414....B7 76
Nagua, Dom. Rep., 13,900.E9 35
Nagykanizsa, Hung.,
39,411...............B3 10

Nagykőrös, Hung.,
20,503 (25,785 ▲)......B4 10
Naha, Jap., 276,380.....F10 17
Nahant, Mass., 4,119....g10 65
Nahariyya, Isr., 24,000...A3 15
Nahunta, Ga., 974.......E5 55
Naicam, Sask., Can., 672.E3 39
Nairn, Scot., 5,367......B5 4
Nairn, co., Scot., 8,304...*B5 4
Nairobi, Ken., 478,000....I5 23
Najin, Kor., 34,338......E5 18
Nakaminato, Jap., 32,873.m19 18
Nakamura, Jap., 33,573...J6 18
Nakatsu, Jap., 43,000
(57,461 ▲)...........J5 18
Nakhichevan [na Arakse],
Sov. Un., 33,000......F7 16
Nakhon Ratchasima,
Thai., 66,071........C2 19
Nakina, Ont., Can., 673..o18 41
Nakło, Pol., 16,800......B4 7
Nakskov, Den., 16,639....J4 11
Nakuru, Ken., 38,181.....I5 23
Nakusp, B.C., Can., 1,163.D9 37
Nalchik, Sov. Un.,
146,000..............*E7 13
Namangan, Sov. Un.,
175,000..............E10 12
Nambour, Austl., 6,744...E9 25
Namcha Barwa, mtn.,
China................F4 17
Nam Dinh, Viet, 86,132...A3 19
Namibia (South West
Africa), country, Afr.,
800,000..............E3 24
Namiquipa, Mex., 4,874...B3 34
Nampa, Idaho, 20,768....F2 57
Nampo (Chinnampo),
Kor., 82,162.........G2 18
Namur, Bel., 32,194
(*88,000)............B6 5
Namur, prov., Bel.,
382,500..............*B6 5

Namwŏn, Kor., 32,000
(46,532 ▲)...........I3 18
Nanaimo, B.C., Can.,
14,948 (*38,760)....E5, f12 37
Nanakuli, Haw.,
6,506.............B3, g9 56
Nanam, Kor., 21,258.....F4 18
Nanao, Jap., 37,500
(47,855 ▲)...........H8 18
Nance, co., Nebr., 5,142...C7 71
Nanchang, China,
520,000..............F8 17
Nanchung, China,
164,700..............E6 17
Nancy, Fr., 123,428
(*260,000)...........C7 5
Nanda Devi, peak, India..B7 20
Nanded, India, 126,538...*E6 20
Nānga Parbat, peak, Pak..A5 20
Nanhai (Fatshan), China,
120,000..............*G7 17
Nanju, Kor., 15,000......I3 18
Nanking (Nanching), China,
1,750,000............E8 17
Nanning, China, 264,000..G6 17
Nanping, China, 29,000...F8 17
Nanterre, Fr., 90,332.....g9 5
Nantes, Fr. 259,208
(*400,000)...........D3 5
Nanticoke, Md., 600.....D6 53
Nanticoke, Pa.,
14,632...........D10, n16 81
Nanton, Alta., Can.,
1,054................D4 38
Nantucket, Mass., 2,461...D7 65
Nantucket, co., Mass.,
3,774................D7 65
Nantung, China,
240,000..............*E9 17
Nanty Glo, Pa., 4,298....F4 81
Nanuet, N.Y., 10,447....g12 75
Nanyang, China, 50,000...E7 17
Naoma, W. Va., 50,000...n13 87
Naousa, Grc., 17,375.....B4 14

Napa, Calif., 35,978......C2 50
Napa, co., Calif., 79,140...C2 50
Napanee, Ont., Can.,
4,638................C8 41
Napanoch, N.Y., 950.....D6 75
Naperville, Ill.,
22,617............B5, k8 58
Napier, N.Z., 41,400
(*91,500)............M16 26
Napierville, Que., Can.,
1,987................D4 42
Napierville, co., Que.,
Can., 11,822.........D4 42
Naples, Fla., 12,042......F5 54
Naples (Napoli), It.,
1,276,800 (*1,920,000)...D5 9
Naples, N.Y., 1,324......C3 75
Naples, Tex., 1,726......C5 84
Napo, riv., Ec., Peru.....B2 31
Napoleon, N. Dak., 1,036..D6 77
Napoleon, Ohio, 7,791....A1 78
Napoleonville, La.,
1,008.............E4, k9 63
Napoli, see Naples. It.
Nappanee, Ind., 4,159....B5 59
Naqadeh, Iran, 10,801....D15 14
Nara, Jap., 208,266......o14 18
Naracoorte, Austl., 4,399..G7 25
Naranja, Fla., 2,900...G6, s13 54
Nārāyanganj, Bngl.,
125,792..............D9 20
Narberth, Pa., 5,151..F11, o20 81
Narbonne, Fr., 38,441....F5 5
Nardò, It., 23,700.......D7 9
Nariño, dept., Col.,
757,600..............C2 32
Narita, Jap., 25,500
(42,514 ▲)...........n19 18
Narmada, riv., India......D6 20
Narodnaya, mtn.,
Sov. Un..............C9 13
Naro-Fominsk, Sov. Un.,
49,000...............D11 12
Narol, Man., Can., 592...D3 40

Narrabri, Austl., 6,875.....F8 25
Narragansett, R.I.,
2,686.................D11 52
Narrandera, Austl., 4,825..F8 25
Narrogin, Austl., 4,843....F2 25
Narrows, Va., 2,421.......C2 85
Narrowsburg, N.Y., 550....D5 75
Narva, Sov. Un., 58,000....B7 12
Narvik, Nor., 13,400.......C7 11
Naryan-Mar, Sov. Un.,
17,000.................C8 13
Nash, Tex., 1,961.........C5 84
Nash, co., N.C., 59,122....A4 76
Nashua, Iowa, 1,712.......B5 60
Nashua, Mont., 513.......B10 70
Nashua, N.H., 55,820
(*92,300)...............F5 73
Nashville, Ark., 4,016.....D2 49
Nashville, Ga., 4,323......E3 55
Nashville, Ill., 3,027......E4 58
Nashville, Mich., 1,558.....F5 66
Nashville, N.C., 1,670.....B5 76
Nashville, Tenn., 447,877
(*521,300).........A5, g10 83
Nashwauk, Minn., 1,341....C5 60
Našice, Yugo., 4,157......C4 10
Nāsik, India, 176,091
(*271,681).............E5 20
Nasirābād, Bngl., 53,256..D9 20
Nassau, Ba., 3,233
(*101,503)..........B5, m17 35
Nassau, N.Y., 1,466......C7 75
Nassau, co., Fla., 20,626..B5 54
Nassau, co., N.Y.,
1,428,838..............E7 75
Nassawadox, Va., 591.....C7 85
Nässjö, Swe., 19,951......I6 11
Nasukoin, mtn., Mont......B2 70
Natagaima, Col., 8,372....C2 32
Natal, Braz., 250,787.....D7 27
Natal, B.C., Can., 829...E10 37
Natal, prov., S. Afr.,
3,600,000..............F6 24
Natalia, Tex., 1,296......E3 84
Natchez, Miss., 19,704....D2 68
Natchitoches, La., 15,974..C2 63
Natchitoches, par., La.,
35,219.................C2 63
Nathanya, Isr., 60,100....B2 15
Natick, Mass., 31,057..B5, g10 65
National City, Calif.,
43,184............F5, o15 50
National Park, N.J.,
3,730.................*D2 74
Natívitas, Mex., 5,067....h9 34
Natoma, Kans., 603......C4 61
Natrona, co., Wyo.,
51,264.................D6 89
Natrona, Heights, Pa.,
14,448............E2, h15 81
Natural Bridge, N.Y., 750..A5 75
Naturita, Colo., 820......C2 51
Nauen, Ger. Dem. Rep.,
12,300.................B6 6
Naugatuck, Conn.,
23,034.................D4 52
Naughton, Ont., Can.,
954...................A3 41
Naumburg [an der Saale],
Ger. Dem. Rep., 36,886..C5 6
Nauru, country, Oceania,
8,000..................G8 2
Nauta, Peru, 689.........B3 31
Nautla, Mex., 1,935..C5, m15 34
Nauvoo, Ill., 1,047.......C2 58
Navajo, co., Ariz., 47,559..B3 48
Navalmoral de la Mata,
Sp., 9,073.............C3 8
Navarre, Ohio, 1,607.....B4 78
Navarre, reg., Sp.,
441,200................A5 8
Navarro, co., Tex.,
31,150.................C4 84
Navasota, Tex., 5,111.....D4 84
Navassa, N.C., 300.......C4 76
Navesink, N.J., 1,500.....C4 74
Navojoa, Mex., 43,817....B3 34
Navolato, Mex., 12,799....C3 34
Navplion, Grc., 9,281.....D4 14
Navy Yard City, Wash.,
2,827.................*B3 86
Nayarit, state, Mex.,
446,400...........C4, m11 34
Nayoro, Jap., 28,000
(35,035 ▲)............D11 18
Nazaré, Braz., 16,285....*E7 27
Nazaré, Port., 9,241......C1 8
Nazareth, Ky., 700.......C4 62
Nazareth, Pa., 5,815.....E11 81
Nazas, Mex., 2,881.......B4 34
Nazca, Peru, 13,587......D3 31
Nazerat (Nazareth), Isr.,
33,300 (*49,000)....B3, g5 15
Nazilli, Tur., 45,159.....D7 14
Ndjemena, Chad, 132,500..F8 22
Ndola, Zambia, 108,000....C5 24
Neah Bay, Wash., 600.....A1 86
Neath, Wales, 28,210.....E5 4

Nebraska, state, U.S.,
1,543,000.............. 71
Nebraska City, Nebr.,
7,441.............D10, h13 71
Necedah, Wis., 740.......D3 88
Nechako, mts., B.C., Can..C5 37
Necochea, Arg., 35,000....D5 28
Nederland, Tex., 16,810...E6 84
Nedrow, N.Y., 3,500.....*C4 75
Needham, Mass., 29,748..g11 65
Needle, mtn., Wyo........B3 89
Needles, Calif., 4,051.....E6 50
Needville, Tex., 1,024....r14 84
Ñeembucu, dept., Par.,
57,878.................E4 29
Neenah, Wis., 22,902..D5, h9 88
Neepawa, Man., Can.,
3,215.................D2 40
Neffs, Ohio, 900.........B5 78
Neffsville, Pa., 1,300.....F9 81
Negaunee, Mich., 5,248...B3 66
Negley, Ohio, 550........B5 78
Negotin, Yugo., 11,376....C6 10
Negra, mts., Peru........C2 31
Negreira, Sp., 7,725......A1 8
Negro, riv., S.A.........D4 27
Negros, isl., Phil........D6 19
Negros Occidental, prov.,
Phil., 1,332,323......*C6 19
Negros Oriental, prov.,
Phil., 597,761........*D6 19
Neguac, N.B., Can., 559...B4 43
Neiba, Dom. Rep., 10,200.E8 35
Neichiang, China, 180,000.F5 17
Neillsville, Wis., 2,750....D3 88
Neiva, Col., 90,400
(107,000 ▲)............C2 32
Nejd, pol. div., Sau. Ar.,
5,000,000.............D3 15
Nekoosa, Wis., 2,409.....D4 88
Neligh, Nebr., 1,764......B7 71
Nellore, India, 133,590....F6 20
Nelson, B.C., Can., 9,400..E9 37
Nelson, Nebr., 746.......D7 71
Nelson, N.Z., 29,800
(*38,900).............N14 26
Nelson, co., Ky., 23,477...C4 62
Nelson, co., N. Dak.,
5,776.................C7 77
Nelson, co., Va., 11,702...C4 85
Nelsonville, Ohio, 4,812...C3 78
Nemacolin, Pa., 1,273....G2 81
Nemaha, co., Kans.,
11,825.................C7 61
Nemaha, co., Nebr.,
8,976................D10 71
Nemunas (Niemen), riv.,
Sov. Un...............D3 12
Nemuro, Jap., 45,381....E12 18
Nenchiang, China, 5,000..B10 17
Neodesha, Kans., 3,295...E8 61
Neoga, Ill., 1,270.......D5 58
Neola, Iowa, 968.........C2 60
Neon, Ky., 705..........C7 62
Neopit, Wis., 1,122......D5 88
Neosho, Mo., 7,517......E3 69
Neosho, co., Kans.,
18,812.................E8 61
Nepal, country, Asia,
11,745,000............C7 20
Nephi, Utah, 2,699......B6 72
Neptune, N.J., 24,000....C4 74
Neptune Beach, Fla...B5, m9 54
Neptune City, N.J.,
5,502.................*C4 74
Nerchinsk, Sov. Un.,
28,700...............D14 13
Nerekhta, Sov. Un.,
26,000...............C13 12
Nerja, Sp., 7,224........D4 8
Nerva, Sp., 12,686.......D2 8
Nesconset, N.Y., 7,500...F4 52
Nescopeck, Pa., 1,897....D9 81
Neshoba, co., Miss.,
20,802.................C4 68
Nesquehoning, Pa.,
3,338................E10 81
Ness, co., Kans., 4,791...D3 61
Ness City, Kans., 1,756...D4 61
Nes Ziyyona, Isr., 11,700..C2 15
Netarts, Oreg., 900......B3 80
Netcong, N.J., 2,858.....B3 74
Netherlands, country,
Eur., 13,550,000.......A6 5
Netherlands Antilles,
dep., N.A., 235,000...*A4 32
Nettleton, Miss., 1,591...A5 68
Nettuno, It., 19,800......k9 9
Neubrandenburg, Ger.
Dem. Rep., 56,339.....B6 6
Neuburg, Ger., Fed. Rep.
of, 19,464.............D5 6
Neuchâtel, Switz., 38,000
(*61,600)..............E3 6
Neuchâtel, canton, Switz.,
168,300................E3 6
Neufchâtel-en-Bray, Fr.,
5,590.................C4 5

Neuilly [sur-Marne], Fr.,
15,082...............g11 5
Neuilly [-sur-Seine], Fr.,
70,995...............g10 5
Neumarkt, Ger. Fed. Rep.
of, 28,735.............D5 6
Neumünster, Ger., Fed.
Rep. of, 86,401........A4 6
Neunkirchen, Aus.,
10,027.................E8 6
Neunkirchen, Ger., Fed.
Rep. of, 42,367
(*124,000)...........*D3 6
Neuquén, Arg., 30,000...B3 28
Neuquén, prov., Arg.,
109,890................B3 28
Neuruppin, Ger. Dem.
Rep., 23,540...........B6 6
Neuss, Ger., Fed. Rep. of,
117,827..............*C3 6
Neustadt, Ont., Can., 493..C4 41
Neustadt [an der Aisch],
Ger., Fed. Rep. of,
10,335.................C5 6
Neustadt an der
Weinstrasse, Ger. Fed.
Rep. of, 50,573.........D4 6
Neustadt [bei Coburg],
Ger., Fed. Rep. of,
13,129.................D4 6
Neustadt im
Schwarzwald, Ger., Fed.
Rep. of, 7,776.........A5 6
Neustadt [in Holstein],
Ger., Fed. Rep. of,
15,470.................C5 6
Neustrelitz, Ger. Dem.
Rep., 27,482...........B6 6
Neu-Ulm, Ger., Fed. Rep.
of, 29,947.............D5 6
Neuville, Que., Can.,
802...............C6, o16 42
Neuwied, Ger., Fed. Rep.
of, 62,848 (*142,000)...C3 6
Nevada, Iowa, 4,952.....B4 60
Nevada, Mo., 9,736......D3 69
Nevada, Ohio, 917.......B2 78
Nevada, co., Ark., 10,111..D2 49
Nevada, co., Calif.,
26,346.................C3 50
Nevada, state, U.S.,
583,000................ 72
Nevada City, Calif., 2,314..C3 50
Nevada de Colima, mtn.,
Mex..................n12 34
Nevada de Toluca, mtn.,
Mex..................n14 34
Nevado del Huilo, peak,
Col...................C2 32
Nevelsk, Sov. Un.,
10,980...............C10 18
Nevers, Fr., 42,422
(*55,000).............D5 5
Nevesinje, Yugo., 2,272...D4 10
Neville Island, Pa.,
2,017................*E1 81
Nevşehir, Tur., 25,685...C10 14
New Albany, Ind.,
38,402.................H6 59
New Albany, Miss., 6,426..A4 68
New Albin, Iowa, 644.....A6 60
New Alexandria, Va., 650.*B5 85
New Amsterdam, Guy.,
14,059.................C5 27
Newark, Ark., 849.......B4 49
Newark, Calif., 27,153....h8 50
Newark, Del., 21,298.....A6 53
Newark, Eng., 24,540.....D6 4
Newark, N.J., 381,930..B4, k8 74
Newark, N.Y., 11,644....B3 75
Newark, Ohio, 41,836....B3 78
Newark Valley, N.Y.,
1,286.................C4 75
New Athens, Ill., 2,000...E4 58
Newaygo, Mich., 1,381...E5 66
Newaygo, co., Mich.,
27,992.................E5 66
New Baden, Ill., 1,953....E4 58
New Baltimore, Mich.,
4,132.................F8 66
New Baltimore, N.Y., 500..C7 75
New Beaver, Pa., 1,426..*E1 81
New Bedford, Mass.,
101,777 (*158,900)......C6 65
Newberg, Oreg.,
6,507.............B4, h12 80
New Berlin, Ill., 754......D4 58
New Berlin, N.Y., 1,369...C5 75
New Berlin, Wis., 26,910..n11 88
New Berlinville, Pa.,
1,145................*F9 81
New Bern, N.C., 14,660...B5 76
Newbern, Tenn., 2,124....A2 83
Newberry, Fla., 1,522....C4 54
Newberry, Mich., 2,334...B5 66
Newberry, S.C., 9,218....C4 82
Newberry, co., S.C.,
29,273.................C4 82

New Bethlehem, Pa.,
1,406.................D3 81
New Bloomfield
(Bloomfield), Pa., 1,032.F7 81
New Boston, Ill., 706.....B3 58
New Boston, Mich., 900..p15 66
New Boston, Ohio, 3,325..D3 78
New Boston, Tex., 4,034..C5 84
New Braunfels, Tex.,
17,859............E3, h7 84
New Bremen, Ohio, 2,185..B1 78
New Brighton, Minn.,
19,507...............*E5 67
New Brighton, Pa., 7,637.E1 81
New Britain, Conn.,
83,441................C5 52
New Britain, Isl.,
Pap. N. Gui..........G7 2
New Brockton, Ala.,
1,374.................D4 46
New Brunswick, N.J.,
41,885................C4 74
New Brunswick, prov.,
Can., 655,000.........C3 43
New Brunswick Heights,
N.J..................*C4 74
New Buffalo, Mich.,
2,784.................G4 66
Newburg, Mo., 806......D6 69
Newburgh, Ont., Can.,
569...................C8 41
Newburgh, Ind., 2,302....I3 59
Newburgh, N.Y., 26,219
(*102,900)............D6 75
Newburgh Heights, Ohio,
3,396................h12 78
Newbury, Eng., 23,940...E6 4
Newbury, Mass., 800.....A6 65
Newburyport, Mass.,
15,807................A6 65
New Caledonia, Fr., dep.,
Oceania, 130,000......H7 2
New Canaan, Conn.,
17,451................E3 52
New Carlisle, Que., Can.,
1,384.................A4 43
New Carlisle, Ind., 1,434..A4 59
New Carlisle, Ohio, 6,112..C1 78
New Cassel, N.Y., 8,721..*E7 75
New Castile, reg., Sp.,
4,833,700.............C4 8
New Castle, Ala., 1,000.B3, f7 46
Newcastle, Austl., 145,718
(*351,010)............F9 25
Newcastle, Calif., 900....C3 50
Newcastle, N.B., Can.,
6,460 (*19,762).......B4 43
Newcastle, Ont., Can.,
1,272.................D6 41
New Castle, Del., 4,814...A6 53
New Castle, Ind., 21,215..E7 59
New Castle, Pa., 38,559..D1 81
Newcastle, Tex., 624.....C3 84
Newcastle, Wyo., 3,432..C8 89
New Castle, co., Del.,
385,856...............A6 53
Newcastle Bridge, N.B.,
Can., 483.............C3 43
Newcastle Mine, Alta.,
Can., 949.............D4 38
New Castle Northwest,
Pa., 1,974...........*E1 81
Newcastle-on-Tyne, Eng.,
221,390 (*1,365,000)....C6 4
New Chicago, Ind., 2,231..A3 59
New City, N.Y.,
26,700...........D7, m15 75
Newcomb, N.Y., 500.....B6 75
Newcomerstown, Ohio,
4,155.................B4 78
New Concord, Ohio, 2,318.C4 78
New Cumberland, Pa.,
9,803.................F8 81
New Cumberland,
W. Va., 1,865......A4, f8 87
New Cumnock, Scot.,
5,508.................C4 4
New Delhi, India,
301,801...............C6 20
New Denver, B.C., Can.,
564...................D9 37
New Eagle, Pa., 2,497...*F1 81
New Egypt, N.J., 1,769...C3 74
Newell, Iowa, 877........B2 60
Newell, W. Va.,
2,300..............A4, e8 87
New Ellenton, S.C., 2,546.E4 82
Newellton, La., 1,403.....B4 63
New England, N. Dak.,
906...................D3 77
Newfane, N.Y., 2,588.....B2 75
Newfield, N.J., 1,487.....D2 74
New Florence, Mo., 635...C6 69
New Florence, Pa., 929...F3 81
Newfoundland, prov.,
Can., 545,000......... 44
Newfoundland, N.J., 900..A4 74
New Franklin, Mo., 1,122.B5 69

New Freedom, Pa., 1,495..G8 81
New Germany, N.S., Can., 623.........E5 43
New Glarus, Wis., 550..F4 88
New Glasgow, N.S., Can., 10,849 (*23,435).......D7 43
New Gretna, N.J., 550...D7 74
New Guinea, isl., Oceania..G6 2
New Guinea, Territory of, see Papua New Guinea, country, Oceania.
Newgulf, Tex., 900....*E5 84
Newhall, Calif., 7,000...E4 50
Newhall, Iowa, 701.......C6 60
New Hamburg, Ont., Can., 3,008 (*10,010)...D4 41
New Hampshire, state, U.S., 788,000.........73
New Hampton, Iowa, 3,621.........A5 60
New Hanover, co., N.C., 82,996.........C5 76
New Harbour, Newf., Can., 756.........E5 44
New Harmony, Ind., 971..H2 59
New Hartford, Conn., 1,076.........B5 52
New Hartford, Iowa, 690..B5 60
New Hartford, N.Y., 2,433.........*B5 75
New Haven, Conn., 137,707 (*493,400)..D5 52
New Haven, Ill., 606....F5 58
New Haven, Ind., 5,728..B7 59
New Haven, Ky., 977....C4 62
New Haven, Mich., 1,855..F8 66
New Haven, Mo., 1,474..C6 69
New Haven, W. Va., 1,538.........C3 87
New Haven, co., Conn., 744,948.........D4 52
New Hebrides, Br. and Fr. dep., Oceania, 88,000...H8 2
New Holland, Ga., 800...B3 55
New Holland, Ohio, 796..C2 78
New Holland, Pa., 3,971..F9 81
New Holstein, Wis., 3,012.........E5, k9 88
New Hope, Ala., 1,300...A3 46
New Hope, Minn., 23,180..*E5 67
New Hope, Pa., 978...F12 81
New Hudson, Mich., 600..o14 66
New Hyde Park, N.Y., 10,116.........G2 52
New Iberia, La., 30,147..D4 63
Newington, Conn., 26,037..C6 52
New Jersey, state, U.S., 7,361,000.........74
New Kensington, Pa., 20,312.........E2, h14 81
New Kent, co., Va., 5,300..C6 85
Newkirk, Okla., 2,173....A4 79
New Knoxville, Ohio, 852..B1 78
New Kowloon, Hong Kong, 1,479,417.........*G7 17
Newland, N.C., 524...A1, e11 76
New Lebanon, Ohio, 4,248.........*C1 78
New Lenox, Ill., 2,855.........B6, k9 58
New Lexington, Ohio 4,921.........C3 78
New Lisbon, Wis., 1,361..E3 88
New Liskeard, Ont., Can., 5,488.........p20 41
New London, Conn., 31,630 (*238,700)..D8 52
New London, Iowa, 1,900..D6 60
New London, Minn., 736..E4 67
New London, Mo., 967....B6 69
New London, N.H., 1,347..E4 73
New London, Ohio, 2,336..A3 78
New London, Wis., 5,801..D5 88
New London, co., Conn., 230,654.........C8 52
New Madison, Ohio, 959..C1 78
New Madrid, Mo., 2,719..E8 69
New Madrid, co., Mo., 23,420.........E8 69
New Malden, Eng., 46,587.........m11 4
Newman, Calif., 2,505...D3 50
Newman, Ill., 1,018.....D6 58
Newman Grove, Nebr., 863.........C8 71
Newmanstown, Pa., 1,532..F9 81
Newmarket, Ont., Can., 18,941.........C5 41
New Market, Ind., 640...E4 59
Newmarket, N.H., 2,645..E6 73
New Market, N.J.......*B4 74
New Market, Va., 718....B4 85
New Martinsville, W. Va., 6,528.........B4 87
New Matamoras, Ohio, 940.........C4 78
New Meadows, Idaho, 605.........E2 57

New Mexico, state, U.S., 1,090,000.........48
New Miami, Ohio, 3,273.........C1, n12 78
New Milford, Conn., 4,606..C3 52
New Milford, N.J., 19,149..h8 74
New Milford, Ohio.......A4 78
New Milford, Pa., 1,143..C10 81
New Monmouth, N.J......C4 74
Newnan, Ga., 11,205....C2 55
New Norfolk, Austl., 6,893.........o15 25
New Orleans, La., 593,471 (*1,052,500).......E5, h11 63
New Oxford, Pa., 1,495...G7 81
New Palestine, Ind., 863..E6 59
New Paltz, N.Y., 6,058...D6 75
New Paris, Ind., 1,080...B6 59
New Paris, Ohio, 1,692..C1 78
New Philadelphia, Ohio, 15,184.........B4 78
New Philadelphia, Pa., 1,528.........E9 81
New Plymouth, Idaho, 986..F2 57
New Plymouth, N.Z., 35,100 (*39,700).....M15 26
Newport, Ark., 7,725....B4 49
Newport, Del., 1,366....A6 53
Newport, Eng., 21,870...E6 4
New Port, Ind., 708.....E3 59
Newport, Ky., 25,998.........A5, h14 62
Newport, Maine, 1,588...D3 64
Newport, Mich., 650....G7 66
Newport, Minn., 2,922...n13 67
Newport, N.H., 3,296...E3 73
Newport, N.J., 400.....E2 74
New Port, N.Y., 908....B5 75
Newport, N.C., 1,735...C6 76
Newport, Ohio, 700.....C4 78
Newport, Oreg., 5,188...C2 80
Newport, Pa., 1,747.....F7 81
Newport, R.I., 34,562 (*76,400).........D11 52
Newport, Tenn., 7,328...D10 83
Newport, Vt., 4,664.....B3 73
Newport, Wales, 111,810 (*315,000).........E5 4
Newport, Wash., 1,418...A8 86
Newport, co., R.I., 94,228.........C11 52
Newport Beach, Calif., 49,582.........F5, n13 50
Newport News (Independent City), Va., 138,177 (*296,800).......D6, k15 85
New Port Richey, Fla., 6,098.........D4 54
Newportville, Pa., 1,300..*F11 81
New Prague, Minn., 2,680..F5 67
New Providence, N.J., 13,796.........B4 74
New Providence, isl., Ba.........B5, m17 35
Newquay, Eng., 13,220...E4 4
New Richland, Minn., 1,113.........G5 67
New Richmond, Que., Can., 3,957.........A4 43
New Richmond, Ohio, 2,650.........D1 78
New Richmond, Wis., 3,707.........C1 88
New Road, N.S., Can., 1,109.........E6 43
New Roads, La., 3,945...D4 63
New Rochelle, N.Y., 75,385.........h13, n15 75
New Rockford, N. Dak., 1,969.........C6 77
Newry, N. Ire., 11,393...C3 4
Newry, S.C., 750.......B2 82
New Salem, N. Dak., 943..D4 77
New Salem, Pa., 384.....*G2 81
New Sarpy, La., 1,643...k11 63
New Sharon, Iowa, 944...C5 60
New Shrewsbury, N.J., 8,395.........C4 74
New Smyrna Beach, Fla., 10,580.........C6 54
New South Wales, state, Austl., 4,780,000.......F8 25
New Straitsville, Ohio, 947..C3 78
New Tazewell, Tenn., 1,192.........C10 83
Newton, Ala., 1,865.....D4 46
Newton, Ill., 3,024......E5 58
Newton, Iowa, 15,619....C4 60
Newton, Kans., 15,439.........D6, f12 61
Newton, Mass., 91,263.........B5, g11 65
Newton, Miss., 3,556....C4 68
Newton, N.J., 7,297.....A3 74
Newton, N.C., 7,857.....B1 76
Newton, Tex., 1,529.....D6 84
Newton, co., Ark., 5,844..B2 49

Newton, co., Ga., 26,282..C3 55
Newton, co., Ind., 11,606..B3 59
Newton, co., Miss., 18,983.........C4 68
Newton, co., Mo., 32,901..E3 69
Newton, co., Tex., 11,657..D6 84
Newton Falls, N.Y., 750.........A6, f9 75
Newton Falls, Ohio, 5,378..A5 78
Newtonville, N.Y., 1,500..*C7 75
Newtown, Newf., Can., 585.........D5 44
Newtown, Conn., 1,963...D3 52
New Town, N. Dak., 1,428.........C3 77
Newtown, Ohio, 2,038.........C1, o13 78
Newtown, Pa., 2,216.....F12 81
Newtown [& Llanllwchaiarn], Wales, 5,621.........D5 4
Newtownards, N. Ire., 15,387.........C4 4
Newtown Square, Pa., 11,081.........p20 81
New Ulm, Minn., 13,051..F4 67
New Vienna, Ohio, 849...C2 78
Newville, Pa., 1,631.....F7 81
New Washington, Ohio, 1,251.........B3 78
New Waterford, N.S., Can., 9,579.........C9 43
New Waterford, Ohio, 735..B5 78
New Westminster, B.C., Can., 42,835.........E6, f13 37
New Whiteland, Ind., 4,200.........E5 59
New Wilmington, Pa., 2,721.........D1 81
New Windsor, Ill., 723...B3 58
New Windsor, Md., 788...A3 53
New Windsor, N.Y., 8,803.........*D6 75
New York, N.Y., 7,895,563 (*17,326,600).......E7, h13 75
New York, co., N.Y., 1,539,233.........k13 75
New York, state, U.S., 18,292,000.........75
New York Mills, Minn., 791.........D3 67
New York Mills, N.Y., 3,805.........*B5 75
New Zealand, country, Oceania, 2,985,000....N15 26
Nezhin, Sov. Un., 56,000..F8 12
Nez Perce, Idaho, 555...C2 57
Nez Perce, co., Idaho, 30,376.........C2 57
Ngaoundéré, Cam......G7 22
Nha Trang, Viet., 59,600..C3 19
Niagara, Wis., 2,347....C6 88
Niagara, co., Ont. Can...D5 41
Niagara, co., N.Y., 235,720.........B2 75
Niagara Falls, Ont., Can., 67,163.........D5 41
Niagara Falls, N.Y., 85,615.........B1 75
Niagara-on-the-Lake, Ont., Can., 12,552.........D5 41
Niagara University, N.Y., 2,000.........*B1 75
Niamey, Niger, 60,000...F5 22
Niantic, Conn., 4,000....D8 52
Niantic, Ill., 705.......D4 58
Nicaragua, country, N.A., 2,100,000.........E7 34
Nicaragua, lake, Nic.....E7 34
Nicastro (Lamezia Terme), It., 26,700 (55,700▲)....E6 9
Nice, Fr., 322,442 (*400,000).........F7 5
Niceville, Fla., 4,155...u15 54
Nichinan, Jap., 39,000 (53,288▲).........K5 18
Nicholas, co., Ky., 6,508..B5 62
Nicholas, co., W. Va., 22,552.........C4 87
Nicholasville, Ky., 5,829..C5 62
Nicholls, Ga., 1,150....E4 55
Nichols, N.Y., 638......C4 75
Nichols, S.C., 549......C9 82
Nichols Hills, Okla., 4,478..B4 79
Nicholson, Pa., 877.....C10 81
Nickerson, Kans., 1,187..D5 61
Nicolet, Que., Can., 4,714..C5 42
Nicolet, co., Que., Can., 30,829.........C5 42
Nicollet, Minn., 618....F4 67
Nicollet, co., Minn., 24,518.........F4 67
Nicoma Park, Okla., 2,560..B4 79
Nicosia (Levkosía), Cyp., 48,000 (*106,000).....A4 23
Nicosia, It., 17,600.....F5 9
Nicotera, It., 9,143.....E5 9
Nicoya, C.R., 3,196.....E7 34

Niedersachsen (Lower Saxony), state, Ger. Fed. Rep. of, 7,270,000.......*B4 6
Nienburg, Ger., Fed. Rep. of, 22,283.........B4 6
Nievre, dept., Fr., 247,702..*D5 5
Niğde, Tur., 26,936.....D10 14
Niger, country, Afr., 4,340,000.........F6 22
Niger, riv., Afr.........F5 22
Nigeria, country, Afr., 60,260,000.........G6 22
Nigríta, Grc., 7,301....B4 14
Niigata, Jap., 383,919...H9 18
Niigata, pref., Jap., 2,360,982.........*H9 18
Niihama, Jap., 126,033...J6 18
Niihau, isl., Haw.......B1 56
Niimi, Jap., 30,966.....I6 18
Níjar, Sp., 2,052.......D4 8
Nijmegen, Neth., 149,205 (*209,164).........B6 5
Nikitovka, Sov. Un., 10,000.........q21 12
Nikko, Jap., 28,502.....H9 18
Nikolayev, Sov. Un., 331,000.........H9 12
Nikopol, Sov. Un., 125,000.........H10 12
Niland, Calif., 950......F6 50
Nile, riv., Afr.........C4 23
Niles, Ill., 31,432......h9 58
Niles, Mich., 12,988....G4 66
Niles, Ohio, 21,581.....A5 78
Nîmes, Fr., 123,292.....F6 5
Ninette, Man., Can., 673..E2 40
Ninety Six, S.C., 2,166..C3 82
Ningan, China, 40,000...D4 18
Ninghsien, China, 5,000..D6 17
Ningpo, China, 280,000...F9 17
Ningsia, see Yinchuan, China
Ningsia Hui, auton. reg., China, 1,810,000....D6 17
Ningte, China, 30,000....F8 17
Ninh Binh, Viet., 25,000..A3 19
Niobrara, Nebr., 602....B7 71
Niobrara, co., Wyo., 2,924..C8 89
Niort, Fr., 53,394......D3 5
Niota, Tenn., 629......D9 83
Nipawin, Sask., Can., 4,057.........D3 39
Nipigon, lake, Ont., Can..o17 41
Nipissing, dist., Ont., Can., 73,533.........A5 41
Nipomo, Calif., 3,642...E3 50
Niquero, Cuba, 11,300 (36,500▲).........D5 35
Nirasaki, Jap., 14,100 (27,267▲).........n17 18
Nis, Yugo., 127,178.....D5 10
Nisa, Port., 5,617......C2 8
Nishinomiya, Jap., 377,043..*I7 18
Nishio, Jap., 57,000 (75,193▲).........o16 18
Nisko, Pol., 8,312......C7 7
Nisswa, Minn., 1,011....D4 67
Niterói, Braz., 291,970..C4, h6 30
Nitra, Czech., 43,596...D5 7
Nitro, W. Va., 8,019....C3 87
Niue, N.Z., dep., Oceania, 4,900.........*H9 2
Nivelles, Bel., 16,433...B6 5
Nivernais, former terr., Fr..D5 5
Niverville, Man., Can., 474.........E3 40
Nixa, Mo., 1,636......D4 69
Nixon, N.J.........B4 74
Nixon, Tex., 1,925.....E4, k8 84
Nizāmābād, India, 115,640.........*E6 20
Nizhneudinsk, Sov. Un., 40,000.........D12 13
Nizhneye, Sov. Un., 10,000.........q21 12
Nizhniy Tagil, Sov. Un., 378,000.........D9 13
Nkangsamba, Cam.......H6 22
Noank, Conn., 1,371....D9 52
Nobel, Ont., Can., 693...B4 41
Nobeoka, Jap., 128,292..J5 18
Noble, Ill., 719.......E5 58
Noble, Okla., 2,241.....B4 79
Noble, co., Ind., 31,382..B7 59
Noble, co., Ohio, 10,428..C4 78
Noble, co., Okla., 10,043..A4 79
Nobles, co., Minn., 23,208..G3 67
Noblesville, Ind., 7,548..D6 59
Noboribetsu, Jap., 46,526..E10 18
Nocatee, Fla., 900.....E5 54
Nochixtán, Mex., 3,235..o15 34
Nocona, Tex., 2,871.....C4 84
Nodaway, co., Mo., 22,467.........A3 69
Noel, Mo., 924.......E3 69
Nogales, Ariz., 8,946...D3 48
Nogales, Mex., 52,108...A2 34
Nogales, Mex., 14,254...n15 34

Nogata, Jap., 55,615.......J5   18
Nogent-le-Rotrou, Fr.,
  11,578.................C4   5
Nogent [sur-Marne], Fr.,
  26,238.................g10   5
Noginsk, Sov. Un.,
  104,000........D12, n18   12
Nogoyá, Arg., 10,911.....A5   28
Nógrád, co., Hung.,
  241,122.............*A4   10
Nohar, India, 16,704......C5   20
Noheji, Jap., 8,881.......F10   18
Noisy-le-Sec, Fr.,
  34,079.................g10   5
Nokomis, Sask., Can., 533.F3   39
Nokomis, Fla., 2,500.....E4   54
Nokomis, Ill., 2,532.....D4   58
Nola, It., 20,500........D5   9
Nolan, co., Tex., 16,220...C2   84
Nome, Alsk., 2,488.......C6   47
Nominingue, Que., Can.,
  744....................C2   42
Nomme, Sov. Un.,
  18,026...............*B5   12
Nonoava, Mex., 972......B3   34
Noranda, Que., Can.,
  10,741...............*o20   41
Nora Springs, Iowa, 1,337.A5   60
Norborne, Mo., 950......B4   69
Norco, Calif., 14,511.....*F5   50
Norco, La., 4,773....D5, h11   63
Norcross, Ga., 2,755...C2, h8   55
Nord, dept., Fr.,
  2,417,899............*B5   5
Nordegg, Alta., Can.,
  96................C2, g7   38
Norden, Ger., Fed. Rep. of,
  24,175...............B3   6
Nordenham, Ger., Fed.
  Rep. of, 27,743......B4   6
Nordhausen, Ger. Dem.
  Rep., 44,377.........C5   6
Nordhorn, Ger., Fed. Rep.
  of, 45,164...........B3   6
Nordland, co., Nor.,
  244,200.............*D6   11
Nördlingen, Ger., Fed. Rep.
  of, 15,885...........D5   6
Nordrhein-Westfalen, state,
  Ger., Fed. Rep. of,
  17,265,000..........*C3   6
Nord-Tröndelag, co.,
  Nor., 117,900.......*E4   11
Nordvik, Sov. Un., 2,500..B14   13
Norfolk, Nebr., 16,607....B8   71
Norfolk, N.Y., 1,379......f9   75
Norfolk (Independent
  City), Va., 307,951
  (*683,000).......D6, k15   85
Norfolk, co., Ont., Can.,
  50,578...............E4   41
Norfolk, co., Eng.,
  616,570.............*D7   4
Norfolk, co., Mass.,
  604,854..............B5   65
Norilsk, Sov. Un.,
  135,000.............C11   13
Norlina, N.C., 969.......A4   76
Norma, N.J., 800........E2   74
Normal, Ala., 3,500.....*A3   46
Normal, Ill., 26,396......C5   58
Norman, co., Minn.,
  10,008...............C2   67
Norman, Okla., 52,117....B4   79
Normandin, Que., Can.,
  1,838...............*G19   36
Normandy, Fla..........*B5   54
Normandy, Mo., 6,236....f13   69
Normandy, former prov.,
  Fr...................C4   5
Normandy Heights, Ohio,
  950.................n12   78
Normandy Park, Wash.,
  4,202...............*B4   86
Norman's Cove, Newf.,
  Can., 571...........*D5   44
Norquay, Sask., Can., 498.F4   39
Norrbotten, co., Swe.,
  259,800.............*E10   11
Norridge, Ill., 16,880.....k9   58
Norridgewock, Maine,
  1,067 (1,964 ▲)......D3   64
Norris, S.C., 757.........B2   82
Norris, Tenn., 1,359......C9   83
Norris Arm, Newf., Can.,
  1,226................D4   44
Norris City, Ill., 1,319....F5   58
Norris Point, Newf.,
  Can., 711............D3   44
Norristown, Pa.,
  38,169...........F11, o20   81
Norrköping, Swe.,
  115,776..........H7, u34   11
Norrtälje, Swe.,
  13,719...........H8, t36   11
Norseman, Austl., 1,757...F3   25
Norte de Santander, dept.,
  Col., 585,800.........B3   32

North, S.C., 1,076.......D5   82
North, isl., N.Z..........L14   26
North, sea, Eur.........D8   3
North Abington,
  Mass., 3,600......B6, h12   65
North Adams, Mass.,
  19,195................A1   65
North Adams, Mich., 574..G6   66
North Albany, Oreg.,
  900.................k11   80
Northam, Austl., 7,109....F2   25
North America, cont.,
  334,200,000..........   33
North Amherst, Mass.,
  2,854................B2   65
North Amityville, N.Y.,
  11,936...............*E7   75
Northampton, Austl., 748..E1   25
Northampton, Eng.,
  126,250..............D6   4
Northampton, Mass.,
  29,664................B2   65
Northampton, Pa., 8,389..E11   81
Northampton, co., Eng.,
  470,380.............*D6   4
Northampton, co., N.C.,
  24,009................A5   76
Northampton, co., Pa.,
  214,545..............E11   81
Northampton, co., Va.,
  14,442................C7   85
North Andover, Mass.,
  16,284................A5   65
North Anson, Maine, 600..D3   64
North Apollo, Pa., 1,618..E2   81
North Arlington, N.J.,
  18,096................h8   74
North Asheboro, N.C.,
  4,836...............*B3   76
North Atlanta, Ga.,
  19,700................h8   55
North Attleboro, Mass.,
  18,665................C5   65
North Augusta, S.C.,
  12,883................E3   82
North Aurora, Ill., 4,833..k8   58
North Babylon, N.Y.,
  21,739.............*n15   75
North Baltimore, Ohio,
  3,143................A2   78
North Bangor, N.Y., 500..f10   75
North Battleford, Sask.,
  Can., 12,698
  (*15,148).......E1, n7   39
North Bay, Ont., Can.,
  49,187...........A5, p20   41
North Bay, Fla., 4,831...*G6   54
North Beach, Md., 761....C4   53
North Belle Vernon, Pa.,
  2,916..............*F2   81
North Bellmore, N.Y.,
  23,400.............*E7   75
North Bellport, N.Y.,
  3,000.............n15   75
North Belmont, N.C.,
  10,759...............B1   76
North Bend, Nebr., 1,350..C9   71
North Bend, Ohio, 638....o12   78
North Bend, Oreg.,
  8,553................D2   80
North Bend, Pa., 700.....D6   81
North Bend, Wash., 1,625..B4   86
North Bennington, Vt.,
  984.................F1   73
North Bergen, N.J.,
  47,751................h8   74
North Berwick, Maine,
  1,449 (2,224 ▲)......E2   64
North Billerica, Mass.,
  5,000............A5, f10   65
North Bonneville, Wash.,
  459.................D4   86
Northboro, Mass., 2,650
  (9,218 ▲).............B4   65
North Brabant, prov.,
  Neth., 1,753,900.....*B6   5
North Braddock, Pa.,
  10,838..............k14   81
North Branch, Mich., 932..E7   66
North Branch, Minn.,
  1,106................E6   67
North Branch, N.J., 2,500.B3   74
Northbridge, Mass., 3,100
  (11,795 ▲)...........B4   65
Northbrook, Ill., 27,297...h9   58
North Brookfield, Mass.,
  2,677 (3,967 ▲)......B3   65
North Brother, mtn.,
  Maine...............C4   64
North Brunswick, N.J.,
  16,691..............*C4   74
North Caldwell, N.J.,
  6,733................B4   74
North Canton, Ga., 300...B2   55
North Canton, Ohio,
  15,228................B4   78
North Carolina, state,
  U.S., 5,274,000........   76

North Catasauqua, Pa.,
  2,941.............*E11   81
North Cedar, Iowa,
  1,900..............*B5   60
North Charleroi, Pa.,
  1,964..............*F1   81
North Charleston, S.C.,
  21,211..........F8, k12   82
North Chelmsford, Mass.,
  6,000................A5   65
North Chicago, Ill.,
  47,275..........A6, h9   58
North Chili, N.Y.,
  3,163..............*B3   75
North Chillicothe, Ill......C4   58
North City, Wash.,
  6,500..............*B3   86
Northcliffe, Austl., 224....F2   25
North Cohasset, Mass.,
  600.................h12   65
North College Hill, Ohio,
  12,363...............o12   78
North Collins, N.Y.,
  1,675................C2   75
North Conway, N.H.,
  1,723................B4   73
North Corbin, Ky., 800...D5   62
North Creek, N.Y., 900...B7   75
Northcrest, Calif., 900...*B1   50
North Dakota, state, U.S.
  632,000..............   77
North Dartmouth, Mass.,
  5,300................C6   65
North Decatur, Ga.,
  10,700.............*C2   55
North Dighton, Mass.,
  1,264................C5   65
North East, Md., 1,818...A6   53
North East, Nor..........E5   13
North East, Pa., 3,846....B2   81
Northeastern Polder,
  prov., Neth., 28,800...*A6   5
Northeast Harbor, Maine,
  600.................D4   64
North Easton, Mass.,
  3,000................B5   65
Northeim, Ger., Fed. Rep.
  of, 22,700...........C4   6
North English, Iowa,
  965.................C5   60
Northern Arm, Newf.,
  Can., 606............D4   44
Northern, reg., Nig.,
  29,758,875..........F6   22
Northern Ireland, reg.,
  U.K., 1,580,000.......C3   4
Northern Territory, ter.,
  Austl., 100,000.......C5   25
North Fairfield, Ohio,
  540.................A3   78
North Falmouth, Mass.,
  600.................C6   65
Northfield, B.C., Can.,
  610.................f2   37
Northfield, Ill., 5,010.....*B6   58
Northfield, Mass., 1,191..A3   65
Northfield, Minn.,
  10,235................F5   67
Northfield, N.H., 1,315...E4   73
Northfield, N.J., 8,875...E3   74
Northfield, Ohio, 4,283...h9   78
Northfield, Vt., 2,139.....C2   73
North Fond du Lac, Wis.,
  3,286............E5, k9   88
North Fork, Calif., 800....D4   50
North Freedom, Wis., 596.E4   88
North Glen Ellyn, Ill.,
  3,000..............*B5   58
Northglenn, Colo., 27,748..B6   51
North Grafton, Mass.,
  4,300................B4   65
North Great River, N.Y.,
  12,080...............n15   75
North Grosvenor Dale,
  Conn., 2,156.........B9   52
North Haledon, N.J.,
  7,614..............*B4   74
North Hampton, Ohio,
  489.................C2   78
North Hartsville, S.C.,
  1,485..............*C7   82
North Hatley, Que., Can.,
  719.................D6   42
North Haven, Conn.,
  22,194................D5   52
North Head, N.S., Can.,
  609.................E3   43
North Henderson, N.C.,
  1,997..............*A4   76
North Highlands, Calif.,
  33,000.............*C3   50
North Holland
  (Noordholland), prov.,
  Neth., 2,229,900....*A6   5
North Hornell, N.Y.,
  919................*C3   75
North Hudson, Wis.,
  1,547...............*D1   88

North Industry, Ohio,
  3,200................B4   78
North Irwin, Pa., 1,306...*F2   81
North Judson, Ind., 1,738..B4   59
North Kamloops, B.C.,
  Can., 11,319.........D7   37
North Kansas City, Mo.,
  5,183................h10   69
North Kingstown, R.I.,
  4,500................C11   52
North Kingsville, Ohio,
  2,458................A5   78
North La Junta, Colo.,
  1,249................C7   51
Northlake, Ill., 14,212....K9   58
North Larchmont, N.Y....*D2   75
North Las Vegas, Nev.,
  35,691................C4   72
North Lewisburg, Ohio,
  840.................B2   78
North Liberty, Ind.,
  1,259................A5   59
North Lima, Ohio, 700....B5   78
North Lindenhurst, N.Y.,
  11,400...............n15   75
North Little Rock,
  Ark., 60,040......C3, h10   49
North Manchester, Ind.,
  5,791................C6   59
North Mankato, Minn.,
  7,347................F4   67
North Massapequa, N.Y.,
  23,200.............*E7   75
North Merrick, N.Y.,
  13,650.............*E7   75
North Miami, Fla.,
  34,767..........G6, s13   54
North Miami Beach, Fla.,
  30,544...............s13   54
Northmoor, Mo., 562....h10   69
North Muskegon, Mich.,
  4,243................E4   66
North New Hyde Park,
  N.Y., 16,100........*E7   75
North Norwich, N.Y.,
  500.................C5   75
North Ogden, Utah,
  5,257............A6, C2   72
North Olmsted, Ohio,
  34,861...............h9   78
North Oxford, Mass.,
  1,550................B4   65
North Palisade, mtn.,
  Calif.................D4   50
North Palm Beach, Fla.,
  9,035..............*F6   54
North Park, Ill., 15,679...A4   58
North Patchogue, N.Y.,
  7,178...............n14   75
North Pembroke, Mass.,
  2,881................B6   65
North Perkin, Ill., 1,885..*C4   58
North Pelham, N.Y.,
  5,184................h13   75
North Plainfield, N.J.,
  21,796................B4   74
North Plains, Oreg.,
  690.............B4, g12   80
North Platte, Nebr.,
  19,447................C5   71
North Platte, riv., U.S....B6   45
North Pleasanton, Tex....*E3   84
Northport, Ala., 9,435....B2   46
Northport, Mich., 594....C5   66
Northport, N.Y., 7,494...n15   75
Northport, Wash., 423....A8   86
North Prairie, Wis., 669..F5   88
North Providence, R.I.,
  24,337...............B11   52
North Quincy, Ill........D2   58
North Reading, Mass.,
  11,264................f11   65
North Richland Hills,
  Tex., 16,514.........C4   84
Northridge, Ohio, 17,000.*C1   78
North Riverside, Ill.,
  8,097..............*B6   58
North Rockville Centre,
  N.Y., 800...........*E7   75
North Rose, N.Y., 850....B4   75
North Royalton, Ohio,
  12,807...............h9   78
North Sacramento, Calif..*C3   50
North Salem, Ind., 601...E4   59
North Salt Lake, Utah,
  2,143..............*A6   72
North Scituate, Mass.,
  4,000................h12   65
North Seaford, N.Y......*E7   75
North Shreveport, La....*B2   63
North Springfield, Va.,
  8,631..............*B5   85
North St. Paul, Minn.,
  11,950...............m13   67
North Sudbury, Mass.,
  700.................g10   65
North Swansea, Mass.,
  700.................C5   65

North Sydney, N.S., Can.,
8,604..................C9 43
North Syracuse, N.Y.,
8,687..................B4 75
North Tarrytown,
N.Y., 8,334......g13, m15 75
North Terre Haute, Ind.,
2,500..................E3 59
North Tewksbury, Mass.,
900....................A5 65
North Tonawanda, N.Y.,
36,012.................B2 75
North Troy, Vt., 774....B3 73
North Turlock, Calif.....*D3 50
North Turner, mtn.,
Mass...................C4 65
Northumberland, Pa.,
4,102..................E8 81
Northumberland, co.,
N.B., Can., 51,711.....B3 43
Northumberland, co.,
Ont., Can., 45,074.....C6 41
Northumberland, co.,
Eng., 795,850.........*C6 4
Northumberland, co., Pa.,
99,190.................D8 81
Northumberland, co., Va.,
9,239..................C6 85
North Uxbridge, Mass.,
1,960..................B4 65
Northvale, N.J., 5,177....g9 74
North Valley Stream,
N.Y., 14,881..........*E7 75
North Vancouver, B.C.,
Can., 31,847.......E6, f12 37
North Vandergrift, Pa.,
1,000.................*E2 81
North Vassalboro, Maine,
800....................D3 64
North Vernon, Ind., 4,582..F6 59
Northville, Mich., 5,400...p15 66
Northville, N.Y., 1,192...B6 75
North Wales, Pa., 3,911...F11 81
North Walsham, Eng.,
6,490..................D7 4
North Warren, Pa., 1,360..C3 81
Northwest Park, Md.,
4,000.................*B3 53
North Westport, Mass......C5 65
North West River, Newf.,
Can., 753..........B1, h9 44
Northwest Territories,
ter., Can., 40,000.....C10 36
North Wilbraham, Mass...B3 65
North Wildwood, N.J.,
3,914..................E3 74
North Wilkesboro, N.C.,
3,357..................A1 76
Northwood, Iowa, 1,950..A4 60
Northwood, Mich.,
1,500.................*E5 66
Northwood, N.H., 350....E5 73
Northwood, N. Dak.,
1,189..................C8 77
Northwoods, Mo., 4,611..*C7 69
North York, Pa., 2,032....G8 81
North York, Ont., Can.,
504,150..........D5, k15 41
Norton, N.S., Can., 846...D4 43
Norton, Kans., 3,627.....C4 61
Norton, Mass., 2,073.....C5 65
Norton, Ohio, 12,308.....A4 78
Norton (Independent
City), Va., 4,172......f9 85
Norton, co., Kans., 7,279..C4 61
Norton Shores, Mich.,
22,271.................E4 66

Nortonville, Kans.,
727............C8, k15 61
Nortonville, Ky., 699......C2 62
Norvelt, Pa., 1,500......*F2 81
Norwalk, Calif., 91,827...n12 50
Norwalk, Conn., 79,288...E3 52
Norwalk, Iowa, 1,745..C4, f8 60
Norwalk, Ohio, 13,386....A3 78
Norwalk, Wis., 432.......E3 88
Norway, Iowa, 554.......C6 60
Norway, Maine, 2,430
(3,595 ▲)..............D2 65
Norway, Mich., 3,033....C3 66
Norway, S.C., 579.......E5 82
Norway, country, Eur.,
3,980,000.............E5 11
Norway House, Man.,
Can., 494..............C3 40
Norwayne, Mich.........*F7 66
Norwell, Mass., 600
(7,796 ▲)............h12 65
Norwich, Ont., Can.,
1,703..................E4 41
Norwich, Conn., 41,739...C8 52
Norwich, Eng., 120,740
(*197,000)............D7 4
Norwich, N.Y., 8,843.....C5 75
Norwood, Ont., Can.,
1,060..................C7 41
Norwood, Mass.,
30,815............B5, h11 65
Norwood, Minn., 1,058...F5 67
Norwood, N.J., 4,398.....h9 74
Norwood, N.Y., 2,098.....f10 75
Norwood, N.C., 1,896....B2 76
Norwood, Ohio, 30,420...o13 78
Norwood, Pa., 7,229.....p20 81
Norwood, Tenn., 400....*D10 83
Norwottock, mtn., Mass...B2 65
Noshiro, Jap., 44,000
(59,795▲)............F10 18
Nossa Senhora das Dores,
Braz., 5,674.........*E7 27
Notch, mtn., Mass........A3 65
Noto, It., 20,700........F5 9
Notodden, Nor., 13,600...H3 11
Notre Dame, Ind., 8,100..*A5 59
Notre-Dame-de-Lourdes,
Man., Can., 511.......E2 40
Notre Dame du Lac,
Que., Can., 2,107......B9 42
Notre-Dame-du-Laus,
Que., Can., 565.......C2 42
Nottingham, Eng.,
296,750 (*650,000)....D6 4
Nottingham, Pa., 3,200..*F11 81
Nottingham, co., Eng.,
972,130.............*D6 4
Nottoway, co., Va.,
14,260.................C4 85
Nouadhibou, Maur., 5,283.D4 21
Nouakchott, Maur., 16,000.E1 22
Nouméa, N. Cal., 34,990.*H8 2
Nova Cruz, Braz., 8,533..*D7 27
Nova Friburgo, Braz.,
65,732...........C4, h6 30
Nova Iguaçu, Braz.,
331,457..............h6 30
Nova Lima, Braz.,
27,386................C4 30
Nova Lisboa, see
Huambo, Ang.
Novara, It., 98,900......B2 9
Nova Scotia, prov., Can.,
810,000...............D6 43
Novato, Calif., 31,006....C2 50

Nova Varos, Yugo.,
3,186..................D4 10
Novaya Ladoga, Sov. Un.,
25,000.................A9 12
Novaya Zemlya, is.,
Sov. Un................B8 16
Nova Zagora, Bul.,
19,258.................D8 10
Nové Zámky, Czech.,
24,628.................E5 7
Novgorod, Sov. Un.,
128,000................B8 12
Novgorod-Severskiy,
Sov. Un., 11,249.......E9 12
Novi, Mich., 9,668......p15 66
Novigrad, Yugo., 531....C2 10
Novi Ligure, It., 32,700..B2 9
Novi Pazar, Bul., 5,461...D8 10
Novi Pazar, Yugo.,
29,072.................D5 10
Novi Sad, Yugo., 141,712..C4 10
Novoaydar, Sov. Un.,
10,000...........G12, q21 12
Novocherkassk, Sov. Un.,
162,000...............H13 12
Novoekonomicheskoye,
Sov. Un., 31,000......q20 12
Novogrudok, Sov. Un.,
25,000.................E5 12
Novo-Kazalinsk,
Sov. Un., 19,499.......E9 16
Novokuznetsk, Sov. Un.,
499,000...............D11 13
Novomoskovsk, Sov. Un.,
61,000................G10 12
Novomoskovsk, Sov. Un.,
134,000 (*340,000)....D12 12
Novorossiysk, Sov. Un.,
133,000...............I11 12
Novoshakhtinsk,
Sov. Un., 102,000.....H12 12
Novosibirsk, Sov. Un.,
1,180,000 (*1,285,000)..D11 13
Novosil, Sov. Un.,
20,000................E11 12
Novoukrainka, Sov. Un.,
20,000.................G8 12
Nový Bohumín, Czech.,
13,104.................D5 7
Nový Bydžov, Czech.,
6,120..................C3 7
Nový Jičín, Czech.,
19,740.................D5 7
Novyye Senzhary,
Sov. Un..............G10 12
Novyy Oskol, Sov. Un.,
10,000................F11 12
Nowa Sól, Pol., 33,300...C3 7
Nowata, Okla., 3,679.....A6 79
Nowata, co., Okla.,
9,773..................A6 79
Nowra-Bomaderry, Austl.,
12,866................G8 26
Nowshera, Pak., 21,516
(*43,757)............B5 20
Nowy Dwór, Pol., 16,900..k13 7
Nowy Sącz, Pol., 41,100...D6 7
Nowy Targ, Pol., 21,900...D6 7
Noxen, Pa., 822....D9, m16 81
Noxubee, co., Miss.,
14,288................B5 68
Noya, Sp., 4,236........A1 8
Noyon, Fr., 11,603......C5 5
Nsawam, Ghana, 20,200...G4 22
Ñuble, prov., Chile,
329,100...............B2 28

Nuckolls, co., Nebr.,
7,404..................D7 71
Nucla, Colo., 949........C2 51
Nueces, co., Tex., 237,544..F4 84
Nueva Atzacoalco, Mex.,
57,456...............*D5 34
Nueva Casas Grandes,
Mex., 20,023.........A3 34
Nueva Ecija, prov., Phil.,
608,362.............*C6 19
Nueva Esparta, state
Ven., 89,492..........A5 32
Nueva Gerona, Cuba,
17,200 (20,100 ▲)......D2 35
Nueva Imperial, Chile,
6,400..................B2 28
Nueva Rosita, Mex.,
34,706................B4 34
Neuva San Salvador, Sal.,
35,106...............*E7 34
Nueva Vizcaya, prov.,
Phil., 138,090.......*B6 19
Nueve de Julio, Arg.,
17,768................B4 28
Nuevitas, Cuba, 20,700
(21,500 ▲)...........D5 35
Nuevo Laredo, Mex.,
148,867...............B5 34
Nuevo León, state, Mex.,
1,290,500.............B5 34
Nukualofa, Tonga,
15,545...............*H9 2
Nules, Sp., 8,460........C5 8
Numazu, Jap., 189,038
(*375,000).......I9, n17 18
Nu Mine, Pa., 475.......E3 81
Nunda, N.Y., 1,254......C3 75
Nungan, China, 35,000...C10 17
Nuoro, It., 28,800......D2 9
Nuquí, Col., 1,500......C3 27
Nuremberg, Pa., 800.....E9 81
Nuri, Mex., 1,887.......B3 34
Nürnberg (Nuremberg), Ger.,
Fed. Rep. of, 514,976
(*850,000)...........D5 6
Nushki, Pak., 2,142.....C4 20
Nutley, N.J., 31,913...B4, h8 74
Nutter Fort, W. Va.,
2,379............B4, k10 87
Nutting Lake, Mass.,
1,500................f10 65
Nuwara Eliya, Sri Lanka,
16,347................G7 20
Nyack, N.Y., 6,659..D7, m15 75
Nyamandhlovu, Rh., 350..D5 24
Nyandoma, Sov. Un.,
23,000...............A13 12
Nyasa, lake, Afr.........C6 24
Nybro, Swe., 15,317......I6 11
Nye, co., Nev., 5,599....B3 72
Nyíregyháza, Hung.,
55,805 (70,640 ▲)......B5 10
Nykøbing Falster, Den.,
23,000................A1 7
Nykøbing Mors, Den.,
9,326.................I3 11
Nykoping, Swe.,
37,175...........H7, u34 11
Nyland Acres, Calif.,
1,200...............*E4 50
Nymburk, Czech.,
13,139...........C3, n19 7
Nynäshamn, Swe.,
11,416...........H7, u35 11
Nyngan, Austl., 2,478....F8 25
Nysa, Pol., 31,800......C4 7
Nyssa, Oreg., 2,620....D10 80

O

Oahu, isl., Haw.......B4, g9 56
Oak Bay, B.C., Can.,
18,426..............h12 37
Oak Bluffs, Mass., 1,385..D6 65
Oakbrook Terrace, Ill.,
1,126...............*F2 58
Oak Creek, Colo., 492....A4 51
Oak Creek, Wis., 13,928...n12 88
Oakdale, Calif., 6,594....D3 50
Oakdale, La., 7,301.....D3 63
Oakdale, Mass., 500.....B4 65
Oakdale, N.Y., 7,334....*n16 75
Oakdale, Pa., 2,136.....k13 81
Oakes, N. Dak., 1,742....D7 77
Oakfield, Maine, 500
(836 ▲)..............B4 64

Oakfield, N.Y., 1,964.....B2 75
Oakford, Pa., 1,500..F12, o22 81
Oak Forest, Ill., 17,870....k9 58
Oak Grove, Ga., 3,500...*C2 55
Oak Grove, La., 1,980....B4 63
Oak Grove, Oreg.,
6,000............B4, h12 80
Oakharbor, Ohio, 2,807...A2 78
Oak Harbor, Wash.,
9,167.................A3 86
Oak Hill, Fla., 747......D6 54
Oak Hill, Mich., 900.....D4 66
Oak Hill, Ohio, 1,642....D3 78
Oak Hill, Tenn.........*A5 83
Oak Hill, W. Va.,
4,738............D3, n13 87

Oakhurst, N.J., 4,600.....C4 74
Oakhurst, Okla., 1,800....A5 79
Oakland, Calif.,
361,561...........D2, h8 50
Oakland, Ill., 1,012.....D5 58
Oakland, Iowa, 1,603....C2 60
Oakland, Maine, 2,261...D3 64
Oakland, Md., 1,786.....m12 53
Oakland, Mo., 1,609.....*C7 69
Oakland, Nebr., 1,355....C9 71
Oakland, N.J., 14,420....A4 74
Oakland, Oreg., 1,010....D3 80
Oakland, Pa., 2,303.....*D1 81
Oakland, co., Mich.,
907,871...............F7 66

Oakland City, Ind.,
3,289.................H3 59
Oaklandon, Ind., 1,000...k11 59
Oakland Park, Fla.,
16,261...........F6, r13 54
Oak Lawn, Ill.,
60,305...........B6, k9 58
Oaklawn, Kans., 5,000...B5 61
Oakley, Idaho, 656......G5 57
Oakley, Kans., 2,327....C3 61
Oakley Park, Mich.,
36,762...............*F7 66
Oaklyn, N.J., 4,626.....*D2 74
Oakman, Ala., 823......B2 46
Oakmont, Pa., 7,550..E2, h14 81
Oak Park, Ill., 62,511..B6, k9 58

Oak Park, Mich., 36,762..p15 66
Oak Ridge, N.C., 900......A3 76
Oakridge, Oreg., 3,422....D4 80
Oak Ridge, Tenn., 28,319..C9 83
Oak Ridges, Ont., Can.,
  1,864..............k15 41
Oaks, Pa., 700......o20 81
Oaktown, Ind., 726......G3 59
Oak View, Calif., 2,448...*E4 50
Oak View, Md., 3,000...*C3 53
Oakville, Ont., Can.,
  61,483............D5 41
Oakville, Conn., 8,000...C4 52
Oakville, Mo., 1,000......g13 69
Oakwood, Ill., 1,367....C6 58
Oakwood, Ohio, 804......A1 78
Oakwood (Oakwood
  Village), Ohio, 3,127...*A4 78
Oakwood (Far Hills),
  Ohio, 10,095.........C1 78
Oakwood, Pa.,......*E1 81
Oakwood, Tex., 547....D5 84
Oakwood Beach, N.J.,
  350...............D1 74
Oakwood Villa, Fla......*B5 54
Oamaru, N.Z., 13,050...P13 26
Oamishirasato, Jap......n19 18
Oaxaca [de Juarez], Mex.,
  99,535.............D5 34
Oaxaca, state, Mex.,
  1,880,700..........D5 34
Ob, river, Sov. Un......C9 13
Obama, Jap., 24,000
  (33,702▲)..........n14 18
Oban, Scot., 6,378......B4 4
Oberhausen, Ger., Fed.
  Rep. of, 242,600......C3 6
Oberlin, Kans., 2,291...C3 61
Oberlin, La., 1,857......D3 63
Oberlin, Ohio, 8,761....A3 78
Oberlin, Pa., 2,000......*F8 81
Oberstdorf, Ger., Fed. Rep.
  of, 11,873..........E5 6
Obetz, Ohio, 2,248...C3, m11 78
Obihiro, Jap., 131,568....E11 18
Obion, Tenn., 1,010......A2 83
Obion, co., Tenn.,
  29,936.............A2 83
Oblong, Ill., 1,860......D6 58
Obluchye, Sov. Un.,
  15,000.............E16 13
O'Brien, co., Iowa,
  17,522.............A2 60
Observation, peak, Calif...B3 50
Obuasi, Ghana, 22,800....G4 22
Ocala, Fla., 22,583......C4 54
Ocaña, Col., 28,028....B3 32
Ocaña, Sp., 6,686......C4 8
Occidental, mts., Peru...D2 31
Ocean, co., N.J., 208,470..D4 74
Oceana, W. Va., 1,580...D3 87
Oceana, co., Mich.,
  17,984.............E4 66
Ocean Bluff, Mass.,
  900...........B6, h13 65
Ocean City, Md., 1,493...D7 53
Ocean City, N.J., 10,575...E3 74
Ocean Falls, B.C., Can.,
  1,085.............C4 37
Ocean Gate, N.J., 1,081..D4 74
Ocean Grove, Mass.,
  2,500.............C5 65
Ocean Grove, N.J., 4,200..C4 74
Oceanlake, Oreg......*C3 80
Oceano, Calif., 1,317....*E3 50
Ocean Park, Wash., 825...C1 86
Oceanport, N.J., 7,503...C4 74
Oceanside, Calif., 40,494
  (*130,900).........F5 50
Oceanside, N.Y., 35,372..*G2 52
Ocean Springs, Miss.,
  9,580..........E5, f8 68
Oceanville, N.J., 600....E4 74
Ocheyedan, Iowa, 545...A2 60
Ochiltree, co., Tex.,
  9,704.............A2 84
Ocilla, Ga., 3,185........E3 55
Ockelbo, Swe., 2,669....G7 11
Ocenle Mari, Rom.,
  4,420.............C7 10
Ocho Rios, Jam.,
  6,900.............E5 35
Ocoee, Fla., 3,937......D5 54
Ocoña, Peru, 932......E3 31
Oconee, co., Ga., 7,915...C3 55
Oconee, co., S.C., 40,728..B1 82
Oconomowoc, Wis., 8,741..E5 88
Oconto, Wis., 4,667......D6 88
Oconto Falls, Wis., 2,517..D5 88
Oconto, co., Wis., 25,553..D6 88
Ocotlán, Mex.,
  35,367........C4, m12 34
Ocracoke, N.C., 500....B7 76
Ocros, Peru, 1,321......D2 31
Oda, Ghana, 19,700....G4 22
Ōdate, Jap., 51,000
  (72,958▲)..........F10 18

Odawara, Jap.,
  156,654..........I9, n18 18
Odda, Nor., 10,100......G2 11
Odebolt, Iowa, 1,323....B2 60
Odell, Ill., 1,076........B5 58
Odem, Tex., 2,130......F4 84
Ödemiş, Tur., 34,630....C7 14
Odendaalsrus, S. Afr.,
  15,344 (*22,000)......F5 24
Odense, Den., 104,400
  (*133,500)..........J4 11
Odense, co., Den., 282,500.*J4 11
Odenton, Md., 5,989....B4 53
Oder (Odra), riv., Eur....B7 6
Odessa, Ont., Can.,
  852...............C8 41
Odessa, Mo., 2,839......A4 69
Odessa, N.Y., 606......C4 75
Odessa, Sov. Un.,
  892,000...........H8 12
Odessa, Tex., 78,380
  (*89,500)..........D1 84
Odessa, Wash., 1,074...B7 86
Odin, Ill., 1,263........E4 58
Odin, mtn., B.C., Can....D8 37
Odon, Ind., 1,433......G4 59
O'Donnell, Tex., 1,148...C2 84
Odorhei, Rom., 14,162...B7 10
Oella, Md., 600........B4 53
Oelsnitz, Ger. Dem. Rep.,
  18,500............C6 6
Oelwein, Iowa, 7,735....B6 60
O'Fallon, Ill., 7,268....E4 58
O'Fallon, Mo., 7,018....f12 69
Offaly, co., Ire., 51,717..*D3 4
Offenbach, Ger., Fed. Rep.
  of, 119,978.........C4 6
Offenburg, Ger., Fed. Rep.
  of, 48,732..........D3 6
Ōfunato, Jap., 32,000
  (38,804▲)..........G10 18
Oga, Jap., 25,000
  (40,907▲)..........G9 18
Ōgaki, Jap., 134,942..I8, n15 18
Ogallala, Nebr., 4,976...C4 71
Ogbomosho, Nig.,
  319,881...........G5 22
Ogden, Iowa, 1,661......B3 60
Ogden, Kans., 1,491....C7 61
Ogden, Pa., 1,600......*G11 81
Ogden, Utah, 70,197
  (*175,600)........A6, C2 72
Ogden Dunes, Ind., 1,361..*A3 59
Ogdensburg, N.J., 2,222..A3 74
Ogdensburg, N.Y., 14,554..f9 75
Ogemaw, co., Mich.,
  11,903............D6 66
Ogle, co., Ill., 42,867....A4 58
Ogles, Ill............*E4 58
Oglesby, Ill., 4,175......B4 58
Oglethorpe, Ga., 1,286...D2 55
Oglethorpe, co., Ga.,
  7,598.............C3 55
Ogletown, Del.,......*A6 53
Ogoamas, mtn., Indon....E6 19
Ogulin, Yugo., 3,519....C2 10
Ogunquit, Maine, 800...E2 64
Ōhara, Jap., 6,865......n19 18
O'Higgins, prov., Chile,
  303,600...........A2 28
Ohio, co., Ind., 4,289....G7 59
Ohio, co., Ky., 18,790...C2 62
Ohio, co., W. Va., 64,197..A4 87
Ohio, state, U.S.,
  10,883,000.........78
Ohio, river, U.S.........C10 45
Ohio City, Ohio, 816....B1 78
Ohioville, Pa., 3,918.....*E1 81
Ohrid, Yugo., 26,370....E5 10
Oil City, La., 907......B2 63
Oil City, Pa., 15,033....D2 81
Oildale, Calif., 22,000...E4 50
Oilton, Okla., 1,087.....A5 79
Oise, dept., Fr., 540,988..*C5 5
Ōita, Jap., 260,584......J5 18
Oita, pref., Jap.,
  1,155,566..........*J5 18
Ojai, Calif., 5,591......E4 50
Ojinaga, Mex., 12,757...B4 34
Ojocaliente, Mex., 7,582..C4 34
Ojos del Salado, mtn.,
  Arg., Chile.........F4 27
Ojus, Fla., 1,400......G6, s13 54
Oka, Que., Can.,
  1,375........D3, q18 42
Oka, Nig., 62,761......E6 22
Oka, river,
  Sov. Un.........D11, o18 12
Okaloosa, co., Fla.,
  88,187............u15 54
Okanagan Landing, B.C.,
  Can., 535..........D8 37
Okanogan, Wash., 2,015..A6 86
Okanogan, co., Wash.,
  25,867............A6 86
Okara, Pak., 68,299......*B5 20
Okarche, Okla., 826....B4 79
Okauchee, Wis., 3,134...*E5 88

Okawville, Ill., 992......E4 58
Okaya, Jap., 60,350..H9, m17 18
Okayama, Jap., 375,106...I6 18
Okayama, pref., Jap.,
  1,707,026..........*I6 18
Okazaki, Jap., 210,515...o16 18
Okecie, Pol., (part of
  Warsaw)........B6, m13 7
Okeechobee, Fla., 3,715...E6 54
Okeechobee, co., Fla.,
  11,233............E5 54
Okeene, Okla., 1,421....A3 79
Okehampton, Eng., 4,050..E4 4
Okemah, Okla., 2,913...B5 79
Okfuskee, co., Okla.,
  10,683............B5 79
Okha, Sov. Un., 31,000...D17 13
Okhotsk, Sov. Un.,
  2,000.............D17 13
Okhotsk, sea, Sov. Un....D17 13
Oklahoma, Pa., 1,084....*F2 81
Oklahoma, co., Okla.,
  526,805...........B4 79
Oklahoma, state, U.S.,
  2,692,000.........79
Oklahoma City, Okla.,
  368,856 (*627,300)....B4 79
Oklawaha, Fla., 950....C5 54
Oklee, Minn., 536......C3 67
Okmulgee, Okla., 15,180...B6 79
Okmulgee, co., Okla.,
  35,358............B5 79
Okolona, Ky., 26,000....g11 62
Okolona, Miss., 3,002...B5 68
Okotoks, Alta., Can.,
  1,043.............D4 38
Oktibbeha, co., Miss.,
  28,752............B5 68
Okushiri, Jap.........E9 18
Olancha, peak, Calif....D4 50
Olanta, S.C., 640......D8 82
Olathe, Kans., 17,919...D9 61
Olavarriá, Arg., 45,000..B4 28
Oława, Pol., 17,700....C4 7
Olbia, It., 11,000......D2 9
Olcott, N.Y., 1,592......B2 75
Old Bethpage, N.Y.,
  7,084.............*E7 75
Old Bridge, N.J., 13,100...C4 74
Old Brookville, N.Y.,
  1,785.............*E7 75
Old Castile, reg., Sp.,
  2,191,200..........B4 8
Oldenburg [in Holstein],
  Ger., Fed. Rep. of, 9,326.A5 6
Oldenburg, Ger., Fed. Rep.
  of, 133,328.........B4 6
Oldenburg, Ind., 758...F7 59
Old Forge, N.Y., 850....B6 75
Old Forge, Pa.,
  9,522........D10, m17 81
Old Fort, N.C., 676......F10 76
Oldham, Eng., 105,530...D5 4
Oldham, co., Ky., 14,687..B4 62
Oldham, co., Tex., 2,258..B1 84
Oldham Village, Mass.,
  600..............*B6 65
Old Hometown, Tenn....*B1 83
Old Man, mtn., Newf.,
  Can...............D3 44
Old Orchard Beach,
  Maine, 5,404......E2, g7 64
Old Perlican, Newf., Can.,
  599..............D5 44
Olds, Alta., Can., 3,376...D3 38
Old Saybrook, Conn.,
  2,281.............*D7 52
Oldsmar, Fla., 1,538....o10 54
Old Speck, mtn., Maine...D2 64
Old Tappan, N.J., 3,917..*B4 74
Old Town, Maine,
  9,057.............D4 64
Oldtown, N.C.........*A2 76
Old Westbury, N.Y.,
  2,667.............*E7 75
Olean, N.Y., 19,169....C2 75
O'Leary Station, P.E.I.,
  Can., 795..........C5 43
Oleiros, Sp., 76......A1 8
Olekminsk, Sov. Un.,
  9,000.............C15 13
Olesno, Pol., 7,481....C5 7
Olhão, Port., 16,017....D2 8
Olímpia, Braz., 19,571...C3 30
Olimpo, dept., Par.,
  3,854.............D4 29
Olin, Iowa, 710........B6 60
Olinda, Braz., 187,553...*D7 27
Oliva, Sp., 14,579......C5 8
Oliva de la Frontera, Sp.,
  12,899............C2 8
Olive Hill, Ky., 1,197...B6 62
Olivehurst, Calif., 6,000..C3 50
Oliveira, Braz., 18,557...C4 30
Olivenza, Sp., 11,469...C2 8
Oliver, B.C., Can., 1,615..E8 37
Oliver, Pa., 1,500......G2 81

Oliver, co., N. Dak.,
  2,322.............C4 77
Oliver Springs, Tenn.,
  3,405.............C9 83
Olivet, Mich., 1,629....F6 66
Olivette, Mo., 9,156....*C7 69
Olivia, Minn., 2,553....F4 67
Olkusz, Pol., 15,800....g11 7
Olla, La., 1,387........C3 63
Olmos, Peru, 2,163......C2 31
Olmos Park, Tex., 2,250..k7 84
Olmsted, Ohio, 6,318....*A4 78
Olmsted, co., Minn.,
  84,104............G6 67
Olmsted Falls, Ohio,
  2,504.............h9 78
Olney, Md., 2,138......B3 53
Olney, Md., 800........B3 53
Olney, Tex., 3,624......C3 84
Olomouc, Czech., 80,563..D4 7
Oloron-Ste. Marie, Fr.,
  13,028............F3 5
Olot, Sp., 17,185......A7 8
Olpe, Kans., 453......D7 61
Olshany, Sov. Un.,
  10,000............F10 12
Olsztyn, Pol., 94,100....B6 7
Olten, Switz., 20,700
  (*48,600).........E3 6
Oltenia, prov., Rom.,
  1,717,982..........*C6 10
Oltenia, reg., Rom.,
  1,564,600..........C6 10
Oltenita, Rom., 14,111...C8 10
Olton, Tex., 1,782......B1 84
Olvera, Sp., 8,341......D3 8
Olympia, Wash., 23,296
  (*63,000).........B3 86
Olympia Fields, Ill.,
  3,478.............*B6 58
Olympus, mtn., Grc....B4 14
Olympus, mtn., Wash....B2 86
Olyphant, Pa.,
  5,422........D10, m18 81
Omagh, N. Ire., 11,953...C3 4
Omaha, Nebr.,
  346,929
  (*525,400)......C10, g13 71
Omak, Wash., 4,164....A6 86
Oman, country, Asia,
  725,000...........F6 15
Omar, W. Va., 900...D3, n12 87
Omdurman (Umm
  Durmān), Sud., 258,532.E4 23
Omega, Ga., 831......E3 55
Omemee, Ont., Can., 809..C6 41
Omerville, Que., Can.,
  1,094.............D5 42
Ometepec, Mex., 7,342...D5 34
Omigawa, Jap.........n19 18
Omiya, Jap., 268,777..I9, n18 18
Omro, Wis., 2,341......D5 88
Ōmuta, Jap., 175,143
  (*230,000).........J5 18
Onalaska, Wis., 4,909...E2 88
Onamia, Minn., 670....D5 67
Onancock, Va., 1,614...C7 85
Onarga, Ill., 1,436......C5 58
Onawa, Iowa, 3,154....B1 60
Onaway, Mich., 1,262...C6 66
Öndör Haan, Mong.,
  4,500.............B7 17
Oneco, Fla., 3,246....E4, q10 54
Onega, Sov. Un., 25,000...C6 13
Onega, lake, Sov. Un....G16 11
Oneida, Ill., 728......B3 58
Oneida, N.Y., 11,658....B5 75
Oneida, Ohio, 1,500....C1 78
Oneida, Tenn., 2,602...C9 83
Oneida, co., Idaho, 2,864..G6 57
Oneida, co., N.Y.,
  273,037...........B5 75
Oneida, co., Wis., 24,427..C4 88
O'Neill, Nebr., 3,753....B7 71
Oneonta, Ala., 4,390....B3 46
Oneonta, N.Y., 16,030...C5 75
Ongjin, Kor., 32,965....H2 18
Onitsha, Nig., 163,032...G6 22
Ono, Jap., 26,000
  (42,241▲)..........n15 18
Onoda, Jap., 42,041....*J15 18
Onomichi, Jap., 101,363..I6 18
Onondaga, N.Y., 1,500...*C4 75
Onondaga, co., N.Y.,
  472,835...........C4 75
Onset, Mass., 1,771....C6 65
Onslow, co., N.C., 103,126.C5 76
Onsong, Kor., 10,116...E4 18
Onsted, Mich., 555......F6 66
Ontake-san, mtn., Jap...n16 18
Ontario, Calif.,
  64,118........E5, m13 50
Ontario, N.Y., 750......B3 75
Ontario, Ohio, 4,345...B3 78
Ontario, Oreg., 6,523...C10 80
Ontario, co., Ont., Can.,
  170,818...........C5 41

Ontario, co., N.Y., 78,849..C3 75
Ontario, prov., Can., 7,990,000.......... 41
Onteniente, Sp., 18,787....C5 8
Ontonagon, Mich., 2,432............B1, m12 66
Ontonagon, co., Mich., 10,548..............m12 66
Oolitic, Ind., 1,155.......G4 59
Oostburg, Wis., 1,309.....E6 88
Oostende, Bel., 71,575 (*81,000)..............B5 5
Ootacamund, India, 63,310.................F6 20
Oot Park, N.Y., 2,000....*B4 75
Opal Cliffs, Calif., 3,825..*D2 50
Opa-Locka, Fla., 11,902...s13 54
Opatów, Pol., 5,636.......C6 7
Opava, Czech., 47,909....D4 7
Opelika, Ala., 19,027......C4 46
Opelousas, La., 20,387.....D3 63
Opochka, Sov. Un., 10,000................C7 12
Opoczno, Pol., 12,100.....C6 7
Opole, Pol., 86,500.......C4 7
Opole Lubelskie, Pol., 3,746................C6 7
Opp, Ala., 6,493..........D3 46
Oppdal, Nor...............F3 11
Oppeln see Opole, Pol.
Oppland, co., Nor., 170,900..............*G4 11
Opportunity, Wash., 16,604............B8, g14 86
Oquawka, Ill., 1,352......C3 58
Oradea, Rom., 122,500 (134,900 ▲)............B5 10
Oradell, N.J., 8,903........h8 74
Oran (Ouahran), Alg., 328,257 (*369,462)......A4 22
Oran, Mo., 1,226.........D8 69
Oran, dept., Alg., 1,990,729.............*B5 22
Orange, Austl., 23,143.....F8 25
Orange, Calif., 77,365....n13 50
Orange, Conn., 13,524....D4 52
Orange, Fr., 18,616.......E6 5
Orange, Mass., 3,847 (6,104▲)...............A3 65
Orange, N.J., 32,566......B4 74
Orange, Ohio, 2,112.....*A4 78
Orange, Tex., 24,457......D6 84
Orange, Va., 2,768........B4 85
Orange, co., Calif., 1,421,233.............F5 50
Orange, co., Fla., 344,311..............D5 54
Orange, co., Ind., 16,968..G4 59
Orange, co., N.Y., 221,657..............D6 75
Orange, co., N.C., 57,707..A3 76
Orange, co., Tex., 71,170..D6 84
Orange, co., Vt., 17,676...D3 73
Orange, co., Va., 13,792...B4 85
Orange, riv., Afr..........F3 24
Orangeburg, N.Y., 3,500...............*D6 75
Orangeburg, S.C., 13,252..E6 82
Orangeburg, co., S.C., 69,789..................E6 82
Orange City, Fla., 1,777...D5 54
Orange City, Iowa, 3,572...............A1 60
Orange Cove, Calif., 3,392................*D4 50
Orange Free State, prov., S. Afr., 1,860,000.......F5 24
Orange Grove, Tex., 1,075..................F4 84
Orange Park, Fla., 7,619............B5, m8 54
Orangevale, Calif., 8,000................*C3 50
Orangeville, Ont., Can., 8,074.................D4 41
Oranienburg, Ger. Dem. Rep., 20,600...........B6 6
Oras, Phil., 4,863........*C7 19
Orăştie, Rom., 10,488.....C6 10
Oraviţa, Rom., 8,175......C5 10
Orchard Avenue, Wash...*B8 86
Orchard Beach, Md., 1,700................*B4 53
Orchard Homes, Mont., 3,500................D2 70
Orchard Lake, Mich., 1,487................*F7 66
Orchard Park, N.Y., 3,732..................C2 75
Orchard Valley, Wyo., 1,015..................E8 89
Orchards, Wash., 9,500....D3 86
Orcotuna, Peru, 3,400.....D2 31
Orcutt, Calif., 1,500......E3 50
Ord, Nebr., 2,439.........C7 71
Órdenes, Sp., 1,311........A1 8
Ordu, Tur., 38,483.......B11 14
Orduña, Sp., 5,950.......A4 8
Ordville, Nebr..........*C2 71
Ordway, Colo., 1,017.....C7 51
Ordzhonikidze, Sov. Un., 236,000.......E7 13
Örebro, Swe., 115,827.H6, t33 11
Örebro, co., Swe., 273,200............*H6 11
Oregon, Ill., 3,539........A4 58
Oregon, Mo., 789.........B2 69
Oregon, Ohio, 16,563..A2, e7 78
Oregon, Wis., 2,553.......F4 88
Oregon, co., Mo., 9,180....E6 69
Oregon, state, U.S., 2,227,000............. 80
Oregon City, Oreg., 9,176............B4, h12 80
Orekhov, Sov. Un., 10,000..............H10 12
Orekhovo-Zuyevo, Sov. Un., 120,000 (*180,000).......D12, n18 12
Orel, Sov. Un., 232,000...E11 12
Oreland, Pa., 9,000.....*F11 81
Orem, Utah, 25,729.......A6 72
Orenburg, Sov. Un., 344,000......D8 13
Orense, prov., Sp., 445,600..............*A2 8
Orestes, Ind., 519.........D6 59
Orestiás, Grc., 10,727......B6 14
Orford, mtn., Que., Can...D5 42
Orfordville, Wis., 888......F4 88
Orgeyev, Sov. Un., 25,800................H7 12
Orick, Calif., 900.........B1 50
Orient, Ill., 502...........F5 58
Orient, N.Y., 600........m16 75
Oriental, N.C., 445........B6 76
Oriente, prov., Cuba, 1,797,606.............D6 35
Orihuela, Sp., 15,873 (44,830 ▲)...............C5 8
Orillia, Ont., Can., 24,040..................C5 41
Orinda, Calif., 18,700.....*D2 50
Orinoco, river, Ven........B5 32
Orion, Ill., 1,801..........B3 58
Oriskany, N.Y., 1,627.....B5 75
Oriskany Falls, N.Y., 927..C5 75
Orissa, state, India, 21,944,615............E7 20
Oristano, It., 19,800.......E2 9
Orizaba, Mex., 92,517 (*210,000)..D5, n15 34
Orkney, co., Scot., 17,137..................*A5 4
Orkney, isl., Scot.........*A5 4
Orland, Calif., 2,884......C2 50
Orlando, Fla., 99,006 (*363,700)............D5 54
Orland Park, Ill., 6,391....k9 58
Orleanais, former prov., Fr.D4 5
Orleans, Calif., 600.......B2 50
Orléans, Ont., Can., 2,810.................h12 41
Orléans, Fr., 95,828 (*170,000)..............D4 5
Orleans, Ind., 1,834.......G5 59
Orleans, Mass., 950 (3,055 ▲)..............C7 65
Orleans, Nebr., 592.......D6 71
Orleans, Vt., 1,138.......B3 73
Orleans, co., N.Y., 37,305..................B2 75
Orleans, co., Vt., 20,153...B3 73
Orleans, par., La., 593,471.................E6 63
Orléansville, see El Asnam, Alg.
Orlovista, Fla., 4,700.....*D5 54
Ormoc, prov., Phil., 13,640...............*C6 19
Ormond Beach, Fla., 14,063..................C5 54
Ormstown, dept., Que., Can., 1,527............D3 42
Orne, dept., Fr., 288,524...............*C3 5
Örnsköldsvik, Swe., 36,336.F8 11
Orocué, Col., 1,600.......C3 32
Orofino, Idaho, 3,883......C2 57
Oro Grande, Calif., 700....E5 50
Oromocto, N.B., Can., 11,427..................D3 43
Orono, Ont., Can., 964....D6 41
Orono, Maine, 9,989......D4 64
Orono, Minn., 6,787......*E5 67
Oronogo, Mo., 492........D3 69
Oroquieta, Phil., 4,265...*D6 19
Orosháza, Hung., 29,146 (33,346 ▲)...........B5 10
Oroville, Calif., 7,536......C3 50
Oroville, Wash., 1,555.....A6 86
Orpington, Eng., 81,600..m13 4
Orrick, Mo., 883..........B3 69
Orrville, Ohio, 7,408......B4 78
Orsainville, Que., Can., 12,520.................n17 42
Orsha, Sov. Un., 101,000..D8 12
Orsk, Sov. Un., 225,000...D8 13
Orsova, Rom., 6,527......C6 10
Orthez, Fr., 5,125.........F3 5
Ortigueria, Sp., 1,590.....A2 8
Orting, Wash., 1,643......B3 86
Ortiz, Mex., 1,133........B2 34
Ortona a Mare, It., 10,700..................C5 9
Ortonville, Mich., 983......F7 66
Ortonville, Minn., 2,665...E2 67
Oruro, Bol., 90,100.......C2 29
Oruro, dept., Bol., 270,500................C2 29
Orvieto, It., 9,500.........C4 9
Orwell, Ohio, 965.........A5 78
Orwigsburg, Pa., 2,661....E9 81
Oryakhovo, Bul., 6,972....D6 10
Osage, Iowa, 3,815........A5 60
Osage, co., Kans., 13,352..D8 61
Osage, co., Mo., 10,994....C6 69
Osage, co., Okla., 29,750.................A4 79
Osage Beach, Mo., 1,091..C5 69
Osage City, Kans., 2,600...D8 61
Ōsaka, Jap., 2,841,937 (*14,175,000).......I7, o14 18
Osaka, Jap...............n16 18
Ōsaka, pref., Jap., 7,620,480..............*I7 18
Osakis, Minn., 1,306.......E3 67
Osawatomie, Kans., 4,294..................D9 61
Osborne, Kans., 1,980.....C5 61
Osborne, co., Kans., 6,416..................C5 61
Osbornsville, N.J., 800....*C4 74
Osburn, Idaho, 2,248......B3 57
Osceola, Ark., 7,204.......B6 49
Osceola, Ind., 1,572.......A5 59
Osceola, Iowa, 3,124......C4 60
Osceola, Mo., 874.........C4 69
Osceola, Nebr., 923.......C8 71
Osceola, Wis., 1,152.......C1 88
Osceola, co., Fla., 25,267...E5 54
Osceola, co., Iowa, 8,555..................A2 60
Osceola, co., Mich., 14,838..................E5 66
Osceola Mills, Pa., 1,671...E5 81
Oschatz, Ger. Dem. Rep., 15,500.................C6 6
Oschersleben, Ger. Dem. Rep., 19,100...........B5 6
Oscoda, Mich., 2,170.....D7 66
Oscoda, co., Mich., 4,726..................D6 66
Osgoode, Ont., Can., 823..B9 41
Osgood, Ind., 1,346.......F7 59
Osh, Sov. Un., 120,000...E10 13
Oshamambe, Jap..........E10 18
Oshawa, Ont., Can., 91,587 (*120,318).......D6 41
Oshkosh, Nebr., 1,067.....C3 71
Oshkosh, Wis., 53,082 (*70,100)....D5, h8 88
Oshogbo, Nig., 208,966....G5 22
Osijek, Yugo., 93,912......C4 10
Osinniki, Sov. Un., 62,000..............*D11 13
Oskaloosa, Iowa, 11,224...C5 60
Oskaloosa, Kans., 955...............C8, k15 61
Oskarshamm, Swe., 22,096 (27,412 ▲)...............I7 11
Oslo, Nor., 487,000 (*715,000).........G4, p28 11
Oslo, co., Nor., 487,600..............*H4 11
Osmaniye, Tur., 46,355..................D11 14
Osmond, Nebr., 883.......B8 71
Osnabrück, Ger., Fed. Rep. of, 163,984 (*255,000)...B4 6
Osorno, Chile, 55,091.....C2 28
Osorno, prov., Chile, 170,400................C2 28
Osoyoos, B.C., Can., 1,022.................E8 37
Osprey, Fla., 1,115........E4 54
Oss, Neth., 42,753.........B6 5
Ossa, mtn., Austl.........o15 25
Osseo, Minn., 2,908......m12 67
Osseo, Wis., 1,356........D2 88
Ossian, Ind., 1,538........C7 59
Ossian, Iowa, 847.........A6 60
Ossining, N.Y., 21,659............D7, m15 75
Ostashkov, Sov. Un., 23,000.................C9 12
Osteen, Fla., 550..........D5 54
Östergötland, co., Swe., 372,500..............*H6 11
Östersund, Swe., 44,491....F6 11
Osterville, Mass., 1,286...C7 65
Östfold, co., Nor., 216,800..............*H4 11
Ostrava, Czech., 278,737 (*670,000).....D5 7
Ostróda, Pol., 21,300......B5 7
Ostrogozhsk, Sov. Un., 30,000..................F12 12
Ostrołęka, Pol., 17,100.....B6 7
Ostrov, Czech., 19,313....C2 7
Ostrov, Sov. Un., 10,000...C7 12
Ostrowiec [Swietokrzyski], Pol., 49,900............C6 7
Ostrów Mazowiecka, Pol., 15,000.................B6 7
Ostrów Wielkopolski, Pol., 49,500............C4 7
Ostrzeszów, Pol., 7,357....C4 7
Ostuni, It., 25,400........D6 9
Ōsuka, Jap..............o16 18
Osuna, Sp., 19,569........D3 8
Oswego, Ill., 1,862.....B5, k8 58
Oswego, Kans., 2,200......E8 61
Oswego, N.Y., 20,913......B4 75
Oswego, co., N.Y., 100,897.B4 75
Oswestry, Eng., 11,215....D5 4
Oświecim, Pol., 39,600............C5, g10 7
Ota, Jap., 98,257........*m18 18
Otaki, Jap...............n19 18
Otaré, mtn., Col..........C3 32
Otaru, Jap., 191,856.....E10 18
Otavalo, Ec., 8,630........A2 31
Otay, Calif., 3,500.......*F5 50
Oteen, N.C., 2,000........f10 76
Otego, N.Y., 956..........C5 75
Otero, co., Colo., 23,523...D7 51
Otero, co., N. Mex., 41,097..................C6 48
Othello, Wash., 4,122.....C6 86
Otho, Iowa, 581...........B3 60
Otis Orchards, Wash., 1,200..................g14 86
Otisville, Mich., 724.......E7 66
Otisville, N.Y., 933......*D6 75
Otoe, co., Nebr., 15,576...D9 71
Otsego, Mich., 3,957.......F5 66
Otsego, co., Mich., 10,422..C6 66
Otsego, co., N.Y., 56,181...C5 75
Ōtsu, Jap., 171,777.......o14 18
Otsuki, Jap., 36,858......n17 18
Ottawa, Ont., Can., 302,341 (*602,510)..B9, h12 41
Ottawa, Ill., 18,716.......B5 58
Ottawa, Kans., 11,036.....D8 61
Ottawa, Ohio, 3,622.......A1 78
Ottawa, co., Kans., 6,183..C6 61
Ottawa, co., Mich., 128,181..................F4 66
Ottawa, co., Ohio, 37,099..A2 78
Ottawa, co., Okla., 29,800..................A7 79
Ottawa, river, Ont., Que., Can.............E18 36
Ottawa-Carleton, co., Ont., Can., 471,931.....B9 41
Ottawa Hills, Ohio, 4,270.............A2, e6 78
Otterbien, Ind., 899.......D3 59
Otter Lake, Mich., 551.....E7 66
Otter River, Mass., 600....A3 65
Otter Tail, co., Minn., 46,097.................D3 67
Otterville, Ont., Can., 725..................E4 41
Ottoville, Ohio, 914.......B1 78
Ottumwa, Iowa, 29,610....C5 60
Otuzco, Peru, 3,534.......C2 31
Otwell, Ind., 600.........H3 59
Otwock, Pol., 39,800.....m14 7
Ouachita, co., Ark., 30,896................D3 49
Ouachita, par., La., 115,387.................B3 63
Ouachita, river, U.S.......D8 45
Ouagadougou, Upper Volta, 77,500..........F4 22
Ouahigouya, Upper Volta, 10,000...........F4 22
Ouargla, Alg., 18,206......B6 22
Oudtshoorn, S. Afr., 26,525................G4 24
Ouezzane, Mor., 33,267....B3 22
Ouidah, Benin, 14,000.....G5 22
Oujda, Mor., 175,532.....C5 21
Oullins, Fr., 26,604.......E6 5
Oulu, Fin., 86,880.......E11 11
Oulu, prov., Fin., 422,700...............*E11 11
Ouray, Colo., 741.........C3 51
Ouray, co., Colo., 1,546...C3 51
Ourinhos, Braz., 40,733....C3 30
Ouro Fino, Braz., 9,122..............C3, m8 30
Ouro Prêto, Braz., 24,050..C4 30
Outagamie, co., Wis., 119,398.................D5 88
Outes, Sp., 869...........A1 8

Outlook, Sask., Can., 1,767..........F2 39
Outreau, Fr., 13,735..........B4 5
Outremont, Que., Can., 28,552..........p19 42
Ovada, It., 9,594..........B2 9
Ovalle, Chile, 25,282..........A2 28
Ovar, Port., 7,298..........B1 8
Overbrook, Kans., 748..........D8 61
Overijssel, prov., Neth., 907,000..........*A7 5
Overland, Mo., 24,819..........f13 69
Overland Park, Kans., 79,034..........m16 61
Overlea, Md., 13,086..........B4, g11 53
Overton, Nebr., 538..........D6 71
Overton, Nev., 900..........C4 72
Overton, Tex., 2,084..........C5 84
Overton, co., Tenn., 14,866..........C8 83
Ovid, Mich., 1,650..........E6 66
Ovid, N.Y., 779..........C4 75
Oviedo, Fla., 1,870..........D5 54
Oviedo, Sp., 152,453..........A3 8
Oviedo, prov., Sp., 1,040,300..........*A3 8
Ovruch, Sov. Un., 10,000..F7 12
Owasso, Okla., 3,491..........A6 79
Owatonna, Minn., 15,341..F5 67
Owego, N.Y., 5,152..........C4 75
Owen, Wis., 1,031..........D3 88
Owen, co., Ind., 12,163..........F4 59
Owen, co., Ky., 7,470..........B5 62
Owens, N.C...........*C4 76
Owensboro, Ky., 50,329 (*61,600)..........C2 62
Owen Sound, Ont., Can., 18,469..........C4 41
Owensville, Ind., 1,056..........H2 59
Ownesville, Mo., 2,416..........C6 69
Owensville, Ohio, 707..........C1 78
Owenton, Ky., 1,280..........B5 62
Owings Mills, Md., 7,360..*B4 53
Owingsville, Ky., 1,381..........B6 62
Owl Creek, mts., Wyo..........C4 89
Owosso, Mich., 17,179..........E6 66
Owsley, co., Ky., 5,023..........C6 62
Owyhee, co., Idaho, 6,422..........G2 57
Oxbow, Sask., Can., 1,380..........H4 39
Oxbow, Mich., 2,000..........*F7 66
Oxelösund, Swe., 14,560..........o35 11
Oxford, Ala., 4,361..........B4 46
Oxford, N.S., Can., 1,473..........D6 43
Oxford, Eng., 110,630 (*210,000)..........E6 4
Oxford, Ga., 1,373..........C3 55
Oxford, Ind., 1,098..........C3 59
Oxford, Iowa, 666..........C6 60
Oxford, Kans., 1,113..........E6 61
Oxford, Maine, 500..........D2 64
Oxford, Md., 750..........C5 53
Oxford, Mass., 6,109..........B4 65
Oxford, Mich., 2,536..........F7 66
Oxford, Miss., 13,846..........A4 68
Oxford, Nebr., 1,116..........D6 71
Oxford, N.J., 1,411..........B3 74
Oxford, N.Y., 1,944..........C5 75
Oxford, N.C., 7,178..........A4 76
Oxford, Ohio, 15,868..........C1 78
Oxford, Pa., 3,658..........G10 81
Oxford, co., Ont., Can., 76,018..........D4 41
Oxford, co., Eng., 388,190..........*E6 4
Oxford, co., Maine 43,457..........D2 64
Oxnard, Calif., 71,225..........E4 50
Oxnard Beach, Calif., 2,000..........*E4 50
Oyama, Jap., 68,000 (105,346 ▲)..........m18 18
Oyo, Nig., 112,349..........G5 22
Oyonnax, Fr., 14,830..........D6 5
Oyster Bay, N.Y., 6,500..........E7, n15 75
Oyster Bay Cove, N.Y., 1,320..........*E7 75
Ozamiz, Phil., 18,434..........D6 19
Ozark, Ala., 13,655..........D4 46
Ozark, Ark., 2,592..........B2 49
Ozark, Mo., 2,384..........D4 69
Ozark, co., Mo., 6,226..........E5 69
Ozaukee, co., Wis., 54,461..........E6 88
Ózd, Hung., 38,637..........A5 10
Ozieri, It., 11,884..........D2 9
Ozona, Fla., 1,200..........o10 54
Ozona, Tex., 2,864..........D2 84
Ozorków, Pol., 18,200..........C5 7
Ozu, Jap., 37,324..........J6 18

P

Paarl, S. Afr., 48,597..........G3 24
Paauilo, Haw., 710..........C6 56
Pabianice, Pol., 62,200..........C5 7
Pābna, Bngl., 40,792..........D8 20
Pacasmayo, Peru, 6,615..........C2 31
Pace, Fla., 1,776..........u14 54
Pacheco, Calif., 2,500..........*C2 50
Pachuca [de Soto], Mex., 83,892..........C5, m14 34
Pacific, Mo., 3,247..........C7, g12 69
Pacific, Wash., 1,831..........f11 86
Pacific, co., Wash., 15,796..C2 86
Pacific, ocean..........F6 2
Pacifica, Calif., 36,020..........h8 50
Pacific Grove, Calif., 13,505..........D3 50
Packard, mtn., Mass..........B3 65
Pacolet, S.C., 1,418..........B4 82
Pacolet Mills, S.C., 1,504..........B4 82
Paczkow, Pol., 6,944..........C4 7
Padang, Indon., 196,339..F2 19
Padangpandjang, Indon., 30,711..........F2 19
Padangsidempuan, Indon., 49,090..........E1, m11 19
Paddock Lake, Wis., 1,470.n11 88
Paden City, W. Va., 3,674..........B4 87
Paderborn, Ger., Fed. Rep. of, 70,706..........C4 6
Padova (Padua), It., 224,200..........B3 9
Paducah, Ky., 31,627..........A2 62
Paducah, Tex., 2,052..........B2 84
Paektu-san, mtn., Kor..........F4 18
Pagadian, Phil., 29,299..........*D6 19
Page, Ariz., 2,500..........A4 48
Page, W. Va., 800..........C3, m13 87
Page, co., Iowa, 18,507..........D2 60
Page, co., Va., 16,581..........B4 85
Pagedale, Mo., 5,044..........*C7 69
Pageland, S.C., 2,122..........B7 82
Page Manor, Ohio, 7,500..........*C1 78
Pago Pago, Am. Sam., 2,451..........*G9 2
Pagosa Springs, Colo., 1,360..........D3 51
Pahala, Haw., 1,507..........D6 56
Pahang, state, Mala., 387,400..........E2 19
Pahoa, Haw., 924..........D7 56
Pahokee, Fla., 5,663..........F6 54
Paia, Haw., 541..........C5 65
Painesdale, Mich., 600..........A2 66
Painesville, Ohio, 16,536..........A4 78
Paint, Pa., 4,233..........*F4 81
Painted Post, N.Y., 2,496..C3 75
Paintsville, Ky., 3,868..........C7 62
Paisley, Ont., Can., 759..........C3 41
Paisley, Scot., 95,067..........C4 4
Paita, Peru, 7,177..........C1 31
Pajaro, Calif., 1,407..........*D3 50
Pakanbaru, Indon., 145,030..........E2 19
Pakistan, country, Asia, 68,720,000..........C4 20
Pakistan, East, see Bangladesh country, Asia
Pakokku, Bur., 30,943..........D10 20
Paks, Hung., 10,452..........B4 10
Pakse, Laos, 25,000..........B3 19
Palacios, Tex., 3,642..........E4 84
Palafrugell, Sp., 7,905..........B7 8
Palaiseau, Fr., 16,326..........h9 5
Palamós, Sp., 7,639..........B7 8
Palana, Sov. Un., 1,000..D18 13
Pālanpur, India, 42,114..........D5 20
Palas de Rey, Sp., 769..........A2 8
Palatine, Ill., 26,050..........A5, h8 58
Palatka, Fla., 9,444..........C5 54
Palawan, prov., Phil., 162,669..........C5 19
Palawan, isl., Phil..........C5 19
Palayankottai, India, 70,050..........*G6 20
Palazzolo Acreide, It., 11,024..........F5 9
Palembang, Indon., 582,961..........F2 19
Palencia, Sp., 56,816..........A3 8
Palencia, prov., Sp., 213,800..........*A3 8
Palermo, It., 659,200..........E4 9
Palestine, Ill., 1,640..........D6 58
Palestine, Tex., 14,525..........D5 84
Palestine, reg., Asia..........D2 15
Palestrina, It., 9,154..........h9 9
Pālghāt, India, 95,788..........F6 20
Palikun (Barkol), China, 10,000..........C3 17
Palisades, Idaho, 150..........*F7 57
Palisades Park, N.J., 13,351..........h8 74
Palma [de Mallorca], Sp., 217,525..........C7 8
Palmares, Braz., 31,281..........*D7 27
Palma Soriano, Cuba, 41,200 (59,600 ▲)..........D5 35
Palm Bay, Fla., 7,176..........D6 54
Palm Beach, Fla., 9,086..........F6 54
Palm Beach, co., Fla., 348,753..........F6 54
Palmdale, Calif., 8,511..........E4 50
Palm Desert, Calif., 5,000..*F5 50
Palmeira dos Indios, Braz., 25,982..........*D7 27
Palmer, Alsk., 1,140..C10, g17 47
Palmer, Mass., 3,649 (11,680 ▲)..........B3 65
Palmer, Mich., 900..........B3 66
Palmer, Tenn., 898..........D8 83
Palmer Heights, Pa., 1,700..........*E11 81
Palmer Park, Md., 8,172..*C4 53
Palmerston, Ont., Can., 1,554..........D4 41
Palmerston North, N.Z., 52,900 (*58,200)..........N15 26
Palmerton, Pa., 5,620..........E10 81
Palmetto, Fla., 7,422..E4, p10 54
Palmetto, Ga., 2,045..........C2 55
Palm Harbor, Fla., 4,500..o10 54
Palmi, It., 15,400..........E5 9
Palmira, Col., 119,100 (157,600 ▲)..........C2 32
Palmira, Cuba, 10,900 (19,000 ▲)..........C3 35
Palm Springs, Calif., 20,936..........F5 50
Palm Springs, Fla., 4,340..*F6 54
Palmyra, Ill., 776..........D4 58
Palmyra, Mo., 3,188..........B6 69
Palmyra, N.J., 6,969..........C2 74
Palmyra, N.Y., 3,776..........B3 75
Palmyra, Pa., 7,615..........F8 81
Palmyra, Wis., 1,341..........F5 88
Palo Alto, Calif., 55,835..........D2, k8 50
Palo Alto, Pa., 1,428..........*E9 81
Palo Alto, co., Iowa, 13,289..........A3 60
Palomar, mtn., Calif..........F5 50
Palombara Sabina, It., 6,215..........g9 9
Palo Pinto, co., Tex., 28,962..........C3 84
Palopo, Indon., 29,724..........F6 19
Palos Heights, Ill., 9,915..*B6 58
Palos Hills, Ill., 6,629..........*B6 58
Palos Park, Ill., 3,297..........k9 58
Palos Verdes Estates, Calif., 13,631..........n12 50
Palouse, Wash., 948..........C8 86
Palpa, Peru, 2,171..........D3 31
Pamekasan, Indon., 41,416..........G4 19
Pamiers, Fr., 13,297..........F4 5
Pamlico, co., N.C., 9,467..B6 76
Pampa, Tex., 21,726..........B2 84
Pampanga, prov., Phil., 617,259..........*B6 19
Pampas, Peru, 1,622..........D3 31
Pampas, reg., Arg..........*G4 27
Pamplico, S.C., 1,068..........C8 82
Pamplona, Col., 25,502..........B3 32
Pamplona, Sp., 145,026..........A5 8
Pana, Ill., 6,326..........D4 58
Panagyurishte, Bul., 18,315..........D7 10
Panaji (Panjim), India, 34,953 (*59,258)..........E5 20
Panama, Okla., 1,121..........B7 79
Panamá, Pan., 348,704 (*465,000)..........B2 32
Panama, country, N.A., 1,585,000..........B2 32
Panama City, Fla., 32,096..........u16 54
Panao, Peru, 954..........C2 31
Panay, isl., Phil..........C6 19
Pancevo, Yugo., 54,269..........C5 10
Pandharpur, India, 53,638..E6 20
Pando, Ur., 6,248..........E1 30
Pando, dept., Bol., 24,800..B2 29
Pandora, Ohio, 857..........B2 78
Panevežys, Sov. Un., 73,000..........D5 12
Panfilov, Sov. Un., 19,000..E10 13
Pangasinan, prov., Phil., 1,124,144..........*B6 19
Pangfou (Pengpu), China, 330,000..........E8 17
Pangkalpinang, Indon., 74,733..........F3 19
Panguitch, Utah, 1,318..........C5 72
Panhandle, Tex., 2,141..........B2 84
Pānīpat, India, 87,981..........*C6 20
Panna, India, 22,316..........D7 20
Panola, co., Miss., 26,829..A3 68
Panola, co., Tex., 15,894..C5 84
Panora, Iowa, 982..........C3 60
Pantelleria, It., 2,294..........F3 9
Pantin, Fr., 47,607..........g10 5
Pánuco, Mex., 14,277..C5, k14 34
Paochi, China, 180,000..........*E7 17
Paola, It., 9,197..........E6 9
Paola, Kans., 4,622..........D9 61
Paoli, Ind., 3,281..........G5 59
Paoli, Pa., 7,000..........o20 81
Paonia, Colo., 1,161..........C3 51
Paoting (Tsingyuan), China, 265,000..........D8 17
Paotou, China, 490,000..........C7 17
Paoying, China, 40,000..........C7 17
Pápa, Hung., 27,775..........B3 10
Papaikou, Haw., 1,888..........D6 56
Papantla [de Olarte], Mex., 26,773..........C5, m15 34
Papeete, Fr. Polynesia 22,278 (*37,485)..........H11 2
Papenburg, Ger., Fed. Rep. of, 26,626..........B3 6
Papillion, Nebr., 5,606..C9, g12 71
Papineau, co., Que., Can., 31,952..........D2 42
Papineauville, Que., Can., 1,300..........D2 42
Papua New Guinea, country, Oceania 2,695,000..........h11 25
Para, state, Braz., 2,197,072..........A4 29
Paracatu, Braz., 17,453..........B3 30
Paracin, Yugo., 21,460..........D5 10
Paradis, La., 900..........k11 63
Paradise, Calif., 14,539..........C3 50
Paradise Valley, Ariz., 7,155..........D2 48
Paragould, Ark., 10,639..........A5 49
Paraguaçu Paulista, Braz., 13,318..........C2 30
Paraguarí, Par., 5,036..........E4 29
Paraguarí, dept., Par., 203,012..........E4 29
Paraguay, country, S.A., 2,735,000..........D4 29
Paraguay, riv., Braz., Par..F5 27
Paraíba do Sul, Braz., 7,675..........h6 30
Paraíba [do Sul], riv., Braz..........F6 27

Paraiso, C.Z., 1,659......*B2 32
Paraíso, Mex., 7,561....D6 34
Paraisópolis, Braz., 6,984...C3 30
Parakhino-Paddubye,
 Sov. Un., 20,000......B9 12
Paramaribo, Sur.,
 102,300 (*175,000)......C5 27
Paramount, Calif.,
 34,734...........*F4 50
Paramus, N.J., 28,381....h8 74
Paraná, Arg., 120,000....A4 28
Paraná, state, Braz.,
 6,997,682..........C2 30
Paraná, riv., S.A.......E4 29
Paranaguá, Braz., 51,510..D3 30
Paray-Le-Monial, Fr.,
 10,716.............D6 5
Parchim, Ger. Dem. Rep.,
 18,900............B5 6
Parchment, Mich., 2,027..F5 66
Pardeeville, Wis., 1,507..E4 88
Pardes Hanna, Isr.,
 13,600............B2 15
Pardubice, Czech., 70,777.C3 7
Parecis, mts., Braz.....E5 27
Parent, Que., Can., 452..k12 42
Parepare, Indon.,
 72,538............F5 19
Paricutín, vol., Mex.....n12 34
Parintins, Braz., 16,721..*D5 27
Paris, Ark., 3,646......B2 49
Paris, Ont., Can., 6,483..D4 41
Paris, Fr., 2,425,000
 (*9,300,000)....C5, g10 5
Paris, Idaho, 615......G7 57
Paris, Ill., 9,971......D6 58
Paris, Ky., 7,823......B5 62
Paris, Mo., 1,442......B6 69
Paris, S.C., 1,000......*B3 82
Paris, Tenn., 9,892......A3 83
Paris, Tex., 23,441.....C5 84
Paris, peak, Idaho......G7 57
Park, co., Colo., 2,185...B5 51
Park, co., Mont., 11,197..E6 70
Park, co., Wyo., 17,752..B3 89
Park City, Ill., 2,855.....*A6 58
Park City, Kans., 2,529..B5 61
Park City, Utah,
 1,193.........A6. D2 72
Parkdale, P.E.I., Can.,
 2,313.............C6 43
Parke, co., Ind., 14,600..E3 59
Parker, Ariz., 1,948......B1 48
Parker, Fla., 4,212......u16 54
Parker, Pa., 843.......D2 81
Parker, S. Dak., 1,005...G8 77
Parker, co., Tex., 33,888..C4 84
Parker City, Ind., 1,179..D7 59
Parkersburg, Iowa, 1,631..B5 60
Parkersburg, W. Va.,
 44,797 (*87,900)......B3 87
Parkers Prairie, Minn.,
 882..............D3 67
Parkes, Austl., 8,849.....F7 26
Parkesburg, Pa., 2,701...G10 81
Park Falls, Wis., 2,953...C3 88
Park Forest, Ill.,
 30,638..........B6, m9 58
Parkhill, Ont., Can.,
 1,169.............D3 41
Park Hills, Ky., 3,999....A7 62
Parkin, Ark., 1,731.....B5 49
Parkland, Pa., 1,800.....*F11 81
Parkland, Wash., 22,200..f11 86
Parklawn, Va., 1,800....*B5 85
Park Place, Pa., 260.....*B3 81
Park Rapids, Minn.,
 2,772.............D3 67
Park Ridge, Ill.,
 42,614.........B6, h9 58
Park Ridge, N.J., 8,709...g8 74
Park Ridge Manor, Ill.,
 900..............*B6 58
Park River, N. Dak.,
 1,680.............B8 77
Parkrose, Oreg., 22,500..*B4 80
Parkside, Pa., 2,343.....*G11 81
Parksley, Va., 903......C7 85
Parkston, S. Dak., 1,611..G8 77
Parksville, B.C., Can.,
 2,169.............E5 37
Parksville, N.Y., 900....D6 75
Parkton, N.C., 550......C4 76
Parkview, Ohio.........*A4 78
Parkview, Pa., 950......*E2 81
Parkville, Md., 35,300...C3 53
Parkville, Mo., 1,253...B3, h10 69
Parkville, Pa., 1,300....*G8 81
Parkwood, Md., 2,800...*B3 53
Parlier, Calif., 1,993....D4 50
Parma, Idaho, 1,228....F2 57
Parma, It., 170,300.....B3 9
Parma, Mich., 880......F6 66
Parma, Ohio, 100,216..A4, h9 78
Parma Heights, Ohio,
 27,192...........h9 78
Parmer, co., Tex., 10,509..B1 84

Parnaíba, Braz., 57,031....D6 27
Parnaíba, riv., Braz......D6 27
Pärnu, Sov. Un., 46,000..B5 12
Parowan, Utah, 1,423....C5 72
Parral, Chile, 14,600.....B2 28
Parramatta, Austl.,
 109,100...........*F8 26
Parras de la Fuente, Mex.,
 18,707............B4 34
Parrish, Ala., 1,742.....B2 46
Parrish, Fla., 850.....E4, p11 54
Parrsboro, N.S., Can.,
 1,807.............D5 43
Parry, is., N.W. Ter.,
 Can.............m28 36
Parry, mtn., B.C., Can....C3 37
Parry Sound, Ont.,
 Can., 5,842.......B4, p20 41
Parry Sound, dist.,
 Ont., Can., 28,335....B4 41
Parshall, N. Dak., 1,246..C3 77
Parsippany, N.J., 7,488...B4 74
Parsons, Kans., 13,015...E8 61
Parsons, Tenn., 2,167....B3 83
Parsons, W. Va., 1,784...B5 87
Parthenay, Fr., 11,334....D3 5
Partinico, It., 27,800.....E4 9
Partizansk, Sov. Un.,
 48,000...........E16 13
Pasadena, Calif.,
 112,951.......E4, m12 50
Pasadena, Md., 1,500....B4 53
Pasadena, Tex., 89,277..r14 84
Pasadena Hills, Mo.,
 1,337.............*C7 69
Pasadena Park, Wash.,
 2,200.............*B8 86
Pasay, Phil., 206,283..C6, o13 19
Pascagoula, Miss.,
 27,264.........E5, f8 68
Paşcani [-Gară], Rom.,
 15,008............B8 10
Pasco, Wash., 13,920
 (*75,300).........C6 86
Pasco, co., Fla., 75,955..D4 54
Pasco, dept., Peru,
 130,507...........D2 31
Pascoag, R.I., 3,132....B2 52
Pas-de-Calais, dept., Fr.,
 1,397,159.........B5 5
Pasewalk, Ger. Dem. Rep.,
 12,400............B7 6
Pasig, Phil., 62,130.....o13 19
Paso de los Libres, Arg.,
 15,054............E4 29
Paso Robles, Calif., 7,168..E3 50
Pasquotank, co., N.C.,
 26,824............A6 76
Pasrur, Pak., 9,403.....B5 20
Passadumkeag, mtn.,
 Maine............C4 64
Passaic, N.J., 55,124...B4, h8 74
Passaic, co., N.J., 460,782..A4 74
Passau, Ger., Fed. Rep. of,
 49,875............D6 6
Pass Christian, Miss.,
 2,979..........E4, g7 68
Passo Fundo, Braz.,
 69,135............D2 30
Passos, Braz., 39,184....D3 30
Pastaza, prov., Ec., 18,600..B2 31
Pasto, Col., 87,800
 (120,100▲)........C2 32
Pasuruan, Indon., 75,266..G4 19
Pataskala, Ohio, 1,851...C3 78
Patchogue, N.Y., 11,582..n15 75
Paternò, It., 47,300.....F5 9
Paterson, N.J., 144,824..B4, h8 74
Pathänkot, India, 76,355..B6 20
Pathfork, Ky., 300......D6 62
Patiāla, India, 148,686...B6 20
Patna, India, 473,001
 (*625,000).........C8 20
Patos, Braz., 39,850....*D7 27
Patos de Minas, Braz.,
 42,215............B3 30
Patrai, Grc., 111,607
 (*120,847)........C3 14
Patrick, co., Va., 15,282..D2 85
Patrocínio, Braz., 19,820..B3 30
Pattani, Thai., 21,938....D2 19
Patten, Maine, 1,068
 (1,266▲)..........C4 64
Patterson, Calif., 3,147..*D3 50
Patterson, La., 4,409....E4 63
Patterson, N.Y., 900....D7 75
Patterson Gardens, Mich.,
 1,000.............*G7 66
Patton, Pa., 2,762.....E4 81
Pattonsburg, Mo., 540...A3 69
Pattullo, mtn., B.C., Can..A3 37
Pátzcuaro, Mex.,
 17,299.........D4, n13 34
Patzicía, Guat., 5,021...*E6 34
Patzún, Guat., 5,103....*E6 34
Pau, Fr., 74,005 (*110,000).F3 5
Paucarbamba, Peru,
 1,173.............D3 31

Paudalho, Braz., 10,707..*D7 27
Pauk, Bur., 5,000......D9 20
Paulding, Ohio, 2,983...A1 78
Paulding, co., Ga., 17,520..C2 55
Paulding, co., Ohio,
 19,329...........A1 78
Paulina (Remy), La.,
 950............D5, h10 63
Paulina, mts., Oreg......D5 80
Paulina, peak, Oreg.....D5 80
Pauline, mtn., B.C., Can...C8 37
Paullina, Iowa, 1,257....B2 60
Paulsboro, N.J., 8,084...D2 74
Pauls Valley, Okla., 5,769..C4 79
Paungde, Bur., 17,286...E10 20
Pavia, It., 85,200......B2 9
Pavlodar, Sov. Un.,
 187,000..........D10 13
Pavlograd, Sov. Un.,
 80,000...........G10 12
Pavlovo, Sov. Un.,
 63,000...........D14 12
Pavlovsk, Sov. Un.,
 30,000...........F13 12
Pavlovskiy Posad,
 Sov. Un., 66,000....n18 12
Pawcatuck, Conn., 5,255..D9 52
Paw Creek, N.C., 1,500..B2 76
Pawhuska, Okla., 4,238..A5 79
Pawling, N.Y., 1,914....D7 75
Pawnee, Ill., 1,936.....D4 58
Pawnee, Okla., 2,443....A5 79
Pawnee, co., Kans.,
 8,484............D4 61
Pawnee, co., Nebr., 4,473..D9 71
Pawnee, co., Okla.,
 11,338............A5 79
Pawnee City, Nebr.,
 1,267.............D9 71
Paw Paw, Mich., 3,160..F5 66
Paw Paw, W. Va., 706...B6 87
Paw Paw Lake, Mich.,
 3,726.............*F4 66
Pawtucket, R.I., 76,984..B11 52
Paxtang, Pa., 2,039.....*F8 81
Paxton, Ill., 4,373.....C5 58
Payen, China, 5,000....C3 18
Payette, Idaho, 4,521...E2 57
Payette, co., Idaho,
 12,401............E2 57
Payne, Ohio, 1,351.....A1 78
Payne, co., Okla., 50,654..A4 79
Paynesville, Minn., 1,920..E4 67
Paysandú, Ur., 51,645...E1 30
Paysandú, dept., Ur.,
 87,229...........*E1 30
Payson, Utah, 4,501..A6, D2 72
Pazardzhik, Bul., 55,430..D7 10
Pazin, Yugo., 3,004.....C1 10
Peabody, Kans., 1,368...D6 61
Peabody, Mass.,
 48,080.........A6, f12 65
Peace, riv., Alta., B.C.,
 Can.............E10 36
Peace Dale, R.I., 3,000..D11 52
Peace River, Alta., Can.,
 5,039.........A2, f7 38
Peach, co., Ga., 15,990..D3 55
Peach Creek, W. Va.,
 700............n12 87
Peaked, mtn., Maine....B4 64
Pearisburg, Va., 2,169...C2 85
Pearl, Miss., 12,165....C3 68
Pearland, Tex., 6,444...r14 84
Pearl Beach, Mich.,
 1,744.............*F8 66
Pearl City, Haw.,
 19,552.........B4, g10 56
Pearl River, La., 1,361..D6 63
Pearl River, N.Y.,
 17,146............g12 75
Pearl River, co., Miss.,
 27,802...........D6 63
Pear Ridge, Tex., 3,697..E2 84
Pearsall, Tex., 5,545....E3 84
Pearsall, peak, Oreg.....E3 80
Pearson, Ga., 1,548.....E4 55
Pebane, Moz.........D7 24
Peć, Yugo., 42,113.....D5 10
Peçanha, Braz., 4,424...B4 30
Pecatonica, Ill., 1,781...A4 58
Pechenga, Sov. Un.,
 13,200...........C6 13
Pechora, riv., Sov. Un....C8 13
Peckville (Blakely), Pa....A9 81
Pecos, N. Mex., 598....*B6 48
Pecos, Tex., 12,682..D1, o13 84
Pecos, co., Tex., 13,748..D1 84
Pecos, riv., N. Mex.,
 Tex.............D6 45
Pécs, Hung., 145,307....B4 10
Pedley, Calif., 4,500....*F5 50
Pedreiras, Braz., 19,539..*D6 27
Pedricktown, N.J., 900...D2 74
Pedro Juan Caballero,
 Par., 21,033.......D4 29
Pedro Velho, Braz.,
 2,420............*D7 27

Peebles, Ohio, 1,629....D2 78
Peebles, Scot., 5,948....C5 4
Peebles, co., Scot.,
 13,360............*C5 4
Peekaboo, mtn., Maine..C5 64
Peekskill, N.Y.,
 19,283.........D7, m15 75
Peel, co., Ont., Can.,
 172,321...........D5 41
Pego, Sp., 8,291......C5 8
Pegu, Bur., 47,378.....E10 20
Pehuajó, Arg., 16,947...B4 28
Peian, China, 18,000....B10 17
Peihai, China, 80,000....G6 17
Peine, Ger., Fed. Rep. of,
 30,550............B5 6
Peiping, see Peking, China
Pekalongan, Indon.,
 111,537...........G3 19
Pekan, Mala., 7,129....E2 19
Pekin, Ill., 31,375.....C4 58
Peking (Peiping), China,
 4,800,000 (7,570,000▲).D8 17
Pelahatchie, Miss., 1,306..C4 68
Pelaihari, Indon.......F4 19
Pelée, mtn., Mart......I14 35
Pelham, Ont., Can., 9,997.D5 41
Pelham, Ga., 4,539.....E2 55
Pelham, N.Y., 2,076....*D7 75
Pelham Manor, N.Y.,
 6,673............h13 75
Pelhrimov, Czech.,
 9,041.............D3 7
Pelican Rapids, Minn.,
 1,835.............D2 67
Pelican, mtn., Alta., Can..B4 38
Pell Lake, Wis., 1,284...n11 88
Pella, Iowa, 6,668.....C5 60
Pella, prov., Grc.,
 126,201..........*B4 14
Pell City, Ala., 5,602....B3 46
Peloponnesos
 (Peloponnesus), reg.,
 Grc..............D4 14
Pelotas, Braz., 150,278...E2 30
Pelzer North, S.C......*B2 82
Pematangsiantar, Indon.,
 129,232...........m11 19
Pemberton, N.J., 1,344...D3 74
Pemberville, Ohio, 1,301..A4 78
Pembina, co., N. Dak.,
 10,728............B8 77
Pembroke, Ont., Can.,
 16,544 (*20,299)...B7, p20 41
Pembroke, Ga., 1,330...D5 55
Pembroke, Mass., 650...B6 65
Pembroke, N.C., 1,982...C3 76
Pembroke, Wales, 14,200.E4 4
Pembroke, co., Wales,
 97,870...........*E4 4
Pembroke Pines, Fla.,
 15,496...........*F6 54
Pemiscot, co., Mo.,
 26,373............E8 69
Penápolis, Braz., 24,597..C2 30
Pen Argyl, Pa., 3,668....E11 81
Peñarroya-Pueblonuevo,
 Sp., 24,152........C3 8
Penbrook, Pa., 3,379....*F8 81
Penchi (Penki), China,
 449,000...........C9 17
Pender, Nebr., 1,229....B9 71
Pender, co., N.C.,
 18,149............C4 76
Pendleton, Ind., 2,243...E6 59
Pendleton, Oreg., 13,197..B8 80
Pendleton, S.C., 2,615...B2 82
Pendleton, co., Ky.,
 9,949.............B5 62
Pendleton, co., W. Va.,
 7,031.............C5 87
Pend Oreille, co., Wash.,
 6,025.............A8 86
Penedo, Braz., 23,411...E7 27
Penetanguishene, Ont.,
 Can., 5,497.......C5 41
Penfield, N.Y., 8,500....*B3 75
Penfield Junction, Ohio..*A3 78
Peniche, Port., 11,357...C1 8
Peninsula, Ohio, 692....A4 78
Penn, Pa., 735.......*F3 81
Pennask, mtn., B.C., Can..E7 37
Penndel, Pa., 2,686....*F12 81
Penne, It., 5,054......C4 9
Penn Hills, Pa., 62,886...F2 81
Pennines, mts., Eng.....C5 4
Pennington, Ala., 301....C1 46
Pennington, N.J., 2,151..C3 74
Pennington, co., Minn.,
 13,266............B2 67
Pennington, co., S. Dak.,
 59,349............G3 77
Pennington Gap, Va.,
 1,886............f8 85
Pennsauken, N.J., 36,394..D2 74
Pennsboro, W. Va., 1,614..B4 87
Pennsburg, Pa., 2,260...F11 81

Penns Grove, N.J., 5,727...D2 74
Pennside, Pa., 3,200.....*F10 81
Pennsville, N.J., 11,014....D1 74
Pennsylvania, state, U.S., 11,874,000.......... 81
Penn Valley, Pa., 6,100..*F11 81
Penn Wynne, Pa., 4,200..*C11 81
Penn Yan, N.Y., 5,293....C3 75
Penny Hill, Del., 1,000...*A6 53
Penobscot, co., Maine, 125,393..........C4 64
Pensacola, Fla., 59,507 (*196,100)..........u14 54
Pentecost, Miss., 75.......B3 68
Penticton, B.C., Can., 18,146..........E8 37
Penton, Miss..........A3 68
Pentwater, Mich., 993.....E4 66
Penza, Sov. Un., 374,000..D7 13
Penzance, Eng., 19,060....E4 4
Penzberg, Ger., Fed. Rep. of, 11,072..........E5 6
Penzhino, Sov. Un., 600..C19 13
Peoria, Ariz., 4,792....C2, D1 48
Peoria, Ill., 126,963 (*299,800)..........C4 58
Peoria, co., Ill., 195,318...C4 58
Peoria Heights, Ill., 7,943..C4 58
Peotone, Ill., 2,345........B6 58
Pepin, Wis., 747..........D1 88
Pepin, co., Wis., 7,319.....D2 88
Pepper Pike, Ohio, 5,382..*A4 78
Pequannock, N.J., 5,900...B4 74
Perak, state, Mala., 1,508,000..........*E2 19
Percy, Ill., 967..........E4 58
Perdido, mtn., Sp..........A6 8
Pereira Barreto, Braz., 17,708..........C2 30
Pereira, Col., 169,300 (216,200 ▲)..........C2 32
Perekop, Sov. Un., 10,000..........H9 12
Pereslavl-Zalesskiy, Sov. Un., 30,000.......C12 12
Pereyaslav-Khmelnitskiy, Sov. Un., 21,000........F8 12
Pergamino, Arg., 48,000...A4 28
Perham, Minn., 1,933.....D3 67
Périgueux, Fr., 37,450 (*57,000)..........E4 5
Perija, mts., Col..........B3 32
Perkasie, Pa., 5,451......F11 81
Perkins, co., Nebr., 3,423..D4 71
Perkins, co., S. Dak., 4,769..........E3 77
Perleberg, Ger. Dem. Rep., 13,500..........B5 6
Perlis, state, Mala., 109,100..........*D2 19
Perl-Mack, Colo., 7,576...*B6 51
Perm, Sov. Un., 850,000...D8 13
Përmet, Alb., 2,302........B3 14
Pernambuco, state, Braz., 5,252,590..........*D7 27
Pernik, Bul., 75,840.......D6 10
Perpignan, Fr., 102,191....F5 5
Perquimans, co., N.C., 8,351..........A6 76
Perrine, Fla., 10,257...G6, s13 54
Perris, Calif., 4,228........F5 50
Perry, Fla., 7,701..........B3 54
Perry Ga., 7,771..........D3 55
Perry, Iowa, 6,906........C3 60
Perry, Mich., 1,531........F6 66
Perry, Mo., 839..........B6 69
Perry, N.Y., 4,538........C3 75
Perry, Ohio, 917..........A4 78
Perry, Okla., 5,341........A4 79
Perry, co., Ala., 15,388....C2 46
Perry, co., Ark., 5,634.....C3 49
Perry, co., Ill., 19,757.....E4 58
Perry, co., Ind., 19,075....H4 59
Perry, co., Ky., 26,259.....C6 62
Perry, co., Miss., 9,065. ..D4 68
Perry, co., Mo., 14,393....D8 69
Perry, co., Ohio, 27,434...C3 78
Perry, co., Pa., 28,615.....F7 81
Perry, co., Tenn., 5,238....B4 83
Perry, peak, Mass..........B1 65
Perry Hall (Fullerton), Md., 5,446..........B5 53
Perry Heights, Ohio, 5,300..........*B4 78
Perryman, Md., 900.......B5 53
Perryopolis, Pa., 2,043....*F2 81
Perrysburg, Ohio, 7,693..........A2, e6 78
Perryton, Tex., 7,810......A2 84
Perryville, Mo., 5,149.....D8 69
Pershing, co., Nev., 2,670..A2 72
Persia, see Iran, country, Asia
Persimmon Grove, Ky., 100..........k14 62
Person, co., N.C., 25,914...A3 76
Perth, Austl., 97,242 (*701,392)..........F2 25
Perth, N.S., Can., 909.....C2 43
Perth, Ont., Can., 5,537...C8 41
Perth, Scot., 42,438.......B5 4
Perth, co., Ont., Can., 60,424..........D3 41
Perth, co., Scot., 124,907..*B5 4
Perth Amboy, N.J., 38,798..........B4, k7 74
Pertuis, Fr., 6,774........F6 5
Peru, Ill., 11,772..........B4 58
Peru, Ind., 14,139........C5 59
Peru, Nebr., 1,380.......D10 71
Peru, country, S.A., 14,140,000..........D3 31
Perugia, It., 88,200 (125,000 ▲)..........C4 9
Pervomaysk, Sov. Un., 59,000..........G8 12
Pervomaysk, Sov. Un., 46,000..........q21 12
Pervouralsk, Sov. Un., 117,000..........D8 13
Pesaro, It., 65,200........C4 9
Pescara, It., 113,500......C5 9
Peshāwar, Pak., 166,273 (*218,691)..........B5 20
Peshtera, Bul., 14,619.....D7 10
Peshtigo, Wis., 2,836......C6 88
Peski, Sov. Un., 25,500...F14 12
Peso da Régua, Port., 5,623..........B2 8
Pesqueira, Braz., 24,421..*D7 27
Pest, co., Hung., 869,864..........*B4 10
Petacas, mtn., Col.........C2 32
Petah Tiqwa, Isr., 92,400..B2 15
Petal, Miss., 6,986........D4 68
Petaling Jaya, Mala, 93,447..........*E2 19
Petaluma, Calif., 24,870...C2 50
Petatlán, Mex., 9,419.....D4 34
Peterborough, Ont., Can., 58,111 (*63,531)........C6 41
Peterborough, Eng., 69,800..........D6 4
Peterborough (Peterboro), N.H., 1,780..........F4 73
Peterborough, co., Ont., Can., 81,959..........C6 41
Peterhead, Scot., 14,384...B6 4
Petermann, ranges, Austl..........D4 25
Peters, mtn., Va..........C2 85
Petersburg, Alsk., 2,042..........D13, m23 47
Petersburg, Ill., 2,632.....C4 58
Petersburg, Ind., 2,697....H3 59
Petersburg, Mich., 1,227...G7 66
Petersburg, Tex., 1,300....C2 84
Petersburg (Independent City), Va., 36,103 (*128,600)........C5, n18 85
Petersburg, W. Va., 2,177..........B5 87
Pétionville, Hai., 35,257...E7 35
Petite-de-Grat, N.S., Can., 865..........D9 43
Petite-Rivière-de-l'Artibonite, Hai., 8,462...E7 35
Petit-Goâve, Hai., 8,779...E7 35
Peto, Mex., 8,362..........C7 34
Petoskey, Mich., 6,342.....C6 66
Petrich, Bul., 20,639.......E6 10
Petrikov, Sov. Un., 10,000..........E7 12
Petrinja, Yugo., 12,145....C3 10
Petrodvorets, Sov. Un., 21,700..........s30 11
Petrokrepost, Sov. Un., 30,000..........s32 11
Petroleum, co., Mont., 675..........C8 70
Petrolia, Ont., Can., 4,044..........E2 41
Petrolina, Braz., 37,801...*D6 27
Petropavlovsk, Sov. Un., 173,000..........D9 13
Petropavlovsk [-Kamchatskiy], Sov. Un., 154,000..........D18 13
Petrópolis, Braz., 116,080..........C4, h6 30
Petros, Tenn., 850........C9 83
Petroseni, Rom., 35,200 (*70,000)..........C6 10
Petrovgrad, see Zrenjanin, Yugo.
Petrovsk, Sov. Un., 19,000..........E15 12
Petrovskoye, Sov. Un., 31,000..........I14 12
Petrovsk-Zabaykalskiy, Sov. Un., 28,000.......D13 13
Petrozavodsk, Sov. Un., 184,000..........A10 12
Pettis, co., Mo., 34,137....C4 69
Petty Harbour, Newf., Can., 908..........E5 44
Pewaukee, Wis., 3,271..........E5, m11 88
Pézenas, Fr., 9,103........F5 5
Pforzheim, Ger., Fed. Rep. of, 94,108 (*212,000)....D4 6
Phalodi, India, 17,379.....C5 20
Phan Rang, Viet., 21,940..C3 19
Phan Thiet, Viet., 58,300..C3 19
Pharr, Tex., 15,829.......F3 84
Phelps, Ky., 770..........C7 62
Phelps, N.Y., 1,989.......C3 75
Phelps, co., Mo., 29,567...D6 69
Phelps, co., Nebr., 9,553...D6 71
Phenix City, Ala., 25,281..C4 46
Phet Buri, Thai., 27,755...C1 19
Phetchabun, Thai., 5,887..B2 19
Phichit, Thai., 9,257.....*B2 19
Philadelphia, Miss., 6,274..........C4 68
Philadelphia, N.Y., 858....A5 75
Philadelphia, Pa., 1,949,996 (*5,282,400)......G11, p21 81
Philadelphia, co., Pa., 1,949,996..........G11 81
Phil Campbell, Ala., 1,230.A2 46
Philip, S. Dak., 983.......C4 77
Philippeville, Bel., 2,143...*B6 5
Philippi, W. Va., 3,002....B4 87
Philippines, country, Asia, 40,665,000........B6 19
Philippolis, S. Afr., 2,173..G5 24
Philipsburg, Mont., 1,128..D3 70
Philipsburg, Pa., 3,700.....E5 81
Phillips, Tex., 2,515.......B2 84
Phillips, Wis., 1,511.......C3 88
Phillips, co., Ark., 40,046..........C5 49
Phillips, co., Colo., 4,131...A8 51
Phillips, co., Kans., 7,888..C4 61
Phillips, co., Mont., 5,386..B8 70
Phillipsburg, Kans., 3,241..........C4 61
Phillipsburg, N.J., 17,849..B2 74
Phillipsville, N.C., 500....*f9 76
Philmont, N.Y., 1,674.....C7 75
Philo, Ohio, 846..........C4 78
Philomath, Ga., 150.......C4 55
Philomath, Oreg., 1,688...C3 80
Phitsanulok, Thai., 33,883..........B2 19
Phnom Penh, Camb., 393,995..........C2 19
Phoenix, Ariz., 582,500 (*947,800)..........C2, D2 48
Phoenix, Ill., 3,596........k9 58
Phoenix, N.Y., 2,617.......B4 75
Phoenixville, Pa., 14,823..........F10, o19 81
Phong Saly, Laos, 10,000..G5 17
Phrae, Thai., 16,006......*B2 19
Phuket, Thai., 34,362.....D1 19
Piacenza, It., 102,800.....B2 9
Pialba, Austl., 3,544.......B9 26
Piaseczno, Pol., 20,500...m14 7
Piatra-Neamt, Rom., 45,900 (*58,400)........B8 10
Piatt, co., Ill., 15,509.....D5 58
Piauí, state, Braz., 1,734,865..........*D6 27
Piazza Armerina, It., 23,100..........F5 9
Picardy (Picardie), former prov., Fr........C5 5
Picayune, Miss., 10,467....E4 68
Picher, Okla., 2,363.......A7 79
Pichincha, prov., Ec., 749,300..........B2 31
Pickaway, co., Ohio, 40,071..........C2 78
Pickens, S.C., 2,954.......B2 82
Pickens, co., Ala., 20,326...B1 46
Pickens, co., Ga., 9,620....B2 55
Pickens, co., S.C., 58,956...B2 82
Pickering, Ont., Can., 2,537..........D5 41
Pickett, co., Tenn., 3,774...C8 83
Pickstown, S. Dak., 275...H7 77
Pico Duarte, peak, Dom. Rep..........E8 35
Pico Rivera, Calif., 54,170..........N12 50
Picton, Ont., Can., 4,875..D7 41
Pictou, N.S., Can., 4,250...D7 43
Pictou, co., N.S., Can., 44,490..........D7 43
Pidurutalagala, peak, Sri Lanka..........G7 20
Piedmont, Ala., 5,063.....B4 46
Piedmont, Calif., 10,917....h8 50
Piedmont, Mo., 1,906.....D7 69
Piedmont, S.C., 2,242.....B3 82
Piedmont, W. Va., 1,763...B5 87
Piedmont, reg., It..........B1 9
Piedrabuena, Sp., 6,210....C3 8
Piedras Negras, Mex., 41,033..........B4 34
Pieksämäki, Fin., 10,600..F12 11
Piélagos, Sp., 8,040.......A4 8
Piemonte, pol. dist., It., 3,914,250..........*B1 9
Piendamó, Col., 3,499.....C2 32
Pierce, Fla..........E5 54
Pierce, Nebr., 1,360.......B8 71
Pierce, co., Ga., 9,281.....E4 55
Pierce, co., Nebr., 8,493....B8 71
Pierce, co., N. Dak., 6,323..B5 77
Pierce, co., Wash., 411,027.C3 86
Pierce, co., Wis., 26,652...D1 88
Pierce City, Mo., 1,097....E3 69
Pierceton, Ind., 1,175......B6 59
Piermont, N.Y., 2,386.....D7 75
Pierre, S. Dak., 9,699.....F5 77
Pierrefitte [sur-Seine], Fr., 14,770..........g10 5
Pierrefonds, Que., Can., 33,010..........q19 42
Pierreville, Que., Can., 1,455 (*2,671)..........C5 42
Pierz, Minn., 893..........E4 67
Piešťany, Czech., 22,601..D4 7
Pietermaritzburg, S. Afr., 112,666 (*158,921)......F6 24
Pietersburg, S. Afr., 27,058..........E5 24
Pigeon, Mich., 1,174......E7 66
Pigeon Cove, Mass., 1,466..A6 65
Piggott, Ark., 3,087.......A5 49
Pigüé, Arg., 5,869........B4 28
Pike, co., Ala., 25,038.....D4 46
Pike, co., Ark., 8,711......C2 49
Pike, co., Ga., 7,316.......C2 55
Pike, co., Ill., 19,185......D3 58
Pike, co., Ind., 12,281.....H3 59
Pike, co., Ky., 61,059.....C7 62
Pike, co., Miss., 31,756....D3 68
Pike, co., Mo., 16,928.....B6 69
Pike, co., Ohio, 19,114....C2 78
Pike, co., Pa., 11,818.....D11 81
Pikes, peak, Colo..........C5 51
Pikesville, Md., 22,600..........B4, g10 53
Piketon, Ohio, 1,347......C2 78
Pikeville, Ky., 5,205......C7 62
Pikeville, Tenn., 1,454.....D8 83
Piła, Pol., 43,700..........B4 7
Pilar, Braz., 9,304........*D7 27
Pilar, Par., 12,506........E4 29
Pilcomayo, riv., S.A.......D3 29
Pilgrim Gardens, Pa., 8,400..........*B11 81
Pilot Mound, Man., Can., 802..........E2 40
Pilot Mountain, N.C., 1,309..........A2 76
Pilot, peak, Wyo..........B3 89
Pilot Point, Tex., 1,663....C4 84
Pilot Rock, Oreg., 1,612...B8 80
Pima, co., Ariz., 351,667...C2 48
Pimmit Hills, Va., 7,600..*B5 85
Pinal, co., Ariz., 68,579....C3 48
Pinang (George Town), Mala., 269,247 (*410,000)..........D2 19
Pinang, state, Mala., 697,000..........D2 19
Pinar del Río, Cuba, 73,200..........C2 35
Pinar del Río, prov., Cuba, 448,442..........C2 35
Pinardville, N.H., 4,200...*E4 73
Pincher Creek, Alta., Can., 3,227..........E4 38
Pinckneyville, Ill., 3,377...E4 58
Pinconning, Mich., 1,320..E7 66
Pindamonhangaba, Braz., 28,213..........C3 30
Pine, co., Minn., 16,821...D6 67
Pine, riv., Mich..........D5 66
Pine Beach, N.J., 1,395...*D4 74
Pine Bluff, Ark., 57,389 (*69,800)..........C3 49
Pine Bluffs, Wyo., 937.....E8 89
Pine Bush, N.Y., 1,183....D6 75
Pine Castle, Fla., 4,700....D5 54
Pine City, Minn., 2,143....E6 67
Pineda, Fla..........D6 54
Pinedale, Ariz., 80........B3 48
Pinedale, Wyo., 948.......D3 89
Pine Falls, Man., Can., 1,122..........D3 40
Pine Grove, Pa., 2,197.....E9 81
Pine Hill, N.J., 5,132.....D3 74
Pine Hills, Fla., 13,882..*D5 54
Pinehurst, Idaho, 1,996....B2 57
Pinehurst, Mass., 5,681....f11 65
Pinehurst, N.C., 1,056.....B3 76
Pinehurst, Wash..........*B3 86
Pine Island, Minn., 1,640..F6 67
Pine Island, N.Y., 800....D6 75
Pine Knot, Ky., 900.......D5 62
Pine Lake, Ind., 1,500....*A4 59
Pine Lake, Mass., 800....g10 65
Pineland, Tex., 1,127......D6 84
Pine Lawn, Mo., 5,745....f13 69
Pinellas, co., Fla., 522,329..........D4 54

Pinellas Park, Fla., 22,287......E4, p10 54
Pine Ridge, S. Dak., 2,768...........G3 77
Pinerolo, It., 31,500....B1 9
Pinetops, N.C., 1,379.....B5 76
Pineville, Ky., 2,817.....D6 62
Pineville, La., 8,951....C3 63
Pineville, N.C., 1,948...B2 76
Pineville, W. Va., 1,187...D3 87
Piney Point, Tex., 2,548..*E5 84
Piney View, W. Va., 500..D7 87
Pinghsiang, China, 7,000...F7 17
Pingliang, China, 60,000...D6 17
Pingtingshan, China, 70,000........*E7 17
Pingtung, Taiwan, 115,000 (145,300▲)..*G9 17
Pinhal, Braz., 18,172..C3, m8 30
Pinhsien, China, 6,000....D3 18
Pinkney (South Gastonia), N.C...........*B1 76
Pinole, Calif., 13,266.....h8 50
Pinon, Ariz., 250........A3 48
Pinos, Mex., 2,254......C4 34
Pinoso, Sp., 5,114.......C5 8
Pinos-Puente, Sp., 8,653..D4 8
Pinsk, Sov. Un., 62,000...E6 12
Pinson, Ala., 1,600.......f7 46
Pioche, Nev., 600........C4 72
Piombino, It., 39,600.....C3 9
Piotrków [Trybunalski], Pol., 59,600.......C5 7
Piper City, Ill., 817.....C5 58
Pipestone, Minn., 5,328...G2 67
Pipestone, co., Minn., 12,791...........F2 67
Piqua, Ohio, 20,741.....B1 78
Piracicaba, Braz., 125,490.......C3, m8 30
Piraçununga, Braz., 25,515.......C3, k8 30
Piraeus, see Piraiévs, Grc.
Piraiévs (Piraeus), Grc., 187,362..........D4 14
Pirajú, Braz., 13,558....C3 30
Pirajuí, Braz., 10,963....C3 30
Piran, Yugo., 5,464......B4 9
Pirapóra, Braz., 18,990..B4 30
Pirgos, Grc., 20,599.....D3 14
Piriápolis, Ur., 4,400....E1 30
Pirmasens, Ger., Fed. Rep. of, 56,214.......D3 6
Pirna, Ger. Dem. Rep., 49,663...........C6 6
Pirot, Yugo., 29,228.....D6 10
Piryatin, Sov. Un., 16,000..F9 12
Pisa, It., 102,700.......C3 9
Piscataquis, co., Maine, 14,285...........C3 64
Piscataway, N.J., 36,418..B4 74
Pisco, Peru, 22,112......D2 31
Písek, Czech., 22,719....D3 7
Pisinimo, Ariz., 140.....C2 48
Pismo Beach, Calif., 4,043..E3 50
Pissis, mtn., Arg........E2 29
Pisticci, It., 13,300.....D6 9
Pistoia, It., 69,400......C3 9
Pitalito, Col., 10,818....C2 32
Pitangui, Braz., 8,687....B4 30
Pitcairn, Pa., 4,741.....k14 81
Piteå, Swe., 14,425.....E9 11
Piteşti, Rom., 60,100....C7 10
Pithiviers, Fr., 8,686....C5 5
Pitkin, co., Colo., 6,185..B4 51
Pitlochry, Scot., 2,461...B5 4
Pitman, N.J., 10,257....D2 74
Pitrufquén, Chile, 6,500..B2 28
Pitt, co., N.C., 73,900...B5 76
Pittsboro, N.C., 1,447...B5 76
Pittsboro, Ind., 867.....E5 59
Pittsburg, Calif., 20,651....g9 50
Pittsburg, Kans., 20,171..E9 61
Pittsburg, Tex., 3,844...C5 84
Pittsburg, co., Okla., 37,521...........C6 79
Pittsburgh, Pa., 520,089 (*2,142,700)...F1, k13 81
Pittsfield, Ill., 4,244....D3 58
Pittsfield, Maine, 3,398..D3 64
Pittsfield, Mass., 57,020 (*101,300)........B1 65
Pittsfield, Mich.......:..*F7 66
Pittsfield, N.H., 1,662...E5 73
Pittsford, N.Y., 1,755....B3 75
Pittston, Pa., 11,113........D10, n17 81
Pittsylvania, co., Va., 58,789...........D3 85
Piura, Peru, 81,683 (*126,702).........C1 31
Piura, dept., Peru, 431,487..........C1 31
Piute, co., Utah, 1,164...B5 72
Pixley, Calif., 1,584....E4 50
Pizzo, It., 9,560.........E6 9
Placentia, Calif., 21,948..*F5 50

Placentia, Newf., Can., 2,211............E5 44
Placer, co., Calif., 77,632..C3 50
Placerville, Calif., 5,416...C3 50
Placetas, Cuba, 32,300 (48,400▲)........C4 35
Placida, Fla., 200........F4 54
Plain City, Ohio, 2,254...B2 78
Plain Dealing, La., 1,300.............B2 63
Plainfield, Conn., 2,923...C9 52
Plainfield, Ill., 2,928..B5, k8 58
Plainfield, Ind., 8,211...E5 59
Plainfield, N.J., 46,862...B4 74
Plainfield, Tenn.......*D10 83
Plainfield Heights, Mich., 3,500............*F5 66
Plainsboro, N.J., 800....C3 74
Plainsville, Pa., 200....*D10 81
Plainview, Minn., 2,093...F6 67
Plainview, Nebr., 1,494...B8 71
Plainview, N.Y., 32,000...........*G3 52
Plainview, Tex., 19,096...B2 84
Plainville, Conn., 16,733..C5 52
Plainville, Kans., 2,627..C4 61
Plainwell, Mich., 3,195...F5 66
Plaisance, Hai., 1,859...E7 35
Plaistow, N.H., 1,500....F5 73
Planada, Calif., 2,506...*D3 50
Plandome, N.Y., 1,593...*E7 75
Plandome Heights, N.Y., 1,032............*E7 75
Plano, Calif...........*D4 50
Plano, Ill., 4,664.......B5 58
Plano, Tex., 17,872..C4, m10 84
Plantagenet, Ont., Can., 854.............B9 41
Plantation, Fla., 23,523..r13 54
Plant City, Fla., 15,451...D4 54
Plantsite, Ariz., 1,552...*D6 48
Plantsville, Conn., 6,000..C5 52
Plaquemine, La., 7,739.........D4, h9 63
Plaquemines, par., La., 25,225..........*D4 63
Plasencia, Sp., 21,297....B2 8
Plaster Rock, N.B., Can., 1,267............C2 43
Plato, Col., 13,364......B3 32
Platón, Sánchez, Mex., 5,367...........m14 34
Platte, S. Dak., 1,351...G7 77
Platte, co., Mo., 32,081...B3 69
Platte, co., Nebr., 26,544..C8 71
Platte, co., Wyo., 6,486...D7 89
Platte City, Mo., 2,022.........B3, h10 69
Platteville, Wis., 9,599....F3 88
Plattsburg, Mo., 1,832...B3 69
Plattsburgh, N.Y., 18,715..f11 75
Plattsmouth, Nebr., 6,371........D10, h13 71
Plauen, Ger. Dem. Rep., 80,871...........C6 6
Pleasant Dale, Nebr., 258..D9 71
Pleasant Gap, Pa., 1,773...E6 81
Pleasant Grove, Ala., 5,090.............g7 46
Pleasant Grove, Utah, 5,327.........A6, D2 72
Pleasant Hill, Calif., 24,610...........h8 50
Pleasant Hill, Ill., 1,064...D3 58
Pleasant Hill, Iowa, 1,535..e8 60
Pleasant Hill, La., 826....C2 63
Pleasant Hill, Mo., 3,396...C3 69
Pleasant Hill, Ohio, 1,025..B1 78
Pleasant Hill, Pa., 10,409..*F9 81
Pleasant Hill, Va........*D6 85
Pleasant Hills, Pa., 10,409...........*F2 81
Pleasanton, Calif., 18,328..h9 50
Pleasanton, Kans., 1,216...D9 61
Pleasanton, Tex., 5,407...E3 84
Pleasant Ridge, Mich., 3,989............*F7 66
Pleasants, co., W. Va., 7,274............B3 87
Pleasant Valley, Mo., 1,535............h11 69
Pleasant Valley, N.Y., 1,372............D7 75
Pleasant View, Colo., 100............*B5 51
Pleasant View, Utah, 2,028..A5 72
Pleasantville, Iowa, 1,297..C4 60
Pleasantville, N.J., 13,778..E3 74
Pleasantville, N.Y., 7,110............m15 75
Pleasantville, Pa., 1,005...C2 81
Pleasure Beach, Conn., 1,394............*E4 52
Pleasure Ridge Park, Ky., 22,000...........g11 62
Pleasureville, Pa., 3,900............*G8 81
Pleiku, Viet., 7,240.....*C3 19

Plenita, Rom., 6,735......C6 10
Plentywood, Mont., 2,381...........B12 70
Plesetsk, Sov. Un., 18,000..C7 13
Plessisville, Que., Can., 7,204............C6 42
Pleszew, Pol., 13,300....C4 7
Pleven, Bul., 78,666.....D7 10
Pleven, co., Bul., 351,585..*D7 10
Pljevlja, Yugo., 13,864...D4 10
Płock, Pol., 71,700.....B5 7
Ploërmel, Fr., 3,840....D2 5
Ploieşti, Rom., 147,000 (*190,700)........C8 10
Plomarion, Grc., 4,353...C6 14
Płońsk, Pol., 11,600....B6 7
Plovdiv, Bul., 225,800...D7 10
Plovdiv, co., Bul., 645,352..*D7 10
Plum, Pa., 21,922......*E1 81
Plumas, co., Calif., 11,707..B3 50
Plymouth, Conn., 1,000...C4 52
Plymouth, Eng., 246,850 (*275,000).......E4 4
Plymouth, Ind., 7,661....B5 59
Plymouth, Mass., 13,400..C6 65
Plymouth, Mich., 11,758........F7, p15 66
Plymouth, Minn., 18,077..*F5 67
Plymouth, Monts., 1,267..H13 35
Plymouth, N.C., 4,774...B6 76
Plymouth, N.H., 3,109...D4 73
Plymouth, Ohio, 1,993...B3 78
Plymouth, Pa., 9,536.......D10, n17 81
Plymouth, Wis., 5,810.......E6, k10 88
Plymouth, co., Iowa, 24,312..........B1 60
Plymouth, co., Mass., 333,314.........C6 65
Plymouth Meeting, Pa., 6,000...........*F11 81
Plymouth Valley, Pa., 8,200...........*F11 81
Plymptonville, Pa., 1,040............*D5 81
Plzeň, Czech., 148,032...D2 7
Pocahontas, Ark., 4,544...A5 49
Pocahontas, Iowa, 2,338...B3 60
Pocahontas, Va., 891.....e10 85
Pocahontas, co., Iowa, 12,729..........B3 60
Pocahontas, co., W. Va., 8,870............C4 87
Pocatello, Idaho, 40,036 (*45,000)........G6 57
Pochep, Sov. Un., 16,000..E9 12
Pochutla, Mex., 4,395...D5 34
Pocomoke City, Md., 3,573............D6 53
Poços de Caldas, Braz., 51,844.........C3, k8 30
Podgorica, see Titograd, Yugo.
Podolsk, Sov. Un., 169,000......D11, n17 12
Podor, Sen., 3,400......E2 22
Poe, S.C., 900.........*B3 82
Poggibonsi, It., 7,236....C3 9
Pohang, Kor., 65,000 (79,451▲)........H4 18
Pohjois-Karjala, prov., Fin., 194,200.....*F13 11
Pohsien, China, 90,000...*E8 17
Poinsett, co., Ark., 26,822..B5 49
Point Comfort, Tex., 1,446...........*E4 84
Pointe-à-Pitre, Guad., 29,522 (*49,000).....H14 35
Pointe-au-Pic, Que., Can., 1,333............B7 42
Pointe-aux-Trembles, Que., Can., 35,567....p20 42
Pointe-Claire, Que., Can., 27,303...D4, q19 42
Pointe Coupee, par., La., 22,002.........D4 63
Pointe-du-Lac, Que., Can., 934........C5 42
Point Edward, Ont., Can., 2,773...........D2 41
Pointe-Gatineau, Que., Can., 15,640......D2 42
Pointe-Noire, Con., 135,000.........I7 22
Point Leamington, Newf., Can., 901........D4 44
Point Lookout, Mo., 900..E4 69
Point Marion, Pa., 1,750...F2 81
Point Pleasant, N.J., 15,968..........C4 74
Point Pleasant Beach, N.J., 4,882...........C4 74
Poissy, Fr., 33,555......C4 5
Poitiers, Fr., 70,681....C4 5
Poitou, former prov., Fr...D3 5
Pokaran, India, 5,284...C5 20
Pokotu, China..........B9 17

Pokrovskoye, Sov. Un., 10,000.........H12 12
Poland, Ohio, 3,097.....*A5 78
Poland, country, Eur., 33,465,000........C5 7
Polgár, Hung., 7,697....B5 10
Poli, China, 35,000.....B11 17
Políkhnitos, Grc., 4,152...C6 14
Polk, Pa., 3,673.......D2 81
Polk, co., Ark., 13,297...C1 49
Polk, co., Fla., 227,222...E5 54
Polk, co., Ga., 29,656...C1 55
Polk, co., Iowa, 286,101..C4 60
Polk, co., Minn., 34,435...C2 67
Polk, co., Mo., 15,415...D4 69
Polk, co., Nebr., 6,468...C8 71
Polk, co., N.C., 11,735...f10 76
Polk, co., Oreg., 35,349...C3 80
Polk, co., Tenn., 11,669..D9 83
Polk, co., Tex., 14,457...D5 84
Polk, co., Wis., 26,666...C1 88
Pollensa, Sp., 8,984....C7 8
Pollocksville, N.C., 456...C5 76
Polo, Ill., 2,542.......B4 58
Polotsk, Sov. Un., 64,000..D7 12
Polson, Mont., 2,464....C2 70
Poltava, Sov. Un., 220,000.........G10 12
Pomabamba, Peru, 2,346..C2 31
Pombal, Braz., 11,405...*D7 27
Pomerania, reg., Pol.....B4 7
Pomeroy, Iowa, 765......B3 60
Pomeroy, Ohio, 2,672....C3 78
Pomeroy, Pa., 690.....*G10 81
Pomeroy, Wash., 1,823...C8 86
Pomoho, Haw., 340......f9 56
Pomona, Calif., 87,384........E5, m13 50
Pompano Beach, Fla., 38,587........F6, r13 54
Pompton Lakes, N.J., 11,397..........A4 74
Pompton Plains, N.J., 8,000............B4 74
Ponca, Nebr., 984......B9 71
Ponca City, Okla., 25,940..A4 79
Ponce, P.R., 128,233 (158,981▲).......G11 35
Ponchatoula, La., 4,545.........D5, h11 63
Pondera, co., Mont., 6,611............B4 70
Pondicherry, India, 90,637 (*153,325)....F6 20
Pondicherry, ter., India, 471,707........*F6 20
Ponferrada, Sp., 37,053...A2 8
Ponoka, Alta., Can., 4,414............C4 38
Ponorogo, Indon., 67,711..*G4 19
Ponta Delgada (Azores Is.), Port., 22,316....m10 22
Ponta Grossa, Braz., 92,344..........D2 30
Pont-A-Mousson, Fr., 13,406 (*20,000).....C7 5
Ponta Porã, Braz., 12,684..C1 30
Pontarlier, Fr., 16,442...D7 5
Pontedera, It., 21,900...C3 9
Ponteix, Sask., Can., 887..H2 39
Ponte Nova, Braz., 28,665..C4 30
Pontevedra, Sp., 21,000 (52,562▲)........A1 8
Pontevedra, prov., Sp., 760,100.........*A1 8
Pontiac, Ill., 10,595.....C5 58
Pontiac, Mich., 85,279........F7, o15 66
Pontiac, co., Que., Can., 20,113..........A7 41
Pontianak, Indon., 217,555.........F3 19
Pontivy, Fr., 8,775.....C2 5
Pont-l'-Abbé, Fr., 6,791...D1 5
Pontoise, Fr., 17,509....C4 5
Pontotoc, Miss., 3,453...A4 68
Pontotoc, co., Miss., 17,363..........A4 68
Pontotoc, co., Okla., 27,867..........C5 79
Pontremoli, It., 4,839....B2 9
Pont-Rouge, Que., Can., 3,272......C6, n16 42
Pont-Viau, Que., Can., 16,077.........*D4 42
Poole, Eng., 106,610....E5 4
Pooler, Ga., 1,517......D5 55
Popasnaya, Sov. Un., 31,000...........q21 12
Popayán, Col., 65,500...C2 32
Pope, co., Ark., 28,607...B2 49
Pope, co., Ill., 3,857....F5 58
Pope, co., Minn., 11,107..E3 67
Poplar, Calif., 1,239....*D4 50
Poplar, Mont., 1,389....B11 70
Poplar Bluff, Mo., 16,653..E7 69
Poplar Heights, Va., 1,100............*B5 85

Poplarville, Miss., 2,312....E4 68
Popocatepetl, vol., Mex....n14 34
Popovka, Sov. Un.,
  10,000................H11 12
Popovo, Bul., 6,469......D8 10
Poquonock, Conn., 900....B6 52
Poquonock Bridge, Conn.,
  2,500.................D8 52
Poquoson, Va., 5,441..C6, h15 85
Porbandar, India, 96,881..D4 20
Porcuna, Sp., 10,516....D3 8
Pordenone, It., 44,000....B4 9
Porec, Yugo., 2,992....C1 10
Pori, Fin., 76,808......G9 11
Porlamar, Ven., 31,985...A5 32
Poronaysk, Shikuka,
  Sov. Un., 24,000.....E17 13
Porrentruy, Switz., 7,095...E3 6
Porsgrunn, Nor., 31,600...p27 11
Portadown, N. Ire.,
  21,906..............C3 4
Portage, Ind., 19,127....A3 59
Portage, Mich., 33,590...F5 66
Portage, Pa., 4,151......F4 81
Portage, Wis., 7,821.....E4 88
Portage, co., Ohio,
  125,868.............A4 78
Portage, co., Wis.,
  47,541..............D4 88
Portage Lakes, Ohio,
  20,400.............*A4 78
Portage-la-Prairie,
  Man., Can., 12,950..E2, h8 40
Portageville, Mo., 3,117...E8 69
Port Alberni, B.C., Can.,
  20,063 (*26,509).....E5 37
Portalegre, Port., 11,017..C2 8
Portales, N. Mex., 10,554..B7 48
Port Alfred, Que., Can.,
  9,228...............A7 42
Port Alfred, S. Afr.,
  8,524...............G5 24
Port Alice, B.C., Can.,
  1,507...............D4 37
Port Allegany, Pa., 2,703...C5 81
Port Allen, La., 5,728..D4, h9 63
Port Angles, Wash.,
  16,367..............A2 86
Port Angeles East, Wash..*A2 86
Port Antonio, Jam.,
  10,400..............E5 35
Port Arthur, Tex., 57,371..E6 84
Port Augusta, Austl.,
  12,095..............F6 25
Port-au-Prince, Hai.,
  458,675.............E7 35
Port Barre, La., 2,133....D4 63
Port Blair, India, 26,218..F9 20
Port Byron, Ill., 1,222....B3 58
Port Byron, N.Y., 1,330...B4 75
Port Carbon, Pa., 2,717...E9 81
Port-Cartier-Ouest, Que.,
  Can., 3,730........k13 42
Port Charlotte, Fla.,
  10,769..............F4 54
Port Chester, N.Y.,
  25,803...........E7, n15 75
Port Chicago, Calif....G8 50
Port Clinton, Ohio,
  7,202...............A3 78
Port Colborne, Ont., Can.,
  21,420..............E5 41
Port Coquitlam, B.C.,
  Can., 19,560......E6, f13 37
Port Crane, N.Y., 1,200...C5 75
Port Credit, Ont.,
  Can., 9,442......D5, m14 41
Port-de-Bouc, Fr., 14,080..F6 5
Port de Kindu, Zaire......I3 23
Port-de-Paix, Hai., 13,913..E7 35
Port Deposit, Md., 906...A5 53
Port Dickinson, N.Y.,
  2,132...............C5 75
Port Dickson, Mala.,
  10,300..............E2 19
Port Dover, Ont., Can.,
  3,407...............E4 41
Port Edward, B.C., Can.,
  887.................B2 37
Port Edwards, Wis.,
  2,126...............D4 88
Port Elgin, N.B., Can.,
  661.................C5 43
Port Elgin, Ont., Can.,
  2,855 (*5,980).......C3 41
Port Elizabeth, S. Afr.,
  386,577, (*470,000)....G5 24
Porter, Ind., 3,058......A3 59
Porter, co., Ind., 87,114..B3 59
Porterdale, Ga., 1,773....C3 55
Porterville, Calif., 12,602..D4 50
Port Ewen, N.Y., 2,882...D7 75
Port-Francqui, see Ilebo,
  Zaire
Port-Gentil, Gabon,
  20,732..............I6 22
Port Gibson, Miss., 2,589..D3 68

Port Hammond, B.C.,
  Can., 1,556........f13 37
Port Harcourt, Nig.,
  179,563.............H6 22
Port Hawkesbury, N.S.,
  Can., 3,372.........D8 43
Port Hedland, Austl.,
  7,172...............D2 25
Port Henry, N.Y., 1,532...A7 75
Port Hope, Ont., Can.,
  8,872...............D6 41
Port Hueneme, Calif.,
  14,295..............E4 50
Port Huron, Mich., 35,794
  (*147,000)..........F8 66
Portimão, Port., 12,129...D1 8
Port Isabel, Tex., 3,067...F4 84
Port Jefferson, N.Y., 5,515..F4 52
Port Jefferson Station,
  N.Y., 7,403........n15 75
Port Jervis, N.Y., 8,852...D6 75
Portland, Austl., 8,212....G7 25
Portland, Conn., 8,812....C6 52
Portland, Ind., 7,115.....D8 59
Portland, Maine, 65,116
  (*192,700).......E2, g7 64
Portland, Mich., 3,817....F6 66
Portland, Oreg.,
  379,967 (*983,600)..B4, g12 80
Portland, Tenn., 2,872....A5 83
Port Lavaca, Tex., 10,491..E4 84
Port Leyden, N.Y., 862....B5 75
Port Lincoln, Austl., 9,158..F6 25
Port Louis, Mau.,
  132,700...........*H24 2
Port McNicoll, Ont.,
  Can., 1,450.........C5 41
Port Macquarie, Austl.,
  9,362...............F9 25
Port Monmouth, N.J.,
  3,600...............C4 74
Port Moody, B.C.,
  Can., 10,778......E6, f13 37
Port Moresby, Pap.,
  41,848.............k12 25
Port Neches, Tex., 10,894..E6 84
Portneuf, Que., Can.,
  1,347 (*3,308).......C5 42
Portneuf, co., Que., Can.,
  51,749..............C5 42
Port Norris, N.J., 1,900...E2 74
Pôrto (Oporto), Port.,
  304,000 (*850,000).....B1 8
Pôrto Alegre, Braz.,
  885,564 (*1,375,000)...E2 30
Porto Alexandre, Ang.,
  2,874...............D2 24
Porto Amélia, Moz.,
  10,000..............C8 24
Porto de Moz, Braz.,
  1,198...............D5 27
Pôrto Feliz, Braz.,
  13,882...........C3, m8 30
Portoferraio, It., 6,500...C3 9
Port of Spain, Trin.,
  67,867 (*310,000).....K14 35
Portogruaro, It., 7,100...B4 9
Portomaggiore, It., 4,300..B3 9
Porto Nacional, Braz.,
  9,027...............E6 27
Porto-Novo, Benin,
  74,500.............G5 22
Port Orange, Fla., 3,781..C6 54
Port Orchard, Wash.,
  3,904...........B3, e10 86
Port Orford, Oreg., 1,037..E2 80
Portolo, Calif., 1,874....C3 50
Porto Torres, It., 9,166...D2 9
Pôrto União, Braz., 14,445..D2 30
Porto Velho, Braz., 41,146..D4 27
Portoviejo, Ec., 41,300...B1 31
Portpatrick, Scot., 681....C4 4
Port Perry, Ont., Can.,
  2,977...............C6 41
Port Pirie, Austl., 15,506..F6 25
Port Reading, N.J., 4,800..k8 74
Port Richey, Fla., 1,259...D4 54
Port Said (Būr Sa'īd),
  Eg., 282,977.........G9 14
Port Saint Joe, Fla.,
  4,401...........C1, v16 54
Port St. Lucie, Fla., 330..E6 54
Port Sewall, Fla., 300....E6 54
Portsmouth, Eng., 204,280
  (*485,000)..........E6 4
Portsmouth, N.H.,
  25,717 (*71,800)......E6 73
Portsmouth, Ohio,
  27,633..............D3 78
Portsmouth, R.I., 3,000...C12 52
Portsmouth,
  (Independent City),
  Va., 110,963......D6, k15 85
Port Stanley, Ont., Can.,
  1,725...............E3 41
Port Sudan, Sud., 110,091..E5 23
Port Sulphur, La., 3,022..E6 63

Port Talbot, Wales, 51,000
  (*130,000)........*E5 4
Port Townsend, Wash.,
  5,241...............A3 86
Portugal, country, Eur.,
  8,770,000............C1 8
Portugal Cove, Newf.,
  Can., 1,141........*E5 44
Portugalete, Sp., 22,584...A4 8
Portuguesa, state, Ven.,
  203,707.............B4 32
Portuguese Guinea, see
  Guinea-Bissau, country,
  Afr.
Port Vue., Pa., 5,862....*F2 81
Port Wakefield, Austl.,
  490...............*F6 25
Port Washington, N.Y.,
  15,923.............h13 75
Port Washington, Wis.,
  8,752...............E6 88
Port Wentworth, Ga.,
  3,905...............D5 55
Posadas, Arg., 95,000.....E4 29
Posadas, Sp., 8,999......D3 8
Posen, Ill., 5,498.......k9 58
Posen, see Poznan, Pol.
Posey, co., Ind., 21,740...H2 59
Poseyville, Ind., 1,035...H2 59
Poshan, China, 250,000
  (875,000 ▲).........D8 17
Poso, Indon., 9,016......F6 19
Poste-de-la-Baleine,
  Que., Can., 987......g11 42
Poste-Mistassini, Que.,
  Can., 3,601.........h12 42
Post Falls, Idaho, 2,371...B2 57
Postojna, Yugo., 4,857....C2 10
Poston, S.C., 250.......D9 82
Postville, Iowa, 1,546....A6 60
Potchefstroom, S. Afr.,
  55,296..............F5 24
Poteau, Okla., 5,500....B7 79
Poteet, Tex., 3,013......E3 84
Potenza, It., 43,700.....D5 9
Potgietersrus, S. Afr.,
  6,550...............E5 24
Poti, Sov. Un., 1,296....E3 14
Potlatch, Idaho, 871....C2 57
Potomac, Md., 1,000....B3 53
Potomac Heights, Md.,
  1,983...............C3 53
Potomac Park, Md.,
  1,250.............k13 53
Potosí, Bol., 70,000......C2 29
Potosi, Mo., 2,761......D7 69
Potosí, dept., Bol.,
  627,000.............C2 29
Pototan, Phil., 5,475....*C6 19
Potsdam, Ger. Dem. Rep.,
  115,468.............B6 6
Potsdam, N.Y., 10,303...f10 75
Pottawatomie, co., Kans.,
  11,755..............C7 61
Pottawatomie, co., Okla.,
  43,134..............B5 79
Pottawattamie, co., Iowa,
  86,991..............C2 60
Potter, co., Pa., 16,395...C6 81
Potter, co., S. Dak., 4,449..F5 77
Potter, co., Tex., 90,511..B2 84
Potterville, Mich., 1,280..*F6 66
Pottstown, Pa., 25,355....F10 81
Pottsville, Pa., 19,715....E9 81
Pouch Cove, Newf., Can.,
  1,324...............E5 44
Poughkeepsie, N.Y., 32,029
  (*150,100)..........D7 75
Poulsbo, Wash., 1,856....B3 86
Poultney, Vt., 1,914.....D1 73
Pound, Va., 995.........e9 85
Pouso Alegre, Braz.,
  29,272..............C3 30
Póvoa, de Varzim, Port.,
  17,696..............B1 8
Powassan, Ont., Can.,
  1,064...............A5 41
Poway, Calif., 9,422.....F5 50
Powder River, co., Mont.,
  2,862...............E11 70
Powell, Mo., 100........E3 69
Powell, Wyo., 4,807......B4 89
Powell, co., Ky., 7,704...C6 62
Powell, co., Mont., 6,660..D4 70
Powell River, B.C., Can.,
  13,726..............E5 37
Powellton, W. Va., 950...C3 87
Power, co., Idaho, 4,864..G6 57
Powers, Oreg., 842.....E2 80
Poweshiek, co., Iowa,
  18,803..............C5 60
Powhatan, co., Va., 7,696..C5 85
Powhatan Point, Ohio,
  2,167...............C5 78
Poynette, Wis., 1,118....E4 88
Požarevac, Yugo., 33,121..C5 10

Poza Rica de Hidalgo,
  Mex., 120,462......m15 34
Poznań, Pol., 469,000
  (*525,000).........B4 7
Pozoblanco, Sp., 16,020..C3 8
Pozzallo, It., 12,253.....F5 9
Pozzuoli, It., 53,100.....D5 9
Prachin Buri, Thai.,
  13,420..............C2 19
Prachuap Khiri Khan,
  Thai., 6,228.......*C1 19
Praco, Ala., 400.........f6 46
Prades, Fr., 5,937......F5 5
Praestö, co., Den.,
  127,000...........*J5 11
Prague (Praha), Czech.,
  1,078,096
  (*1,175,000).....C3, n17 7
Prague, Okla., 1,802.....B5 79
Praha, see Prague, Czech.
Praia, C. V., 13,100.....n12 22
Prairie, co., Ark., 10,249..C4 49
Prairie, co., Mont.,
  1,752..............D11 70
Prairie City, Iowa, 1,141..C4 60
Prairie du Chien, Wis.,
  5,540...............E2 88
Prairie du Sac, Wis.,
  1,902...............E4 88
Prairie Grove, Ark., 1,582..B1 49
Prairie Village, Kans.,
  28,138.............*B9 61
Pran Buri, Thai.........C1 19
Prato, It., 137,500
  (*174,000)..........C3 9
Pratt, Kans., 6,736.....E5 61
Pratt, Minn...........*C6 87
Pratt, co., Kans., 10,056..E5 61
Prattville, Ala., 13,116...C3 46
Prattville, Okla.......*A5 79
Pravdinsk (Friedland),
  Sov. Un., 10,000.....A6 7
Pravia, Sp., 1,804......A2 8
Preble, co., Ohio, 34,719..C1 78
Premont, Tex., 3,282....F3 84
Prentiss, Miss., 1,789....D4 68
Prentiss, co., Miss., 20,133..A5 68
Prenzlau, Ger., 19,700...F6 6
Přerov, Czech., 38,963...D4 7
Prescott, Ariz., 13,283...B2 48
Prescott, Ark., 3,921....D2 49
Prescott, Ont., Can.,
  5,165...............C9 41
Prescott, Wis., 2,331....D1 88
Prescott, co., Ont., Can.,
  27,155.............B10 41
Presidencia Roque Sáenz
  Peña, Arg., 14,381....E3 29
Presidente Hayes, dept.,
  Par., 29,870.........D4 29
Presidente Prudente, Braz.,
  91,188..............C2 30
Presidio, Tex., 950.....p12 84
Presidio, co., Tex., 4,842..o12 84
Prešov, Czech., 41,163...D6 7
Presque Isle, Maine,
  11,452..............B4 64
Presque Isle, co., Mich.,
  12,836..............C6 66
Preston, Eng., 96,790
  (*240,000)..........D5 4
Preston, Idaho, 3,310...G7 57
Preston, Ky., 200.......B6 62
Preston, Minn., 1,413...G6 67
Preston, co., W. Va.,
  25,455..............B5 87
Preston, peak, Calif......B2 50
Prestonburg, Ky., 3,422...C7 62
Prestonville, Ky., 252....B4 62
Prestwick, Scot., 13,438..C4 4
Pretoria, S. Afr., 543,950,
  (*575,000)..........F5 24
Préveza, Grc., 11,439....C3 14
Préveza, prov., Grc.,
  56,616............*C3 14
Prey Veng, Camb., 8,800..*C3 19
Příbram, Czech., 29,724..D3 7
Price, Que., Can.,
  2,740............*G20 36
Price, Utah, 6,218......B6 72
Price, co., Wis., 14,520..C3 88
Pricedale, Pa., 1,600...*F2 81
Prichard, Ala., 41,578...E1 46
Priestly, mtn., B.C., Can..B3 37
Priest River, Idaho,
  1,493...............A2 57
Prilep, Yugo., 48,242...E5 10
Priluki, Sov. Un., 57,000..F9 12
Primera, Tex., 902....*F4 84
Primghar, Iowa, 995....A2 60
Primorsk, Sov. Un.,
  8,000...............A6 7
Primorsko-Akhtarsk,
  Sov. Un., 26,000....H12 12
Primos, Pa., 1,100....*G11 81
Primrose, Pa., 800....*E9 81
Prince, co., P.E.I., Can.,
  42,688..............C5 43

Prince Albert, Sask.,
Can., 28,464..........D3, n7 39
Prince Edward, co., Ont.,
Can., 21,307...........C7 41
Prince Edward, co., Va.,
14,379................C4 85
Prince Edward Island,
prov., Can., 115,000....C6 43
Prince George, B.C., Can.,
33,101 (*49,100)...C6, n18 37
Prince George, co., Va.,
29,092................C5 85
Prince Georges, co., Md.,
661,082...............C4 53
Prince of Wales, isl., N.
W. Ter., Can.........B14 36
Prince Rupert, B.C., Can.,
15,747 (*16,766)...B2, n16 37
Princess Anne, Md.,
975...................D6 53
Princeton, Ala., 200......A3 46
Princeton, B.C., Can.,
2,601.................E7 37
Princeton, Fla.,
1,300.............G6, s13 54
Princeton, Ill., 6,959....B4 58
Princeton, Ind., 7,431....H2 59
Princeton, Ky., 6,292.....C2 62
Princeton, Minn., 2,531...E5 67
Princeton, Mo., 1,328.....A4 69
Princeton, N.J., 12,311...C3 74
Princeton, N.C., 1,044....B4 76
Princeton, W. Va.,
7,253.................D3 87
Princeton, Wis., 1,446....E4 88
Princeville, Que., Can.,
3,829.................C6 42
Princeville, Ill., 1,455...C4 58
Princeville, N.C., 654....B5 76
Prince William, co., Va.,
111,102...............B5 85
Prineville, Oreg., 4,101..C6 80
Prineville Southeast, Oreg. *C6 80
Pringle, Pa., 1,155.....*D10 81
Prinsburg, Minn., 448....F3 67
Priozersk, Sov. Un.,
17,000...............G14 11
Pristina, Yugo.,
69,524................D5 10
Pritzwalk, Ger. Dem. Rep.,
9,416.................B6   6
Privas, Fr., 10,080......E6   5
Privolnoye, Sov. Un.,
9,000.................H9 12
Prizren, Yugo., 41,661...D5 10
Prizzi, It., 9,752........F4   9
Probolinggo, Indon.,
82,008................G4 19
Proctor, Minn., 3,123....D6 67
Proctor, Vt., 2,095......D1 73
Proctorville, Ohio, 881...D3 78
Progreso, Hond., 6,921...*D7 34
Progreso, Mex., 17,518...C7 34
Progress, Pa., ,3,500....*F8 81
Prokopyevsk, Sov. Un.,
274,000 (*405,000)....D11 13
Prokuplje, Yugo.,
20,049................D5 10
Proletarskaya, Sov. Un.,
10,000...............H13 12
Prome, Bur., 36,997.....E10 20

Prophetstown, Ill., 1,915...B4 58
Propriá, Braz., 18,386....*D7 27
Proserpine, Austl., 2,955..D8 25
Prosotsáni, Grc., 3,775...*B4 14
Prospect, Conn., 6,543....C5 52
Prospect, Ohio, 1,031.....B2 78
Prospect, Pa., 973........E1 81
Prospect Heights, Ill.,
7,200................*B6 58
Prospect Park, N.J., 5,176..B4 74
Prospect Park, Pa., 7,250..p20 81
Prosser, Wash., 2,954.....C6 86
Prostějov, Czech., 36,980..D4   7
Provadiya, Bul., 12,463...D8 10
Provence, former prov., Fr. F7   5
Providence, Ky., 4,270....C2 62
Providence, R.I., 179,116
(*892,800)...........B11 52
Providence, Tenn........*A5 83
Providence, Utah, 1,608..*A6 72
Providence, co., R.I.,
581,470..............B10 52
Provincetown, Mass.,
2,911.................B7 65
Provins, Fr., 11,432......C5   5
Provo, Utah, 53,131
(*134,800)..........A6, D2 72
Provost, Alta., Can., 1,022..C5 38
Prowers, co., Colo., 13,258.D8 51
Prozor, Yugo., 5,506.....D3 10
Prudnik, Pol., 20,300.....C4   7
Pruszków, Pol.,
42,900............B6, m13   7
Pruzhany, Sov. Un.,
10,000................E5 12
Pryor, Okla., 7,057......A6 79
Pryor, mts., Mont........E8 70
Przasnysz, Pol., 11,100...B6   7
Przemyśl, Pol., 53,200....D7   7
Przeworsk, Pol., 7,853....C7   7
Pskov, Sov. Un., 127,000..C7 12
Pszczyna, Pol., 17,900..D5, h9   7
Ptolemaís, Grc., 16,588..*B3 14
Ptuj, Yugo., 7,365.......B2 10
Puebla, state, Mex.,
2,148,300..........D5, n14 34
Puebla de Don Fadrique,
Sp., 7,142............D4   8
Puebla del Caramiñal,
Sp., 8,337............A1   8
Puebla [de Zaragoza],
Mex., 401,603......D5, n14 34
Pueblo, Colo., 97,453
(*111,600)...........C6 51
Pueblo, co., Colo.,
118,238...............C6 51
Puenteareas, Sp., 14,634..A1   8
Puente Ceso, Sp., 9,780...A1   8
Puentedeume, Sp., 7,755..A2   8
Puente-Genil, Sp., 24,836
(30,185 ▲)...........D3   8
Puerto Alvaro Obregón,
Mex., 8,320.........*D6 34
Puerto Armuelles, Pan.,
12,015..............*B1 32
Puerto Barrios, Guat.,
19,696................D7 34
Puerto Berrío, Col.,
15,812................B3 32
Puerto Cabello, Ven.,
73,380................A4 32

Puerto Casado, Par.,
6,708................D4 29
Puerto Cortés, Hond.,
17,048................D7 34
Puerto de la Cruz, Sp.,
5,855................m13   8
Puerto Eten, Peru, 2,576..C2 31
Puerto La Cruz, Ven.,
63,276................A5 32
Puertollano, Sp., 53,674...C3   8
Puerto Maldonado, Peru,
3,500.................D4 31
Puerto Montt, Chile,
41,681................C2 28
Puerto Padre, Cuba,
16,500 (23,300 ▲).....D5 35
Puerto Peñasco, Mex.,
8,452.................A2 34
Puerto Pinasco, Par.,
7,576.................D4 29
Puerto Plata, Dom. Rep.,
32,200................E8 35
Puerto Rico, U.S., dep.,
N.A., 2,875,000......G11 35
Puerto Sastre, Par., 5,058..D4 29
Puerto Supe, Peru, 2,180..D2 31
Puerto Tejada, Col.,
14,863................C2 32
Puerto Vallarto, Mex.,
24,155............C3, m11 34
Puerto Wilches, Col.,
4,635.................B3 32
Puglia, pol. dist., It.,
3,421,217...........*D6   9
Pugwash, N.S., Can.,
815...................D6 43
Puhi, Haw., 772.........B2 56
Puhsi, China, 5,000......B2 18
Pukchong, Kor., 30,709...F4 18
Puksubaek-san, mtn., Kor. F3 18
Pula, Yugo., 47,414......C1 10
Pulaski, Miss., 150.......C4 68
Pulaski, N.Y., 2,480......B4 75
Pulaski, Tenn., 6,989.....B4 83
Pulaski, Va., 10,279......C2 85
Pulaski, Wis., 1,717......D5 88
Pulaski, co., Ark., 287,189..C3 49
Pulaski, co., Ga., 8,066...D3 55
Pulaski, co., Ill., 8,741...F4 58
Pulaski, co., Ind., 12,534..B4 59
Pulaski, co., Ky., 35,234..C5 62
Pulaski, co., Mo., 53,967..D5 69
Pulaski, co., Va., 29,564..C2 85
Puławy, Pol., 34,800.....C6   7
Pul-I-Khumri, Afg., 12,246.A4 20
Pullman, Wash., 20,509...C8 86
Pulog, mtn., Phil........n13 19
Pułtusk, Pol., 12,600.....B6   7
Pune (Poona), India,
856,105 (*1,175,000)..E5 20
Pungsan, Kor., 17,453....F4 18
Punjab, state, India
13,551,060...........B5 20
Puno, Peru, 41,166.......E3 31
Puno, dept., Peru, 646,385..E3 31
Punta Alta, Arg., 51,000..B4 28
Punta Arenas, Chile,
49,504...............h11 28
Punta Gorda, Fla.,
3,879.................F4 54

Puntarenas, C.R., 22,500..*F8 34
Puntarenas, prov., C.R.,
189,700..............*F8 34
Punxsutawney, Pa., 7,792..E4 81
Puquio, Peru, 6,183......D3 31
Purcell, Mo., 325........D3 69
Purcell, Okla., 4,076.....B4 79
Purcellville, Va., 1,775...A5 85
Purèpero, Mex., 11,198...n12 34
Puri, India, 72,674.......E8 20
Purnea, India, 56,484
(*71,311)............C8 20
Pursat, Camb., 14,500...C2 19
Pursglove, W. Va., 600...B4 87
Purúlia, India, 57,708....D8 20
Purús, riv., Peru........D3 31
Purvis, Miss., 1,860......D4 68
Purwokerto, Indon.,
94,023..............*G3 19
Pusan, Kor., 1,880,710...I4 18
Pushkin, Sov. Un., 73,000..B8 12
Pushkino, Sov. Un.,
10,000...........C11, m17 12
Pushmataha, Ala., 150....C1 46
Pushmataha, co., Okla.,
9,385.................C6 79
Püspökladány, Hung.,
15,735................B5 10
Pustelnik, Pol., 5,000....k14   7
Putao, Bur., 10,000.....C10 20
Puteaux, Fr., 37,946......g9   5
Putehachi (Yalu), China,
10,000................B9 17
Putivl, Sov. Un., 15,000...F9 12
Putnam, Conn., 6,918....B9 52
Putnam, co., Fla., 36,290..C5 54
Putnam, co., Ga., 8,394...C3 55
Putnam, co., Ill., 5,007...B4 58
Putnam, co., Ind., 26,932..E4 59
Putnam, co., Mo., 5,916..A4 69
Putnam, co., N.Y., 56,696..D7 75
Putnam, co., Ohio, 31,134..B1 78
Putnam, co., Tenn., 35,487.C8 83
Putnam, co., W. Va.,
27,625................C3 87
Puttalam, Sri Lanka,
17,982................G6 20
Putumayo, comisaría,
Col., 67,900..........C2 32
Puukolii, Haw., 250......C5 56
Puunene, Haw., 1,132....C5 56
Puxico, Mo., 759........E7 69
Puyallup, Wash.,
14,742............B3, f11 86
Puy-de-Dôme, dept., Fr.,
547,743.............*E5   5
Puyo, Ec., 2,290.........B2 31
Pwllheli, Wales, 3,910....D4   4
Pyapon, Bur., 19,174....E10 20
Pyatigorsk, Sov. Un.,
93,000..............*E7 13
Pyinmana, Bur., 22,066...E10 20
Pyongchang, Kor., 5,000
(18,781 ▲)...........H4 18
Pyongtaek, Kor., 28,000
(41,697 ▲)...........H3 18
Pyŏngyang, Kor., 840,000..G2 18
Pyrénées-Orientales, dept.,
Fr., 281,976.........*F5   5
Pyskowice, Pol., 23,000...g9   7
Pyu, Bur., 10,443.......E10 20

Q

Qānā, Leb., 3,000.......A3 15
Qaṣr al Farāfirah, Eg.,
1,010.................C3 23
Qatar, country, Asia,
200,000...............D5 15
Qazvīn, Iran, 88,106.....B5 15
Qina, Eg., 68,536........C4 23
Qiryat Shemona, Isr.,
15,200................A3 15
Qiryat Yam, Isr., 19,800..B3 15
Qom, Iran, 134,292......C5 15
Quakenbruck, Ger. Fed.
Rep. of, 10,180.......B3   6
Quaker Hill, Conn., 2,068..D8 52
Quakertown, Pa., 7,276..F11 81
Quanah, Tex., 3,948.....B3 84
Quang Ngai, Viet., 8,640..B3 19
Quang Tri, Viet., 10,740..B3 19
Quantico, Va., 719.......B5 85
Quapaw, Okla., 967.....A7 79
Quaraí, Braz., 13,373....E1 30

Quarryville, Pa., 1,571...G9 81
Quartu Sant' Elena, It.,
27,500................E2   9
Quartz Hill, Calif., 4,935..*E4 50
Quay, co., N. Mex.,
10,903................B7 48
Québec, Que.,
Can., 186,088
(*480,502)........C6, n17 42
Québec, co., Que., Can.,
383,092...............B5 42
Québec, prov., Can.,
6,115,000............42
Québec-Quest, Que.,
Can., 8,733.........*C6 42
Quedlinburg, Ger. Dem.
Rep., 30,143..........C5   6
Queen Annes, co., Md.,
18,422................B5 53
Queen Bess, mtn., B.C.,
Can..................D5 37

Queen City, Tex., 1,227..*C5 84
Queen Elizabeth, is.,
N.W. Ter., Can.......m31 36
Queens, borough and co.,
N.Y., 1,987,174.......E7 75
Queens, co., N.B., Can.,
10,940................D4 43
Queens, co., N.S., Can.,
12,807................E4 43
Queens, co., P.E.I., Can.,
47,832................C6 43
Queensland, state, Austl.,
1,930,000............D7 25
Queenstown, S. Afr.,
39,552................G5 24
Quelimane, Moz.........D7 24
Querétaro, Mex.,
112,993..........C4, m13 34
Querétaro, state,
Mex., 390,400.....C4, m13 34
Quesada, Sp., 7,609......D4   8

Quesnel, B.C., Can., 6,252.C6 37
Questa, N. Mex., 1,095...A6 48
Quetta, Pak., 79,493
(*106,633)...........B4 20
Quezaltenango, Guat.,
45,977................E6 34
Quezaltepeque, Sal.,
12,641..............*E7 34
Quezon, prov., Phil.,
653,426.............*C6 19
Quezon City, Phil.,
754,452...............C6 19
Quibdó, Col., 19,989.....B2 32
Quidnessett, R.I., 700...C11 52
Quidnick, R.I., 3,000....C10 52
Quiindy, Par., 2,150......E4 29
Quilá, Mex., 2,175.......C3 34
Quillota, Chile, 29,447...A2 28
Quilon, India, 124,208...G6 20

R

Quilpie, Austl., 747......E7 25
Quilpué, Chile, 26,588.....A2 28
Quimper, Fr., 52,496......C2 5
Quimperlé, Fr., 10,698....D2 5
Quincy, Calif., 2,500....C3 50
Quincy, Fla., 8,334.......B2 54
Quincy, Ill., 45,288......D2 58

Quincy, Mass., 87,966.B5, h11 65
Quincy, Mich., 1,540......G6 66
Quincy, Wash., 3,237.....B6 86
Qui Nhon, Viet., 50,000...C3 19
Quinnville, R.I., 400......B11 52
Quintana de la Serena,
Sp., 7,861.............C3 8

Quintanar, Sp., 9,483.....C4 8
Quintana Roo, state,
Mex., 69,800.........D7 34
Quinter, Kans., 930.......C3 61
Quinton, Okla., 1,262.....B6 79
Quiroga, Sp., 8,380......A2 8
Quitman, Ga., 4,818......F3 55

Quitman, Miss., 2,702.....C5 68
Quitman, Tex., 1,494......C5 84
Quitman, co., Ga., 2,180...E1 55
Quitman, co., Miss.,
15,888.............A3 68
Quito, Ec., 496,400......B2 31
Quixadá, Braz., 16,905...*D7 27

Raba, Indon., 29,881.....G5 19
Rabat, Mor., 367,620
(*540,000)...........B3 22
Rabaul, Pap. N. Gui.,
10,600..............h13 25
Rabun, Ala., 200........D2 46
Rabun, co., Ga., 8,327....B3 55
Raceland, Ky., 1,857......B7 62
Raceland, La., 4,880..E5, k10 63
Rach Gia, Viet., 56,000...*C2 19
Racibórz, Pol., 40,400....C5 7
Racine, Wis., 95,162
(*132,300)........F6, n12 88
Racine, co., Wis., 170,838..F5 88
Radauti, Rom., 15,949....B7 10
Radcliff, Ky., 7,881......C4 62
Radeberg, Ger. Dem. Rep.,
38,588.............C6 6
Radford (Independent
City), Va., 11,596.......C2 85
Radiant Valley, Md.,
1,500...............C4 53
Radnor, Pa., 1,000.....*G11 81
Radnor, co., Wales,
18,270.............*D5 4
Radom, Pol., 158,600.....C6 7
Radomir, Bul., 5,778......D6 10
Radomsko, Pol., 31,100....C5 7
Radville, Sask., Can.,
1,024...............H3 39
Radzionków, Pol., 27,800...g9 7
Rãe Bareli, India, 38,765...C7 20
Raeford, N.C., 3,180......C3 76
Rafaela, Arg., 43,000......A4 28
Rafah, Gaza Strip, 49,812..C2 15
Ragland, Ala., 1,239......B3 46
Ragusa, It., 52,900.......F5 9
Rahīmyār-Khān, Pak.,
14,919.............C5 20
Rahway, N.J., 29,114..B4, k7 74
Rāichūr, India, 79,831.....E6 20
Raigarh, India, 46,745....*D7 20
Rainbow City, Ala.,
3,107..............*A3 46
Rainbow City, C.Z.,
2,375..............*B2 32
Rainier, Oreg., 1,731.....A4 80
Rainier, mtn., Wash......C4 86
Rains, co., Tex., 3,752....C5 84
Rainsville, Ala., 2,099.....A4 46
Rainy River, Ont., Can.,
1,196..............*o16 41
Rainy River, dist., Ont.,
Can., 25,816.........o16 41
Raipur, India, 174,518
(*205,986)..........D7 20
Rājahmundry, India,
165,912 (*188,805)...E7 20
Rajapalaiyam, India,
86,952.............*G6 20
Rājasthān, state, India,
25,765,806..........C5 20
Rājkot, India, 300,612....D5 20
Rājshāhi, Bngl., 56,885...D8 20
Rakovník, Czech., 12,927..C2 7
Rakvere, Sov. Un.,
18,000.............B6 12
Raleigh, N.C., 123,793
(*216,900)..........B4 76
Raleigh, W. Va., 800.....n13 87
Raleigh, co., W. Va.,
70,080.............D3 87
Ralls, Tex., 1,962.......C2 84
Ralls, co., Mo., 7,764....B6 69
Ralston, Nebr., 4,731....g12 71
Rām Allāh, Jordan,
14,759.............C3 15
Ramat Gan, Isr., 120,100..B2 15
Ramat HaSharon, Isr.,
20,100.............*B2 15
Rambervillers, Fr., 7,042..C7 5
Ramea, Newf., Can., 970..E3 44
Ramenskoye, Sov. Un.,
61,000...........D12, n18 12
Ramla, Isr., 34,100......C2 15
Ramleh, Eg., 52,000.....*G8 14

Ramona, Calif., 3,554.....F5 50
Rāmpur, India, 161,417...C6 20
Ramsay, Mich., 1,068.....n12 66
Ramseur, N.C., 1,328.....B3 76
Ramsey, N.J., 12,571.....A4 74
Ramsey, co., Minn.,
476,255............E5 67
Ramsey, co., N. Dak.,
12,915.............B7 77
Ramsgate, Eng., 39,770...E7 4
Rancagua, Chile, 53,318..A2 28
Ranches of Taos, N. Mex.,
1,600..............A6 48
Rānchi, India, 175,934
(*255,551)...........D8 20
Rancho Cordova, Calif.,
35,300.............*C3 50
Rand, W. Va., 2,600.....m12 87
Randall, co., Tex., 53,885..B2 84
Randallstown, Md., 15,000.B4 53
Randers, Den., 42,000
(*57,500)...........I4 11
Randers, co., Den.,
184,100............*I4 11
Randleman, N.C., 2,312...B3 76
Randolph, Maine, 1,741...D3 64
Randolph, Mass.,
27,035...........B5, h11 65
Randolph, Nebr., 1,130...B8 71
Randolph, Vt., 2,115.....D2 73
Randolph, Wis., 1,582....E4 88
Randolph, co., Ala.,
18,331.............B4 46
Randolph, co., Ark.,
12,645.............A4 49
Randolph, co., Ga.,
8,734..............E2 55
Randolph, co., Ill., 31,379.E4 58
Randolph, co., Ind.,
28,915.............D7 59
Randolph, co., Mo.,
22,434.............B5 69
Randolph, co., N.C.,
76,358.............B3 76
Randolph, co., W. Va.,
24,596.............C5 87
Randolph Hills, Md.,
4,500..............*B3 53
Rangely, Colo., 1,591....A2 51
Ranger, Tex., 3,094......C3 84
Rangoon, Bur., 821,800..E10 20
Rangpur, Bngl., 31,759...C8 20
Rāniganj, India, 40,104...D8 20
Rankin, Pa., 3,704......k14 81
Rankin, Tex., 1,105......D2 84
Rankin, co., Miss., 43,933..C4 68
Ranlo, N.C., 2,092......*B1 76
Ranshaw, Pa., 950......*E9 81
Ransom, co., N. Dak.,
7,102..............D8 77
Ranson, W. Va., 2,189....B7 87
Rantoul, Ill., 25,562.....C5 58
Rapallo, It., 25,300......B2 9
Rapid City, S. Dak.,
43,836 (*59,800).......F2 77
Rapides, par., La.,
118,078............C3 63
Rappahannock, co., Va.,
5,199..............B4 85
Raritan, N.J., 6,691......B3 74
Raseiniai, Sov. Un., 6,181..A7 7
Rashīd (Rosetta), Eg.,
36,711.............G8 14
Rasht, Iran, 143,557.....A7 23
Rasskazovo, Sov. Un.,
40,000.............E13 12
Rastatt, Ger., Fed. Rep. of,
37,032.............D4 6
Rat Buri, Thai., 32,271....C1 19
Rathenow, Ger. Dem. Rep.,
31,841.............B6 6
Ratibor, see Raciborz, Pol.
Ratlām, India, 106,666
(*119,247)..........*D6 20
Ratnāgiri, India, 37,551...E5 20
Raton, N. Mex., 6,962....A6 48

Rauch, Arg., 6,953.......B5 28
Rauma, Fin., 26,520......G9 11
Raurkela, India, 90,287..*D7 20
Ravalli, co., Mont.,
14,409.............D2 70
Rava-Russkaya, Sov. Un.,
10,000.............F4 12
Raven, Va., 1,819.......e10 85
Ravena, N.Y., 2,797......C7 75
Ravenna, It., 82,500
(130,100 ▲)..........B4 9
Ravenna, Ky., 784.......C6 62
Ravenna, Nebr., 1,356....C7 71
Ravenna, Ohio, 11,780....A4 78
Ravensburg, Ger. Fed.
Rep. of, 35,525.......E4 6
Ravenswood, W. Va.,
4,240..............C3 87
Rāwalpindi, Pak., 197,370
(*340,175)..........B5 20
Rawa Mazowiecka, Pol.,
10,700.............C6 7
Rawdon, Que., Can.,
2,740..............C4 42
Rawicz, Pol., 14,100.....C4 7
Rawlins, Wyo., 7,855.....E5 89
Rawlins, co., Kans., 4,393..C2 61
Ray, Ariz.............C3, D3 48
Ray, N. Dak., 776.......B2 77
Ray, co., Mo., 17,599.....B3 69
Raybon, Ga............E5 55
Raychikhinsk, Sov. Un.,
30,000.............B4 18
Raymond, Alta., Can.,
2,156..............E4 38
Raymond, Miss., 1,620....C3 68
Raymond, Wash., 3,126...C2 86
Raymond Terrace, Austl.,
6,001..............F8 26
Raymondville, Tex., 7,987.F4 84
Rayne, La., 9,510........D3 63
Raynham Center, Mass.,
800...............C5 65
Raytown, Ga...........C4 55
Raytown, Mo., 33,306....h11 69
Rayville, La., 3,962......B4 63
Razgrad, Bul., 26,289....D8 10
Razlog, Bul., 6,857.......E6 10
Reading, Eng., 133,360
(*195,000)..........E6 4
Reading, Mass.,
22,539...........A5, f11 65
Reading, Mich., 1,125....G6 66
Reading, Ohio,
14,617...........C1, o13 78
Reading, Pa., 87,643
(*204,100)..........F10 81
Reagan, co., Tex., 3,239..D2 84
Real, co., Tex., 2,013....E3 84
Ream, Camb., 5,000.....*C2 19
Ream, W. Va...........*D3 87
Reamstown, Pa., 1,050...F9 81
Recanati, It., 6,288......C4 9
Rechitsa, Sov. Un.,
48,000.............E8 12
Recife (Pernambuco), Braz.,
1,060,752 (*1,750,000)...D7 27
Recklinghausen, Ger. Fed.
Rep. of, 124,907......C3 6
Reconquista, Arg., 21,000..E4 29
Rector, Ark., 1,990......A5 49
Red, riv., U.S...........D8 45
Red, sea, Afr...........D9 21
Red, sea, Asia..........D9 21
Red Bank, N.J., 12,847...C4 74
Red Bank, Tenn.,
12,715.............D8 83
Red Bay, Ala., 2,464.....A1 46
Red Bluff, Calif., 7,676...B2 50
Red Boiling Springs,
Tenn., 726..........C8 83
Red Bud, Ill., 2,559......E4 58
Redcliff, Alta., Can.,
2,255..............D5 38
Red Cloud, Nebr., 1,531...D7 71

Red Deer, Alta., Can.,
27,674...........C4, g8 38
Reddell, La., 250........D3 63
Redding, Calif., 16,659...B2 50
Redfield, Iowa, 921......C3 60
Redfield, S. Dak., 2,943...F7 77
Redford Township, Mich.,
71,901.............p15 66
Red Hill, Pa., 1,201.....*F11 81
Red Hook, N.Y., 1,680....D7 75
Redington Beach, Fla.,
1,583..............*E4 54
Redington Shores, Fla.,
1,733..............*E4 54
Red Jacket, W. Va., 850...D2 87
Red Key, Ind., 1,667.....D7 59
Red Lake, Ont., Can.,
2,155..............o16 41
Red Lake, co., Minn.,
5,388..............C2 67
Red Lake Falls, Minn.,
1,740..............C2 67
Redlands, Calif., 36,355...E5 50
Red Lion, Pa., 5,645.....G8 81
Red Lodge, Mont., 1,844..E7 70
Redmond, Oreg., 3,721...C5 80
Redmond, Wash., 11,020..e11 86
Red Oak, Ga., 1,200.....h7 55
Redon, Fr., 9,363.......D3 5
Redondela, Sp., 3,261....A1 8
Redondo Beach, Calif.,
57,451.............n12 50
Redore, Minn...........C6 67
Red River, co., Tex.,
14,298.............C5 84
Red River, par., La.,
9,226..............B2 63
Red Springs, N.C., 3,383...C3 76
Redstone, Colo., 150.....B3 51
Red Tank, C.Z., 1,949...*B2 32
Redtop, Mo............D4 69
Redwater, Alta., Can.,
1,135..............C4 38
Red Willow, co., Nebr.,
12,191.............D5 71
Red Wing, Minn., 10,441..F6 67
Redwood, co., Minn.,
20,024.............F3 67
Redwood City, Calif.,
55,686...........D2, k8 50
Redwood Estates, Calif.,
1,100..............*D3 50
Redwood Falls, Minn.,
4,774..............F3 67
Reed City, Mich., 2,286...E5 66
Reedley, Calif., 8,131....D4 50
Reedsburg, Wis., 4,585...E3 88
Reeds Lake, Mich........*F5 66
Reedsport, Oreg., 4,039...D2 80
Reedsville, Pa., 950......E6 81
Reese Village, Tex.,
2,545..............*C2 84
Reeves, co., Tex., 16,526..o13 84
Reform, Ala., 1,893......B1 46
Refuge, Tex............D5 84
Refugio, co., Tex., 9,494..E4 84
Regensburg, Ger. Fed.
Rep. of, 133,501
(*182,000)..........D6 6
Reggio di Calabria, It.,
138,600 (164,800 ▲)....E5 9
Reggio nell 'Emilia, It.,
98,600 (126,900 ▲).....B3 9
Reghin, Rom., 18,091....B7 10
Regina, Sask., Can.,
139,469 (*140,734)..G3, n8 39
Region Occidental
(Chaco), dept., Par.,
54,277.............*D3 29
Regla, Cuba, (part of
Havana).............C2 35
Rehoboth Beach, Del.,
1,614..............C7 53
Rehovot, Isr., 39,200.....C2 15
Reichenbach, Ger. Dem.
Rep., 27,832.........C6 6

Reidsville, Ga., 1,806.....D4 55
Reidsville, N.C., 13,636....A3 76
Reigate, Eng.,
  56,320...........E6, m12 4
Reims, Fr., 152,967......C6 5
Reinbeck, Iowa, 1,711....B5 60
Reindeer, lake, Can...E13 36
Reinosa, Sp., 10,044....A3 8
Reisterstown, Md., 13,000.B4 53
Rembertów, Pol., (part of
  Warsaw)........B6, k14 7
Remedios, Cuba, 13,100
  (20,900 ▲)........C4 35
Remerton, Ga., 523......F3 55
Remington, Ind., 1,127...C3 59
Remiremont, Fr., 9,312
  (*16,000)........C7 5
Remscheid, Ger., Fed. Rep.
  of, 135,547.......C3 6
Remsen, Iowa, 1,367.....B2 60
Rendsburg, Ger., Fed. Rep.
  of, 34,636.........A4 6
Renfrew, Ont., Can.,
  9,173............B8 41
Renfrew, co., Ont., Can.,
  89,453...........B7 41
Renfrew, co., Scot.,
  361,616..........*C4 4
Rengo, Chile, 11,000....A2 28
Rennes, Fr., 180,943....C3 5
Reno, Nev., 72,863
  (*118,000)........B2 72
Reno, co., Kans., 60,765...E5 61
Renovo, Pa., 2,620......D6 81
Rensselaer, Ind., 4,688...C3 59
Rensselaer, N.Y., 10,136..C6 75
Rensselaer, co., N.Y.,
  152,510..........C7 75
Renton, Wash., 25,878.B3, f11 86
Renville, Minn., 1,252....F3 67
Renville, co., Minn.,
  21,139...........F3 67
Renville, co., N. Dak.,
  3,828............B4 77
Republic, Mich., 950....B3 66
Republic, Mo., 2,411....D4 69
Republic, Pa., 1,500.....G2 81
Republic, Wash., 862....A7 86
Republic, co., Kans.,
  6,498............C7 61
Requena, Sp., 8,228.....C5 8
Reserve, La., 6,381......h10 63
Resistencia, Arg.,
  112,000 (*135,000)......E4 29
Resita, Rom., 56,700
  (121,500 ▲)........C5 10
Restigouche, co., N.B.,
  Can., 41,121......B2 43
Reston, Va., 22,000......B5 85
Reszel, Pol., 4,208......A6 7
Retalhuleu, Guat., 20,222.E6 34
Rethímni (Rhethymnon),
  prov., Grc., 60,856....*E5 14
Réthimnon, Grc., 14,969..E5 14
Reus, Sp., 59,904.......B6 8
Reutlingen, Ger., Fed. Rep.
  of, 90,007 (*145,000)...D4 6
Revel, Fr., 4,288.......F5 5
Revelo, Ky., 550........D5 62
Revelstoke, B.C., Can.,
  4,867............D8 37
Revere, Mass., 43,159....g11 65
Revere, Minn., 166......F3 67
Revin, Fr., 12,156......C6 5
Revloc, Pa., 750........F4 81
Rewa, India, 69,182.....D7 20
Rewāri, India, 43,885....C6 20
Rexburg, Idaho, 8,272....F7 57
Rey, Iran, 102,825.......C5 15
Reykjavík, Ice., 81,600
  (*107,500)........n22 11
Reynolds, Ga., 1,253.....D2 55
Reynolds, co., Mo., 6,106..D6 69
Reynoldsburg, Ohio,
  13,921........C3, m11 78
Reynoldsville, Pa., 2,771..D4 81
Reynosa (Reinosa), Mex.,
  137,383..........B5 34
Rezāīyeh (Urmia), Iran,
  110,749..........B4 15
Rezé, Fr., 33,509.......D3 5
Rezekne, Sov. Un., 30,600.C6 12
Rhea, co., Tenn., 17,202..D9 83
Rheden, Neth., 10,700....A7 9
Rhein (Rhine), riv., Eur..C3 6
Rheine, Ger., Fed. Rep. of,
  50,951...........B3 6
Rheinland-Pfalz, state,
  Ger., Fed. Rep. of,
  3,725,000.........C3 6
Rheydt, Ger., Fed. Rep. of,
  101,872..........*C3 6
Rhinebeck, N.Y., 2,336...D7 75
Rhineland, reg., Ger., Fed.
  Rep. of...........C3 6
Rhinelander, Wis., 8,218..C4 88
Rhode Island, state, U.S.,
  968,000...........52

Rhodesia, country, Afr.,
  5,975,000.........D5 24
Rhodhiss, N.C., 784.....B1 76
Rhondda, Wales, 88,990..E5 4
Rhône, dept., Fr.,
  1,325,611.........*E6 5
Rhyl, Wales, 21,600.....D5 4
Rialto, Calif., 28,370....m14 50
Rianjo, Sp., 9,971......A1 8
Ribadavia, Sp., 7,031....A1 8
Ribadeo, Sp., 9,567.....A2 8
Ribadesella, Sp., 8,228...A3 8
Ribatejo, prov., Port.,
  464,874..........*C1 8
Ribe, co., Den., 200,400...*J3 11
Ribeirão Prêto, Braz.,
  190,897........C3, k8 30
Ribera, It., 18,547......F4 9
Ričany, Czech., 6,376....o18 7
Rice, co., Kans., 12,320...D5 61
Rice, co., Minn., 41,582..F5 67
Rice Lake, Wis., 7,278...C2 88
Riceville, Iowa, 877.....A5 60
Rich, Miss., 90........A3 68
Rich, co., Utah, 1,615....A6 72
Richardson, Tex., 48,582..n10 84
Richardson, co., Nebr.,
  12,277...........D10 71
Richelieu, co., Que.,
  Can., 44,835......D4 42
Richfield, Calif.......C2 50
Richfield, Minn., 47,231..n12 67
Richfield, Utah, 4,471....B5 72
Richfield Springs, N.Y.,
  1,540............C6 75
Richford, Vt., 1,527.....B3 73
Rich Hill, Mo., 1,661....C3 69
Richibucto, N.B., Can.,
  1,375............C5 43
Richland, Ga., 1,823.....D2 55
Richland, Mo., 1,783....D5 69
Richland, Pa., 1,444.....*F9 81
Richland, Wash., 26,290..C6 86
Richland, co., Ill., 16,829.E5 58
Richland, co., Mont.,
  9,837............C12 70
Richland, co., N.Dak.,
  18,089...........D9 77
Richland, co., Ohio,
  129,997..........B3 78
Richland, co., S.C.,
  233,868..........D6 82
Richland, co., Wis.,
  17,079...........E3 88
Richland, par., La.,
  21,774...........B4 63
Richland Center, Wis.,
  5,086............E3 88
Richland Hills, Tex.,
  8,865............*C4 84
Richlands, N.C., 935....C5 76
Richlands, Va., 4,843....e10 85
Richmond, Calif.,
  79,043........D2, h8 50
Richmond, Que., Can.,
  4,317............D5 42
Richmond, Ind., 43,999...E8 59
Richmond, Ky., 16,861...C5 62
Richmond, Maine,
  1,449..........D3, f8 64
Richmond, Mich., 3,234..F8 66
Richmond, Mo., 4,948...B4 69
Richmond, Tex.,
  5,777..........E5, r14 84
Richmond, Utah, 1,000...A6 72
Richmond
  (Independent City),
  Va., 249,431
  (*489,500)......C5, m18 85
Richmond (Staten Island),
  borough and co., N.Y.,
  295,443..........E6 75
Richmond, co., N.S.,
  Can., 11,218......D9 43
Richmond, co., Que.,
  Can., 41,426......D5 42
Richmond, co., Ga.,
  162,437..........C4 55
Richmond, co., N.C.,
  39,889...........B3 76
Richmond, co., Va 6,504..C6 85
Richmond Beach, Wash.,
  7,700............B3 86
Richmond Heights, Fla.,
  6,663............s13 54
Richmond Heights, Mo.,
  13,802...........f13 69
Richmond Highlands,
  Wash., 20,100.....*B3 86
Richmond Hill, Ont.,
  Can., 32,384....D5, k15 41
Richmond Hill, N.C.,
  1,500............*B3 76
Richmond-Windsor, Austl.,
  11,357...........F8 26
Rich Square, N.C., 1,254..A5 76
Richton, Miss., 1,110....D5 68
Richwood, Ohio, 2,072...B2 78

Richwood, W. Va., 3,717..C4 87
Riddle, Oreg., 1,042.....E3 80
Ridge, Va..........*C5 85
Ridgecrest, Calif., 7,629..*E5 50
Ridgecrest, Wash., 4,500..*B3 86
Ridgedale, Mo., 135.....E4 69
Ridgedale, Tenn.......C10 83
Ridge Farm, Ill., 1,015...D6 58
Ridgefield, Conn., 5,878..D3 58
Ridgefield, N.J., 11,308..h8 74
Ridgefield Park, N.J.,
  13,990.........B4, h8 74
Ridgeland, S.C., 1,165...G6 82
Ridgeley, W. Va., 1,112..B6 87
Ridgely, Tenn., 1,657....A2 83
Ridgetown, Ont., Can.,
  2,836............E3 41
Ridgeville, Ga., 200.....E5 55
Ridgeville, Ind., 924.....D7 59
Ridgewood, Ill., 3,500....B5 58
Ridgewood, N.J., 27,547..B4 74
Ridgewood Heights, Ohio,
  2,000............*C1 78
Ridgway, Ill., 1,160.....F5 58
Ridgway, Pa., 6,022.....D4 81
Ridley Farms, Pa.,
  1,200............*G11 81
Ridley Park, Pa., 9,025...p20 81
Ried, Aus., 10,526......D6 6
Riegelsville, Pa., 1,050...B2 81
Riesa, Ger. Dem. Rep.,
  49,392...........C6 6
Rieti, It., 29,900.......C4 9
Rifle, Colo., 2,150......B3 51
Rīga, Sov. Un., 743,000
  (*810,000)........C5 12
Rigaud, Que., Can., 2,138.D3 42
Rigby, Idaho, 2,324.....F7 57
Riihimäki, Fin., 23,187...G11 11
Rijeka (Fiume), Yugo.,
  132,933..........C2 10
Riley, co., Kans., 56,788..C7 61
Rimbey, Alta., Can.,
  1,266............C3 38
Rimersburg, Pa., 1,146...D2 81
Rimini, It., 95,600
  (114,500 ▲)........B4 9
Rîmnicu-Sărat, Rom.,
  19,095...........C8 10
Rîmnicu-Vîlcea, Rom.,
  18,984...........C7 10
Rimouski, Que., Can.,
  26,887 (*28,956)....A9 42
Rimouski, co., Que., Can.,
  65,629...........A9 42
Rincon, Ga., 1,854.....D5 55
Rindjani, peak, Indon....G5 19
Ringgold, Ga., 1,381....B1 55
Ringgold, La., 1,731.....B2 63
Ringgold, co., Iowa,
  6,373............D3 60
Ringkøbing, co., Den.,
  224,900..........*I3 11
Ringling, Okla., 1,206...C4 79
Ringsaker, Nor.......G4 11
Ringsted, Den., 9,694...A1 7
Ringwood, N.J., 10,393..A4 74
Rio Arriba, co., N. Mex.,
  25,170...........A5 48
Riobamba, Ec., 49,300...B2 31
Rio Blanco, co., Colo.,
  4,842............B2 51
Rio Branco, Braz., 34,531.C4 31
Río Caribe, Ven., 7,774...A5 32
Rio Claro, Braz.,
  69,240.........C3, m8 30
Río Cuarto, Arg., 78,000..A4 28
Rio de Janeiro, Braz.,
  4,252,009
  (*7,000,000)......C4, h6 30
Rio de Janeiro, state,
  Braz., 9,110,324...C4, h6 30
Rio Dell, Calif., 2,817....B1 50
Río Gallegos, Arg.,
  26,000.........E3, h12 28
Rio Grande, Braz.,
  98,863...........E2 30
Río Grande, Mex., 11,651 .C4 34
Rio Grande, N.J., 1,203...E3 74
Rio Grande, co., Colo.,
  10,494...........D4 51
Rio Grande (Rio Bravo
  del Norte), river, Mex.-
  U.S..............E6 45
Rio Grande do Norte,
  state, Braz., 1,611,606..*D7 27
Rio Grande do Sul, state,
  Braz., 6,755,458.....E2 30
Ríohacha, Col., 11,708....A3 32
Rio Hondo, Tex., 1,167...F4 84
Rio Linda, Calif., 7,524..*C3 50
Riom, Fr., 15,467......E5 5
Río Muni, reg., Equat.
  Gui., 195,000......H7 22
Rio Negro, Braz.,
  12,681...........D3 30
Río Negro, dept. Ur.,
  46,852...........*E1 30

Río Negro, prov., Arg.,
  193,292..........C3 28
Rionero in Vulture, It.,
  14,378...........D5 9
Rio Pardo, Braz., 16,857..D2 30
Río Piedras, P.R.,
  65,406...........*G11 35
Río Tercero, Arg., 22,000..A4 28
Río Verde, Braz., 22,337..B2 30
Río Verde (Ríoverde),
  Mex., 16,804.......m13 34
Rio Vista, Calif., 3,135...C3 50
Ripley, Miss., 3,482.....A5 68
Ripley, N.Y., 1,173.....C1 75
Ripley, Ohio, 2,745.....D2 78
Ripley, Tenn., 4,794....B2 83
Ripley, W. Va., 3,244....C3 87
Ripley, co., Ind., 21,138..F7 59
Ripley, co., Mo., 9,803...E7 69
Ripoll, Sp., 9,034......A7 8
Ripon, Calif., 2,679.....*D3 50
Ripon, Eng., 11,800.....C6 4
Ripon, Wis., 7,053......E5 88
Rishon leZiyyon, Isr.,
  51,900...........C2 15
Rising Star, Tex., 1,009...C3 84
Rising Sun, Ind., 2,305...G8 59
Rison, Ark., 1,214......D3 49
Ritchey, Mo., 101......E3 69
Ritchie, co., W. Va.,
  10,145...........B3 87
Rittman, Ohio, 6,308....B4 78
Ritzville, Wash., 1,876...B7 86
Riva, It., 8,400.......B3 9
Rivadavia, Arg., 215.....A3 28
Rive-de-Gier, Fr., 16,855
  (*35,000).........E6 5
Rivera, Ur., 41,266.....E1 30
Rivera, dept., Ur.,
  77,496...........*E1 30
Riverbank, Calif., 3,949..D3 50
Riverdale, Calif., 1,722..D4 50
Riverdale, Ill., 15,806...k9 58
Riverdale, Md., 5,724..C4, f9 53
Riverdale, N.J., 2,729...B4 74
Riverdale, N. Dak., 700..C4 77
Riverdale, Oreg.......*B4 80
Riverdale, Utah, 3,704...*A6 72
Riverdale Heights, Md.,
  1,100............*C4 53
River Edge, N.J., 12,850..h8 74
River Falls, Wis., 7,238...D1 88
River Forest, Ill., 13,402..k9 58
River Grove, Ill., 11,465..k9 58
Riverhead, N.Y., 7,600...n15 75
River Hebert, N.S.,
  Can., 1,382.......D5 43
River Hills, Wis., 1,561..m12 88
Riverina, reg., Austl....F7 25
Riverland Terrace, S.C...k12 82
River Pines, Mass., 3,000.*A5 65
River Plaza, N.J., 1,900..*C4 74
River Rouge, Mich.,
  15,947........F7, p15 66
Rivers, Man., Can.,
  1,175............D1 40
Riverside, Calif.,
  140,089........F5, n14 50
Riverside, Ont., Can.,
  18,089...........E2 41
Riverside, Colo.......B5 51
Riverside, Ill., 10,432...k9 58
Riverside, Mich., 800....*F6 66
Riverside, Mo., 2,123...*B3 69
Riverside, N.J., 8,591...C3 74
Riverside, N.Y., 911....*C3 75
Riverside, Pa., 1,905....E8 81
Riverside, S.C., 2,200...*B3 82
Riverside, co., Calif.,
  459,074..........F5 50
Riverton, Ill., 2,090.....D4 58
Riverton, N.J., 3,412....C3 74
Riverton, Utah, 2,820....D2 72
Riverton, Wyo., 7,995...C4 89
Riverton Heights, Wash.,
  33,200...........*B3 86
River Vale, N.J., 8,883...*A5 74
River View, Ala., 1,171...C4 46
Riverview, Fla., 2,225...p11 54
Riverview, Mich., 11,342..p15 66
Riverview, Mo., 3,741...*C7 69
Riverview (Pasco West),
  Wash., 3,809......*C6 86
Rives, Mo., 120.......E7 69
Rivesville, W. Va.,
  1,108..........B4, h10 87
Riviera Beach, Fla.,
  21,401...........F6 54
Riviera Beach, Md.,
  7,464............*B4 53
Rivière-Bleue, Que., Can.,
  1,540............B8 42
Rivière-du-Loup, Que.,
  Can., 12,760......B8 42
Rivière-du-Loup, co.,
  Que., Can., 40,324...B9 42
Rivière-du-Moulin, Que.,
  Can., 4,393........A6 42

Riyadh (Ar Riyāḍ), Sau. Ar., 225,000......E4 15
Rizal, Prov., Phil., 1,456,362......*B6 19
Rize, Tur., 30,532......B13 14
Rjukan, Nor., 5,677......H3 11
Roachdale, Ind., 1,004...E4 59
Roane, co., Tenn., 38,881..D9 83
Roane, co., W. Va., 14,111............C3 87
Roan Mountain, Tenn., 850............C11 83
Roanne, Fr., 53,373 (*78,000)......D5 5
Roanoke, Ala., 5,251....B4 46
Roanoke, Ill., 2,040....C4 58
Roanoke, Ind., 858......C7 59
Roanoke (Independent City), Va., 92,115 (*192,900)......C3 85
Roanoke, co., Va., 67,339............C2 85
Roanoke Rapids, N.C., 13,508............A5 76
Roanoke Rapids West, N.C., 2,260......*A5 76
Roaring Springs, Pa., 2,811............F5 81
Robbins, Ill., 9,641......k9 58
Robbins, N.C., 1,059....B3 76
Robbinsdale, Minn., 16,845......E5, m12 67
Robersonville, N.C., 1,910............B5 76
Robert Lee, Tex., 1,119..D2 84
Roberts, co., S. Dak., 11,678............E9 77
Roberts, co., Tex., 967..B2 84
Robertsdale, Pa., 700....F5 81
Robertsdale, Ala., 2,078..E2 46
Robertson, co., Ky., 2,163..B5 62
Robertson, co., Tenn., 29,102............A5 83
Robertson, co., Tex., 14,389............D4 84
Robertsonville, Que., Can., 1,156............C6 42
Roberval, Que., Can., 8,330............A5 42
Robesonia, Pa., 1,685....*F9 81
Robeson, co., N.C., 84,842 .C3 76
Robinson, Ill., 7,178....D6 58
Robinson, Pa., 900......F3 81
Robinson, Tex., 3,807....*D4 84
Robinsonville, Miss., 135 .A3 68
Roblin, Man., Can., 1,753............D1 40
Robson, mtn., Can.......C1 38
Robstown, Tex., 11,217..F4 84
Roby, Mo., 100............D5 69
Roby, Tex., 784..........C2 84
Roccastrada, It., 3,109...C3 9
Rocha, Ur., 19,484......E2 30
Rocha, dept., Ur., 55,523............*E2 30
Rochdale, Eng., 91,470...D5 4
Rochdale, Mass., 1,320...B4 65
Rochefort, Fr., 29,226...E3 5
Rochelle, Ga., 1,380....E3 55
Rochelle, Ill., 8,594....B4 58
Rochelle Park, N.J., 6,380............h8 74
Rochester, Ind., 4,631...B5 59
Rochester, Mich., 7,054..F7 66
Rochester, Minn., 53,766 (*73,300)......F6 67
Rochester, N.H., 17,938..E6 73
Rochester, N.Y., 296,233 (*805,400)............B3 75
Rochester, Pa., 4,819....E1 81
Rock, co., Minn., 11,346..G2 67
Rock, co., Nebr., 2,231...B6 71
Rock, co., Wis., 131,970..F4 88
Rockaway, N.J., 6,383...B3 74
Rockaway, Oreg., 665....B3 80
Rockbridge, co., Va., 16,637............C3 85
Rockcastle, co., Ky., 12,305............C5 62
Rockcliffe Park, Ont., Can., 2,138............*B9 41
Rock Creek Hills, Md., 2,000............*B3 53
Rockdale, Ill., 2,085...B5, m8 58
Rockdale, Md., 2,500....*B4 53
Rockdale, Tex., 4,655....D4 84
Rockdale, co., Ga., 18,152..C2 55
Rock Falls, Ill., 10,287..B4 58
Rockford, Ill., 147,370 (*244,900)............A4 58
Rockford, Iowa, 902......A5 60
Rockford, Mich., 2,428...E5 66
Rockford, Ohio, 1,207...B1 78
Rockford, Tenn., 430............D10, n14 83
Rock Hall, Md., 1,125....B5 53
Rockhampton, Austl., 49,141............D9 25

Rock Hill, Mo., 6,815...*C7 69
Rock Hill, S.C., 33,846 (*51,100)............B5 82
Rockingham, N.C., 5,852..C3 76
Rockingham, co., N.H., 138,951............E5 73
Rockingham, co., N.C., 72,402............A3 76
Rockingham, co., Va., 47,890............B4 85
Rock Island, Que., Can., 1,341 (*2,533)......D5 42
Rock Island, Ill., 50,166..B3 58
Rock Island, co., Ill., 166,734............B3 58
Rockland, Ont., Can., 3,649............B9 41
Rockland, Maine, 8,505...B3 64
Rockland, Mass., 15,674............B6, h12 65
Rockland, co., N.Y., 229,903............D6 75
Rockledge, Fla., 10,523..D6 54
Rockledge, Pa., 2,564....o21 81
Rocklin, Calif., 3,039...*C3 50
Rockmart, Ga., 3,857....B1 55
Rockport, Ind., 2,565....I3 59
Rockport, Maine, 900....D3 64
Rockport, Mass., 4,166...A6 65
Rock Port, Mo., 1,575....A2 69
Rockport, Tex., 3,879....F4 84
Rock Rapids, Iowa, 2,632.A1 60
Rocksprings, Tex., 1,221..D2 84
Rock Springs, Wyo., 11,657............E3 89
Rockton, Ill., 2,099.....A4 58
Rock Valley, Iowa, 2,205.A1 60
Rockville, Conn......B7 52
Rockville, Ind., 2,820...E3 59
Rockville, Md., 41,821...B3 53
Rockville Centre, N.Y., 27,444............n15 75
Rockwall, Tex., 3,121............C4, n10 84
Rockwall, co., Tex., 7,046 .C4 84
Rockwell City, Iowa, 2,396............B3 60
Rockwood, Mich., 3,225...F7 66
Rockwood, Pa., 1,051....F3 81
Rockwood, Tenn., 5,259..D9 83
Rocky Ford, Colo., 4,859..C7 51
Rocky Grove, Pa.......D2 81
Rocky Hill, Conn., 11,103............C6 52
Rocky Mount, N.C., 34,284............B5 76
Rocky Mount, Va., 4,002..C3 85
Rocky Mountain House, Alta., Can., 2,968......C3 38
Rocky Point, N.Y., 3,500............*n15 75
Rocky Point, Wash., 1,733............*B3 86
Rocky Ripple, Ind......k10 59
Rocky River, Ohio, 22,958............A4, h9 78
Roddickton, Newf., Can., 1,185............C3, h10 44
Rodeo, Calif., 5,356.....*D3 50
Roderfield, W. Va., 1,000............D3 87
Rodessa, La., 273........B1 63
Rodez, Fr., 23,328 (*31,000)............E5 5
Rodgers Forge, Md......*B4 53
Rodhópi (Rhodope), prov., Grc., 107,618..*B5 14
Ródhos, Grc., 32,092....D7 14
Rodney, Ont., Can., 1,016............E3 41
Rodney Village, Del., 2,127............B6 53
Roebling, N.J., 3,600....C3 74
Roeland Park, Kans., 9,974............B9 61
Roermond, Neth., 36,383............B6 5
Roeselare, Bel., 40,473...B5 5
Roessleville, N.Y., 5,476 .*C7 75
Rogachev, Sov. Un., 16,000............E8 12
Rogaland, co., Nor., 262,800............*H1 11
Rogatica, Yugo., 3,044...D4 10
Roger Mills, co., Okla., 4,452............B2 79
Rogers, Ark., 11,050....A1 49
Rogers, Tex., 1,030......D4 84
Rogers, Va., 50..........f10 85
Rogers, co., Okla., 28,425..A6 79
Rogers City, Mich., 4,275..C7 66
Rogers Heights, Md., 3,200............*C4 53
Rogersville, Tenn., 4,076..C10 83
Rogoźno, Pol., 7,395....B4 7
Rohnerville, Calif., 1,300 .*B1 50
Rohtak, India, 124,755...*C6 20
Roi Et, Thai., 13,055....B2 19

Rojas, Arg., 9,446......A4 28
Rokitno, Sov. Un., 9,000..F6 12
Rokycany, Czech., 12,567..D2 7
Roland Terrace, Md.....*B4 53
Rolette, co., N. Dak., 11,549............B6 77
Rolfe, Iowa, 767........B3 60
Rolla, Mo., 13,571......D6 69
Rolla, N. Dak., 1,458....A6 77
Rolling Fork, Miss., 2,034..C3 68
Rolling Hills, Kans......B5 61
Rolling Hills Estates, Calif., 6,735......*F4 50
Rolling Meadows, Ill., 19,178............h8 58
Rollingwood, Calif., 3,000............*D2 50
Roma, Austl., 5,860.....E8 25
Roma, Tex., 2,154......F3 84
Roma, see Rome, It.
Roman, Rom., 39,000...B8 10
Romania, country, Eur., 21,190,000............B7 10
Romans [-sur-Isère], Fr., 31,545 (*43,000)......E6 5
Romblon, Phil., 4,241...*C6 19
Romblon, prov., Phil., 131,658............*C6 19
Rome, Ga., 30,759......B1 55
Rome, Ill., 1,919........C4 58
Rome, N.Y., 50,148.....B5 75
Rome, Ohio, 90.........*A5 78
Rome (Roma), It., 2,731,400 (*2,925,000)......D4, h8 9
Romeo, Ill., 12,674......*B5 58
Romeo, Mich., 4,012....F7 66
Romilly [-sur-Seine], Fr., 17,038............C5 5
Romita, Mex., 11,947...m11 34
Romney, W. Va., 2,364...B6 87
Romny, Sov. Un., 48,000..F9 12
Romorantin, Fr., 14,096..D4 5
Romulus, Mich., 22,879..p15 66
Ronan, Mont., 1,347....C2 70
Ronceverte, W. Va., 1,981.D4 87
Ronciglione, It., 7,079...C4 9
Ronda, Sp., 17,703.....D3 8
Rondônia, ter., Braz., 70,783............B3 29
Ronkonkoma, N.Y., 14,800.F4 52
Rønne, Den., 12,900....A3 7
Ronse, Bel., 25,087.....B5 5
Roodhouse, Ill., 2,357...D3 58
Rooks, co., Kans., 7,628..C4 61
Roosendaal, Neth., 49,526.B6 5
Roosevelt, N.Y., 15,000..G2 52
Roosevelt, Utah, 2,005...A6 72
Roosevelt, co., Mont., 10,365............B11 70
Roosevelt, co., N. Mex., 16,479............B7 48
Roosevelt, riv., Braz......B3 29
Roosevelt Park, Mich., 4,176............E4 66
Roquetas, Sp., 5,514....B6 8
Rorschach, Switz., 11,600 (*24,400)............E4 6
Rosa, mtn., It., Switz....B2 9
Roraima, ter., Braz., 41,638............C5 32
Rosario, Arg., 705,000 (*875,000)............A4 28
Rosário, Braz., 8,518....*D6 27
Rosario, Mex., 10,376...C3 34
Rosario, Par., 6,058....D4 29
Rosario, Ur., 7,600.....E1 30
Rosário do Sul, Braz., 24,399............E2 30
Rosario Tala, Arg., 10,584.A5 28
Rosburg, Wash., 50......B5 89
Roscoe, N.Y., 800......D6 75
Roscoe, Pa., 1,176......F2 81
Roscoe, Tex., 1,580.....C2 84
Roscommon, co., Ire., 56,228............*D2 4
Roscommon, co., Mich., 9,892............D6 66
Roseau, Dominica, 10,417.I14 35
Roseau, Minn., 2,552....B3 67
Roseau, co., Minn., 11,569............B3 67
Roseboro, N.C., 1,235...C4 76
Rosebud, Tex., 1,597....D4 84
Rosebud, co., Mont., 6,032............D10 70
Roseburg, Oreg., 14,461..D3 80
Rosedale, Fla., 150......*E4 54
Rosedale, Miss., 2,599...B2 68
Rosedale Station, Alta., Can.............D4 38
Rose Hill, Kans., 387....E6 61
Rose Hill, N.C., 1,448...C4 76
Roseland, Fla., 500......E6 54
Roseland, Ind., 895.....A5 59
Roseland, La., 1,273....D5 63
Roseland, N.J., 4,453....*B4 74
Roseland, Ohio, 3,000...B3 78
Roselle, Ill., 6,207......k8 58

Roselle, N.J., 22,585.....k7 74
Roselle Park, N.J., 14,277.k7 74
Rosemead, Calif., 40,972..*F4 50
Rosemère, Que., Can., 6,710............p19 42
Rosemont, Ill., 4,825....*E3 58
Rosemont, Pa., 4,500....*F11 81
Rosemount, Minn., 1,337..F5 67
Rosenberg, Tex., 12,098............E5, r14 84
Rosendael, Fr., 19,591...B5 5
Rosendale, N.Y., 1,220...*C6 75
Rosenheim, Ger., Fed. Rep. of, 38,060............E6 6
Roseto, Pa., 1,538......E11 81
Rosetown, Sask., Can., 2,614............F1, n7 39
Roseville, Calif., 18,221..C3 50
Roseville, Ill., 1,111.....C3 58
Roseville, Mich., 60,529...o16 66
Roseville, Minn., 34,438..m12 67
Roseville, Ohio, 1,767...C3 78
Rosewood, Calif., 900...*B1 50
Rosewood Heights, Ill., 6,620............*E3 58
Rosiclare, Ill., 1,421....F5 58
Roşiori-de-Vede, Rom., 17,320............C7 10
Roskilde, co., Den., 107,497............*J5 11
Roslavl, Sov. Un., 49,000..E9 12
Roslyn, N.Y., 2,607.....*E7 75
Roslyn, Pa., 13,400.....*F11 81
Roslyn, Wash., 1,031....B4 86
Roslyn Estates, N.Y., 1,420............*G2 52
Roslyn Harbor, N.Y., 1,125............*E7 75
Roslyn Heights, N.Y., 7,242............D2, h13 75
Rosny-sous-Bois, Fr., 30,705............g10 5
Ross, Calif., 2,742......*C2 50
Ross, co., Ohio, 61,211...C2 78
Ross and Cromarty, co., Scot., 58,037......*B4 4
Rossano, It., 12,400....E6 9
Rossford, Ohio, 5,302...A2, e6 78
Rossiter, Pa., 900......E4 81
Rossland, B.C., Can., 3,896............E9 37
Rossmoor, Calif., 12,922 .*F5 50
Rossmoyne, Ohio.......*C1 78
Rossosh, Sov. Un., 36,000............F12 12
Rossville, Ga., 3,957....B1 55
Rossville, Ill., 1,420....C6 58
Rosthern, Sask., Can., 1,431............E2 39
Rostock, Ger. Dem. Rep., 207,285............A6 6
Rostov, Sov. Un., 31,000..C12 12
Rostov [-na-Donu], Sov. Un., 789,000 (*905,000)............H12 12
Roswell, Ga., 5,430.....B2 55
Roswell, N. Mex., 33,908..C6 48
Rotan, Tex., 2,404......C2 84
Rotenburg [an der Fulda], Ger., Fed. Rep. of, 16,723............B4 6
Rothenburg ob der Tauber, Ger., Fed. Rep. of, 12,221............D5 6
Rothesay, Scot., 6,373...C4 4
Rothschild, Wis., 3,141...D4 88
Rothsville, Pa., 1,318....F9 81
Rotondella, It., 5,643....D6 9
Rotorua, N.Z., 32,600 (*41,300)............M16 26
Rotterdam, Neth., 654,024 (*1,115,000)............B6 5
Rotterdam, N.Y., 25,700..*C6 75
Rottweil, Ger., Fed. Rep. of, 23,465............D4 6
Roubaix, Fr., 114,547...B5 5
Roudnice [nad Labem], Czech., 11,279......n17 7
Rouen, Fr., 120,471 (*1,120,000)............C4 5
Roulette, Pa., 1,100....C5 81
Round Lake, Ill., 1,531...h8 58
Roundlake, Miss., 100...A3 68
Round Lake Beach, Ill., 5,717............h8 58
Round Lake Heights, Ill., 1,144............*h8 58
Round Lake Park, Ill., 3,148............*h8 58
Round Pond, Ark., 150...B5 49
Round Rock, Tex., 2,811..D4 84
Roundup, Mont., 2,116...D8 70
Rouses Point, N.Y., 2,250.f11 75
Rouseville, Pa., 877.....D2 81
Routt, co., Colo., 6,592...A3 51
Rouville, co., Que., Can., 29,171............D4 42

Rouzerville, Pa., 1,419....G7 81	Royse City, Tex., 1,535....C4 84	Rush Springs, Okla., 1,381............C4 79	Ruth, Nev., 750........B4 72
Rovaniemi, Fin., 27,281..D11 11	Royston, Ga., 2,428......B3 55	Rushville, Ill., 3,300.....C3 58	Ruthenia, reg., Sov. Un...D7 7
Rovato, It., 6,288.......B2 9	Rožňava, Czech., 11,509..D6 7	Rushville, Ind., 6,686....E7 59	Rutherford, N.J., 20,802............B4, h8 74
Rovenki, Sov. Un., 61,000............G12, q22 12	Rtishchevo, Sov. Un., 37,000............E14 12	Rushville, Nebr., 1,137...B3 71	Rutherford, Tenn., 1,385..A3 83
Rovereto, It., 28,000.....B3 9	Ruapehu, mtn., N.Z....M15 26	Rusk, Tex., 4,914.......D5 84	Rutherford, co., N.C., 47,337............B1 76
Rovigo, It., 38,600.......B3 9	Rubezhnoye, Sov. Un., 58,000............p21 12	Rusk, co., Tex., 34,102...C5 84	Rutherford, co., Tenn., 59,428............B5 83
Rovinj, Yugo., 7,156.....C1 10	Rubidoux, Calif., 12,400..n14 50	Rusk, co., Wis., 14,238...C2 88	Rutherford Heights, Pa., 3,300............*F8 81
Rovno, Sov. Un., 116,000..F6 12	Ruda Śląska, Pol., 142,400............*C5 7	Ruskin, Fla., 2,414..E4, p11 54	Rutherfordton, N.C., 3,245............B1, f11 76
Rovnoye, Sov. Un., 10,000............F16 12	Rudbar, Afg., 5,000......B3 20	Russas, Braz., 9,955.....*D7 27	Rutland, Mass., 1,751....B4 65
Rowan, co., Ky., 17,010...B6 62	Rudolf, lake, Afr........F9 21	Russell (Russell City), Calif............*D3 50	Rutland, Vt., 19,293.....D2 73
Rowan, co., N.C., 90,035..B2 76	Rudolstadt, Ger. Dem. Rep., 31,564..........C5 6	Russell, Man., Can., 1,526.D1 40	Rutland, co., Eng., 29,230.*D6 4
Rowan Mill, N.C., 1,184..*B2 76	Rueil-Malmaison, Fr., 60,804............g9 5	Russell, Kans., 5,371....D5 61	Rutland, co., Vt., 52,637..D1 73
Rowes Run, Pa., 800......*F2 81	Rufino, Arg., 13,771......A4 28	Russell, Ky., 1,982......B7 62	Rutledge, Pa., 1,167.....*G11 81
Rowland, N.C., 1,358.....C3 76	Rufisque, Sen., 49,700...F1 22	Russell, co., Ala., 45,394..C4 46	Ruvo [di Puglia], It., 23,300............D6 9
Rowland, Pa., 125.......D11 81	Rugby, Eng., 57,200.....D6 4	Russell, co., Kans., 9,428..D5 61	Ruxton, Md............*B4 53
Rowlesburg, W. Va., 829..B5 87	Rugby, N. Dak., 2,889....B6 77	Russell, co., Ky., 10,542..C4 62	Ruzayevka, Sov. Un., 41,000............D15 12
Rowlett, Tex., 2,243.....*C4 84	Ruidoso, N. Mex., 2,216..C6 48	Russell, co., Va., 24,533..f9 85	Ružomberok, Czech., 21,380............D5 7
Rowley, Mass., 1,325......A6 65	Rule, Tex., 1,024.......C3 84	Russell Gardens, N.Y., 1,207............*E7 75	Rwanda, country, Afr., 4,100,000............I3 23
Roxana, Ill., 1,882......f13 69	Ruleville, Miss., 2,351...B3 68	Russells Point, Ohio, 1,104............*B2 78	Ryazan,Sov.Un.,350,000.D12 12
Roxas (Capiz), Phil., 19,641............C6 19	Ruma, Yugo., 23,941.....C4 10	Russell Springs, Ky., 1,641............C4 62	Rybinsk, Sov. Un., 218,000............B12 12
Roxboro, N.C., 5,370......A4 76	Rumford, Maine, 6,198...D2 64	Russellton, Pa., 1,597...E2 81	Rybnik, Pol., 43,400...C5, g9 7
Roxburgh, co., Scot., 41,821............*C5 4	Rumoi, Jap., 38,691.....E10 18	Russellville, Ala., 7,814...A2 46	Rydal, Pa., 2,200.......*F11 81
Roxton Falls, Que., Can., 972............D5 42	Rumson, N.J., 7,421......C4 74	Russellville, Ark., 11,750..B2 49	Ryde, Eng., 22,790.....E6 4
Roy, N. Mex., 476.......D5 42	Runge, Tex., 1,147......E4 84	Russellville, Ky., 6,456...D3 62	Rye, N.Y., 15,869...h13, n15 75
Roy, Utah, 14,356...A5, C2 72	Runnels, co., Tex., 12,108..D3 84	Russian Soviet Federated Socialist Republic, rep., Sov. Un., 133,975,000..C8 12	Rylsk, Sov. Un., 16,000...F10 12
Royal, Fla., 300.........D4 54	Runnemede, N.J., 10,475..D2 74	Russiaville, Ind., 844....D5 59	Ryotsu, Jap., 12,800 (23,483▲)............G9 18
Royal Center, Ind., 987...C4 59	Rupert, Idaho, 4,563.....G5 57	Rustavi, Sov. Un., 98,000.B15 14	Rypin, Pol., 10,000......B5 7
Royal Mills, N.C., 300...A4 76	Rupert, W. Va., 1,027....D4 87	Ruston, La., 17,365......B3 63	Ryukyu Islands, Jap., 980,000............F10 17
Royal Oak, Mich., 86,238............F7, o15 66	Rural Hall, N.C., 2,338...A2 76	Rutchenkovo, Sov. Un., 25,000............r20 12	Rzeszów, Pol., 82,100....C6 7
Royal Oak Township, Mich., 6,326...........*F7 66	Ruse (Ruschuk), Bul., 131,700............*D7 10	Rute, Sp., 10,077.......D3 8	Rzhev, Sov. Un., 61,000..C10 12
Royalton, Ill., 1,166.....F4 58	Ruse (Ruschuk), co., Bul., 273,226..........*D8 10	Ruteng, Indon., 15,814...G6 19	
Royalton, Pa., 1,040.....*F8 81	Rush, co., Ind., 20,352...E7 59	Ruth, Miss., 150........D3 68	
Royan, Fr., 17,292 (*27,000)............E3 5	Rush City, Minn., 1,130..E6 67		
Royersford, Pa., 4,235...F10 81	Rush, co., Kan., 5,117...D4 61		
	Rushford, Minn., 1,318...G7 67		

S

Saalfeld, Ger. Dem. Rep., 33,653............C5 6	Sa'dah, Yemen, 25,000....F3 15	Saida (Sidon), Leb., 35,600............F10 14	Ste. Anne-de-la-Pérade, Que., Can., 1,184......C5 42
Saar, state, Ger., Fed. Rep. of, 1,120,000............D3 6	Saddle Brook, N.J., 15,975............*A4 74	Saidpur, Bngl., 60,628....C8 20	St. Anselme, Que., Can., 1,131............C7 42
Saarbrücken, Ger., Fed. Rep. of, 125,900 (*375,000)............D3 6	Saddle River, N.J., 2,437............*A4 74	Saigo, Jap., 5,330.......H6 18	St. Ansgar, Iowa, 944....A5 60
Saarlouis, Ger., Fed. Rep. of, 40,107 (*99,000)...D3 6	Saddle Rock, N.Y., 895............*G2 52	Saigon, see Ho Chi Minh City, Viet.	St. Anthony, Newf., Can., 2,593............C4 44
Sabac, Yugo., 42,307.....C4 10	Saegertown, Pa., 1,348...C1 81	Saijo, Jap., 38,000 (51,127▲)............*I6 18	St. Anthony, Minn., 9,239............*F5 67
Sabadell, Sp., 158,311...B7 8	Saeki, Jap., 32,000......J5 18	Saiki, Jap., 40,500 (50,698▲)............J5 18	St. Antoine des Laurentides, Que., Can., 3,005......*D3 42
Sabae, Jap., 42,000 (52,614▲)............n15 18	Safety Harbor, Fla., 3,103............D4, p10 54	St. Affrique, Fr., 5,670....F5 5	St. Apollinaire, Que., Can., 968...........C6, o16 42
Sabah (North Borneo), reg., Mala., 725,000.....D5 19	Safford, Ariz., 5,333.....C4 48	St. Agapit, Que., Can., 1,117............C6 42	St. Aubert, Que., Can., 735............B7 42
Sabana de la Mar, Dom. Rep., 6,800............E9 35	Safi, Mor., 129,113......B3 22	Ste. Agathe-des-Monts, Que. Can., 5,532.......C3 42	St. Augustine, Fla., 12,352............C5, n9 54
Sabana Grande, P.R., 5,561 (16,343▲)........*G11 35	Safranbolu, Tur., 12,470..B9 14	St. Alban, Que., Can., 786.C5 42	St. Avold, Fr., 16,280 (*25,000)............C7 5
Sabanalarga, Col., 20,254..A3 32	Saga, Jap., 143,454......J5 18	St. Alban's, Newf., Can., 1,941............E4 44	St. Barthélémy, Que., Can., 620............C4 42
Sabang, Indon., 17,625...k11 19	Saga, pref., Jap., 838,468..*J5 18	St. Albans, Eng., 52,690............E6, k12 4	St. Basile [-de-Portneuf], Que., Can., 1,709......C6 42
Sabará, Braz., 18,696.....B4 30	Sagadahoc, co., Maine, 23,452............E3 64	St. Albans, W. Va., 14,356.C3 87	St. Bernard, Ohio, 6,080..o12 78
Sabaudia, It., 6,262......D4 9	Sagaing, Bur., 15,439....D10 20	St. Albans, Vt., 8,082....B1 73	St. Bernard, par., La., 51,185............E6 63
Sabetha, Kans., 2,376....C8 61	Sagamihara, Jap., 278,326............*I9 18	St. Albans Bay, Vt., 200..B1 73	St. Bernice, Ind., 900....E2 59
Sabina, Ohio, 2,160......C2 78	Sagamore, Pa., 850......E3 81	St. Albert, Alta., Can., 11,800............C4 38	St. Bonaventure, N.Y., 1,800............*C2 75
Sabinal, Tex., 1,554......E3 84	Sagamore Hills, Ohio, 6,000............h9 78	St. Alexandre [-de-Kamouraska], Que., Can., 872........B8 42	St. Bride, mtn., Alta., Can............D3 38
Sabinas, Mex., 20,538....B4 34	Sāgar, India, 118,574 (*154,785)............D6 20	St. Alexis-des-Monts, Que., Can., 1,964......C3 42	St. Brieuc, Fr., 50,281....C2 5
Sabinas Hidalgo, Mex., 17,439............B4 34	Sagara, Jap............o17 18	St. Amand-Mont-Rond, Fr., 11,495............D5 5	St. Bruno-Lac-St. Jean, Que., Can., 1,158......A6 42
Sabine, co., Tex., 7,187...D6 84	Sag Harbor, N.Y., 2,363..n16 75	St. Ambroise-de-Chicoutimi, Que., Can., 1,629......A6 42	St. Camille [-de-Belle-chasse], Que., Can., 689............C7 42
Sabine, par., La., 18,638..C2 63	Saginaw, Mich., 91,849 (*181,600)............E7 66	St. André-Avellin, Que., Can., 1,066............D2 42	St. Casimir, Que., Can., 1,386............C5 42
Sablé [-sur-Sarthe], Fr., 6,885............D3 5	Saginaw, Tex., 2,382.....n9 84	St. Andrews, N.B., Can., 1,812............D2 43	St. Catharines, Ont., Can., 109,722 (*303,429)....D5 41
Sabzawar, Afg., 10,000...B3 20	Saginaw, co., Mich., 219,743............E6 66	St. Andrews, Scot., 11,944..B5 4	Ste. Catherine, Que., Can., 893...........C6, n16 42
Sac, co., Iowa, 15,573....B2 60	Sagle, Idaho, 100........A2 57	St. Andrews, S.C., 5,000............F7, k11 82	St. Césaire, Que., Can., 2,279............D4 42
Sac City, Iowa, 3,268....B2 60	Saguache, Colo., 642....C4 51	St. Andrews East, Que., Can., 1,183............D3 42	St. Chamond, Fr., 37,728..E6 5
Sachsen, former state, Ger. Dem. Rep., 5,558,566..*C6 6	Saguache, co., Colo., 3,827............C4 51	St. Ann, Mo., 18,215.....*C7 69	St. Charles, Ill., 12,945...B5 58
Sachsen-Anhalt (Saxony-Anhalt), former state, Ger. Dem. Rep., 4,160,539............*C5 6	Sagua de Tánamo, Cuba, 9,600 (40,100▲)........D6 35	Ste. Anne, Man., Can., 900.D4 42	St. Charles, Mich., 2,046..E6 66
Sackets Harbor, N.Y., 1,202.B4 75	Sagua la Grande, Cuba, 35,800 (41,900▲)......C3 35	Ste. Anne, Guad., 3,190..H14 35	St. Charles, Minn., 1,942..G6 67
Sackville, N.B., 3,180.....D5 43	Saguenay, co., Que., Can., 107,663..........A8 42	St. Anne, Ill., 1,271......B6 58	St. Charles, Mo., 31,834............C7, f12 69
Saco, Maine, 11,678...E2, g7 64	Sagunto, Sp., 40,293....C5 8	Ste. Anne-de-Beaupré, Que., Can., 1,797......B7 42	
Sacramento, Calif., 257,105 (*703,200)....A6 50	Sahagún, Col., 11,560....B2 32	Ste. Anne [-de-Bellevue], Que., Can., 4,976......q19 42	
Sacramento, co., Calif., 634,190............C3 50	Sahāranpur, India, 225,396............C6 20		
Sacré-Coeur Saguenay, Que., Can., 1,108......A8 42	Sahiwal, Pak., 115,000...B5 20		
	Sahuaripa, Mex., 4,710...B3 34		
	Sahuayo [de Díaz], Mex., 28,727............m12 34		

St. Charles, co., Mo., 92,954.................C7 69
St. Charles, par., La., 29,550.................E5 63
St. Charles [-de-Bellechasse], Que., Can., 981.......C7 42
St. Chrysostome, Que., Can., 972.........D4 42
St. Clair, Mich., 4,770....F8 66
St. Clair, Mo., 2,978.....C6 69
St. Clair, Pa., 4,576.....E9 81
St. Clair, co., Ala., 27,956..B3 46
St. Clair, co., Ill., 285,176..E3 58
St. Clair, co., Mich., 120,175.............F8 66
St. Clair, co., Mo., 7,667...C4 69
Ste. Claire, Que., Can., 1,838.............C7 42
St. Clair Haven, Mich., 2,177............*F8 66
St. Clair Shores, Mich., 88,093............*F8 66
St. Clairsville, Ohio, 4,754..B5 78
St. Claude, Man., Can., 609...............E2 40
St. Claude [-sur-Bienne], Fr., 12,114........D6 5
St. Cloud, Fla., 5,041.....D5 54
St. Cloud, Fr., 28,162.....g9 5
St. Cloud, Minn., 39,691 (*63,800).......E4 67
St. Constant, Que., Can., 4,139.............q19 42
St. Croix, Que., Can., 1,363.........C6, o16 42
St. Croix, co., Wis., 34,354.............C1 88
St. Croix Falls, Wis., 1,425.............C1 88
St. Cyrille [-de-L'Islet], Que., Can., 655.....B7 42
St. Cyrille [-de-Wendover], Que., Can., 1,138......D5 42
St. Damase, Que., Can., 879...............D4 42
St. Davids, Pa., 1,500....*G11 81
St. Denis, Fr., 99,268..C5, g10 5
St. Denis, Reunion, 67,550 (88,444 ▲)..........*H24 2
St. Denis [-de-la-Bouteillerie], Que., Can., 269.......B8 42
St. Denis [River Richelieu], Que., Can., 1,063.............D4 42
St. Dié, Fr., 25,117......C7 5
St. Dizier, Fr., 36,616....C6 5
St. Donat-de-Mont-calm, Que., Can., 1,414.....C3 42
St. Edward, Nebr., 853....C8 71
St. Éleuthère, Que., Can., 1,014.............B8 42
St. Elias, mts., N.A......C11 47
St. Elmo, Ill., 1,676......D5 58
Ste. Émélie-de-l'Énergie, Que., Can., 566......C4 42
St. Ephrem, Que., Can., 898...............C7 42
St. Esprit, Que., Can., 778..D4 42
St. Étienne, Fr., 213,468 (*330,000)..........E6 5
St. Eustache, Que., Can., 16,890.........D4, p19 42
St. Fabien, Que., Can., 1,466.............A9 42
St. Felicien, Que., Can., 4,952.............A5 42
St. Félix-de-Valois, Que., Can., 1,399......C4 42
St. Ferdinand, Que., Can., 2,415............C6 42
St. Flavien, Que., Can., 610...............C6 42
St. Flour, Fr., 5,997.....E5 5
Ste. Foy, Que., Can., 68,385............C6 42
St. Francis, Kans., 1,725...C2 61
St. Francis, Wis., 10,489...E2 88
St. Francis, co., Ark., 30,799.............B4 49
St. François [-du-Lac], Que., Can., 977......C5 42
St. Francisville, Ill., 997..E6 58
St. Francisville, La., 1,603..D4 63
St. Francois, co., Mo., 36,818.............D7 69
St. Fulgence, Que., Can., 1,094.............A7 42
St. Gabriel [-de-Brandon], Que., Can., 3,383.....C4 42
St. Gallen, see Sankt Gallen, Switz.
St. Gaudens, Fr., 7,949....F4 5
Ste. Genevieve, Mo., 4,468..D7 69
Ste. Genevieve, co., Mo., 12,867...........D7 69

Ste. Geneviève-de-Pierrefonds, Que., Can., 2,397............*D4 42
St. George, Austl., 2,184...E8 25
St. George, N.B., Can., 977...............D3 43
St. George, Ont., Can., 791...............D4 41
St. George, Mo., 2,033....*C7 69
St. George, S.C., 1,806....E6 82
St. Georges, Que., Can., 2,061.............C5 42
St. George's, Grenada, 8,099 (*21,730).....J14 35
St. Georges [-de-Windsor], Que., Can., 345......D6 42
St. Georges-Ouest, Que., Can., 6,000.....*C7 42
St. Gérard, Que., Can., 662...............D6 42
St. Germain, [-de-Grantham], Que., Can., 1,015......D5 42
St. Germain-en-Laye, Fr., 38,308.............g9 5
St. Gervais, Que., Can., 576...............C7 42
St. Gilles, Que., Can., 822...............C6 42
St. Gilles-du-Gard, Fr., 4,791.............F6 5
St. Girons, Fr., 7,971....F4 5
St. Helena, Calif., 3,173...A5 50
St. Helena, Br. dep., Afr., 6,000.............H20 2
St. Helena, par., La., 9,937.............D5 63
St. Helens, Eng., 102,800 (*153,000).........*D5 4
St. Helens, Oreg., 6,212...B4 80
St. Helier, Jersey, 28,135 (*45,000).........F5 4
St. Henry, Ohio, 1,276....B1 78
St. Hilaire Est, Que., Can., 2,911.........D4 42
St. Hyacinthe, Que., Can., 24,562 (*39,693)....D5 42
St. Hyacinthe, co., Que., Can., 48,842.....D4 42
St. Ignace, Mich., 2,892...C6 66
St. Jacobs, Ont., Can., 669...............D4 41
St. Jacques, Que., Can., 1,975.............D4 42
St. James, Man., Can., 35,685.............E3 40
St. James, Minn., 4,027...G4 67
St. James, Mo., 2,929.....D6 69
St. James, N.Y., 10,500...F4 52
St. James, par., La., 19,733.............D5 63
St. Jean, Que., Can., 32,863 (*47,044).....D4 42
St. Jean, co., Que., Can., 41,621............D4 42
St. Jean-Baptiste, Man., Can., 521.........E3 40
St. Jean-D'Angély, Fr., 9,739.............E3 5
St. Jean-de-Dieu, Que., Can., 1,177.........A9 42
St. Jean-de-Luz, Fr., 10,841 (*21,000).....F3 5
St. Jean-de-Matha, Que., Can., 846.........*C4 42
St. Jean-Eudes, Que., Can., 2,873.........*A7 42
St. Jérôme, Que., Can., 26,524 (*35,335).....D3 42
Saint John, N.B., Can., 89,039 (*106,744)....D3 43
St. John, Ind., 1,757.....B3 59
St. John, Kans., 1,477....E5 61
St. John, co., N.B., Can., 92,926............D4 43
St. John's, Antigua, 21,595............H14 35
St. John's, Newf., Can., 88,102 (*131,814)....E5 44
St. Johns, Ariz., 1,320....B4 48
St. Johns, Mich., 6,672...F6 66
St. Johns, Mo., 8,960....*C7 69
St. Johns, co., Fla., 30,727............B5 54
St. Johnsbury, Vt., 6,400..C3 73
St. Johnsville, N.Y., 2,089............*B6 75
St. John the Baptist, par., La., 23,813........D5 63
St. Joseph, Ill., 1,554....C5 58
St. Joseph, La., 1,864....C4 63
St. Joseph, Mich., 11,042.............F4 66
St. Joseph, Minn., 1,786...E4 67
St. Joseph, Mo., 72,748 (*88,200).........B3 69
St. Joseph, co., Ind., 245,045...........A5 59

St. Joseph, co., Mich., 47,392............G5 66
St. Joseph-de-Beauce, Que., Can., 2,893......C7 42
St. Joseph-de-Sorel, Que., Can., 3,290.....*D4 42
St. Joseph-de-St. Hyacinthe, Que., Can., 4,945............*D5 42
St. Jovite, Que., Can., 3,132.............C3 42
St. Junien, Fr., 8,449.....E4 5
St. Kitts-Nevis-Anguilla, Br., dep., N.A., 67,000.......G13, H13 35
St. Lambert, Que., Can., 18,616............p19 42
St. Landry, par., La., 80,364............D3 63
St. Laurent, Man., Can., 869...............D3 40
St. Laurent, Que., Can., 62,955............p19 42
St. Lawrence, Newf., Can., 2,173.........E4 44
St. Lawrence, Pa., 1,256..*F10 81
St. Lawrence, co., N.Y., 112,309...........A6 75
St. Lawrence, riv., N.A....G20 36
St. Léonard, N.B., Can., 1,666.............B2 43
St. Léonard [-de-Noblat], Fr., 3,671.........E4 5
St. Lô, Fr., 18,615.......C3 5
St. Louis, Mich., 4,101...E6 66
St.-Louis, Sen., 48,800...E1 22
St. Louis (Independent City), Mo., 622,236 (*2,295,700).......C37 69
St. Louis, co., Minn., 220,693...........C6 67
St. Louis, co., Mo., 951,353...........C7 69
St. Louis Park, Minn., 48,883............n12 67
St. Lucie, co., Fla., 50,836............E6 54
St. Maixent-l' École, Fr., 7,706.............D3 5
St. Malo, Fr., 42,297....C2 5
St. Mandé, Fr., 23,044...g10 5
St. Marc, Hai., 17,263....E7 35
St. Marc [-des-Carrières], Que., Can., 2,650....C5 42
Ste. Marie-Beauce, Que., Can., 4,307.........C6 42
St. Maries, Idaho, 2,571...B2 57
St. Martin, par., La., 32,453............D4 63
St. Martinville, La., 7,153.............D4 63
St. Mary, par., La., 60,752............E4 63
St. Mary, peak, Austl....*F6 25
St. Mary-of-the-Woods, Ind., 800.........E3 59
St. Mary's, Ont., Can., 4,650.............D3 41
St. Marys, Ga., 3,408....F5 55
St. Marys, Ind., 1,700....A5 59
St. Marys, Kans., 1,434...C7 61
St. Marys, Ohio, 7,699...B3 78
St. Marys, Pa., 7,470....D4 81
St. Marys, W. Va., 2,348.............B3 87
St. Marys, co., Md., 47,388............D4 53
St. Matthews, Ky., 13,152..........B4, g11 62
St. Matthews, S.C., 2,403..D6 82
St. Maur-des-Fossés, Fr., 77,251............g10 5
St. Maurice, co., Que., Can., 112,695......C4 42
St. Michael, Minn., 1,021..E5 67
St. Michael, Pa., 1,248...*E4 81
St. Michaels, Md., 1,456...C5 53
St. Nazaire, Fr., 63,289 (*110,000)..........D2 5
St. Noël, Que., Can., 1,124............*G20 36
St. Norbert, Man., Can., 695...............E3 40
St. Omer, Fr., 18,205 (*27,000)..........B5 5
St. Ouen, Fr., 48,886.....g10 5
St. Pacôme, Que., Can., 1,242.............B8 42
St. Pamphile, Que., Can., 3,542.............C8 42
St. Paris, Ohio, 1,646....B2 78
St. Pascal, Que., Can., 2,513.............B8 42
St. Paul, Alta., Can., 4,161.............B5 38
St. Paul, Minn., 309,866.........E5, n12 67

St. Paul, Nebr., 2,026.....C7 71
St. Paul, Va., 949.........f9 85
St. Paulin, Que., Can., 920...............C4 42
St. Paul Park, Minn., 5,587.........F5, n12 67
St. Pauls, N.C., 2,011....C4 76
St. Peter, Minn., 8,339...F5 67
St. Peter Port, Guernsey, 16,303 (*36,000).....F5 4
St. Petersburg, Fla., 216,159 (*509,300)..E4, p10 54
St. Petersburg Beach, Fla., 8,024.........p10 54
St. Pie, Que., Can., 1,434..D5 42
St. Pierre, Mart., 5,556...I14 35
St. Pierre-Jolys, Man., Can., 856.........E3 40
St. Pierre & Miquelon, Fr. dep., N.A., 5,500....E3 44
St. Pol-de-Léon, Fr., 6,037.............C2 5
St. Pourçain [-sur-Sioule], Fr., 3,182.........D5 5
St. Prosper, Que., Can., 158............*C7 42
St. Quentin, N.B., Can., 2,089.............B2 43
St. Quentin, Fr., 64,196...C5 5
St. Raphaël, Que., Can., 1,134.............C7 42
St. Raphaël, Fr., 9,470....F7 5
St. Raymond, Que., Can., 4,036.............C6 42
St. Rémi, Que., Can., 2,282.........D4, q19 42
St. Romuald, Que., Can., 8,394.........C6, n17 42
Ste. Rosalie, Que., Can., 2,210............*D5 42
Ste. Rose, Que., Can., 7,571............*D4 42
Ste. Rose, Guad., 2,237...H14 35
St. Rose, La., 2,106......k11 63
Ste. Rose-du-Dégelé, Que., Can., 1,943......B9 42
Ste. Rose-du-Lac, Man., Can., 790.........D2 40
Saintes, Fr., 26,507......E3 5
St. Sauveur [-des-Monts], Que., Can., 1,702.....D3 42
Ste. Savine, Fr., 11,622...C5 5
St. Siméon, Que., Can., 1,186.............B8 42
St. Simons Island, Ga., 3,199.............E5 55
St. Stephen, N.B., Can., 3,409 (*5,302).....D2 43
St. Stephen, S.C., 1,506...E8 82
St. Tammany, par., La., 63,585............D5 63
Ste. Thérèse-de-Blainville, Que., Can., 17,175.......D4, p19 42
St. Thomas, Ont., Can., 25,545............E3 41
St. Tite, Que., Can., 3,130.............C5 42
St. Ulric, Que., Can., 1,021...........*k13 42
St. Vincent-de-Paul, Que., Can., 11,214...*D4 42
St. Walburg, Sask., Can., 656...............D1 39
St. Yrieix-la-Perche, Fr., 4,368.............E4 5
Saintonge, former prov., Fr., 286,000.......E3 5
Saitama, pref., Jap., 3,866,472...........*I9 18
Sajama, mtn., Bol........C2 29
Saka, China.............C8 20
Sakai, Jap., 594,367.....o14 18
Sakākah, Sau. Ar.........D3 15
Sakania, Zaire, 12,100....C5 24
Sakashita, Jap...........n16 18
Sakata, Jap., 70,000 (96,072 ▲)..........G9 18
Sakchu, Kor., 13,568.....F2 18
Sakhalin, isl., Sov. Un...D17 16
Sakon Nakhon, Thai., 15,997............B2 19
Sakti, India, 10,754.....*D7 20
Sala, Swe., 12,219....H7, t34 11
Sala Consilina, It., 6,897..D5 9
Saladillo, Arg., 13,293....B5 28
Salado, riv., Arg.........A3 28
Salamà, Guat., 2,760....*D7 34
Salamanca, Mex., 61,039...........m13 34
Salamanca, N.Y., 7,877....C2 75
Salamanca, Sp., 122,241...B3 8
Salamanca, prov., Sp., 386,200...........*B3 8
Salamina, Col., 14,263....B2 32
Salamis, Grc., 18,317....D4 14
Salas, Sp., 2,522........A2 8
Salatiga, Indon., 69,831..*G4 19

Sal-San 181

Salavat, Sov. Un., 114,000 . *D8 13
Salaverry, Peru, 3,403 ..... C2 31
Salcedo, Ec., 3,442 ..... B2 31
Saldanha, S. Afr., 4,916 .. G3 24
Saldus, Sov. Un., 10,000 .. C4 12
Sale, Austl., 10,404 ..... I6 26
Salé, Mor., 155,557 ..... B3 22
Salekhard, Sov. Un., 22,000 ..... C9 13
Salem, Ill., 6,187 ..... E5 58
Salem, India, 308,716 ..... F6 20
Salem, Ind., 5,041 ..... G5 59
Salem, Mass., 40,556 .. A6, f12 65
Salem, Mo., 4,363 ..... D6 69
Salem, N.H., 10,000 ..... F5 73
Salem, N.J., 7,648 ..... D2 74
Salem, N.Y., 1,025 ..... B7 75
Salem, Ohio, 14,186 ..... B5 78
Salem, Oreg., 68,480 (*141,300) C4, k12 80
Salem, S. Dak., 1,391 ..... G8 77
Salem, Utah, 1,081 ..... D2 72
Salem, Va. (Independent City), 21,982 ..... C2 85
Salem, W. Va., 2,597 .. B4, k9 87
Salem, co., N.J., 60,346 .... D2 74
Salem Depot, N.H F5 73
Salem Heights, Oreg *C4 80
Salemi, It., 13,300 ..... F4 9
Salerno, It., 148,100 (*220,000) D5 9
Salford, Eng., 131,330 ..... D5 4
Salgótarján, Hung., 37,212 . A4 10
Salida, Calif., 1,109 ..... *D3 50
Salida, Colo., 4,355 ..... C5 51
Salies-de-Béarn, Fr., 2,859 ..... F3 5
Salihli, Tur., 34,478 ..... *C7 14
Salin, Bur., 5,000 ..... *D9 20
Salina, Kans., 37,714 (*41,300) D6 61
Salina, Okla., 1,024 ..... A6 79
Salina, Utah, 1,494 ..... B6 72
Salinas, Calif., 58,896 (*78,200) D3 50
Salinas, P.R., 3,666 ..... *G11 35
Salina Springs, Ariz A4 48
Saline, Mich., 4,811 ..... F7 66
Saline, co., Ark., 36,107 ... C3 49
Saline, co., Ill., 25,721 .... F5 58
Saline, co., Kans., 46,592 .. D6 61
Saline, co., Mo., 24,837 .... B4 69
Saline, co., Nebr., 12,809 .. D8 71
Salineville, Ohio, 1,686 .... B5 78
Salisbury, Eng., 35,500 .... E6 4
Salisbury, Md., 15,252 .... D6 53
Salisbury, Mass., 1,500 .... A6 65
Salisbury, Mo., 1,960 ..... B5 69
Salisbury, N.C., 22,515 (*54,700) B2 76
Salisbury, Rh., 210,000 (*380,000) D6 24
Salisbury West, N.C *B2 76
Sallisaw, Okla., 4,888 ..... B7 79
Salmon, Idaho, 2,910 ..... D5 57
Salmon Arm, B.C., Can., 1,981 ..... D8 37
Salmon Falls, N.H E6 73
Salo, Fin., 11,000 ..... G10 11
Salon-de-Provence, Fr., 25,174 ..... F6 5
Salonta, Rom., 16,276 ..... B5 10
Salsk, Sov. Un., 50,000 ... H13 12
Salsomaggiore, It., 8,600 ... B2 9
Salta, Arg., 172,000 ..... D2 29
Salta, prov., Arg., 412,854 . D2 29
Saltillo, Mex., 161,114 ..... B4 34
Salt Lake, co., Utah, 458,607 ..... A5 72
Salt Lake City, Utah, 175,885 (502,900) ... A6, C2 72
Salto, Braz., 19,060 ..... m8 30
Salto, Ur., 57,714 ..... E1 30
Salto, dept., Ur., 92,216 .. *E1 30
Saltpond, Ghana, 9,900 ... G4 22
Salt River, Ky., 400 ..... C4 62
Saltsburg, Pa., 1,037 ..... F3 81
Salt Springs, Fla., 900 .... C5 54
Saltville, Va., 2,527 ..... f10 85
Saluda, S.C., 2,442 ..... D4 82
Saluda, co., S.C., 14,528 ... C4 82
Saluda Gardens, S.C *D5 82
Sālūr, India, 30,929 ..... E7 20
Saluzzo, It., 11,100 ..... B1 9
Salvador, Braz., 1,007,744 (*1,020,000) E7 27
Salvatierra, Mex., 18,975 ..... m13 34
Salween, riv., Asia D10 20
Salyersville, Ky., 1,196 .... C6 62
Salzburg, Aus., 127,455 (*150,000) E6 6
Salzburg, state, Aus., 388,600 ..... E6 6
Salzgitter, Ger., Fed. Rep. of, 117,640 ..... B5 6
Salzwedel, Ger. Dem. Rep., 20,890 ..... B5 6
Samani, Jap E11 18
Samaniego, Col., 3,181 .... C2 32
Samar, prov., Phil., 867,994 ..... C7 19
Samar, isl., Phil C7 19
Samarinda, Indon., 137,521 ..... F5 19
Samarkand, Sov. Un., 267,000 ..... F9 13
Sāmarrā', Iraq, 24,746 .... E14 14
Sambalpur, India, 64,675 .. D7 20
Sambas, Indon., 12,000 .... E3 19
Sambhal, India, 86,323 ... *C6 20
Sambor, Sov. Un., 29,000 . G4 12
Samchŏk, Kor., 28,500 (38,815 ▲) H4 18
Samchonpo, Kor., 33,000 (54,945 ▲) I4 18
Samokov, Bul., 21,611 ..... D6 10
Samos, prov., Grc., 41,687 ..... *D6 14
Samoset, Fla., 4,070 ..... q10 54
Sampson, co., N.C., 44,954 ..... B4 76
Samson, Ala., 2,257 ..... D3 46
Samsun, Tur., 134,061 .... B11 14
Samtown, La., 3,750 ..... *C3 63
San'ā', Yemen, 89,000 ..... F3 15
San Agustín, Col., 3,250 .. C2 32
Sanandaj, Iran, 54,748 .... B4 15
San Andreas, Calif., 1,800 .. C3 50
San Andrés de Giles, Arg., 5,392 ..... g7 28
San Andrés Tuxtla, Mex., 24,267 ..... D5 34
San Angelo, Tex., 63,884 (*65,900) D2 84
San Anselmo, Calif., 13,031 ..... h7 50
San Antonio, Chile, 26,917 . A2 28
San Antonio, Tex., 654,153 (*835,200) ... E3, k7 84
San Antonio de Areco, Arg., 9,249 ..... g7 28
San Antonio de los Baños, Cuba, 25,300 (30,000 ▲) . C2 35
San Antonio Heights, Calif., 2,000 ..... *E5 50
San Augustine, Tex., 2,539 ..... D5 84
San Augustine, co., Tex., 7,858 ..... D5 84
San Bartolomeo [in Galdo], It., 8,767 .... D5 9
San Benedetto del Tronto, It., 35,600 ..... C4 9
San Benito, Tex., 15,176 ... F4 84
San Benito, co., Calif., 18,226 ..... D3 50
San Bernardino, Calif., 104,251 (*577,000) . E5, m14 50
San Bernardino, co., Calif., 682,233 ..... E5 50
San Bernardo, Chile, 45,207 ..... A2 28
Sanborn, Iowa, 1,456 ..... A2 60
Sanborn, co., S. Dak., 3,697 ..... G7 77
San Bruno, Calif., 36,254 ..... D2, h8 50
San Carlos, Arg., 809 ..... C2 28
San Carlos, Calif., 26,053 .. k8 50
San Carlos, Chile, 16,097 ... B2 28
San Carlos, Phil., 23,633 (90,058 ▲) o13 19
San Carlos, Ur., 13,695 .... E2 30
San Carlos [de Bariloche], Arg., 23,000 ..... C2 28
San Cataldo, It., 22,500 ... F4 9
Sanch'ung, Tai., 166,300 .. *G9 17
San Clemente, Calif., 17,063 ..... F5 50
San Clemente, Sp., 6,948 .. C4 8
San Cristóbal, Dom. Rep., 25,800 ..... E8 35
San Cristóbal, Ven., 152,239 ..... B3 32
San Cristóbal Las Casas, Mex., 25,700 ..... D6 34
Sancti-Spíritus, Cuba, 57,700 (66,500 ▲) D4 35
Sanda, Jap., 33,090 ..... o14 18
Sandakan, Mala., 42,413 .. D5 19
Sandefjord, Nor., 7,000 ... p28 11
Sanders, co., Mont., 7,093 .. C1 70
Sandersville, Ga., 5,546 ... D4 55
Sandia, Peru, 1,482 ..... D4 31
San Diego, Calif., 697,027 (*1,206,800) F5, o15 50
San Diego, Tex., 4,490 .... F3 84
San Diego, co., Calif., 1,357,854 ..... F5 50
Sandikli, Tur., 11,056 ..... C8 14
Sandīla, India, 22,365 ..... C7 20
San Dimas, Calif., 15,692 .. *F4 50
Sandoa, Zaire B4 24
Sandomierz, Pol., 16,800 ... C6 7
Sandoná, Col., 6,776 ..... C2 32
San Donà di Piave, It., 18,500 ..... B4 9
Sandoval, Ill., 1,332 ..... E4 58
Sandoval, co., N. Mex., 17,492 ..... B5 48
Sandpoint, Idaho, 4,144 .... A2 57
Sandspit, B.C., Can., 466 .. C2 37
Sands Point, N.Y., 2,916 .. *G2 52
Sand Springs, Okla., 10,565 ..... A5 79
Sandstone, Minn., 1,641 ... D6 67
Sandusky, Mich., 2,071 .... E8 66
Sandusky, Ohio, 32,674 .... A3 78
Sandusky, co., Ohio, 60,983 ..... A2 78
Sandusky South, Ohio, 4,724 ..... *A3 78
Sandviken, Swe., 43,489 ... G7 11
Sandwich, Ill., 5,056 ..... B5 58
Sandwich, Mass., 1,305 .... C7 65
Sandy, Oreg., 1,544 ..... B4 80
Sandy, Pa., 2,000 ..... *D4 81
Sandy, Utah, 6,438 ..... D2 72
Sandy Beach, N.Y., 1,691 . *C2 75
Sandy Hook, Conn., 900 .. D3 52
Sandy Springs, Ga., 16,000 ..... h8 55
San Elizario, Tex., 950 .... o11 84
San Estanislao, Par., 10,948 ..... D4 29
San Felipe, Chile, 19,048 ... A2 28
San Felipe, N. Mex., 1,187 ..... B5, D6 48
San Felipe, Ven., 43,801 ... A4 32
San Felipe de Jesus, Mex., 59,932 ..... *D5 34
San Felíu de Guixols, Sp., 10,307 ..... B7 8
San Fernando, Arg., 119,565 ..... A5, g7 28
San Fernando, Calif., 16,571 ..... m12 50
San Fernando, Chile, 21,774 ..... A2 28
San Fernando, Phil., 11,084 ..... B6, n13 19
San Fernando, Phil., 33,335 ..... o13 19
San Fernando, Sp., 57,235 ..... D2 8
San Fernando, Trin., 37,313 (*68,000) A5 32
San Fernando de Apure, Ven., 38,960 ..... B4 32
San Fernando de Atabapo, Ven., 898 ..... C4 32
Sanford, Fla.,17,393 ..... D5 54
Sanford, Maine, 10,457 .... E4 64
Sanford, N.C., 11,716 ..... B3 76
San Francisco, Arg., 44,000 ..... A4 28
San Francisco, Calif., 715,674 (*4,274,800) D2, h8 50
San Francisco, Col., 1,248 ..... C2 32
San Francisco del Oro, Mex., 12,116 ..... B3 34
San Francisco del Rincón, Mex., 27,079 ..... m13 34
San Francisco de Macorís, Dom. Rep., 43,900 ..... E8 35
San Gabriel, Calif., 29,336 ..... m12 50
San Gabriel, Ec., 6,803 .... A2 31
San Gabriel Chilac, Mex., 6,707 ..... D5, n15 34
Sangamon, co., Ill., 161,335 ..... D4 58
Sanger, Calif., 10,088 ..... D4 50
Sanger, Tex., 1,603 ..... C4 84
Sangerhausen, Ger. Dem. Rep., 32,084 ..... C5 6
San Germán, P.R., 11,613 (27,990 ▲) *G11 35
San Gil, Col., 18,518 ..... B3 32
San Giovanni in Fiore, It., 17,400 ..... E6 9
Sangju, Kor., 28,000 (52,504 ▲) H4 18
Sāngli, India, 115,138 (*201,597) *E5 20
San Gorgonio, mtn., Calif E5 50
San Ignacio, Par., 6,116 ... E4 29
Sanilac, co., Mich., 35,181 ..... E8 66
San Isidro, Arg., 250,008 ... g7 28
San Jacinto, Calif., 4,385 ... F5 50
San Jacinto, co., Tex., 6,702 ..... D5 84
San Javier, Chile, 8,500 .... B2 28
Sanjo, Jap., 77,814 ..... H9 18
San Joaquin, co., Calif., 291,073 ..... C3 50
San Jose, Ariz., 100 ..... C4 48
San Jose, Calif., 446,537 ..... D3, k9 50
San José, C.R., 201,100 (*385,000) F8 34
San Jose, Ill., 681 ..... C4 58
San José, Ur., 21,200 ..... E1 30
San José, dept., Ur., 77,300 ..... *E1 30
San José, prov., C.R., 563,800 ..... *F8 34
San José de Feliciano, Arg., 3,721 ..... A5 28
San José de los Molinos, Peru, 1,221 ..... D2 31
San Juan, Arg., 112,500 (*210,000) A3 28
San Juan, Colo., 100 ..... D6 51
San Juan, Dom. Rep., 32,200 ..... E8 35
San Juan, P.R., 452,749 (*936,693) *G11 35
San Juan, Tex., 5,070 ..... G2 84
San Juan, co., Colo., 831 .. D3 51
San Juan, co., N. Mex., 52,517 ..... A4 48
San Juan, co., Utah, 9,606 ..... C6 72
San Juan, co., Wash., 3,856 ..... A2 86
San Juan, prov., Arg., 352,387 ..... A3 28
San Juan Bautista, Calif., 1,164 ..... *D3 50
San Juan Bautista, Par., 6,457 ..... E4 29
San Juan Capistrano, Calif., 3,781 ..... F5 50
San Juan de los Lagos, Mex., 19,570 ..... m12 34
San Juan de los Morros, Ven., 37,817 ..... B4 32
San Juan del Río, Mex., 15,422 ..... m13 34
San Julián, Arg., 3,649 .... D3 28
San Justo, Arg., 659,193 .. *B5 28
S[ank]t Gallen, Switz., 80,500 (*114,000) E4 6
Sankt Gallen, canton, Switz., 381,000 ..... *E4 6
Sankt Pölten, Aus., 50,144 ..... D7 6
Sankt Veit an der Glan, Aus., 11,058 ..... E7 6
San Leandro, Calif., 68,698 ..... h8 50
San Lorenzo, Arg., 28,000 .. A4 28
San Lorenzo, Calif., 27,000 ..... *D2 50
San Lorenzo, P.R., 7,702 (27,755 ▲) *G12 35
San Lorenzo del Escorial, Sp., 7,965 .. B3, o16 8
Sanlúcar, Sp., 32,580 (40,335 ▲) D2 8
San Luis, Arg., 50,000 ..... A3 28
San Luis, Colo., 781 ..... D5 51
San Luis, Cuba, 17,400 (35,000 ▲) D6 35
San Luis, prov., Arg., 174,316 ..... A3 28
San Luis de la Paz, Mex., 12,654 ..... m13 34
San Luis Obispo, Calif., 28,036 ..... E3 50
San Luis Obispo, co., Calif., 105,690 ..... E3 50
San Luis Potosí, Mex., 230,039 ..... C4, k13 34
San Luis Potosí, state, Mex., 1,145,900 .... C4, k13 34
San Manuel, Ariz., 4,332 ..... *C3 48
San Marco [in Lamis], It., 19,014 ..... D5 9
San Marcos, Tex., 18,860 ..... E4, h8 84
San Marino, Calif., 14,177 ..... m12 50
San Marino, country, Eur., 20,000 ..... C4 9
San Martín, Arg., 26,000 .. A3 28
San Martín (General San Martín), Arg., 278,751 ..... g7 28
San Martin, Calif., 1,162 ..... *D3 50
San Martín, dept., Peru, 120,913 ..... C2 31
San Mateo, Calif., 78,991 .. h8 50
San Mateo, Ven., 1,849 .... B5 32
San Mateo, co., Calif., 556,605 ..... D2 50
San Miguel, Sal., 59,304 ... E7 34
San Miguel, co., Colo., 1,949 ..... D2 51
San Miguel, co., N. Mex., 21,951 ..... B6 48
San Miguel de Allende, Mex., 24,286 ..... m13 34

San Miguel del Padrón,
Cuba, 156,200........*C2 35
San Miguel de Tucumán,
Arg., 310,000........F4 27
San Nicolás, Arg., 49,082..A4 28
San Nicolás Totolapan,
Mex., 7,110............h9 34
Sannois, Fr., 19,060.....g10 5
Sano, Jap., 71,573....m18 18
Sanok, Pol., 21,600....D7 7
San Onofre, Col., 10,737..B2 32
San Pablo, Calif., 21,461..*D2 50
San Patricio, co., Tex.,
47,288.............E4 84
San Pedro, Arg., 15,354...D3 29
San Pedro, Arg.,
19,000...........A5, f7 28
San Pedro, Par., 16,691...D4 29
San Pedro, Tex., 5,294...*F4 84
San Pedro, dept., Par.,
91,804............D4 29
San Pedro de las Colonias,
Mex., 26,882..........B4 34
San Pedro de Lloc, Peru,
5,286.............C2 31
San Pedro de Macorís,
Dom. Rep., 42,500......E9 35
San Pedro Mártir, mts.,
Mex.............A1 34
San Pedro Sula, Hond.,
58,632.............D7 34
Sanpete, co., Utah,
10,976.............B6 72
San Rafael, Arg., 54,000...A3 28
San Rafael, Calif.,
38,977.........D2, h7 50
San Rafael, mts., Calif....E4 50
San Ramon, Peru, 1,275...D2 31
San Ramon, Ur., 5,672....g9 28
San Remo, It., 50,000....C1 9
San Roque, Sp., 13,676...D3 8
San Saba, Tex., 2,555...D3 84
San Saba, co., Tex.,
5,540.............D3 84
San Salvador, Sal.,
337,171 (*600,000)......E7 34
San Salvador de Jujuy,
Arg., 67,000..........F4 27
San Sebastián, P.R.,
7,169 (30,157 ▲)....*G11 35
San Sebastián, Sp.,
161,293 (*240,000).....A4 8
San Sepolcro, It., 7,242...C4 9
San Severo, It., 52,500....D5 9
Sansom Park Village,
Tex., 4,771..........*C4 84
Sans Souci, S.C., 4,500...*B3 82
Santa, Peru, 1,089.......C2 31
Santa Ana, Calif.,
156,601.........F5, n13 50
Santa Ana, Mex., 7,020...A2 34
Santa Ana, Sal., 96,306...E7 34
Santa Ana, mts., Calif....n13 50
Santa Anita, Mex.,
19,433.............h9 34
Santa Anna, Tex., 1,310...D3 84
Santa Bárbara d'Oeste,
Braz., 22,358.........m8 30
Santa Barbara, Calif.,
70,215 (*148,700)......E4 50
Santa Bárbara, Mex.,
16,978.............B3 34
Santa Barbara, co., Calif.,
264,324............E3 50
Santa Catalina, isl.,
Calif.............F4 50
Santa Catarina, state,
Braz., 2,930,411.......D2 30
Santa Clara, Calif.,
87,839.........D2, k9 50
Santa Clara, Cuba,
131,500 (154,500 ▲).....C4 35
Santa Clara, Ur., 2,499...E2 30
Santa Clara, co., Calif.,
1,066,932...........D3 50
Santa Cruz, Bol., 85,600...C3 29
Santa Cruz, Calif.,
32,076.............D2 50
Santa, Cruz, C.R., 3,849...E7 34
Santa Cruz, co., Ariz.,
13,966.............D3 48
Santa Cruz, co., Calif.,
123,790............D2 50
Santa Cruz, prov., Arg.,
52,908.............D3 28
Santa Cruz de la Palma,
Sp., 8,835.........m13 8
Santa Cruz de la Zarza,
Sp., 5,588..........C4 8
Santa Cruz del Sur,
Cuba, 10,800........D5 35
Santa Cruz de Tenerife,
Sp., 142,305........m13 8
Santa Cruz de Tenerife,
prov., Sp., 583,200...*m13 8
Santa Cruz do Rio Pardo,
Braz., 16,252........C3 30

Santa Cruz do Sul., Braz.,
30,496............D2 30
Santa Elena, Tex., 75....F3 84
Santa Eugenia [de
Ribeira], Sp., 4,543....A1 8
Santa Eulalia del Río,
Sp., 7,564..........C6 8
Santa Fe, Arg., 245,000...A4 28
Santa Fé, Cuba, (part of
Havana)............D2 35
Santa Fe, Mex., 9,430....h9 34
Santa Fe, N. Mex.,
41,167.........B6, D6 48
Santafé, Sp., 8,387......D4 8
Santa Fe, co., N. Mex.,
53,756............B5 48
Santa Fe, prov., Arg.,
1,884,918...........A4 28
Santa Fe Springs, Calif.,
14,750.............F4 50
Santai, China, 24,000....E6 17
Santa Inés Ahuatempan,
Mex., 3,657.........n14 34
Santa Isabel, P.R.,
4,712............*G11 35
Santa Lucía, Cuba,
3,700 (30,100 ▲)......D6 35
Santa Lucia, Ur., 12,647...E1 30
Santa Margarita, Calif.,
950.............E3 50
Santa Maria, Braz.,
120,667............D2 30
Santa Maria, Calif.,
32,749.............E3 50
Santa Maria [Capua
Vetere], It., 31,500.....D5 9
Santa Maria Colotepec,
Mex., 1,012.........D5 34
Santa María del Oro,
Mex., 4,231.........B3 34
Santa Marta, Col.,
129,200............A3 32
Santa Marta, Sp., 5,142...C2 8
Santa Monica, Calif.,
88,349............m12 50
Santana, Port., 4,953....h12 8
Santana do Livramento,
Braz., 48,448........E1 30
Santander, Col., 11,426...C2 32
Santander, Sp., 148,845...A4 8
Santander, dept., Col.,
1,087,500...........B3 32
Santander, prov., Sp.,
462,000...........*A4 8
Santanoni, peak, N.Y....A6 75
Santañy, Sp., 6,295.....C7 8
Santa Paula, Calif.,
18,001.............E4 50
Santaquin, Utah, 1,236...B6 72
Santarém, Braz., 51,123...D5 27
Santarém, Port., 16,449...C1 8
Santa Rita, Braz., 29,794.*D7 27
Santa Rita, Guam, 1,630..*F6 2
Santa Rita, N. Mex., 300..C4 48
Santa Rosa, Arg., 35,000...B4 28
Santa Rosa, Calif., 50,006
(*118,200)..........C2 50
Santa Rosa, N. Mex.,
1,813.............B6 48
Santa Rosa, co., Fla.,
37,741............G2 54
Santa Rosa de Copán,
Hond., 7,946.......*E7 34
Santa Rosa, de Osos,
Col., 6,860.........B2 32
Santa Rosalia, Mex.,
7,356.............B2 34
Santa Susana, Calif....*E4 50
Santa Tomé de Guayana,
Ven., 75,000........B5 32
Santa Úrsula Coapa,
Mex., 6,813.........h9 34
Santa Venetia, Calif.,
4,000............*D2 50
Santa Vitória do Palmar,
Braz., 10,879........E2 30
Santee, Calif., 9,000....o16 50
Santiago, Braz., 22,055...D2 30
Santiago, Chile, 510,246
(*2,900,000)........A2 28
Santiago, Dom. Rep.,
155,200............E8 35
Santiago, Mex., 877.....C3 34
Santiago, Pan., 14,595....B1 32
Santiago, Par., 7,834....E4 29
Santiago, Sp., 46,000....A1 8
Santiago, prov., Chile,
3,038,400...........A2 28
Santiago, mts., Tex.....D1 84
Santiago, peak, Calif....n14 50
Santiago, peak, Tex....p13 84
Santiago de Cao, Peru,
957.............C2 31
Santiago de Cuba, Cuba,
276,000............D6 35
Santiago del Estero, Arg.,
105,000 (*135,000)....E3 29

Santiago del Estero, prov.,
Arg., 476,503........E3 29
Santiago Ixcuintla,
Mex., 17,321.....C3, m11 34
Santiago Tepalcatlalpan,
Mex., 5,773.........h9 34
Santisteban, del Puerto,
Sp., 8,678..........C4 8
Santo Amaro, Braz.,
20,767............*E7 27
Santo Andre, Braz.,
230,196...........*m8 30
Santo Ângelo, Braz.,
36,020............D2 30
Santo Antônio, Braz.,
3,731............*E7 27
Santo Domingo, Dom.
Rep., 671,400........E9 35
Santo Domingo Pueblo,
N. Mex., 900........B5 48
San Tomas, Calif.......*D3 50
Santoña, Sp., 9,082.....A4 8
Santos, Braz., 341,317
(*610,000).........C3, m8 30
Santos Dumont, Braz.,
27,004..........C4, g6 30
Santo Tomás, Peru, 877..D3 31
Santo Tomas, Ven., 100...B5 32
Santo Tomé de Guayana,
Ven., 75,000........B5 22
San Valentín, mtn.,
Chile.............H3 27
San Vicente, Sal., 18,872..E7 34
San Vicente de Alcántara,
Sp., 8,212..........C2 8
San Vincente del Caguán,
Col., 1,764.........C3 32
San Vito al Tagliamento,
It., 5,065..........B4 9
San Ygnacio, Tex., 800...F3 84
São Bernardo [do
Campo], Braz.,
187,368.........C3, m8 30
São Borja, Braz., 28,875..D1 30
São Carlos, Braz.,
74,835..........C3, m8 30
São Caetano do Sul, Braz.,
150,171...........*m8 30
São Cristovão, Braz.,
10,168............*E7 27
São Francisco, riv.,
Braz.............A4 30
São Francisco do Sul,
Braz., 12,868........D3 30
São Gabriel, Braz.,
27,685............E2 30
São João da Boa Vista,
Braz., 33,051.......C3, k8 30
São João del Rei, Braz.,
45,019..........C4, g5 30
São Joao de Meriti, Braz.,
163,934...........*h6 30
São José do Rio Pardo,
Braz., 16,425........k8 30
São José do Rio Prêto,
Braz., 108,319........C3 30
São José dos Campos,
Braz., 130,118.....C3, m9 30
São Leopoldo, Braz.
62,861............D2 30
São Lourenço, Braz.,
18,124............C3 30
São Luís, Braz., 167,529...D6 27
São Luís Gonzaga, Braz.,
17,131............D2 30
São Manuel, Braz.,
12,756.........C3, m7 30
Saône-et-Loire, dept.,
Fr., 550,362........*D6 5
São Paulo, Braz., 5,921,796
(*8,050,000)......C3, m8 30
São Paulo, state, Braz.,
17,958,693........C3, m8 30
São Roque, Braz., 16,474..m8 30
São Sebastião do Paraíso,
Braz., 19,037........C3 30
São Tomé, São Tomé &
Principe, 17,380......H6 22
Sao Tome & Principe,
country, Afr., 77,000...H5 22
São Vicente, Braz.,
116,075............C3 30
São Vicente, Port., 6,663..h11 8
Sapai, Grc., 2,456......B5 14
Sapele, Nig., 61,007.....G6 22
Saposoa, Peru, 3,243....C2 31
Sapozhok, Sov. Un.,
10,000............E13 12
Sapphire, mts., Mont.....D3 70
Sappington, Mo., 10,603..f13 69
Sapporo, Jap., 1,130,828..E10 18
Sapri, It., 6,188........D5 9
Sapulpa, Okla., 15,159...B5 79
Sara Buri, Thai., 18,861..*C2 19
Sarah, Miss., 100.......A3 68
Sarajevo, Yugo.,
244,045............D4 10

Sara Kaeo, Thai.......*C2 19
Saraland, Ala., 7,840.....E1 46
Saranac, Mich., 1,223....F5 66
Saranac, N.Y., 600.....f11 75
Saranac Lake, N.Y.,
6,086.............B3 75
Saranap, Calif........*D2 50
Sarandí del Yí, Ur.,
4,437.............E1 30
Sarandi Grande, Ur.,
4,539.............E1 30
Saransk, Sov. Un.,
191,000............D15 12
Sarapul, Sov. Un.,
97,000............D8 12
Sarasota, Fla., 40,237
(*187,800).......E4, q10 54
Sarasota, co., Fla.,
120,413............E4 54
Saratoga, Calif., 27,110...*D3 50
Saratoga, Tex., 900.....D5 84
Saratoga, Wyo., 1,181...E6 89
Saratoga, co., N.Y.,
121,674............B7 75
Saratoga Place, Va.....*D6 85
Saratoga Springs, N.Y.,
18,845.............B7 75
Saratov, Sov. Un.,
757,000 (*935,000)....F15 12
Saravane, Laos, 25,000..*B3 19
Sarawak, reg., Mala.,
1,065,000...........E4 19
Sarayköy, Tur., 8,925....D7 14
Sarcelles, Fr., 51,674....g10 5
Sarcoxie, Mo., 1,175....D3 69
Sardegna, pol. dist., It.,
1,419,362..........*E2 9
Sardinia, Ohio, 824......C2 78
Sardinia, isl., It........D2 9
Sardis, Ala., 368.......C3 46
Sardis, B.C., Can., 898...f14 37
Sardis, Miss., 2,391.....A4 68
Sardis, Ohio, 500......C5 78
Sarepta, La., 882.......B2 63
Sargent, Nebr., 789.....C6 71
Sargent, co., N. Dak.,
5,937.............D8 77
Sargodha, Pak., 83,141
(*129,291).........*B5 20
Sarh, Chad, 35,000.....G1 23
Sarikamiş, Tur., 20,343..B14 14
Sarina, Austl., 2,516....D8 25
Sariwon, Kor., 42,957...G2 18
Sarlat, Fr., 5,251......E4 5
Sarmiento, mtn., Chile...I3 27
Sarnia, Ont., Can.,
57,644 (*78,444).....E2 41
Sarny, Sov. Un., 15,000...F6 12
Saronno, It., 30,900.....B2 9
Sárospatak, Hung., 14,173.A5 10
Sarpsborg, Nor., 13,100
(*35,000)..........p29 11
Sarpy, co., Nebr., 66,200..C9 71
Sarreguemines, Fr.,
17,866............C7 5
Sartell, Minn., 1,323.....E4 67
Sartène, Fr., 4,067.......D2 9
Sarthe, dept., Fr.,
461,839...........*D4 5
Sartrouville, Fr., 40,277...g9 5
Sárvár, Hung., 12,721....B3 10
Sarzana, It., 9,082......B2 9
Sāsarām, India, 48,282...D7 20
Sasebo, Jap., 247,898....J4 18
Saskatchewan, prov., Can.,
915,000...........39
Saskatchewan, riv., Can..F13 36
Saskatoon, Sask., Can.,
126,449.........E2, n7 39
Sasovo, Sov. Un.,
27,000............D13 12
Sassafras, mtn., S.C....A2 82
Sassari, It., 89,100
(105,000 ▲).........D2 9
Satah, mtn., B.C., Can....C5 37
Satanta, Kans., 1,161....E3 61
Saticoy, Calif., 2,250....E4 50
Satka, Sov. Un., 44,000...D8 13
Sátoraljaújhely, Hung.,
17,000............A5 10
Satsuma, Ala., 2,035.....E1 46
Sattahip, Thai., 4,478...*C2 19
Satu-Mare, Rom., 68,300..B6 10
Saucillo, Mex., 8,467....B3 34
Sauda, Nor., 5,723......H2 11
Saudi Arabia, country,
Asia, 8,530,000......D3 15
Saugatuck, Mich., 1,022..F4 66
Saugerties, N.Y., 4,190...C7 75
Saugus, Mass.,
25,110..........B5, g11 65
Sauk, co., Wis., 39,057...E4 88
Sauk Centre, Minn.,
3,750.............E4 67
Sauk City, Wis., 2,385...E4 88
Sauk Rapids, Minn.,
5,051.............E4 67

Sauk Village, Ill., 7,479...*B6 58
Saukville, Wis., 1,389...E6 88
Sault-au-Mouton, Que., Can., 876...A8 42
Sault Ste. Marie, Mich., 15,136...B6 66
Sault Ste. Marie, Ont., Can., 80,332 (*81,270) . p18 41
Saumur, Fr., 21,551 (*33,000)...D4 5
Saunders, co., Nebr., 17,018...C9 71
Sauquoit, N.Y., 2,100...*B5 75
Sausalito, Calif., 6,158...D2, h8 50
Sava, Yugo...C4 10
Savage, Md., 2,116...B4 53
Savage, Minn., 3,611...F5, n11 67
Savanna, Ill., 4,942...A3 58
Savanna, Okla., 948...C6 79
Savanna-la-Mar, Jam., 12,000...E4 35
Savannah, Ga., 118,349 (*193,400)...D5 55
Savannah, Mo., 3,324...B3 69
Savannah, N.Y., 636...B4 75
Savannah, Tenn., 5,576...B3 83
Savannah Beach, Ga., 1,786...D6 55
Saveni, Rom., 6,470...B8 10
Saverne, Fr., 9,682...C7 5
Savigliano, It., 14,800...B1 9
Savoie, dept., Fr., 288,921...*F3 5
Savona, B.C., Can., 532...D7 37
Savona, It., 78,200 (*114,000)...B2 9
Savona, N.Y., 933...C3 75
Savonlinna, Fin., 18,259..G13 11
Savoy (Savoie), former prov., Fr...E7 5
Savran, Sov. Un., 10,000..G8 12
Sawahlunto, Indon., 12,427...F2 19
Sawakin, Sud., 4,228...E5 23
Sawan Khalok, Thai., 7,873...B1 19
Sawbill Landing, Minn., 30...C7 67
Sawhāj, Eg., 74,753...C4 23
Sawtooth, mts., Idaho...E3 57
Sawyer, Mich., 500...G4 66
Sawyer, co., Wis., 9,670...C2 88
Sawyerville, Que., Can., 789...D6 42
Sawyerwood, Ohio, 3,000...*A4 78
Saxapahaw, N.C., 600...B3 78
Saxis, Va., 451...C7 85
Saxon, S.C., 1,100...B4 82
Saxony, reg., Ger. Dem. Rep...C6 6
Saxonburg, Pa., 1,191...E2 81
Saxton, Pa., 858...F5 81
Sayabec, Que., Can., 1,789...*G19 36
Sayán, Peru, 1,229...D2 31
Saybrook, Ill., 814...C5 58
Sahyūt, P.D.R. of Yem...F5 15
Sayre, Ala., 350...B3 46
Sayre, Okla., 2,712... B2 79
Sayre, Pa., 7,473...C9 81
Sayreton, Ala., 550...B3, f7 46
Sayreville, N.J., 32,508...C4 74
Sayula, Mex., 14,339...D4, n12 34
Sayville, N.Y., 15,300...G4 52
Scafell Pikes, mtn., Eng...C4 4
Scalp Level, Pa., 1,353...F4 81
Scandia, Kans., 567...C6 61
Scanlon, Minn., 1,132...D6 67
Scansano, It., 8,560...C3 9
Scapegoat, mtn., Mont...C4 70
Scappoose, Oreg., 1,859...B4 80
Scarboro, Maine, 800 (7,845 ▲)...E2, g7 64
Scarborough, Ont., Can., 334,310...m15 41
Scarborough, Eng., 43,070...C6 4
Scarborough, Trin., 1,931.K14 35
Scarbro, W. Va., 400...n13 87
Scarsdale, N.Y., 19,229...h13 75
Sceaux, Fr., 19,913...g10 5
Schaefferstown, Pa., 800...F9 81
Schaerbeek, Bel., 118,570..*B6 5
Schaffhausen, Switz., 36,600 (*56,400)...E4 6
Schaffhausen, canton, Switz., 72,200...*E4 6
Schaghticoke, N.Y., 860...C7 75
Schaller, Iowa, 835...B2 60
Schaumburg, Ill., 18,730...h8 58
Schefferville, Que., Can., 3,271...h13 42
Schenectady, N.Y., 77,958...C7 75
Schenectady, co., N.Y., 161,078...C6 75
Schererville, Ind., 3,663...B3 59
Schertz, Tex., 4,061...h7 84
Schiedam, Neth., 81,202...B6 5
Schiller Park, Ill., 12,712...k9 58
Schiltigheim, Fr., 29,198...C7 5
Schio, It., 32,200...B3 9
Schivelbein, see Swidwin, Pol.
Schleicher, co., Tex., 2,277...D2 84
Schleswig, Ger., Fed. Rep. of, 31,665...A4 6
Schleswig, Iowa, 835...B2 60
Schleswig-Holstein, reg., Ger., Fed. Rep. of...A4 6
Schleswig-Holstein, state, Ger., Fed. Rep. of, 2,545,000...A4 6
Schley, co., Ga., 3,097...D2 55
Schlüchtern, Ger., Fed. Rep. of, 13,188...C4 6
Schmalkalden, Ger. Dem. Rep., 14,968...C5 6
Schneidemuhl, see Pila, Pol.
Schofield, Wis., 2,577...D4 88
Schoharie, N.Y., 1,125...C6 75
Schoharie, co., N.Y., 24,750...C6 75
Schönebeck, Ger. Dem. Rep., 45,661...B5 6
Schongau, Ger., Fed. Rep. of, 10,929...E5 6
Schoolcraft, Mich., 1,277...F5 66
Schoolcraft, co., Mich., 8,092...B4 66
Schooley, mtn., N.J...B3 74
Schramberg, Ger., Fed. Rep. of, 20,133...D4 6
Schram City, Ill., 657...D4 58
Schriever, La., 650...E5, k10 63
Schrobenhausen, Ger., Fed. Rep. of, 11,725...D5 6
Schroon Lake, N.Y., 800...B7 75
Schulenburg, Tex., 2,294...E4 84
Schuyler, Nebr., 3,597...C8 71
Schuyler, co., Ill., 8,135...C3 58
Schuyler, co., Mo., 4,665...A5 69
Schuyler, co., N.Y., 16,737...C4 75
Schuylerville, N.Y., 1,402..B7 75
Schuylkill, co., Pa., 160,089.E9 81
Schuylkill Haven, Pa., 6,125...E9 81
Schwabach, Ger., Fed. Rep. of, 32,024...D5 6
Schwäbisch Gmünd, Ger., Fed. Rep. of, 55,938...D4 6
Schwäbisch Hall, Ger., Fed. Rep. of, 30,502...D4 6
Schwandorf, Ger., Fed. Rep. of, 22,669...D6 6
Schwaner, mts., Indon...F4 19
Schwaz, Aus., 10,264...E5 6
Schwedt, Ger. Dem. Rep., 42,854...B7 6
Schweinfurt, Ger., Fed. Rep. of, 57,154 (*103,000)...C5 6
Schwerin, Ger. Dem. Rep., 102,897...B5 6
Schwyz, Switz., 12,100...E4 6
Schwyz, canton, Switz., 91,000...*E4 6
Sciacca, It., 29,600...F4 9
Scio, Ohio, 1,002...B4 78
Scioto, co., Ohio, 76,951...D2 78
Sciotodale, Ohio, 800...*D2 78
Scituate, Mass., 5,000 (11,214▲)...B6, h13 65
Scobey, Mont., 1,486...B11 70
Scone, Austl., 3,259...F8 26
Scotch Plains, N.J., 22,279...B4 74
Scotia, Calif., 950...B1 50
Scotia, N.Y., 7,370...C7 75
Scotland, Ont., Can., 612..D4 41
Scotland, S. Dak., 984...G8 77
Scotland, co., Mo., 5,499...A5 69
Scotland, co., N.C., 26,929...C3 76
Scotland, reg., U.K., 5,240,000...B4 4
Scotland Neck, N.C., 2,869...A5 76
Scotlandville, La., 24,000...D4, g9 63
Scotstown, Que., Can., 1,038...D6 42
Scott, La., 1,334...D3 63
Scott, co., Ark., 8,207...C1 49
Scott, co., Ill., 6,096...D3 58
Scott, co., Ind., 17,144...G6 59
Scott, co., Iowa, 142,687...C7 60
Scott, co., Kans., 5,606...D3 61
Scott, co., Ky., 17,948...B5 62
Scott, co., Minn., 32,423...F5 67
Scott, co., Miss., 21,369...C4 68
Scott, co., Mo., 33,250...D8 69
Scott, co., Tenn., 14,762...C9 83
Scott, co., Va., 24,376...f9 85
Scott, mtn., Idaho...E3 57
Scott, mtn., Okla...C3 79
Scott, mtn., Oreg...E4 80
Scott, peak, Idaho...E6 57
Scott City, Kans., 4,001...D3 61
Scott City, Mo., 2,464...D8 69
Scottdale, Ga., 9,200...h8 55
Scottdale, Pa., 5,818...F2 81
Scotts, mtn., N.J...B2 74
Scottsbluff, Nebr., 14,507..C2 71
Scotts Bluff, co., Nebr., 36,432...C2 71
Scottsboro, Ala., 9,324...A3 46
Scottsburg, Ind., 4,791...G6 59
Scottsdale, Ariz., 67,823...C3, D2 48
Scottsville, Ky., 3,584...D3 62
Scottsville, N.Y., 1,967...B3 75
Scottville, Mich., 1,202...E4 66
Scranton, Iowa, 875...B3 60
Scranton, Kans., 575...D8 61
Scranton, Pa., 102,696 (*225,500)...D10, m18 81
Scranton, S.C., 732...D8 82
Screven, Ga., 936...E4 55
Screven, co., Ga., 12,591...D5 55
Scribner, Nebr., 1,031...C9 71
Scunthorpe, Eng., 70,480..D6 4
Scurry, co., Tex., 15,760..C2 84
Seaboard, N.C., 611...A5 76
Sea Bright, N.J., 1,339...C5 74
Seabrook, Md., 6,500...*C4 53
Seabrook, N.J., 1,569...E2 74
Seabrook, Tex., 3,811...r14 84
Sea Cliff, N.Y., 5,890...F2 52
Seadrift, Tex., 1,092...E4 84
Seaford, Del., 5,537...C6 53
Seaford, N.Y., 17,379...G3 52
Seaford, Va., 1,200...h15 85
Seaforth, Ont., Can., 2,134...D3 41
Sea Girt, N.J., 2,207...C4 74
Seagoville, Tex., 4,390...n10 84
Seagraves, Tex., 2,440...C1 84
Sea Isle City, N.J., 1,712...E3 74
Seal Beach, Calif., 24,441 .*F5 50
Seal Cove, N.B., Can., 549...E3 43
Sealevel, N.C., 500...C6 76
Sealy, Tex., 2,685...E4 84
Seaman, Ohio, 866...D2 78
Searcy, Ark., 9,040...B4 49
Searcy, co., Ark., 7,731...B3 49
Searsport, Maine, 1,110 (1,951 ▲)...D4 64
Seaside, Calif., 35,935...*D3 50
Seaside, Oreg., 4,402...B3 80
Seaside Heights, N.J., 1,248...D4 74
Seaside Park, N.J., 1,432...D4 74
Seat Pleasant, Md., 7,217...C4, f9 53
Seattle, Wash., 530,831 (*1,816,100)...B3, e11 86
Seaview, Wash., 600...C1 86
Sebastian, Fla., 825...E6 54
Sebastian, co., Ark., 79,237...B1 49
Sebastopol, Calif., 3,993...C2 50
Sebeka, Minn., 668...D3 67
Sebeş, Rom., 11,628...C6 10
Sebewaing, Mich., 2,053...E7 66
Şebinkarahisar, Tur., 10,255...B12 14
Sebnitz, Ger. Dem. Rep., 14,800...C7 6
Sebree, Ky., 1,092...C2 62
Sebring, Fla., 7,223...E5 54
Sebring, Ohio, 4,454...B4 78
Sebringville, Ont., Can., 520...D3 41
Secane, Pa., 4,700...*B11 81
Secaucus, N.J., 13,228...h8 74
Sechura, Peru, 3,826...C1 31
Sector Popular, Mex., 21,258...h9 34
Security, Colo., 8,700...C6 51
Sedalia, Mo., 22,847...C4 69
Sedan, Fr., 23,037...C6 5
Sedan, Kans., 1,555...E7 61
Sedgefield, N.C., 750...*A3 76
Sedgewick, Alta., Can., 655...C5 38
Sedgwick, Kans., 1,083...E6, g12 61
Sedgwick, co., Colo., 3,405...A8 51
Sedgwick, co., Kans., 350,694...E6 61
Sedro Woolley, Wash., 4,598...A3 86
Seekonk, Mass., 11,116...C5 65
Seeley, Calif., 900...F6 50
Seeley Lake, Mont., 500...C3 70
Seelyville, Ind., 1,195...F3 59
Segorbe, Sp., 7,538...C5 8
Ségou, Mali., 30,000...F3 22
Segovia, Sp., 40,816...B3 8
Segovia, prov., Sp., 179,600...*B3 8
Segré, Fr., 5,959...D3 5
Seguin, Tex., 15,934...E4, h8 84
Sehwān, Pak., 3,827...C4 20
Seiling, Okla., 1,033...A3 79
Seinäjoki, Fin., 20,852...F10 11
Seine, dept., Fr., 5,646,446...C5, g1 5
Seine-et-Marne, dept., Fr., 604,340...*C5 5
Seine-et-Oise, dept., Fr., 2,298,931...*C5 5
Seine-Maritime, dept., Fr., 1,113,977...C4 5
Seixal, Port., 4,125...f9 8
Seki, Jap., 49,078...o15 18
Sekondi-Takoradi, Ghana, 110,800 (181,000 ▲)...H4 22
Selah, Wash., 3,311...C5 86
Selangor, state, Mala., 1,276,200...E2 19
Selanovtsi, Bul., 7,259...D7 10
Selb, Ger., Fed. Rep. of, 17,681...C6 6
Selby, S. Dak., 957...E5 77
Selbyville, Del., 1,099...D7 53
Selden, N.Y., 18,000...*E3 75
Sélestat, Fr., 14,635...C7 5
Selidovka, Sov. Un., 10,000...q20 12
Selinsgrove, Pa., 5,116...E8 81
Selkirk, Man., Can., 9,331...D3 40
Selkirk, Scot., 5,694...C5 4
Selkirk, co., Scot., 20,588..*C5 4
Selle, Pic la, peak, Hai...E8 35
Sellersburg, Ind., 3,177...H6 59
Sellersville, Pa., 2,829...F11 81
Selma, Ala., 27,379...C2 46
Selma, Calif., 7,459...D4 50
Selma, Ind., 890...D7 59
Selma, N.C., 4,356...B4 76
Selmer, Tenn., 3,495...B3 83
Selvas, reg., Braz...*D4 27
Selwyn, mtn., B.C., Can...B6 37
Semarang, Indon., 646,590...G4 19
Sembilan, state, Mala., 466,300...*E2 19
Semenovka, Sov. Un., 9,000...E9 12
Semeru, mtn., Indon...G4 19
Seminoe, mts., Wyo...D6 89
Seminole, Ala., 250...E2 46
Seminole, Fla., 22,000...*E4 54
Seminole, Okla., 7,878...B5 79
Seminole, Tex., 5,007...C1 84
Seminole, co., Fla., 83,692...D5 54
Seminole, co., Ga., 7,059...F2 55
Seminole, co., Okla., 25,144...B5 79
Semipalatinsk, Sov. Un., 236,000...D11 13
Semnān, Iran, 31,058...A8 23
Senador Pompeu, Braz., 9,057...*D7 27
Senath, Mo., 1,484...E7 69
Senatobia, Miss., 4,247...A4 68
Sendai, Jap., 545,065 (*690,000)...G10 18
Sendai (Kagoshima, Perf.) Jap., 35,000 (62,374 ▲)..K5 18
Seneca, Ill., 1,781...B5 58
Seneca, Kans., 2,182...C7 61
Seneca, Mo., 1,577...E3 69
Seneca, Pa., 980...D2 81
Seneca, S.C., 6,382...B2 82
Seneca, co., N.Y., 35,083...C4 75
Seneca, co., Ohio, 60,696..A2 78
Seneca Falls, N.Y., 7,794...C4 75
Senegal, country, Afr., 4,265,000...F2 22
Senftenberg, Ger. Dem. Rep., 24,301...C6 6
Senhor do Bonfim, Braz., 21,414...*E7 27
Senigallia, It., 25,100...C4 9
Senlis, Fr., 11,169...C5 5
Senneterre, Que., Can., 4,303...B2 42
Sens, Fr., 23,035...C5 42
Senta, Yugo., 24,714...C5 10
Sentinel, Okla., 984...B2 79
Sentinel, peak, B.C., Can..B6 37
Seoul (Sŏul), Kor., 5,536,377 (*5,900,000)..H3 18
Sept Iles (Seven Islands), Que., Can., 24,320...h13 42

Sequatchie, co., Tenn., 6,331 . . . D8 83
Sequim, Wash., 1,549 . . . A2 86
Sequoia, Calif. . . . D4 50
Sequoyah, co., Okla., 23,370 . . . B7 79
Serafimovich, Sov. Un., 8,800 . . . G14 12
Seraing, Bel., 40,885 . . . B6 5
Serampore, India, 102,023 . . . *D8 20
Serang, Indon., 56,263 . . . G3 19
Serbia, reg., Yugo. . . . D5 10
Serbia, rep., Yugo., 7,642,227 . . . *D5 10
Serdobsk, Sov. Un., 34,000 . . . E15 12
Sered, Czech., 11,412 . . . D4 7
Seremban, Mala., 80,921 . . E2 19
Sergeant Bluff, Iowa, 1,153 . . . B1 60
Sergipe, state, Braz., 911,251 . . . *E7 27
Seria, Bru., 17,595 . . . E4 19
Seringapatam, India, 14,100 . . . F6 20
Serón, Sp., 7,091 . . . D4 8
Serov, Sov. Un., 101,000 . . . D9 13
Serowe, Bots., 34,182 . . . E5 24
Serpa, Port., 7,273 . . . D2 8
Serpukhov, Sov. Un., 124,000 . . . D11 12
Sérrai, Grc., 39,897 . . . B4 14
Sérrai, prov., Grc., 202,771 . . . *B4 14
Serra Talhada, Braz., 21,589 . . . *D7 27
Serrinha, Braz., 15,971 . . . *E7 27
Sesser, Ill., 2,125 . . . E4 58
Sesto [Fiorentino], It., 36,300 . . . C3 9
Sestri Levante, It., 20,800 . . B2 9
Sestroretsk, Sov. Un., 25,200 . . . A8 12
Setana, Jap. . . . E9 18
Setauket, N.Y., 2,000 . . . F4 52
Sète, Fr., 40,476 . . . F5 5
Sete Lagoas, Braz., 61,063 . . B4 30
Seth, W. Va., 400 . . . C3, m12 87
Seth Ward, Tex., 950 . . . *B2 84
Sétif, Alg., 98,337 . . . A6 22
Seto, Jap., 92,681 . . . I8, n16 18
Settat, Mor., 42,325 . . . B3 22
Setúbal, Port., 44,435 . . . C1 8
Sevastopol, Sov. Un., 229,000 . . . I9 12
Seven Devils, mts., Idaho . . D2 57
Seven Harbors, Mich., 3,170 . . . *F7 66
Seven Hills, Ohio, 12,700 . *A4 78
Seven Mile, Ohio, 699 . . . C1 78
Sevenoaks, Eng., 18,280 . . m13 4
Severn, Md., 800 . . . B4 53
Severna Park, Md., 16,358 . . . B4 53
Sevier, co., Ark., 11,272 . . . D1 49
Sevier, co., Tenn., 28,241 . . . D10 83
Sevier, co., Utah, 10,103 . . . B6 72
Sevierville, Tenn., 2,661 . . D10 83
Sevilla, Col., 26,757 . . . C2 32
Sevilla (Seville), Sp., 545,692 . . . D3 8
Sevilla (Seville), prov., Sp., 1,434,900 . . . *D3 8
Seville, Fla., 650 . . . C5 54
Seville, Ohio, 1,402 . . . A4 78
Sevlievo, Bul., 20,423 . . . D7 10
Sevran, Fr., 17,969 . . . g11 5
Sèvres, Fr., 20,083 . . . g9 5
Sewanee, Tenn., 1,900 . . . B6 83
Seward, Alsk., 1,587 . . C10, g17 47
Seward, Nebr., 5,294 . . . D8 71
Seward, co., Kans., 15,744 . . . E3 61
Seward, co., Nebr., 14,460 . . . D8 71
Sewaren, N.J., 2,600 . . . k7 74
Sewell, N.J., 1,900 . . . D2 74
Sewickley, Pa., 5,660 . . E1, h13 81
Sewickley Heights, Pa., 797 . . . *E1 81
Sexsmith, Alta., Can., 531 . . B1 38
Seychelles, Br. dep., Afr., 55,000 . . . G24 2
Seymour, Conn., 12,776 . . . D4 52
Seymour, Ind., 13,352 . . . G6 59
Seymour, Iowa, 1,153 . . . D4 60
Seymour, Mo., 1,208 . . . D5 69
Seymour, Tex., 3,469 . . . C3 84
Seymour, Wis., 2,194 . . D5, g9 88
Seymourville, La., 2,506 . . . h9 63
Sezimbra, Port., 6,957 . . . C1 8
Sezze, It., 7,544 . . . D4 9
Sfax, Tun., 70,472 . . . B7 22
Sfîntul-Gheorghe, Rom., 17,638 . . . C7 10
's Gravenhage, see The Hague, Neth.
Shabbona, Ill., 730 . . . B5 58
Shackelford, co., Tex., 3,323 . . . C3 84
Shady Cove, Oreg., 613 . . . E4 80
Shady Side, Md., 1,562 . . . C4 53
Shadyside, Ohio, 5,070 . . . C5 78
Shaft (William Penn), Pa., 450 . . . *E9 81
Shafter, Calif., 5,327 . . . E4 50
Shāhjahanpur, India, 135,604 (*144,065) . . . C7 20
Shāhrūd, Iran, 17,058 . . . B6 15
Shaker Heights, Ohio, 36,306 . . . A4, h9 78
Shakhty, Sov. Un., 205,000 . . . H13 12
Shaki, Nig., 76,290 . . . G5 22
Shakopee, Minn., 6,876 . . . F5, n11 67
Shalimar, Fla., 578 . . . u15 54
Shallowater, Tex., 1,339 . . . C2 84
Shām, Jabal ash, mtn., Om. . . . D2 20
Shamokin, Pa., 11,719 . . . E8 81
Shamokin Dam, Pa., 1,562 . E8 81
Shamrock, Fla., 200 . . . C3 54
Shamrock, Tex., 2,644 . . . B2 84
Shandaken, N.Y., 500 . . . C6 75
Shandī, Sud., 11,031 . . . E4 23
Shangshui, China, 134,400 . E7 17
Shanghai, China, 7,900,000 (10,820,000 ▲) . E9 17
Shanhaikuan, China, 35,000 . . . C8 17
Shannon, Ga., 1,563 . . . B1 55
Shannon, Ill., 848 . . . A4 58
Shannon, co., Mo., 7,196 . . D6 69
Shannon, co., S. Dak., 8,198 . . . G3 77
Shannontown, S.C., 7,491 . *D7 82
Shansi, prov., China, 15,960,000 . . . D7 17
Shantung, prov., China, 54,030,000 . . . D8 17
Shaohsing, China, 130,600 . . E9 17
Shaokuan, China, 81,700 . . G7 17
Shaoyang, China, 170,000 . . F7 17
Shari, Jap., 8,692 . . . E12 18
Sharkey, co., Miss., 8,937 . . . C3 68
Sharon, Mass., 12,367 . B5, h11 65
Sharon, Pa., 22,653 . . . D1 81
Sharon, Tenn., 1,188 . . . A3 83
Sharon, Wis., 1,216 . . . F5 88
Sharon Hill, Pa., 7,464 . . . p20 81
Sharon Park, Ohio, 600 . . . n12 78
Sharon Springs, Kans., 1,012 . . . D2 61
Sharonville, Ohio, 11,393 . . n13 78
Sharp, co., Ark., 8,233 . . . A4 49
Sharpes, Fla., 700 . . . D6 54
Sharpsburg, Md., 833 . . . B2 53
Sharpsburg, Pa., 5,453 . . . k14 81
Sharpsville, Ind., 672 . . . D5 59
Sharpsville, Pa., 6,126 . . . D1 81
Sharptown, Md., 660 . . . C6 53
Shashih, China, 85,800 . . . E7 17
Shasta, co., Calif., 77,640 . . B3 50
Shasta, mtn., Calif. . . . B2 50
Shastsk, Sov. Un., 10,000 . . D13 12
Shattuck, Okla., 1,546 . . . A2 79
Shaunavon, Sask., Can., 2,244 . . . H1 39
Shavertown, Pa., 2,300 . . . *B8 81
Shaw, Miss., 2,513 . . . B3 68
Shawano, Wis., 6,488 . . . D5 88
Shawano, co., Wis., 32,650 . D5 88
Shawbridge, Que., Can., 1,034 . . . D3 43
Shawinigan, Que., Can., 27,792 (*57,246) . . . C5 42
Shawinigan-Sud, Que., Can., 11,470 . . . C5 43
Shawmut, Ala., 2,181 . . . C4 46
Shawnee, Kans., 20,946 . . k16 61
Shawnee, Ohio, 914 . . . C3 78
Shawnee, Okla., 25,075 . . . B5 79
Shawnee, co., Kans., 155,322 . . . D8 61
Shawneetown, Ill., 1,742 . . . F5 58
Shawville, Que., Can., 1,534 . . . B8 41
Shchelkovo, Sov. Un., 78,000 . . . n18 12
Shchetovo, Sov. Un., 10,000 . . . q22 12
Shchigry, Sov. Un., 17,000 . . . F11 12
Shchors, Sov. Un., 10,000 . . F8 12
Sheartown, Newf., Can., 680 . . . *E5 44
Sheboygan, Wis., 48,484 (*70,500) . . . E5, k10 88
Sheboygan, co., Wis., 96,660 . . . E6 88
Sheboygan Falls, Wis., 4,771 . . . E5, k10 88
Shediac, N.B., Can., 2,203 . . . C5 43
Sheep, mtn., Wyo. . . . B5 89
Sheep, mtn., Wyo. . . . C2 89
Sheeps Heaven, mtn., Mass. . . . A1 65
Sheet Harbour, N.S., Can., 883 . . . E7 43
Sheffield, Ala., 14,000 . . . A2 46
Sheffield, Eng., 515,950 (*725,000) . . . D6 4
Sheffield, Ill., 1,038 . . . B4 58
Sheffield, Iowa, 1,070 . . . B4 60
Sheffield, Ohio, 1,730 . . . A3 78
Sheffield, Pa., 1,564 . . . C3 81
Sheffield Lake, Ohio, 8,734 . . . *A3 78
Shefford, co., Que., Can., 60,161 . . . D5 42
Sheila, N.B., Can., 553 . . . B5 43
Shelagyote, peak, B.C., Can. . . . B4 37
Shelbiana, Ky., 500 . . . C7 62
Shelbina, Mo., 2,060 . . . B5 69
Shelburn, Ind., 1,281 . . . F3 59
Shelburne, N.S., Can., 2,689 . . . F4 43
Shelburne, Ont., Can., 1,790 . . . C4 41
Shelburne, co., N.S., Can., 16,284 . . . F4 43
Shelburne Falls, Mass., 2,183 . . . A2 65
Shelby, Ind., 500 . . . B3 59
Shelby, Iowa, 537 . . . C2 60
Shelby, Mich., 1,703 . . . E4 66
Shelby, Miss., 2,645 . . . B3 68
Shelby, Mont., 3,111 . . . B5 70
Shelby, Nebr., 647 . . . C8 71
Shelby, N.C., 16,328 . . . B1 76
Shelby, Ohio, 9,847 . . . B3 78
Shelby, co., Ala., 38,037 . . . B3 46
Shelby, co., Ill., 22,589 . . . D5 58
Shelby, co., Ind., 37,797 . . . E6 59
Shelby, co., Iowa, 15,528 . . C2 60
Shelby, co., Ky., 18,999 . . . B4 62
Shelby, co., Mo., 7,906 . . . B5 69
Shelby, co., Ohio, 37,748 . . B1 78
Shelby, co., Tenn., 722,014 . . . B2 83
Shelby, co., Tex., 19,672 . . D5 84
Shelby City, Ky., 700 . . . C5 62
Shelby Village, Mich., 1,200 . . . *F7 66
Shelbyville, Ill., 4,887 . . . D5 58
Shelbyville, Ind., 15,094 . . . F6 59
Shelbyville, Ky., 4,182 . . . B4 62
Shelbyville, Mo., 601 . . . B5 69
Shelbyville, Tenn., 12,262 . . B5 83
Sheldon, Ill., 1,455 . . . C6 58
Sheldon, Iowa, 4,535 . . . A2 60
Shell Beach, Calif. . . . *E3 50
Shellbrook, Sask., Can., 1,042 . . . D2 39
Shell Camp, Tex. . . . *C5 84
Shelley, Idaho, 2,614 . . . F6 57
Shell Lake, Wis., 928 . . . C2 88
Shellman, Ga., 1,166 . . . E2 55
Shellman Bluff, Ga., 250 . . . E5 55
Shell Rock, Iowa, 1,159 . . . B5 60
Shellsburg, Iowa, 740 . . . B6 60
Shelter Island, N.Y., 700 . . m16 75
Shelton, Conn., 27,165 . . . D4 52
Shelton, Nebr., 1,028 . . . D7 71
Shelton, Wash., 6,515 . . . B2 86
Shenandoah, Iowa, 5,968 . . D2 60
Shenandoah, Pa., 8,287 . . . E9 81
Shenandoah, Va., 1,714 . . . B4 85
Shenandoah, co., Va., 22,852 . . . B4 85
Shenandoah, mtn., Va. . . . B3 85
Shenandoah Heights, Pa., 1,471 . . . *E9 81
Shenorock, N.Y., 1,600 . . . *D7 75
Shensi, prov., China, 18,130,000 . . . E6 17
Shenyang (Mukden), China, 2,423,000 . . . C9 17
Shepetovka, Sov. Un., 39,000 . . . F6 12
Shepherd, Mich., 1,416 . . . E6 66
Shepherd Brook, mtn., Maine . . . B3 64
Shepherdstown, W. Va., 1,688 . . . B7 87
Shepherdsville, Ky., 2,769 . . . C4, g11 62
Shepparton, Austl., 19,409 . . . H5 26
Sheppton, Pa., 650 . . . E9 81
Sherborn, Mass., 500 (3,309 ▲) . . . h10 65
Sherbrooke, Que., Can., 80,711 (*84,570) . . . D6, k12 42
Sherbrooke, co., Que., Can., 93,199 . . . D5 42
Sherburn, Minn., 1,190 . . . G4 67
Sherburne, N.Y., 1,613 . . . C5 75
Sherburne, co., Minn., 18,344 . . . E5 67
Shereshevo, Sov. Un., 10,000 . . . B8 7
Sheridan, Ark., 2,480 . . . C3 49
Sheridan, Colo., 4,787 . . . B6 51
Sheridan, Ind., 2,137 . . . D5 59
Sheridan, Mich., 653 . . . E5 66
Sheridan, Mont., 636 . . . E4 70
Sheridan, Oreg., 1,881 . . . B3 80
Sheridan, Wyo., 10,856 . . . B8 89
Sheridan, co., Kans., 3,859 . . . C3 61
Sheridan, co., Mont., 5,779 . . . B12 70
Sheridan, co., Nebr., 7,285 . . . B3 71
Sheridan, co., N. Dak., 3,232 . . . C5 77
Sheridan, co., Wyo., 17,852 . . . B5 89
Sheridan, mtn., Wyo. . . . B2 89
Sheridan Beach, Wash., 2,000 . . . *B3 86
Sheringham, Eng., 4,680 . . . D7 4
Sherman, N.Y., 769 . . . C1 75
Sherman, Tex., 29,061 (*63,100) . . . C4 84
Sherman, co., Kans., 7,792 . . . C2 61
Sherman, co., Nebr., 4,725 . . . C6 71
Sherman, co., Oreg., 2,139 . . . B6 80
Sherman, co., Tex., 3,657 . . A2 84
Sherridon, Man., Can., 40 . . B1 40
Sherrill, N.Y., 2,986 . . . B5 75
's Hertogenbosch, Neth., 84,914 (*173,114) . . . B6 5
Sherwood, Ark., 2,754 . C3, h10 49
Sherwood, Ohio, 784 . . . A1 78
Sherwood, Oreg., 1,396 . . . h12 80
Sherwood, Tenn., 450 . . . B6 83
Sherwood Park, Alta., Can., 14,282 . . . C4 38
Sheshebee, Minn., 100 . . . D5 67
Shetland, co., Scot., 17,535 . . . *g10 4
Shetland, is., Scot. . . . g1 4
Shiawassee, co., Mich., 62,957 . . . F6 66
Shibām, P.D.R. of Yem., 8,000 . . . F4 15
Shibarghan (Shibargan), Afg., 22,464 . . . A4 20
Shibata, Jap., 49,000 (74,459▲) . . . H9 18
Shibecha, Jap., 5,234 . . . E12 18
Shibetsu, Jap., 17,000 (33,004 ▲) . . . D11 18
Shibetsu, Jap. . . . E12 18
Shibīn al Kawm, Eg., 66,290 . . . G8 14
Shickshinny, Pa., 1,685 . . . D9 81
Shidler, Okla., 717 . . . A5 79
Shiga, pref., Jap., 889,768 . . *I8 18
Shihchiachuang, China, 750,000 . . . D7 17
Shihchu, China . . . B10 20
Shikārpur, Pak., 53,910 . . . C4 20
Shikoku, isl., Jap. . . . J6 18
Shilka, Sov. Un., 16,000 . . D14 13
Shillington, Pa., 6,249 . . . F10 81
Shillong, India, 87,659 (*122,752) . . . C9 20
Shiloh, Ohio, 817 . . . B3 78
Shiloh, Ohio, 10,000 . . . C1 78
Shimabara, Jap., 33,500 (44,475▲) . . . J5 18
Shimada, Jap., 66,489 . . . o17 18
Shimane, pref., Jap., 773,575 . . . *I16 18
Shimanovsk, Sov. Un., 17,000 . . . D15 13
Shimizu, Jap., 234,966 . . . I9, n17 18
Shimoda, Jap., 11,049 . . . o17 18
Shimodate, Jap., 34,000 (53,863▲) . . . m18 18
Shimoga, India, 102,709 . . . F6 20
Shimonoseki, Jap., 258,425 . . I5 18
Shimotsuma, Jap., 13,000 (27,699 ▲) . . . m18 18
Shiner, Tex., 2,102 . . . E4 84
Shinglehouse, Pa., 1,320 . . . C5 81
Shingu, Jap., 38,808 . . . J7 18
Shinjo, Jap., 28,000 (42,120▲) . . . G10 18
Shinkolobwe, Zaire, 10,900 . . . C5 24
Shinnston, W. Va., 2,576 . . . B4, k10 87
Shinshiro, Jap., 32,597 . . . o16 18
Shiocton, Wis., 830 . . . D5, h8 88
Shiogama, Jap., 58,772 . . . G10 18
Shiojiri, Jap., 26,000 (42,265 ▲) . . . m16 18

Ship Bottom, N.J., 1,079...D4 74
Shipman, Va., 400.........C4 85
Shippegan, N.B., Can.,
2,043................B5 43
Shippegan Gully, N.B.,
Can., 761............*B5 43
Shippensburg, Pa., 6,536...F7 81
Shirane-san, mtn., Jap....H9 18
Shīrāz, Iran, 269,865.....G8 16
Shīrbin, Eg., 13,293......G8 14
Shiremanstown, Pa.,
1,773................*F8 81
Shiribeshi-yama, mtn.,
Jap.................E10 18
Shirley, Ind., 958........E6 59
Shirley, Mass., 1,718
(4,909 ▲)............A4 65
Shirley, Mont............D11 70
Shirley, N.Y., 6,280......*n15 75
Shirley, mtn., Wyo........D6 89
Shirntoru, see Makarov,
Sov. Un.
Shiroishi, Jap., 25,000
(40,886▲)..........G10 18
Shirotori, Jap...........n15 18
Shitara, Jap.............n16 18
Shively, Ky., 19,139..B4, g11 62
Shizuoka, Jap., 416,378
(*680,000)........I9, o17 18
Shizuoka, pref., Jap.,
3,089,895...........*I9 18
Shkodër (Scutari), Alb.,
49,800..............A2 14
Shkodër (Scutari), pref.,
Alb., 150,000........*A2 14
Shoal Lake, Man., Can.,
774.................D1 40
Shoals, Ind., 1,039.......G4 59
Shoemakersville, Pa.,
1,427...............E10 81
Sholāpur, India, 398,361...E6 20
Shore Acres, Calif.,
4,000...............*D2 50
Shore Acres, Mass., 1,200.h13 65
Shoreview, Minn.,
10,978..............*F5 67
Shorewood, Minn.,
4,223...............*F5 67
Shorewood, Wis.,
15,576...........E6, m12 88
Shorewood Hills, Wis.,
2,206...............*E4 88
Short Beach, Conn.,
1,500...............D5 52
Shortsville, N.Y., 1,516....C3 75
Shoshone, Idaho, 1,233....G4 57
Shoshone, co., Idaho,
19,718..............B3 57
Shoshoni, Wyo., 562.......C4 89
Show Low, Ariz., 2,129....B3 48
Shpola, Sov. Un., 20,000...G8 12
Shreve, Ohio, 1,635.......B3 78
Shreveport, La., 182,064
(*263,800)..........B2 63
Shrewsbury, Eng.,
56,630..............D5 4
Shrewsbury, Mass., 19,196..B4 65
Shrewsbury, Mo., 5,896....*C7 69
Shrewsbury, N.J., 3,315....C4 74
Shrewsbury, Pa., 1,716....G8 81
Shropshire, co., Eng.,
341,960.............*D5 4
Shrub Oak, N.Y., 2,200....*D7 75
Shuangcheng, China,
80,000..............D3 18
Shuangliao, China,
177,000.............C9 17
Shuangshan, China,
5,000...............E1 18
Shuangyang, China,
5,000...............E2 18
Shuangyashan, China,
110,000.............C5 18
Shubenacadie, N.S., Can.,
579.................D6 43
Shubrā al Khaymah, Eg.,
104,139.............*G8 14
Shuksan, mtn., Wash......A4 86
Shulan, China, 5,000......D3 18
Shulaps, peak, B.C., Can..D6 37
Shullsburg, Wis., 1,376....F3 88
Shumen, Bul., 59,293......D8 10
Shumen, co., Bul.,
243,416.............*D8 10
Shumerlya, Sov. Un.,
34,000..............D16 12
Shuya, Sov. Un., 69,000...C13 12
Shuzenji, Jap............o17 18
Shwebo, Bur., 17,842......D10 20
Shwegyin, Bur., 10,000....*B1 19
Siālkot, Pak., 143,889
(*164,346)..........B5 20
Siam, see Thailand, Asia
Sian (Hsian), China,
1,368,000...........E6 17
Siauliai, Sov. Un.,
93,000..............D4 12
Sibenik, Yugo., 30,090....D2 10

Sibert, Ky., 800..........C6 62
Sibi, Pak., 11,842........C4 20
Sibiu, Rom., 109,500......C7 10
Sibley, Iowa, 2,749.......A2 60
Sibley, La., 869..........B2 63
Sibley, co., Minn., 15,845..F4 67
Sibolga, Indon., 42,223....E1 19
Sibsāgar, India, 27,426....C9 20
Sibu, Mala., 50,635.......E4 19
Sicard, La...............B3 63
Sicilia, pol. dist., It.,
4,900,000...........*F4 9
Sicily, isl., It..........F4 9
Sicily Island, La., 630....C4 63
Sicklerville, N.J., 850....D3 74
Sicuaní, Peru, 10,664.....D3 31
Siderno Marina, It., 6,915..E6 9
Sidhirokastron, Grc.,
6,363...............B4 14
Sidi-bel-Abbès, Alg.,
91,527..............A4 22
Sidi Ifni, Mor., 13,650....C2 22
Sidmouth, Eng., 10,000....E5 4
Sidney, B.C., Can.,
4,868.............E6, g12 37
Sidney, Iowa, 1,061.......D2 60
Sidney, Mont., 4,543......C12 70
Sidney, Nebr., 6,403......C3 71
Sidney, N.Y., 4,789.......C5 75
Sidney, Ohio, 16,332......B1 78
Sidney Center, N.Y., 500...C5 75
Siedlce, Pol., 38,900......B7 7
Siegburg, Ger., Fed. Rep.
of, 35,286...........C3 6
Siegen, Ger., Fed. Rep. of,
56,864 (*151,000)....C4 6
Siemianowice Śląskie,
Pol., 67,200........g10 7
Siem Reap, Camb.,
10,200..............C2 19
Siena, It., 54,300........C3 9
Sieradz, Pol., 18,500.....C5 7
Siero, Sp., 30,931........A3 8
Sierpc, Pol., 12,700......B5 7
Sierra, co., Calif., 2,365...C3 50
Sierra, co., N. Mex., 7,189..C5 48
Sierra Blanca, Tex., 800...o12 84
Sierra Leone, country,
Afr., 2,690,000......G2 22
Sierra Madre, Calif.,
12,140.............m12 50
Sierra Nevada, mts., Calif..C3 50
Sierraville, Calif., 300....C3 50
Sierra Vieja, mts., Tex....o12 84
Sierra Vista, Ariz., 6,689..*D3 48
Sifton, Man., Can., 245...D1 40
Sighet, Rom., 22,361.....B6 10
Sighișoara, Rom., 25,100..B7 10
Sigli, Indon., 4,519......k11 19
Signal, mtn., Va..........g11 85
Signal Hill, Calif., 5,588..*F4 50
Signal Hill, Ill., 2,000....*E3 58
Signal Mountain, Tenn.,
4,839............D8, h11 83
Sigourney, Iowa, 2,319....C5 60
Siguiri, Guinea, 12,700....F3 22
Sihaus, Peru, 1,432.......C2 31
Siirt, Tur., 29,544.......D13 14
Sīkar, India, 70,987......C6 20
Sikasso, Mali, 13,600.....F3 22
Sikeston, Mo., 14,699.....E8 69
Sikionía, Grc., 7,392.....C4 14
Sikkim, country, Asia,
215,000.............C8 20
Silao, Mex., 31,825......m13 34
Silchar, India, 52,596....D9 20
Siler City, N.C., 4,689....B3 76
Silesia, reg., Pol........C4 7
Siletz, Oreg., 596........C3 80
Silifke, Tur., 14,624......D9 14
Silīguri, India, 97,484....C8 20
Silistra, Bul., 33,019.....C8 10
Sillery, Que., Can.,
13,932.............n17 42
Siloam Springs, Ark.,
6,009...............A1 49
Silsbee, Tex., 7,271......D5 84
Siluria, Ala., 678........B3 46
Silva, Mo., 100..........D7 69
Silva Jardim, Braz., 1,774..h6 30
Silver Bay, Minn., 3,504...C7 67
Silver Bow, co., Mont.,
41,981..............E4 70
Silver Bow Park, Mont.,
5,524...............D4 70
Silver City, N. Mex.,
8,557...............C4 48
Silver Creek, N.Y., 3,182..C1 75
Silverdale, Wash., 900.B3, e10 86
Silver Grove, Ky., 1,365..h14 62
Silver Hill, Md., 5,000....f9 53
Silver Lake, Ind., 588.....B6 59
Silver Lake, Mass., 5,000..f11 65
Silver Lake, Minn., 694....F4 67
Silver Lake, Ohio, 3,637..*A4 78
Silver Lake, Wis.,
1,210............F5, n11 88

Silver Spring, Md.,
81,000............C3, f8 53
Silver Springs, N.Y., 823..C2 75
Silverthrone, mtn., B.C.,
Can.................D4 37
Silvertip, mtn., Mont......C3 70
Silverton, Colo., 797......D3 51
Silverton, Idaho, 800......B3 57
Silverton, Ohio, 6,588....o13 78
Silverton, Oreg.,
4,773...........B4, h12 80
Silverton, Tex., 1,026.....B2 84
Silvia, Col., 3,180........C2 32
Silvis, Ill., 5,907........B3 58
Silvis Heights, Ill., 2,000.*B3 58
Silwān, Jordan, 5,000....*C3 15
Simav, Tur., 10,183......C7 14
Simcoe, Ont., Can.,
10,793..............E4 41
Simcoe, co., Ont., Can.,
149,132.............C4 41
Simferopol, Sov. Un.,
249,000.............I10 12
Simi, Calif., 59,832......m11 50
Simití, Col., 2,825.......B3 32
Simla, India, 55,368......B6 20
Simleul-Silvaniei, Rom.,
8,560...............B6 10
Simmesport, La., 2,027....D4 63
Simpson, N.C., 450.......B5 76
Simpson, Pa., 2,200......C11 81
Simpson, co., Ky.,
13,054..............D3 62
Simpson, co., Miss.,
19,947..............D4 68
Simpsonville, S.C., 3,308..B3 82
Simsbury, Conn., 4,994....B5 52
Sinaia, Rom., 9,006......C7 10
Sinajana, Guam, 2,861...*F6 2
Sinaloa [de Leyva], Mex.,
1,998...............B3 34
Sinaloa, state, Mex.,
950,600.............C3 34
Sinanju, Kor., 16,493.....G2 18
Sincé, Col., 10,631.......B2 32
Sincelejo, Col., 49,800....B2 32
Sinclair, Wyo., 445.......E5 89
Sinclairville, N.Y., 772....C1 75
Sind, reg., Pak..........C4 20
Sinelnikovo, Sov. Un.,
30,000.............G10 12
Sines, Port., 4,893.......D1 8
Singapore, Singapore,
2,122,466 (*2,250,000)...E2 19
Singapore, country, Asia,
2,265,000...........E2 19
Singaraja, Indon., 42,289..G5 19
Singkawang, Indon.,
35,169..............E3 19
Singleton, Austl., 7,181...*F9 25
Sinhung, Kor., 7,583......F3 18
Siniscola, It., 6,559......D2 9
Sinj, Yugo., 4,133........D3 10
Sinjah, Sud., 15,500......F4 23
Sinkiang, auton. reg.,
China, 8,500,000.....F11 13
Sinking Spring, Pa.,
2,862...............*F9 81
Sînnicolau-Mare, Rom.,
9,956...............B5 10
Sinnūris, Eg., 23,537.....H8 14
Sinop, Tur., 15,096......A10 14
Sinpo, Kor., 26,086.......F4 18
Sintang, Indon., 9,013....E4 19
Sint-Niklaas, Bel., 49,320..B6 5
Sinton, Tex., 5,563.......E4 84
Sintra, Port., 7,705......f9 8
Sinuiju, Kor., 118,414....F2 18
Sion, Switz., 22,200......E3 6
Sioux, co., Iowa, 27,996...A1 60
Sioux, co., Nebr., 2,034...B2 71
Sioux, co., N. Dak.,
3,632...............D5 77
Sioux Center, Iowa, 3,450..A1 60
Sioux City, Iowa, 85,925
(*99,500)...........B1 60
Sioux Falls, S. Dak.,
72,488 (*80,800)....G9 77
Sioux Lookout, Ont.,
Can., 2,530........o17 41
Sioux Rapids, Iowa, 813...B2 60
Sipes (Midway), Fla.....*D5 54
Sipsey, Ala., 608........B2 46
Siracusa, It., 84,900
(*101,500)..........F5 9
Sirājganj, Bngl., 47,152...D8 20
Sir Douglas, mtn., Alta.,
Can.................C3 38
Siren, Wis., 639.........C1 88
Siret, Rom., 5,664.......B8 10
Síros, Grc., 13,502
(*16,082)...........D5 14
Sirpur, India, 5,619......E6 20
Sirsa, India, 48,808......C6 20
Sir Wilfrid, mtn., Que.,
Can.................C2 42
Sisak, Yugo., 38,421.....C3 10

Siskiyou, co., Calif.,
33,225..............B2 50
Sisseton, S. Dak., 3,094...E9 77
Sister Bay, Wis., 483.....C6 88
Sisters, Oreg., 516.......C5 80
Sistersville, W. Va., 2,246..B4 87
Sītāpur, India, 66,715....C7 20
Sitionuevo, Col., 5,969....A3 32
Sitka, Alsk., 3,370......D12 47
Sittwe, Burma, 81,000....D9 20
Sivas, Tur., 133,979......C11 14
Siverek, Tur., 34,146....D12 14
Sivrihisar, Tur., 8,429....C8 14
Skagit, co., Wash., 52,381..A4 86
Skamania, co., Wash.,
5,845...............D3 86
Skanderborg, co., Den.,
147,400.............*I3 11
Skaneateles, N.Y., 3,005...C4 75
Skara, Swe., 11,480......H5 11
Skegness, Eng., 13,270....D7 4
Skellefteå, Swe., 41,262...E9 11
Skidmore, Tex., 700......E4 84
Skien, Nor., 44,800
(*76,400).........H3, p27 11
Skierniewice, Pol., 25,500..C6 7
Skihist, mtn., B.C., Can...D7 37
Skikda (Philippeville),
Alg., 72,742........A6 22
Skokie, Ill., 68,322....A6, h9 58
Skole, Sov. Un., 5,000....D7 7
Skopin, Sov. Un., 24,000..E13 12
Skopje (Skoplje), Yugo.,
312,092.............D5 10
Skövde, Swe., 44,721....H5 11
Skovorodino, Sov. Un.,
26,000.............D15 13
Skowhegan, Maine, 6,571
(7,601 ▲)...........D3 64
Skradin, Yugo., 928......D2 10
Skvira, Sov. Un., 16,000...G7 12
Skyland, N.C., 2,177.....f10 76
Sky Manor, N.J..........C4 74
Slagelse, Den., 22,600....A1 7
Slamet, mtn., Indon......G3 19
Slănic, Rom., 6,842......C7 10
Slany, Czech., 12,739....n17 7
Slater, Iowa, 1,094....C4, e8 60
Slater, Mo., 2,576.......B4 69
Slater, S.C., 800........A3 82
Slatersville, R.I., 2,000..B10 52
Slatina, Rom., 13,381....C7 10
Slatington, Pa., 4,687....E10 81
Slaton, Tex., 6,583......C2 84
Slavgorod, Sov. Un.,
33,000.............D10 13
Slavonia, reg., Yugo......C3 10
Slavonska Pozega, Yugo.,
18,183..............C3 10
Slavyanoserbsk, Sov.
Un., 5,000..........q21 12
Slavyansk, Sov. Un.,
124,000.........G11, q20 12
Slavyanskaya, Sov. Un.,
83,000..............I12 12
Slayton, Minn., 2,351.....G3 67
Sleepy Eye, Minn., 3,461..F4 67
Sleepy Hollow, Calif.,
1,200...............*D2 50
Sleepy Hollow, Va.,
1,200...............*B5 85
Slickville, Pa., 1,066......F2 81
Slidell, La., 16,101...D6, h12 63
Slide, mtn., N.Y..........C6 75
Sliderock, mtn., Mont.....D3 70
Slieve Donard, mtn.,
N. Ire..............C3 4
Sligo, Ire., 14,080.......C2 4
Sligo, Pa., 825..........D3 81
Sligo, co., Ire., 51,263...*C2 4
Slinger, Wis., 1,022......E5 88
Slingerlands, N.Y., 1,500..*C7 75
Slippery Rock, Pa., 4,949..D1 81
Sliven, Bul., 68,384......D8 10
Sloan, Iowa, 799.........B1 60
Sloan, N.Y., 5,216.......C2 75
Sloatsburg, N.Y., 3,134...A4 75
Slobozia, Rom., 9,632....C8 10
Slocomb, Ala., 1,883.....D4 46
Slonim, Sov. Un., 30,000..E5 12
Slope, co., N. Dak., 1,484..D2 77
Slough, Eng., 87,660.....k11 4
Slovakia (Slovensko),
reg., Czech., 4,542,092..D5 7
Slovan, Pa., 900........F1 81
Slovenia, reg., Yugo......C2 10
Slovenia, rep., Yugo.,
1,584,368...........*C2 10
Słupca, Pol., 5,077......B4 7
Słupsk, Pol., 68,300.....A4 7
Slutsk, Sov. Un., 36,000..s31 11
Slyudyanka, Sov. Un.,
21,000.............D13 13
Smackover, Ark., 2,058...D3 49
Smederevo, Yugo., 40,289..C5 10
Smela, Sov. Un., 55,000...G8 12
Smelterville, Idaho, 967...B2 57
Smethport, Pa., 1,883....C5 81

186 Sme-Sou

Smethwick (Warley), Eng., 163,270.............D5 4
Smidovich, Sov. Un., 5,000................B6 18
Smith, co., Kans., 6,757...C5 61
Smith, co., Miss., 13,561...C4 68
Smith, co., Tenn., 12,509..C8 83
Smith, co., Tex., 97,096...C5 84
Smith, peak, Idaho......A2 57
Smith Center, Kans., 2,389................C5 61
Smithers, B.C., Can., 3,864................B4 37
Smithers, W. Va., 2,020..............C3, m13 87
Smithfield, N.C., 6,677...B4 76
Smithfield, Ohio, 1,245...B5 78
Smithfield, Pa., 2,488....*E5 81
Smithfield, Pa., 969......G2 81
Smithfield, Utah, 3,342...A6 72
Smithfield, Va., 2,713.D6, k14 85
Smithmill, Pa., 600......E5 81
Smith River, Calif., 900...B1 50
Smithsburg, Md., 671.....A2 53
Smiths Falls, Ont., Can., 9,585 (*14,044).....C8 41
Smithton, Austl., 3,203...o15 25
Smithtown, N.Y., 22,500..E4 52
Smithville, Mo., 1,785.B3, h10 69
Smithville, Ohio, 1,278...B4 78
Smithville, Tenn., 2,997..D8 83
Smithville, Tex., 2,959...D4 84
Smock, Pa., 950.........*G2 81
Smokey Dome, mtn., Idaho................F4 57
Smoky, mts., Idaho.......F4 57
Smoky Lake, Alta., Can., 626.................B4 38
Smolensk, Sov. Un., 211,000.............D8 12
Smooth Rock Falls, Ont., Can., 1,131..........o19 41
Smyre, N.C., 600.......*B1 76
Smyrna, Del., 4,243......B6 53
Smyrna, Ga., 19,157..C2, h7 55
Smyrna, Tenn., 5,698....B5 83
Smyrna, see Izmir, Tur.
Smyth, co., Va., 31,349...f10 85
Snake, riv., U.S..........B3 45
Sneads, Fla., 1,550......B2 54
Sneads Ferry, N.C., 400...C5 76
Sneek, Neth., 21,100.....A6 5
Snezhnoye, Sov. Un., 64,000...........q21 12
Snohomish, Wash., 5,174..B3 86
Snohomish, co., Wash., 265,236...........A4 86
Snoqualmie, Wash., 1,260.B4 86
Snow, mtn., Calif.........C2 50
Snow, mtn., Maine.......C2 64
Snow, peak, Wash........A7 86
Snowdon, mtn., Wales....D4 4
Snowflake, Ariz., 1,977...B3 48
Snow Hill, Md., 2,201....D7 53
Snow Hill, N.C., 1,359...B5 76
Snow Lake, Man., Can., 1,011................B1 40
Snowshoe, peak, Mont....B1 70
Snowyside, peak, Idaho...F4 57
Snyatyn, Sov. Un., 10,000..A7 10
Snyder, Okla., 1,671.....C3 79
Snyder, Tex., 11,171.....C2 84
Snyder, co., Pa., 29,269...E7 81
Soap Lake, Wash., 1,064...B6 86
Soatá, Col., 4,361.......B3 32
Sobinka, Sov. Un., 23,000.D13 12
Sobota Rimavská, Czech., 13,615...........D6 7
Sobral, Braz., 51,864....*D6 27
Socaste, S.C., 900.......D9 82
Sochaczew, Pol., 20,500...B6 7
Soche (Yarkand), China, 80,000.............F10 16
Sochi, Sov. Un., 224,000..*E6 13
Society, is., Fr. Polynesia..H10 2
Society Hill, S.C., 806....B8 82
Socorro, Col., 13,716.....B3 32
Socorro, N. Mex., 5,849...B5 48
Socorro, co., N. Mex., 9,763................C5 48
Soc Trang, Viet., 16,890..D3 19
Socuéllamos, Sp., 14,828..C4 8
Soda Springs, Idaho, 2,977................G7 57
Soddy-Daisy, Tenn., 7,569............D8, h11 83
Söderhamn, Swe., 17,094..G7 11
Södertälje, Swe., 77,875...t35 11
Sodus, N.Y., 1,813.......B3 75
Soest, Ger., Fed. Rep. of, 40,338...............C4 6
Sofia (Sofiya), Bul., 840,100 (*940,000).....D6 10
Sofiya, see Sofia, Bul.
Sofiya, co., Bul., 317,596..*D6 10
Sofiyevka, Sov. Un., 10,000...............G9 12
Sogamoso, Col., 32,274...B3 32

Sogn og Fjordane, co., Nor., 101,000.......*G1 11
Sointula, B.C., Can., 682..D4 37
Soissons, Fr., 25,890 (*40,000)...........C5 5
Sokal, Sov. Un., 10,000...F5 12
Sokcho, Kor., 73,096.....G4 18
Söke, Tur., 30,000......*D6 14
Soke of Peterborough, co., Eng., 74,442.....*D6 4
Sokol, Sov. Un., 48,000...B13 12
Sokołów, Pol., 8,068.....B7 7
Sokoto, Nig., 89,817.....F6 22
Solana, Fla., 1,286.......F5 54
Solana Beach, Calif., 5,023..............*F5 50
Solano, Phil., 12,095....*B6 19
Solano, co., Calif., 171,989.............C2 50
Soldiers Grove, Wis., 514..E3 88
Soledad, Calif., 4,222....D3 50
Soledad, Col., 37,617....A3 32
Solihull, Eng., 108,400...*D6 4
Solikamsk, Sov. Un., 89,000...............D8 13
Soliman, Tun., 6,980.....F3 9
Solingen, Ger., Fed. Rep. of, 176,734.........C3 6
Sollefteå, Swe., 10,278...F7 11
Sóller, Sp., 6,817.......C7 8
Solna, Swe., 55,430......H7 11
Solomon, Kans., 973.....D6 61
Solomon Is., Br. dep., Oceania, 175,000.....G7 2
Solon, Iowa, 837........C6 60
Solon, Maine, 500 (712 ▲)..D3 64
Solon, Ohio, 11,519.....A4 78
Solonika, see Thessaloniki, Grc.
Solon Springs, Wis., 598..B2 88
Solothurn, Switz., 17,100 (*36,000)...........E3 6
Solothurn, canton, Switz., 223,000.............E3 6
Solovyevsk, Sov. Un., 10,000...............D15 13
Soltau, Ger., Fed. Rep. of, 15,852..............B4 6
Solvang, Calif., 1,325....*E3 50
Solvay, N.Y., 8,280......B4 75
Soma, Tur., 20,900......*C6 14
Somalia, country, Afr., 3,055,000............H6 23
Sombor, Yugo., 43,971...C4 10
Sombra, Ont., Can., 520..E2 41
Sombrerete, Mex., 11,077..C4 34
Somerdale, N.J., 6,510...D2 74
Somers, Conn., 1,274....B7 52
Somers, Mont., 800......B2 70
Somerset, Man., Can., 587..E2 40
Somerset, Ky., 10,436....C5 62
Somerset, Md., 1,303....*C3 53
Somerset, Mass., 18,088..C5 65
Somerset, Ohio, 1,417....C3 78
Somerset, Pa., 6,269.....F3 81
Somerset, Wis., 778......C1 88
Somerset, co., Eng., 686,230............*E5 4
Somerset, co., Maine, 40,597.............C2 64
Somerset, co., Md., 18,924.............D6 53
Somerset, co., N.J., 198,372.............C3 74
Somerset, co., Pa., 76,037..............G3 81
Somerset, isl., N. W. Ter., Can..............B15 36
Somerset East, S. Afr., 10,246.............G5 24
Somers Point, N.J., 7,919..E3 74
Somersworth, N.H., 9,026..E6 73
Somerton, Ariz., 2,225....C1 48
Somervell, co., Tex., 2,793..C4 84
Somerville, Mass., 88,779............B5, g11 65
Somerville, N.J., 13,652...B3 74
Somerville, Tenn., 1,816..B2 83
Somerville, Tex., 1,250...D4 84
Somme, dept., Fr., 512,113............C5 5
Somogy, co., Hung., 363,510...........*B3 10
Somonauk, Ill., 1,112....B5 58
Sonchon, Kor., 22,725....G2 18
Sønderborg, Den., 22,900..A4 6
Sønderborg, co., Den., 49,604............*A4 6
Sondershausen, Ger. Dem. Rep., 23,374........C5 6
Sondrio, It., 22,440......A2 9
Sonepur, India, 8,084....D7 20
Songjin, see Kimchaek, Kor.
Songkhla, Thai., 41,193...D2 19
Songnim (Kyomipo), Kor., 53,035..........G2 18
Son La, Viet., 10,000....G5 17

Sonneberg, Ger. Dem. Rep., 29,287........C5 6
Sonobe, Jap........n14 18
Sonoma, Calif., 4,112....C2 50
Sonoma, co., Calif., 204,885.............C2 50
Sonora, Ariz........C3, D3 48
Sonora, Calif., 3,100....D3 50
Sonora, Tex., 2,149.....D2 84
Sonora, state, Mex., 967,500.............B2 34
Sonsón, Col., 16,955.....B2 32
Sonsonate, Sal., 33,562..E7 34
Son Tay, Viet., 16,640...G6 17
Soperton, Ga., 2,596.....D4 55
Sophia, W. Va., 1,303....D3 87
Sopot, Pol., 47,500......A5 7
Sopron, Hung., 44,950...B3 10
Sora, It., 9,000.........D4 9
Sorbas, Sp., 5,961......D4 8
Sorel, Que., Can., 19,347..C4 42
Sorento, Ill., 625.......E4 58
Soresina, It., 9,100......B2 9
Soria, Sp., 24,455.......B4 8
Soria, prov., Sp., 124,600..*B4 8
Soriano, dept., Ur., 78,234.............*E1 30
Sorø, co., Den., 139,400..*J4 11
Sorocaba, Braz., 165,990...........C3, m8 30
Soroki, Sov. Un., 21,700..G7 12
Sorong, Indon., 8,000....F8 19
Soroti, Ug., 6,645.......H4 23
Sorrento, It., 10,500.....D5 9
Sorrento, La., 1,182..D5, h10 63
Sorrento, Maine, 185....*D5 64
Sorsogon, Phil., 19,008...C6 19
Sorsogon, prov., Phil., 347,771...........*C6 19
Sortavala, Sov. Un., 22,000.............G14 11
Sor Trondelag, co., Nor., 229,900...........*F4 11
Sosnovka, Sov. Un., 10,000...............E13 12
Sosnowiec, Pol., 144,600..........C5, g10 7
Sotteville-lès-Rouen, Fr., 34,495.............C4 5
Soudan, Minn., 850......C6 67
Souderton, Pa., 6,366....F11 81
Souflíon, Grc., 5,637.....B6 14
Soufriere, St. Lucia, 2,692..............J14 35
Souk-el Arba, Tun., 6,469................F2 9
Soul, see Seoul, Kor.
Soulanges, co., Que., Can., 10,757.........D3 42
Sound Beach, N.Y., 4,900.............*n15 75
Soure, Braz., 8,958.....*D6 27
Souris, Man., Can., 1,674................E1 40
Souris East, P.E.I., Can., 1,393................C7 43
Sourlake, Tex., 1,694....D5 84
Sousse, Tun., 58,161....A7 22
South, div., Ice., 13,416............*n21 11
South, isl., N.Z.........O12 26
South Acton, Mass., 3,000................g10 65
South Africa, country, Afr., 23,910,000......F5 24
South Amboy, N.J., 9,338............C4, m7 74
South America, cont., 205,500,000.........27
South Amherst, Mass., 600.................B2 65
South Amherst, Ohio, 2,913................A3 78
Southampton, Ont., Can., 2,036................C3 42
Southampton, Eng., 213,550 (*390,000).....E6 4
Southampton, N.Y., 4,904.............n16 75
Southampton, Pa., 9,500.............*F11 81
Southampton, co., Va., 18,582.............D5 85
Southampton Island, Can................D16 36
South Apopka, Fla.....*D5 54
South Arabia, see Yemen, People's Democratic Republic of, country, Asia
South Ashburnham, Mass., 1,181............A4 65
South Australia, state, Austl., 1,220,000.....E5 25
South Barre, Mass., 800..B3 65
South Bathurst, N.S., Can., 1,390.........*B4 43
South Bay, Fla., 2,958...F6 54

South Bellingham, Mass., 3,000................B5 65
South Belmar, N.J., 1,490..C4 74
South Belmont, N.C.....*B1 76
South Beloit, Ill., 3,804..A4 58
South Bend, Ind., 125,580 (*380,800).........A5 59
South Bend, Wash., 1,795..C2 86
South Bennettsville, S.C..*B8 82
South Berwick, Maine, 1,863................E2 64
South Boise, Idaho.....*F2 57
Southboro, Mass., 1,500............B4, g9 65
South Boston (Independent City), Va., 6,889...........D4 85
South Bound Brook, N.J., 4,525................B3 74
Southbridge, Mass., 17,057.............B3 65
South Broadway, Wash., 3,298.............*C5 86
South Brook, Newf., Can., 621............*D3 44
South Burlington, Vt., 10,032.............*C1 73
South Carolina, state, U.S., 2,700,000.........82
South Charleston, Ohio, 1,500................C2 78
South Charleston, W. Va., 16,333...........m12 87
South Chelmsford, Mass., 3,000................C1 65
South Chicago Heights, Ill., 4,923............m9 58
South China, sea, Asia...H14 16
South Cleveland, Tenn....*D9 83
South Clinton, Tenn., 1,356.............*C9 83
South Coatesville, Pa., 1,583............*G10 81
South Coffeyville, Okla., 646.................A6 79
South Congaree, S.C., 1,434................D5 82
South Connellsville, Pa., 2,385................G2 81
South Corning, N.Y., 1,414................*C3 75
South Dakota, state, U.S., 680,000............77
South Dartmouth, Mass., 7,000................C6 65
South Dayton, N.Y., 688...C1 75
South Daytona, Fla., 24,000.............*C5 54
South Decatur, Ga., 4,979................*C2 55
South Deerfield, Mass., 1,628................B2 65
South Dennis, Mass., 1,000.C7 65
South Dum-Dum, India, 174,538...........*D8 20
South Duxbury, Mass., 2,075................B6 65
South Easton, Mass., 1,200.B5 65
South Elgin, Ill., 4,289............B5, h8 58
South El Monte, Calif., 14,960...........*E5 50
Southend-on-Sea, Eng., 162,420.............E7 4
Southern Cross, Austl., 896.................F2 25
Southern Pines, N.C., 5,937................B3 76
Southern Rhodesia, see Rhodesia
Southern Shops, S.C., 2,864..............*B4 82
Southern View, Ill., 1,504..............*D4 58
Southern Yemen, see Yemen, Peoples Democratic Republic of, country, Asia
South Essex, Mass., 700...A6 65
South Euclid, Ohio, 29,579.............g9 78
South Fallsburg, N.Y., 1,590................D6 75
South Farmingdale, N.Y., 20,500.............*E7 75
South Fayetteville, N.C...*B3 76
Southfield, Mass., 150....B1 65
Southfield, Mich., 69,285..o15 66
South Floral Park, N.Y., 1,032.............*E7 75
South Fork, Pa., 1,661...F4 81
South Fort George, B.C., Can., 1,964..........C6 37
South Fulton, Tenn., 3,122................A3 83
South Gate, Calif., 56,909.............n12 50
Southgate, Ky., 3,212...h14 62

Southgate, Mich., 33,909..p15 66
South Glastonbury, Conn.,
 1,600..................C6 52
South Glens Falls, N.Y.,
 4,013.................*B7 75
South Grafton, Mass.,
 3,000..................B4 65
South Greensburg, Pa.,
 3,288.................*F2 81
South Greenwood, S.C....C3 82
South Hackensack, N.J.,
 2,412.................*B4 74
South Hadley, Mass.,
 6,000..................B2 65
South Hadley Falls, Mass.,
 9,000..................B3 65
South Hamilton,
 Mass., 3,500......A6, f12 65
South Hanover, Mass.,
 900..................h12 65
South Harriman, Tenn...*D9 83
South Harwich, Mass.,
 600...................C7 65
South Haven, Mich.,
 6,471.................F4 66
South Hempstead, N.Y.,
 3,000................*E7 75
South Henderson, N.C.,
 1,843.................*A4 76
South Hill, Va., 3,858....D4 85
South Holland, Ill.,
 23,931................k9 58
South Holland
 (Zuid-Holland), prov.,
 Neth., 2,943,600.......*A6 5
South Hooksett, N.H.,
 1,200.................D4 73
South Houston, Tex.,
 11,527...............r14 84
South Huntington, N.Y.,
 9,115................*D3 75
South Hutchinson, Kans.,
 1,879................f11 61
Southington, Conn.,
 16,000................C5 52
South International Falls,
 Minn., 2,116..........B5 67
South Jacksonville, Ill.,
 2,950.................D3 58
South Jordan, Utah,
 2,942................*A6 72
Southkent, Mich......*F5 66
South Laguna, Calif.,
 2,000................*F5 50
Southlake, Tex., 2,031...*C4 84
South Lake Tahoe, Calif.,
 21,921................C4 50
South Lancaster, Mass.,
 2,679.................B4 65
Southland, Mich.,
 2,000................*F6 66
Southlawn, Ill., 3,000...*D4 58
South Lebanon, Ohio,
 3,014.................C1 78
South Lyon, Mich.,
 2,675.............F7, p14 66
South Mansfield, La., 439..B2 63
South Miami, Fla.,
 11,780...........G6, s13 54
South Milwaukee,
 Wis., 23,297......F6, n12 88
South Modesto, Calif.,
 9,000................*D3 50
South Monroe, Mich.,
 1,200................*G7 66
Southmont, N.C., 600....B2 76
Southmont, Pa., 2,653....*F4 81
South Montrose, Pa.,
 500.................C10 81
South Mt. Vernon, Ohio,
 1,044................*B3 78
South Nelson, N.S., Can.,
 792.................*C4 43
South Nelson Village,
 B.C., Can., 939......*E9 37
South New Castle, Pa.,
 940.................*D1 81
South Nyack, N.Y.,
 3,435.................g9 75
South Ogden, Utah,
 9,991.............A6, C2 72
Southold, N.Y., 2,030....m16 75
South Orange, N.J.,
 16,971................B4 74
South Oroville, Calif.,
 3,704................*C3 50
South Paris, Maine,
 2,315.................D2 64
South Park, Ill., 2,500...*B5 58
South Pasadena, Calif.,
 22,979................*E4 50
South Patrick Shores,
 Fla., 10,313.........D6 54
South Pekin, Ill., 955....C4 58
South Pittsburg, Tenn.,
 3,613.................D8 83
South Plainfield, N.J.,
 21,142................B4 74

South Point, Ohio, 2,243..D3 78
South Porcupine, Ont.,
 Can., 4,843..........o19 41
Southport, Austl., 66,558..E9 25
Southport, Eng., 84,870...D5 4
Southport, Fla., 1,560....u16 54
Southport, Ind.,
 2,342............E5, m10 59
Southport, N.Y., 8,685...*C4 75
Southport, N.C., 2,220...D4 76
South Portland, Maine,
 23,267............E2, g7 64
South Pottstown, Pa.,
 800.................*F10 81
South Range, Mich., 898..A2 66
South Renovo, Pa., 662...D6 81
South Revelstoke, B.C.,
 Can., 737............D8 37
South River, Ont., Can.,
 1,044.................B5 42
South River, N.J.,
 15,428................C4 74
South Rockwood, Mich.,
 1,477................*F7 66
South Roxana, Ill.,
 2,241................*E4 58
South Russell, Ohio,
 2,673................*A4 78
South St. Paul, Minn.,
 25,016............F5, n12 67
South Salisbury, N.C.,
 2,199................*B2 76
South Salt Lake, Utah,
 7,810.................C2 72
South San Francisco,
 Calif., 46,646........h8 50
South San Gabriel,
 Calif., 26,213.......*F4 50
South Shields, Eng.,
 100,220...............C6 4
South Shore, Mo., 200....f12 69
Southside Estates, Fla...*B5 54
South Side Place, Tex.,
 1,466................r14 84
South Sioux City, Nebr.,
 7,920.................B9 71
South Stickney, Ill......k9 58
South Streator, Ill.,
 1,869................*B5 58
South Swansea, Mass.,
 1,500.................C5 65
South Taft, Calif.,
 1,910................*E4 50
South Temple, Pa.,
 1,600................*F10 81
South Toms River, N.J.,
 3,981................D4 74
South Torrington, Wyo.,
 250..................D8 89
South Trail, Fla........q10 54
South Tucson, Ariz.,
 6,220.................C3 48
South Uniontown, Pa.,
 3,546................*G2 81
South Walpole, Mass.,
 600.................h10 65
South Waverly, Pa.,
 1,307................C8 81
South Webster, Ohio,
 825..................D3 78
Southwest, Pa., 700.....F2 81
South West, div., Ice.,
 77,976...............n22 11
South West Africa, see
 Namibia, country, Afr.
South Westbury, N.Y.,
 10,978...............*E7 75
Southwest Dillon, S.C...*C9 82
Southwestern, mts., Va...B4 85
South West Fargo,
 N. Dak..............D9 77
Southwest Greensburg,
 Pa., 3,186...........*F2 81
Southwest Harbor, Maine,
 900..................D4 64
South Whitley, Ind.,
 1,632.................B6 59
Southwick, Mass., 1,263...B2 65
South Williamson, Ky.,
 700..................C7 62
South Williamsport, Pa.,
 7,153.................D7 81
South Wilmington, Ill.,
 725..................B5 58
South Windermere, S.C...*F8 82
South Windham, Maine,
 1,453............E2, g7 64
South Windsor, Conn.,
 10,200................B6 52
Southwood Acres, Conn.,
 10,000...............*B6 52
South Yarmouth, Mass.,
 5,380.................C7 65
South Zanesville, Ohio,
 1,436.................C3 78
Sovetsk (Tilsit), Sov. Un.,
 38,000................A6 7

Sovetskaya Gavan, Sov.
 Un., 28,000..........E17 13
Soviet Union (U.S.S.R.),
 country, Eur., Asia,
 251,050,000........... 13
Spa, Bel., 9,557........B6 5
Spain, country, Eur.,
 34,905,000........... 8
Spalding, Eng., 16,970...D6 4
Spalding, Nebr., 676....C7 71
Spalding, co., Ga., 39,514..C2 55
Spanaway, Wash., 5,768...B3 86
Spangler, Pa., 3,109......E4 81
Spaniard's Bay, Newf.,
 Can., 1,764..........E5 44
Spanish, Ont., Can., 1,257..A2 41
Spanish Fork, Utah,
 7,284.............A6, D2 72
Spanish Sahara, see
 Western Sahara, Afr.
Spanish Town, Jam.,
 41,600................F5 35
Sparkill, N.Y., 1,200....*D6 75
Sparkman, Ark., 663.....D3 49
Sparks, Ga., 1,337.......E3 55
Sparks, Nev., 24,187.....B2 72
Sparlingville, Mich.,
 1,845................*F8 66
Sparrows Point, Md.,
 2,750.................B5 53
Sparta, Ga., 2,172.......C4 55
Sparta, Ill., 4,307......E4 58
Sparta, Mich., 3,094.....E5 66
Sparta, N.J., 6,262......A3 74
Sparta, N.C., 1,304......A1 76
Sparta, Tenn., 4,930.....D8 83
Sparta, Wis., 6,258......E3 88
Sparta, mtn., N.J........B3 74
Spartanburg, S.C.,
 44,546 (*125,000)......B4 82
Spartanburg, co., S.C.,
 173,631...............B3 82
Sparti (Sparta), Grc.,
 10,549 (*13,432)......D4 14
Spassk-Dalniy, Sov. Un.,
 45,000...............E16 13
Spearfish, S. Dak., 4,661..F2 77
Spearman, Tex., 3,435....A2 84
Spearville, Kans., 738...E4 61
Speed, Ind., 640.........H6 59
Speedway, Ind.,
 14,649............E5, k10 59
Speers, Pa., 1,408......*F2 81
Speight, Ky., 230........C7 62
Spenard, Alsk.........*C10 47
Spencer, Ind., 2,553.....F4 59
Spencer, Iowa, 10,278.....A2 60
Spencer, Mass., 5,895....B4 65
Spencer, Nebr., 606......B7 71
Spencer, N.Y., 854.......C4 75
Spencer, N.C., 3,075.....B2 76
Spencer, Ohio, 758.......A3 78
Spencer, Okla., 3,714....*B4 79
Spencer, W. Va., 2,271...C3 87
Spencer, Wis., 1,181.....D3 88
Spencer, co., Ind., 17,134..H4 59
Spencer, co., Ky., 5,488...B4 62
Spencerport, N.Y., 2,929..B3 75
Spencerville, Ohio, 2,241..B1 78
Sperry, Okla., 1,123......A6 79
Speyer, Ger., Fed. Rep. of,
 43,415................D4 6
Spiceland, Ind., 957.....E7 59
Spinazzola, It., 10,850....D6 9
Spindale, N.C., 3,848.....B1 76
Spink, co., S. Dak., 10,595..F7 77
Spirit Lake, Idaho, 622...B3 57
Spirit Lake, Iowa, 3,014...A2 60
Spirit River, Alta., Can.,
 1,091.................B1 38
Spiro, Okla., 2,057......B7 79
Spišská Nová Ves, Czech.,
 22,554................D6 7
Spittal an der Drau, Aus.,
 12,556................E6 6
Split, Yugo., 151,875.....D3 10
Spokane, Wash., 170,516
 (*259,000).......B8, g14 86
Spokane, co., Wash.,
 287,487...............B8 86
Spoleto, It., 26,300.....C4 9
Spooner, Wis., 2,444......C2 88
Spotswood, N.J., 7,891...C4 74
Spotsylvania, co., Va.,
 16,424................B5 85
Sprague, W. Va., 1,500...n13 87
Spray, N.C..............A3 76
Spreckels, Calif., 750...*D3 50
Spreckelsville, Haw., 120..*C5 56
Spremberg, Ger. Dem.
 Rep., 22,900..........C7 6
Spring, Tex., 950.......q14 84
Spring Arbor, Mich., 1,832.F6 66
Springboro, Ohio, 2,799...C1 78
Spring City, Pa., 3,578...F10 81
Spring City, Tenn., 1,756..D9 83
Springdale, Ark., 16,783...A1 49

Springdale, Newf., Can.,
 3,224.................D3 44
Springdale, Ohio, 8,127...n13 78
Springdale, Pa., 5,202.E2, h14 81
Springdale, S.C., 2,638...*D5 82
Springer, N. Mex., 1,574...A6 48
Springfield, Colo., 1,660..D8 51
Springfield, Fla., 5,949...v16 54
Springfield, Ill., 91,753
 (*137,400)...........D4 58
Springfield, Ky., 2,961....C4 62
Springfield, Mass., 163,905
 (*500,000)...........B2 65
Springfield, Minn., 2,530...F4 67
Springfield, Mo., 120,096
 (*151,400)...........D4 69
Springfield, Nebr.,
 795..............C9, g12 71
Springfield, N.J., 15,740...B4 74
Springfield, Ohio, 81,941...C2 78
Springfield, Oreg., 27,047..C4 80
Springfield, Pa., 29,006...*B11 81
Springfield, S.C., 724.....E5 82
Springfield, S. Dak.,
 1,566.................H8 77
Springfield, Tenn., 9,720...A5 83
Springfield, Vt., 5,632....E3 73
Springfield, Wis., 11,613..g12 85
Springfield Place, Mich...*F5 66
Spring Glen, Fla.......*B5 54
Spring Green, Wis., 1,199..E3 88
Spring Grove, Minn.,
 1,290.................G7 67
Spring Grove, Pa., 1,669...G8 81
Springhill, N.S., Can.,
 5,262.................D6 43
Spring Hill, Kans., 1,186..D9 61
Springhill, La., 6,496.....A2 63
Spring Hill, Pa., 500....*F4 81
Spring Hope, N.C., 1,334...B4 76
Spring Lake, Mich., 3,034..E4 66
Spring Lake, N.J., 3,896...C4 74
Spring Lake, N.C., 3,968...B3 76
Spring Lake Heights, N.J.,
 4,602.................C4 74
Spring Lake Park, Minn.,
 6,411................*E5 67
Springlee, Ky., 583.....*H6 62
Spring Mills, S.C., 900...*B6 82
Springmont, Pa., 600....*F10 81
Springport, Mich., 723....F6 66
Springs, S. Afr., 99,047..*F5 24
Springsure, Aust., 820.....B8 25
Springvale, Maine, 2,914...E2 64
Spring Valley, Calif.,
 34,400...............o16 50
Spring Valley, Ill., 5,605..B4 58
Spring Valley, Minn.,
 2,572.................G6 67
Spring Valley, N.Y.,
 18,112...............g12 75
Spring Valley, Ohio, 667..C1 78
Spring Valley, Tex.,
 3,170................*E5 84
Springville, Iowa, 970....B6 60
Springville, N.Y., 4,350...C2 75
Springville, Utah,
 8,790.............A6, D2 72
Spruce Knob, mtn.,
 W. Va................C5 87
Spruce Pine, N.C., 2,333..f10 76
Spur, Tex., 1,747........C2 84
Squamish, B.C., Can.,
 1,597.................E6 37
Squatteck, Que., Can.,
 1,088.................B9 42
Squaw Lake, Minn., 113...C4 67
Squaw Rapids, Sask.,
 Can., 1,024...........D4 39
Srbobran, Yugo., 14,150...C4 10
Sredne-Kolymsk, Sov.
 Un., 2,500...........C18 13
Sremska Mitrovica, Yugo.,
 31,921................C4 10
Sretensk, Sov. Un.,
 13,900...............D14 13
Sri Lanka, country, Asia,
 13,065,000...........G7 20
Srīnagar, India, 403,413
 (*415,271)...........B6 20
Ssuping (Szeping), China,
 130,000...............C9 17
Staatsburg, N.Y., 800....D7 75
Stade, Ger., Fed. Rep. of,
 40,687................B4 6
Stafford, Eng., 54,120....D5 4
Stafford, Kans., 1,414....E5 61
Stafford, Tex., 2,906....*E5 84
Stafford, co., Eng.,
 1,860,200............*D5 4
Stafford, co., Kans.,
 5,943.................D5 61
Stafford, co., Va., 24,587..B5 85
Stafford Springs, Conn.,
 3,339.................B7 52
Staffordsville, Ky., 700..C7 62
Staines, Eng., 56,370.....m11 4
Stains, Fr., 32,169......g10 5

Stambaugh, Mich., 1,458..B2 66
Stamford, Conn., 108,798..E2 52
Stamford, N.Y., 1,286......C6 75
Stamford, Tex., 4,558......C3 84
Stamps, Ark., 2,448.......D2 49
Stanaford, W. Va.,
 950............D3, n13 87
Stanberry, Mo., 1,479.....A3 69
Standale, Mich..........*F5 66
Standerton, S. Afr.,
 20,782.............F5 24
Standish, Mich., 1,184....E7 66
Stanfield, Oreg., 891.....B7 80
Stanford, Calif., 8,691...*D2 50
Stanford, Ky., 2,474......C5 62
Stanford, Mont., 505......C6 70
Stanhope, N.J., 3,040.....B3 74
Stanislaus, co., Calif.,
 194,506............D3 50
Stanke Dimitrov, Bul.,
 35,806.............D6 10
Stanley, Falk. Is., 1,050..I5 27
Stanley, N.C., 2,336......B1 76
Stanley, N. Dak., 1,581...B3 77
Stanley, Va., 1,208.......B4 85
Stanley, Wis., 2,049......D3 88
Stanley, co., S. Dak.,
 2,457.............F5 77
Stanleytown, Va., 500.....D3 85
Stanleyville, N.C., 2,362.*A2 76
Stanly, co., N.C., 42,833..B2 76
Stanstead, Que., Can.,
 1,192.............D5 42
Stanstead, co., Que., Can.,
 37,247............D5 42
Stanthorpe, Austl., 3,606..E9 25
Stanton, Calif., 18,149...*F5 50
Stanton, Del., 3,000......*A6 53
Stanton, Mich., 1,089.....E5 66
Stanton, Nebr., 1,363.....C8 71
Stanton, Tex., 2,117......C2 84
Stanton, co., Kans., 2,287..E2 61
Stanton, co., Nebr., 5,758..C8 71
Stantonsburg, N.C., 869...B5 76
Stanwood, Wash., 1,347...A3 86
Staples, Minn., 2,657.....D4 67
Star, N.C., 892..........B3 76
Starachowice, Pol.,
 42,800............C6 7
Staraya Russa, Sov. Un.,
 35,000............C8 12
Stara Zagora, Bul.,
 88,621............D7 10
Stara-Zagora, co., Bul.,
 352,350...........*D7 10
Starbuck, Minn., 1,138...E3 67
Star City, Ark., 2,032....D4 49
Star City, W. Va., 1,312..B5 87
Stargard, Pol., 44,400....B3 7
Stargo, Ariz., 1,194......C4 48
Starjunction, Pa., 1,150..*F2 81
Stark, co., Ill., 7,510....B4 58
Stark, co., N. Dak.,
 19,613............D3 77
Stark, co., Ohio, 372,210..B4 78
Starke, Fla., 4,848.......C4 54
Starke, co., Ind., 19,280..B4 59
Starkey, Va., 100........C3 85
Starkville, Miss., 11,369..B5 68
Starobelsk, Sov. Un.,
 22,000............G12 12
Starodub, Sov. Un.,
 15,000............E9 12
Starogard, Pol., 33,400...B5 7
Starr, co., Tex., 17,707..F3 84
Startex, S.C., 1,203......B3 82
Staryy Oskol, Sov. Un.,
 52,000............F11 12
Stassfurt, Ger. Dem. Rep.,
 26,272............C5 6
State Center, Iowa, 1,232..B4 60
State College, Miss.,
 4,595.............B5 68
State College, Pa., 33,778..E6 81
State Road, N.C., 650.....A2 76
Statesboro, Ga., 14,616...D5 55
Statesville, N.C., 20,007..B2 76
Staunton, Ill., 4,396.....D4 58
Staunton (Independent
 City), Va., 24,504......B3 85
Stavanger, Nor., 80,800
 (*111,000)...........H1 11
Stavropol, Sov. Un.,
 198,000............I13 12
Stawell, Austl., 5,826....H4 26
Stayner, Ont., Can.,
 1,671.............C4 41
Stayton, Oreg.,
 3,170..........C4, k12 80
Steamboat Springs, Colo.,
 2,340.............A4 51
Stearns, Ky., 950........D5 62
Stearns, co., Minn., 95,400 E4 67
Steblev, Sov. Un., 10,000..G8 12
Steele, Mo., 2,107.......E8 69
Steele, co., Minn., 26,931..F5 67
Steele, co., N Dak., 3,749..C8 77
Steeleville, Ill., 1,957...E4 58

Steelton, Pa., 8,556......F8 81
Steelville, Mo., 1,392....D6 69
Steep Rock Lake, Ont.,
 Can., 40.........o17 41
Stefanesti, Rom., 7,770...B8 10
Steger, Ill., 8,104....B6, m9 58
Steiermark (Styria),
 state, Aus., 1,137,865...*E7 6
Steilacoom, Wash.,
 2,850..........B3, f10 86
Steinbach, Man., Can.,
 5,197.............E3 40
Stellarton, N.S., Can.,
 5,357.............D7 43
Stendal, Ger. Dem. Rep.,
 38,927............B5 6
Stephen, Minn., 904......B2 67
Stephens, Ark., 1,184....D2 49
Stephens, co., Ga.,
 20,331............B3 55
Stephens, co., Okla.,
 35,902............C4 79
Stephens, co., Tex.,
 8,414.............C3 84
Stephens City, Va., 802...A4 85
Stephenson, Mich., 800...C3 66
Stephenson, co., Ill.,
 48,861............A4 58
Stephenville, Newf., Can.,
 7,770.............D2 44
Stephenville, Tex., 9,277..C3 84
Stephenville Crossing,
 Newf., Can., 2,129.....D2 44
Sterling, Colo., 10,636...A7 51
Sterling, Ill., 16,113....B4 58
Sterling, Kans., 2,312....D5 61
Sterling, Mass., 950
 (4,247 ▲)..........B4 65
Sterling, co., Tex., 1,056..D2 84
Sterling City, Tex., 780..D2 84
Sterling Heights, Mich.,
 61,365............o15 66
Sterlington, La., 1,118....B3 63
Sterlitamak, Sov. Un.,
 185,000............D8 13
Šternberk, Czech.,
 12,441............D4 7
Stettin, see Szczecin, Pol.
Stettler, Alta., Can.,
 4,168.............C4 38
Stetson, mtn., Maine.....C4 64
Steuben, co., Ind.,
 20,159............A7 59
Steuben, co., N.Y.,
 99,546............C3 75
Steubenville, Ohio,
 30,771 (*138,200)....B5 78
Stevenage, Eng., 61,700...*E6 4
Stevens, co., Kans., 4,198..E3 61
Stevens, co., Minn.,
 11,218............E2 67
Stevens, co., Wash.,
 17,405............A7 86
Stevenson, Ala., 2,390....A4 46
Stevenson, Wash., 916....D4 86
Stevens Point, Wis.,
 23,479............D4 88
Stevensville, Mich., 1,107..F4 66
Stevensville, Mont., 829..D2 70
Steveston, B.C., Can.,
 4,000.............F12 37
Stewardson, Ill., 729.....D5 58
Stewart, Minn., 666......F4 67
Stewart, co., Ga., 6,511..D2 55
Stewart, co., Tenn., 7,319..A4 83
Stewart Manor, N.Y.,
 2,183.............*E7 75
Stewartstown, Pa., 1,157..G8 81
Stewartsville, N.J., 900...B2 74
Stewartville, Minn.,
 2,802.............G6 67
Stewiacke, N.S., Can.,
 1,042.............D6 43
Steyr, Aus., 40,587
 (*54,000)..........D7 6
Stickney, Ill., 6,601.....*B6 58
Stigler, Okla., 2,347.....B6 79
Stillwater, Minn.,
 10,191............E6 67
Stillwater, N.Y., 1,428...C7 75
Stillwater, Okla., 31,126..A4 79
Stillwater, co., Mont.,
 4,632.............E7 70
Stilwell, Okla., 2,134....B7 79
Stinnett, Tex., 2,014.....B2 84
Štip, Yugo., 27,289......E6 10
Stirling, Ont., Can.,
 1,315.............C7 41
Stirling, N.J., 200.......B4 74
Stirling, Scot., 29,788
 (*56,000)..........B5 4
Stirling, co., Scot.,
 208,840...........*B5 4
Stittsville, Ont., Can.,
 1,994.............B9 41
Stockbridge, Ga., 1,561...C2 55
Stockbridge, Mass., 900...B1 65

Stockbridge, Mich., 1,190..F6 66
Stockdale, Tex., 1,132..E4, k8 84
Stockerau, Aus., 12,564...D8 6
Stockholm, Swe.,
 699,238
 (*1,350,929)......H8, t36 11
Stockholm, co., Swe.,
 1,436,400...........*H8 11
Stockport, Eng., 139,530...D5 4
Stockton, Ala., 150.......E2 46
Stockton, Calif.,
 109,963 (*241,800)..D3, h10 50
Stockton, Ill., 1,930.....A3 58
Stockton, Kans., 1,818....C4 61
Stockton, Mo., 1,063.....D4 69
Stoddard, co., Mo.,
 25,771............E8 69
Stoke-on-Trent, Eng.,
 263,610 (*445,000)....D5 4
Stokes, co., N.C., 23,782..A2 76
Stokesdale, N.C., 800....A3 76
Stokke, Nor., 801........p28 11
Stolberg, Ger., Fed. Rep.
 of, 56,910..........C3 6
Stone, Ky., 400.........C7 62
Stone, co., Ark., 6,838...B3 49
Stone, co., Miss., 8,101..E4 68
Stone, co., Mo., 9,921...E4 69
Stoneboro, Pa., 1,129....D1 81
Stonega, Va., 600........f9 85
Stoneham, Mass., 20,725..g11 65
Stone Harbor, N.J., 1,089..E3 74
Stonehaven, Scot., 4,748..B5 4
Stoneleigh, Md........*B4 53
Stone Mountain, Ga.,
 1,899...........C2, h8 55
Stone Park, Ill., 4,421...*B6 58
Stones River Homes,
 Tenn............*B5 83
Stoneville, N.C., 1,030...A3 76
Stonewall, Man., Can.,
 1,583.............D3 40
Stonewall, Miss., 1,161...C5 68
Stonewall, co., Tex.,
 2,397.............C2 84
Stoney Creek, Ont., Can.,
 7,243.............D5 41
Stonington, Conn.,
 1,413.............D9 52
Stonington, Ill., 1,096...D4 58
Stonington, Maine, 800
 (1,291 ▲)..........D4 64
Stony Brook, N.Y.,
 6,391............*n15 75
Stony Creek Mills, Pa.,
 2,500............*F10 81
Stony Mountain, Can.,
 1,268.............D3 40
Stony Plain, Alta., Can.,
 1,770.............C3 38
Stony Point, N.Y., 8,270..A5 75
Stony Point, N.C., 1,001..B1 76
Stony Prairie, Ohio,
 1,913.............*A2 78
Storey, co., Nev., 695....B2 72
Storm Lake, Iowa, 8,591..B2 60
Stormont, co., Ont., Can.,
 59,550............B9 41
Stornoway, Scot., 5,266...A3 4
Storozhinets, Sov. Un.,
 10,000............G5 12
Storrs, Conn., 10,691....B7 52
Story, co., Iowa, 62,783..B4 60
Story City, Iowa, 2,104...B4 60
Stottville, N.Y., 1,106...C7 75
Stoughton, Sask., Can.,
 606..............H4 39
Stoughton, Mass.,
 23,459..........B5, h11 65
Stoughton, Wis., 6,091...F4 88
Stovall, Miss., 50.......A3 68
Stover, Mo., 849.........C4 69
Stow, Ohio, 19,847......A4 78
Stowe, Pa., 4,038.......F10 81
Stowe Township, Pa.,
 10,119............*E2 81
Stoyoma, mtn., B.C., Can..E7 37
Strabane, N. Ire., 9,325...C3 4
Strabane, Pa., 1,900.....F1 81
Strafford, Mo., 491......D4 69
Strafford, Pa., 4,500....*G10 81
Strafford, co., N.H.,
 70,431............E5 73
Strakonice, Czech.,
 17,093............D2 7
Straldzha, Bul., 5,348...D8 10
Stralsund, Ger. Dem. Rep.,
 72,244............A6 6
Strängnäs, Swe., 8,300...t35 11
Stranraer, Scot., 9,894...C4 4
Strasbourg, Sask., Can.,
 636..............F3 39
Strasbourg, Fr.,
 249,396 (*355,000)....D3 5
Strasburg, N. Dak., 642..D5 77
Strasburg, Ohio, 1,874...B4 78
Strasburg, Pa., 1,897....G9 81
Strasburg, Va., 2,431....B4 85

Stratford, Calif., 800......D4 50
Stratford, Ont., Can.,
 24,508............D3 41
Stratford, Conn., 49,775...E4 52
Stratford, Iowa, 710.....B4 60
Stratford, N.J., 9,801....D2 74
Stratford, Okla., 1,278...C5 79
Stratford, Tex., 2,139....A1 84
Stratford, Wis., 1,239....D3 88
Stratford Hills, Va......*C5 85
Stratford-on-Avon, Eng.,
 19,280............D6 4
Strathmore, Calif., 1,221..D4 50
Strathmore, Alta., Can.,
 924..............D4 38
Strathroy, Ont., Can.,
 6,592.............E3 41
Straubing, Ger., Fed. Rep.
 of, 44,546.........D6 6
Strawberry, mts., Oreg....C8 80
Strawberry Point, Calif.,
 3,300............*C2 50
Strawberry Point, Iowa,
 1,281.............B6 60
Strawn, Tex., 786.......C3 84
Strážnice, Czech., 4,989..D4 7
Streamwood, Ill., 18,176..*A5 58
Streator, Ill., 15,600....B5 58
Streetsboro, Ohio, 7,966.*A4 78
Streetsville, Ont., Can.,
 6,840............m14 41
Strehaia, Rom., 8,545....C6 10
Stringtown, Ky., 350.....B5 62
Stromsburg, Nebr., 1,215..C8 71
Strong City, Kans., 545...D7 61
Stronghurst, Ill., 836....C3 58
Strongsville, Ohio, 15,182..A4 78
Stroud, Okla., 2,502.....B5 79
Stroudsburg, Pa., 5,451..E11 81
Stroudsburg West, Pa.,
 1,777............*E11 81
Struer, Den., 8,335......I3 11
Strum, Wis., 738........D2 88
Strumica, Yugo., 23,071..E6 10
Struthers, Ohio, 15,343..A5 78
Stryker, Ohio, 1,296.....A1 78
Stryy, Sov. Un., 48,000..G4 12
Strzegom, Pol., 14,000...C4 7
Strzelce, Pol., 14,700...C5 7
Strzelin, Pol., 8,462....C4 7
Strzelno, Pol., 5,403....B5 7
Strzemieszyce, Pol.,
 11,400............g10 7
Stuart, Fla., 4,820......E6 54
Stuart, Iowa, 1,354......C3 60
Stuart, Nebr., 561......B6 71
Stuart, Va., 947.........D2 85
Stuarts Draft, Va., 950...B3 85
Stung Treng, Camb.,
 3,400.............C3 19
Sturbridge, Mass., 800...B3 65
Sturgeon, Mo., 787......B5 69
Sturgeon, Pa., 850......*F1 81
Sturgeon Bay, Wis., 6,776..D6 88
Sturgeon Falls, Ont.,
 Can., 6,662........A5 41
Sturgis, Sask., Can., 611..F4 39
Sturgis, Ky., 2,210......C2 62
Sturgis, Mich., 9,295....G5 66
Sturgis, S. Dak., 4,536...F2 77
Sturtevant, Wis.,
 3,376...........F6, n12 88
Stutsman, co., N. Dak.,
 23,550............C7 77
Stuttgart, Ark., 10,477...C4 49
Stuttgart, Ger., Fed. Rep.
 of, 630,390 (*1,650,000)..D4 6
Styria, reg., Aus........E7 6
Suao, Taiwan, 5,000.....*G9 17
Sublette, Kans., 1,208....E3 61
Sublette, co., Wyo., 3,755..D2 89
Subotica, Yugo., 88,787...B4 10
Succasunna, N.J., 7,400..B3 74
Suceava, Rom., 37,700...B8 10
Sucha, Pol., 6,599.......D5 7
Suchitoto, Sal., 5,540...*E7 34
Suchou (Soochow), China,
 725,000............E9 17
Sucre, Bol., 48,000......C2 29
Sucre, state, Ven.,
 401,992............A5 32
Sucy-en-Brie, Fr., 17,206..g11 5
Sudan, Tex., 976........B1 84
Sudan, country, Afr.,
 17,085,000..........E8 21
Sudan, reg., Afr........E7 21
Sudbury, Ont., Can.,
 90,535 (*155,424)..A4, p19 41
Sudbury, Mass.,
 2,500...........B5, g10 65
Sudbury, dist., Ont.,
 Can., 174,102......A3 41
Sudbury Center, Mass.,
 2,000............*B5 65
Sudirman, mts., Indon...F9 19
Sudzha, Sov. Un.,
 10,000............F10 12
Sueca, Sp., 20,612......C5 8

Suez, Eg., 264,098........H9 14
Suffern, N.Y.,
 8,273.............D6, m14 75
Suffield, Conn., 1,500.....B6 52
Suffolk (Independent
 City), Va., 47,400..D6, k14 85
Suffolk, co., Eng.,
 553,980.............*D7 4
Suffolk, co., Mass.,
 735,190.............B5 65
Suffolk, co., N.Y.,
 1,127,030............n15 75
Sugar, mtn., Mich........k9 66
Sugar Creek, Mo., 4,755..h11 69
Sugarcreek, Ohio, 1,771..*B4 78
Sugar Grove, Va.,
 500.............D1, f10 85
Sugar Hill, Ga., 1,745...B2 55
Sugar Land, Tex.,
 3,318............E5, r14 84
Sugarloaf, mtn., Maine....C2 64
Sugar Notch, Pa., 1,333...n17 81
Şuḥār, Om., 4,000........E6 15
Suhl, Ger. Dem. Rep.,
 36,187.............C5 6
Suihua, China, 55,000....B10 17
Suileng, China, 5,000....C3 18
Suipin, China, 5,000.....C5 18
Suita, Jap., 259,619.....*I7 18
Suitland, Md., 28,000....f9 53
Sukabumi, Indon., 96,242..G3 19
Sukaradja, Indon., 16,632.F4 19
Sukarnapura, see Jayapura,
 Indon.
Sukhumi, Sov. Un.,
 102,000.............A13 14
Sukumo, Jap., 25,028.....J6 18
Sukkur, Pak., 103,216....C4 20
Sulawesi, see Celebes, isl.,
 Indon.
Sullana, Peru, 34,501
 (*53,000)............B1 31
Sulligent, Ala., 1,762....B1 46
Sullivan, Ill., 4,112.....D5 58
Sullivan, Ind., 4,683.....F3 59
Sullivan, Mo., 5,111......C6 69
Sullivan, co., Ind.,
 19,889.............F3 59
Sullivan, co., Mo., 7,572..A4 69
Sullivan, co., N.H.,
 30,949.............E3 73
Sullivan, co., N.Y.,
 52,580.............D6 75
Sullivan, co., Pa., 5,961...D8 81
Sullivan, co., Tenn.,
 127,329............C11 83
Sullivans Island, S.C.,
 1,426.............k12 82
Sully, Iowa, 685..........C5 60
Sully, co., S. Dak., 2,362..F5 77
Sulmona, It., 18,300......C4 9
Sulphur, La., 14,959......D2 63
Sulphur, Okla., 5,158.....C5 79
Sulphur South, La.......*D2 63
Sulphur Springs, Tex.,
 10,642.............C5 84
Sultan, Wash, 1,119......B4 86
Sulu, prov., Phil.,
 326,898.............*D6 19
Sumach, Wash., 500.....*C5 86
Sumas, Wash., 722.......A3 86
Sumatra, isl., Indon......F2 19
Sumenep, Indon., 26,823..G4 19
Sumiton, Ala., 2,374......B2 46
Summerdale, Pa., 800....*F8 81
Summerfield, N.C., 750...A3 76
Summerland, B.C., Can.,
 5,551.............E8 37
Summers, co., W. Va.,
 13,213.............D4 87
Summerside, P.E.I., Can.,
 9,439 (*14,004)......C6 43
Summersville, W. Va.,
 2,429.............C4, m14 87
Summerton, S.C., 1,305...D7 82
Summerville, Ga., 5,043...B1 55
Summerville, Pa., 859....D3 81
Summerville, S.C.,
 3,839.............E7, h11 82
Summit, Ill., 11,569......k9 58
Summit, Miss., 1,640.....D3 68
Summit, N.J., 23,620......B4 74
Summit, co., Colo., 2,665..B4 51
Summit, co., Ohio,
 553,371.............A4 78
Summit, co., Utah, 5,879..A6 72
Summit Hill, Pa.,
 3,811.............E10 81
Summitville, Ind., 1,104...D6 59
Sumner, Ill., 1,201.......E6 58
Sumner, Iowa, 2,174......B5 60
Sumner, Wash., 4,325....B3 86
Sumner, co., Kans.,
 23,553.............E6 61

Sumner, co., Tenn.,
 56,106.............A5 83
Sumoto, Jap., 36,000
 (44,499 ▲)............I7 18
Šumperk, Czech., 23,080..D4 7
Sumter, S.C.,
 24,555 (*68,700)......D7 82
Sumter, co., Ala., 16,974..C1 46
Sumter, co., Fla., 14,839..D4 54
Sumter, co., Ga., 26,931..D2 55
Sumter, co., S.C., 78,885..D7 82
Sumy, Sov. Un., 159,000..F10 12
Sun, La., 288............D6 63
Sunburst, Mont., 604.....B5 70
Sunbury, Ohio, 1,820.....B3 78
Sunbury, Pa., 13,025......E8 81
Sunbury, co., N.B., Can.,
 25,011.............D3 43
Sunchŏn, Kor., 61,000
 (90,910 ▲)............I3 18
Sunchŏn, Kor., 20,682....G2 18
Sun City, Ariz., 13,670...D1 48
Suncook, N.H., 4,280.....E5 73
Sun Crest, Calif., 2,000...*F5 50
Sundance, Wyo., 1,056....B8 89
Sundance, mtn., Wyo......B8 89
Sundbyberg, Swe.,
 28,400.............t35 11
Sunderland, Ont., Can.,
 634.............C5 41
Sunderland, Eng.,
 215,650.............C6 4
Sundown, Tex., 1,129.....C1 84
Sundre, Alta., Can., 853..D3 38
Sundsvall, Swe., 65,712
 (*98,388)............F7 11
Sunfield, Mich., 497......F5 66
Sunflower, co., Miss.,
 37,047.............B3 68
Sungari, riv., China......C5 18
Sungchiang, China,
 40,000.............E7 17
Sungurlu, Tur., 16,993....B10 14
Suniland, Fla...........*G6 54
Sunman, Ind., 707........F7 59
Sunnyland, Fla., 800.....q11 54
Sunnyland, Ill., 4,000....*C4 58
Sunnymead, Calif.,
 6,708.............*F5 50
Sunnyside, Utah, 485.....B6 72
Sunnyside, Wash., 6,751..C5 86
Sunnyvale, Calif., 95,408..k8 50
Sunol, Calif., 450........h9 50
Sun Prairie, Wis., 9,935...E4 88
Sunray, Tex., 1,854.......B2 84
Sunridge, Ont., Can., 756.B5 41
Sunrise Heights, Mich.,
 1,626.............*F5 66
Sunset, La., 1,675........D3 63
Sunset, Utah, 6,268......*A5 72
Sunset Beach, Calif.,
 1,500.............*F5 50
Sunset Hills, Mo.,
 4,126.............*C7 69
Sunset Park, Kans., 750..*B5 61
Superior, Ariz., 4,975..C3, D3 48
Superior, Mont., 993.....C2 70
Superior, Nebr., 2,779....E7 71
Superior, W. Va., 350....*D3 87
Superior, Wis., 32,237....B1 88
Superior, Wyo., 5........E4 89
Superior, lake, Can.,
 U.S.............A9 45
Suquamish, Wash., 900...B3 86
Şūr (Tyre), Leb., 12,500..F10 14
Şur, Om...............E6 15
Surabaja, see Surabaya,
 Indon.
Surabaya, Indon.,
 1,556,255............G4 19
Surakarta, Indon., 414,285.G4 19
Šurany, Czech., 5,381....D5 7
Surat, India, 471,656
 (*493,001)...........D5 20
Suresnes, Fr., 40,616.....g9 5
Surfside, Fla., 3,614......s13 54
Surgoinsville, Tenn.,
 1,285.............C11 83
Surgut, Sov. Un., 3,500...C10 13
Sūri, India, 30,110.......D8 20
Surigao, Phil., 26,099....D7 19
Surigao del Norte, prov.,
 Phil., 194,981.......*D7 19
Surigao del Sur, prov.,
 Phil., 165,016.......*D7 19
Surinam, dep., S.A.,
 445,000.............C5 27
Suriname, riv., Sur.......C5 27
Surrey, co., Eng.,
 1,011,230...........*E6 4
Surry, N.H., 200.........E3 73
Surry, co., N.C., 51,415..A2 76
Surry, co., Va., 5,882....C6 85
Susa, It., 5,891.........B1 9

Susana Knolls, Calif......*E4 50
Susanville, Calif., 6,608...B3 50
Sušice, Czech., 6,793.....D2 7
Susquehanna, Pa., 2,319..C10 81
Susquehanna, co., Pa.,
 34,344.............C10 81
Sussex, N.B., Can.,
 3,942.............D4 43
Sussex, N.J., 2,038.......A3 74
Sussex, Wis., 2,758......m11 88
Sussex, co., Del., 80,356..C6 53
Sussex, co., Eng.,
 1,244,560.............*E7 4
Sussex, co., N.J., 77,528..A3 74
Sussex, co., Va., 11,464...D5 85
Susurluk, Tur., 12,354....C7 14
Sutersville, Pa., 830.....*F2 81
Sutherland, Iowa, 875....B2 60
Sutherland, Nebr., 840....C4 71
Sutherland, co., Scot.,
 12,974.............*B4 4
Sutherlin, Oreg., 3,070...D3 80
Sutter, Calif., 1,488......*C3 50
Sutter, co., Calif., 41,935..C3 50
Sutter Creek, Calif., 1,508.C3 50
Sutton, Que., Can.,
 1,684.............D5 42
Sutton, Nebr., 1,361......D8 71
Sutton, W. Va., 1,031....C4 87
Sutton, co., Tex., 3,175...D2 84
Sutton-in-Ashfield, Eng.,
 40,240.............D6 4
Sutton West, Ont., Can.,
 2,500.............C5 41
Suttsu, Jap.............E10 18
Suva, Fiji, 54,157
 (*80,269)............H8 2
Suwa, Jap., 48,125.......m17 18
Suwałki, Pol., 25,300....A7 7
Suwannee, Fla., 250......C3 54
Suwannee, co., Fla.,
 15,559.............B3 54
Suwŏn, S. Kor., 140,000
 (170,518▲)...........H3 18
Suyo, Peru, 744.........B1 31
Suzuka, Jap., 85,000
 (121,185▲)...........o15 18
Svalbard (Spitzbergen),
 Nor., dep............B5 13
Svedala, Swe., 3,114.....A2 7
Svendborg, co., Den.,
 146,500.............*J4 11
Sverdlovsk, Sov. Un.,
 1,048,000 (*1,230,000)..D9 13
Sverdrup, is., Can.......m30 36
Svetlaya, Sov. Un.,
 10,000.............C9 18
Svilajnac, Yugo., 5,905...C5 10
Svilengrad, Bul., 9,918...E8 10
Svirstroy, Sov. Un.,
 10,000.............A9 12
Svishtov, Bul., 21,539....D7 10
Svitavy, Czech., 13,868...D4 7
Svobodnyy, Sov. Un.,
 63,000.............D15 13
Swain, co., N.C., 7,861...f9 76
Swainsboro, Ga., 7,325...D4 55
Swampscott, Mass.,
 13,578.............B6, g12 65
Swan Hill, Aust., 7,693...G7 25
Swan Hills, Alta., Can.,
 643.............B3 38
Swanlake, Idaho, 135.....G6 57
Swan Lake, Miss., 300....B3 68
Swannanoa, N.C., 1,966..f10 76
Swan River, Man., Can.,
 3,522.............C1 40
Swansboro, N.C., 1,207...C5 76
Swansea, Ill., 5,432......f14 69
Swansea, Mass., 300......C5 65
Swansea, S.C., 691.......D5 82
Swansea, Wales, 171,320
 (*270,000)...........E5 4
Swansea Center, Mass.,
 700.............*C5 65
Swanton, Ohio, 2,927....A2 78
Swanton, Vt., 2,630......B1 73
Swarthmore, Pa., 6,156..p20 81
Swartz Creek, Mich.,
 4,928.............F7 66
Swatow (Shantou), China,
 250,000.............G8 17
Swayzee, Ind., 1,073.....C6 59
Swaziland, country,
 Afr., 445,000.......F6 24
Swea City, Iowa, 774.....A3 60
Swedeborg, Mo., 175.....D5 69
Swedeland, Pa., 600......o20 81
Sweden, country, Eur.,
 8,165,000...........F7 11
Swedesboro, N.J., 2,287..D2 74
Sweeny, Tex., 3,191......r14 84
Sweet, Idaho, 65........F2 57
Sweet Briar, Va., 900....C3 85

Sweet Grass, co., Mont.,
 2,980.............E7 70
Sweet Home, Oreg., 3,799.C4 80
Sweetsburg, Que., Can.,
 958.............D5 42
Sweetsers, Ind., 1,076....C6 59
Sweet Springs, Mo., 1,716.C4 69
Sweetwater, Tenn., 4,340..D8 83
Sweetwater, Tex., 12,020..C2 84
Sweetwater, co., Wyo.,
 18,391.............E3 89
Swepsonville, N.C., 800...A3 76
Swidnica, Pol., 47,500....C4 7
Swidwin, Pol., 12,500.....B3 7
Swiebodzice, Pol., 18,400.C4 7
Swiebodzin, Pol., 14,900..B3 7
Świecie, Pol., 17,900.....B5 7
Świętochłowice, Pol.,
 57,600.............g9 7
Swift, co., Minn., 13,177..E3 67
Swift Current, Sask.,
 Can., 15,415........G2, n7 39
Swindon, Eng., 90,670....E6 4
Swinemünde, see
 Swinoujscie, Pol.
Świnoujście, Pol., 27,900..B3 7
Swisher, co., Tex., 10,373.B2 84
Swissvale, Pa., 13,819....k14 81
Switzer, W. Va., 900.....D3 87
Switzerland, co., Ind.,
 6,306.............G7 59
Switzerland, country,
 Eur., 6,550,000......E4 6
Swoyerville, Pa.,
 6,786.............D10, n17 81
Sycamore, Ill., 7,843.....B5 58
Sycamore, Ohio, 1,096...B2 78
Sycemore Hills, Mo., 821.*C7 69
Sydenham, Ont., Can., 803.C8 41
Sydney, Austl., 61,940
 (*2,799,634).........F9 25
Sydney, N.S., Can.,
 33,230 (*91,162).....C9 43
Sydney Mines, N.S., Can.,
 8,991 (*34,026)......C9 43
Sykesville, Md., 1,399....B4 53
Sykesville, Pa., 1,311....D4 81
Syktyvkar, Sov. Un.,
 125,000.............C8 13
Sylacauga, Ala., 12,255...B3 46
Sylhet, Bngl., 37,740.....D9 20
Sylva, N.C., 1,561.......f9 76
Sylvan, Oreg...........g12 80
Sylvan Beach, N.Y., 699..B5 75
Sylvania, Ala., 476......A4 46
Sylvania, Ga., 3,199......D5 55
Sylvania, Ky............g11 62
Sylvania, Ohio, 12,031.A2, e6 78
Sylvan Lake, Alta., Can.,
 1,597.............C3 38
Sylvester, Ga., 4,226.....E3 55
Syosset, N.Y., 10,084....F2 52
Syracuse, Ind., 1,546.....B6 59
Syracuse, Kans., 1,720...E2 61
Syracuse, Nebr.,
 1,562.............D9, h12 71
Syracuse, N.Y., 197,297
 (*546,900)...........B4 75
Syracuse, Ohio, 681......D4 78
Syracuse, Utah, 1,843....C2 72
Syr Darya, riv., Sov. Un...E9 13
Syria, country, Asia,
 7,015,000...........F6 16
Syriam, Bur., 15,070.....*B1 19
Syzran, Sov. Un., 173,000.D7 13
Szabadszállás, Hung.,
 4,878.............B4 10
Szabolcs-Szatmár, co.,
 Hung., 592,186......*B5 10
Szamotuly, Pol., 14,600..B4 7
Szarvas, Hung., 14,245
 (19,478 ▲)...........B5 10
Szczebrzeszyn, Pol., 4,989.C7 7
Szczecin (Stettin), Pol.,
 337,200.............B3 7
Szczecinek, Pol., 28,600..B4 7
Szechwan, prov., China,
 72,160,000..........E5 17
Szeged, Hung., 118,490...B5 10
Székesfehérvár, Hung.,
 72,490.............B4 10
Szekszárd, Hung., 22,565
 (24,201 ▲)...........B4 10
Szentendre, Hung., 12,744.B4 10
Szentes, Hung., 28,336
 (32,492 ▲)...........B5 10
Szolnok, Hung., 61,418...B5 10
Szolnok, co., Hung.,
 449,827.............*B5 10
Szombathely, Hung.,
 64,745.............B3 10

T

Tabaco, Phil., 8,308...... *C6 19
Tabasco, state, Mex., 573,500.............. D6 34
Taber, Alta., Can., 4,765.. E4 38
Taboada, Sp., 81,62....... A2 8
Tábor, Czech., 21,949..... D3 7
Tabor, Iowa, 957......... D2 60
Tabor, N.J., 1,500....... *B4 74
Tabora, Tan., 15,361...... B6 24
Tabor City, N.C., 2,400... C4 76
Tabrīz, Iran, 403,413...... B4 15
Tabūk, Sau. Ar........... D2 15
Tachikawa, Jap., 117,057.. n18 18
Táchira, state, Ven., 399,163................ B3 32
Tacloban, Phil., 49,908.... C6 19
Tacna, Peru, 55,752....... E5 31
Tacna, dept., Peru, 42,874.. E3 31
Tacoma, Wash., 154,407........... B3, f11 86
Tacuarembó, Ur., 29,011.. E1 30
Tacuarembó, dept., Ur., 77,409................ *E1 30
Tadoussac, Que., Can., 1,010.................. A8 42
Tadzhik, rep., Sov. Un., 3,155,000.............. F9 16
Taegu, Kor., 1,082,750..... I4 18
Taejon, Kor., 414,598..... H3 18
Tafalla, Sp., 7,320........ A5 8
Taff Viejo, Arg., 15,374... E2 29
Tafí Viejo, Arg., 25,000.... E2 29
Taft, Calif., 4,285......... E4 50
Taft, Fla., 1,183.......... D5 54
Taft, Tex., 3,274.......... F4 84
Taft Heights, Calif., 2,108................. *E4 50
Taft Southwest, Tex., 2,026................. *F4 84
Taganrog, Sov. Un., 254,000.............. H12 12
Tahat, mtn., Alg.......... D6 22
Tahlequah, Okla., 9,254... B7 79
Tahoka, Tex., 2,956....... C2 84
Tahoua, Niger, 12,400..... F6 22
Taian, China, 35,000..... *D8 17
Taichou, China, 159,800.. *E8 17
T'aichung, Taiwan, 280,000 (410,200 ▲)..... G9 17
Taihsien, China, 2,600..... E6 17
Taikang, China, 5,000..... C2 18
Tailai, China, 5,000....... C1 18
T'ainan, Taiwan, 340,000 (443,800 ▲)........... G9 17
Taipei, Taiwan, 1,614,100 (*2,150,000)........... G9 17
Taiping, Mala., 54,645.... E2 19
T'aitung, Taiwan, 46,000.. G9 17
Taiwan (Formosa), country (Nationalist China), Asia, 16,370,000............ G9 17
Taiyüan (Yangkü), China, 1,350,000....... D7 17
Taizz, Yemen, 25,000..... G3 15
Tajimi, Jap., 63,522... I8, n16 18
Tajrīsh, Iran, 157,486.... *B5 15
Tājūrā', Libya, 2,670...... B7 22
Tak, Thai., 13,398....... *B1 19
Takada, Jap., 56,000 (75,053 ▲)............ H9 18
Takamatsu, Jap., 274,367.. I7 18
Takaoka, Jap., 159,664 (*205,000)............ H8 18
Takasaki, Jap., 193,072.......... H9, m17 18
Takatsuki, Jap., 231,129.. o14 18
Takawa, Jap., 64,233..... *J5 18
Takayama, Jap., 56,459 (62,019 ▲).. H8, m16 18
Takefu, Jap., 46,500 (62,019▲)............. n15 18
Takeo, Camb., 7,400..... *C2 19
Takingeun, Indon., 8,412................ *m11 19
Takoma Park, Md., 18,455.. f8 53
Takut, Bur., 5,000...... *D10 20
Talā, Eg., 18,570........ *G8 14
Tala, Mex., 15,744....... m12 34
Tala, Ur., 3,213.......... E1 30
Talagante, Chile, 11,560... A2 28
Talai, China, 24,921...... D2 18
Talara, Peru, 27,957...... B1 31
Talavera de la Reina, Sp., 31,900............ C3 8
Talbert, Ky., 30.......... C6 62
Talbot, co., Ga., 6,625.... D2 55
Talbot, co., Md., 23,682... C5 53
Talbotton, Ga., 1,045..... D2 55
Talca, Chile, 68,148....... B2 28
Talca, prov., Chile, 242,100................ B2 28
Talcahuano, Chile, 112,100................ B2 28
Tālcher, India, 11,794..... D8 20
Talco, Tex., 837.......... C5 84
Taliaferro, co., Ga., 2,423.. C4 55
Talihina, Okla., 1,227..... C6 79
Talisayan, Phil., 10,646... *D6 19
Talladega, Ala., 17,662.... B3 46
Talladega, co., Ala., 65,280................. B3 46
Tallahassee, Fla., 72,624 (*92,900)............. B2 54
Tallahatchie, co., Miss., 19,338................. B3 68
Tallapoosa, Ga., 2,896..... C1 55
Tallapoosa, co., Ala., 33,840................ C4 46
Tallassee, Ala., 4,809...... C4 46
Talleyville, Del., 5,000... *A6 53
Tallinn, Sov. Un., 371,000.. B5 12
Tallmadge, Ohio, 15,274.. A4 78
Tallulah, La., 9,643....... B4 63
Talnoye, Sov. Un., 10,000.. G8 12
Talsi, Sov. Un., 10,000.... C4 12
Taltal, Chile, 4,901........ E1 29
Tama, Iowa, 3,000........ C5 60
Tama, co., Iowa, 20,147... B5 60
Tamale, Ghana, 40,400.... G4 22
Taman, Sov. Un., 10,000.. I11 12
Tamano, Jap., 68,446...... I6 18
Tamanrasset, Alg., 1,714.. D6 22
Tamaqua, Pa., 9,246..... E10 81
Tamatave, Mad., 50,200... D9 24
Tamaulipas, state, Mex., 1,210,200.............. C5 34
Tamazula de Gordiano, Mex., 13,521.......... n12 34
Tambov, Sov. Un., 230,000.............. E13 12
Tamil Nadu, state, India, 41,199,168.............. F6 20
Tampa, Fla., 277,753 (*439,400)......... E4, p11 54
Tampere, Fin., 161,257 (*200,000)........... G10 11
Tampico, Mex., 179,584 (*305,000).. C5, k15 34
Tams, W. Va., 500........ D3 87
Tamworth, Austl., 24,076.. F9 25
Tanabe, Jap., 49,000 (63,368 ▲)............. J7 18
Tananarive, see Antananarive, Mad.
Tanchon, Kor., 32,761..... F4 18
Tandag, Phil., 5,085...... *D7 19
Tăndărei, Rom., 2,353.... C8 10
Taney, co., Mo., 13,023.... E4 69
Taneytown, Md., 1,731.... A3 53
Tanga, Tan., 60,935....... B7 24
Tanganyika, lake, Afr..... C6 24
Tanger (Tangier), Mor., 187,894................ A3 22
Tangermünde, Ger. Dem. Rep., 13,046............ B5 6
Tangier, Va., 814......... C7 85
Tangipahoa, par., La., 65,875............... D5 63
Tangshan, China, 900,000.............. *D8 17
Tangtan, China......... C11 20
Tangyüan, China, 5,000... C4 18
Tanjay, Phil., 12,355..... *D6 19
Tanjore, see Thanjāvūr, India
Tanjungkarang-Telukbetung, Indon., 198,986............... G3 19
Tanjungpandan, Indon., 29,412................ F3 19
Tānk, Pak., 10,582........ B5 20
Tanque Verde, Ariz., 200. *C4 48
Tanshui, Taiwan, 10,000.. *F9 17
Ţanţā, Eg., 229,978....... G8 14
Tantung (Antung), China, 370,000............... C9 17
Tanzania, country, Afr., 14,550,000............ B6 24
Taoan, China, 65,000..... B9 17
Taormina, It., 6,600....... F5 9
Taos, N. Mex., 2,475...... A6 48
Taos, co., N. Mex., 17,516.. A6 48
Tapachula, Mex., 60,620... E6 34
Tappahannock, Va., 1,111.................. C6 85
Tappan, N.Y., 7,424...... g13 75
Taquara, Braz., 11,282.... D2 30
Taquaritinga, Braz., 11,624................. k7 30
Tara, Mo................ *C7 69
Tara, Sov. Un., 22,000... D10 13
Ţarābulus, see Tripoli, Leb.
Tarakan, Laos, 10,000.... *B2 19
Tarancon, Sp., 7,714...... B4 8
Taranto, It., 216,600...... D6 9
Tarapacá, prov., Chile, 155,900.............. D1 29
Tarapoto, Peru, 13,907.... C2 31
Tarare, Fr., 12,296........ E6 5
Tarascon-sur-Ariège, Fr., 3,680.................. F6 5
Tarazona, Sp., 12,059..... B5 8
Tarbes, Fr., 55,375 (*73,000).............. F4 5
Tarboro, N.C., 9,425...... B5 76
Taree, Austl., 11,914...... E9 26
Tarentum, Pa., 7,379.. E2, h14 81
Tarfaya, Mor., 1,104...... C2 22
Tarifa, Sp., 7,737......... D3 8
Tarija, Bol., 26,100....... D3 29
Tarija, dept., Bol., 143,900. D3 29
Tarkio, Mo., 2,517........ A2 69
Tarkwa, Ghana, 13,500 (*25,232).............. G4 22
Tarlac, Phil., 23,547 (135,128 ▲)........ B6, o13 19
Tarlac, prov., Phil., 426,647............... *B6 19
Tarma, Peru, 15,452...... D2 31
Tarn, dept., Fr., 332,011.. *F5 5
Tarn-et-Garonne, dept., Fr., 183,572............... *E4 5
Tarnobrzeg, Pol., 18,800... C6 7
Tarnów, Pol., 85,500...... C6 7
Tarnowskie Góry, Pol., 34,200................. g9 7
Taroudant, Mor., 22,272... B3 22
Tarpon Springs, Fla., 7,118................. D4 54
Tarquinia, It., 9,776...... C3 9
Tarragona, Sp., 77,275.... B6 8
Tarragona, prov., Sp., 416,500............... *B6 8
Tarrant, Ala., 6,835.... B3, f7 46
Tarrant, co., Tex., 716,317................ C4 84
Tarrasa, Sp., 136,952...... B7 8
Tarrytown, N.Y., 11,115............ D7, m15 75
Tarsney, Mo., 401........ k11 69
Tarsus, Tur., 74,510..... D10 14
Tartu, Sov. Un., 90,000... B6 12
Tashkent, Sov. Un., 1,424,000 (*1,590,000)... E9 13
Tashkurghan, Afg., 20,000................ A4 20
Tasikmalaja, Indon., 136,004.............. *G3 19
Tasmania, state, Austl., 405,000............... o14 25
Tatabánya, Hun., 65,130... B4 10
Tatamagouche, N.S., Can., 581............. D6 43
Tatarbunary, Sov. Un., 10,000................ C9 10
Tate, Ga., 900............ B2 55
Tate, co., Miss., 18,544.... A4 68
Tateville, Ky., 725........ D5 62
Tateyama, Jap., 40,000 (55,236 ▲)... I9, n18 18
Tatta, Pak., 9,716......... D4 20
Tattnall, co., Ga., 16,557.. D4 55
Tatuí, Braz., 30,895... C3, m8 30
Tatum, N. Mex., 982...... C7 48
Tatung, China, 228,500... C7 17
Taubaté, Braz., 98,933.... C3 30
Taung, S. Afr., 1,288...... F4 24
Taungdwingyi, Bur., 16,233.............. D10 20
Taunggyi, Bur., 8,652.... D10 20
Taunton, Eng., 38,640..... E5 4
Taunton, Mass., 43,756 (*57,200).............. C5 65
Taurage, Sov. Un., 19,500.. D4 12
Tauranga, N.Z., 29,500 (*42,300)............. L16 26
Taurianova, It., 14,300.... E6 9
Tauste, Sp., 6,634........ B5 8
Tavares, Fla., 3,261....... D5 54
Tavas, Tur., 7,110....... *D7 14
Tavda, Sov. Un., 47,000... D9 13
Tavira, Port., 7,496....... D2 8
Tavistock, Ont., Can., 1,490................. D4 41
Tavoy, Bur., 40,312...... F10 20
Tavsanli, Tur., 11,500.... *C7 14
Tawas City, Mich., 1,666.. D7 66
Taylor, Mich., 70,020.... p15 66
Taylor, Pa., 6,977.. D10, m18 81
Taylor, Tex., 9,616........ D4 84
Taylor, co., Fla., 13,641... B3 54
Taylor, co., Ga., 7,865.... D2 55
Taylor, co., Iowa, 8,790... D3 60
Taylor, co., Ky., 17,138... C4 62
Taylor, co., Tex., 97,853... C3 84
Taylor, co., W. Va., 13,878. B4 87
Taylor, co., Wis., 16,958................. C3 88
Taylor Mill, Ky., 4,228................. k14 62
Taylors, S.C., 6,831....... B3 82
Taylorsport, Ky., 100..... h13 62
Taylorsville, Ky., 897...... B4 62
Taylorsville, Miss., 1,299.. D4 68
Taylorsville, N.C., 1,231... B1 76
Taylorville, Ill., 10,927.... D4 58
Tayshet, Sov. Un., 34,000............... D12 13
Taza, Mor., 55,157........ B4 22
Tazewell, Tenn., 1,860... C10 83
Tazewell, Va., 4,168...... e10 85
Tazewell, co., Ill., 118,649. C4 58
Tazewell, co., Va., 39,816. e10 85
Tbilisi, Sov. Un., 907,000 (*1,025,000).... E7 13
Tchula, Miss., 1,729....... B3 68
Tczew, Pol., 40,700....... A5 7
Teague, Tex., 2,867....... D4 84
Teaneck, N.J., 42,355...... h8 74
Tecuala, Mex., 12,461..... C3 34
Tecuci, Rom., 23,400...... C8 10
Tecumseh, Ont., Can., 5,165.................. E2 41
Tecumseh, Mich., 7,120... F7 66
Tecumseh, Nebr., 2,058... D9 71
Tecumseh, Okla., 4,451.... B5 79
Tegal, Indon., 105,752... *G3 19
Tegucigalpa, Hond., 205,000................ E7 34
Teguise, Sp., 5,547....... m15 8
Tehachapi, Calif., 4,211... E4 50
Tehama, co., Calif., 29,517. B2 50
Tehrān, Iran, 2,875,000 (*3,250,000)........... B5 15
Tehuacan, Mex., 47,497............ D5, n15 34
Tehuantepec, Mex., 16,179................ D5 34
Teide, Pico de, peak, Sp., (Can. Is.)........ m13 8
Tejo (Tagus), riv., Eur..... C1 8
Tekamah, Nebr., 1,848.... C9 71
Tekax de Alvaro Obregón, Mex., 10,326.. C7 34
Tekirdağ, Tur., 35,387..... B6 14
Teko, China............ B10 20
Tekoa, Wash., 808........ B8 86
Tela, Hond., 13,619...... *D7 34
Tel Aviv-Yafo (Tel Aviv Jaffa), Isr., 362,200 (*1,150,000). B2, g5 15
Telde, Sp., 11,761....... m14 8
Telemark, co., Nor., 156,600.............. *H3 11
Telfair, co., Ga., 11,381.... E3 55
Telford, Pa., 3,409....... F11 81
Tell, Wis................ I4 59
Tell City, Ind., 7,933...... I4 59
Teller, co., Colo., 3,316.... C5 51
Telluride, Colo., 553...... D3 51
Telok Anson, Mala., 44,524................. E2 19
Teloloapan, Mex., 10,335............ D5, n14 34
Temirtau, Sov. Un., 166,000.............. *D10 13
Témiscouata, co., Que., Can., 25,902............ B9 42
Temora, Austl., 4,462..... *F8 25
Tempe, Ariz., 63,550.. C3, D2 48
Temperance, Mich., 3,000................. G7 66
Tempio Pausania, It., 8,300................. D2 9
Temple, Okla., 1,354...... C3 79
Temple, Pa., 1,667....... F10 81
Temple, Tex., 33,431...... D4 84
Temple City, Calif., 31,004................ *F5 50
Temple Hill, Ky., 130..... D4 62
Temple Terrace, Fla., 7,347................. o11 54
Templeton, Que., Can., 3,684................. D2 42
Templeton, Mass., 750..... A3 65
Templin, Ger. Dem. Rep., 11,600................ B6 6
Temryuk, Sov. Un., 23,000................ I11 12
Temuco, Chile, 101,000.... B2 28
Tenafly, N.J., 14,827... B5, h9 74
Tenaha, Tex., 1,094....... D5 84
Tenāli, India, 102,937.... *E7 20
Tenancingo, [de Degollado], Mex., 12,807...... D5, n14 34
Tenango del Valle, Mex., 8,849................. n14 34
Tenasserim, Bur., 1,194... F10 20

Tengchung, China.......F4 17
Tengri Khan, mtn., China.............E11 13
Tenino, Wash., 962......C3 86
Tennessee, state, U.S., 4,072,000.............. 83
Tennessee, riv., U.S.......D9 45
Tensas, par., La., 9,732...B4 63
Teocaltiche, Mex., 13,745.............C4, m12 34
Teófilo Otoni, Braz., 64,568.............B4 30
Tepatitán [de Morelos], Mex., 29,292....C4, m12 34
Tepic, Mex., 87,540...C4, m11 34
Teplice, Czech., 52,982....C2 7
Teramo, It., 33,300.......C4 9
Teresina, Braz., 181,071...D6 27
Teresópolis, Braz., 53,462.............C4, h6 30
Termez, Sov. Un., 35,000..F9 13
Termini Imerese, It., 24,600.............F4 9
Termoli, It., 9,686......C5 9
Ternate, Indon., 24,287....E7 19
Terneuzen, Neth., 17,600..B5 5
Terney, Sov. Un., 10,000..D8 18
Terni, It., 105,000......C4 9
Ternopol, Sov. Un., 85,000.............G5 12
Terra Alta, W. Va., 1,474..B5 87
Terrace, B.C., Can., 7,820 (*13,902).......B3 37
Terrace Park, Ohio, 2,266.............*C1 78
Terracina, It., 21,900....D4 9
Terra Linda, Calif., 5,000.............*D2 50
Terrebonne, Que., Can., 9,212......D4, p19 42
Terrebonne, co., Que., Can., 122,781......D3 42
Terrebonne, par., La., 76,049.............E5 63
Terre Haute, Ind., 70,335 (*117,700).........F3 59
Terre Hill, Pa., 1,129....F9 81
Terrell, Tex., 14,182.....C4 84
Terrell, co., Ga., 11,416..E2 55
Terrell, co., Tex., 1,940..D1 84
Terrell Hills, Tex., 5,225..k7 84
Terry, Mont., 870......D11 70
Terry, co., Tex., 14,118..C1 84
Terrytown, La., 13,832...*k11 63
Terrytown, Nebr., 747...C2 71
Terryville, Conn., 3,200..C4 52
Teruel, Sp., 20,668......B5 8
Teruel, prov., Sp., 184,400 *B5 8
Tesanj, Yugo., 3,150.....C3 10
Teterow, Ger. Dem. Rep., 11,100.............B6 6
Teton, co., Idaho, 2,351..F7 57
Teton, co., Mont., 6,116..C4 70
Teton, co., Wyo., 4,823..C2 89
Tétouan, Mor., 139,105...A3 22
Tetovo, Yugo., 35,792...D5 10
Tetu, China, 22,024.....B3 18
Teutopolis, Ill., 1,249...D5 58
Teverya (Tiberias), Isr., 23,800.............B3, g5 15
Tewantin-Noosa, Austl., 4,053.............C9 26
Tewksbury, Mass., 4,000..........A5, f11 65
Texarkana, Ark., 21,682..D1 49
Texarkana, Tex., 30,497 (*69,600).........C5 84
Texas, Md., 1,200......B4 53
Texas, co., Mo., 18,320...D5 69
Texas, co., Okla., 16,352..e9 79
Texas, state, U.S., 11,885,000.............. 84
Texas City, Tex., 38,908.............E5, r15 84
Texhoma, Okla., 921.....e9 79
Teziutlán, Mex., 23,948.............D5, n15 34
Thailand (Siam), country, Asia, 37,715,000......B2 19
Thames, N.Z., 5,810....L15 26
Thamesville, Ont., Can., 1,028.............E3 41
Thăna, India, 170,675....*E5 20
Thanh Hoa, Viet., 31,211..B3 19
Thanjāvūr (Tanjore), India, 140,547.............F6 20
Thann, Fr., 8,318 (*26,000).........D7 5
Thaon [-les-Vosges], Fr., 7,622.............C7 5
Tharptown, Pa., 950.....*E8 81
Tharrawaddy, Bur., 8,977.E10 20
Thatcher, Ariz., 2,320....C4 54
Thatcher, Idaho, 50.....G7 57
Thaton, Bur., 38,047....E10 20
Thayer, Mo., 1,609......E6 69
Thayer, co., Nebr., 7,779..D8 71

Thayetmyo, Bur., 11,164.............*E10 20
The Dalles, Oreg., 10,423..B5 80
The Entrance, Austl., 13,661.............F8 26
The Father, mtn., N. Gui.............k13 25
The Hague ('s Gravenhage), Neth., 510,360 (*810,000)......A6 5
The Pas, Man., Can., 6,062.............C1, g7 40
The Plains, Ohio, 1,568...C3 78
Theresa, N.Y., 956......A5, f9 75
Thermalito, Calif., 4,217..*C3 50
Thermopolis, Wyo., 3,063..C4 89
Thesprotía, prov., Grc., 40,547.............*C3 14
Thessalon, Ont., Can., 1,879.............p19 41
Thessaloníki (Salonika), Grc., 345,799 (*557,360).........B4 14
Thessaloníki(Salonika), prov., Grc., 703,350....*B4 14
Thessaly, reg., Grc.......C4 14
Thetford Mines, Que., Can., 22,003 (*26,126)..C6 42
The Village, Okla., 13,695.............*B4 79
Thibodaux, La., 15,028.............E5, k10 63
Thief River Falls, Minn., 8,618.............B2 67
Thiensville, Wis., 3,182.............E6, m12 88
Thiers, Fr., 12,418......E5 5
Thiès, Sen., 69,000......F1 22
Thimbu, Bhu.............C8 20
Thionville, Fr., 38,133 (*63,000).........C7 5
Thisted, co., Den., 82,700.............*I3 11
Thivai (Thebes), Grc., 15,971.............C4 14
Thomas, Okla., 1,336....B3 79
Thomas, W. Va., 713....B5 87
Thomas, co., Ga., 34,515..F3 55
Thomas, co., Kans., 7,501..C2 61
Thomas, co., Nebr., 954...C5 71
Thomason, Ga., 10,024...D2 55
Thomaston, Ala., 824....C2 46
Thomaston, Conn., 3,500..C4 52
Thomaston, Maine, 2,160..D3 64
Thomaston, N.Y., 2,811..*E7 75
Thomasville, Ala., 3,769..D2 46
Thomasville, Ga., 18,155..F3 55
Thomasville, N.C., 15,230..B2 76
Thompson, Conn., 500...B9 52
Thompson Falls, Mont., 1,356.............C1 70
Thompsonville, Conn., 15,000.............A6 52
Thomson, Ga., 6,503....C4 55
Thon Buri, Thai., 627,989.*C2 19
Thorburn, N.S., Can., 1,000.............D7 43
Thornbury, Ont., Can., 1,220.............C4 41
Thorndale, Tex., 1,031....D4 84
Thornton, Colo., 13,326..*B6 51
Thornton, Idaho, 150....F7 57
Thornton, Ill., 3,714.....*B6 58
Thornton, Miss., 200....B3 68
Thorntown, Ind., 1,399...D4 59
Thornwood, N.Y., 4,500..*D7 75
Thorofare, N.J., 1,400...D2 74
Thorold, Ont., Can., 15,065.............D5 41
Thorp, Wis., 1,469......D3 88
Thorpe, W. Va.............D3 87
Thorsby, Ala., 944......C3 46
Thorshavn, Faer. Is., 9,738.C6 3
Thouars, Fr., 11,787.....D3 5
Thousand Oaks, Calif., 35,873.............*E4 50
Three Forks, Mont., 1,188.............E5 70
Three Hills, Alta., Can., 1,491.............D4 38
Three Oaks, Mich., 1,750..G4 66
Three Rivers, Mass., 3,366..B3 65
Three Rivers, Mich., 7,355.............G5 66
Three Rivers, Miss.......E5 68
Three Rivers, Tex., 1,761..E3 84
Throckmorton, Tex., 1,105.............C3 84
Throckmorton, co., Tex., 2,205.............C3 84
Throop, Pa., 4,307......m18 81
Thule, Grnld., 206......*B14 33
Thun, Switz., 36,600 (*63,200).........E3 6
Thunder Bay, Ont., Can., 108,411 (*112,093)..o17 41
Thunder Bay, dist., Ont., Can., 143,673......o17 41

Thunderbolt, Ga., 2,750..D5 55
Thurgau, canton, Switz., 180,000.............*E4 6
Thüringia, former state, Ger. Dem. Rep., 2,927,497.............*C5 6
Thuringia, reg., Ger. Dem. Rep.............C5 6
Thurles, Ire., 6,840......D3 4
Thurmont, Md., 2,359....A3 53
Thurrock, Eng., 124,800..*E7 4
Thursday Island, Austl., 2,216.............B7 25
Thurso, Que., Can., 3,219.............D2 42
Thurso, Scot., 9,025.....A5 4
Thurston, co., Nebr., 6,942.............B9 71
Thurston, co., Wash., 76,894.............C3 86
Tibet, prov., China, 1,480,000.............B8 20
Tiburon, Calif., 6,209...*C2 50
Tice, Fla., 7,254........F5 54
Ticino, canton, Switz., 256,000.............*E4 6
Tickfaw, La., 370.......D5 63
Ticonderoga, N.Y., 3,268..B7 75
Ticul, Mex., 14,341.....C7 34
Tidioute, Pa., 939......C3 81
Tiehling, China, 65,000..C9 17
Tienen, Bel., 24,013....B6 5
Tienshui, China, 63,000..E6 17
Tientsin (Tienching), China, 3,800,000 (4,280,000 ▲).......D8 17
Tie Plant, Miss., 500....B4 68
Tierra Blanca, Mex., 22,727.............D5, n15 34
Tierra del Fuego, isl., Chile.............h12 28
Tietê, Braz., 10,602...C3, m8 30
Tiff City, Mo., 100......E3 69
Tiffin, Ohio, 21,596.....A2 78
Tiflis, see Tbilisi, Sov. Un.
Tift, co., Ga., 27,288....E3 55
Tifton, Ga., 12,179.....E3 55
Tiftona, Tenn., 2,200...*D8 83
Tigard, Oreg., 5,302....h12 80
Tigil, Sov. Un., 1,200...D18 13
Tignish, P.E.I., Can.,994..C6 43
Tigre, Arg., 152,335.....g7 28
Tigris, riv., Asia.......F7 13
Tijuana, Mex., 277,306..A1 34
Tikhvin, Sov. Un., 34,000.B9 12
Tiksi, Sov. Un., 1,000...B15 13
Tilburg, Neth., 154,069...B6 5
Tilbury, Ont., Can., 3,580.E2 41
Tilden, Ill., 909........E4 58
Tilden, Nebr., 947......B8 71
Tilghman, Md., 900.....C5 53
Tiline, Ky., 100........e9 62
Tillamook, Oreg., 3,968..B3 80
Tillamook, co., Oreg., 18,034.............B3 80
Tillicum, Wash.........*B2 86
Tillman, co., Okla., 12,901.............C2 79
Tillsonburg, Ont., Can., 6,608.............E4 41
Tilton, Ill., 2,544......C6 58
Tilton, N.H., 1,105.....E4 73
Tiltonsville, Ohio, 2,123..B5 78
Timaru, N.Z., 28,600 (*29,300).........P13 26
Timbaúba, Braz., 26,515..*D7 27
Timberlake, Va., 2,500...*C3 85
Times Beach, Mo., 1,265..*C7 69
Timiskaming, dist., Ont., Can., 47,154.......o19 41
Timişoara, Rom., 174,400 (193,000 ▲).........C5 10
Timmins, Ont., Can., 28,542 (*41,473)......o19 41
Timmonsville, S.C., 2,246.............C8 82
Timoneng, Guam, 5,380..*F6 2
Timor, isl., Indon.......G6 19
Timor Portuguese, see Portuguese Timor, dep., Asia
Timpson, Tex., 1,254....D5 84
Tineo, Sp., 21,338......A2 8
Tinley Park, Ill., 12,382..k9 58
Tinsley, Miss., 200......C3 68
Tioga, N. Dak., 1,667...B2 77
Tioga, co., N.Y., 46,513..C4 75
Tioga, co., Pa., 39,691...C7 81
Tippah, co., Miss., 15,852.A5 68
Tipp City, Ohio, 5,090...C1 78
Tippecanoe, co., Ind., 109,378.............D4 59
Tipperary, Ire., 4,631...D3 4
Tipperary, co., Ire., 122,812.............*D3 4
Tipton, Calif., 950......D4 50
Tipton, Ind., 5,313.....D5 59
Tipton, Iowa, 2,877.....C6 60

Tipton, Mo., 1,914......C5 69
Tipton, Okla., 1,206....C2 79
Tipton, co., Ind., 16,650..D5 59
Tipton, co., Tenn., 28,001..B2 83
Tiptonville, Tenn., 2,407..A2 83
Tiranë (Tirana), Alb., 169,300.............B2 14
Tiranë (Tirana), pref., Alb.............*B2 14
Tirano, It., 7,517......A3 9
Tiraspol, Sov. Un., 105,000.............H7 12
Tire, Tur., 28,018......C6 14
Tîrgovişte, Rom., 27,200..C7 10
Tîrgu-jiu, Rom., 30,800..C6 10
Tîrgul-Neamt, Rom., 10,373.............B8 10
Tîrgul-Ocna, Rom., 11,227.............B8 10
Tîrgu-Mureş, Rom., 86,500 (*104,900).......B7 10
Tîrgu-Sacuesc, Rom., 7,500.............B8 10
Tîrnaveni, Rom., 14,883..B7 10
Tîrnavos, Grc., 10,451...*C4 14
Tirol, state, Aus., 462,899.E5 6
Tirol, reg., Aus.........E5 6
Tiruchchirāppalli, India, 307,400 (*475,000)......F6 20
Tirunelveli, India, 108,498 (*266,688).....G6 20
Tiruppur, India, 113,302.*F6 20
Tisdale, Sask., Can., 2,798.E3 39
Tishomingo, Okla., 2,663..C5 79
Tishomingo, co., Miss., 14,940.............A5 68
Tiskilwa, Ill., 973......B4 58
Tisza, riv., Hung., Yugo..B5 10
Tiszafüred, Hung., 10,318.B5 10
Tiszakécske, Hung., 6,626.B5 10
Titicaca, lake, Bol., Peru..C2 29
Titograd, Yugo., 54,509..D4 10
Titovo Užice, Yugo., 34,312.............D4 10
Titov Veles, Yugo., 36,026.............E5 10
Titus, co., Tex., 16,702...C5 84
Titusville, Fla., 30,515 (*41,800).........D6 54
Titusville, N.J., 900....C3 74
Titusville, Pa., 7,331....C2 81
Tiverton, Eng., 15,660...E5 4
Tiverton, R.I., 7,500....C12 52
Tivoli, It., 40,500....D4, h9 9
Tivoli, Tex., 500.......E4 84
Tixtla, Mex., 10,334....o14 34
Tizapán, Mex., 7,476....h9 34
Tizimín, Mex., 18,343...C7 34
Tizi-Ouzou, Alg., 25,852..A5 22
Tiznit, Mor., 11,391....C3 22
Tjiandjur, Indon., 144,803.............*G3 19
Tjimahi, Indon., 72,367..*G3 19
Tjirebon, Indon., 178,529..G3 19
Tlalpan, Mex., 22,128...h9 34
Tlaxcala, state, Mex., 377,900.............D5 34
Tlaxiaco, Mex., 4,477...D5 34
Tlemcen, Alg., 87,210...B4 22
Toast, N.C., 2,635......A2 76
Toba, Jap., 29,462.....o15 18
Tobarra, Sp., 8,243.....C5 8
Tobol, riv., Sov. Un.....D9 13
Tobolsk, Sov. Un., 49,000.D9 13
Tobyhanna, Pa., 700....D11 81
Tocantins, riv., Braz.....D6 27
Toccoa, Ga., 6,971.....B3 55
Toccoa Falls, Ga., 350...B3 55
Tochigi, Jap., 78,345.H9, m18 18
Tochigi, pref., Jap., 1,580,021.............*H9 18
Tocopilla, Chile, 21,580..D1 29
Todd, co., Ky., 10,823...D2 62
Todd, co., Minn., 22,114..D4 67
Todd, co., S. Dak., 6,606..G5 77
Togo, country, Afr., 2,175,000.............G5 22
Tokat, Tur., 44,110.....B11 14
Tokenon, Kor., 15,711...G2 18
Toki, Jap., 60,786......*n16 18
Tokorozawa, Jap., 136,611.n18 18
Tokushima, Jap., 223,451..I7 18
Tokushima, pref., Jap., 791,111.............*I7 18
Tokuyama, Jap., 98,520 (*185,000).........I5 18
Tōkyō, Jap., 8,738,997 (*23,300,000)....I9, n18 18
Tokyo, pref., Jap., 11,408,071.............*I9 18
Tolbukhin (Dobrich), Bul., 55,150.............D8 10
Toledo, Ill., 1,068......D5 58
Toledo, Iowa, 2,361.....B5 60
Toledo, Ohio, 383,105 (*566,700).......A2, e6 78
Toledo, Oreg., 2,818....C3 80
Toledo, Sp., 44,190.....C3 8

Toledo, prov., Sp., 490,000 ... *C3 8
Toler, Ky., 500 ... C7 62
Tolima, dept., Col., 879,800 ... C2 32
Tolland, co., Conn., 103,440 ... B7 52
Tolleson, Ariz., 3,881 ... D1 48
Tolmin, Yugo., 1,638 ... B1 10
Tolna, Hung., 8,748 ... B4 10
Tolna, co., Hung., 259,267 ... *B4 10
Tolono, Ill., 2,027 ... D5 58
Tolosa, Sp., 16,281 ... A4 8
Toluca, Ill., 1,319 ... B4 58
Toluca [de Lerdo], Mex., 114,079 ... D5, n14 34
Tolyatti, Sov. Un., 251,000 ... *D7 13
Tomah, Wis., 5,647 ... E3 88
Tomahawk, Wis., 3,419 ... C4 88
Tomakomai, Jap., 101,573 ... E10 18
Tomakovka, Sov. Un., 10,000 ... H10 12
Tomar, Port., 8,034 ... C1 8
Tomari, Sov. Un., 16,100 ... E17 13
Tomaszow Lubelski, Pol., 12,300 ... C7 7
Tomaszow Mazowiecki, Pol., 54,900 ... C6 7
Tomball, Tex., 2,734 ... D5 84
Tombouctou (Timbuktu), Mali, 9,000 ... E4 22
Tombstone, Ariz., 1,241 ... D4 48
Tomé, Chile, 26,942 ... B2 28
Tomelloso, Sp., 27,815 ... C4 8
Tom Green, co., Tex., 71,047 ... D2 84
Tomkins Cove, N.Y., 800 ... D7, m14 75
Tommot, Sov. Un., 6,600 ... D15 13
Tompkins, co., N.Y., 77,064 ... C4 75
Tompkinsville, Ky., 2,207 ... D4 62
Tom Price, Austl., 3,370 ... D2 25
Tomsk, Sov. Un., 338,000 ... D11 13
Toms River, N.J., 7,303 ... D4 74
Tonalá, Mex., 15,611 ... D6 34
Tonasket, Wash., 951 ... A6 86
Tonawanda, N.Y., 21,898 ... B2 75
Tondano, Indon., 22,678 ... E6 19
Tønder, Den., 7,192 ... A4 6
Tønder, co., Den., 43,200 ... *J3 11
Tonga, Br. dep., Oceania, 95,000 ... H9 2
Tonganoxie, Kans., 1,717 ... C8, k15 61
Tonk, India, 55,866 ... C6 20
Tonka Bay, Minn., 1,397 ... *F5 67
Tonkawa, Okla., 3,337 ... A4 79
Tonkin, reg., Viet., 11,000,000 ... A3 19
Tonopah, Nev., 1,716 ... B3 72
Tönsberg, Nor., 11,400 (*34,500) ... H4, p28 11
Tooele, Utah, 12,539 ... A5, D2 72
Tooele, co., Utah, 21,545 ... A5 72
Toole, co., Mont., 5,839 ... B5 70
Toombs, co., Ga., 19,151 ... D4 55
Toowoomba, Austl., 59,476 ... E9 25
Topanga, Calif., 1,800 ... *F4 50
Topeka, Kans., 125,011 (*151,900) ... C8, k13 61
Topol'čany, Czech., 12,757 ... D5 7
Topolovgrad, Bul., 6,591 ... D8 10
Toppenish, Wash., 5,744 ... C5 86
Topsfield, Mass., 2,200 ... A6 65
Topsham, Maine, 2,700 ... E3, g8 64
Topton, Pa., 1,744 ... F10 81
Torbay, Newf., Can., 2,090 ... E5 44
Torez, Sov. Un., 93,000 (*275,000) ... q21 12
Torhout, Bel., 15,413 ... B5 5
Toride, Jap., 40,287 ... n19 18
Torino, see Turin, It.
Toro, Sp., 10,218 ... B3 8
Törökszentmiklós, Hung., 20,988 (24,229 ▲) ... B5 10
Toronto, Ont., Can., 712,786 (*2,628,043) ... D5, m15 41
Toronto, Ohio, 7,705 ... B5 78
Toropets, Sov. Un., 17,000 ... C8 12
Torquay (Torbay), Eng., 105,050 ... E5 4
Torrance, Calif., 134,968 ... n12 50
Torrance, co., N. Mex., 5,290 ... B5 48
Torre Annunziata, It., 63,100 ... D5 9
Torre del Greco, It., 80,100 ... D5 9
Torredonjimeno, Sp., 14,204 ... D4 8
Torrelavega, Sp., 13,612 ... A3 8
Torremaggiore, It., 17,318 ... D5 9
Torrens, lake, Austl. ... F6 25
Torrente, Sp., 24,042 ... C5 8
Torreón, Mex., 223,104 (*410,000) ... B4 34
Torre Pacheco, Sp., 9,541 ... D5 8
Torres Novas, Port., 7,291 ... C1 8
Torrevieja, Sp., 9,234 ... D5 8
Torrington, Conn., 31,952 ... B4 52
Torrington, Wyo., 4,237 ... D8 89
Torrox, Sp., 7,384 ... D4 8
Tortilla Flat, Ariz., 15 ... C3 48
Tortona, It., 23,000 ... B2 9
Tortosa, Sp., 18,674 (43,267 ▲) ... B6 8
Toruń, Pol., 129,100 ... B5 7
Torzhok, Sov. Un., 46,000 ... C10 12
Toscana, pol. dist., It., 3,286,160 ... *C3 9
Tosno, Sov. Un., 20,000 ... C10 12
Tosya, Tur., 16,698 ... B10 14
Totana, Sp., 9,949 ... D5 8
Totkomlós, Hung., 8,122 ... B5 10
Totonicapán, Guat., 8,727 ... D6 34
Totowa, N.J., 11,580 ... B4 74
Tottori, Jap., 113,151 ... I7 18
Tottori, pref., Jap., 568,777 ... *I7 18
Totz, Ky., 350 ... D6 62
Toubkal, Jbel, mtn., Mor ... B3 22
Tougaloo, Miss., 1,300 ... C3 68
Touggourt, Alg., 26,486 (50,159 ▲) ... B6 22
Toul, Fr., 14,780 (*20,000) ... C3 68
Toulon, Fr., 174,746 (*340,000) ... F6 5
Toulon, Ill., 1,207 ... B4 58
Toulouse, Fr., 370,796 (*440,000) ... F4 5
Toungoo, Bur., 31,589 ... E10 20
Touraine, former prov., Fr ... D4 5
Tourcoing, Fr., 98,755 ... B5 5
Tourlaville, Fr., 12,062 ... C3 5
Tours, Fr., 128,120 (*205,000) ... D4 5
Towaco, N.J., 1,400 ... B4 74
Towanda, Kans., 1,190 ... E7, k12 61
Towanda, Pa., 4,224 ... C9 81
Tower City, Pa., 1,774 ... E8 81
Town and Country, Mo., 2,645 ... *C7 69
Towner, N. Dak., 870 ... B5 77
Towner, co., N. Dak., 4,645 ... B6 77
Townley, Ala., 500 ... B2 46
Town of Pines, Ind., 1,007 ... *A4 59
Town of Tonawanda, N.Y., 86,302 ... *B2 75
Towns, co., Ga., 4,565 ... B3 55
Townsend, Mass., 1,329 ... A4 65
Townsend, Mont., 1,371 ... D5 70
Townsville, Austl., 71,109 ... C8 25
Towson, Md., 80,000 ... B4, g11 53
Toyama, Jap., 269,276 ... H8 18
Toyama, pref., Jap., 1,029,695 ... *H8 18
Toyohashi, Jap., 258,547 ... I8, o16 18
Toyokawa, Jap., 85,860 ... *I8 18
Toyonaka, Jap., 368,498 ... o14 18
Toyota, Jap., 197,193 ... n16 18
Tozeur, Tun., 11,820 ... B6 22
Trabzon, Tur., 80,795 ... B12 14
Tracadie, N.B., Can., 2,222 ... B5 43
Tracy, Calif., 14,724 ... D3, h10 50
Tracy, Minn., 2,516 ... F3 67
Tracy City, Tenn., 1,388 ... D7 83
Traer, Iowa, 1,682 ... B5 60
Trafford, Pa., 4,383 ... k14 81
Traiguén, Chile, 10,000 ... B2 28
Trail, B.C., Can., 11,149 (*17,177) ... E9, o19 37
Trail Creek, Ind., 2,697 ... A4 59
Trailer Estates, Fla., 1,759 ... *E4 54
Traill, co., N. Dak., 9,571 ... C8 77
Trainer, Pa., 2,336 ... *G11 81
Tralee, Ire., 12,287 ... D2 4
Tranås, Swe., 18,959 ... H6 11
Trani, It., 41,500 ... D6 9
Transilvania, prov., Rom., 3,420,859 ... *B6 10
Transvaal, prov., S. Afr., 8,000,000 ... E5 24
Transylvania, co., N.C., 19,713 ... f10 76
Transylvania, reg., Rom ... B6 10
Trapani, It., 66,700 ... E4 9
Trappe, Pa., 1,676 ... *F11 81
Traralgon, Austl., 14,624 ... I6 26
Trás-os-Montes, reg., Port., 582,800 ... B2 8
Trás-os-Montes e Alto Douro, prov., Port., 639,846 ... *B2 8
Traunstein, Ger., Fed. Rep. of, 15,079 ... E6 6
Travelers Rest, S.C., 2,241 ... B3 82
Traverse, co., Minn., 6,254 ... E2 67
Traverse City, Mich., 18,048 ... D5 66
Travis, co., Tex., 295,516 ... D4 84
Travnik, Yugo., 12,977 ... C3 10
Treasure, co., Mont., 1,069 ... D9 70
Treasure Island, Fla., 6,120 ... *E4 54
Třebíč, Czech., 21,417 ... D3 7
Trebinje, Yugo., 4,072 ... D4 10
Trebišov, Czech., 11,142 ... D6 7
Trego, co., Kans., 4,436 ... D4 61
Treinta y Tres, Ur., 21,035 ... E2 30
Treinta y Tres, dept., Ur., 43,623 ... *E2 30
Trélazé, Fr., 11,664 ... D3 5
Trelew, Arg., 21,000 ... C3 28
Trelleborg, Swe., 29,038 ... J5 11
Tremont, Ill., 1,942 ... C4 58
Tremont, Pa., 1,833 ... E9 81
Tremonton, Utah, 2,794 ... A5 72
Trempealeau, co., Wis., 23,344 ... D2 88
Trenčín, Czech., 28,746 (*39,000) ... D5 7
Trengganu, state, Mala., 346,000 ... *D2 19
Trenque Lauquén, Arg., 13,263 ... B4 28
Trentino-Alto-Adige, pol. dist., It., 785,967 ... *A3 9
Trento, It., 88,500 ... A3 9
Trenton, N.S., Can., 3,331 ... D7 43
Trenton, Ont., Can., 14,589 (*28,650) ... C7 41
Trenton, Fla., 1,074 ... C4 54
Trenton, Ga., 1,523 ... B1 55
Trenton, Ill., 2,328 ... E4 58
Trenton, Mich., 24,127 ... F7, p15 66
Trenton, Mo., 6,063 ... A4 69
Trenton, Nebr., 770 ... D4 71
Trenton, N.J., 104,786 ... C3 74
Trenton, Ohio, 5,278 ... C1 78
Trenton, Tenn., 4,226 ... B3 83
Trentwood, Wash., 1,800 ... *B8 86
Tres Arroyos, Arg., 37,000 ... B4 28
Tresckow, Pa., 1,146 ... E10 81
Trés Coraçoes, Braz., 25,707 ... C3 30
Três Lagoas, Braz., 40,137 ... C2 30
Treutlen, co., Ga., 5,647 ... D4 55
Treviglio, It., 21,600 ... B2 9
Treviso, It., 88,100 ... B4 9
Trevorton, Pa., 2,196 ... E8 81
Trevose, Pa., 7,000 ... *F12 81
Trevose Heights, Pa., 3,000 ... *F12 81
Treynor, Iowa, 472 ... C2 60
Trezevant, Tenn., 877 ... A3 83
Triangle, Va., 3,021 ... B5 85
Tribbett, Miss., 90 ... B3 68
Tribune, Kans., 1,013 ... D2 61
Trichinopoly, see Tiruchchirāppalli, India
Trichūr, India, 76,241 ... F6 20
Trier, Ger., Fed. Rep. of, 102,752 ... D3 6
Trieste, It., 279,400 ... B4 9
Trigg, co., Ky., 8,620 ... D2 62
Triglav, mtn., Yugo ... B1 10
Trigueros, Sp., 6,454 ... D2 8
Trikkala, Grc., 34,794 ... C3 14
Trikkala, prov., Grc., 131,820 ... *C3 14
Tri Lakes, Ind., 1,193 ... *B7 59
Trimble, co., Ky., 5,349 ... B4 62
Trimont, Minn., 835 ... G4 67
Trincomalee, Sri Lanka, 41,784 ... G7 20
Tring-Jonction, Que., Can., 1,283 ... C6 42
Trinidad, Bol., 16,800 ... B3 29
Trinidad, Colo., 9,901 ... D6 51
Trinidad, Cuba., 31,500 (37,000 ▲) ... D4 35
Trinidad, Tex., 1,079 ... C4 84
Trinidad, Ur., 16,599 ... E1 30
Trinidad & Tobago, country, N.A., 1,110,000 ... A5 32
Trinité, Mart., 3,631 ... I14 35
Trinity, Tex., 2,512 ... D5 84
Trinity, co., Calif., 7,615 ... B2 50
Trinity, co., Tex., 7,628 ... D5 84
Trinity, mts., Calif ... B2 50
Trino, It., 8,100 ... B2 9
Trion, Ga., 1,965 ... B1 55
Tripoli, Iowa, 1,345 ... B5 60
Tripolis, Grc., 20,209 ... D4 14
Tripoli (Ṭarābulus), Leb., 157,320 ... f5 15
Tripoli (Ṭarābulus), Libya, 157,320 ... B7 22
Tripp, S. Dak., 851 ... G8 77
Tripp, co., S. Dak., 8,171 ... G6 77
Tripura, state, India, 1,556,342 ... D9 20
Tristate Village, Ill., 1,700 ... *B5 58
Triumph, La., 1,600 ... E6 63
Trivandrum, India, 409,627 ... G6 20
Trnava, Czech., 38,634 (*46,000) ... D4 7
Trois-Pistoles, Que., Can., 4,678 ... A8 42
Trois-Rivières, Que., Can., 55,869 (*97,930) ... C5 42
Troitsk, Sov. Un., 85,000 ... D9 13
Trollhättan, Swe., 48,840 ... H5 11
Troms, co., Nor., 135,900 ... *C8 11
Tromsö, Nor., 37,200 ... C8 11
Trona, Calif., 1,500 ... E5 50
Trondheim, Nor., 123,600 ... F4 11
Troodos, mtn., Cyp ... E9 14
Tropea, It., 6,702 ... E5 9
Trotwood, Ohio, 6,997 ... C1 78
Troup, Tex., 1,668 ... C5 84
Troup, co., Ga., 44,466 ... C1 55
Trousdale, co., Tenn., 5,155 ... A5 83
Trouville, Fr., 6,429 (*15,000) ... C3 5
Trowbridge, Eng., 19,380 ... E5 4
Troy, Ala., 11,482 ... D4 46
Troy, Ill., 2,144 ... E4 58
Troy, Kans., 1,047 ... C8 61
Troy, Mich., 39,419 ... o15 66
Troy, Mo., 2,538 ... C7 69
Troy, N.Y., 62,918 ... C7 75
Troy, N.C., 2,429 ... B3 76
Troy, Ohio, 17,186 ... B1 78
Troy, Pa., 1,315 ... C8 81
Troyes, Fr., 74,898 (*115,000) ... C6 5
Trubchevsk, Sov. Un., 10,000 ... E9 12
Trucial States, see United Arab Emirates, country, Asia
Trucksville, Pa., 2,200 ... *D10 81
Trujillo, Peru, 127,535 ... C2 31
Trujillo, Sp., 13,326 ... C3 8
Trujillo, Ven., 25,921 ... B3 32
Trujillo, state, Ven., 326,634 ... B3 32
Truman, Minn., 1,137 ... G4 67
Trumann, Ark., 6,023 ... B5 49
Trumansburg, N.Y., 1,803 ... C4 75
Trumbull, Conn., 31,394 ... E4 52
Trumbull, co., Ohio, 232,579 ... A5 78
Truro, N.S., Can., 13,047 (*24,914) ... D6 43
Truro, Eng., 15,100 ... E4 4
Trussville, Ala., 2,985 ... B3, f7 46
Truth or Consequences, N. Mex., 4,656 ... C5 48
Trutnov, Czech., 24,666 ... C3 7
Tryon, N.C., 1,951 ... f10 76
Trysil, Nor., 787 ... G5 11
Tsangwu, see Wuchou, China
Tselinograd, Sov. Un., 180,000 ... D10 13
Tsinan (Chinan), China, 882,000 ... D8 17
Tsinghai (Chinghai), prov., China, 2,050,000 ... D8 17
Tsingtao (Chingtao), China, 1,350,000 ... D9 17
Tsingyuan, see Paoting, China
Tskhinvali, Sov. Un., 30,000 ... A14 14
Tsu, Jap., 125,203 ... I8, o15 18
Tsuchiura, Jap., 89,958 ... H10, m19 18
Tsuni, China, 200,000 ... F6 17
Tsun Wan, Hong Kong, 267,670 ... *G7 17
Tsuruga, Jap., 56,445 ... I8, n15 18
Tsuruoka, Jap., 74,000 (95,136 ▲) ... G9 18
Tsushima, Jap., 51,441 ... n15 18
Tsuyama, Jap., 54,000 (76,368 ▲) ... I7 18
Tubarão, Braz., 51,121 ... D3 30

Tübingen, Ger., Fed. Rep. of, 69,261.............D4 6
Ţubruq, (Tobruk), Libya, 15,900.................B2 23
Tuchola, Pol., 8,114........B4 7
Tuckahoe, N.Y., 6,236....h13 75
Tucker, Ga., 12,500......h8 55
Tucker, co., W. Va., 7,447................B5 87
Tuckerman, Ark., 1,731..B4 49
Tuckerton, N.J., 1,926...D4 74
Tucson, Ariz., 262,933 (*325,000)...........C3 48
Tucumán, Arg., 280,000...E2 29
Tucumán, prov., Arg., 773,972.............E2 29
Tucumcari, N. Mex., 7,189...............B7 48
Tudela, Sp., 16,456......A5 8
Tuguegarao, Phil., 14,116.B6 19
Tuktoyaktuk, N.W. Ter., Can., 596...........C7 36
Tukwila, Wash., 3,509....f11 86
Tula, Sov. Un., 462,000 (*545,000)..........D11 12
Tulancingo, Mex., 35,799..............C5, m14 34
Tulare, Calif., 16,235....D4 50
Tulare, co., Calif., 188,322.............D4 50
Tularosa, N. Mex., 2,851..C5 48
Tulcán, Ec., 20,300......A2 31
Tulcea, Rom., 35,600.....C9 10
Tuléar, Mad., 40,400.....E8 24
Tulelake, Calif., 857.....B3 50
Tulia, Tex., 5,294.......B2 84
Tülkarm, Jordan, 15,275..B3 15
Tullahoma, Tenn., 15,311..............B5 83
Tullamore, Ire., 6,809...D3 4
Tulle, Fr., 20,016.......E4 5
Tullytown, Pa., 2,194....*F12 81
Tulsa, Okla., 330,350 (*460,300)...........A6 79
Tulsa, co., Okla., 400,709.B6 79
Tuluá, Col., 59,300......C2 32
Tulufan (Turfan), China, 25,000..............C2 17
Tulun, Sov. Un., 49,000..D13 13
Tulungagung, Indon., 68,899.............G4 19
Tumaco, Col., 25,145.....C2 32
Tumbarumba, Austl., 1,511...............G7 26

Tumbes, Peru, 32,972.....B1 31
Tumen, China, 28,000....C10 17
Tumkür, India, 70,476....F6 20
Tumuti, Austl., 5,525....*G8 25
Tumwater, Wash., 5,373...B3 86
Tunbridge Wells, Eng., 44,610..............E7 4
Tunchi, China, 50,000....*F8 17
Tunghsien, China, 55,000..............*D8 17
Tunghua, China, 129,100..F2 18
Tungliao, China, 40,000..C9 17
Tungurahua, prov., Ec., 245,600.............B2 31
Tunhua, China, 35,000...C10 17
Tunica, Miss., 1,685.....A3 68
Tunica, co., Miss., 11,854.A3 68
Tunis, Tun., 469,997 (*685,000)............A7 22
Tunisia, country, Afr., 5,575,000...........A6 22
Tunja, Col., 40,451......B3 32
Tunkhannock, Pa., 2,251...............C10 81
Tuntutuliak, Alsk., 158...C7 47
Tuolumne, Calif., 1,365...D3 50
Tuolumne, co., Calif., 32,169..............C4 50
Tupelo, Miss., 20,471....A5 68
Tupper Lake, N.Y., 4,584............A6, f10 75
Tupungato, mtn., Arg....A3 28
Tura, Sov. Un., 2,000...C13 13
Turbaco, Col., 14,255....A2 32
Turčiansky Svaty Martin, Czech., 22,400......D5 7
Turda, Rom., 42,300 (*69,800)............B6 10
Turek, Pol., 18,500......B5 7
Turfan, see Tulufan, China
Turgay, Sov. Un., 5,800...E9 13
Turgovishte, Bul., 25,502.D8 10
Turgutlu, Tur., 40,986...C6 14
Turin (Torino), It., 1,177,000 (*1,560,000)..........B1 9
Turka, Sov. Un., 10,000..G4 12
Turkestan, Sov. Un., 54,000..............E9 13
Túrkeve, Hung., 10,103 (11,415 ▲).........B5 10
Turkey, Tex., 680........B2 84
Turkey, country, Asia, Eur., 38,355,000........C9 14

Turkmen, S.S.R., rep., Sov. Un., 2,330,000....*F8 16
Turks & Caicos Islands, Br. dep., N.A., 6,000...D8 35
Turku (Åbo), Fin., 155,497 (*204,000)....G10 11
Turku-Pori, prov., Fin., 678,000............*G10 11
Turley, Okla., 6,300.....A6 79
Turlock, Calif., 13,992...D3 50
Turner, co., Ga., 8,790...E3 55
Turner, Kans...........B8 61
Turner, co., S. Dak.,9,872.G8 77
Turners Falls, Mass., 4,470. A2 65
Turner Valley, Alta., Can., 702................D3 38
Turnhout, Bel., 38,194...B6 5
Turnov, Czech., 13,077...C3 7
Turnovo, Bul., 37,269....D7 10
Turnu Măgurele, Rom., 18,055.............D7 10
Turnu Severin, Rom., 45,400.............C6 10
Turquino, peak, Cuba....D5 35
Turtkul, Sov. Un., 19,000.E9 13
Turtle Creek, Pa., 8,308..k14 81
Turukhansk, Sov. Un., 5,000..............C11 13
Tuscaloosa, Ala., 65,773 (*98,200)...........B2 46
Tuscaloosa, co., Ala., 116,029.............B2 46
Tuscany, reg., It.........C3 9
Tuscarawas, co., Ohio, 77,211.............B4 78
Tuscola, Ill., 3,917.....D5 58
Tuscola, co., Mich., 48,285.............E7 66
Tusculum College, Tenn., 1,180............*C5 83
Tuscumbia, Ala., 8,828...A2 46
Tuskegee, Ala., 11,028...C4 46
Tuskegee Institute, Ala...C4 46
Tustin, Calif., 21,178....*F5 50
Tuticorin, India, 155,310 (*181,913)..........G6 20
Tutrakan, Bul., 7,203....C8 10
Tuttlingen, Ger., Fed. Rep. of, 32,212.........E4 6
Tutwiler, Miss., 1,103....A3 68
Tuxedo, Md., 1,000......C4 53
Tuxedo Park, N.Y., 861..............D6, m14 75

Tuxpan, Mex., 20,322.........C3, m11 34
Tuxpan, Mex., 14,693....n12 34
Tuxpan de Rodriguez Cano, Mex., 33,901......C5, m15 34
Tuxtla Gutiérrez, Mex., 66,857............D6 34
Tuy, Sp., 2,779.........A1 8
Tuyün, China, 60,000....F6 17
Tuzla, Yugo., 53,825.....C4 10
Tweed, Ont., Can., 1,738..............C7 41
Twenty-Nine Palms, Calif., 5,667...........E5 50
Twig, Minn., 175........D6 67
Twiggs, co., Ga., 8,222..D3 55
Twillingate, Newf., Can., 1,437............D4 44
Twin City, Ga., 1,119....D4 55
Twin Falls, Idaho, 21,914.G4 57
Twin Falls, co., Idaho, 41,807............G4 57
Twin Lakes, Calif., 2,300..............*D2 50
Twin Lakes, Ohio, 1,200..*A4 78
Twin Lakes, Wis., 2,276...........F5, n11 88
Twin Oaks, Pa., 1,600...*G11 81
Twin Orchards, N.Y., 1,500............*C5 75
Twin Rocks, Pa., 700.....F4 81
Twinsburg, Ohio, 6,432...A4 78
Two Harbors, Minn., 4,437.............C7 67
Two Rivers, Wis., 13,553..........D6, h10 88
Tyler, Minn., 1,069......F2 67
Tyler, Tex., 57,770 (*77,100)...C5 84
Tyler, co., Tex., 12,417...D5 84
Tyler, co., W. Va., 9,929..B4 87
Tyler Park, Va., 1,650....*B5 85
Tylertown, Miss., 1,736...D3 68
Tyndall, S. Dak., 1,245...H8 77
Tynemouth, Eng., 68,740..C6 4
Tyre, see Sūr, Leb.
Tyrrell, co., N.C., 3,806..B6 76
Tyrone, Pa., 7,072.......E5 81
Tyrone, co., N. Ire., 138,975...........*C3 4
Tyumen, Sov. Un., 269,000.............D9 13
Tzukung, China, 280,000..F5 17

U

Ubá, Braz., 29,025.....C4, g6 30
Ube, Jap., 152,935 (*203,000)............J5 18
Ubeda, Sp., 28,956......C4 8
Uberaba, Braz., 108,576..B3 30
Uberlândia, Braz., 110,463.B3 30
Ubon Ratchathani, Thai., 40,650.............B2 19
Uccle, Bel., 79,225......B6 5
Udaipur, India, 161,278..D5 20
Uddevalla, Swe., 47,306..H4 11
Udine, It., 95,700 (*115,000)............A4 9
Udon Thani, Thai., 56,218.............B2 19
Ueda, Jap., 93,198...H9, m17 18
Uelen, Sov. Un., 800....C21 13
Uelkal, Sov. Un., 800....C21 13
Uelzen, Ger., Fed. Rep. of, 37,819...........B5 6
Ueno, Jap., 41,000 (57,666 ▲)..........o15 18
Ufa, Sov. Un., 771,000...D8 13
Uganda, country, Afr., 10,940,000..........H4 23
Uglegorsk (Esutoru), Sov. Un., 20,000......B11 18
Uglich, Sov. Un., 35,000..............C12 12
Uherské Hradiště, Czech., 15,796 (*32,000).....D4 7
Uhrichsville, Ohio, 5,731..B4 78
Uijongbu, Kor., 94,518...H3 18
Uinta, co., Wyo., 7,100...E2 89
Uintah, co., Utah, 12,684.B7 72
Uitenhage, S. Afr., 69,048.............G5 24
Uji, Jap., 103,497......*o14 18

Ujjain, India, 203,278 (*208,561)...........D6 20
Ujung Pandang, Indon., 434,766............G5 19
Ukhta, Sov. Un., 63,000..C8 13
Ukiah, Calif., 10,095....C2 50
Ukraine (S.S.R.), rep., Sov. Un., 48,810,000...*E6 16
Ulan Bator (Urga), Mong., 262,600............B6 17
Ulan-Ude, Sov. Un., 254,000............D13 13
Ulhasnagar, India, 168,462...........*E5 20
Ulla, Sov. Un., 10,000...D7 12
Ulm, Ger., Fed. Rep. of, 93,407 (*200,000)......D4 6
Ulman, Mo., 100........C5 69
Ulsan, Kor., 108,000 (159,340 ▲)........I4 18
Ulster, co., N.Y., 141,241.D6 75
Ulster, prov., Ire., 208,303...........*C3 4
Ulugh Muztagh, mtn., China..............A8 20
Ulverston, Eng., 12,010..C5 4
Ulyanovsk, Sov. Un., 351,000............D7 13
Ulysses, Kans., 3,779....E2 61
Uman, Sov. Un., 63,000..G8 12
Umatilla, Fla., 1,600....D5 54
Umatilla, co., Oreg., 44,923............B7 80
Umbria, pol. dist., It., 794,745...........*C4 9
Umbria, reg., It., 783,200.C4 9
Umeå, Swe., 57,898......F9 11
Umm Durmān, see Omdurman, Sud.

Umm Ruwābah, Sud., 7,805.............F4 23
'Umrān, Yemen, 20,000...F3 15
Umtali, Rh., 50,000 (*54,000)...........D6 24
Umvuma, Rh., 1,750.....D6 24
Una, S.C., 2,000.......*B4 82
Unadilla, Ga., 1,457....D3 55
Unadilla, N.Y., 1,489....C5 75
'Unayzah, Sua., Ar., 50,000.............D3 15
Uncasville, Conn., 1,350..D8 52
Uncompahgre, mts., Colo..C3 51
Underwood, N. Dak., 781..C4 77
Unecha, Sov. Un., 22,000.E9 12
Unggi, Kor., 20,882.....E5 18
Unicoi, co., Tenn., 15,254............C11 83
Unidad de San Juan de Aragón, Mex., 61,525..*D5 34
Union, Miss., 1,856......C4 68
Union, Mo., 5,183.......C6 69
Union, N.J., 53,077.....B4 74
Union, Ohio, 3,654......C1 78
Union, Oreg., 1,531.....B9 80
Union, S.C., 10,775.....B4 82
Union, co., Ark., 45,428..D3 49
Union, co., Fla., 8,112...B4 54
Union, co., Ga., 6,811...B2 55
Union, co., Ill., 16,071..F4 58
Union, co., Ind., 6,582...E8 59
Union, co., Iowa, 13,557..C3 60
Union, co., Ky., 15,882...C1 62
Union, co., Miss., 19,096..A4 68
Union, co., N.J., 543,116..B4 74
Union, co., N. Mex., 4,925.............A7 48
Union, co., N.C., 54,714.............B2 76

Union, co., Ohio, 23,786.............B2 78
Union, co., Oreg., 19,377............B8 80
Union, co., Pa., 28,603...E7 81
Union, co., S.C., 29,133..B4 82
Union, co., S. Dak., 9,643.............H9 77
Union, co., Tenn., 9,072.............C10 83
Union, par., La., 18,447............B3 63
Union Beach, N.J., 6,472..C4 74
Union City, Calif., 14,724.h8 50
Union City, Ga., 3,031...C2 55
Union City, Ind., 3,995...D8 59
Union City, Mich., 1,740..F5 66
Union City, N.J., 57,305..h8 74
Union City, Ohio, 1,808...B1 78
Union City, Pa., 3,638...C2 81
Union City, Tenn., 11,925.A2 83
Uniondale, N.Y., 22,400..*G2 52
Unión de Reyes, Cuba, 7,000 (9,200 ▲)......C3 35
Union Gap, Wash., 2,040.C5 86
Union Grove, Wis., 2,703.............F5, n11 88
Union Lake, Mich., 9,000.............*F7 66
Union of Soviet Socialist Republics, country, Europe, Asia, 251,050,000.. 13
Union Park, Fla., 3,166...*D5 54
Union Point, Ga., 1,624...C3 55
Union Springs, Ala., 4,324.............C4 46
Union Springs, N.Y., 1,183.............C4 75
Uniontown, Ala., 2,133...C2 46

Uniontown, Ky., 1,255...C2   62
Uniontown, Ohio, 900....B4   78
Uniontown, Pa., 16,282..G2   81
Union Village, R.I.,
  1,500................B10   52
Unionville, Conn., 3,500..B5   52
Unionville, Mo., 2,075....A4   69
United, Pa., 950.........F3   81
United Arab Emirates,
  country, Asia, 215,000...E5   15
United Arab Republic, see
  Egypt, country, Afr.
United Kingdom of
  Great Britain and
  Northern Ireland
  country, Eur.,
  56,340,000............   4
United States, country,
  N.A., 211,300,000.......   45
United States Air Force
  Acad., Colo., 8,000....C6   51
Unity, Sask., Can., 2,294..E1   39
University, Miss........A4   68
University City, Mo.,
  47,527.........C7, f13   69
University Gardens, Md.,
  1,200................*C4   53
University Heights, Ohio,
  17,055................h9   78
University Hills, Md.,
  2,000................*C4   53
University Park, Md.,
  2,926................*C4   53
University Park, N.Mex.,
  3,700................*C5   48
University Park, Tex.,
  23,498...............n10   84
University View, Ohio,
  2,500................*C3   78
Unterwalden, canton,
  Switz., 50,300........*E4   6
Ünye, Tur., 19,448....B11   14

Upington, S. Afr., 28,234...F4   24
Upland, Calif.,
  32,551..........E5, m13   50
Upland, Ind., 3,202......D7   59
Upland, Pa., 3,930......*G10   81
Upper Arlington, Ohio,
  38,727.........B3, k10   78
Upper Brookville, N.Y.,
  1,182................*E7   75
Upper Darby, Pa.,
  51,700.........G11, p20   81
Upper Nyack, N.Y.,
  2,096................*D7   75
Upper Saddle River, N.J.,
  7,949................A4   74
Upper Sandusky, Ohio,
  5,645................B2   78
Upper Silesia, reg., Pol.....g9   7
Upper Volta, country,
  Afr., 5,785,000.......F4   22
Uppsala, Swe.,
  132,560..........H7, t35   11
Uppsala, co., Swe.,
  195,500..............*H7   11
Upshur, co., Tex., 20,976..C5   84
Upshur, co., W. Va.,
  19,092...............C4   87
Upson, co., Ga., 23,505....D2   55
Upton, Mass., 1,130...B4, h9   65
Upton, Wyo., 987.......B8   89
Upton, co., Tex., 4,697...D2   84
Ural, riv., Sov. Un......E8   13
Uralsk, Sov. Un.,
  134,000..............D8   13
Urania, La., 874.........C3   63
Uranium City, Sask.,
  Can., 1,867..........E12   36
Uravan, Colo., 800.......C2   51
Urawa, Jap., 269,397..I9, n18   18
Urbana, Ill., 33,739......C5   58
Urbana, Ohio, 11,237....B2   78
Urbancrest, Ohio, 754...m10   78

Urbandale, Iowa,
  14,434.........C4, e8   60
Urbino, It., 7,200.......C4   9
Urfa, Tur., 100,654.....D12   14
Uri, canton, Switz.,
  33,400..............E4   6
Urla, Tur., 12,600......*C6   14
Urmia, salt lake, Iran....D15   14
Uruapan del Progreso,
  Mex., 82,677......D4, n13   34
Uruguaiana, Braz., 60,667.D1   30
Uruguay, country, S.A.,
  3,015,000............E1   30
Uruguay, riv., Arg., Ur....E1   30
Urumchi (Wulumuchi),
  China, 320,000........C2   17
Urusha, Sov. Un.,
  10,000...............D15   13
Uryupinsk, Sov. Un.,
  38,000...............F14   12
Uşak, Tur., 46,392......C7   14
Üsküdar, Tur., 143,527...B7   14
Usman, Sov. Un.,
  20,000...............E12   12
Usolye-Sibirskoye, Sov.
  Un., 87,000..........D13   13
Ussuriysk, Sov. Un.,
  128,000..............E16   13
Ústí nad Labem, Czech.,
  74,425 (*93,000).......C3   7
Ust-Kamenogorsk, Sov.
  Un., 230,000.........E11   13
Ust-Kut, Sov. Un.,
  33,000...............D13   13
Ust-Maya, Sov. Un.,
  2,300................C16   13
Ust-Srednikan, Sov. Un.,
  800..................C18   13
Ust-Tsilma, Sov. Un.,
  7,900................C8   13
Ust-Usa, Sov. Un.,
  2,500................C8   13

Ustyuzhna, Sov. Un.,
  10,000...............B11   12
Usumbura, see
  Bujumbura, Burundi
Utah, co., Utah, 137,776...A6   72
Utah, state, U.S.,
  1,160,000............   72
Utica, Ill., 974.........B4   58
Utica, Mich., 3,504...F7, o15   66
Utica, N.Y., 91,340
  (*282,000)...........B5   75
Utica, Ohio, 1,977......B3   78
Utica, S.C., 1,218......*B1   82
Utica Heights, Mich., 500.*F8   66
Utiel, Sp., 10,076......C5   8
Utrecht, Neth., 269,574
  (*464,053)...........A6   5
Utrecht, prov., Neth.,
  784,400.............*A6   5
Utrera, Sp., 25,935.....D3   8
Utsunomiya, Jap.,
  301,231.............H9   18
Uttaradit, Thai., 9,109...*B2   19
Uttar Pradesh, state,
  India, 88,341,144......C6   20
Utuado, P.R., 11,573
  (35,494 ▲)..........*G11   35
Uusimaa, prov., Fin.,
  983,800.............*G11   11
Uvalde, Tex., 10,764....E3   84
Uvalde, co., Tex., 17,348..E3   84
Uvaly, Czech., 4,706....n18   7
Uwajima, Jap., 64,262...J6   18
Uxbridge, Ont., Can.,
  3,077................C5   41
Uxbridge, Mass., 3,380...B4   65
Uzbek S.S.R., rep.,
  Sov. Un., 12,760,000...*E9   16
Uzhgorod, Sov. Un.,
  65,000...............G4   12
Uzunköprü, Tur., 23,326...B6   14

V

Vaasa, Fin., 49,442......F9   11
Vaasa, prov., Fin.,
  448,400.............*F9   11
Vác, Hung., 27,946......B4   10
Vacaville, Calif., 21,690..C3   50
Vacherie, La., 2,145....h10   63
Vadnais Heights, Minn.,
  3,411...............*F5   67
Vaduz, Liech., 3,790....E4   6
Vail Homes, N.J., 1,164..*C4   74
Valais, canton, Switz.,
  206,000.............E3   6
Valatie, N.Y., 1,288.....C7   75
Val-Barrette, Que., Can.,
  557................*G20   36
Val-David, Que., Can.,
  1,118...............C3   42
Valdepeñas, Sp., 25,706...C4   8
Valdese, N.C., 3,182....B1   76
Valdivia, Chile, 61,334...B2   28
Valdivia, prov., Chile
  298,500.............B2   28
Val-d' Or, Que., Can.,
  17,421 (*19,165)......o20   41
Valdosta, Ga., 32,303....F3   55
Vale, Oreg., 1,448......D9   80
Valença, Braz., 20,743..E7   27
Valence, Fr., 62,358
  (*92,000)...........E6   5
Valencia, Sp., 13,159....C2   8
Valencia, Sp., 648,003
  (*890,000)..........C5   8
Valencia, Ven., 366,154..A4   32
Valencia, co., N. Mex.,
  40,539.............B4   48
Valencia, prov., Sp.,
  1,654,300..........*C2   8
Valenciennes, Fr., 46,626
  (*240,000)..........B5   5
Valentine, Nebr., 2,662...B5   71
Valera, Ven., 74,353....B3   32
Valhalla, N.Y.,
  5,500............D7, m15   75
Valjevo, Yugo., 26,367...C4   10
Valka, Sov. Un., 25,000...C6   12
Valki, Sov. Un., 10,000..G10   12
Valladolid, Sp., 233,974...B3   8
Valladolid, prov., Sp.,
  392,300............*B3   8
Valle d' Aosta, pol. dist.,
  It., 100,959.........*B1   9

Valle de la Pascua, Ven.,
  36,809..............B4   32
Valle del Cauca, dept.,
  Col., 1,973,800.....   C2   32
Valle de Santiago, Mex.,
  16,517.............m13   34
Valledupar, Col., 61,300
  (110,500 ▲).........A3   32
Vallée-Jonction, Que.,
  Can., 1,405.........C7   42
Vallejo, Calif.,
  71,710..............C2   50
Valletta, Malta, 15,400
  (*202,000)..........A7   22
Valley, Nebr., 1,595..C9, g12   71
Valley, co., Idaho,
  3,609..............*E3   57
Valley, co., Mont.,
  11,471.............B10   70
Valley, co., Nebr., 5,783...C6   71
Valley Brook, Okla.,
  1,197..............*B4   79
Valley Center, Kans.,
  2,551...........E6, g12   61
Valley City, N. Dak.,
  7,843..............D7   77
Valley Cottage, N.Y.,
  6,007..............g13   75
Valleydale, Calif., 1,500..*F4   50
Valley Falls, Kans.,
  1,169.............C8, k15   61
Valleyfield, Que., Can.,
  30,173 (*37,430)..D3, q18   42
Valley Mills, Tex., 1,022..D4   84
Valley Park, Miss., 100....C3   68
Valley Park, Mo., 3,662..f12   69
Valley Station, Ky.,
  20,000.............g11   62
Valley Stream, N.Y.,
  40,413.............k13   75
Valley View, Ill., 1,723..*B5   58
Valley View, Ohio,
  1,422..............*A4   78
Valley View, Pa., 1,585...E9   81
Valmiera, Sov. Un.,
  20,400.............C5   12
Valparai, India, 94,939..*F6   20
Valparaíso, Chile, 289,500
  (*540,000)..........A2   28
Valparaiso, Fla., 6,504...u15   54
Valparaiso, Ind., 20,020..B3   59

Valparaíso, prov., Chile,
  618,112.............A2   28
Valverde, Dom. Rep.,
  27,100..............E8   35
Val Verde, co., Tex.,
  27,471..............E2   84
Van, Tex., 1,593........C5   84
Van, Tur., 46,751.......C14   14
Van, prov., Tur.,
  326,100............*C14   14
Van Alstyne, Tex., 1,981..C4   84
Van Buren, Ark., 6,373....B1   49
Van Buren, Ind., 1,057....C6   59
Van Buren, Maine,
  3,429...............A5   64
Van Buren, co., Ark.,
  8,275...............B3   49
Van Buren, co., Iowa,
  8,643...............D5   60
Van Buren, co., Mich.,
  55,182..............F4   66
Van Buren, co., Tenn.,
  3,758...............D8   83
Vance, co., N.C.,
  32,691..............A4   76
Vanceburg, Ky., 1,773...B6   62
Vancouver, B.C., Can.,
  426,256(*1,082,352).E6, f12   37
Vancouver, Wash.,
  41,859.............D3   86
Vancouver, isl., B.C., Can.G8   36
Vandalia, Ill., 5,160....E4   58
Vandalia, Mo., 3,160.....B6   69
Vandalia, Ohio, 10,796...*C1   78
Vanderbilt, Pa., 755.....F2   81
Vanderburgh, co., Ind.,
  168,772.............H2   59
Vandercook Lake, Mich.,
  5,000...............*F6   66
Vandergrift, Pa., 7,889...E2   81
Vanderhoof, B.C., Can.,
  1,653...............C5   37
Vandling, Pa., 633......C11   81
Vänern (Väner), lake,
  Swe.................H5   11
Vänersborg, Swe., 21,007..H5   11
Van Horn, Tex., 2,889...o12   84
Vankleek Hill, Ont.,
  Can., 1,691.........B10   41
Van Lear, Ky., 1,033....C7   62
Vannes, Fr., 36,576.....D2   5

Vanves, Fr., 25,138......g10   5
Van Wert, Ohio, 11,320...B1   78
Van Wert, co., Ohio,
  29,194..............B1   78
Van Winkle, Miss., 2,000..C3   68
Van Yen, Viet., 10,000...*G5   17
Van Zandt, co., Tex.,
  22,155..............C5   84
Var, dept., Fr., 555,926..*F7   5
Varanasi (Benares), India,
  583,856 (*606,271)....C7   20
Varaždin, Yugo., 34,270..B3   10
Varazze, It., 9,200......B2   9
Varberg, Swe., 23,839...I5   11
Varel, Ger., Fed. Rep. of,
  24,589..............B4   6
Varennes, Que., Can.,
  2,382............D4, p20   42
Varese, It., 80,300......B2   9
Varginha, Braz., 36,447..C3   30
Varkaus, Fin., 24,004...F12   11
Varmland, co., Swe.,
  285,400............*H5   11
Värnamo, Swe., 20,895..I6   11
Varna (Stalin), Bul.,
  184,400.............D8   10
Varnsdorf, Czech.,
  13,968.............*C3   7
Varnville, S.C., 1,555...*F5   82
Vas, co., Hung., 280,842..*B3   10
Vasilkov, Sov. Un.,
  27,000..............F8   12
Vaslui, Rom., 14,850....B8   10
Vassar, Mich., 2,802....E7   66
Västerås, Swe.,
  117,946..........H7, t34   11
Västerbotten, co., Swe.,
  234,700............*F9   11
Västernörrland, co., Swe.,
  276,500............*F8   11
Västervik, Swe., 22,123..I7   11
Västmanland, co., Swe.,
  257,100............*H7   11
Vasto, It., 12,600......C5   9
Vatican City, country,
  Eur., 1,000......D4, h8   9
Vaucluse, dept., Fr.,
  353,966............*F6   5
Vaud, canton, Switz.,
  512,000............*E2   6

Vaudreuil, Que., Can., 3,843........D3, a18 42
Vaudreuil co., Que., Can., 34,053..........D3 42
Vaughan, Ont., Can., 15,873...........D5, k14 41
Vaughn, N. Mex., 867.....B6 48
Vaupés, comisaría, Col., 15,800..............C3 32
Växjö, Swe., 43,411........I6 11
Veachland, Ky., 700.......B4 62
Veazie, Maine, 1,556.....*D4 64
Vecsés, Hung., 15,537.....B4 10
Veedersburg, Ind., 2,198...D3 59
Vegas Heights, Nev......*G6 72
Vegreville, Alta., Can., 3,691................C4 38
Vejle, Den., 32,300 (*44,000)...............J3 11
Vejle, co., Den., 233,400..*J3 11
Velbert, Ger., Fed. Rep. of, 55,400..............*C3 6
Velda Village Hills, Mo., 1,205...............*C7 69
Vélez-Rubio, Sp., 4,484...D4 8
Velikiye Luki, Sov. Un., 85,000...............C8 12
Velikiy Ustyug, Sov. Un., 37,000...............C7 13
Velizh, Sov. Un., 10,000...D8 12
Velletri, It., 22,200....D4, h9 9
Vellore, India, 139,082 (*178,554)............F6 20
Velma, Okla., 611........C4 79
Velsen, Neth.............B2 6
Velsk, Sov. Un., 22,000...C7 13
Velva, N. Dak., 1,241.....B5 77
Venado Tuerto, Arg., 30,000...............A4 28
Venango, co., Pa., 62,353..D2 81
Vendée, hills, Fr.........*D3 5
Venetian Village, Ill., 2,554...............*A6 58
Veneto, pol. dist., It., 3,846,562............*B4 9
Veneto, reg., It., 4,054,000.A3 9
Venezia, see Venice, It.
Venezuela, country, S.A., 11,560,000............C4 27
Venice, Fla., 6,648........E4 54
Venice, Ill., 4,680.........E3 58
Venice (Venezia), It., 367,600 (*420,000)......B4 9
Vénissieux, Fr., 47,613.....E6 5
Venlo, Neth., 62,675 (*86,000).............B7 5
Ventimiglia, It., 21,000....C1 9
Ventnor City, N.J., 10,385................E4 74
Ventspils, Sov. Un., 40,000................C3 12
Ventura, Calif., 57,964 (*246,800)............E4 50
Ventura, co., Calif., 378,497................E4 50
Ventura North (Chrisman), Calif......*E4 50
Veracruz [Llave], Mex., 214,072 (*270,000).D5, n15 34
Veracruz, state, Mex., 3,144,600.........D5, n15 34
Veradale, Wash., 2,400...*B8 86
Verāval, India, 58,771 (*75,520)............D5 20
Vercelli, It., 56,100.......B2 9
Verchères, Que., Can., 1,840................D4 42
Verchères, Que., Can., 30,885...............D9 42
Verden, Ger., Fed. Rep. of, 23,420...............B4 6
Verdun, Que., Can., 74,718...............g19 42
Verdun [-Sur-Meuse], Fr., 22,013...............C6 5
Verdunville, W. Va., 900..D2 87
Vereeniging, S. Afr., 169,553 (*250,000)......F5 24
Verga, N.J., 600.........*D2 74
Vergennes, Vt., 2,242.....C1 73
Verkhneye, Sov. Un., 10,000..........G12, q21 12
Verkhoyansk, Sov. Un., 1,400...............C16 13
Vermilion, Alta., Can., 2,915.................C5 38
Vermilion, Ohio, 9,872....A3 78
Vermilion, co., Ill., 97,047...............C6 58
Vermilion, par., La., 43,071................E3 63
Vermilion Heights, Ill.,....*C6 58
Vermillion, S. Dak., 9,128.H9 77
Vermillion, co., Ind.,
Vermilion Heights, Ill....*C6 58
Vermont, state, U.S., 469,000................ 73
Vernal, Utah, 3,908.......A7 72
Vernon, Ala., 2,190.......B1 46
Vernon, B.C., Can., 13,283..........D8, n19 37
Vernon, Fr., 17,247.......C4 5
Vernon, N.Y., 1,108......*B5 75
Vernon, Tex., 11,454......B3 84
Vernon, co., Mo., 19,065..D3 69
Vernon, co., Wis., 24,557..E3 88
Vernon, par., La., 53,794..C2 63
Vernonia, Oreg., 1,643....B3 80
Vernon Valley, N.Y......n15 75
Vernona, N.J., 15,067......B4 74
Vernona, Pa., 3,737......k14 81
Vernona, Wis., 2,334......E4 88
Vero Beach, Fla., 11,908...E6 54
Véroia, Grc., 29,528.......B4 14
Verona, It., 254,900.......B3 9
Verona Park, Mich., 2,107................*F5 66
Verplanck, N.Y., 2,400...*D7 75
Versailles, Fr., 90,829..C4, g9 5
Versailles, Ind., 1,020.....F7 59
Versailles, Ky., 5,697......B5 62
Versailles, Mo., 2,244.....C5 69
Versailles, Ohio, 2,441.....B1 78
Versailles, Pa., 2,754.....*F2 81
Verviers, Bel., 33,063 (*81,000).............B6 5
Veseloye, Sov. Un., 25,000..............H10 12
Vesoul, Fr., 16,352........D7 5
Vest-Agder, co., Nor., 121,100..............*H2 11
Vestal, N.Y., 6,800........C4 75
Vestavia Hills, Ala., 8,311..................g7 46
Vestfold, co., Nor., 171,600..............*H4 11
Vestry, Miss.............E5 68
Vesuvius, vol., It..........D5 9
Veszprém, Hung., 35,158................B3 10
Veszprem, co., Hung., 408,989...............*B3 10
Veszto, Hung., 9,645......B5 10
Vevay, Ind., 1,463........G7 59
Vevey, Switz., 17,900 (*61,100).............E3 6
Vezirköprü, Tur., 10,132..B10 14
Viadana, It., 5,587........B3 9
Vian, Okla., 1,131........B7 79
Viareggio, It., 54,500......C3 9
Viborg, co., Den., 167,700................*I3 11
Vibo Valentia, It., 22,300...................E6 9
Vicco, Ky., 377...........C6 62
Vicente López, Arg., 285,178................*g7 28
Vicenza, It., 111,200......B3 9
Vichada, comisaría, Col., 10,300................C3 32
Vichy, Fr., 33,506 (*57,000)..............D5 5
Vicksburg, Mich., 2,139....F5 66
Vicksburg, Miss., 25,478...C3 68
Victor, N.Y., 2,187........C3 75
Victor Harbour, Austl., 3,533.................G2 26
Victoria, Arg., 15,108......A4 28
Victoria, B.C., Can., 61,761 (*195,800)...E6, f12 37
Victoria, Newf., Can., 1,601..................E5 44
Victoria, Chile, 14,200.....B2 28
Victoria, Hong Kong, 521,612 (*3,575,000)....G7 17
Victoria, Kans., 1,246.....D4 61
Victoria, Tex., 41,349.....E4 84
Victoria, Va., 1,408.......D4 85
Victoria, co., N.B., Can., 19,694..................B2 43
Victoria, co., N.S., Can., 8,001...................C9 43
Victoria, co., Ont., Can., 30,917..................C6 43
Victoria, co., Tex., 53,766..................E4 84
Victoria, state, Austl., 3,645,000..............G7 25
Victoria, isl., Can........B11 36
Victoria, lake, Afr.........I4 23
Victoria, mtn., Pap........k12 25
Victoria de las Tunas, Cuba, 53,700 (65,000 ▲).D5 35
Victoria Harbour, Ont., Can., 1,243............C5 41
Victoriaville, Que., Can., 22,047 (*26,526)........C6 42
Victor Mills, S.C.........*B3 82
Victorville, Calif., 10,845...E5 50
Victory Gardens, N.J., 1,027..................*B3 74
Victory Heights, N.Y......*C4 75
Vidal, Calif...............E6 50
Vidalia, Ga., 9,507........D4 55
Vidalia, La., 5,538........C4 63
Vidin, Bul., 36,835........D6 10
Vidor, Tex., 9,738........D6 84
Vienna (Wien), Aus., 1,614,841 (*1,940,000)..D8 6
Vienna, Ga., 2,341........D3 55
Vienna, Ill., 1,325.........F5 58
Vienna, Va., 17,146...B5, g12 85
Vienna, W. Va., 11,549....B3 87
Vienne, Fr., 29,057.......E6 5
Vienne, dept., Fr., 340,256...............*D4 5
Vientiane, Laos, 190,200...B2 19
Vierzon, Fr., 33,775.......D5 5
Vieste, It., 12,679........D6 9
Vietnam, country, Asia, 42,760,000..............B3 19
View Park, Calif., 5,000...*E4 50
Vigan, Phil., 30,252.......B6 19
Vigevano, It., 66,400......B2 9
Vigo, Sp., 198,815.........A1 8
Vigo, co., Ind., 114,528.....F3 59
Vijayawāda, India, 317,258 (*344,607)......E7 20
Vila Nova de Gaia, Port., 45,739..................B1 8
Vilas, co., Wis., 10,958....B4 88
Vila Velha, Braz., 31,027..C4 30
Vileyka, Sov. Un., 10,000..D6 12
Viljandi, Sov. Un., 20,600..................B5 12
Vilkovo, Sov. Un., 20,000..I7 12
Villacarrillo, Sp., 13,090...C4 8
Villach, Aus., 50,993......E6 6
Villa Dolores, Arg., 16,730.................A3 28
Villafranca, It., 15,712.....B3 9
Villafranca de los Barros, Sp., 16,671............C2 8
Villafranca del Panadés, Sp., 11,985............B6 8
Villafranca di Verona, It., 6,015...................B3 9
Villagarcía, de Arosa, Sp., 4,986..................A1 8
Village-Richelieu, Que., Can., 1,612............*D4 42
Villa Grove, Ill., 2,605....D5 58
Villaguay, Arg., 12,463....A5 28
Villa Heights, Md., 500..*C4 53
Villahermosa, Mex., 99,565................D6 34
Villa María, Arg., 48,000..................A4 28
Villanova, Pa., 6,600....*G11 81
Villanueva de Córdoba, Sp., 15,719............C3 8
Villanueva del Arzobispo, Sp., 9,712.............C4 8
Villanueva de La Serena, Sp., 20,812............C3 8
Villanueva y Geltrú, Sp., 25,669.................B6 8
Villa Obregón, Mex., 3,904...................h9 34
Villa Park, Ill., 25,891......k8 58
Villa Rica, Ga., 3,922......C2 55
Villarreal, Sp., 20,025.....C5 8
Villarrica, Par., 17,687....E4 29
Villarrobledo, Sp., 21,356.................C4 8
Villas, N.J., 3,155.........E3 74
Villavicencio, Col., 62,500..................C3 32
Villefranche-sur-Saône, Fr., 26,338 (*36,000)....E6 5
Villejuif, Fr., 51,120......g10 5
Ville Marie, Que., Can., 1,995..................p20 41
Villemomble, Fr., 28,756.................g10 5
Villeneuve-le-Roi, Fr., 23,074.................h10 5
Villeneuve-St. Georges, Fr., 30,488..............h10 5
Villeneuve-sur-Lot, Fr., 17,295..................E4 5
Ville Platte, La., 9,692.....D3 63
Ville St. Georges, Que., Can., 7,554 (*13,554)...C7 42
Villeta, Par., 14,729.......E4 29
Villeurbanne, Fr., 119,879.................E6 5
Villigen-Schwenningen, Ger., Fed. Rep. of, 78,436.................*D4 6
Villisca, Iowa, 1,402......D3 60
Vilnius, Sov. Un., 386,000.................D5 12
Vilvoorde, Bel., 34,400.....B6 5
Vilyuy, riv., Sov. Un......C15 13
Vilyuysk, Sov. Un., 1,500..................C15 13
Vimianzo, Sp., 654.......A1 8
Viña del Mar, Chile, 149,300.................A2 28
Vinalhaven, Maine, 800...D4 64
Vincennes, Fr., 49,143....g10 5
Vincennes, Ind., 19,867....G3 59
Vincent, Ala., 1,419.......B3 46
Vincent, Ohio, 1,700.....*A3 78
Vindeln, Swe., 1,875.......E8 11
Vine Grove, Ky., 2,987....C4 62
Vine Hill (Martinez East), Calif., 2,000.....*C2 50
Vineland, N.J., 47,399 (*86,700)...............E2 74
Vineyard Haven (Tisbury), Mass., 2,257...........D6 65
Vinh Yen, Viet., 3,820.....G6 17
Vinita, Okla., 5,847.......A6 79
Vinita Park, Mo., 2,905...*C7 69
Vinkovci, Yugo., 29,072...C4 10
Vinnitsa, Sov. Un., 212,000...............G7 12
Vinson Massif, mtn., Ant..L15 2
Vinton, Iowa, 4,845........B5 60
Vinton, La., 3,454.........D2 63
Vinton, Va., 6,347..........C3 85
Vinton, co., Ohio, 9,420...C3 78
Vintondale, Pa., 812.......F4 81
Virden, Man., Can., 2,823..................E1 40
Virden, Ill., 3,504........D4 58
Virginia, Ill., 1,814.......D3 58
Virginia, Minn., 12,450....C6 67
Virginia, state, U.S., 4,849,000................ 85
Virginia Beach (Independent City), Va., 172,106.......D7, k16 85
Virginia City, Nev., 600...B2 72
Virginia Gardens, Fla., 2,524.................*G6 54
Virgin Islands, Br. dep., N.A., 11,000..........G12 35
Virgin Islands of the U.S., dep., N.A., 74,000.....G12 35
Viroflay, Fr., 16,004.......g9 5
Viroqua, Wis., 3,739......E3 88
Virovitica, Yugo., 16,339..................C3 10
Visalia, Calif., 27,482.....D4 50
Visby, Swe., 22,946........I8 11
Vishākhapatnam, India, 352,504 (*363,467).......E7 20
Vista, Calif., 24,688.......F5 50
Vista Park, Calif., 2,000..*E4 50
Vitanovak, Yugo., 1,127...D5 10
Vitebsk, Sov. Un., 231,000...............D8 12
Viterbo, It., 37,500........C4 9
Vitim, Sov. Un., 2,300...D14 13
Vitória, Braz., 121,978 (*345,000).............C4 30
Vitoria, Sp., 132,963......A4 8
Vitória da Conquista, Braz., 82,477...........A4 30
Vitry [-sur-Seine], Fr., 77,846.................g10 5
Vittoria, It., 46,900.......F5 9
Vittorio Veneto, It., 24,200..................B4 9
Vivian, La., 4,046.........B2 63
Vizcaya, prov., Sp., 973,400.................*A4 8
Vizianagaram, India, 86,608..................E7 20
Vizzini, It., 10,806........F5 9
Vlaardingen, Neth., 81,785..................B6 5
Vladimir, Sov. Un., 234,000...............C13 12
Vladimiro Aleksandrovskoye, Sov. Un., 10,000........E6 18
Vladimir Volynskiy, Sov. Un., 28,000........F5 12
Vladivostok, Sov. Un., 441,000.................E5 18
Vlasotince, Yugo., 5,924...D6 10
Vlissingen, Neth., 42,639...B5 5
Vlonë, pref., Alb., 58,000...............*B2 14
Vlorë, Alb., 50,400........B2 14
Vodnany, Czech..........*D3 7
Voeune Sai, Camb., 10,000..................F7 22
Voghera, It., 34,800.......B2 9
Voiron, Fr., 17,587 (*27,000)..............E6 5
Volga, riv., Sov. Un.......E7 13
Volgograd, Sov. Un., 818,000 (*1,015,000)...G14 12
Volkhov, Sov. Un., 47,000..B9 12
Volkovysk, Sov. Un., 23,000..................E5 12
Vologda, Sov. Un., 178,000................B12 12
Volokolamsk, Sov. Un., 15,000...............C10 12
Volos, Grc., 51,290 (*88,096)..............C4 14
Volsk, Sov. Un., 69,000..*D7 13
Volta Redonda, Braz., 120,645 (*205,000)..C4, h5 30
Volterra, It., 10,500.......C3 9

Volusia, co., Fla., 169,487 ..C5 54
Volzhskiy, Sov. Un.,
  142,000 ....G15 12
Voorheesville, N.Y.,
  2,826 ....*C7 75
Vorarlberg, state, Aus.,
  508,200 ....E4 6
Vordingborg, Den.,
  11,780 ....A1 7
Vorkuta, Sov. Un.,
  90,000 ....C9 13

Voronezh, Sov. Un.,
  660,000 ....F12 12
Voroshilovgrad (Lugansk),
  Sov. Un., 383,000 .G12, q22 12
Vosges, dept., Fr.,
  388,201 ....*C7 5
Votkinsk, Sov. Un.,
  74,000 ....*D8 13
Voznesensk, Sov. Un.,
  36,000 ....H8 12
Vranje, Yugo., 25,685 .....D5 10

Vratsa, Bul., 39,091 ....D6 10
Vratsa, co., Bul., 308,852 ..D6 10
Vršac, Yugo., 34,231 .....C5 10
Vsetín, Czech., 22,092 .....D5 7
Vukovar, Yugo., 30,149 ..C4 10
Vulcan, Alta., Can.,
  1,310 ....D4 38
Vulcan, Mo., 100 ....D7 69
Vung Tau, Viet., 54,200 ..*C3 19
Vyazma, Sov. Un.,
  44,000 ....D10 12

Vyazniki, Sov. Un.,
  43,000 ....C14 12
Vyborg, Sov. Un.,
  65,000 ....A7 12
Vyksa, Sov. Un.,
  46,000 ....D14 12
Vyshniy Volochek,
  Sov. Un., 74,000 ......C10 12
Vysoké Tatry, Czech......D6 7
Vytegra, Sov. Un.,
  11,800 ....A11 12

W

Wabana (Bell Island),
  Newf., Can., 5,421 ....E5 44
Wabash, Ind., 13,379 ....C6 59
Wabash, co., Ill., 12,841 ..E6 58
Wabash, co., Ind., 35,553 ..C6 59
Wabasha, Minn., 2,371 ....F6 67
Wabasha, co., Minn.,
  17,224 ....F6 67
Wabasso, Fla., 600 ....E6 54
Wabaunsee, co., Kans.,
  6,397 ....D7 61
Wacissa, Fla., 300 ....B3 54
Waco, Tex., 95,326
  (*127,700) D4 84
Waconia, Minn., 2,445 ....F5 67
Waddington, B.C., Can....F8 36
Waddington, N.Y., 955 ...f9 75
Wadena, Sask., Can.,
  1,311 ....F4 39
Wadena, Minn., 4,640 ...D3 67
Wadena, co., Minn.,
  12,412 ....D4 67
Wadesboro, N.C., 3,977 ...C2 76
Wadley, Ga., 1,989 ......D4 55
Wad Madani, Sud., 63,700 .F4 23
Wadsworth, Ohio, 13,142 ..A4 78
Waelder, Tex., 1,138 .....E4 84
Wagga Wagga, Austl.,
  28,814 ....G8 25
Wagner, S. Dak., 1,655 ...G7 77
Wagoner, Okla., 4,959 ...B6 79
Wagoner, co., Okla.,
  22,163 ....B6 79
Wagon Mound, N. Mex.,
  630 ....B6 48
Wągrowiec, Pol., 15,600 ..B4 7
Wah Cantonment, Pak.,
  109,000 ....*B5 20
Wahiawa, Haw.,
  17,598 ....B3, f9 56
Wahkiakum, co., Wash.,
  3,592 ....C2 86
Wahneta, Fla., 2,733 .....*E5 54
Wahoo, Nebr., 3,835 .C9, g11 71
Wahpeton, N. Dak., 7,076 .D9 77
Waialua, Haw., 4,047 .B3, f9 56
Waianae, Haw., 3,302 .B3, g9 56
Waikabubak, Indon.,
  3,934 ....G5 19
Wailua, Haw., 1,379 .....A2 56
Wailuku, Haw., 7,979 ....C5 56
Waimanalo, Haw.,
  2,081 ....B4, g11 56
Waimea, Haw., 1,569 ....B2 56
Waimea, Haw., 756 ......f9 56
Wainwright, Alta., Can.,
  3,872 ....C5 38
Waipahu, Haw., 22,798 .B3, g9 56
Waipio Acres, Haw.,
  2,146 ....g9 56
Waite Park, Minn., 2,824 ..E4 67
Waitsburg, Wash., 953 ...C7 86
Wajima, Jap., 18,500
  (33,652 ▲) H8 18
Wakarusa, Ind., 1,160 ...A5 59
Wakaw, Sask., Can., 974 .E3 39
Wakayama, Jap.,
  365,267 ....I7, o14 18
Wakayama, pref., Jap.,
  1,042,736 ....*I7 18
Wake, co., N.C., 228,453 ..B4 76
Wakefield, Mass.,
  25,402 ....B5, f11 65
Wakefield, Mich., 2,757 .n12 66
Wakefield, Nebr., 1,160 ..B9 71
Wakefield, R.I., 3,300 ...D11 52
Wakefield, Va., 942 .....D6 85
Wake Forest, N.C., 3,148 ..B4 76
Wakkanai, Jap., 54,493 ...D10 18
Wakulla, co., Fla., 6,308 ..B2 54
Walbridge, Ohio, 3,208 ...e6 78

Wałbrzych, Pol., 125,000
  (*160,000) C4 7
Walden, N.Y., 5,277 ....D6 75
Waldo, Ark., 1,658 ......D2 49
Waldo, co., Maine,
  28,328 ....D3 64
Waldorf, Md., 6,000 .....C4 53
Waldron, Ark., 2,132 ....C1 49
Waldwick, N.J., 12,313 ...A4 74
Wales, reg., U.K.,
  2,775,000 ....D5 4
Walhalla, N. Dak., 1,471 .A8 77
Walhalla, S.C., 3,662 ....B1 82
Walker, La., 1,363 ......g10 63
Walker, Mich., 11,492 ...E5 66
Walker, Minn., 1,073 ....C4 67
Walker, co., Ala., 56,246 ..B2 46
Walker, co., Ga., 50,691 ..B1 55
Walker, co., Tex., 27,680 .D5 84
Walkersville, Md., 1,269 ..B3 53
Walkerton, Ont., Can.,
  4,479 ....C3 41
Walkerton, Ind., 2,006 ...B5 59
Walkertown, N.C., 1,652 .A2 76
Walkerville, Mont., 1,097 .D4 70
Wall, Pa., 1,265 ....*F2 81
Wallace, Idaho, 2,206 ...B3 57
Wallace, N.C., 2,095 ....C4 76
Wallace, co., Kans., 2,215 .D2 61
Wallaceburg, Ont., Can.,
  10,550 ....E2 41
Wallasey, Eng., 97,470 ...D5 4
Walla Walla, Wash.,
  23,619 ....C7 86
Walla Walla, co., Wash.,
  42,176 ....C7 86
Walled Lake, Mich.,
  3,759 ....o15 66
Waller, Tex., 1,123 ......D5 84
Waller, co., Tex., 14,285 ..E4 84
Wallingford, Conn.,
  35,714 ....D5 52
Wallingford, Vt., 800 ....E2 73
Wallington, Eng.,
  32,500 ....m12 4
Wallington, N.J., 10,284 ..h8 74
Wallis, Tex., 1,033 ......E4 84
Wallkill, N.Y., 1,849 ....D6 75
Wallowa, Oreg., 811 .....B9 80
Wallowa, co., Oreg., 6,247 .B9 80
Wallsend, Eng., 45,950 ...C6 4
Walnut, Calif., 5,992 ...*F4 50
Walnut, Ill., 1,295 ......B4 58
Walnut Cove, N.C., 1,213 .A2 76
Walnut Creek, Calif.,
  39,844 ....h8 50
Walnut Heights, Calif.,
  700 ....*D2 50
Walnut Park, Calif.,
  8,925 ....*F4 50
Walnutport, Pa., 1,942 ...E10 81
Walnut Ridge, Ark., 3,800 .A5 49
Walpole, Mass., 8,500 .B5, h10 65
Walsall, Eng., 184,380 ....D6 4
Walsenburg, Colo., 4,329 ..D6 51
Walsh, co., N. Dak.,
  16,251 ....B8 77
Walterboro, S.C., 6,257 ...F6 82
Walters, Okla., 2,611 ....C3 79
Walthall, co., Miss.,
  12,500 ....D3 68
Waltham, Mass.,
  61,582 ....B5, g11 65
Walthill, Nebr., 897 .....B9 71
Walton, Ind., 1,054 ......C5 59
Walton, Ky., 1,801 .B5, k13 62
Walton, N.Y., 3,744 ....C5 75
Walton, co., Fla., 16,087 .u15 54
Walton, co., Ga., 23,404 ..C3 55
Walton Hills, Ohio,
  2,508 ....*A4 78
Walvisbaai, S. Afr., 21,725 .E2 24

Walworth, Wis., 1,637 ....F5 88
Walworth, co., S. Dak.,
  7,842 ....E5 77
Walworth, co., Wis.,
  63,444 ....F5 88
Wamac, Ill., 1,347 ......E4 58
Wamego, Kans., 2,507 ...C7 61
Wampum, Pa., 1,189 ....E1 81
Wanamassa, N.J., 4,000 ..C4 74
Wanaque, N.J., 8,636 ....A4 74
Wanganui, N.Z., 35,750
  (*38,000) M15 26
Wangaratta, Austl.,
  15,535 ....H6 26
Wangching, China......C10 17
Wanhsien, China, 90,000 ..E6 17
Wankie, Rh., 23,000 .....D5 24
Wantagh, N.Y., 22,300 ...G2 52
Wapakoneta, Ohio, 7,324 .B1 78
Wapato, Wash., 2,841 ...C5 86
Wapello, Iowa, 1,873 ....C6 60
Wapello, co., Iowa, 42,149 .C5 60
Wappingers Falls, N.Y.,
  5,607 ....D7 75
War, W. Va., 2,004 ......D3 87
Warangal, India, 207,520 ..E6 20
Ward, W. Va., 125 ......m13 87
Ward, co., N. Dak., 58,560 .B4 77
Ward, co., Tex., 13,019 ...D1 84
Warden, Wash., 1,254 ...C6 86
Ward Ridge, Fla., 8 .....*C1 54
Wardville, La., 1,087 ....*C3 63
Ware, Mass., 6,509 ......B3 65
Ware, co., Ga., 33,525 ...E4 55
Wareham, Mass., 2,024 ...C6 65
Warehouse Point, Conn.,
  700 ....B6 52
Waren, Ger. Dem. Rep.,
  19,700 ....B6 6
Ware Shoals, S.C., 2,480 ..C3 82
Warfield, B.C., Can.,2,132 .E9 37
Warner Robins, Ga.,
  33,491 ....D3 55
Warr Acres, Okla., 9,887 ..B4 79
Warragul, Austl., 7,103 ..*G8 25
Warren, Ark., 6,433 .....D3 49
Warren, Ill., 1,523 ......A4 58
Warren, Ind., 1,229 .....C7 59
Warren, Mass., 1,688 ....B3 65
Warren, Mich.,
  179,260 ....F7, p16 66
Warren, Minn., 1,999 ....B2 67
Warren, Ohio, 63,494 ....A5 78
Warren, Pa., 12,998 .....C3 81
Warren, R.I., 10,523 ....C11 52
Warren, co., Ga., 6,669 ...C4 55
Warren, co., Ill., 21,595 ..C3 58
Warren, co., Ind., 8,705 ..D3 59
Warren, co., Iowa, 27,432 .C4 60
Warren, co., Ky., 57,432 ..C3 62
Warren, co., Miss., 44,981 .C3 68
Warren, co., Mo., 9,699 ..C6 69
Warren, co., N.J., 73,960 .B3 74
Warren, co., N.Y., 49,402 .B7 75
Warren, co., N.C., 15,810 .A4 76
Warren, co., Ohio, 85,505 .C1 78
Warren, co., Pa., 47,682 ..C3 81
Warren, co., Tenn.,
  26,972 ....D8 83
Warren, co., Va., 15,301 ..B4 85
Warrensburg, Mo., 13,125 .C4 69
Warrensburg, N.Y., 2,743 .B7 75
Warrensville Heights,
  Ohio, 18,925 ....h9 78
Warrenton, Ga., 2,073 ...C4 55
Warrenton, Mo., 2,057 ..C6 69
Warrenton, N.C., 1,035 ..A4 76
Warrenton, Oreg., 1,825 ..A3 80
Warrenton, Va., 4,027 ...B5 85
Warrenville, Ill., 3,281 ...k8 58
Warrensville, S.C., 1,059 ..D4 82
Warri, Nig., 55,254 ......G6 22

Warrick, co., Ind., 27,972 ..H3 59
Warrington, Eng.,
  67,890 (*135,000) D5 4
Warrington, Fla., 15,848 .u14 54
Warrior, Ala., 2,621 .....B3 46
Warrnambool, Austl.,
  18,663 ....G7, n14 25
Warroad, Minn., 1,086 ...B3 67
Warsaw, Ill., 1,758 .....C2 58
Warsaw, Ind., 7,506 ....B6 59
Warsaw, Mo., 1,423 ....C4 69
Warsaw, N.Y., 3,619 ....C2 75
Warsaw, N.C., 2,701 ....B4 76
Warsaw (Warszawa),
  Pol., 1,308,100
  (*1,760,000) B6, m14 7
Warson Woods, Mo.,
  2,544 ....*C7 69
Warwick, Que., Can.,
  2,847 ....D6 42
Warwick, Eng., 18,040 ...D6 4
Warwick, N.Y.,
  3,604 ....D6, m14 75
Warwick, R.I., 83,694 ....C10 52
Warwick, co., Eng.,
  2,081,900 ....*D6 4
Wasatch, co., Utah, 5,863 .A6 72
Wasco, Calif., 8,269 .....E4 50
Wasco, co., Oreg., 20,133 .B5 80
Waseca, Minn., 6,789 ....F5 67
Waseca, co., Minn.,
  16,663 ....F5 67
Washabaugh, co., S. Dak.,
  1,389 ....G4 77
Washakie, co., Wyo.,
  7,569 ....C5 89
Washburn, Ill., 1,173 ....C4 58
Washburn, Maine, 1,098 ..B4 64
Washburn, Wis., 1,957 ...B3 88
Washburn, co., Wis.,
  10,601 ....C2 88
Washington, D.C.,
  756,510
  (*2,964,500) C3, f8 53
Washington, Ga., 4,094 ...C4 55
Washington, Ill., 6,790 ...C4 58
Washington, Ind., 11,358 .G3 59
Washington, Iowa, 6,317 ..C6 60
Washington, Kans., 1,584 .C6 61
Washington, La., 1,473 ...D3 63
Washington, Mo., 8,499 ..C6 69
Washington, N.J., 5,943 ..B3 74
Washington, N.C., 8,961 ..B5 76
Washington, Pa., 19,827 ..F1 81
Washington, co., Ala.,
  16,241 ....D1 46
Washington, co., Ark.,
  77,370 ....A1 49
Washington, co., Colo.,
  5,550 ....B7 51
Washington, co., Fla.,
  11,453 ....u16 54
Washington, co., Ga.,
  17,480 ....C3 55
Washington, co., Idaho,
  7,633 ....E2 57
Washington, co., Ill.,
  13,780 ....E4 58
Washington, co., Ind.,
  19,278 ....G5 59
Washington, co., Iowa,
  18,967 ....C6 60
Washington, co., Kan.,
  9,249 ....C6 61
Washington, co., Ky.,
  10,728 ....C4 62
Washington, co., Maine,
  27,859 ....D5 64
Washington, co., Md.,
  103,829 ....A2 53
Washington, co., Minn.,
  82,948 ....E6 67

Washington, co., Miss., 70,581................B3 66
Washington, co., Mo., 15,086.................D7 69
Washington, co., Nebr., 13,310.................C9 71
Washington, co., N.Y., 52,725.................B7 75
Washington, co., N.C., 14,038.................B6 76
Washington, co., Ohio, 57,160.................C4 78
Washington, co., Okla., 42,277.................A6 79
Washington, co., Oreg., 157,920................B3 80
Washington, co., Pa., 210,876.................F1 81
Washington, co., R.I., 85,706.................D10 52
Washington, co., Tenn., 73,924.................C10 83
Washington, co., Tex., 18,842.................D4 84
Washington, co., Utah, 13,669.................C5 72
Washington, co., Vt., 47,659.................C2 73
Washington, co., Va., 40,835.................f9 85
Washington, co., Wis., 63,839.................E5 88
Washington, par., La., 41,987.................D5 63
Washington, state, U.S., 3,423,000................86
Washington, mtn., N.H....C5 73
Washington Court House, Ohio, 12,495..........C2 78
Washington Heights, N.Y., 1,204.........*D6 75
Washington North, Pa., 2,855.............*F1 81
Washington Park, Ill., 9,524.................E3 58
Washington Terrace, Utah, 7,241.........*A5 72
Washingtonville, N.Y., 1,887.............*D6 75
Washington West, Pa., 3,297.............*F1 81
Washita, co., Okla., 12,141.B2 79
Washoe, co., Nev., 121,068.A2 72
Washougal, Wash., 3,388..D3 86
Washtenaw, co., Mich., 234,103................F7 66
Waskom, Tex., 1,460....C5 84
Watauga, co., N.C., 23,404.A1 76
Watchung, N.J., 4,750....*B4 74
Waterbury, Conn., 108,033 (*203,400)......C4 52
Waterbury, Vt., 2,840....C2 73
Waterford, Calif., 2,243..*D3 50
Waterford, Ont., Can., 2,403.................E4 41
Waterford, Conn., 4,400..D8 52
Waterford, Ire., 31,968....D3 4
Waterford, N.Y., 2,879...C7 75
Waterford, Pa., 1,468.....C1 81
Waterford, Wis., 1,922.................F5, n11 88
Waterford, co., Ire., 73,080.................*D3 4
Waterloo, Ont., Can., 36,677.................D4 41
Waterloo, Que., Can., 4,936.................D5 42
Waterloo, Ill., 4,546......E3 58
Waterloo, Ind., 1,876.....B7 59
Waterloo, Iowa, 75,533 (*125,200)........B5 60
Waterloo, N.Y., 5,418....C4 75
Waterloo, Wis., 2,253....E5 88
Waterloo, co., Ont., Can., 216,728................D4 41
Waterman, Ill., 990......B5 58
Waterproof, La., 1,438....C4 63
Watertown, Fla., 200....B4 54
Watertown, Conn., 6,500..C4 52
Watertown, Mass., 39,307................g11 65
Watertown, Minn., 1,390..*F5 67
Watertown, N.Y., 30,787..B5 75
Watertown, S. Dak., 13,388................F8 77
Watertown, Tenn., 1,061..A5 83
Watertown, Wis., 15,683..E5 88
Water Valley, Miss., 3,285.A4 68
Waterville, Que., Can., 1,330.................D6 42
Waterville, Maine, 18,192.D3 64
Waterville, Minn., 1,539..F5 67
Waterville, N.Y., 1,808...C5 75
Waterville, Ohio, 2,940.................A2, f6 78
Waterville, Wash., 919...B5 86
Watervliet, Mich., 2,059..F4 66
Watervliet, N.Y., 12,404..C7 75

Watford, Ont., Can., 1,293.................E3 41
Watford City, N. Dak., 1,768.................C2 77
Watkins Glen, N.Y., 2,716..C4 75
Watonga, Okla., 3,696....B3 79
Watonwan, co., Minn., 13,298................F4 67
Watrous, Sask., Can., 1,541.................F3 39
Watseka, Ill., 5,294......C6 58
Watsontown, Pa., 2,514...D8 81
Watsonville, Calif., 14,569.D3 50
Wattrelos, Fr., 43,754....B5 5
Wattsville, S.C., 1,181....B4 82
Wauchope, Austl., 3,351..E9 26
Wauchula, Fla., 3,007....E5 54
Wauconda, Ill., 5,460.....h8 58
Waukegan, Ill., 65,269..A6, h9 58
Waukesha, Wis., 39,695...E5 88
Waukesha, co., Wis., 231,335................E5 88
Waukon, Iowa, 3,883.....A6 60
Waunakee, Wis., 2,181...E4 88
Waupaca, Wis., 4,342....D4 88
Waupaca, co., Wis., 37,780................D5 88
Waupun, Wis., 7,946.....E5 88
Waurika, Okla., 1,833....C4 79
Wausau, Wis., 32,806 (*56,600)...........D4 88
Wauseon, Ohio, 4,932....A1 78
Waushara, co., Wis., 14,795................D4 88
Wautoma, Wis., 1,624....D4 88
Wauwatosa, Wis., 58,676................m11 88
Waverly, Ill., 1,442......D4 58
Waverly, Iowa, 7,205.....B5 60
Waverly, N.Y., 5,261.....C4 75
Waverly, Ohio, 4,858.....C3 78
Waverly, Tenn., 3,794....A4 83
Waverly, Va., 1,717......C5 85
Waxahachie, Tex., 13,452...........C4, n10 84
Waycross, Ga., 18,996....E4 55
Wayland, Ky., 384.......C7 62
Wayland, Mass., 4,000....g10 65
Wayland, Mich., 2,054...F5 66
Wayland, N.Y., 2,022....C3 75
Waymart, Pa., 1,122.....C11 81
Wayne, Mich., 21,054....p15 66
Wayne, Nebr., 5,379.....B8 71
Wayne, N.J., 49,141.....B4 74
Wayne, Pa., 8,900...F11, o20 81
Wayne, W. Va., 1,385....C2 87
Wayne, co., Ga., 17,858...E4 55
Wayne, co., Ill., 17,004..E5 58
Wayne, co., Ind., 79,109..E7 59
Wayne, co., Iowa, 8,405..D4 60
Wayne, co., Ky., 14,268..D5 62
Wayne, co., Mich., 2,670,368.............F7 66
Wayne, co., Miss., 16,650.D5 68
Wayne, co., Mo., 8,546...D7 69
Wayne, co., Nebr., 10,400.B8 71
Wayne, co., N.Y., 79,404..B3 75
Wayne, co., N.C., 85,408..B4 76
Wayne, co., Ohio, 87,123..B4 78
Wayne, co., Pa., 29,581...C11 81
Wayne, co., Tenn., 12,365.B4 83
Wayne, co., Utah, 1,483..B6 72
Wayne, co., W. Va., 37,581................C2 87
Waynesboro, Ga., 5,530...C4 55
Waynesboro, Miss., 4,368..D5 68
Waynesboro, Pa., 10,011..G6 81
Waynesboro, Tenn., 1,983..B4 83
Waynesboro (Independent City), Va., 16,707....B4 85
Waynesburg, Ohio, 1,337..B4 78
Waynesburg, Pa., 5,152...G1 81
Waynesville, Mo., 3,375...D5 69
Waynesville, N.C., 6,488..f10 76
Waynesville, Ohio, 1,638..C1 78
Waynoka, Okla., 1,444...A3 79
Wayzata, Minn., 3,700...*F5 67
Weakley, co., Tenn., 28,827................A3 83
Weatherford, Okla., 7,959.B3 79
Weatherford, Tex., 11,750..C4 84
Weatherly, Pa., 2,254....E10 81
Weaver, Ala., 2,091......B4 46
Weaverville, Calif., 1,489..B2 50
Weaverville, N.C., 1,280..f10 76
Webb, co., Tex., 72,859...F3 84
Webb City, Mo., 6,923....D3 69
Weber, co., Utah, 126,278..A6 72
Weber City, Va., 1,676....*f9 85
Webster, Mass., 14,917...B4 65
Webster, N.Y., 5,037.....B3 75
Webster, S. Dak., 2,252...E8 77
Webster, co., Ga., 2,362..D2 55
Webster, co., Iowa, 48,391.B3 60
Webster, co., Ky., 13,282..C2 62
Webster, co., Miss., 10,047.B4 68
Webster, co., Mo., 15,562.D5 69
Webster, co., Nebr., 5,396.D7 71

Webster, co., W. Va., 9,809.................C4 87
Webster, par., La., 39,939................B2 63
Webster City, Iowa, 8,488.................B4 60
Webster Groves, Mo., 27,457................f13 69
Webster Springs (Addison), W. Va., 1,038.................C4 87
Wedgeport, N.S., Can., 665.................F4 43
Wedowee, Ala., 842.....B4 46
Weed, Calif., 2,983......B2 50
Weed Heights, Nev., 650..*B2 72
Weedon, Que., Can., 1,429.................D6 42
Weedsport, N.Y., 1,900...B4 75
Weehawken, N.J., 13,383..h8 74
Weeks, La.................E4 63
Weeping Water, Nebr., 1,143.......D9, h12 71
Weert, Neth., 24,400.....B6 5
Weiden, Ger., Fed. Rep. of, 43,436................D6 6
Weifang, China, 190,000..D8 17
Weihai, China, 45,000....D9 17
Weilheim, Ger., Fed. Rep. of, 15,343...........E5 6
Weimar, Ger. Dem. Rep., 63,265................C5 6
Weimar, Tex., 2,104......E4 84
Weinan, China............E6 17
Weinheim, Ger., Fed. Rep. of, 41,332...........D4 6
Weippe, Idaho, 713.......C3 57
Weirton, W. Va., 27,131..........A4, f8 87
Weiser, Idaho, 4,108......E2 57
Weissenburg [in Bayern], Ger., Fed. Rep. of, 16,362.................D5 6
Weissenfels, Ger. Dem. Rep., 43,994..........*C5 6
Wejherowo, Pol., 33,600..A5 7
Welborn, Kans...........B8 61
Welch, W. Va., 4,149....D3 87
Welcome, S.C., 1,600....*B3 82
Weld, co., Colo., 89,297..A6 51
Weldon, N.C., 2,304.....A5 76
Weleetka, Okla., 1,199...B5 79
Welkom, S. Afr., 66,217 (*132,000).........*F5 24
Welland, Ont., Can., 44,397................E5 41
Wellesley, Mass., 28,051...........B5, g10 65
Wellford, S.C., 1,298....B3 82
Wellington, Austl., 5,534..F7 26
Wellington, Ont., Can., 1,064.................D7 41
Wellington, Kans., 8,072..E6 61
Wellington, N.Z., 136,400 (*328,800).........N15 26
Wellington, Ohio, 4,137..A3 78
Wellington, Tex., 2,884...B2 84
Wellington, Utah, 922....B6 72
Wellington, co., Ont., Can., 94,177...........D4 41
Wellman, Iowa, 977......C6 60
Wells, B.C., Can., 409....C7 37
Wells, Minn., 2,791......G5 67
Wells, Nev., 1,081.......A4 72
Wells, co., Ind., 23,821..C7 59
Wells, co., N. Dak., 7,847.................C6 77
Wellsboro, Pa., 4,003....C7 81
Wellsburg, W. Va., 4,600...........A4, f8 87
Wellston, Mo., 7,050.....f13 69
Wellston, Ohio, 5,410....C3 78
Wellsville, Kans., 1,183..D8 61
Wellsville, Mo., 1,565....B6 69
Wellsville, N.Y., 5,815...C3 75
Wellsville, Ohio, 5,891...B5 78
Wellsville, Utah, 1,267...A6 72
Wels, Aus., 47,081 (*59,000)...........D7 6
Welsh, La., 3,203.......D3 63
Wembley, Eng., 124,600..k11 4
Wenatchee, Wash., 16,912..B5 86
Wenchou (Yunghia), China, 210,000.....F9 17
Wendell, Idaho, 1,122....G4 57
Wendell, N.C., 1,929....B4 76
Wenham, Mass., 3,849...........A6, f12 65
Wenona, Ill., 1,080.....*B4 58
Wenonah, N.J., 2,364....D2 74
Wentworth, co., Ont., Can., 394,299.........D4 41
Wentzville, Mo., 3,223...C7 69
Werdau, Ger. Dem. Rep., 22,601................C6 6
Wernersville, Pa., 1,761..*F9 81
Wernigerode, Ger. Dem. Rep., 33,479..........C5 6

Wesel, Ger., Fed. Rep. of, 46,387................C3 6
Weslaco, Tex., 15,313...F3 84
Weslaco North, Tex.....*F3 84
Wesleyville, Newf., Can., 1,285.................D5 44
Wesleyville, Pa., 1,761...B2 81
Wessington Springs, S. Dak., 1,300.......F7 77
Wesson, Miss., 1,253....D3 68
West, Tex., 2,406.......D4 84
West Alexandria, Ohio, 1,553.................C1 78
West Allis, Wis., 71,649..m12 88
West Amityville, N.Y., 6,424.................*E7 75
West Babylon, N.Y., 30,680................*n15 75
West Baden Springs, Ind., 930.................G4 59
West Barrington, R.I., 4,000.................B11 52
West Baton Rouge, par., La., 16,864..........D4 63
West Belmar, N.J., 2,700..*C4 74
West Bend, Iowa, 865....B3 60
West Bend, Wis., 16,555..E5 88
West Bengal, state, India, 44,312,011.........*D8 20
West Berlin, N.J., 3,300..D3 74
West Blocton, Ala., 1,172..B2 46
West Bountiful, Utah, 1,246.................*A6 72
West Boylston, Mass., 4,000.................B4 65
West Branch, Iowa, 1,322.C6 60
West Branch, Mich., 1,912.................D6 66
West Bridgewater, Mass., 1,920.................B5 65
West Bridgewater, Pa., 966.................*E1 81
West Bromwich, Eng., 166,560................D6 4
Westbrook, Maine, 14,444...........E2, g7 64
Westbrook, Minn., 990.................F3 67
West Brookfield, Mass., 1,536.................B3 65
Westbrook Park, Pa., 5,700................*B11 81
West Brownsville, Pa., 1,426.................*F2 81
West Brunswick, N.J.....*C4 74
West Burlington, Iowa, 3,139.................D6 60
Westbury, N.Y., 15,362..E7 75
Westby, Wis., 1,568.....E3 88
West Caldwell, N.J., 11,913................*B4 74
West Cape May, N.J., 1,005.................F3 74
West Carroll, par., La., 13,028................B4 63
West Carrollton, Ohio, 10,748................C1 78
West Carthage, N.Y., 2,047.................B5 75
Westchester, Ill., 20,033..k9 58
West Chester, Pa., 19,301................G10 81
Westchester, co., N.Y., 894,406...............D7 75
West Chicago, Ill., 10,111..k8 58
West City, Ill., 637......F5 58
West Clarkston, Wash., 2,000.................*C8 86
West Collingswood, N.J..*D2 74
West Collingswood Heights, N.J., 1,100...*D2 74
West Columbia, S.C., 7,838.................D5 82
West Columbia, Tex., 3,335............E5, r14 84
West Concord, Mass., 4,000............B5, g10 65
West Concord, N.C., 3,400.................*B2 76
West Conshohocken, Pa., 2,194................o20 81
West Corners, N.Y., 3,000.................*C5 75
West Covina, Calif., 68,034...............m13 50
Westdale, Ill., 3,500....*B6 58
West Decatur, Pa., 600...E5 81
West Derry, Pa., 750....*F3 81
West Des Moines, Iowa, 16,441............C4, e8 60
West Easton, Pa., 1,123..*E11 81
West Elizabeth, Pa., 848..*F2 81
West Elkton, Ohio, 291..*C1 75
West Elmira, N.Y., 5,901.................*C4 75
West End, Fla...........*C4 54
West End, N.Y., 1,692...*C5 75

West End Anniston, Ala.,
5,515.............*B4　46
West Endicott, N.Y.,
3,000.............*C5　75
Westerly, R.I., 14,400.....D9　52
Western, reg., Nig.,
10,265,846.............G5　22
Western Australia, state,
Austl., 1,085,000.......D3　25
Western Hills, Colo.,
4,500.............*B6　51
Western Peninsula, div.,
Ice., 11,394.............*m21　11
Westernport, Md., 3,106..m12　53
Western Sahara, country,
Afr., 106,000.............D2　22
Western Samoa, country,
Oceania, 150,000........G9　2
Western Springs, Ill.,
13,029.............k9　58
Westerville, Ohio,
12,530.............B3, k11　78
West Fairview, Pa., 1,388..F8　81
West Farmington, Maine,
500.............D2　64
West Feliciana, par., La.,
11,376.............D4　63
Westfield, Ind., 1,837.....D5　59
Westfield, Mass., 31,433...B2　65
Westfield, N.J., 33,720....B4　74
Westfield, N.Y., 3,651.....C1　75
Westfield, Pa., 1,273.....C6　81
Westfield, Wis., 884.....E4　88
West Flanders, prov.,
Bel., 1,046,800.......*B5　5
West Frankfort, Ill.,
8,854.............F5　58
Westgate, Fla., 1,900......F6　54
West Glens Falls, N.Y.,
3,363.............*B7　75
West Grove, Pa., 1,870...G10　81
Westhampton Beach,
N.Y., 1,926.............n16　75
West Hartford, Conn.,
68,031.............B6　52
West Hartsville, S.C.,....*C7　82
West Haven, Conn.,
52,851.............D5　52
West Haverstraw, N.Y.,
8,558.............*D7　75
West Hazleton, Pa., 6,059..E9　81
West Helena, Ark., 11,007..C5　49
West Hempstead, N.Y.,
26,200.............*G2　52
West Hillsboro, N.C., 700.*A3　76
West Hollywood, Calif.,
34,400.............*E4　50
West Hollywood, Fla.,
3,700.............r13　54
West Homestead, Pa.,
3,789.............*F2　81
West Indies, reg., Atl. O.....35
West Islip, N.Y., 20,613...*n15　75
West Jefferson, N.C.,
889.............A1　76
West Jefferson, Ohio,
3,664.............C2, m10　78
West Jordan, Utah,
4,221.............A5, D2　78
West Kingston, R.I., 900..D10　52
West Kittanning, Pa.,
956.............*E3　81
West Lafayette, Ind.,
19,157.............D4　59
West Lafayette, Ohio,
1,719.............B4　78
Westlake, La., 4,082......D2　63
Westlake, Ohio, 15,689....h9　78
Westland, Mich., 86,749..p15　66
Westlands, Mass., 4,000...f10　65
West Lanham Hills, Md.,
1,200.............*C4　53
West Lawn, Pa., 1,973....F10　81
West Lebanon, Pa., 986...*F9　81
West Leechburg, Pa.,
1,422.............*E2　81
West Leisenring, Pa., 700..G2　81
West Liberty, Iowa,
2,296.............C6　60
West Liberty, Ky., 1,387...C6　62
West Liberty, Ohio,
1,580.............B2　78
West Liberty, W. Va.,
2,400.............f8　87
West Linn, Oreg.,
7,091.............B4, h12　80
Westlock, Alta., Can.,
3,246.............B4　38
West Long Branch, N.J.,
6,845.............C4　74
West Lorne, Ont., Can.,
1,070.............E3　41
West Lothian, Scot.,
108,463.............*C5　4
West Malaysia, reg., Mala.,
9,505,000.............E2　19
West Manayunk, Pa.,
1,900.............*F11　81

West Marion, N.C.,
2,000.............*f10　76
West Mayfield, Pa.,
2,152.............*E1　81
Westmeath, co., Ire.,
52,900.............*D3　4
West Medway, Mass.,
2,269.............B5, h10　65
West Melbourne, Fla.,
3,050.............*D6　54
West Memphis, Ark.,
25,892.............B5　49
West Miami, Fla., 5,494...s13　54
West Middlesex, Pa.,
1,293.............D1　81
West Mifflin, Pa., 28,070...F2　81
West Milton, Ohio, 3,696..C1　78
West Milwaukee, Wis.,
4,405.............m12　88
Westminster, Calif.,
59,865.............n12　50
Westminster, Colo., 19,432.A6　51
Westminster, Md., 7,207...A4　53
Westminster, Mass., 1,200..A4　65
Westminster, S.C., 2,521...B1　82
West Monroe, La., 14,868..B3　63
Westmont, Ill., 8,920.....k9　58
Westmont, N.J., 5,700....D2　74
Westmont, Pa., 6,673.....F4　81
Westmoreland, co., Pa.,
376,935.............F2　81
Westmoreland, co., Va.,
12,142.............B6　85
Westmoreland City, Pa.,
1,300.............*F2　81
Westmorland, Calif.,
1,175.............F6　50
Westmorland, co., N.B.,
Can., 95,181.............C5　43
Westmorland, co., Eng.,
71,830.............*C5　4
Westmount, Que., Can.,
23,606.............*D4　42
West Mystic, Conn., 1,150.D9　52
West Newton, Pa., 3,648...F2　81
West New York, N.J.,
40,627.............h8　74
West Nyack, N.Y., 5,510..*D7　75
Weston, Ont., Can.,
11,047.............m14　41
Weston, Conn., 700......E3　52
Weston, Mass., 10,870...g10　65
Weston, Mo., 1,267...B3, h10　69
Weston, Ohio, 1,269......A2　78
Weston, W. Va., 7,323....B4　87
Weston, co., Wyo., 6,307..C8　89
Weston-Super-Mare, Eng.,
49,540.............E5　4
West Orange, N.J., 43,715..B4　74
West Orange, Tex.,
4,820.............*D6　84
Westover, W. Va.,
5,086.............B5, h11　87
West Palm Beach, Fla.,
57,375 (*232,900).......F6　54
West Paterson, N.J.,
11,692.............*B4　74
West Pensacola, Fla.,
23,000.............v14　54
West Pittston, Pa., 7,074..m17　81
West Plains, Mo., 6,893....E6　69
West Point, Ga., 4,232....D1　55
West Point, Ky., 1,741....C4　62
West Point, Miss., 8,714...B5　68
West Point, Nebr., 3,385..C9　71
West Point, N.Y.,
5,200.............D7, m15　75
West Point, Va., 2,600....C6　85
Westport, Conn., 27,318...E3　52
West Portland, Oreg......*B4　80
West Portland Park, Oreg.*B4　80
West Portsmouth, Ohio,
3,396.............D2　78
West Pueblo, Colo.......*C6　51
West Rockingham, N.C.,
700.............*B3　76
West Rutland, Vt., 2,381...D1　73
West Sacramento, Calif.,
12,002.............*C3　50
West Salem, Ill., 979.....E5　58
West Salem, Ohio, 1,058...B3　78
West Salem, Wis., 2,180...E2　88
West Sayville, N.Y.,
3,650.............G4　52
West Seneca, N.Y.,
48,404.............*C2　75
West Slope, Oreg., 8,000..g12　80
West Spitsbergen, isl.,
Nor.............A21　2
West Springfield, Mass.,
28,461.............B2　65
West St. Paul, Minn.,
18,799.............n12　67
West Terre Haute, Ind.,
2,704.............F3　59
West Union, Iowa, 2,624...B6　60
West Union, Ohio, 1,951...D2　78

West Union, W. Va.,
1,141.............B4, k9　87
West Unity, Ohio, 1,589...A1　78
West University Place,
Tex., 13,317.............r14　84
West Van Lear, Ky., 900...C7　62
West View, Ohio, 2,523....h9　78
West View, Pa., 8,312....h13　81
Westville, Ill., 3,655.....C6　58
Westville, N.J., 5,170....D2　74
Westville Grove, N.J.,
3,100.............*D2　74
West Virginia, state, U.S.,
1,780,000.............87
West Warren, Mass.,
1,237.............B3　65
West Warwick, R.I.,
24,323.............C10　52
Westwego, La., 11,402....k11　63
West Wenatchee, Wash.,
2,134.............*B5　86
West Winfield, N.Y., 1,018.C5　75
West Winter Haven, Fla.,
7,716.............*D5　54
Westwood, Calif., 1,862...B3　50
Westwood, Kans., 2,329...k16　61
Westwood, Ky., 777.....B7　62
Westwood, Mass.,
8,000.............B5, h11　65
Westwood, Mich., 9,143..*F5　66
Westwood, N.J.,
11,105.............D5, h8　74
Westwood Lakes, Fla.,
12,811.............s13　54
Westworth Village, Tex.,
4,578.............*C4　84
West Wyalong, Austl.,
3,438.............F6　26
West Wyoming, Pa.,
3,659.............n17　81
West Wyomissing, Pa.,
3,000.............*F9　81
West Yarmouth, Mass.,
3,699.............C7　65
West York, Pa., 5,314....G8　81
West Yuma, Ariz.......*C1　48
Wetaskiwin, Alta., Can.,
6,267.............C4　38
Wethersfield, Conn.,
26,662.............C6　52
Wetumka, Okla., 1,687....B5　79
Wetumpka, Ala., 3,912....C3　46
Wetzel, co., W. Va.,
20,314.............B4　87
Wetzlar, Ger., Fed. Rep. of,
37,721 (*100,000).......C4　6
Wewahitchka, Fla., 1,733..B1　54
Wewoka, Okla., 5,284....B5　79
Wexford, Ire., 11,849....D3　4
Wexford, co., Ire.,
83,437.............*D3　4
Wexford, co., Mich.,
19,717.............D5　66
Weyauwega, Wis., 1,377...D5　88
Weyburn, Sask., Can.,
8,815.............H4, o8　39
Weymouth, N.S., Can.,
671.............E4　43
Weymouth, Mass.,
54,610.............B6, h12　65
Weymouth [& Melcombe
Regis], Eng., 41,420.....E5　4
Whangarei, N.Z.,
31,300 (*34,600).....K15　26
Wharton, N.J., 5,535....B3　74
Wharton, Tex., 7,881....E4　84
Wharton, W. Va., 400....D6　87
Wharton, co., Tex.,
36,729.............E4　84
Wharton West, Tex......*E4　84
What Cheer, Iowa, 868...C5　60
Whatcom, co., Wash.,
81,950.............A4　86
Wheatland, Wyo., 2,498...D8　89
Wheatland, co., Mont.,
2,529.............D7　70
Wheatley, Ont., Can.,
1,362.............E2　41
Wheaton, Ill., 31,138...B5, k8　58
Wheaton, Md., 70,000....*B3　53
Wheaton, Minn., 2,029....E2　67
Wheat Ridge, Colo.,
29,778.............*B5　51
Wheeler, Tex., 1,116.....B2　84
Wheeler, co., Ga., 4,596...D4　55
Wheeler, co., Nebr.,
1,051.............C7　71
Wheeler, co., Oreg.,
1,849.............C6　80
Wheeler, co., Tex.,
6,434.............B2　84
Wheeler, peak, N. Mex.....A6　48
Wheelersburg, Ohio,
3,709.............D3　78
Wheeling, Ill., 14,746.....h9　58
Wheeling, W. Va.,
48,188 (*158,600)....A4, f8　87
Wheelwright, Ky., 793....C7　62

Whippany, N.J., 6,800.....B4　74
Whitaker, Pa., 1,797.....*F2　81
Whitakers, N.C., 926.....A5　76
Whitby, Ont., Can.,
25,324.............D6　41
Whitby, Eng., 12,850.....C6　4
Whitchurch-Stouffville,
Ont., Can., 11,262..D5, k15　41
White, co., Ark., 39,253...B4　49
White, co., Ga., 7,742....B3　55
White, co., Ill., 17,312....E5　58
White, co., Ind., 20,995...C4　59
White, co., Tenn.,
16,355.............D8　83
White Bear Lake,
Minn., 23,313....E5, m12　67
White Castle, La.,
2,206.............D4, h9　63
White City, Fla., 700.....C1　54
White Cloud, Mich.,
1,044.............E5　66
White Deer, Tex., 1,092...B2　84
Whitefield, N.H., 1,093...C4　73
Whitefish, Mont., 3,349...B2　70
Whitefish Bay, Wis.,
17,402.............*E6　88
White Hall, Ill., 2,979....D3　58
Whitehall, Mich., 3,017...E4　66
Whitehall, Mont., 1,035...E4　70
Whitehall, N.Y., 3,764....B7　75
Whitehall, Ohio, 25,263..m11　78
Whitehall, Pa., 16,450...*F1　81
Whitehall, Wis., 1,486...D2　88
Whitehaven, Eng., 26,420..C5　4
White Haven, Pa.,
2,134.............D10　81
Whitehorse, Yukon, Can.,
11,217.............D6　36
Whitehouse, Ohio,
1,542.............A2, e6　78
White Lake, Mich., 1,330.*F7　66
Whiteland, Ind., 1,492...*E5　59
White Oak, N.C., 150....C4　76
White Oak, Ohio........o12　78
White Oak, Pa., 9,304...*F2　81
White Oak, Tex., 2,300...*C5　84
White Pigeon, Mich.,
1,455.............G5　66
White Pine, co., Nev.,
10,150.............B4　72
White Pine, Tenn.,
1,532.............C10　83
White Plains, N.Y.,
50,346.............D7, m15　75
White River Junction,
Vt., 2,379.............D3　73
White Rock, B.C.,
Can., 10,349.....E6, f13　37
White Salmon, Wash.,
1,585.............D4　86
Whitesboro, N.Y.,
4,805.............*B5　75
Whitesboro, Tex., 2,927...C4　84
Whitesburg, Ky., 1,137...C7　62
Whites Creek, Tenn.....g10　83
White Settlement, Tex.,
13,449.............*B5　84
Whiteside, co., Ill.,
62,877.............B3　58
White Stone, Va., 381....C6　85
White Sulphur Springs,
Mont., 1,200.............D6　70
White Sulphur Springs,
W. Va., 2,869.............D4　87
Whitesville, W. Va., 781..n12　87
Whiteville, N.C., 4,195....C4　76
Whitewright, Tex., 1,742..C4　84
Whitfield, co., Ga.,
55,108.............B1　55
Whiting, Ind., 7,152.....A3　59
Whiting, Wis., 1,782....D4　88
Whitinsville, Mass.,
5,210.............B4　65
Whitley, co., Ind.,
23,395.............B6　59
Whitley, co., Ky., 24,145..D5　62
Whitley City, Ky., 1,060...D5　62
Whitman, Mass.,
13,059.............B6, h12　65
Whitman, co., Wash.,
37,900.............B8　86
Whitmire, S.C., 2,226....N4　82
Whitmore City, Haw.,
2,015.............f9　56
Whitnel, N.C.............B1　76
Whitney, Idaho.............F2　57
Whitney, S.C., 1,100.....B4　82
Whitney, Tex., 1,371....D4　84
Whitney, mtn., Calif.....D4　50
Whitney Point, N.Y.,
1,058.............C5　75
Whittier, Calif.,
72,863.............F4, n12　50
Whitwell, Tenn., 1,669...D8　83
Wiarton, Ont., Can.,
2,222.............C3　41
Wibaux, co., Mont.,
1,465.............D12　70

Wichita, Kans., 276,554
(*350,400).........E6, g12 61
Wichita, Oreg...........*B4 80
Wichita, co., Kans., 3,274..D2 61
Wichita, co., Tex.,
  121,862..............B3 84
Wichita Falls, Tex.,
  96,265 (*115,000)......C3 84
Wickenburg, Ariz.,
  2,698................C2 48
Wickett, Tex., 598.......D1 84
Wickliffe, Ky., 1,211.....A2 62
Wickliffe, Ohio,
  21,354...............A4, g9 78
Wickliffe, Ohio, 7,500...*A5 78
Wicklow, co., Ire.,
  60,428...............*D3 4
Wicomico, co., Md.,
  54,236...............D6 53
Wiconisco, Pa., 1,236....E8 81
Widnes, Eng., 55,100.....*D5 4
Wieluń, Pol., 14,300.....C6 7
Wiener Neustadt, Aus.,
  34,707 (*41,000).......E8 6
Wiesbaden, Ger., Fed. Rep.
  of, 252,232 (*640,000)..C4 6
Wiggins, Miss., 2,995.....E4 68
Wigtown, co., Scot.,
  27,251...............*C4 4
Wilbarger, co., Tex.,
  15,355...............B3 84
Wilber, Nebr., 1,483.....D9 71
Wilberforce, Ohio, 4,400..C2 78
Wilbur, Wash., 1,074.....B7 86
Wilburton, Okla., 2,504...C6 79
Wilcox, co., Ala.,
  16,303...............D2 46
Wilcox, co., Ga., 6,998...E3 55
Wilder, W.Va., 1,328.....D3 73
Wildwood, Fla., 2,082....D4 54
Wildwood, N.J., 4,110....F3 74
Wildwood, Pa., 500.......*E2 81
Wildwood Crest, N.J.,
  3,483................F3 74
Wilhelm, mtn., N. Gui....k12 25
Wilhelmina, mtn., Indon..F9 19
Wilhelm-Pieck-Stadt
  Guben, Ger. Dem. Rep.,
  31,979...............C7 6
Wilhelmshaven, Ger., Fed.
  Rep. of, 104,333.......B4 6
Wilkes, co., Ga., 10,184..C4 55
Wilkes, co., N.C., 49,524..A1 76
Wilkes-Barre, Pa.,
  58,856
  (*244,000)......D10, n17 81
Wilkesboro, N.C., 1,974..A1 76
Wilkie, Sask., Can.,
  1,642................E1 39
Wilkin, co., Minn.,
  9,389................D2 67
Wilkinsburg, Pa.,
  26,780.............F2, k14 81
Wilkinson, co., Ga.,
  9,393................D3 55
Wilkinson, co., Miss.,
  11,099...............D2 68
Will, co., Ill., 249,498...B6 58
Willacoochee, Ga., 1,120..E3 55
Willacy, co., Tex.,
  15,570...............F4 84
Willamina, Oreg., 1,193..B3 80
Willard, Ohio, 5,510.....A3 78
Willcox, Ariz., 2,568.....C4 48
Willemstad, Neth. Antilles,
  43,547 (*94,133)......A4 32
Williams, Ariz., 2,386....B2 48
Williams, Calif., 1,571....C2 50
Williams, co., N. Dak.,
  19,301...............B2 77
Williams, co., Ohio,
  33,669...............A1 78
Williams Bay, Wis., 1,554..F5 88
Williamsburg, Iowa,
  1,544................C5 60
Williamsburg, Ky., 3,687..D5 62
Williamsburg, Ohio,
  2,054................C1 78
Williamsburg, Pa., 1,579..F5 81
Williamsburg
  (Independence City),
  Va., 9,069............C6 85
Williamsburg, co., S.C.,
  34,203...............D8 82
Williams Lake, B.C., Can.,
  4,072 (*11,407)....C6, n18 37
Williamson, N.Y., 1,991..B3 75
Williamson, W. Va.,
  5,831................D2 87
Williamson, co., Ill.,
  49,021...............F4 58
Williamson, co., Tenn.,
  34,330...............A5 83
Williamson, co., Tex.,
  37,305...............D4 84
Williamsport, Ind., 1,661..D3 59
Williamsport, Md., 2,270..A2 53

Williamsport, Pa., 37,918
  (*85,200).............D7 81
Williamston, Mich., 2,600..F6 66
Williamston, N.C., 6,570..B5 76
Williamston, S.C., 3,991..B3 82
Williamstown, Ky., 2,063..B5 62
Williamstown, Mass.,
  4,285................A1 65
Williamstown, N.J.,
  4,075................D3 74
Williamstown, Pa., 1,919..E8 81
Williamstown, W. Va.,
  2,743................B3 87
Williamsville, N.Y., 6,835..C2 75
Willimantic, Conn.,
  14,402...............C8 52
Willingboro (Levittown),
  N.J., 43,386..........*C3 74
Willis Beach, Nebr., 100..B9 71
Williston, Fla., 1,939....C4 54
Williston, N. Dak., 11,280..B2 77
Williston, S.C., 2,594....E5 82
Williston Park, N.Y., 9,154..G2 52
Willits, Calif., 3,091.....C2 50
Willmar, Minn., 12,869...E3 67
Willoughby, Ohio, 18,634..A4 78
Willow Brook, Calif.,
  31,300...............*F4 50
Willow Grove, Pa.,
  21,200...........F11 o21 81
Willowick, Ohio,
  21,237..............A4, g9 78
Willow Run, Mich.,
  6,400................p14 66
Willows, Calif., 4,085....C2 50
Willow Springs, Ill., 3,318..k9 58
Willow Springs, Mo.,
  2,045................E6 69
Wills Point, Tex., 2,636..*C5 84
Wilmer, Tex., 1,922......n10 84
Wilmerding, Pa., 3,218...B6 81
Wilmette, Ill., 32,134...A6, h9 58
Wilmington, Del., 80,386..A6 53
Wilmington, Ill., 4,335....B5 58
Wilmington, Mass.,
  4,500..............A5, f11 65
Wilmington, N.C., 46,169
  (*83,000).............C5 76
Wilmington, Ohio, 10,051..C2 78
Wilmington Manor, Del.,
  1,200................*A6 53
Wilmore, Ky., 3,466.....C5 62
Wilson, Ark., 1,009......B5 49
Wilson, Conn...........B6 52
Wilson, Kans., 870......D5 61
Wilson, N.Y., 1,284......B2 75
Wilson, N.C., 29,347....B5 76
Wilson, Okla., 1,569......C4 79
Wilson, Pa., 8,406......E11 81
Wilson, co., Kans.,
  11,317...............E8 61
Wilson, co., N.C., 57,486..B5 76
Wilson, co., Tenn.,
  36,999...............A5 83
Wilson, co., Tex., 13,041..E3 84
Wilton, Conn., 5,300.....E3 52
Wilton, Maine, 2,225.....D2 64
Wilton, N.H., 1,161......F4 73
Wilton Junction (Wilton),
  Iowa, 1,873...........C6 60
Wilton Manors, Fla.,
  10,948...............*F6 54
Wiltshire, co., Eng.,
  489,370..............*F6 4
Winamac, Ind., 2,341....B4 59
Winchendon, Mass.,
  3,997................A3 65
Winchester, Ont., Can.,
  1,429................B9 41
Winchester, Eng., 31,670..E6 4
Winchester, Ill., 1,788...D3 58
Winchester, Ind., 5,493..D8 59
Winchester, Ky., 13,402..C5 62
Winchester, Mass.,
  22,269...............g11 65
Winchester, Mo., 2,329..*C7 69
Winchester, Tenn., 5,256..B5 83
Winchester (Independent
  City), Va., 14,643.....A4 85
Windber, Pa., 6,332......F4 81
Winder, Ga., 6,605......C3 55
Windfall, Ind., 946......D6 59
Windgap, Pa., 2,270.....E11 81
Windham, Ohio, 3,360...A4 78
Windham, co., Conn.,
  84,515...............B8 52
Windham, co., Vt.,
  33,476...............F3 73
Windhoek, Namibia,
  61,260...............E3 24
Wind Lake, Wis., 2,000..F5 88
Windom, Minn., 3,952...G3 67
Windsor, Newf., Can.,
  6,644................D4 44
Windsor, N.S., Can.,
  3,775................E5 43
Windsor, Ont., Can.,
  203,300 (*258,643).....E1 41

Windsor, Que., Can.,
  6,023................D5 42
Windsor, Colo., 1,564....*A6 51
Windsor, Conn., 16,000...B6 52
Windsor, Ill., 1,126......D5 58
Windsor, Mo., 2,734.....C4 69
Windsor, N.C., 2,191.....B6 76
Windsor, Pa., 1,298......G8 81
Windsor, Vt., 3,000......E3 73
Windsor, co., Vt.,
  44,082...............D2 73
Windsor Heights, Iowa,
  6,303................e8 60
Windsor Hills, Calif.,
  7,270................*F4 50
Windsor Locks, Conn.,
  15,080...............B6 52
Windward Islands, see
  Dominica, Grenada,
  St. Lucia and St.
  Vincent, Br. dep., N.A.
Windy Hill, S.C., 1,671..*C8 82
Windy Hills, Ky., 1,692..*H6 62
Winfield, Ala., 3,292....B2 46
Winfield, Ill., 4,285......*B5 58
Winfield, Kans., 11,405..E7 61
Winfield, N.J., 2,184.....k7 74
Wingate, N.C., 2,569....C2 76
Wingham, Ont., Can.,
  2,913................D3 41
Wink, Tex., 1,023.......D1 84
Winkelman, Ariz., 974...C3 48
Winkler, Man., Can.,
  2,983................E3 40
Winkler, co., Tex., 9,640..D1 84
Winn, par., La., 16,369...C3 63
Winneab, Ghana, 25,400..G4 22
Winnebago, Ill., 1,258....A4 58
Winnebago, Minn., 1,791..G4 67
Winnebago, co., Ill.,
  246,623..............A4 58
Winnebago, co., Iowa,
  12,990...............A4 60
Winnebago, co., Wis.,
  129,946..............H9 88
Winneconne, Wis., 1,611..D5 88
Winnemucca, Nev., 3,587..A3 72
Winner, S. Dak., 3,789...G6 77
Winneshiek, co., Iowa,
  21,758...............A6 60
Winnetka, Ill., 13,998...A6, h9 58
Winnfield, La., 7,142.....C3 63
Winnie, Tex., 1,543......*E5 84
Winnipeg, Man., Can.,
  548,573.............E3, h8 40
Winnipeg, lake, Man.,
  Can..................C2 40
Winnipegosis, Man.,
  Can., 887............D2 40
Winnipegosis, lake, Man.,
  Can., 980............C2 40
Winnsboro, La., 5,349....B4 63
Winnsboro, S.C., 3,411...C5 82
Winnsboro, Tex., 3,064...C5 84
Winnsboro Mills, S.C.,
  3,411................*C5 82
Winona, Minn., 26,438...F7 67
Winona, Miss., 5,521.....B4 68
Winona, co., Minn.,
  44,409...............F7 67
Winona Lake, Ind., 2,811..B6 59
Winooski, Vt., 7,309.....C1 73
Winschoten, Neth.,
  18,595...............A7 5
Winslow, Ariz., 8,066....B3 48
Winslow, Ind., 1,030.....H3 59
Winslow, Maine, 5,389...D3 64
Windslow, Wash., 1,461..e10 86
Winsted, Conn., 8,954...B4 52
Winsted, Minn., 1,266...F4 67
Winston, Fla., 4,505.....D4 54
Winston, Oreg., 2,468...*D3 80
Winston, co., Ala., 16,654..A2 46
Winston, co., Miss., 18,406..B4 68
Winston-Salem, N.C.,
  133,683 (*235,900).....A2 76
Winter Garden, Fla.,
  5,153................D5 54
Winter Haven, Fla.,
  16,136...............D5 54
Winter Park, Fla.,
  21,895...............D5 54
Winters, Calif., 2,419....C2 50
Winters, Tex., 2,907.....D3 84
Winterset, Iowa, 3,654...C4 60
Wintersville, Ohio, 4,921..B5 78
Winterthur, Switz.,
  92,000 (*109,600)......E4 6
Winterton, Newf., Can.,
  808..................E5 44
Winterville, N.C., 1,437..B5 76
Winthrop, Maine, 2,571..D3 64
Winthrop, Mass.,
  20,335..............B6 g12 65
Winthrop, Minn., 1,391..F4 67
Winthrop Harbor, Ill.,
  4,794...............A6, h9 58
Wirt, co., W. Va., 4,154...B3 87

Wisbech, Eng., 16,950...D7 4
Wiscasset, Maine, 950...D3 64
Wisconsin, state, U.S.,
  4,547,000............B8 45
Wisconsin Dells, Wis.,
  2,401................E4 88
Wisconsin Rapids, Wis.,
  18,587...............D4 88
Wise, Va., 2,891........f9 85
Wise, co., Tex., 19,687...C4 84
Wise, co., Va., 35,947....e9 85
Wishek, N. Dak., 1,275...D6 77
Wisla, riv., Pol..........B5 7
Wismar, Ger. Dem. Rep.,
  56,724...............B5 6
Wisner, La., 1,339......C4 63
Wisner, Nebr., 1,315.....C9 71
Withamsville, Ohio, 3,000..C1 78
Witt, Ill., 1,040........D4 58
Wittenberg, Ger. Dem.
  Rep., 48,614..........C6 6
Wittenberge, Ger. Dem.
  Rep., 33,186..........B5 6
Wixom, Mich., 2,010....o14 66
Włocławek, Pol., 77,100..B5 7
Woburn, Mass.,
  37,406.............B5, g11 65
Wolcott, Conn., 4,500....C5 52
Wolcott, N.Y., 1,617.....B4 75
Wolfe, co., Que., Can.,
  16,793...............D6 42
Wolfe, co., Ky., 5,669....C6 62
Wolfeboro, N.H., 1,500...D5 73
Wolfe City, Tex., 1,433...C4 84
Wolfenbüttel, Ger., Fed.
  Rep. of, 40,291.......B5 6
Wolf Lake, Mich., 2,258..E4 66
Wolf Point, Mont., 3,095..B11 70
Wolfsburg, Ger., Fed. Rep.
  of, 130,156...........B5 6
Wolfville, N.S., Can.,
  2,861................D5 43
Wollongong, Austl.,
  160,902 (*198,768).....F9 25
Wolseley, Sask., Can.,
  1,031................G4 39
Wolverhampton, Eng.,
  268,380..............D5 4
Wolverine Lake, Mich.,
  4,301................*F7 66
Wolverton, Eng., 13,800..D6 4
Womelsdrof, Pa., 1,551..F9 81
Wonder Lake, Ill.,
  4,806..............A5, h8 58
Wŏnju, Kor., 111,972....H3 18
Wonsan, Kor., 112,952...G3 18
Wood, co., Ohio, 89,722..A2 78
Wood, co., Tex., 18,589...C5 84
Wood, co., W. Va.,
  86,818...............B3 87
Wood, co., Wis., 65,362..D3 88
Woodbine, Iowa, 1,349...C2 60
Woodbine, N.J., 2,625....E3 74
Woodbourne, N.Y., 1,155..D6 75
Woodbridge, Conn.,
  7,673................D4 52
Woodbridge, N.J.,
  14,200..............B4, k7 74
Woodbridge, Va., 32,400..B5 85
Woodburn, Oreg.,
  7,495..............B4, h12 80
Woodbury, Conn., 1,342..C4 52
Woodbury, Ga., 1,422....D2 55
Woodbury, N.J., 12,408..D2 74
Woodbury, N.Y., 2,200...*E7 75
Woodbury, Tenn., 1,725..B5 83
Woodbury, co., Iowa,
  103,052..............B1 60
Woodbury Heights, N.J.,
  3,621................*D2 74
Woodcliff Lake, N.J.,
  5,506................g8 74
Woodcroft, Ind.........*E5 59
Wood Dale, Ill., 8,831....k9 58
Woodford, Eng., 61,259..k13 4
Woodford, co., Ill.,
  28,012...............C4 58
Woodford, co., Ky.,
  14,434...............B5 62
Wood Green, Eng.,
  47,100..............k12 4
Woodlake, Calif., 3,371...D4 50
Woodland, Calif., 20,677..C3 50
Woodland, Maine, 1,534..C5 64
Woodland, Pa., 1,264....E5 81
Woodland, Wash., 1,622..D3 86
Woodland Beach, Mich.,
  2,249................*G7 66
Woodlawn, Ky., 525......A2 62
Woodlawn, Md., 7,500...*B4 53
Woodlawn, Md., 3,000...*C4 53
Woodlawn, Ohio, 3,251..n13 78
Woodlawn Beach,
  N.Y., 2,000...........C2 75
Woodlawn Orchards,
  Mich................*F6 66
Woodley Hills, Va.,
  1,200................*B5 85

Woodlyn, Pa., 6,000.....*B10 81
Wood Lynne, N.J.,
3,101................*D2 74
Woodmere, N.Y.,
20,000................G2 52
Wood-Ridge, N.J., 8,311...h8 74
Woodridge, N.Y., 1,071...*D6 75
Wood River, Ill., 13,186...E3 58
Woodroffe, mtn., Austl....E5 25
Woodruff, S.C., 4,690....B3 82
Woodruff, co., Ark.,
11,566................B4 49
Woodruff Place, Ind.....*E5 59
Woods, co., Okla., 11,920..A3 79
Woodsboro, Tex., 1,839...E4 84
Woods Cross, Utah, 3,124..C2 72
Woodsfield, Ohio, 3,239...C4 78
Woodside, Calif., 4,734...*D2 50
Woodson, co., Kans.,
4,789.................E8 61
Woodson Terrace, Mo.,
5,880.................*C7 69
Woodstock, N.B., Can.,
4,846.................C2 43
Woodstock, Ont., Can.,
26,173................D4 41
Woodstock, Ill., 10,226...A5 58
Woodstock, Vt., 1,154....D2 73
Woodstock, Va., 2,338....B4 85
Woodsville, N.H., 1,336...C3 73
Woodville, Calif., 1,031..*D4 50
Woodville, Miss., 1,734...D2 68
Woodville, Ohio,
1,834................A2, f7 78
Woodville, Tex., 2,662...D5 84
Woodward, Ala.,
1,000................B3, g7 46
Woodward, Iowa, 1,010...C4 60
Woodward, Okla., 9,412...A2 79

Woodward, co., Okla.,
15,537................A2 79
Woodway, Tex., 4,819....*D4 84
Woolwich, Eng.,
148,700...............m13 4
Woonsocket, R.I.,
46,820................A10 52
Woonsocket, S. Dak.,
852..................F7 77
Wooster, Ohio, 18,703....B4 78
Worcester, Eng., 72,970...D5 4
Worcester, Mass., 176,572
(*334,000)............B4 65
Worcester, N.Y., 799....C6 75
Worcester, S. Afr.,
40,610................G3 24
Worcester, co., Eng.,
695,760...............*D5 4
Worcester, co., Md.,
24,442................D7 53
Worcester, co., Mass.,
637,079...............A3 65
Worden, Ill., 1,091....E4 58
Workington, Eng.,
28,540................C5 4
Worland, Wyo., 5,055....B5 89
World, 3,859,000,000....... 2
Wormleysburg, Pa.,
3,192................*F8 81
Worms, Ger., Fed. Rep. of,
76,658................D4 6
Worth, Ill., 11,999....k9 58
Worth, co., Ga., 14,770...E3 55
Worth, co., Iowa, 8,968...A4 60
Worth, co., Mo., 3,359...A3 69
Wortham, Tex., 1,036....D4 84
Worthing, Eng., 87,780...E6 4
Worthington, Ind., 1,691..F4 59
Worthington, Ky., 1,364...B7 62

Worthington, Minn.,
9,916.................G3 67
Worthington, Ohio,
15,326................B2, k10 78
Wrangel, isl., Sov. Un...B21 13
Wrangell, Alsk.,
2,029.............D13, m23 47
Wrangell, mtn., Alsk.....f19 47
Wray, Colo., 1,953.......A8 51
Wrens, Ga., 2,204.......C4 55
Wrentham, Mass., 1,723...B5 65
Wrexham, Wales,
38,650................D5 4
Wright, co., Iowa, 17,294..B4 60
Wright, co., Minn.,
38,933................E4 67
Wright, co., Mo., 13,667...D5 69
Wright City, Okla., 1,068..C6 79
Wrightstown, N.J., 2,719..C3 74
Wrightsville, Ga., 2,106...D4 55
Wrightsville, Pa., 2,668...F8 81
Wrocław (Breslau), Pol.,
523,300...............C4 7
Wuchou, China, 120,000...G7 17
Wuhan, China, 2,900,000..E7 17
Wuhsi (Wusih), China,
650,000...............E9 17
Wuhsing, China, 120,000..E9 17
Wuhu, China, 240,000....E8 17
Wulumuchi, see Urumchi,
China
Wuppertal, Ger., Fed. Rep.
of, 413,153 (*920,000)...C3 6
Württemberg, reg., Ger.,
Fed. Rep. of..........D4 6
Würzburg, Ger., Fed. Rep.
of, 114,106 (*178,000)...D4 6
Wurzen, Ger. Dem. Rep.,
24,033................C6 6
Wusu, China, 10,000.....C1 17

Wutungchiao, China,
140,000...............C11 20
Wyandanch, N.Y.,
15,716................*n15 75
Wyandot, co., Ohio,
21,826................B2 78
Wyandotte, Mich.,
41,061..............F7, p15 66
Wyandotte, co., Kans.,
186,845...............C9 61
Wyckoff, N.J., 16,039....*A4 74
Wymore, Nebr., 1,790....D9 71
Wyncote, Pa., 5,300....*F11 81
Wyndmoor, Pa., 5,800...*F11 81
Wynne, Ark., 6,696......B5 49
Wynnewood, Okla.,
2,374................C4 79
Wynnewood, Pa., 7,700..*F11 81
Wynyard, Austl., 4,013...o15 25
Wynyard, Sask., Can.,
1,932...............F3, n8 39
Wyoming, Del., 1,062....B6 53
Wyoming, Ill., 1,563....B4 58
Wyoming, Mich., 56,560...F5 66
Wyoming, Minn., 695.....E6 67
Wyoming, Ohio, 9,089....c13 78
Wyoming, Pa., 4,195....n17 81
Wyoming, co., N.Y.,
37,688................C2 75
Wyoming, co., Pa.,
19,082................D9 81
Wyoming, co., W. Va.,
30,095................D3 87
Wyoming, state, U.S.,
343,000...............89
Wyomissing, Pa., 7,136...F10 81
Wythe, co., Va.,
22,139................D1 85
Wytheville, Va.,
6,069.................D1 85

X

Xánthi, Grc.,
24,867................B5 14

Xavier, Kans............B8 61
Xenia, Ohio, 25,373.....C2 78

Xilitla, Mex., 3,213.....m14 34
Xingú, riv., Braz.........D5 27

Xochimilco, Mex.,
43,067................h9 34

Y

Yaan, China, 55,200......F5 17
Yadkin, co., N.C.,
24,599................A2 76
Yadkinville, N.C., 2,232...A2 76
Yaizu, Jap., 82,737......o17 18
Yakima, Wash., 45,588
(*78,300).............C5 86
Yakima, co., Wash.,
144,971...............C5 86
Yakutsk, Sov. Un.,
108,000...............C15 13
Yalobusha, co., Miss.,
11,915................A4 68
Yalta, Sov. Un., 62,000...I10 12
Yalvaç, Tur., 13,545.....C8 14
Yamachiche, Que., Can.,
1,147.................C5 42
Yamagata, Jap.,
204,127...............*G10 18
Yamagata, pref., Jap.,
1,225,618.............*G10 18
Yamaguchi, Jap.,
73,000 (101,041 ▲)......I5 18
Yamaguchi, pref, Jap.,
1,511,448.............*I5 18
Yamanashi, pref., Jap.,
762,029...............*I9 18
Yamaska, co., Que., Can.,
15,535................C5 42
Yambol, Bul., 58,465.....D8 10
Yamethin, Bur., 12,030...D10 20
Yamhill, co., Oreg.,
40,213................B3 80
Yanam, India, 8,291.....E7 20
Yanbu', Sau. Ar., 20,000...E2 15
Yancey, co., N.C., 12,629..f10 76

Yanceyville, N.C., 1,274...A3 76
Yangchou, China, 160,000..E8 17
Yangchüan, China,
200,000...............D7 17
Yangtze, riv., China......E8 17
Yankton, S. Dak.,
11,919................H8 77
Yankton, co., S. Dak.,
19,039................G8 77
Yao, Jap., 227,778......*I7 18
Yaoundé, Cam.,
101,000...............H7 22
Yaracuy, state, Ven.,
175,291...............A4 32
Yardley, Pa., 2,616......F12 81
Yarim, Yemen, 20,000....G3 15
Yarmouth, N.S., Can.,
8,516.................F3 43
Yarmouth, Maine,
2,441..............E2, g7 64
Yarmouth, co., N.S.,
Can., 23,552..........F4 43
Yaroslavl, Sov. Un.,
517,000...............C12 12
Yartsevo, Sov. Un.,
37,000................D9 12
Yarumal, Col., 16,823....B2 32
Yasinovataya, Sov. Un.,
37,000................q20 12
Yass, Austl., 4,240.....G7 26
Yates, co., N.Y., 19,831...C3 75
Yates Center, Kans.,
1,967.................E8 61
Yatsushiro, Jap., 76,000
(101,866 ▲)...........J5 18

Yauco, P.R., 12,922
(35,103 ▲)...........*G11 35
Yavapai, co., Ariz.,
36,837................B2 48
Yavorov, Sov. Un., 10,000.G4 12
Yawatahama, Jap.,
36,000 (46,903 ▲).....J6 18
Yazd (Yezd), Iran, 93,241..B8 23
Yazoo, co., Miss., 27,304..C3 68
Yazoo City, Miss., 11,688..C3 68
Yeadon, Pa., 12,136.....p20 81
Yeagertown, Pa., 1,363...E6 81
Yecla, Sp., 18,400......C5 8
Yefremov, Sov. Un.,
48,000................E12 12
Yegoryevsk, Sov.
Un., 67,000.......D12, n19 12
Yelan, Sov. Un., 10,000...F14 12
Yelets, Sov. Un., 101,000..E12 12
Yell, co., Ark., 14,208....B2 49
Yellow, see Huang Ho,
riv., China
Yellow, sea, China.......D9 17
Yellowknife, N.W. Ter.,
Can., 6,122...........D11 36
Yellow Medicine, co.,
Minn., 14,516.........F2 67
Yellow Springs, Ohio,
4,624.................C2 78
Yellowstone, co., Mont.,
87,367................D8 70
Yellowstone, riv., U.S.....B2 89
Yellowstone National Park
(part), co., Wyo., 64...B2 89
Yemen, country, Asia
6,280,000.............F3 15

Yemen, People's Democratic
Republic of, country,
Asia, 1,565,000........H7 16
Yenakiyevo, Sov. Un.,
92,000................q20 12
Yenangyaung, Bur.,
11,098................*G4 17
Yencheng, China, 50,000..*E9 17
Yenchi (Karashahr), China,
10,000................C2 17
Yenchi, China, 80,000....C10 17
Yenisey, riv., Sov. Un.....C11 16
Yeniseysk, Sov. Un.,
20,000................D12 13
Yentai (Chefoo), China,
140,000...............D9 17
Yeovil, Eng., 25,760....E5 4
Yeppoon, Austl., 4,440...D9 25
Yerevan, Sov. Un.,
791,000...............E7 13
Yerupaja, mtn., Peru.....D2 31
Yessey, Sov. Un., 10,000..C13 13
Yevpatoriya, Sov. Un.,
79,000................I9 12
Yeysk, Sov. Un., 64,000...H12 12
Yiannitsá, Grc., 18,151...*B4 14
Yinchuan (Ningsia),
China, 91,000.........D6 17
Yingkou, China, 131,400...C9 17
Yoakum, Tex., 5,755.....E4 84
Yoakum, co., Tex., 7,344..C1 84
Yogyakarta, Indon.,
342,267...............G4 19
Yoichi, Jap., 16,713.....E10 18
Yokkaichi, Jap.,
229,000............I8, o15 18

Yokohama, Jap.,
2,494,975 . . . . .I9, n18   18
Yokosuka, Jap.,
347,576 . . . . .I9, n18   18
Yokote, Jap., 28,000
(43,363 ▲) G10   18
Yolo, co., Calif., 91,788 . . . .C2   50
Yolyn, W. Va., 700 . . . . . . .D5   87
Yonago, Jap., 109,096 . . . . .I6   18
Yonezawa, Jap., 72,000
(92,764 ▲) H10   18
Yonghung, Kor., 18,445 . . .G3   18
Yonkers, N.Y.,
204,297 . . . . .E7, n15   75
Yonne, dept., Fr., 283,376 . *D5   5
Yorba Linda, Calif.,
11,856 . . . . *F5   50
York, Ala., 3,044 . . . . .C1   46
York, Ont., Can.,
145,721 . . . . *m15   41
York, Eng., 105,210
(*140,000) D6   4
York, Maine, 1,900 . . . . . .E1   64
York, Nebr., 6,778 . . . . . . .D8   71
York, Pa., 50,335
(*177,500) G8   81

York, S.C., 5,081 . . . . .B5   82
York, co., N.B., Can.,
58,470 . . . . .C3   43
York, co., Ont., Can.,
2,018,019 . . . . .D5   43
York, co., Eng., 5,064,530 . *D6   4
York, co., Maine, 111,576 . .E2   64
York, co., Nebr., 13,685 . . .D8   71
York, co., Pa., 272,603 . . .G8   81
York, co., S.C., 85,216 . . . .A5   82
York, co., Va., 33,203 . . . . .C6   85
Yorkshire, N.Y., 450 . . . . . .C2   75
Yorkton, Sask., Can.,
13,430 . . . . .F4, n8   39
Yorktown, Ind., 1,673 . . . . .D6   59
Yorktown, N.Y., 4,000 . . . .*D7   75
Yorktown, Tex., 2,411 . . . . .E4   84
Yorktown Heights, N.Y.,
6,805 . . . .*D7   75
Yorktown Manor, R.I.,
900 . . . . .C11   52
Yorkville, Ill., 2,049 . . . . . .B5   58
Yorkville, N.Y., 6,805 . . . . .B5   75
Yorkville, Ohio, 1,656 . . . . .B5   78
Yoshkar-Ola, Sov. Un.,
166,000 . . . .*D7   13

Yŏsu, Kor., 113,651 . . . . . . .I3   18
Young, Austl., 6,062 . . . . . .*F8   25
Young, co., Tex., 15,400 . . .C3   84
Youngstown, N.Y., 2,169 . . .B2   75
Youngstown, Ohio,
140,909 (*501,500) A5   78
Youngsville, La., 1,002 . . . .D3   63
Youngsville, Pa., 2,158 . . . .C3   81
Youngtown, Ariz., 1,886 . . .D1   48
Youngwood, Pa., 3,057 . . . .F2   81
Yozgat, Tur., 27,047 . . . . . .C10   14
Ypacaraí, Par., 5,195 . . . . .E4   29
Ypsilanti, Mich.,
29,538 . . . . .F7, p4   66
Yreka, Calif., 5,394 . . . . . . .B2   50
Ystad, Swe., 16,388 . . . . . .J5   11
Yuanling, China, 28,000 . . .F7   17
Yuba, co., Calif., 44,736 . . .C3   50
Yuba City, Calif., 13,986 . . .C3   50
Yuba City South, Calif.,
5,352 . . . .*C3   50
Yūbari, Jap., 69,871 . . . . . .E10   18
Yucatán, state, Mex.,
661,500 . . . . .C7   34
Yugoslavia, country, Eur.,
21,055,000 . . . . .C3   10

Yukon, Okla., 8,411 . . . . . .B4   79
Yukon, ter., Can.,
20,000 . . . . .D6   36
Yukon, riv., N.A. C9   47
Yuma, Ariz., 29,007
(*40,700) C1   48
Yuma, Colo., 2,259 . . . . . . .A8   51
Yuma, co., Ariz., 60,827 . . .C1   48
Yuma, co., Colo., 8,544 . . . .A8   51
Yümen, China, 200,000 . . . .C4   17
Yunnan, prov., China,
19,100,000 . . . . .G5   17
Yurécuaro, Mex.,
13,611 . . . . .m12   34
Yuryevets, Sov. Un.,
20,000 . . . . .C14   12
Yuryev-Polskiy, Sov. Un.,
22,000 . . . . .C12   12
Yuty, Par., 16,262 . . . . .E4   29
Yützu, China, 100,000 . . . .*D7   17
Yuzha, Sov. Un.,
24,000 . . . . .C13   12
Yuzhno-Sakhalinsk,
Sov. Un., 106,000 . . . . . .E17   13
Yverdon, Switz., 20,400 . . . .E3   6

Z

Zabkowice, Pol., 13,800 . . . .C4   7
Zabrze, Pol., 197,200 . . .C5, g9   7
Zacatecas, Mex., 50,251 . . .C4   34
Zacatecas, state, Mex.,
895,400 . . . . .C4, m12   34
Zachary, La., 4,964 . . . . . . .D4   63
Zadar, Yugo., 43,187 . . . . . .C2   10
Zagorsk, Sov. Un., 92,000 .C12   12
Zagreb, Yugo., 566,084 . . . .C2   10
Zāhedān, Iran, 39,732 . . . . .G9   16
Zaḥlah, Leb., 29,500 . . . .F10   14
Zaire, country, Afr.,
23,600,000 . . . . .B4   24
Zaječar, Yugo., 27,677 . . . .D6   10
Zákinthos, Grc., 9,339 . . . . .D3   14
Zákinthos (Zante),
prov., Grc., 30,156 . . . .*D3   14
Zakopane, Pol., 27,000 . . . .D5   7
Zala, co., Hung., 267,184 . .*B3   10
Zalaegerszeg, Hung.,
39,176 . . . . .B3   10
Zalău, Rom., 13,378 . . . . . .B6   10
Zambales, prov., Phil.,
213,442 . . . .*B5   19
Zambezi, riv., Afr. H8   21
Zambia (Northern
Rhodesia), country,
Afr., 4,600,000 . . . . .D5   24
Zamboanga, Phil.,
41,750 (199,901 ▲) D6   19
Zamboanga del Norte,
prov., Phil., 281,429 . . . .*D6   19
Zamboanga del Sur,
prov., Phil., 742,404 . . . .*D6   19
Zamora, Sp., 48,691 . . . . . .B3   8
Zamora, prov., Sp.,
270,000 . . . .*B3   8
Zamora de Hidalgo,
Mex., 57,775 . . . . . .C4, m12   34
Zamość, Pol., 34,700 . . . . .C7   7

Zanesville, Ohio, 33,045 . . .C4   78
Zanjān, Iran, 58,714 . . . . . .A7   23
Zanzibar, Tan.,
68,380 . . . . .B7   24
Zapata, Tex., 2,300 . . . . . . .F3   84
Zapata, co., Tex.,
4,352 . . . . .F3   84
Zaporozhye, Sov. Un.,
658,000 . . . . .H10   12
Zaragoza, Sp., 469,366 . . . .B5   8
Zaragoza, prov., Sp.,
731,500 . . . .*B5   8
Zárate, Arg., 51,000 . . .A5, g7   28
Zaraysk, Sov. Un.,
24,000 . . . . .D12   12
Zaria, Nig., 166,170 . . . . . .F6   22
Zashiversk, Sov. Un.,
800 . . . . .C17   13
Žatec, Czech., 16,303 . . . . .C2   7
Zavala, co., Tex.,
11,370 . . . . .E3   84
Zavitaya, Sov. Un.,
14,500 . . . . .D15   13
Zawiercie, Pol.,
39,400 . . . . .C5, g10   7
Zaysan, Sov. Un., 15,600 . .E11   13
Zdolbunov, Sov. Un.,
21,000 . . . . .F6   12
Zduńska Wola, Pol.,
29,000 . . . . .C5   7
Zebulon, N.C., 1,839 . . . . . .B4   76
Zeeland, Mich., 4,734 . . . . .F5   66
Zeeland, prov., Neth.,
301,800 . . . . .B5   5
Zefat (Safad), Isr.,
13,600 . . . . .B3, g5   15
Zehdenick, Ger. Dem. Rep.,
12,800 . . . . .B6   6
Zeigler, Ill., 1,940 . . . . .F4   58
Zeist, Neth., 57,155 . . . . . . .A6   5

Zeitz, Ger. Dem. Rep.,
44,675 . . . . .C6   6
Zelienople, Pa., 3,602 . . . . .E1   81
Zella-Mehlis, Ger. Dem.
Rep., 16,400 . . . . .C5   6
Zemetchino, Sov. Un.,
10,000 . . . . .E14   12
Zenica, Yugo., 51,279 . . . . .C3   10
Zephyrhills, Fla., 3,369 . . . .D4   54
Zerbst, Ger. Dem. Rep.,
19,401 . . . . .C6   6
Zeya, Sov. Un., 17,000 . . . .D15   13
Zgierz, Pol., 42,800 . . . . . . .C5   7
Zhdanov, Sov. Un.,
417,000 . . . . .H11   12
Zhitomir, Sov. Un.,
161,000 . . . . .F7   12
Zhizdra, Sov. Un.,
10,000 . . . . .E10   12
Zhmerinka, Sov. Un.,
36,000 . . . . .G7   12
Ziebach, co., S. Dak.,
2,221 . . . . .F4   77
Zielona Gora, Pol.,
73,100 . . . . .C3   7
Ziguinchor, Sen.,
29,800 . . . . .F1   22
Zile, Tur., 27,429 . . . . .B10   14
Žilina, Czech., 41,806 . . . . .D5   7
Zilwaukee, Mich., 2,072 . . .E7   66
Zima, Sov. Un.,
42,000 . . . . .D13   13
Zimnicea, Rom., 12,445 . . .D7   10
Zinder, Niger, 13,300 . . . . .F6   22
Zion, Ill., 17,268 . . . . . .A6, h9   58
Zionsville, Ind.,
1,857 . . . . .E5, k9   59
Zipaquirá, Col., 22,648 . . . .B3   32
Zitácuaro, Mex., 36,911 . . .n13   34

Zittau, Ger. Dem. Rep.,
42,428 . . . . .C7   6
Zlatoust, Sov. Un.,
180,000 . . . . .D8   13
Zlynka, Sov. Un., 10,000 . . .E8   12
Znamenka, Sov. Un.,
27,000 . . . . .G9   12
Znojmo, Czech., 25,905 . . .D4   7
Zolochev, Sov. Un.,
28,600 . . . . .G5   12
Zolotonosha, Sov. Un.,
28,000 . . . . .G9   12
Zomba, Malawi, 19,000 . . .D7   24
Zonguldak, Tur., 77,135
(*145,000) B8   14
Zrenjanin (Petrovgrad),
Yugo., 59,580 . . . . .C5   10
Zug, Switz., 23,000
(*50,000) E4   6
Zug, canton, Switz.,
69,500 . . . .*E4   6
Zulia, state, Ven., 919,863 .B3   32
Zumbrota, Minn., 1,929 . . .F6   67
Zuni, N. Mex., 3,958 . . . . . .B4   48
Zürich, Switz., 412,200
(*770,000) *E4   6
Zürich, canton, Switz.,
1,108,000 . . . .*E4   6
Zutphen, Neth., 27,718 . . . .A7   5
Zvenigorodka, Sov. Un.,
20,000 . . . . .G8   12
Zvolen, Czech., 25,354 . . . .D5   7
Zweibrücken, Ger., Fed.
Rep. of, 37,522 . . . . .D3   6
Zwickau, Ger. Dem. Rep.,
123,830 (*175,000) C6   6
Zwolle, La., 2,169 . . . . .C2   63
Zwolle, Neth., 77,122 . . . . .A7   5
Zyrardów, Pol.,
33,100 . . . . .B6, m12   7